*Livestock Feeds
and Feeding*

THIRD EDITION

Livestock Feeds and Feeding

D. C. Church, Ph.D

PRENTICE HALL, Englewood Cliffs, New Jersey 07632

Library of Congress Cataloging-in-Publication Data

CHURCH, D. C.
    Livestock feeds and feeding / D. C. Church.—3rd ed.
        p. cm.
    Includes bibliographical references and index
    ISBN 0-13-538760-4
    1. Feeds. 2. Animal feeding. 3. Animal nutrition. I. Title.
    SF95.C48 1991
    636.08′4—dc20   90-49517
                                                                CIP

Tables from *Nutrient Requirements of Dairy Cattle: Update 1989, Sixth Revised Edition,* © 1989 by the National Academy of Sciences, Washington DC; *Nutrient Requirements of Goats: Angora, Dairy, and Meat Goats in Temperate and Tropical Countries,* © 1981 by the National Academy of Sciences; *Nutrient Requirements of Swine, Ninth Revised Edition, 1988,* © 1988 by the National Academy of Sciences; *Nutrient Requirements of Poultry, Eighth Revised Edition, 1984,* © 1984 by the National Academy of Sciences; *Nutrient Requirements of Horses, Fifth Revised Edition, 1989,* © 1989 by the National Academy of Sciences; *Nutrient Requirements of Beef Cattle, Sixth Revised Edition, 1984,* © 1984 by the National Academy of Sciences; *Nutrient Requirements of Sheep, Sixth Revised Edition, 1985,* © 1985 by the National Academy of Sciences. Acknowledgments to CAB International, Wallingford, Oxon, UK for permission to reproduce tables and figures from *The Nutrient Requirements of Ruminant Livestock.*

*Editorial/production supervision and
    interior design: Joan L. Stone*
Cover design: Bruce Kenselaar
Cover photo: Dick Dietrick/FPG
Prepress buyer: Mary McCartney
Manufacturing buyer: Ed O'Dougherty

Printed in the United States of America
10 9 8 7 6 5 4 3 2 1

ISBN 0-13-538760-4

PRENTICE-HALL INTERNATIONAL (UK) LIMITED, *London*
PRENTICE-HALL OF AUSTRALIA PTY. LIMITED, *Sydney*
PRENTICE-HALL CANADA INC., *Toronto*
PRENTICE-HALL HISPANOAMERICANA, S.A., *Mexico*
PRENTICE-HALL OF INDIA PRIVATE LIMITED, *New Delhi*
PRENTICE-HALL OF JAPAN, INC., *Tokyo*
SIMON & SCHUSTER ASIA PTE. LTD., *Singapore*
EDITORA PRENTICE-HALL DO BRASIL, LTDA., *Rio de Janeiro*

Contents

Preface

It has been seven years since the last edition of *Livestock Feeds and Feeding* was published. During that period of time there have been many dramatic things happening in international relationships, politics, medicine, and other areas of science. Information is still being developed in the human and animal nutrition fields, although perhaps at a somewhat slower rate than during the previous decade or so. It seems to be the sign of the times that far too many unsubstantiated experiments get national or worldwide publicity; sometimes the information turns out to be fact and at other times to be fiction.

In the practical field of feeding animals, we are usually concerned with growing and raising animals for a profit, although the profit motive may not apply to pets and a few other situations. When profit is one of the driving forces, it is imperative to try to increase efficiency of animal production by using less expensive feed, providing deficient nutrients and thus improving animal production, or processing feed when desirable and carrying out the feeding management of animals in such ways as to get faster growth or more milk production, and so forth. There has been a gradual improvement in all of these areas as well as in the genetic potential for rapid-growing animals.

In this book we have attempted to present enough information to provide the reader with the needed background on various topics and to put that information into practice. The editor gave the following charge to all co-authors: "Please write your chapter in a manner so that the users will be able to understand the material and have confidence that he/she can feed a particular type of livestock with the expectation that they will be good producers." Only the user will eventually know if this challenge was successful. We sincerely hope that it is.

D. C. Church

*Livestock Feeds
and Feeding*

1

Feeds and Feeding

Information available in print on the nutrition and feeding of livestock has been developed from countless experiments carried out on a worldwide basis, primarily in the past 100 to 125 years. The bulk of this information has been developed by public institutions (land grant universities in the United States, for example). More limited studies have been done by private institutions or individuals, and all of the published data are backed up by observations of herders, farmers, ranchers, veterinarians, and nutritionists. As a result of the accumulation of this vast amount of data, we can, within reasonable limits, define animal needs for specific nutrients, and we can classify and describe accurately most animal feeds with regard to their nutritional value and/or problems that may be associated with them. Even though the science of animal nutrition and feeding has been advanced significantly by this type of information, our knowledge is still not complete (see Ch. 3 and 13 to 25).

Competition between humans and animals for feedstuffs often used for feeding animals (for example, cereal grains) is almost inevitably going to become keener in the future. Relatively large famines have occurred in several African countries in recent years—largely caused by adverse weather, but in some cases apparently abetted by the local political situation. If these large-scale famines are not to occur at increasing intervals, more efficient use must be made of rangelands, forages, and other materials such as agricultural and industrial wastes in the feeding of animals *if* livestock flocks and herds are to be maintained at about their present levels. Livestock feeders and nutritionists must learn to be more conservative of ration components and nutrients in critical supply and to utilize those in surplus more effectively. For example, if more of the vast tonnage of crop residues—straws, fodders, and so on—could be made into higher-quality livestock feed *at acceptable costs*, feed could be provided for millions of animals from otherwise poorly utilized residues.

Nutritional value of feedstuffs, critical nutrient requirements, and ration formulation in practical feeding situations will be emphasized in this book. Thus this book is intended to provide for the reader and student a better understanding of and practice in integration of these important factors in livestock production.

1

INFORMATION NEEDED
FOR SUCCESSFUL FEEDING

The fundamental principles in economical feeding were outlined very well by Professor W. O. Atwater (1) in 1878:

> The right feeding of stock, then is not merely a matter of so much hay and grain and roots, but rather of so much water, starch, gluten, etc., of which they are composed. To use fodder economically, we must so mix and deal it out that the ration shall contain just the amounts of the various nutrients needed for maintenance and for the particular form of production that is required. . . . we must consider: What is the chemical composition of our fodder materials? How many pounds of . . . (nutrients) . . . are contained in a hundred pounds of hay, clover, potatoes, meal, etc? Of these various ingredients of food, what proportions of each are digestible and consequently nutritious? What part does each of these food ingredients play in the animal economy? . . . How much of each do different animals, as oxen and cows, need for maintenance of life and production of meat, milk, etc.? And finally, how must different kinds of fodder be mixed and fed so that the digestible material shall be most fully digested and utilized, and the least quantity wasted?

The statements by Professor Atwater, which were published more than one hundred years ago, are still quite applicable in our modern agriculture. However, some additional comment and elaboration of some of the factors are in order.

A knowledge of the nutrient needs of animals is of primary importance if we wish to achieve maximum performance on minimal nutrient intake. This need is well recognized, and there is a constant and continual research effort to refine and extend existing knowledge of animal requirements. In modern agriculture it is obvious that many factors may affect animal nutrient requirements over and above those normally considered. For example, two factors may operate to cause a reduction in nutrient needs. First, herd health has been improved by control of many diseases and parasites. In addition, livestock management, in general, has improved in recent years. Both of these factors should result in less wastage of feeds and nutrients. On the other hand, there has been a general in-

crease in the genetic capabilities of animals, allowing improved production. This may alter requirements, perhaps resulting in a higher requirement of nutrient concentration/unit of feed. However, if an animal grows more rapidly, the amount of feed needed/unit of gain is nearly always less.

Still another factor to consider is that the development of large livestock operations undoubtedly puts more stress of various types on confined animals. Greater emphasis on the production of high-yielding crops may sometimes result in trace mineral deficiencies or higher levels of toxic compounds such as nitrates in some plants. In addition, increasing use of waste and by-product feedstuffs requires an improved knowledge of nutrient requirements as some of these products may be quite deficient in some nutrients or they may contain excesses of nutrients that are toxic. Also, there has been an increasing utilization of synthetic and purified products, such as urea, which require that other components of the diet must be examined more critically.

As Professor Atwater pointed out, animal needs are best described as needs for specific nutrients. While animal needs could be described in terms of weight units of feedstuffs, this is not feasible under many situations, primarily because feedstuffs vary in composition due to environmental factors such as soil fertility, weather, varietal differences, and harvesting methods. Consequently, a kilogram of alfalfa hay produced in one area may have a different feeding value than hay produced in a different locality or at a different time. In addition, with the wide variety of feedstuffs available in some locations, there would still be a need for some means of relative evaluation; that is, if a kilogram of alfalfa is worth so much, how much is corn worth if half alfalfa and half corn are fed? Thus it is more feasible to express requirements as the need for specific nutrients.

For maximum production, something must be known for different animal species and which feedstuffs are preferred, because this becomes more critical when it is desired to achieve high levels of feed intake. By the same token we must be knowledgeable of different feed preparatory and preservation methods because they may affect feed consumption and utilization in the gastrointestinal tract.

The feeder and/or nutritionist must be aware of feedstuffs that are harmful. For example, cottonseed meal has a relatively high amount of gossypol. This compound is relative-

TABLE 1-1

Estimated world production of wheat, rice, corn, and coarse grains* (in millions of metric tons)

	Crop Year		
	1981–82	1983–84	1986–87
Wheat	449.4	489.4	522.4
Rice	412.4	453.8	465.8
Corn	440.0	347.5	475.1
Coarse grains	766.0	687.7	838.0
Total	2067.8	1978.4	2301.3

*Coarse grains include barley, oats, and sorghum.
Source: USDA (2).

ly toxic to swine and poultry, thus cottonseed meal must be restricted in rations for these animals or a more expensive type must be used which is produced from varieties of cotton that have low levels of gossypol.

When formulating and evaluating diets, it is quite useful to have a general knowledge of nutrient concentration in groups of similar feedstuffs. For example, a student of this subject should learn the general similarities of the cereal grains, the oil seed meals, and different types of hays.

It is certainly necessary to have some background knowledge of supplemental feedstuffs—those used in relatively small amounts to make up for inadequacies in the principal ingredients. It is a must to have some knowledge of different nonnutritive additives in common usage—antibiotics, hormones, medicants, and others. Last, but certainly not least, the cost of different sources of nutrients must be given due consideration. When it is realized that feed is the major cost in production of all livestock enterprises, it is easy to visualize that cost of individual feedstuffs and rations may determine whether the feeder stays in business or ends up in backruptcy.

This brief discussion is meant to highlight some of the factors necessary for a complete knowledge of this subject. The beginning student will understand that it is a complex problem, but these factors will be discussed in other chapters in more detail so that a gradual understanding should be developed.

FOOD PRODUCTION AND ANIMAL CONSUMPTION

Food and feed production vary each year depending on governmental regulatory practices, price of the product and estimated future price, environmental factors, particularly weather, and the cost of other factors such as labor, fertilizer, machinery, and money.

In order to give some perspective to the world and national feed production and consumption, some recent statistics will be presented on this topic. In the 1986–87 crop year, estimates for world production of food and feed grains (Table 1–1) show production to be at a level of 2301 million metric tons (T), up appreciably from 2067.8 million metric T for 1981–82. Some of the increased production is due to wider use of improved varieties and perhaps more use of fertilizer and irrigation or other cultural practices. In any case, as shown in Table 1–2, over the past 10 years estimated

TABLE 1-2

Estimated world production and consumption of feed grains (in millions of metric tons)

	Crop Year		
	1976–77	1981–82	1986–87[a]
Production	704.8	766.3	834.1
Consumption	685.1	738.2	805.4
End stocks	85.1	120.4	211.6

[a]Estimated amounts.
Source: USDA (3).

TABLE 1-3

Acreage devoted to major crop production in the United States for the 1985 crop year

Crop	Acreage, Millions	Percent of Grain
Grains[a]		
Corn	82.28	43.97
Wheat	64.73	34.59
Rye	0.72	0.38
Rice	2.50	1.34
Oats	8.15	4.36
Barley	11.55	6.17
Sorghum[a]	17.19	9.19
Grain total	187.12	
All hays	60.55	
Total crops	247.67	

[a]Includes acreage harvested for silage.
Source: USDA (4).

world production of feed grains has increased from 704.8 to 834.1 million metric T, an increase of 131 million metric T, or 18.6 percent. All of this has occurred in the face of high fuel costs, increasing labor costs (in many countries), and increasing population growth on a worldwide basis. During this same period, consumption of feed grains increased from 685.1 to 805.4 million metric T (17.4 percent).

In the United States, production (in million metric T) of these same grains for 1986–87 was estimated to be (percent of the world total is given in parentheses): wheat, 309.9 (59.3); rice, 6.1 (1.3); corn, 209.6 (44.1); and coarse grains, 252.9 (30.2). Coarse grains include barley, oats, and sorghums.

The acreage devoted to the major grains and hay crops is shown in Table 1–3 for the United States. Note that a total of 187.1 million acres (ac) of land was harvested with grains on it and 60.5 million ac with hays. The feed grains (all except wheat, rye, and rice) were grown on about 119 million ac (48.2 million hectares [ha]). An additional 26.7 million ha (65.9 million ac) were devoted to soybean production. Other data on production of specific crops and manufactured by-products are listed and discussed in Ch. 6, 7, and 8.

Total feed units (all feed equilibrated to the feeding value of corn) consumed in the United States are shown in Table 1–4. Note in the past 5 years (the time span in the table) that use of concentrates (grains and other nonroughage feeds) has increased from 193 to 210 million T, an increase of 8.8 percent. Harvested roughage use has declined by 21.6 percent and pasture production by 4.3 percent. For 1985 (the last

year for which data were available), concentrates amounted to 41 percent of the total feed units produced. This is up from 36.6 percent for 1980. Of course, if the total feed and pasture produced were expressed on a straight tonnage basis, the concentrates would be a much lower percentage, because they have a higher feeding value than hay or pasture.

FEED PRODUCTION BY THE FEED MILLING INDUSTRY

The milling of food grains for flour, other food products, or various industrial uses results in the production of a number of by-products used as animal feeds (see Ch. 7 and 8). These by-products are used by the feed milling industry, a very important segment of the livestock industry in any highly industrialized country. This is evident by the amounts of manufactured feeds produced.

TABLE 1-4

Estimated total feeds consumed by livestock and poultry in the United States (in millions of tons)

Feed Source	Amount[a]		
	1980	1984	1985[b]
Concentrates	193	206	210
Harvested roughage	102	82	80
Pasture	232	227	222
Total	527	515	512

[a]Values are expressed in equivalent feeding value to corn grain.
[b]Estimated values.
Source: USDA (4).

TABLE 1-5

Primary feed* production in the United States (in millions of tons)

Type of Feed	Year			
	1980	1983	1986	1987
Starter/grower/layer/ breeder chickens	12.8	12.3	14.0	14.2
Broiler chickens	16.8	17.5	21.7	23.4
Turkey	4.0	4.0	6.2	7.2
Dairy	14.6	15.1	18.2	17.4
Beef/sheep	14.8	14.7	18.3	18.1
Hog	13.7	12.4	13.0	14.5
All other	5.1	5.0	6.6	6.9
Total, all feeds	81.9	81.0	98.2	101.8

*Primary feed is defined as that which is mixed with individual ingredients, sometimes with the addition of a premix at a rate of less than 100 lb/ton of finished feed.

Source: Anon. (5).

Manufactured feeds are frequently listed as primary or secondary feeds. A **primary feed** is defined as one which is mixed with individual ingredients, sometimes with the addition of a premix at a rate of less than 100 lb/T of finished feed. A **secondary feed** is defined as that which is mixed with one or more ingredients and a formula feed supplement (which is a primary feed). These supplements are normally used at a rate of 300 lb or more per ton of finished feed.

Production (estimated) of primary feeds for 1980, 1983, 1986, and 1987 is shown in Table 1-5. During that period the amount produced increased from 81.9 to 101.8 million T (24.3 percent) and the production of feed for all different livestock groups increased. Naturally, the normal cycles in price and production that occur will have some effect on these trends, but the overall trend is up, as is the production of feed grains. Poultry are normally fed very little hay or other coarse feeds. With respect to primary feeds, all poultry use accounted for 44.8 million T in 1987, or 44.0 percent of the total manufactured primary feeds. The amount of secondary feeds produced is not as well documented. Based on a survey by the USDA, secondary feed production in 1986 amounted to about 11 million T, or 10 percent of the total manufactured feed (5).

Because of the complexity of the rations used, a high percentage of the feeds fed to poultry are prepared in feed mills. Only in very large units are growers likely to have their own feed mills. Table 1-6 illustrates the variety of manufactured ingredients or grains used in broiler rations in the United States for the 1984 year. Although corn and soybean meal account for 73.4 percent of the total ingredients shown

in this table, numerous other ingredients are normally used, although the variety in any particular ration in any given area would be less than indicated by the ingredient list shown in Table 1-6.

TABLE 1-6

Broiler feed ingredients used in the United States in 1984 (in thousands of tons)

Ingredient	Amount
Corn	5283.2
Sorghum	659.1
Barley	9.6
Oats	0.6
Wheat	225.8
Other grains	26.4
Total grain	6204.6
Soybean meal	1792.0
Other oil meals	9.6
Corn gluten meal	235.0
Wheat millfeeds	23.4
Other millfeeds	39.1
Meat & bone meal	209.9
Fish meal	253.6
Poultry by-product	221.7
Other animal proteins	102.0
Calcium sources	65.8
Phosphorus sources	72.1
Salt	26.3
Other minerals	34.8
Fats	250.7
Molasses	6.8
Alfalfa products	1.9
Other by-products	259.4
Total ingredients	9639.2

Source: USDA (4).

In other types of livestock units, with the possible exception of growing-finishing operations for pigs, the tendency for most producers is to use considerably less primary feed. They would normally supply other ingredients such as grains or hays or, if not grown by the feeder, they would more likely be purchased separately and processed at the site of feeding. Large beef feeders generally have their own milling equipment and normally would purchase only supplemental feed (secondary feeds) containing proteins, minerals, and additives of various types.

SUMMARY

Although there have been many dire predictions of decreasing availability of feed grains for animal use (including some by the writer), worldwide statistics show that production continues to increase, even in the face of high fuel and fertilizer costs. Eventually, either the human population will have to be stabilized at a slower growth rate or fewer feed grains will be available to animals. Expansion of the feed industry continues in the United States (in volume of feed use). Many different feed ingredients are utilized by the milling industry in addition to the feed grains. Development of more information on nutrient requirements and feeding management of livestock will help to increase the efficiency of utilization of feeds and to put off the time when feeds are increasingly priced out of the market for livestock.

REFERENCES

1. Atwater, W. O. 1877–88 *Report of work of the Agricultural Experiment Station.* Middletown, CN: Agricultural Experiment Station.
2. USDA. 1987. *World grain situation and outlook.* Washington, D.C.: USDA, Foreign Agr. Service Cir. Series FG-2-87 (January).
3. USDA. 1987. *Feed situation and outlook report.* Washington, D.C.: USDA, Econ. Res. Service, FDS-304 (November).
4. USDA. 1987. *Agricultural statistics 1986.* Washington, D.C.: USDA.
5. Anon. 1988. *Feedstuffs reference issue.* Minnetonka, MN: Miller.

2

The Gastrointestinal Tract and Nutrient Utilization

The gastrointestinal tract (GI tract) is vitally important to the animal because it is made up of a number of organs that are responsible for utilization of foods and nutrients. Furthermore, some knowledge of its anatomy and function is helpful in evaluating feedstuffs and in formulation of diets (rations) and thus it is of some concern to those readers interested in the nutrition and feeding of animals.

Some knowledge in how the GI tract digests feeds and factors that affect feed utilization is important because losses in digestibility have a marked affect on efficiency of feed utilization. In addition, many feed-related factors may alter normal functioning of the GI tract. Consequently, some degree of familarity with its anatomy and function are important for a reasonable understanding of practices and problems in feeding livestock. Information presented in this chapter will be very brief. Additional information is available from many other sources; some that the author would recommend are listed at the end of the chapter (1, 2, 3).

The GI tract of simple-stomached mammalian species includes the mouth and associated structures and salivary glands, esophagus, stomach, small and large intestines, pancreas, and liver. These various organs, glands, and other structures are concerned with procuring, chewing, and swallowing food, and with the digestion and absorption of nutrients as well as with some excretory functions.

Digestion and absorption are terms that will be referred to frequently in this and other chapters. **Digestion** has been defined simply as the preparation of food for absorption. It may include mechanical forces such as chewing (or mastication) or muscular contractions of the GI tract, chemical action of hydrogen chloride (HCl) in the stomach or physiochemical action of bile (from the liver) in the small intestine, or activity from enzymes produced in the GI tract or from microorganisms in various sites in the tract. The overall function of the various digestive processes is to reduce food particles to a size or solubility that will allow for absorption. **Absorption** includes various processes that allow small molecules to pass through the membranes of the GI tract into the blood or lymph systems.

7

MAJOR ANATOMICAL FEATURES OF THE STOMACH AND INTESTINES

As might be imagined, the GI tract of different types of domestic animals varies considerably. Generally, animal species are divided into groups based on what the main ingredient in their diet is. **Herbivores** are primarily vegetarians, **carnivores** eat other animals, and **omnivores** eat a combination of vegetable and animal matter. If we wanted to include all animal species, there are many other subgroupings that could be included; for example, with birds we have those which are fish eaters, insect eaters, fruit eaters, and so forth.

When discussing digestive physiology of domestic species, it is also common to describe animals as having a simple stomach, often referred to as **monogastric** (or **nonruminant**), or as **ruminant** animals. Ruminant animals are herbivorous and include cattle, sheep, goats, deer, and many other wild species. Horses and mules are herbivorous animals, but they have a simple stomach and a rather large, complex large intestine. Rabbits are herbivores with a simple stomach with a relatively complex large gut. Swine are omnivorous simple-stomached species. Poultry are omnivorous with a complex foregut (three organs replacing the normal stomach) and a relatively simple intestinal tract.

A picture of the partially dissected stomach and intestines of a pig is shown in Fig. 2–1; it will serve as our model for a simple-stomached (nonruminant) or monogastric species.

The shape of the stomach of different animal species varies, as does the relative size within species as well as among species. In swine, for example, the stomach is relatively large, with a capacity in the adult on the order of 6–8 liters. The weight of the stomach and its contents is about 4 percent of body weight as compared to 1 percent in humans.

Most of the stomach is lined with mucosal cells which produce mucus that serves to protect the stomach lining from gastric secretions. In the central part of the stomach there are gastric glands which produce mixed secretions of HCl, enzymes, and mucus. These gastric juices are effective in initiating digestion in the stomach.

In the pig the small intestine is relatively long (15–20 m). The small intestine is generally much shorter in carnivores. The first short section, the duodenum, is the site of production of various digestive juices, and other juices enter the duodenum from the bile duct. These latter

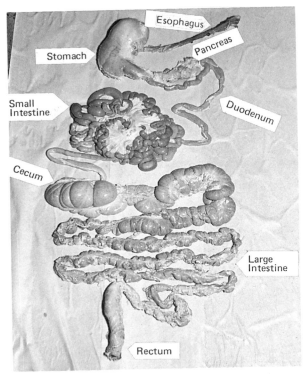

Figure 2–1. The esophagus, stomach, pancreas, and intestines of the pig. Photo by D. C. Church.

juices are derived either from the liver (bile) or the pancreas. The small intestine is lined with small, fingerlike projections, the villi, which serve to increase surface area for absorption (Fig. 2–2).

The large intestine is made up of the cecum, colon, and rectum. The relative length, diameter, and sacculation differ considerably in different species of animals. These organs tend to be much larger (relatively) in herbivorous species.

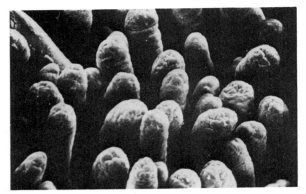

Figure 2–2. A scanning electron micrograph showing the intestinal villi of the baby pig. Courtesy of H. Moon, USDA, ARS, National Animal Disease Center, Ames, IA.

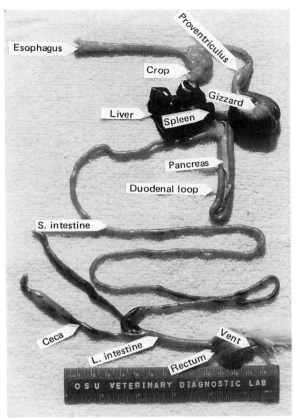

Figure 2-3. The digestive tract of the chicken. Photo by Don Helfer, Oregon State University Diagnostic Laboratory.

In avian species, the crop, proventriculus, and gizzard replace the simple stomach found in monogastric species (Fig. 2–3). Even here there are variations between different types of birds, because most insect-eating or fish-eating species have no crops.

Where a crop is present, ingested food goes directly to it and the crop serves as a temporary storage site; it is an organ which in many species has great capacity for expansion. The proventriculus of birds is the site of production of gastric juices. The gizzard is a very muscular organ with a tough lining. It normally contains grit—small stones and other hard materials. The gizzard serves some of the same functions of teeth in mammalian species, acting to physically reduce particle size of food. With regard to the intestinal tract, birds have a relatively long small intestine, two rather large ceca, and a very short section of large intestine. Birds also differ from mammals in that urine is excreted in semisolid form along with the feces.

In ruminant species the major modification of the GI tract is in the stomach, an organ which has a very complex pattern of motility and physical structure. In most ruminant species the stomach is divided into four compartments, the reticulum, rumen, omasum, and abomasum (Fig. 2–4). In a few species—the camel and related species (pseudoruminants)—the stomach has only three compartments.

The stomach of the ruminant is quite large when measured on the basis of the total GI tract or on the basis of body weight. Whereas the stomach (and its contents) of the pig is about 4 percent of body weight, the stomach of sheep and cattle will be more on the order of 25–28 percent of body weight. If expressed as a percentage of the total GI tract, the pig stomach is about 14 percent of the total, while the stomach of sheep and cattle are about 37 and 45 percent, respectively.

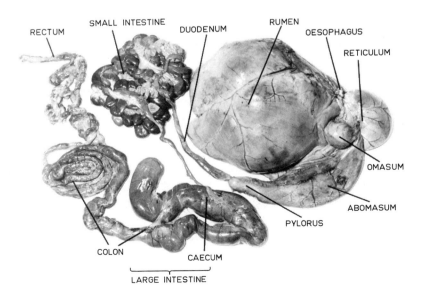

Figure 2-4. The stomach and intestines of the sheep. Courtesy of CSIRO, Canberra, Australia.

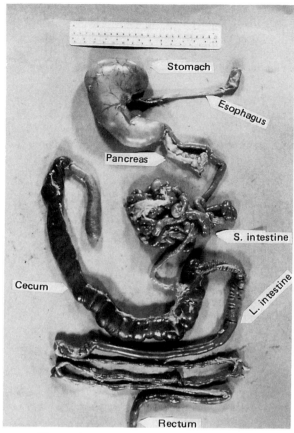

Figure 2–5. The digestive tract of the rabbit. Photo by D. C. Church.

The first three compartments of the ruminant stomach are lined with cell types (stratified *squamous epithelium*) not normally associated with organs that have absorptive surfaces. Yet research evidence indicates that substantial amounts of some materials may be absorbed here.

The reticulum gets its name from a lining of cells arranged in a network resembling the cell shape of a honeycomb, thus its common name of honeycomb. The rumen, or paunch, is lined with papillae, which cover most of the surface but are more dense in the ventral parts of the rumen of most species. It is partially divided into different sacs by pillars which function to control contractions of the organs. The omasum is a spherical-shaped organ containing leaves of different sizes, and it is normally tightly packed with fine particulate matter. The omasum empties into the abomasum, which is comparable in function to the gastric stomach of simple-stomached species in that it produces the usual gastric juices. It differs physically in that there are spiral folds, about 12 in number, extending around the interior of the organ; these

apparently act to provide more surface area for proliferation of the gastric glands.

As with other herbivorous species, the intestinal tract of ruminants is relatively long and moderately complex. The cecum is large, but relatively smaller than that of other herbivorous species such as the rabbit or horse. The large intestine is also relatively large as compared to omnivorous species, although relatively smaller than in the horse.

The rabbit is one example of a herbivorous species that has a simple stomach (Fig. 2–5) accompanied by a very voluminous cecum. Both the cecum and colon are sacculated. The horse is another example of a herbivore with a relatively large sacculated cecum and an extremely large sacculated colon. Both species are examples of animals in which extensive microbial fermentation occurs in the large gut (cecum and/or colon).

FUNCTIONS OF THE GASTROINTESTINAL TRACT

Monogastric and Avian Species

In mammalian animal species, the mouth and associated structures—tongue, lips, teeth—are used for grasping and masticating food. The degree of use of any organ depends on the species of animal and the nature of its food. In omnivorous species, such as humans or swine, the incisor teeth are used primarily to bite off pieces of the food and the molar teeth are adapted to mastication of nonfibrous materials. The tongue is used relatively little. In carnivorous species the canine teeth are adapted to tearing and rending of muscle and bone, while the molars are pointed and adapted to only partial mastication and the crushing of bones. Herbivorous species, such as the horse, have incisor teeth adapted to nipping off plant material, and the molars have relatively flat surfaces that are used to grind plant fibers. The jaws are used in both vertical and lateral movements which shred plant fibers efficiently. Ruminants, on the other hand, have no upper incisors and depend on an upper dental pad and lower incisors for biting off plant material. With regard to avian species, they have no teeth, thus the beak and/or claws serve to reduce food to a size that may be swallowed.

In the process of mastication (chewing), saliva is added, primarily from three bilateral pairs of glands. Saliva aids in forming food into a bolus that may be swallowed easily, and it has other functions such as keeping the mouth moist, aiding in the taste mechanisms, and providing a source of some enzymes that contribute to the digestive process.

In the stomach, gastric juices continue the digestive processes initiated by mastication and ensalivation in the mouth. Hydrochloric acid provides for an acidic pH, and the enzymes initiate digestion of protein and, in young mammals, of fats. The partially digested food, now called chyme, passes into the duodenum, where it is subjected to the action of intestinal juices and bile, which gradually raises the pH into the alkaline range. Bile also aids in emulsification of fats, a necessary step in their solubilization and absorption. Enzymes from the pancreas continue enzymic digestion of proteins, fats, and carbohydrates, and these are complemented by additional enzymes produced by glands in the wall of the duodenum. Enzymic activity continues as the food passes into the jejunum and ileum, the other segments of the small intestine. These sections are also the site of most of the absorption of nutrients that occurs in the intestinal tract. Most of the organic nutrients that are absorbed have been absorbed by the time the digesta passes into the cecum. The cecum, although a blind sac, appears to empty and refill itself by means of rhythmatic contractions.

Bacterial growth develops in the ileum, cecum, and colon. By the time the digesta reaches the cecum there is a high population of many different organisms, the amount and type depending upon the species of animal and its diet. Absorption of some organic acids and other organic compounds such as ammonia occurs in the cecum and large intestine. Large amounts of water are absorbed by the large intestine, also. This may be one of the major functions of the cecum and of large (or long) and sacculated colons (3).

In addition to the digestion and absorption that occurs, the GI tract is the major route of excretion of many compounds. This statement applies particularly to bile, which is produced by the liver. The liver is a very active site of detoxification of many toxins found in plants or microbes or drugs that may be administered to the animal. The liver also excretes many metallic elements, and it is the site of degradation and excretion of many body compounds such as most of the hormones. These different compounds or detoxified chemicals are excreted via the bile. In the large intestine some net excretion of mineral elements occurs, particularly calcium, magnesium, and phosphorus.

One other important activity that occurs in the GI tract is that of nutrient synthesis. Many different research studies have shown that the microbial population in the cecum and large gut are capable of extensive synthesis of a number of water-soluble vitamins and other organic components of microbial tissues—amino acids and proteins, different carbohydrates, and some lipids. Intestinal synthesis, particularly of some of the vitamins, reduces or eliminates the dependence of the animal on a dietary supply of vitamins that may be produced there.

The amount of absorption of vital nutrients, such as vitamins, that occurs in the lower gut is not clear, although it is usually assumed that relatively little absorption of organic molecules takes place past the ileum. In some animals, particularly rodents such as rabbits and rats, this potential lack of absorption is circumvented by the practice of coprophagy (feces eating). These species typically produce night feces with a different physical character; night feces are believed to originate mainly from the cecum. This material is high in vitamin content and, perhaps, in essential amino acids. The consequence of this is that the animal may survive on diets which would otherwise not have sufficient vitamins and essential amino acids to support life.

Ruminant Species

In the GI tract of the ruminant, ingested food is exposed to very extensive pregastric fermentation. Most of the ingesta is fermented by microbes before it is exposed to typical gastric and intestinal digestive chemicals and enzymes; thus this is quite a different system than that of typical monogastric animal species.

The reticulo-rumen provides a very favorable environment for microbial activity and survival. It is moist and warm, and there is an irregular introduction of new digesta and a more or less continual removal of fermented digesta and end products of digestion. A wide variety of bacterial types may be found in the rumen and typical bacterial counts range from 25 to 80 billion/ml. In addition to bacteria, some 35+ species of ciliate protozoa have been identified from the rumen of animals in different situations, although the variety that may be found in any one animal is considerably less. Protozoal numbers vary widely, but typical counts are on the order of 20,000 to 500,000/ml. These organisms are much larger than bacteria and, although the numbers are less, they represent about the same amount of microbial protoplasm as from the bacteria.

In addition, flagellated protozoa are often present in the rumen, particularly in young animals, and very high numbers of phages (bacterial viruses) have been observed, although little is known of their importance. Yeast sometimes occur in appreciable numbers, as do other types of organisms, but the bacteria and protozoa are believed to be the most important microbes. The fate of rumen microorganisms is that eventually they pass into the abomasum and intestine and are then digested by the host animal.

The net effect of this thriving microbial population is that it has a marked effect on nutrient requirements and metabolism of the host animal. Fibrous feeds are digested more efficiently in the rumen than in the large intestine or cecum. Cellulose and hemicellulose, in particular, can be digested by microbes, whereas animals do not produce the necessary enzymes. In addition, bacteria can utilize simple forms of nitrogen, such as ammonia or urea, to synthesize their cellular proteins. This reduces the dependence of the animal on high-quality dietary proteins and allows the use of compounds such as urea as protein replacements in their diets. A further benefit is that rumen synthesis is extensive for all vitamins except vitamins A, D, and E and, as a result, the animal is not dependent upon a dietary source of these vitamins with rare exceptions.

One of the chief disadvantages of rumen fermentation is that most dietary proteins are partially degraded and the ammonia produced is resynthesized into microbial protein. This is a wasteful process. In addition, readily available carbohydrates such as sugars and starches are rapidly and completely degraded, the major end products being the volatile fatty acids—acetic, propionic, and butyric. While these acids are used readily by the animal's tissues, they are used less efficiently for energy than the original carbohydrates. Furthermore, in the fermentation process as much as 8–10 percent of the energy consumed is converted to methane, a gas which the animal cannot utilize and which is wasted as a result of microbial fermentation.

These different factors illustrate in a simplified manner why feed coversion of ruminants is low as compared to that of monogastric species. Feed conversion (units of feed consumed/unit of product produced) for ruminants is often twice or more that of monogastric species.

The overall effect of rumen fermentation is that these animals can survive and do well on less complex and lower-quality diets than monogastric species can, but, on the other hand, they use good-quality dietary ingredients less efficiently than do monogastric species.

Associated with rumen fermentation in ruminants is the production of vast amounts of saliva, perhaps as much as 150+ liters/day in mature cows. Saliva contains large amounts of sodium bicarbonate which is vital in maintaining an appropriate pH in the rumen by buffering the acids produced. Saliva is also important in maintaining an optimum moisture content.

In the young ruminant the reticulum, rumen, and omasum are relatively underdeveloped at birth because the suckling animal depends primarily on the abomasum and intestine for digestive functions. As soon as the animal starts to consume solid food, the other compartments develop rapidly, and they attain relative mature proportions by about 8 weeks in lambs and kids, 3-4 months in deer, and 6-9 months in domestic bovines.

An anatomical peculiarity of ruminant species is that they have a structure called the reticular (or esophageal) groove. This structure begins at the lower end of the esophagus and, when closed, forms a tube from the esophagus into the omasum. Its function is to allow milk consumed by the suckling animal to bypass the rumen and thus escape bacterial fermentation. The groove does not appear to remain functional in older animals unless they continue to suckle liquid diets.

In the ruminant stomach there is a well-developed pattern of rhythmic contractions of the various stomach compartments which act to circulate ingesta into and throughout the rumen, into and through the omasum, and on to the abomasum. Of importance also are contractions that aid in regurgitation during rumination. This is a phenomenon peculiar to ruminants. In effect, **rumination** is a controlled form of vomiting, allowing semiliquid material to be regurgitated up the esophagus, followed by swallowing of the liquids and a deliberate remastication of and reswallowing of the solids. Ruminants may spend 8 hours per day or more in rumination, the amount of time depending upon the nature of their diet. Course, fibrous diets result in more rumination time.

Eructation (belching of gas) is another mechanism that is quite important to ruminants. Microbial fermentation in the rumen results in the production of large amounts of gases (primarily carbon dioxide and methane) which must be eliminated. This is accomplished by contractions of the upper sacs of the rumen which force the gas forward and down; the esophagus then dilates and allows the gas to escape. During this process much of the gas penetrates into the trachea and lungs, after which it is exhaled through the nostrils.

A common problem in ruminants is bloat, a condition which results, for the most part, from formation of froth in the rumen, particularly after consumption of some legume species or in some feedlot situations. Froth, if found in the area where the esophagus enters the rumen, inhibits eructation. This is a safety mechanism which prevents inhalation of froth into the lungs. Bloat may be a very servere problem in cattle, resulting in many deaths or reduced production in affected animals.

RELATION OF THE TYPE OF GI TRACT AND TYPE OF DIET REQUIRED

The information that has been presented on the anatomy and function of the GI tract of different animals gives some indication of the type of diet (physical nature, chemical composition) which may be optimal for different animals. For example, the GI tract of avian species is relatively short and simple and does not provide for extensive fermentation in the intestines. Some fermentation does occur in the ceca but relatively much less than in most other species. Consequently, avian species do not have the ability to eat fibrous plant material to any degree. In order for most birds to consume their needed nutrients, they must have a diet relatively low in fiber and one that is moderately to highly digestible. This rules out the use of large amounts of feed ingredients such as ground alfalfa hay or of the fibrous grains such as barley and oats if we wish to have maximal consumption and productivity.

In omnivorous species such as swine, the GI tract is capable of utilizing relatively more fiber than avian species but much less than herbivorous species. Some ground legumes can be used in dry rations or adult pigs can be grazed on pastures for a portion of their sustenance, but if the pig must depend entirely on pasture, it must be excellent pasture indeed if productivity is not to suffer greatly. Hogs that run wild

depend on other food items such as nuts, roots, and similar plant material in addition to herbage, but their productivity on this type of diet is much too low to be feasible commercially.

Horses, as an example of nonruminant herbivorous species, can survive and do well on plant material of much lower quality than that required by swine. Data of a recent nature are insufficient to clearly quantitate needs of nutrients, such as the amino acids and vitamins. Hard-working horses clearly require more than roughage in order to maintain body weight and performance, but a substantial amount of roughage is conducive to optimal functioning of their GI tract.

The ruminant GI tract is adapted primarily to a diet of mainly fibrous plant materials. Although cattle can be fed high- or all-concentrate diets, if this practice is carried on for any great length of time (several months), digestive disturbances are likely and much better management of the cattle and care in formulation and milling of their rations is required to obtain maximal performance. Except for recent times when there have been grain surpluses, cattle and other domestic ruminants have traditionally been fed on pasture, hay, or coarse fodders which are of little use to chickens, swine, or humans as food. Present trends suggest a return to these practices to some degree. Although a greater dependence on roughages will reduce productivity, it will probably result in fewer problems with the animals and, perhaps, a more efficient overall utilization of our total agricultural resources.

SUMMARY

The gastrointestinal tract of our common domestic animals varies considerably in anatomy from species to species. In those animals which consume large amounts of coarse herbage, there are adaptations in either the stomach or the intestine. These various modifications allow for either pregastric microbial fermentation of the food consumed (as in ruminants) or in postgastric fermentation in the large intestine (as in the horse) or cecum (as in the rabbit). Omnivorous species such as the pig (or human) have less complex digestive tracts. Thus the type of digestive tract has a major effect on what kind of food can be consumed (over an extended period) and on how efficiently the food will be utilized. Animals with simple stomachs and intestines (for example pigs and poultry) cannot utilize large amounts of coarse, fibrous herbage. Those with more complex anatomies can utilize the fibrous herbage, and they are apt to have many problems if they are restricted to a diet containing very little fibrous material.

The gastrointestinal tract serves the animal well by providing the means of digesting the food it eats, absorbing the digested nutrients in the food, as well as recycling water (and thereby reducing water requirements). The GI tract is also the site of excretion of various chemicals by way of bile from the liver or through the walls of the intestines.

REFERENCES

1. Church, D. C. 1988. *The ruminant animal.* Englewood Cliffs, NJ: Prentice Hall.
2. Church, D. C., and W. G. Pond. 1988. *Basic animal nutrition and feeding.* 3d ed. New York: Wiley.
3. Swenson, M. J. (ed.). 1987. *Dukes' physiology of domestic animals.* 10th ed. Ithaca, NY: Cornell University Press.

3

The Nutrients, Their Metabolism, and Feeding Standards

INTRODUCTION

Nutrition, of both plants and animals, is one of the major biological sciences. A very considerable volume of scientific literature is available on the topic. The coverage of this topic in this book is intended to provide the reader with some familiarity with the names of the various nutrients, to give a brief amount of information on nutrient function and deficiencies of problem nutrients, and to discuss feeding standards briefly. Further details on these topics can be found in a variety of reference books listed at the end of the chapter (1, 2, 3, 4).

The nutrients required by animals are water, protein, energy, lipids, minerals, and vitamins. In most instances there are differences in requirements among different species of animals, but in practical situations the livestock feeder need not be concerned with a very long list of problem (critical) nutrients in any given situation because the usual feeds consumed will provide an adequate supply of most nutrients.

WATER

Water is an extremely important compound (nutrient) for livestock because it makes up 71–73 percent of the fat-free animal body weight. It has numerous functions of vital importance and, in general, is the most vital material ingested by animals, since a lack of water will have more immediate and drastic effects on animal physiology than the lack of any other nutrient.

Water Functions and Metabolism

Water has many functions. It acts as a solvent for many different compounds. It serves to transport fluids and semisolid ingesta through the GI tract. It transports materials in the blood and other body tissues so that nutrients are moved to the cells and wastes away from the cells. It serves in the elimination of body wastes via urine and, last but not least, is used for evaporative cooling of the animal body when temperatures are elevated.

Water available to an animal's tissues comes from drinking water, water contained in or on feed, and metabolic water produced by chemical reactions (primarily oxidation) of organic compounds in the animal's tissues. The importance of these different sources of water varies from animal species to species. Animals adapted to an arid climate get a higher percentage of their total water from sources other than drinking water than do animals adapted to more humid climates.

Water is lost from the body by way of the kidneys as urine, from the GI tract in the feces, from the lungs and skin as water vapor, and from the sweat glands as sweat. Water losses are increased greatly in a warm environment because the animal must increase evaporative losses from the lungs and body surface to maintain body temperatures within a range that allows the animal to survive. Water losses will be increased by greater consumption of high-protein diets (more water is required for urinary excretions), diets high in salts of various kinds, high-fiber diets, and by greater consumption of food, in general. Consequently, if a limited amount of water is available, it would be better to cut down on food consumption before water became restrictive. Certainly, a reduced supply of water will reduce feed consumption and animal productivity, especially for high-producing animals.

Further details on water requirements are given in Ch. 13–25. It is important to remember that water is more critical in warm and hot periods of the year and when productivity is high. Given a chance, animals can reduce somewhat the amount of water required, but this is not a desirable situation unless reduced water intake is a matter of animal survival during a long-term drought.

Water Quality

Water quality, as well as quantity, may affect feed consumption and animal health, because low-quality water will normally result in reduced water and feed consumption. As generally defined, good-quality water should contain less than 2,500 mg/ℓ of total solids; even though 15,000 mg/ℓ (1.5 percent) may be tolerated, production will likely be decreased at this level. Substances which may reduce palatability of water include various saline salts. At high rates of consumption these salts may be toxic, of course. Substances which may be toxic without much affect, if any, on palatability include nitrates and fluorine as well as salts of various heavy metals. Other materials which may affect palatability or be toxic include pathogenic microorganisms of a wide variety, algae and/or protozoa, hydrocarbons and other oily substances, pesticides of various types, and many industrial chemicals which sometimes pollute water supplies.

The various salts likely to be found in water include chlorides, sulfates and bicarbonates of sodium (Na), calcium (Ca), magnesium (Mg), and potassium (K). The tolerance of animals to salts in water depends on factors such as water requirements, species, age, physiological condition, season of the year, and salt content of the total diet as well as the type and quantity of salts present in the water. Animals will not normally choose to drink saline water if given a choice of good-quality (low salt) water, but within limits they can adjust and will drink saline waters that will be refused at first. However, sudden changes in water quality may cause acute salt poisoning and rapid death. Generally, water containing more than 1 percent NaCl (common salt) is generally not considered good quality because cattle and sheep can tolerate only about 1 percent NaCl without decreasing production in warm climates, and some animals, such as chickens and swine, will not tolerate even this much salt. Levels of 100-200 parts per million (ppm) nitrates are potentially toxic, and 1 g of sulfate/ℓ may result in diarrhea. Thus if there is a question of water quality, the water should be tested, especially in dairy, broiler, layer, or swine water supplies.

Water as a Source of Mineral Nutrients

Water is normally overlooked as a source of nutrients that may be dissolved in it. Granted, the dissolved materials in water vary greatly depending on the source (ground water, surface water, open lakes, closed lakes, and so on) and the mineral content of the soils. If average values are used for mineral content, computations suggest that cattle might receive from 20 to 40 percent of their NaCl requirements, 7 to 28 percent of Ca needs, 6 to 9 percent of Mg needs, and 20 to 45 percent of sulfur requirements (5). In areas where mineral imbalances might be a problem, water supplies should not be overlooked as a source of excess mineral elements.

PROTEIN

Proteins are essential constituents of the tissues of all biological organisms and, in animals, are found in higher concentration in organ and muscular tissue than any other constituent except water. All cells synthesize proteins for part or all of their life cycle, and without protein synthesis life could not exist. Thousands of different proteins are found in the various tissues. They may range from very insoluble types such as feather, hair, wool, and hooves to liquid and highly soluble proteins such as plasma globulins. Proteins are large molecules with molecular weights ranging from 35,000 to several hundred thousand. Each protein has a distinctive function in the animal body (or other biological organisms), ranging from protection of the body surface (hair, skin) to defense against invading organisms. Structurally, proteins have important functions as components of muscle, cell membranes, skin, hair, and hooves. Metabolically important proteins are the blood serum proteins, enzymes, hormones, and immune antibodies, which all have important specialized functions in the body (1). Proteins are synthesized in plant and animal cells where the cell nucleus contains genetic material that determines the nature of the newly synthesized protein. The genetic material, commonly referred to as DNA (deoxyribonucleic acid), is transferred from one generation to another. The nuclear DNA controls the synthesis of all proteins regardless of their function. Thus proteins are vital to animals and must be provided in the diet in one form or other.

Composition

A characteristic of all proteins is that they are composed of long chains of amino acids. An amino acid is an organic acid, such as acetic, which also contains one or more amino groups ($-NH_2$) attached to the basic molecule. The physical and chemical characteristics of proteins are altered by the different proportions of amino acids, the sequence in which they are bound together, any cross-linking which may occur, and by the presence of other nonamino acid groups or compounds. For example, some proteins may contain metals (for example, hemoglobin, which contains iron); others may contain carbohydrates (glycoproteins) or lipids (lipoproteins). Some, such as casein, an important protein in milk, contain rather large amounts of P (phosphorus).

Although there are more than two hundred naturally occurring compounds that have been classified as amino acids, most proteins contain about twenty different amino acids, regardless of whether the protein is of plant or animal origin. Plants are capable of synthesizing all of these amino acids from inorganic nitrogen (N) sources such as ammonia or nitrate and organic compounds of various types. Many microorganisms also have this capability, but higher animals are not capable of synthesizing all amino acids required by the various tissues, the result being that some amino acids are required in the diet of most animals. The liver is the principal site of synthesis for amino acids.

Essential Amino Acids

The amino acids required in the diets of animals are referred to as essential (or nondispensable) amino acids. Those not specifically required in the diet are called nonessential (or dispensable). Both groups are listed below:

Essential	Nonessential
Arginine	Alanine
Histidine	Aspartic acid
Isoleucine	Citrulline
Leucine	Cystine
Lysine	Glutamic acid*
Methionine	Glycine*
Phenylalanine	Hydroxyproline
Threonine	Proline*
Tryptophan	Serine
Valine	Tyrosine

*Amino acids required in addition to the essential amino acids by the chick for optimal growth.

Extensive studies with rats, mice, dogs, pigs, chicks, and humans have been carried out to evaluate the requirements of these different species. Such studies have been done using purified diets that contain such components as starch, sugar(s), lard or corn oil, purified vitamin and mineral sources, and various combinations of individual amino acids.

These studies have indicated that arginine is required in the diet of some species for maximum growth but not for maintenance; neither is it required by young calves. Asparagine (a derivative of aspartic acid) is required for maximum growth during the first few days of consumption of a crystalline amino acid diet.

Because there are situations in which one or more amino acids may be essential or give an added response (in growth or other production) when included in the diet, some authors prefer to list the amino acids as essential, semiessential, and nonessential. If divided up in this manner, the lists would be as follows:

Essential	Semiessential	Nonessential
Isoleucine	Arginine	Alanine
Leucine	Cystine	Aspartic acid
Lysine	Glycine	Citrulline
Methionine	Histidine	Glutamic acid
Phenylalanine	Proline	Hydroxyproline
Threonine	Tyrosine	Serine
Tryptophan		
Valine		

In practical animal nutrition, the amino acids most likely to be deficient are lysine, methionine (which contains sulfur), and tryptophan. Primary energy feeds such as corn and milo are quite low in these amino acids, and diets based on high percentages of these grains usually require supplementation with proteins which contain higher levels of these amino acids. Data on the amino acid content of some feedstuffs are presented in Ch. 9 and in the Appendix.

Ruminants (and some other herbivores) do not require dietary amino acids to the same extent as monogastric species. This is so because the rumen and intestinal microorganisms are capable of synthesizing the essential (and nonessential) amino acids from simple compounds such as urea (or ammonia) and organic acids produced from carbohydrate metabolism. Although ruminants can survive and produce at moderate levels on N sources such as urea, optimum productivity cannot be obtained with such diets. Evidence with high-producing animals, particularly with dairy cows, suggests that they may not necessarily receive optimal amounts of lysine or methionine (2).

Biological Availability of Proteins

The biological availability of dietary proteins is affected by the ability of an animal to digest proteins to amino acids, to absorb these amino acids, and to utilize them in the body to synthesize new proteins. In simple-stomached species of animals, dietary proteins are digested in the stomach with the aid of HCl and pepsin. Further digestion of protein occurs in the lower GI tract as enzymes from the pancreas (trypsin, chymotrypsin) and duodenum (various peptidases) complete the digestion process. Proteins must be hydrolyzed into smaller particles (amino acids) before they can be absorbed. An exception to this statement is the case of very young mammals. They are capable of absorbing some milk proteins in the early hours of life in order to pick up passive immunity to various diseases.

Protein metabolism in body tissues is a very active process with constant synthesis of new proteins and constant degradation of dead cells. During this process the amino group will be removed from the amino acid (deamination). It may be used in the synthesis of nonessential amino acids or, if in excess, will be further metabolized for excretion. In mammalian species the end product of protein catabolism (degradation) is urea, which is excreted via the urine. In avian species, uric acid is the primary form in which N is excreted from the kidneys.

The digestibility of proteins from different sources is quite different and varies among animal species. As a rule of thumb, we might say that most protein sources used as animal feed will be digested to the extent of 75–80 percent. However, many things may affect this value. For instance, many plant sources contain inhibitors of one type or another (see Ch. 8), and proper processing of animal proteins is generally critical in order to ensure high digestibility.

Efficient utilization of absorbed amino acids for resynthesis of body proteins is primarily related to the distribution of essential amino acids. Dietary proteins vary greatly in the extent to which they may be digested by animals (see Ch. 8). Those that contain essential amino acids at levels needed by the animal are referred to as high-quality proteins. Such proteins are normally highly digestible, but there are many exceptions to such a statement.

There are various means of ranking dietary proteins in addition to the content of amino acids which, by itself, does not provide information on animal utilization. The amount (concentration) of protein is one method. Digestibility of dietary protein is a second method, one often used in selection of dietary protein sources when formulating diets. Biological value (BV) is another way. BV is defined as the percentage of digested and absorbed N (protein) that is retained in the body for productive functions; it is an indirect means of evaluating how well a specific protein supplies the essential amino acids. Whole egg protein has a BV of about 100; meat proteins, 72–79; cereal proteins, 50–65; and gelatin, 12–16. Of course, in practice an animal would normally consume proteins from several sources in any given meal. Thus the inadequacies of a poor-quality protein are apt to be balanced out by others of higher quality. When this does not occur, then the animal's tissues are limited in the amount of new protein that can be synthesized. For example, if absorbed lysine is in short supply but is required for the proteins being synthesized, the amount of synthesis will be governed by the available lysine. Other essential amino acids present over and above the amount that can be used with the lysine will then be used primarily as an energy source and will not function as amino acids. This situation leads to poor performance and low feed efficiency if continued for any length of time.

Other measures of protein adequacy are the protein efficiency ratio (PER) and net protein value (NPV). PER is by definition the number of grams of body weight gain of an animal per unit of protein consumed. NPV measures efficiency of growth by comparing body N resulting from feeding a test protein with that resulting from feeding a comparable group of animals a protein-free diet for the same period of time. NPV can also be computed by multiplying the digestibility of a protein by the BV. Further details on this topic can be found in other sources (1).

In general, protein quality is less important to ruminant animals than to simple-stomached species. In the rumen a high proportion of dietary proteins are hydrolyzed by rumen microbes to amino acids, many of which are further degraded to organic acids, ammonia, and carbon dioxide. The free ammonia in rumen fluid is utilized by bacteria to synthesize new amino acids essential for their function. The bacteria, in turn, may be ingested by protozoa which go through the same type of cycle of degradation and resynthesis of proteins. Eventually, bacterial, protozoal, and undegraded dietary proteins pass into the intestinal tract, where they are digested to some degree and the amino acids absorbed. Bacterial and protozoal proteins are generally lower in BV than are high-quality proteins found in egg and milk, but they are of higher quality than many plant sources. Thus the tendency is to degrade the value of very high-quality proteins and upgrade that of low-quality dietary proteins. These various mechanisms allow the use of nonprotein-N compounds such as urea to be used as a feed ingredient in ruminant diets, although there are some limitations to its usage.

The value of a protein to a ruminant animal is related to how soluble the protein is in the rumen and how much of it will be de-

graded by rumen microorganisms. Some high-quality protein sources, such as fish meals, are not degraded to a great extent in the rumen. If such proteins pass into the intestinal tract and are digested rather completely, they are, therefore, able to supply the animal with a greater abundance of amino acids, such as lysine and methionine, which might otherwise be limiting. There must, of course, be an adequate supply of soluble and degradable protein to nourish the rumen microorganisms. Further information on this topic is presented in Ch. 8.

Protein Requirements

This topic is discussed to some extent in the section on feeding standards and in more detail in the chapters on feeding livestock (13–25), but some comments are in order here.

As explained earlier, the requirement for monogastric and avian species is for the essential amino acids. Although there are substantial volumes of data on the amino acid content of all major feedstuffs, chemical analyses do not tell us how much of a given amino acid will be digested and absorbed. Thus the requirements (given in various appendix tables) are usally expressed in amounts of total protein with additional information on some of the limiting amino acids.

Requirements are always highest (in terms of concentration in the diet) for young, rapidly growing animals. The needs decrease as the growth rate declines. Requirements are lowest for adult animals in a maintenance situation. They are increased during pregnancy and increased markedly during periods of peak lactation or egg production. Further details will be given in other chapters.

Protein Deficiency

Protein deficiency can be a result of one or more limiting amino acids or an inadequate protein consumption. Signs of protein deficiency include poor growth rate and reduced N retention by the body, poor utilization and lower consumption of feed, lowered birth weights often accompanied by high infant mortality, reduced milk or egg production, and infertility in both males and females. The severity of the symptoms will be highly related to the severity of the deficiency. From a practical point of view, insufficient protein will most noticeably affect young, rapidly growing animals, lactating females, or laying hens. Normally, a protein deficiency will be accompanied by deficiencies of one or more other nutrients, energy in particular for herbivore species.

Subclinical deficiencies (those which cannot be diagnosed by examination of the animal) are probably relatively common in many countries. One reason is that proteins are expensive feed ingredients to purchase, and the tendency of livestock feeders is to reduce the level or quality fed if possible. Sometimes, such mild deficiencies can be detected by lowered blood proteins, reduced growth rates, and so on, but it is usually difficult to be quite sure that the animal is deficient. Only in the case of lysine is there a specific sign of a deficiency. In black feathered turkeys, a lysine deficiency produces a white barring of the primary flight feathers.

Excess Protein

Free-ranging herbivorous animals in a natural habitat would normally encounter excess protein only during periods of lush growth of vegetation in the spring months (or early in the rainy season in the tropics). With confined domestic animals it is not a common problem because of the costs associated with protein supplements. Most of the studies that have been done do not suggest any marked adverse effects from consuming excess protein, particularly if the protein is of adequate quality and consumption is not continued for long periods of time. However, there is some information on dairy cattle indicating a decline in fertility of cows consuming high levels of protein (6).

Toxicity and death can occur in ruminant animals fed urea as a N source, particularly if fed without an adequate supply of carbohydrates such as starch or sugar. This situation arises when animals are consuming low-quality forage which results in a relatively high pH in the rumen. In this condition, urea is rapidly hydrolyzed to ammonia. The ammonia is absorbed quickly, overloading the liver system, which would normally detoxify it, resulting in a buildup in the blood and tissues and, if present in sufficient amounts, toxicity and/or death. It can also occur in other conditions if animals are not adapted to urea or if feeds have been poorly mixed, allowing the consumption of excess amounts of urea.

CARBOHYDRATES

Although plants synthesize many different carbohydrates, the basic compound is glucose, from which more complex or different carbohydrates are synthesized. In plant tissues, carbohydrates may comprise 50 percent of the dry matter of forages and as much as 80 percent in the kernels of some cereal grains. Thus, carbohydrates are the major dietary components for all herbivorous animals. For the animal, carbohydrates serve as a source of energy or as bulk in the diet, but there is no specific requirement for any individual carbohydrate compound.

Dietary Carbohydrates

Chemically, carbohydrates are classified on the basis of the number of carbon (C) atoms each molecule contains or on the numbers of simple sugar molecules contained in more complex compounds. The various classes are shown in the following table, along with the most common carbohydrates in each class.

Monosaccharides (1 sugar molecule)	
Pentoses (5-C sugars)	
Arabinose	
Ribose	
Xylose	
Hexoses (6-C sugars)	
Fructose	
Galactose	
Glucose	
Mannose	

Disaccharides (contain 2 sugar molecules)	
Cellobiose	glucose-glucose*
Lactose	glucose-galactose*
Maltose	glucose-glucose*
Sucrose	glucose-fructose*

Trisaccharides	
Raffinose	glucose-fructose-galactose*

Polysaccharides (contain multiple sugars)	
Pentosans (contain pentose sugars)	
Araban	arabinose*
Xylan	xylose*
Hexosans	
Cellulose	glucose*
Glycogen	glucose*
Inulin	fructose*
Starch	glucose*

Mixed Polysaccharides	
Gums	pentoses & hexoses*
Hemicellulose	pentoses & hexoses*
Pectins	pentoses & hexoses*

*sugars contained

Glucose (also called dextrose) and fructose are the most common simple sugars in feed and food ingredients. They occur as the simple sugars in both plant and animal tissues, but only in low concentrations. Fructose is converted readily to glucose in the animal body and is, therefore, available to body metabolism as glucose. As indicated in the listing, other simple sugars are present in feeds, but in even smaller amounts than those mentioned previously.

The disaccharides (sugars containing two units of simple sugar) and polysaccharides (those containing numerous units of simple sugars) are present in plant tissues in much higher concentrations than the simple sugars. Sucrose (common table sugar) is a combination of glucose and fructose and is found in high concentrations in plants such as sugar cane or sugar beets. Lactose (milk sugar) contains glucose and galactose and is found only in milk. Maltose, which is an intermediate compound between glucose and starch, is composed of two glucose units.

Starch is the most important polysaccharide of a nonfibrous nature found in plants, particularly in grains and tubers or other root crops. It is composed of units of glucose. There are two main types of starch designated as amylose and amylopectin. The major difference between them is the amount of side chains attached to the primary chain of glucose units. Starches from different plant sources vary in the ratio of amylose and amylopectin and in their microscopic physical structure, presumably because of differences in the protein matrix within which the starch has been deposited. Even though these differences exist, starches are generally highly digestible by animals.

The fibrous plant polysaccharides provide structural support for plant tissues. In forages the most important are cellulose and hemicellulose. In woody tissues high levels of xylans are present.

Like starch, cellulose is synthesized from glucose units, but the glucose molecules are linked in a manner that makes it rather insoluble and difficult to degrade. Hemicellulose includes a broad group of plant components that are long chains of five- and six-carbon sugars, and it is also resistant to degradation, although it is more soluble in some solvents than cellulose.

Absorption and Metabolism

Dietary carbohydrates must be digested to simple sugars before they can be absorbed by simple-stomached animals. A very small amount of amylase (starch digesting enzyme) is present in the saliva of some species. The pancreas produces a potent enzyme (pancreatic amylase) which will degrade the starches and other similar polysaccharides. Other enzymes capable of hydrolyzing the disaccharides are produced by mucosal cells in the duodenum.

The simple sugars are absorbed rapidly by the small intestine (duodenum, jejunum), some studies generally indicating that glucose and galactose are absorbed most rapidly while some of the five-carbon sugars, such as xylose and arabinose, are absorbed at a slower rate. A high proportion of simple sugars will be converted to glucose in the wall of the small intestine. Those that are not will be modified by the liver or metabolized in other ways. Thus all absorbed sugars become available to the body cells for energy or other metabolic processes. The animal body stores very little energy as carbohydrate, but some glucose is converted to glycogen, a type of starch, which is stored in the liver and muscle tissues in small amounts and provides a readily available source of quick energy for the tissues. The ready availability of glycogen is one reason that animals can maintain blood glucose levels within a relatively narrow range. Because they are relatively soluble and/or easily digested, the mono- and disaccharides and starch are frequently referred to as **readily available carbohydrates**.

For some reason animals never developed the ability to produce enzymes capable of digesting cellulose, hemicellulose, and other fibrous carbohydrates. Although digestion of these compounds does, indeed, take place in their GI tract, it is a result of microbial action. A wide variety of microbes are capable of digesting fibrous carbohydrates, and a number of these species may be found in the large intestine (cecum and colon). Of the various domestic simple-stomached species, the horse digests the most fiber. Poultry digest very little. Swine and rabbits are intermediate.

When a young ruminant begins to eat solid food, it gradually develops a bacterial and protozoal population in its rumen. These microorganisms, in turn, can digest dietary carbohydrates. With regard to the readily available carbohydrates, they are attacked rapidly and metabolized almost completely to carbon dioxide, water, heat, and the volatile fatty acids (primarily acetic, propionic, and butyric). The volatile fatty acids are absorbed through the rumen wall or the intestine and provide a source of energy for the animal. In the case of animals being fed high-grain diets at high levels, sometimes a substantial amount of starch may pass through the stomach into the intestine. Here, some of the starch will be digested as with monogastric species. However, the amount of amylase produced by the pancreas of ruminant animals is quite low, a factor which limits starch digestion. Consequently, if a high level of starch passes into the ruminant gut, some will be digested normally, some will be digested by microbes in the cecum and colon, and some may be excreted in the feces. In addition, other enzymes needed for digestion of disaccharides are low, with the exception of lactase in suckling animals. Ruminants do not produce sucrase, the enzyme needed for digestion of sucrose.

Ruminant animals are the most efficient of herbivorous species at digesting fibrous carbohydrates. The fibrous carbohydrates are usually retained in the rumen for some period of time—perhaps as long as 6 to 10 days by cattle fed long straw, although higher-quality forage (alfalfa hay, for example) will be retained for a much shorter period of time. At any rate, forages are retained long enough for action by the microbes. A combination of microbial action and chewing during rumination act to reduce particle size so that eventually the fibrous particles are either digested or chewed to a point where they will pass out of the rumen. The end products of rumen (or gut) digestion of fibrous carbohydrates are the same as with the readily available carbohydrates, except that higher levels of acetic acid and lower levels of propionic acid are characteristic of fibrous carbohydrates.

A comment is in order about lignin. Lignin is a long-chain polymer (similar to some plastics) which is present as a structural component in plant tissues. It is not a carbohydrate, but it is important from a nutritional point of view in that it is essentially undigestable but at the same time it interferes with the digestion of the plant tissues. Lignin content generally is found in higher concentration in forages of poor quality. In legumes, for example, much more lignin is present in the stems than in the leaves, and the overall content tends to be higher in legumes than in grasses.

LIPIDS

Lipids are organic compounds that are insoluble in water but soluble in organic solvents. Quite a variety of different types of compounds are found in both plant and animal tissues, all of which serve some important biochemical or physiological function. Chemically, lipids range from fats and oils to complex sterols. Lipoproteins are important constituents of all cell structures. Fats serve as a concentrated form of stored energy—one gram of fat yields about 9.45 kilocalories (kcal) of heat when completely combusted compared to about 4.1 kcal for a typical carbohydrate. Phospholipids and glycolipids are compounds containing fatty acids and P or a carbohydrate, respectively. They are involved in numerous biochemical functions in biological systems. Sterols range from compounds such as cholesterol to vitamin D and, likewise, are involved in numerous functions in animal tissues.

Nutritionally, the important lipids are fats and oils, the two being differentiated on the basis of melting points. Fats are solid at room temperature, while oils will be liquid at room temperature. Fats are composed of fatty acids of varying lengths and structures and one molecule of glycerol. They are referred to as mono-, di-, and triglycerides, depending on the number of fatty acids present. Fatty acids consist of chains of C atoms ranging from 2 to 24 or more Cs in length with a carboxyl (acid) group on the end. If all of the available positions on the C atoms are taken up with hydrogen, the fatty acid is referred to as saturated. If one or more double bonds are present (in place of hydrogen), the fatty acid is unsaturated. The most common fatty acids found in fats are listed in the table following.

Fatty Acid	Abbreviated Designation*
Saturated acids	
Acetic	C2:0
Propionic	C3:0
Butyric	C4:0
Caproic	C6:0
Caprylic	C8:0
Capric	C10:0
Lauric	C12:0
Myristic	C14:0
Palmitic	C16:0
Stearic	C18:0
Arachidic	C20:0
Lignoceric	C24:0
Unsaturated acids	
Palmitoleic	C16:1
Oleic	C18:1
Linoleic	C18:2
Linolenic	C18:3
Arachidonic	C20:4

*For acetic acid, the C2 means that it contains two C atoms and :0 means that no double bonds are present.

Most fatty acids found in animal tissues are straight-chained and contain an even number of Cs. Branched-chain fatty acids and those with an odd number of Cs are often produced by microorganisms, and, in the case of ruminant animals, body fats may contain substantial amounts of such fatty acids. Other differences in structure and position of double bonds occur but are outside the scope of this discussion (1, 2). Oils found in plant seeds are generally triglycerides. However, in forage, a high percentage of the lipids are diglycerides with a molecule of galactose (simple sugar) attached to the glycerol molecule.

Metabolism

In simple-stomached animals, fats are digested in the small intestine, primarily as a result of the action of bile, which emulsifies the fat, thus greatly increasing the surface area, and by pancreatic lipase, an enzyme which hydrolyzes fatty acids from the glycerol molecule. Some diglycerides are absorbed, but the majority of absorption is as monoglycerides and fatty acids. The majority of the longer-chain fatty acids are absorbed by lacteals into the lymph system and enter the blood stream just before the *vena cava* vein enters the heart.

In ruminant animals the rumen microbes present are capable of altering dietary fatty acids. When fats are ingested in amounts typical of common feed ingredients (2-6 percent), a high proportion of the unsaturated fatty acids will be saturated by the rumen microorganisms. If abnormal amounts of fat are ingested, many of the unsaturated fatty acids will not be saturated and an abnormal rumen fermentation may result. Fats in feeds can be protected from rumen action by treating the feed with aldehydes such as formaldehyde. Such compounds inhibit rumen metabolism of proteins, which in turn protects the fats in the plant or animal feed material.

Absorption of fatty acids is usually quite high, depending on the amount in the diet. For example, in one study absorption by chicks of different fats was shown to be as follows: soybean oil, 96 percent, corn oil, 94 percent; lard, 92 percent; beef tallow, 70 percent; and menhaden oil, 88 percent. Generally, oils are absorbed more completely than are highly saturated fats. Fats in the diet also stimulate absorption of the fat-soluble vitamins (A, D, E, K) and other fat-soluble substances.

After absorption as a fatty acid or monoglyceride, triglycerides are resynthesized in the mucosal tissues of the gut. The fats are then transported to the various tissues, particularly the liver, where they are used in synthesis of various compounds required by the body, or they are stored in the tissues (fat depots) or metabolized as a source of energy. The end products of energy metabolism are carbon dioxide, water, and heat. In instances where animals are fasting or if abnormal situations develop (diabetes, ketosis in dairy animals), intermediate products known as ketones may be present in high amounts. If present in moderate amounts, these compounds can be further metabolized for energy by most tissues, but if present in excessive amounts, they are detrimental to the animal and will normally be excreted in urine, milk, or via the lungs.

Animals may synthesize large amounts of body fat even though the dietary intake of fat is quite low. The mechanism for synthesis is relatively complex, but in simple terms it can be said that acetyl units (structure similar to acetic acid) are the basis of synthesis of most body fats. Such units can be provided by carbohydrate metabolism or metabolism of some of the amino acids.

Essential Fatty Acids

Linoleic and linolenic acids are required in the diets of monogastric species at a level of about 1 percent of the energy in the diet. A third acid, arachidonic, can be synthesized from linolenic acid, but it may be required in the diet if linolenic acid levels are marginal. The essential fatty acids are important because they are an integral part of the lipid-protein structure of cell membranes and they appear to be important in the structure of prostaglandins, hormone-like compounds that have a number of important effects on body biochemistry. Deficiencies of the essential fatty acids have been demonstrated in pigs, chickens, calves, dogs, mice, and guinea pigs. Such signs as scaly skin and necrosis of the tail, growth and reproductive failure, edema, subcutaneous hemorrhages, and poor feathering (chicks) have been observed. It is rather puzzling that deficiencies have not been shown in adult ruminants fed purified diets with no added fat, because the rumen microorganisms are capable of saturating these particular fatty acids.

Deficiencies of the fatty acids have, in most cases, been produced on purified diets or diets of natural feed ingredients quite low in fat. Thus it is not a common problem and is of no dietary significance for domestic animals except for poultry. Fortunately, the essential fatty acids are distributed widely among most fats and feed supplements. Corn and soybean oils and animal fats are excellent sources of linoleic and linolenic acids.

Composition of Body Fat

Body (depot) fat in simple-stomached species may be influenced markedly by the type and amount of dietary fat consumed. It has been known for many years that feeding of high levels of a particular fat (± 10 percent) will alter the nature of normal body depot fat. If an oil is fed—from a source such as peanut, safflower, or fish—it will result in body fat less saturated, softer, and with a lower melting point than that typical of the species. Especially with pork, this is objectional because of the soft, oily lard and cuts of meat. If fish oil is fed, flavor associated with the oil will be present in the meat also.

Minor changes in the diet do not have a marked influence on body fat deposits of ruminant animals, primarily because of the effect of rumen microorganisms on dietary fats. However, it is possible to feed protected fats (treated with aldehydes) and substantially alter the fatty acid composition of body or milk fat. Limited research on the topic indicates that the keeping qualities of milk are reduced and at this point it is strictly of academic interest.

MINERALS

The mineral nutrients are solid, crystalline elements which cannot be decomposed or synthesized by ordinary chemical reactions. With respect to animal nutrition, the minerals that are dietary essentials are classified as the **major** or **macrominerals** and the **trace** or **microminerals**. The major minerals are normally present in animal carcasses at levels greater than 100 ppm. Included in this group are calcium (Ca), chlorine (Cl), magnesium (Mg), phosphorus (P), potassium (K), sodium (Na), and sulfur (S). The trace minerals are usually present in the carcass at levels less than 100 ppm. Included are chromium (Cr), cobalt (Co), copper (Cu), fluorine (F), iron (Fe), iodine (I), manganese (Mn), molybdenum (Mo), nickel (Ni), selenium (Se), silicon (Si), and zinc (Zn).

Mineral Function

The most obvious function of mineral elements in the body is to provide structural support in the form of the skeleton. Bone is formed through the deposition of Ca and P in a complex salt in a protein matrix. Small amounts of some elements such as Mg and Na are present, as are some of the trace elements such as Zn, Mo, and Mn. Another example of a structural function is the use of Ca by birds to produce egg shells.

Most of the mineral elements are also involved in complex biochemical reactions. Those involved in enzyme activity include Ca, Mg, Fe, Co, Mn, Mo, and Zn. Fe is, of course, an essential constituent of hemoglobin in the blood and myoglobin in muscle tissues. Co is a constituent of a vitamin (B_{12}). Iodine is a component of thyroid hormone. In addition, other minerals such as Ca, K, Mg, and Na are involved in activity of the nervous system. Na, K, and Cl are necessary for the regulation of osmotic pressure and pH of intestinal and systemic fluids. This short list gives only a brief description of the many activities that minerals are involved with in the body of animals.

Mineral Metabolism

Mineral elements are absorbed from the GI tract by either an active or passive method. Active absorption means that the mineral is "pumped" by the intestinal wall from the digesta in the GI tract into intestinal cells. Mineral elements that are actively absorbed include Ca, P, and Na. However, most minerals are absorbed in a passive manner. These elements simply diffuse from the digesta across the intestinal wall at a rate determined by the concentrations of the mineral in both the digesta and the mucosal intestinal cells. Thus with passive absorption the concentration of an element in the feed and in the body greatly affects the amount absorbed.

Mineral elements are absorbed primarily in the ionic form. Therefore, digesta components that bind (chelate) minerals will reduce their absorption. Phytates, oxalates, and fats are compounds that may bind some elements and reduce absorption. Ca is particularly affected in this way. On the other hand Ca as Ca-lactate is absorbed more efficiently.

Interference with absorption of some essential minerals by other elements is an important nutritional problem that must be considered in formulating livestock rations. Minerals sometimes interfere with the utilization of other essential elements. Excess Ca is particularly a problem, as it interferes with P utilization and with Zn absorption.

Other factors can alter the degree to which

minerals are absorbed. Young animals are more efficient and old animals are less efficient in absorbing essential elements. The form of the element (organic versus inorganic) and the pH of the intestinal tract can also affect absorption.

The ash content (total mineral content) of the animal carcass is about 3.5 percent of carcass weight, or 17.5 kg of minerals/500 kg of carcass (cattle). Ca represents about 46 percent and P about 29 percent of the total. K, S, Na, Cl, and Mg together account for about 24 percent, while essential trace elements constitute less than 0.3 percent of the total.

The distribution of these minerals within the body's tissues is not uniform because some tissues selectively concentrate specific elements. Bone is the primary storage site for many of the essential elements, including Ca, P, Mg, K, Na, Mn, Mo, and Zn. Some organs, particularly the liver, kidney, and spleen, serve as major storage sites for Mg, Co, Cu, Fe, Mn, Mo, Ni, Se, and Zn. The thyroid gland is the most specific storage site for I, and the gland contains 70-80 percent of total body I.

Mineral Requirements and Deficiencies

Mineral requirements for the various species are listed in the appendix tables. Some information is also given in Ch. 13–25 on species or classes of farm livestock. Additional information may be obtained in other reference books (2, 6, 7).

The essential macro minerals most likely to be deficient or imbalanced in livestock rations are Ca, Mg, Na, and P. Clinical signs and symptoms vary somewhat from species to species, so only general signs will be mentioned here. A deficiency of Ca or P (or vitamin D) or an imbalance (ratios outside of about 3–5:1 of Ca:P) may result in rickets in young animals, which is manifested by inadequate mineralization of the bones, crooked legs, and enlarged joints as well as other abnormalities. In older animals the minerals are withdrawn from the bones, resulting in osteoporosis, a condition in which the mineral content is low and bones are porous and much more subject to fractures. Mild to severe P deficiencies are not uncommon, particularly in grazing species of animals. It results in a depraved appetite (pica) which is manifested by animals chewing bones, rocks, boards, and other abnormal objects. Reproduction and growth will be affected markedly. With regard to Na, it is widely recognized that livestock need added salt (NaCl). When salt is not fed and the soil or water supplies do not contain much Na,

deficiencies may result. Clinical signs are a craving for salt, emaciation, listlessness, and poor performance. A deficiency of K is not likely except in animals fed very high grain diets. Deficiency signs are similar to those of Na deficiency. Mg deficiency is not common in most livestock except for grazing ruminants. Various factors prevent normal utilization of Mg during cool, cloudy weather in the late winter and early spring or with similar light and temperature conditions in the fall, resulting in a metabolic deficiency called grass tetany (2). This condition results in irritability, convulsions, coma, and death (if not treated) in many instances. Mature animals are more likely to be affected, particularly lactating females.

With regard to the trace minerals, Fe is always deficient for very young pigs. A deficiency occurs because body reserves of newborn pigs are low, young pigs grow very rapidly, and milk is a poor source of Fe. The result will be anemia (insufficient hemoglobin in the blood) if the pig is not provided some source of Fe (see Ch. 21). With chicks and other poultry species, Mn may be deficient, the signs showing up as perosis, a condition in which the hock joint is enlarged and deformed such that the bird has great difficulty in moving about. Iodine may be deficient for most species, depending on the source of their feed. An iodine deficiency results in goiter, an enlargement of the thyroid gland. Co is deficient in some soil types. A Co deficiency results in a deficiency of vitamin B_{12} because Co is an essential constituent of this vitamin. Animals appear listless and will develop a particular type of anemia. In some cases Cu may be deficient and in others an excess of Mo and/or sulfate may result in poor utilization of Cu and the appearance of deficiency signs. Typical signs are a light hair color, partial paralysis of the rear quarters, and other manifestations depending on the age of the affected animal. Se is deficient in many areas for domestic livestock. A clinical deficiency shows up as white muscle disease (also called nutritional muscular dystrophy), primarily in young animals. In pigs it also affects the liver. The muscles of affected animals appear lighter than normal, and they may contain high levels of Ca-P salts. High death rates are common in newly born animals with a severe deficiency. Zn deficiencies are also relatively common and can be made more severe by high levels of Ca consumption. One sign is parakeratosis, which is a dermatitis manifested by itching, skin lesions, and other changes to the skin.

All deficiencies will, sooner or later, affect animal performance (growth, lactation, egg production, and so on), even though the appearance of the animal may not, in some cases, be affected to a great degree. In some cases multiple deficiencies of nutrients may occur, such as protein-energy, energy-mineral, energy-vitamin, and the like. Mild deficiencies may be difficult to detect because the only apparent effect on the animal may be somewhat lower production than would be expected. Such situations require careful evaluation by people trained in such matters to determine what the problem may be.

Mineral Toxicity

As a general rule, mineral toxicity is much less of a problem than mineral deficiencies. Water containing high levels of some alkali salts may be toxic, but such water would not normally be consumed if better-quality water is available. Of the macro minerals, NaCl can be a problem for both poultry and swine but is not often a problem for other species.

With regard to the trace minerals, flourine can be obtained in sufficient amounts in rock phosphates to produce toxicity over a period of months (or years). Contamination of vegetation downwind from mills processing ores high in F may also result in chronic toxicity. F toxicity results in enlarged, soft bones, teeth that wear off much more rapidly than normal, difficulty in walking, and generally poor performance. Cu toxicity can, at times, be a problem for young lambs, particularly if feed is contaminated or intake of Mo and sulfates is low. Cu toxicity affects the liver and, eventually, the blood and may result in a relatively high death rate in affected animals. Se is present in soil and vegetation in high enough levels in some areas (in the north central states in the United States) to cause chronic toxicity manifested by elongated hooves, loss of tail and mane (horses), difficulty in walking, and so on.

It should be noted that any mineral can be toxic to some degree if fed in excessive amounts. However, except for those mentioned, such conditions are not common and are usually the result of carelessness or outright mistakes in mixing feed or in animal feeding management.

VITAMINS

Vitamins are organic substances that are required by animal tissues in very small amounts. All vitamins are essential for animal tissues, but some species of animals are able to synthesize certain vitamins in their tissues or they are able to utilize vitamins synthesized by microorganisms in their GI tract. Consequently, vitamins needed in the diet vary from animal species to species. For example, humans, guinea pigs, monkeys, and some other species require vitamin C (ascorbic acid), but most animal species do not, because they can synthesize their own vitamin C.

Vitamins are divided into water-soluble or fat-soluble compounds. The water-soluble vitamins are C (ascorbic acid) and the B-complex vitamins, namely thiamin (B_1), riboflavin (B_2), niacin, pyridoxine (B_6), pantothenic acid, folacin, cyanocobalamin (B_{12}), biotin, choline, inositol, and paraaminobenzoic acid (PABA). The fat-soluble group includes vitamin A (retinal or retinoic acid) or its precursor, carotene; vitamin D, of which there are several forms; vitamin E, α-tocopherol; and vitamin K, which has several active forms. In nutritional use, vitamins A, D, and E are frequently quantitated in international units because there are several different compounds that have vitamin activity. The other vitamins are quantitated in weight units.

Functions

The primary functions of many water-soluble vitamins are as coenzymes (a substance associated with and which activates an enzyme). Water-soluble vitamins that do not act as coenzymes include choline, ascorbic acid, inositol, and PABA. The fat-soluble vitamins do not serve as coenzymes. Vitamin A, for example, is concerned with vision and with maintenance of epithelial cells (cells which line body cavities and cover body surfaces). Vitamin D is important in absorption and metabolism of Ca and in bone metabolism. Vitamin E functions as a metabolic antioxidant, and vitamin K is concerned with the blood clotting mechanism.

Tissue Distribution

The major storage site for most vitamins is the liver, with lesser amounts in the kidney, spleen, and other tissues or organs. Most are stored bound to specific proteins. Vitamins stored in the tissues are released at a rate necessary to maintain a relatively constant level in the blood.

The presence of vitamins in milk is important because milk often provides the sole food source for newborn animals. Colostrum is especially high in all vitamins, thus ensuring a high intake for the young mammal early in life.

Vitamin Metabolism

Vitamins are absorbed primarily from the small intestine. The B-complex vitamins and vitamin K are synthesized by microorganisms in the intestines of monogastric species and in the rumen of ruminating animals. Ruminants, with one or two exceptions, have no dietary requirements for these vitamins because sufficient quantities are produced in the rumen and absorbed from the intestinal tract.

The ability of monogastric animals to absorb vitamins synthesized in their intestinal tract varies with the vitamin and the species of animal. Vitamin K is synthesized and absorbed in such quantities that a deficiency is almost impossible to produce in animals other than poultry. Pantothenic acid and B_{12} are synthesized in the intestine, but little of the synthesized vitamins is absorbed and, consequently, monogastric species are dependent on dietary sources of these vitamins. Swine absorb enough of the folacin from the gut to meet most of their needs, while poultry absorb none of it and are entirely dependent on dietary sources. In the upper intestine, absorption of fat-soluble vitamins is less efficient than that of the water-soluble compounds. Some dietary lipid and the presence of bile salts are required for absorption.

Vitamin D, on the basis of present knowledge, is a unique vitamin. Plants contain a precursor, ergosterol, which can be converted to vitamin D_2 (calciferol) in the animal body if exposed to some ultraviolet light. Most mammals can use this form, but birds require vitamin D_3 (7-dehydrocholesterol), which is mainly of animal origin. However, in the animal body both D_2 and D_3 are converted by the liver to a more active form, which in turn is metabolized to another compound in the kidney, and the latter compound (1,25-dihydroxycholecalciferol) has direct effect on Ca metabolism in the tissues.

With regard to vitamin A, plants produce many different carotinoid pigments, but only a few can be converted to vitamin A. This takes place in the wall of the small intestine or the liver. Plants, themselves, contain no vitamin A.

Vitamin Deficiences

Many of the signs of the various vitamin deficiencies are similar. These include anorexia (poor appetite), reduced growth, dermatitis, weakness, and muscular incoordination. Some vitamin deficiencies cause additional specific symptoms (1, 2). For example, vitamin A deficiency can cause various kinds of blindness, including night, color, and total blindness. Vitamin D deficiency causes rickets and related bone disorders, and vitamin K deficiency causes hemorrhaging in the tissues. If niacin is absent, lesions develop on the tongue, lips, and mouth.

Vitamins that may be deficient under practical conditions often vary among different classes of livestock and with age of the animal. With ruminants the main concern is with vitamin A, possibly with vitamin E, and probably with vitamin D in specialized circumstances, although recent evidence indicates that carotene is required for normal ovarian function in cattle. Swine feeders must be concerned about dietary requirements of riboflavin, niacin, pantothenic acid, B_{12}, and choline of the B-complex and with vitamins A, D, and possibly E of the fat-soluble group. Poultry raisers must monitor the intake of all vitamins except ascorbic acid, inositol, and PABA.

ENERGY

Quantitatively, energy is the most important item in an animal's diet, and all feeding standards and ration formulation (Ch. 12) are based on some measure of energy with additional inputs on protein or amino acids, essential fatty acids, vitamins, and minerals.

The animal derives energy by partial or complete oxidation of organic molecules that are absorbed from the GI tract, including some of the amino acids or fat. In practice the individual nutrients are ignored and some form of energy is utilized when computing animal requirements or formulating rations. Thus it is necessary to discuss energy terminology, although a complete discussion of energy is beyond the scope of this chapter and the reader is referred to other books for more detail (1, 2, 3, 4).

Terminology

Energy is defined as the capacity to do work. In nutritional use it is quantitated by measuring heat production resulting from biochemical oxidations in the body or loss of energy from body excretions. Energy may be expressed in units such as calories, British Thermal Units (BTU), or joules. In the United States the calorie (cal), kilocalorie (kcal) or megacalorie (Mcal) are commonly used in animal nutrition. European countries have changed to the use of the joule, but it makes no difference whether calories or joules are the basal measure. A cal is the amount of heat required to raise the temperature of 1 g (gram) of water 1 degree C (= 4.1855 joules). A kcal = 1,000 cal and a Mcal (or therm) = 1,000 kcal. Animal use of energy is partitioned in the following way.

Gross Energy (GE). GE is the amount of heat resulting from oxidation of feed in an instrument called an oxygen bomb calorimeter. This is a reference point which tells how much energy is in the feed, but values are of little use otherwise because the energy value of a poorly digested and low-quality feed, such as straw, may be similar to a highly digestible ingredient such as sucrose. It is, however, the term used for energy in human diets. For humans it is more appropriate, because the average diet is highly digestible.

Digestible Energy (DE). DE is a measure of the amount of energy absorbed by the animal after consuming a particular feed or diet. The values are obtained by subtracting fecal energy from GE consumed. It is not strictly a measure of absorbed energy, because some of the energy of fecal excretion is derived from body tissues rather than undigested food. However, DE is a common energy base that is used in the United States and other countries as well.

Metabolizable Energy (ME). ME is determined by subtracting energy losses in urine and combustible gases from DE consumed. It is slightly more accurate than DE but is more expensive to obtain data on most species except for birds. It is the common base used for feeding standards and ration formulation for birds, and it is the common standard used in European countries for other domestic animals.

Net Energy (NE). NE is measured by subtracting energy losses in rumen fermentation and tissue metabolism from ME. It is energy available for maintenance or some type of production such as work or lactation. In theory, it is more accurate than DE or ME. In practice, information is not available on very many feed-stuffs or production situations. If an animal is outside its normal comfort zone (temperature range where nutrients are not oxidized to keep the body warm or cool), NE values will be different than if determined within the comfort zone. Nevertheless, NE values are currently in vogue and are often used in formulating rations or estimating animal performance. NE may also

be divided into NEm (NE for maintenance) and NEg (NE for gain) or expressed as NEℓ (lactation) when applied to lactating animals.

Total Digestible Nutrients (TDN). TDN is an old method of calculating energy and is the sum of digestible crude protein, crude fiber, nitrogen-free extract (carbohydrates), plus ether extract × 2.25. The ether extract (lipids) is multipled by 2.25 in an attempt to give it an increased value equivalent to the higher caloric value of fats. The chief criticism of TDN is that it tends to overvalue roughages as compared to ME or NE methods. Nevertheless, it is still widely used, and some nutritionists feel that it works as well as ME or NE bases. TDN is quite similar to DE, but DE or NE are gradually taking the place of TDN in the United States.

Energy Metabolism and Requirements

Energy metabolism is a very complex topic that is beyond the scope of this book. However, there are a few points that should be made for clarity if the reader is not familiar with the topic.

In the process of digesting and metabolizing energy, the greatest loss is that of undigested material excreted in feces. However, this general statement is subject to many modifications. For example, monogastric species generally consume more digestible diets than herbivorous species, thus the digestibility of energy will usually be higher. Young animals, particularly mammals, also consume more digestible diets than do adults, so digestibility will be higher. High-quality diets fed to poultry or swine may be digested to the extent of 85+ percent. At the other extreme, poor-quality diets such as straw fed to ruminants may be less than 35 percent digestible. In ruminants, digestibility will decrease as the level of feed intake increases, but there is little effect in other species. Factors which disturb the normal intestinal or stomach functions—diarrhea, toxins, parasite infections, and the like—will normally result in reduced digestibility. Digestibility can usually be enhanced in many species by proper feed processing.

Other losses occur in energy metabolism. Energy lost through urine and methane production in the GI tract will amount to about 10 percent of GE in ruminants, but less in most monogastric species. Losses after absorption can vary greatly, depending on level of intake, quality of the diet, and other factors. Heat is produced as a result of microbial fermentation in the stomach or gut (heat of fermentation). While such heat can be used to warm the body if necessary, the animal is not capable of storing the heat by chemical means such as synthesis of fat. In addition, heat is produced by oxidation of nutrients (particularly amino acids); this is referred to as the heat increment. Proteins produce the greatest losses, followed by carbohydrates and then fats. As with the heat of fermentation, such heat can be used to warm the body but cannot be stored. Thus both the heat of fermentation and the heat increment are detrimental in a situation where the animal is heat stressed.

Energy requirements are affected by many different factors, such as age, species, activity of the animal, level of production, environmental temperature, nutrient deficiencies, and various other factors. However, for a healthy animal, energy requirements are directly related to body surface area; this is so because heat is lost or gained in proportion to the area exposed. If body weight is multiplied by a fractional power (0.75 is commonly used), this gives a reasonably good means of relating weight to surface area for different species and sizes of animals (see reference 1, 3). This method of calculating energy requirements for the various domestic species is used in all current feeding standards.

Effective surface area can be altered in various ways. For example with sheep, shearing increases their susceptibility to cold temperatures but reduces heat stresses. Winter hair coats provide more insulation as does a thick layer of fat under the skin. In dry areas, sprinkling animals with water during hot periods will increase evaporation from the body surface and help to reduce heat stress as a result. Other examples could be given, but these will suffice to illustrate the point.

All homotherms (species which maintain a rather constant body temperature) operate within a so-called comfort zone. Within this temperature range the animal does not need to increase oxidation of nutrients to either cool or warm itself. The comfort zone will be affected greatly by humidity because evaporation from the body surface or from the lungs will be decreased when humidity is high and evaporation is the most efficient means of increasing heat loss. Likewise, wind will increase heat loss greatly in a cold climate and add to discomfort in a very hot situation, particularly if humidity is high. Normal activity or an increased level of feeding will increase body heat production and

lower the temperature at which the animal is comfortable. Immersion in cold water greatly intensifies heat loss. If an animal, such as a human, with little body surface protection is immersed in cold water for any length of time, body temperature will decrease rapidly to the point at which the animal cannot survive.

Energy Deficiency

Many wild species go through alternating periods of energy surplus, adequacy, and deficiency as the seasons change or as they go from dry to rainy seasons in tropical areas. This also may happen to free-ranging domestic animals, but usually the extremes of deficiency are less severe because of supplementary feed supplied by the livestock feeder. Such extremes should not occur with animals in confinement. Energy deficiency, if severe, results in a loss of body fat, weight losses, and emaciation. Pregnancy may be interrupted by resorption or abortion, milk or egg production will be decreased drastically, and animal fertility will inevitably be reduced. Energy deficiency is usually accompanied by deficiencies of other nutrients, but the overriding importance of body energy need may prevent the appearance of signs of the other deficiencies.

FEEDING STANDARDS

Feeding standards are statements of quantitative descriptions of the amounts of nutrients needed by animals. Use of such standards dates back to the early 1800s. There has been a gradual development over the years to the point where nutrient requirements for farm animals may be specified with a reasonable degree of accuracy, particularly for growing chicks and pigs. Although there are still many situations where nutrient needs of animals cannot be specified with great accuracy, nutrient needs of some domestic animals have been defined more completely than those of humans. This is due to the simple fact that people do not lend themselves to the types of experimentation needed to collect good quantitative data.

In the United States the most widely used standards are those published by the various committees of the National Research Council (4) under the auspices of the National Academy of Science. These standards (see the appendix tables) are revised and reissued at intervals of a few years. In England, the standards in use are put out by the Agricultural Research Council (3). Other countries have similar bodies which update information and make recommendations on animal nutrient requirements.

Terminology Used in Feeding Standards

Feeding standards are usually expressed in quantities of nutrients required per day or as a percentage of a diet, the former being used for animals given exact quantities of a diet and the latter more commonly when rations are fed ad libitum. With respect to the various nutrients, most are expressed in weight units, percentage, or ppm (parts per million). Some vitamins—A, D, E—are often given in international units. Protein requirements are sometimes given in terms of digestible protein (DP), although crude protein is used more commonly and amino acids can be substituted for DP in monogastric species when adequate information is at hand. Energy is expressed in a variety of different forms. The NRC uses ME for chickens and turkeys; DE, ME, or TDN for swine; DE, ME, and TDN for sheep; ME and TDN for beef cattle, with alternative use of NEm and NEg for growing and fattening cattle. For dairy cattle, values are given in DE, ME, TDN, NEm, and NEg, with additional values as NEℓ for lactating cows. The ARC uses ME almost exclusively, with energy expressed in terms of MJ (megajoules) rather than Mcal (megacalories). Other European standards are based on starch equivalents, Scandinavian Feed Units, and so forth. Regardless of the units used, feeding standards are based on some estimate of animal needs and have been derived from data obtained from a great many experimental studies done under a wide variety of conditions with a diverse list of feed ingredients.

Some comments are in order regarding the use of NEm and NEg for beef cattle and growing dairy cattle and NEℓ for lactating cows by the NRC publications. If one looks at the tables on feed composition in the respective publications, it is apparent that values are given in this energy terminology for almost all of the feedstuffs listed except for mineral supplements. The reader should be aware that most of these NE values have been calculated from older data that were generally expressed in other ways. Most of it was originally given as TDN or DE, as there is a wealth of older data expressed in these forms. Some values have also been derived from ME. Only a few feedstuffs have been evaluated directly in terms of NEm, NEg, or NEℓ.

However applicable these values may be for these respective classes of cattle, recalculating from existing data does not necessarily improve the original data.

Inaccuracies in Feeding Standards

The means and methods of arriving at quantitative values for feeding standards have been discussed elsewhere (1, 3, 4). For the nutritionist, feeding standards provide a useful base from which to formulate rations or to estimate feed requirements of animals. Feeding standards should not, however, be considered as the final answer on nutrient needs, but should be used as a guide. Current NRC recommendations are specified in terms believed by the committees to be minimum requirements for a population of animals of a given species, age, weight, and productive status. Some of the earlier versions were called allowances and, as such, included a safety factor on top of what was believed to be required. It is well known that animal requirements vary considerably, even within a relatively uniform herd. For example, a protein intake that may be satisfactory for most animals in a given situation will probably not be sufficient for a few of the more rapid gainers or high producers; conversely, some of the herd will probably be overfed. With our present production methods, this usually is the most feasible basis of feeding. The poor producers would be culled and the high producers can be given extra allowances.

It is quite obvious from published literature that management and feeding methods may alter an animal's needs or efficiency of feed utilization apart from known breed differences in nutrient metabolism and requirements. In addition, most current recommendations provide no basis for increasing intake in severe weather or reduction in mild climates. The effect of climate may be very great. For example, recent data show that pregnant cows with no shelter have metabolic rates which were 18–36 percent higher than cows provided with shelter.

Nor is any allowance made for the effect of other stresses such as disease, parasitism, surgery, and so forth. Furthermore, beneficial effects of additives, hormones, or feed preparatory methods are not always considered when devising quantitative requirements in feeding standards. Thus many variables may alter nutrient needs and nutrient utilization, and these variables are not normally built into the feeding standards.

Nutrient Needs and the Productive Functions

The remainder of this section will be devoted to some general discussion which will relate the effect of various productive functions on nutrient requirements. This should give the reader a better understanding of nutrient requirements as affected by growth, fattening, reproduction, lactation, and work.

Maintenance. Maintenance may be defined as the condition in which an animal is neither gaining nor losing body energy (or other nutrients). With productive animals there are only a few times when a true maintenance situation is approached. It is closely approximated or attained in adult male breeding animals other than during the breeding season and, perhaps, for a few days or weeks in adult females following the cessation of lactation and before pregnancy increases requirements substantially. However, as a reference point for evaluating nutritional needs, maintenance is a commonly used benchmark.

Other things being equal, nutrient needs are minimal during maintenance. In field conditions during dry periods of the year or during winter months, we may find that range animals need to expend considerable energy just to obtain enough plant material for their needs, as opposed to the amount of energy expended when forage growth is more lush, but this does not alter the fact that nutrient needs are less during maintenance than when an animal is performing some productive function.

Growth and Fattening. Growth, as measured by increase in body weight, is at its most rapid rate early in life. When expressed as a percentage increase in body weight, the growth rate gradually declines until puberty, followed by an even slower rate until maturity. As animals grow, different tissues and organs develop at differential rates and it is quite obvious that the conformation of most newborn animals is different from that of adults; this differential development has, no doubt, some effect on changing nutrient requirements. Growth rate probably decreases because the biological stimulus to grow is lessened, because young animals cannot continue to eat as much per unit of metabolic size, and, as measured by increase in body weight, because relatively more of the tissue of older animals is fat, which has a much higher caloric value than muscle tissue.

Nutrient requirements per unit of body weight or metabolic size (body weight$^{0.75}$) are greatest for very young animals. These needs gradually taper off as the growth rate declines and as the animal approaches maturity. In young mammals, nutrient needs are so great that, because the capacity of the GI tract is relatively limited in space and function, they must have milk (or a milk replacer) or milk and additional highly digestible food to approach maximum growth rates. As the young mammal grows, quality of the diet generally decreases as more and more of its food is from nonmilk sources, with the result that digestibility is lower and the dry matter of food is used less efficiently.

Dry matter consumption for all young animals is usually far greater per unit of body weight during their early life than in later periods. This high level of food consumption provides a large margin above maintenance needs, thus allowing a high proportion to be used for growth and development. Due to differences in capability of the GI tract for food utilization and because the rate, duration, and character of body growth vary with age and animal species, nutrient requirements may be quite different for different animal species. Nevertheless, it is characteristic for all species that nutrient requirements (nutrient concentration/unit of diet) are highest for the very young and then gradually decline as the animal matures. Naturally, total food and nutrient consumption are less for young animals because of their smaller size.

Nutrient deficiencies show up quite rapidly in young animals, particularly when the young are dependent in the early stages of life on tissue reserves obtained while *in utero*. With few exceptions, tissue reserves in newborn animals are low. Milk or other food may be an inadequate nutrient source, so that deficiencies may occur frequently until the food supply changes or the young animal develops a capability to eat the existing food supply. The young pig is an example. Iron reserves are low and rapid growth soon depletes body reserves; because milk is a poor source of iron, young pigs often become anemic unless supplemented with iron.

It should be pointed out that young mammals are dependent upon an intake of colostrum early in life. In very early life the intestinal tract is permeable to large protein molecules. Colostrum has a large supply of globulins and other proteins that provide nutrition as well as a temporary supply of antibodies which greatly increase resistance to many diseases. In addition, colostrum is a rich source of most of the vitamins and trace minerals, and the young animal's tissues can be supplied with needed nutrients which may not have been provided adequately *in utero*.

From a production point of view, nutrient requirements per unit of gain are least and gross efficiency (total production divided by total food consumption) is greatest when animals grow at maximal rates. However, net efficiency (total production divided by nutrient needs above maintenance) may not be altered greatly. In a number of instances it may not be desirable or economical to attempt to achieve maximal gain. For example, if we want to market a milk-fed veal calf at an early age, maximal gain and fattening are desired. On the other hand, if the calf is being grown out for a herd replacement, then less than maximal gain will be just as satisfactory and considerably cheaper.

The biological stimulus to grow cannot be suppressed to a marked degree in young animals without resultant permanent stunting. It is possible to maintain young animals for a period during which they do not increase body energy reserves, yet they will—if other nutrients are adequate—continue to increase in stature. Following a period of subnormal growth due to energy restriction, most young animals will gain weight at faster than normal rates when given adequate rations. This response is termed compensatory growth. This phenomenon has practical application when young calves are wintered at low to moderate levels (submaximal). When new grass is available in the spring or if calves are put in the feedlot, weight gain occurs at a very rapid rate initially. Efficiency for the total period and especially for a given amount of gain is greater, however, if the animal is fed at near maximal rates, but feeding at a lower level may allow the use of much cheaper feedstuffs or deferred marketing and, as a result, be a profitable management procedure.

Lactation

Heavy lactation results in more nutritional stress in mature animals than any other production situation, with the exception of very heavy, sustained muscular exercise. During a year, high-producing cows or goats typically produce milk with a dry-matter content equivalent to four- to fivefold that of the animal's body, and some animals reach production levels as high as sevenfold that of body dry matter. High-producing cows give so much milk that it is impossible for them to consume enough feed to prevent weight loss during peak periods of lactation.

Milk of most domestic species runs 80-88 percent water; thus water is a critical nutrient needed to sustain lactation. All nutrient needs are increased during lactation, however, as milk components are either supplied directly via the blood or synthesized in the mammary gland and, thus, are derived from the animal's tissue or from food consumed. All recognized nutrients are secreted to some extent in milk, although the major components of milk are fat, protein, and lactose, with substantial amounts of ash, primarily Ca and P.

Milk yield varies widely among and within species. In cows, peak yields usually occur between 60 and 90 days after parturition and then gradually taper off; thus the peak demand for nutrients follows the typical milk flow characteristic for the species concerned. Milk composition and quantity in ruminants may be altered by the type of ration. This is true particularly of the fat content and, to a lesser extent, the protein and lactose. In monogastric species, diet may affect fat, mineral, and vitamin composition of milk.

Limiting water or energy intake of the lactating cow (and probably any other species) results in a marked drop in milk production, whereas protein restriction has a less noticeable effect, particularly during a short period of time. Although deficiencies of minerals do not affect milk composition markedly, they will result in rapid depletion of the lactating animal's reserves. The need for elements such as Cu, Fe, and Se will be increased during lactation, even though they are found in very low concentrations in milk. The effects of marked nutrient deficiencies during lactation will often carry over into pregnancy and the next lactation.

Reproduction

Although nutrient needs of animals for reproduction are generally considerably less critical than during rapid growth or heavy lactation, they are certainly more critical than for maintenance. If nutrient deficiencies occur prior to breeding, the result may be sterility, low fertility, silent estrus, or failure to establish or maintain pregnancy.

It has been demonstrated many times that underfeeding (of energy and protein) during growth will result in delayed sexual maturity and that both underfeeding and overfeeding (of energy) will usually result in reduced fertility as compared to animals fed on a medium intake. Of the two, overfeeding is usually more detrimental to fertility.

Energy needs for most species during pregnancy are more critical during the last one-third of the pregnancy. Information on deposition of nutrients in fetal tissues suggests only relatively small percentages of total animal requirements are needed for this function, even late in the term, however other information indicates a somewhat greater need. Pregnant animals have a greater appetite and will spend more time grazing and searching for food than will nonpregnant animals. Furthermore, the basal metabolic rate of pregnant animals is higher. By the end of pregnancy the basal rate of a cow is about 1.5-fold that of a nonpregnant identical twin.

Protein deposition in the products of conception follows the same trend as energy, but protein is relatively more critical for development of the fetus in the late stages than early in pregnancy as is true for Ca, P, other minerals, and vitamins.

Inadequate nutrition of the mother during pregnancy may have variable results, depending on the species of animal, the degree of malnutrition, the nutrient involved, and the stage of pregnancy. Nutrient deficiencies are usually more serious in late pregnancy, although there are exceptions to this statement. With a moderate deficiency, fetal tissues tend to have a priority over the mother's tissues; thus body reserves of the mother may be withdrawn to nourish the fetus. However, a very severe deficiency will usually result in partial depletion of the mother's tissues and such detrimental effects as resorption of the fetus, abortion, malformed young, or birth of dead, weak, or undersized young with, sometimes, long-term effects on the mother. When the mother's tissues are depleted of critical nutrients, then tissue storage in the young animal is almost always low, nutrients excreted in colostrum are also low, milk production may be nil, and survival of the young animal is much less certain than when nutrition of the mother is at an adequate level.

Work

Experimental studies with humans and animals indicate that work (physical effort) results in an increased energy demand in proportion to the work done and the efficiency with which it is accomplished. Carbohydrates are said to be more efficient sources of energy for work than fats. With respect to protein, balance studies show little, if any, increase in N excretion in horses or humans as a result of muscular exercise, provided energy intake is adequate and protein does not need to be metabolized for energy. Although this evidence has been obtained in a number of studies, data on men indicate reduced quality and quantity of work when protein intake is on the low side, but still above maintenance levels.

If appreciable sweating occurs, work may be expected to increase the need of Na and Cl, particularly. P intake should be increased during work, as it is a vital nutrient in many energy-yielding reactions. Likewise, the B-vitamins involved in energy metabolism, particularly thiamin, niacin, and riboflavin, probably should be increased as work output increases, although data on this subject are not clear.

COMMON NUTRITIONAL ANALYSES

It is necessary for the reader and user of this book to have some idea of the common methods and terms used in analyzing and describing nutrients in feeds and other items. This topic, of course, could be one for a book by itself. For the reader interested in the details of standard methods used in most nutrition laboratories, the writer would recommend the book entitled *Official Methods of Analysis* (8).

There are thousands of different kinds of analyses that might be done on feeds (or foods), animal tissues, excreta, and the like at one time or another. These can be lumped broadly into qualitative tests (which can be used to indicate the presence of a substance, for example, mold) and quantitative tests which will provide information on how much of a given substance is present in the food.

Qualitative tests are used like keys for classifying a plant, bird, or animal. Many things can be eliminated very quickly. For example, is the material liquid or solid? Is it soluble in water or one of many different types of solvents? Does it melt when heated or does it decompose and burn?

In recent years there have been marked improvements in the instrumentation, much of which is automated, for doing analyses on nutrients. Consequently, quantitative information is obtained more easily and qualitative tests are used less frequently. Discussion follows on the most common methods in use.

Dry Matter

Although water is a useful substance to the animal, its presence in feed acts as a diluent. Therefore, most feeds are analyzed and the data presented either on a dry matter (DM) basis or an as-is basis with information shown on the moisture content. DM is determined by grinding the material (unless it is not feasible to grind) and drying in an oven of one type or another. Microwave ovens make this a very speedy process. Older ovens using temperatures of 60 to 105°C require 24 hours or more, depending on the nature of the product.

Crude Protein

For common nutritional use, most feedstuffs are analyzed with a procedure called the Kjeldahl process, which measures the N content of the feed, regardless of its source. For this method, feeds are digested in hot, concentrated sulfuric acid, with eventual measurement of ammonia expressed as percent N. This is done because all proteins contain N, although not all N-containing compounds are proteins. The average protein contains about 16 percent N; thus multiplying the percent N $\times$ 6.25 gives the crude protein equivalent ($16 \times 6.25 = 100$).

The N from the Kjeldahl analysis could be from urea, manure, an insoluble protein such as uncooked feathers, or from high-quality proteins in milk, but this method will not provide any measure of quality, only of quantity of N present. The advantages of the procedure are that it is relatively rapid and repeatable, it has been used for many years, and most people are somewhat familiar with it.

If more precise information is needed, there are many different types of analysis that could be used. Automated methods are available for analyzing for amino acids, but they require quite a bit of time and are much more expensive. Analyses are available for different types of proteins, for solubility of proteins, for protein bound in an undigestible manner to other components, and so on.

Ether Extract (Crude Fat)

Crude fat is the product resulting from extracting a feed item with hot ethyl ether or some other organic solvent or combination of solvents

such as chloroform + ethyl alcohol. A small sample of feed is put in the proper container and the hot solvent drips through it. The ether extract resulting from this process may contain many things other than true fats. For example, most plant leaves are covered with a certain amount of waxy material which, although soluble in ether, is essentially undigestible and of no nutritional value to animals. As with the crude protein analysis, the information provided is quantitative rather than qualitative in nature. No information is provided on the different types of fatty acids or different types of lipids. In the event that such information is needed, there are methods available for determination of fatty acids, for different types of lipids, and so on (8).

Crude Fiber

The analysis for crude fiber was developed many years ago. It involves boiling the ground feed (usually fat-extracted first) in a weak solution of acid, filtration and boiling in a weak solution of alkali, filtration, and drying. This was an attempt to simulate digestion in the stomach and then the intestine. The procedure is intended to be an analysis for cellulose, hemicellulose, xylans, lignin, and any other components associated with fibrous carbohydrates. It has a number of disadvantages. It is slow and tedious, not very repeatable, and the information is less applicable to some feeds than to others. The reason for the latter statement is that some hemicelluloses will be dissolved by the chemical treatment and, if protein is bound to the lignin or other chemicals in an insoluble form, it will also show up in the crude fiber fraction. Unfortunately, most state regulatory agencies still require crude fiber analyses on commercial feedstuffs (see Ch. 5).

Neutral-Detergent Fiber, Acid-Detergent Fiber

Methods using detergents have been developed to overcome some of the problems with the crude fiber analysis. If feed is extracted with the appropriate neutral-detergent solution, the solution will extract (remove) materials that are essentially the same as the contents of the cell, thus dividing the feed into fractions of cell contents and cell walls. Neutral-detergent fiber and cell wall content are synonymous terms. Most of the soluble material in the cell contents (proteins, lipids, sugars, starch, pectins, other solubles) are highly utilizable by animals of all types, whereas the cell walls contain most of the fibrous carbohydrates, lignin, heat-damaged protein (if any), and silica. Now, if the cell walls (or neutral-detergent fiber) are extracted with an acid-detergent solution, the hemicellulose is removed, leaving acid-detergent fiber which contains cellulose, lignin, heat-damaged protein (if any), and silica. Hemicellulose and cellulose utilization is low to moderate by ruminants, and they are only partially utilized by nonruminant species. The other materials in acid-detergent fiber are indigestible by all species for all practical purposes.

Ash

As the term implies, ash is obtained by burning feed at a temperature of 350-600°C until nothing is left but metallic oxides or contaminants such as rocks and soil. No qualitative information is provided. If information is needed on individual mineral elements, there are many different methods available. However, nutritional information on some of the trace elements is not too precise because the very low concentrations make analytical results less certain.

Nitrogen-Free-Extract (NFE)

This fraction of feed, which is primarily composed of readily available carbohydrates (sugars, dextrins, starches), is one utilized in an old scheme called the **proximate analysis**. In this scheme all of the other analyzed items are subtracted from 100, leaving NFE. The formula is as follows:

$$NFE = 100 - [crude\ protein + crude\ fat \\ + crude\ fiber + ash]$$

Analysis was done in this manner because there were no quick, simple analytical methods (at that time) for starch, which must be hydrolyzed to sugar, and then an analysis must be done for sugars.

The values on NFE for the grains and other components high in sugar and starch are a reliable estimate of the readily available carbohydrates, but they are not for feeds high in hemicellulose if the crude fiber procedure is used. This is so because a substantial portion of hemicellulose is dissolved in the crude fiber analysis and, using the formula above, would end up in the NFE fraction. If the detergent methods are used, this criticism would be taken care of.

Energy

Energy content of feed is obtained with an instrument called an oxygen bomb calorimeter. A small sample of ground feed is introduced into a thick-walled container (bomb) which is then filled with oxygen under pressure. The bomb is then placed in a container of water, the feed is ignited, and the increase in the temperature of the water is determined. In this way the fuel value (gross energy) of the feed can be determined. In order to develop information on animal utilization of the feed, animal trials of one type or another must be carried out (see the previous section on energy).

SUMMARY

Animals needs an adequate source of good-quality water for maximum levels of production. At times water may contain too many mineral salts or other contaminants, but water can also be an important source of mineral elements. Animals need nitrogen or amino acids in their diet. Ruminant animals can use largely nonprotein N sources, but the simple-stomached animals need at least nine essential amino acids in their diet. Other amino acids needed for protein synthesis can, usually, be synthesized by the animal's tissues. Carbohydrates provide the majority of most animal diets (except for carnivores), but no specific carbohydrate is required to the diet. Sugars and starches are highly utilized. Fibrous carbohydrates such as hemicellulose and cellulose are utilized by animals only because of digestion in the gastrointestinal tract by microbial organisms; animals do not produce the enzymes needed to digest these compounds. Lipids are normally only a small percentage of animal diets. There are two essential fatty acids, but only in very rare situations are they likely to be inadequate.

Many different mineral elements are required in animal diets. Those that may be a problem at times include Ca, P, and Mg, of the major elements. Of the trace minerals, Cu, Fe, I, Mn, and Zn are usually most likely to be insufficient in animal diets. Vitamins may also be problems in animal diets. Vitamin A is usually thought to be limiting for many species. Vitamin D may be deficient at times. With the B vitamins, the most likely problems are with poultry, which may need to have diets supplemented with a number of these vital nutrients.

Energy is often a limiting dietary component for free-ranging animals, but it would not, normally, be a problem for confined animals raised under intensive situations. Energy utilization can be affected markedly by deficiencies of other nutrients and by feed preparatory methods.

Feeding standards were discussed. Feeding standards are intended to define nutrient needs of domestic animals of different species and at different ages or in various production situations. They are reworked and redefined from time to time in an effort to improve them. There are a number of inadequacies in most standards, but they serve as a most useful base from which to project animal needs for feed.

Common nutritional analyses of feedstuffs were discussed, and some of the problems associated with analytical work were pointed out.

REFERENCES

1. Church, D. C., and W. G. Pond. 1988. *Basic animal nutrition and feeding*. 3d ed. New York: Wiley.
2. Church, D. C. ed. 1988. *The ruminant animal*. Englewood Cliffs, NJ: Prentice Hall.
3. ARC. 1980. *The nutrient requirements of ruminant livestock*. London, UK: Agr. Res. Council, Commonwealth Agr. Bureaux.
4. NRC. *Nutrient requirements of domestic animals*. Washington, D.C.: Nat. Academy Press. Publications are available on all domestic animals including cats, dogs, and rabbits as well as on laboratory animals, warm and coldwater fishes, nonhuman primates, and mink and foxes.
5. NRC. 1980. *Mineral tolerance of domestic animals*. Washington, D.C.: Nat. Academy Press.
6. Church, D. C., ed. 1979. *Digestive physiology and nutrition of ruminants. Vol. 2: Nutrition*. 2d ed. Corvallis, OR: O & B Books.
7. Underwood, E. J. 1981. *The mineral nutrition of livestock*. 2d ed. London, UK: Commonwealth Agr. Bureaux.
8. AOAC. 1984. *Official methods of analysis*. 14th ed. Washington, D.C.: Assoc. of Official Analytical Chemists.

4

Introduction to Feedstuffs

A tremendous variety of feedstuffs is used for animal feeding throughout the world; the variety in a given location will depend on the local products grown or harvested and the class and species of animal involved. Well over two thousand different products have been characterized to some extent for animal feeds, not counting varietal differences in various forages and grains.

The number of feedstuffs is so great that it is not feasible to present information on many of them. Rather, the discussion will deal with major feeds in the various classes, with comments on particular characteristics (in Ch. 6, 7, 8). Further information will be presented in Ch. 13 through 25 regarding utilization and suitability of specific feedstuffs for the animals discussed in any given chapter.

Readers desiring data on nutrient composition of feedstuffs can find a wealth of information in the literature, although many times it may not be as complete as one would wish. There are at least four books in English dealing almost entirely with compositional data. They include the NAS publication (1) which gives data on feedstuffs utilized in North American and other

temperate climates. A second book on this topic is published in Utah (2). Another book published by the University of Florida (3) provides data on Latin American feedstuffs, and one published by FAO (4) provides information on tropical feeds. In addition to the sources mentioned, a number of texts dealing with domestic animals may also present data on a variety of feedstuffs. Reasonably complete information on feedstuff composition is given in appendix tables in this book.

CLASSIFICATION OF FEEDSTUFFS

A **feedstuff** may be defined as any component of a diet (ration) that serves some useful function. Most feedstuffs provide a source of one or more nutrients that can be used by the animal. However, feed ingredients may also be included to provide bulk (reduce physical density), reduce oxidation of readily oxidized nutrients, emulsify fats, or provide flavor, color, desirable odor, or other factors related to acceptability rather than serving strictly as a source of nutrients. As a rule, medicinal compounds are usually excluded from lists of feedstuffs. The usual classification of feedstuffs, essentially as given by NRC (1) but with a number of added items, is as follows:

Roughages
  Pasture, range plants, and plants fed green
    Grazed plants
      Growing
      Dormant
    Soilage or green chop
    Cannery and food crop residues
  Dry forages and roughages
    Hay
      Legume
      Grass-legume
      Nonlegume
    Straw and chaff
    Fodder, stover
    Other products with > 18 percent crude fiber
      Corn cobs
      Cottonseed hulls, gin trash
      Milling by-products
      Shells and hulls
      Sugar cane bagasse
      Paper, wood products
  Silages
    Corn, sorghum
    Grass, grass-legume, legume
    Miscellaneous
Energy feeds (< 18 percent crude fiber and > 20 percent crude protein)
  Cereal grains
  Milling by-products of cereal grains
  Beet and citrus pulp
  Molasses of various types
  Seed and mill screenings
  Animal, marine, and vegetable fats
  Roots and tubers, fresh or ensiled
  Miscellaneous
Protein supplements (with 20 percent or more crude protein)
  Animal, avian, and marine sources
  Milk and milk by-products
  Legume seeds
  Dehydrated legume plants
  Milling by-products of grains
  Brewery and distillery by-products
  Single-cell sources (bacteria, yeast, algae)
  Nonprotein nitrogen (urea, ammonia, biuret, etc.)
Mineral supplements
Vitamin supplements
Nonnutritive additives
  Antibiotics, antimicrobials, antifungals
  Antioxidants
  Bacterial preparations

Buffers
Colors and flavors
Emulsifying agents
Enzymes
Hormones
Medicines
Miscellaneous

In the commercial feed trade it is a common practice to use collective terms on feed labels (see Ch. 5) rather than listing a long string of feed ingredients. Because there is some difference in the terminology used as compared to that used by the NRC, the listings used for the collective terms will be given even though there will be some duplication. The listings which follow are as defined by the American Feed Control Officials (5). They are as shown for feedstuffs used in manufactured feeds.

Animal Protein Products
Animal products
  Dried animal blood
  Meat meal
  Meat and bone meal
  Meat meal tankage
  Meat and bone meal tankage
  Animal liver and glandular meal
  Extracted animal liver meal
  Poultry by-product meal
  Dried meat solubles
  Poultry
  Poultry parts
  Poultry by-products
  Hydrolyzed poultry by-product aggregate
  Animal by-product meal
  Fleshings hydrolsate
  Whole dressed chicken
  Hydrolyzed feather meal
  Hydrolyzed leather meal

Marine products (except fish oil)
  Fish meal
  Fish residue meal
  Fish liver and glandular meal
  Crab meal
  Shrimp meal
  Condensed fish solubles
  Dried fish solubles
  Fish protein concentrate
  Fish by-product

Milk products
  Dried buttermilk
  Condensed buttermilk
  Dried skim milk

Condensed skimmed milk
Dried cultured skimmed milk
Condensed cultured skim milk
Dried whey
Condensed whey
Dried whey solubles
Condensed whey solubles
Dried hydrolyzed whey
Condensed hydrolyzed whey
Condensed whey product
Dried whey product
Condensed cultured whey
Casein
Cheese rind
Dried milk albumin
Dried whole milk
Dried milk protein
Dried hydrolyzed casein

Forage Products

Suncured alfalfa meal
Dehydrated alfalfa meal
Alfalfa leaf meal
Flax plant product
Lespedeza meal
Dehydrated corn plant
Corn plant pulp
Ground grass
Dehydrated silage (ensilage pellets)
Ground alfalfa hay
Ground soybean hay
Lespedeza stem meal

Grain Products

Barley
Ground grain sorghums
Rolled grain sorghums
Corn feed meal
Ground corn
Cracked corn
Screened cracked corn
Flaked corn
Heat-processed corn
Toasted corn flakes
Kibbled corn
Oats and mixed feed oats
Ground rough rice or ground paddy rice
Ground brown rice
Chipped or broken rice
Brewers rice
Rye
Wheat

Plant Protein Products

Algae meal
Beans

Coconut meal
Cottonseed meal
Cottonseed cake
Cottonseed flakes
Whole pressed cottonseed
Low gossypol cottonseed meal
Guar meal
Rapeseed meal
Linseed meal
Peanut meal
Safflower meal
Ground soybeans
Soybean feed
Soybean meal
Kibbled soybean meal
Sunflower meal
Dehulled sunflower meal
Primary dried yeast
Heat-processed soybeans
Soy protein concentrate
Peas
Active dry yeast
Dried yeast
Brewers yeast
Grain distillers dried yeast
Molasses distillers dried yeast
Torula dried yeast
Yeast culture

Processed Grain By-products

Corn bran
Peanut skins
Rice bran
Wheat bran
Brewers dried grains
Distillers dried grains
Distillers dried grains/solubles
Molasses distillers dried solubles
Molasses distillers condensed solubles
Condensed distillers solubles
Partially aspirated gelatinized sorghum grain
    flour
Gelatinized sorghum grain flour
Corn flour
Soy grits
Soy flour
Wheat feed flour
Grain sorghum germ cake
Grain sorghum germ meal
Corn germ meal (wet and dry milled)
Wheat germ meal
Defatted wheat germ meal
Corn gluten feed
Distillers dried solubles
Grain sorghum grits
Corn grits

Soy grits
Flour
Oat groats
Hominy feed
Malt sprouts
Buckwheat middlings
Rye middlings
Pearl barley by-products
Rice polishings
Wheat shorts
Wheat mill run
Wheat red dog
Feeding oat meal
Grain sorghum mill feed

Roughage Products
Corn cob fractions
Ground corn cob
Barley hulls
Barley mill by-product
Malt hulls
Cottonseed hulls
Ground almond hulls
Buckwheat hulls
Sunflower hulls
Oat hulls
Clipped mill by-product
Oatmill by-product
Peanut hulls
Rice hulls
Rice mill by-product
Bagasse
Rye mill run
Soybean hulls
Soybean mill feed
Soybean mill run
Husks
Dried citrus pulp
Dried citrus meal
Citrus seed meal
Corn plant pulp
Dried apple pomace
Dried apple pectin pulp
Dried beet pulp
Dried tomato pomace
Flax straw by-product
Ground straw

Molasses Products
Beet molasses
Cane molasses
Citrus molasses
Starch molasses
Dried beet pulp with molasses
Dried beet molasses product

It will be obvious to the experienced reader that the NAS listing is intended to divide feeds into groups based on the major nutrient provided, while the AFCO listing is primarily intended to identify the source of the feed ingredient. Both serve useful purposes and, because the AFCO listing is used commercially, the reader should be aware of the types of ingredients that might be included under these different headings.

MEASUREMENT OF FEEDSTUFF VALUE

Animal feeds may be evaluated in many different ways. Regardless of the method, the ultimate objectives are to know if the animal will eat the feed, to have a quantitative assessment of usable nutrients the feed contains, and to know if there are undesirable factors such as plant, mineral, or microbial toxins present which may be harmful to the animal. In this section some of the methods will be discussed briefly. Most of the methods will be illustrated in greater detail in appropriate chapters in other parts of the book.

Chemical Analyses

The principal groups of nutrients of concern are: water, protein, carbohydrates, lipids (fats), mineral elements, and vitamins. These are discussed in more detail in Ch. 3.

Many different chemical methods may be used to determine the content of specific nutrients, such as one of the vitamins or a given mineral element or for groups of nutrients. In evaluation of feedstuffs, the proximate analysis or some modification of it is normally utilized. While this method has received much criticism from nutritionists, it is still utilized widely although often supplemented with additional analyses.

Regardless of the chemical methods employed, the question still remains, how well does the animal utilize the nutrient in the feed? The problem is that utilization varies with different feedstuffs, and it may be different for different animal species or age groups. Although various equations have been derived to predict utilization, primarily for protein and energy in forages (see Ch. 6), the relationship between chemical content and animal usage is difficult to predict with certainty. Thus it is necessary to resort to other methods which are, invariably, more costly and time-consuming.

Digestion and Balance Trials

In digestion trials the technique requires that feed consumed by an animal be carefully measured over a period of time. Fecal excretion in a corresponding period of time is also determined and, as a result, it is possible to account for consumption and excretion of a given nutrient except for that which may be excreted via urine, skin, or lungs. The formula for calculating digestibility is as follows:

$$\text{Digestibility (\%)} = \frac{\text{feed consumption} - \text{fecal excretion}}{\text{feed consumption}} \times 100$$

The number derived from this formula is called the coefficient of apparent digestibility; the adjective "apparent" is used because this information does not give a measure of true digestibility. This is so because some materials are excreted from the intestinal tract even if no food is consumed.

All important feedstuffs have been studied in digestion trials. In feed utilization and metabolism, the greatest losses occur as a result of incomplete digestion, the exact amounts depending on the animal species and the type of feed being consumed. Thus valid digestibility data give a more accurate estimate of the nutritive value of a feed than do chemical analyses. As indicated, because there is some intestinal excretion anyway, this excretion tends to result in a slightly lower value for digestibility than that which really occurs (true digestibility) for any component which is excreted by the body. On the other hand, if it is realized that some diet organic matter may be converted to gases, particularly to methane in ruminants, and that these gases are not accounted for with digestion trial methods, this gives an overestimate of nutritive value.

Balance trials differ from digestion trials in that excretions via urine, lungs, and sometimes the skin may be included so that a complete measure of intake and excretion is obtained. The result is that determination can be made as to whether or not the animal is in a state of equilibrium or in a state of negative or positive balance. Additional information on digestion and balance trial methods is available in other references (6, 7).

Feeding Trials

Feeding trials are used extensively in order to evaluate feedstuffs, nutrient levels, additives, feed processing methods, and the like. The experiments may be designed to evaluate the growth response of young animals, production of eggs, lactation or growth in the feedlot—conditions which require a high-quality diet if maximum performance is to be achieved. In less demanding circumstances, the trials may be related to needs of mature animals during maintenance or pregnancy.

A typical experiment with some product, such as a new protein supplement, would be to include it in graded amounts as a replacement for a protein supplement of known quality. For example, from 0 to 100 percent of soybean meal might be replaced in a broiler ration. The rations would then be fed to different groups of chicks and data obtained on growth and feed conversion. Other data might be obtained, for example, information on blood proteins or some index of carcass quality. Experiments of this nature will quickly show how the new product compares. We can readily find out if animals will eat the ration with untested ingredients, if there is any marked effect on production or body weight gain, and if there is any evidence of undesirable effects as a result of including it in the ration.

The usual response is that small amounts of the unknown ingredient may be satisfactory but replacement of all of the standard ingredient is apt to result in less desirable performance. This is not always the case, but this type of response is more common than not. On the other hand, an evaluation might be made of the requirement for an essential nutrient. A very poor performance may result with no addition to the ration and a dramatic increase with initial additions. The animal response with further additions will normally taper off. It may eventually decline if too much is added.

There are many different types of experiments with different objectives and responses. It might seem logical to do digestion and balance trials before doing feeding trials, but feeding trials are often the first means of obtaining experimental evidence, sometimes even before chemical data of any consequence are available. Whatever the objectives or product, feeding trials are the most common method of evaluating animal performance in nutritional studies. Feeding trials are often subject to some criticism, mainly because animal response, as a result of other environmental factors, is apt to be variable (especially growth rates), and it is often difficult to show that experimental differences are repeatable. Fortunately, more time and further experimentation will usually sort out these differences. Another objection is that feeding trials, by themselves, do not provide the type of data needed to explain differences in performance that may be observed. For this reason, other types of data must usually be collected to understand what has happened in the metabolism of unknown ingredients.

Physical Appearance

Physical appearance of many feedstuffs often offers a clue as to the relative feeding value. For example, with roughages such as alfalfa, we can see from the color if hay has been poorly cured and get an estimate of its carotene (provitamin A) content. It may be possible to see or smell mold or to see differences in the relative number of leaves or stem size, all factors which are associated with feeding value. In addition, we might see that undesirable weeds are present or that the hay has a high proportion of grass. Smell is sometimes a reasonably good criteria of good or poor hay. Unfortunately, none of these are good quantitative estimates, but they are useful nonetheless.

With grains or other concentrate feeds, it may be possible to observe things that may have some effect on feeding value; for example, shriveled seeds, presence of other grains, weed seeds, molds, foreign material such as hair, dirt, and dust, rodent pellets, and so on. With processed feeds, we can sometimes see that rolled grains have been poorly rolled or in pelleted concentrates that there is a high percentage of fines (unpelleted meal) or in meals that the texture is too fine or dusty. As with the roughages, visual appraisal is not quantitative, but it is an important means of quickly evaluating some feedstuffs.

Cultural Information

A general knowledge of soil fertility and fertilization practices used with a given crop often provides useful information on likely nutrient problems. For example, if we know that a given crop is grown in an area where a required nutrient is deficient (P or I, for example), we can expect that the plant material may be low in this nutrient. Or, if the crop comes from an area where soil levels of an element are quite high, some potential toxicity might be anticipated to some animals from elements such as selenium or molybdenum. If high N fertilization has been used and there has been a shortage of water for the plant, an undesirable and toxic accumulation of nitrates might be anticipated.

Some knowledge of the stage of maturity at which a crop was harvested often gives a clue as to the relative feeding value. Most grasses, for example, decrease rapidly in feeding value as they mature. Thus if hay is made at a mature stage, the feeding value is likely to be relatively low.

Some consideration should be given, where known, to conditions of storage. Has the feed been treated to prevent insect infestations? Is there insect damage? How long has the feed been in storage? Has it been subjected to excessive heat? These and other factors may have some effect on nutritive value of many different feedstuffs.

Cost of Feedstuffs

In any commercial operation consideration must be given to the cost of feedstuffs. Although discussed in more detail in other chapters, a few brief comments are in order here.

Feed costs rarely stay the same throughout the year. For crops that are harvested annually, the price is usually lowest at harvest and increases in later months, even in a stable economy without any high level of inflation. One reason is that costs increase with added handling and storage. A second factor is that the moisture content (of grain or hay) will usually decrease somewhat after harvest, resulting in more nutrients per unit of product purchased. Of course, costs increase with the distance from where feeds are grown or processed. For example, it is a common practice in the United States to price soybean meal at a location in Indiana. Thus if the user lives close by, transportation costs will be quite low; however, if the user lives in California, the transportation costs will be an appreciable portion of the total cost.

Estimating Energy Values of Feedstuffs

Feedstuffs, particularly roughages, are apt to be quite variable in composition and nutritive value. Furthermore, the nutritive value of a given batch of roughage may be different for sheep than for cattle or other species, or it may be influenced by level of feeding, nature of other feedstuffs, the environment, and so on. Even so, a feeder or feed manufacturer is faced with making some estimate of nutritive value in practical feeding situations. We can go to appropriate tables and use digestion coefficients to calculate digestible protein or some measure of energy (DE, ME, NE, TDN); when no analytical information is available, this is about all that can be done. It has been demonstrated that *in vitro* rumen digestion gives a better estimate of digestibility of roughages for ruminants than do chemical analyses, but *in vitro* digestion data are rarely available, certainly not on a routine basis anywhere that the writer is familiar with.

If a minimal amount of analytical information is at hand for the roughage of interest, then various formulas are available for estimating digestible protein and energy in several different forms. Most feed analytical laboratories use something like this to give values for energy of analyzed feeds (see the formula in Fig. 6–10). There are numerous formulas that have been published in the literature, but taking the space to discuss them is not warranted in this book. For the reader who wants more information on this topic, most of the NRC publications on nutrient requirements of the various classes of animals have some discussion. Added information is given in a bulletin by Fonnesbeck et al. (15).

NUTRIENT VALUES OF MAJOR FEEDSTUFF GROUPS

For the benefit of inexperienced readers, a brief introduction will be given on relative nutrient contents of major feed ingredients. These are shown in Table 4–1. Except for fats and some mineral supplements, all feedstuffs provide several nutrients for animals, but they are often much more important as a source of one type of nutrient than for others. For example, oil seed proteins and animal proteins are purchased and used primarily because of the protein content. However, these products also supply energy, minerals, and vitamins in varying amounts.

VARIABILITY IN FEEDSTUFF COMPOSITION

At this point it is appropriate to discuss and illustrate some of the variations that may occur in feedstuffs fed to animals. There are many examples in the literature to illustrate these variations but, unfortunately, this problem is not always recognized by people concerned with feedstuff utilization and animal feeding.

One good example of the variation to be expected in the grade of milo and corn is shown in Table 4–2. The data in this table show the percentage of each grade received at a large feedlot in Texas. Unfortunately, information relating grade to nutritional quality is not well documented. It may be that there is relatively little difference; on the other hand, foreign material may be expected to reduce nutritive value, and other factors, such as broken grains or small seeds, make it more difficult to produce a uniform product when processing methods such as steam flaking are utilized.

A second example of the variability to be expected in milo is shown in Fig. 4–1. These data were accumulated from a feedlot in Arizona. The graphs show the tremendous range in protein and starch content of milo and the correlations with bushel weight. Note that the protein content (moisture-free basis) ranged from a low of 7.4 percent to a high of almost 16 percent and the starch from a low of about 55.6 percent to

TABLE 4-1

Nutrient contributions of major feedstuff groups

Feedstuff Group	Relative Value[a]						
			Minerals		Vitamins		
	Protein	Energy	Macro	Trace	Fat-Sol.	B-Complex	Bulk
High-quality roughage	+ + +	+ +	+ +	+ +	+ + +	+	+ + +
Low-quality roughage	+	+	+	+	−	−	+ + + +
Cereal grains	+ +	+ + +	+	+	+	+	+
Grain millfeeds	+ +	+ +	+ +	+ +	+	+ +	+ +
Feeding fats	−	+ + + +	−	−	−	−	−
Molasses	+	+ + +	+ +	+ +	−	+	−
Fermentation products	+ + +	+ +	+	+ +	−	+ + + +	±
Oil seed proteins	+ + +	+ + +	+ +	+ +	+	+ +	+
Animal proteins	+ + + +	+ + +	+ + +	+ + +	+ +	+ + +	+

[a]Relative values are indicated by number of +. Feeding values (nutrient content and availability) of any product depends on many different factors which are discussed in the text of Ch. 6–10.

TABLE 4-2

Grades of grain received at a feed yard in Texas (expressed as % of loads in each grade)

Grade	April	May	June	July	August	Sept
			Month			
Milo						
#1	5	4	2	1	1	1
#2	40	44	41	55	41	41
#3	37	40	54	38	51	40
#4	6	5	3	4	4	9
#5	0	0	0	0	0	0
Sample	12	7	0	2	3	9
	100	100	100	100	100	100
Corn						
#1	6	1	4	4	0	0
#2	31	32	40	21	9	2
#3	21	20	13	21	25	5
#4	13	11	15	15	4	10
#5	12	12	15	18	10	14
Sample	17	24	13	21	52	69
	100	100	100	100	100	100

Source: Fleming (8).

a high of 80 percent. Obviously, this tremendous range in these two important nutrients must have an important effect on the nutritive value of milo. Further information of this type on corn has been compiled and published elsewhere.

A third example of variation in legume-grass forage is shown in Table 4–3. Note the tremendous range observed in most of the listed nutrients. The author points out that nutritionists should probably have less concern with energy than some of the other nutrients, as the energy content (TDN) varies much less. For example, there was a 7.5-fold difference in protein,

TABLE 4-3

Range in nutritive content (dry basis) of mixed legume-grass forage

Nutrient	Mean	Range	Fold Difference
TDN, %	59.4	51.0–71.7	1.4
Crude protein, %	16.4	5.5–40.3	7.5
Potassium, %	2.26	0.42–9.63	22.9
Calcium, %	1.02	0.01–2.61	261.0
Phosphorus, %	0.29	0.07–0.74	10.6
Magnesium, %	0.22	0.07–0.75	10.7
Sulfur, %	0.23	0.04–0.38	9.5
Manganese, ppm	48.1	6.0–265	44.2
Iron, ppm	222	10.0–2,599	259.9
Copper, ppm	13.1	2.0–92	46.0
Zinc, ppm	27.2	8.0–300	37.5

Source: Adams (10).

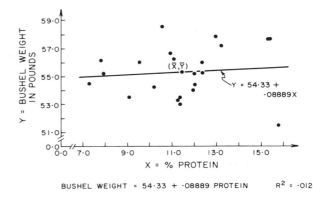

BUSHEL WEIGHT vs. MOISTURE-FREE PROTEIN IN ARIZONA MILO

BUSHEL WEIGHT = 54·33 + ·08889 PROTEIN R^2 = ·012

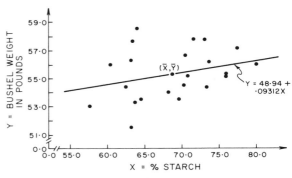

BUSHEL WEIGHT vs. MOISTURE-FREE STARCH IN ARIZONA MILO

BUSHEL WEIGHT = 48·94 + ·09312 STARCH R^2 = ·095

FIGURE 4-1. Relationship between bushel weight of milo and the protein and starch content of the grain. From Cardon (9).

about a 10-fold difference for most of the major mineral elements, and about a 45-fold difference for most of the trace minerals.

These illustrations show clearly that average book values of nutrient composition may be very misleading when used in formulation of animal diets. When appropriate analytical data are not available, there is little that can be done about it except to try to find analytical values from the region where the feedstuff originated, and this may or may not be helpful.

DAMAGED AND SPOILED FEED

Miscellaneous Damage

Many different environmental situations can result in damage to the feeding value of feedstuffs prior to harvest, during harvest, or while in storage. Consequently, the reader should be familiar with some of the problems that can result from feeding damaged or spoiled feed. Several relatively recent papers are available on the topic (11, 12, 13, 14).

Rainfall and very high humidity will delay drying of forage cut for hay. If drying is delayed, particularly at a relatively high temperature, it allows enzymes in the plant tissues to continue action after cuttiing (see sections on hay and silage making in Ch. 6). Such action will result in some metabolism of amino acids to nonprotein compounds and a reduction in the amount of sugar in the plant tissues. Heating will usually occur, especially if the forage is rather tightly packed. All of these result in some loss of nutritive value. Excess exposure to sunlight will result in a rapid loss of carotenes (provitamin A) from green plant tissues.

Grains and other crops may be damaged by insects, rodents, birds, and other species before harvest or during storage. Contamination of stored grains by rodent fecal pellets, urine, hairs, and other foreign matter will make the feed less palatable even if no other losses occur. In addition, a variety of beetles and their larva may infest stored grain. If beetles or larvae are present in large enough numbers, the damage done may be quite severe. This is usually combated by storage in clean bins and use of various chemicals to inhibit insect infestations.

Molds and Other Fungi

All harvested grains, forage, and many other feedstuffs are suitable mediums for growth of a wide variety of molds, provided temperature and moisture conditions allow growth to occur. Although feedstuffs may frequently have detectable and very substantial mold populations, the degree of visible mold infestation is not necessarily an indication of the amount of toxin present; mold may not be apparent at all after milling or processing of feed.

More than one hundred different molds that grow on standing crops or feeds are known to produce toxins (mycotoxins), and about twenty of these mycotoxins have been associated with naturally occurring diseases in humans or animals. However, the evidence suggests that toxicity is seldom diagnosed (14). Subclinical toxicity may result in lowered production, reduced weight gains, and impaired resistance to infections.

Molds may begin spoiling grain while the crop is still growing in the field. For example, wheat, barley, other cereal grains, and some grasses may be infested with scab, caused by a *fusarium* fungi. The affected kernels appear bleached, shriveled, and with pinkish mold. This mold produces two potent toxins, zearalenone and vomitoxin. The former interferes with the estrus cycle and the latter causes vomiting. Cattle are generally less affected than swine or poultry. Cereal grains, especially rye, may also be infested with ergot, a fungus which produces a variety of clinical effects (11).

Many of the toxins from molds and other fungi are heat-stable and survive pelleting and other feed processing methods, thus the only sure method of controlling molds is to have the moisture content of the feed and the humidity where it is stored low enough to prevent growth. While various mold inhibitors are satisfactory for preserving high-moisture feeds (propionic acid, for example), very little can be done to make moldy feeds satisfactory for animals if the feed is highly contaminated. Treatment of corn with gaseous ammonia has been shown to reduce mold toxins, but the method is still experimental.

Molds may be a serious economic problem in stored feeds if the feed is stored in a manner so that the moisture level is relatively high. The moisture of most feeds must be below 14 percent to be safe. In some cases, feeds will mold with 10 percent or less moisture. There are exceptions, of course. Molasses, a high-moisture feed, does not mold, because the osmotic pressure of the fluid is high enough that molds cannot survive, although they might grow on the surface. Failure to cool pelleted or flaked feeds and to remove moisture added while processing will invariably result in mold if the feeds are stored for several days, because of condensation of moisture in the bin.

Although some molds will grow at freezing temperatures, most grow most rapidly at temperatures between 20 and 30°C, and temperatures above 50-55°C will inactivate most molds. It has been shown that *Aspergillus candidus* and *A. flavus* predominate when grain heats at temperatures up to 50-55°C. Above this temperature thermophilic (heat-loving) fungi predominate, and then thermophilic bacteria, which may raise the temperature to 70-75°C. The combination of mold infestation, oxidation of material from the feed, and long-term heating reduces the value of the feed drastically (see Table 6–12), to say nothing of creating fire hazards.

Molds require oxygen for growth, and this is the reason that feeds such as silage will have higher concentrations of mold on the surface and around the edges. Rapid fermentation of silage depletes the oxygen supply, thus reducing the potential for mold growth. Likewise, the reduction in pH has a preservative effect. In addition, the development of an impervious (or semi-impervious) layer of moldy feed limits penetration of oxygen into the silage.

Molds may cause clinical symptoms ranging from photosensitivity of the skin to death (11, 12, 14). Unfortunately, it is quite difficult to determine in the field whether a particular batch of feed is poisonous. Some aflatoxins can be detected in a dark area with the use of ultraviolet light, which will cause the toxin to fluoresce. Rapid-screening laboratory tests have been developed, also, but the question the feeder asks still remains, should I feed moldy feed to my animals? There are marked differences between animal species in susceptibility to a given mold toxin. Generally, young animals are more sensitive than adults. Wilcox (14) has suggested the following criteria for determining whether to feed spoiled feed: (a) apparent kind of spoilage (yeast, blight, mold); (b) extent of spoilage: less than 10 percent, chancy; 10 to 50 percent, definitely risky; over 50 percent, discard the feed; (c) age and species of livestock to be fed: young, fast-growing animals are most adversely affected within a species; breeding animals may not be severely affected but the developing embryos are endangered; trout, ducks, geese, turkeys, chickens, fish, swine, other simple-stomached animals, cattle, and sheep are affected in decreasing order; (d) willingness to chance toxic effects on livestock; (e) estimated value of the questionable feedstuff minus the possible detrimental effects compared to cost of "good feedstuffs"; (f) what past experience has taught you—send a sample to a laboratory for analysis or go back to (d).

FEED MANUFACTURING TERMINOLOGY

It is appropriate to present in this chapter a listing of some of the terms used in feed manufacturing, because many of the terms will be used in succeeding chapters in discussions of various feedstuffs. The terminology is as defined by the American Feed Control Officials (5). The terms and their definitions follow:

Additive. An ingredient or combination of ingredients added to the basic feed mix or parts thereof to fulfill a specific need. Usually used in micro quantities and requires careful handling and mixing.

Antibiotics. A class of drug. They are usually synthesized by a living microorganism and in proper concentration inhibit the growth of other microorganisms.

Artificially dried. (Process) Moisture having been removed by other than natural means.

Aspirated, aspirating. Having removed chaff, dust, or other light materials by use of air.

Balanced. A term that may be applied to a diet, ration, or feed having all known required nutrients in proper amount and proportion based upon recommendations of recognized authorities in the field of animal nutrition, such as the National Research Council, for a given set of physiological animal requirements. The species for which it is intended and the functions such as maintenance or maintenance plus production (growth, fetus, fat, milk, eggs, wool, feathers, or work) shall be specified.

Blending. (Process) To mingle or combine two or more ingredients of feed. It does not imply a uniformity of dispersion.

Blocked, blocking. (Process) Having agglomerated individual ingredients or mixtures into a large mass.

Blocks. (Physical form) Agglomerated feed compressed into a solid mass cohesive enough to hold its form and weighing over two pounds, and generally weighing 30-50 pounds.

Brand name. Any word, name, symbol, or device or any combination thereof identifying the commercial feed of a distributor and distinguishing it from that of others.

By-product. (Part) Secondary products produced in addition to the principal product.

Cake. (Physical form) The mass resulting from the pressing of seeds, meat, or fish in order to remove oils, fats, or other liquids.

Carriers. An edible material to which ingredients are added to facilitate uniform incorporation of the latter into feeds. The active particles are absorbed, impregnated, or coated into or onto the edible material in such a way as to physically carry the active ingredient.

Chaff. (Part) Glumes, husks, or other seed covering together with other plant parts separated from seed in threshing or processing.

Cleaned, cleaning. (Process) Removal of material by such methods as scalping, aspirating, magnetic separation, or by any other method.

Cleaning. (Part) Chaff, weed seeds, dust, and other foreign matter removed from cereal grains.

Clipped, clipping. (Process) Removal of the ends of whole grain.

Commercial feed. The term "commercial feed" (as defined in the Uniform Feed Bill) means all materials distributed for use as feed or for mixing in feed, for animals other than humans except as follows: (A) Option A—Unmixed seed, whole or processed, made directly from the entire seed. Option B—

Unmixed or unprocessed whole seeds. (B) Hay, straw, stover, silage, cobs, husks, and hulls (a) when unground, and (b) when unmixed with other materials. (C) Individual chemical compounds when not mixed with other materials.

Complete feed. A nutritionally adequate feed for animals other than humans, which by specific formula is compounded to be fed as the sole ration and is capable of maintaining life and/or promoting production without any additional substance being consumed except water.

Concentrate. A feed used with another to improve the nutritive balance of the total and intended to be further diluted and mixed to produce a supplement or a complete feed.

Condensed, condensing. (Process) Reduced to denser form by removal of moisture.

Conditioned, conditioning. (Process) Having achieved predetermined moisture characteristics and/or temperature of ingredients or a mixture of ingredients prior to further processing.

Cooked, cooking. (Process) Heated in the presence of moisture to alter chemical and/or physical characteristics or to sterilize.

Cooled, cooling. (Process) Temperature reduced by air movement, usually accompanied by a simultaneous drying action.

Cracked, craking. (Process) Particle size reduced by a combined breaking and crushing action.

Crumbled, crumbling. (Process) Pellets reduced to granular form.

Crumbles. (Physical form) Pelleted feed reduced to granular form.

Cubes. (Physical form) See Pellets.

Cubes, range. (Physical form) See Pellets, Range cubes.

Dehulled, dehulling. (Process) Having removed the outer covering from grains or other seeds.

Dehydrated, dehydrating. (Process) Having been freed of moisture by thermal means.

Diet. Feed ingredient or mixture of ingredients, including water, which is consumed by animals.

Dilute. (Physical form) An edible substance used to mix with and reduce the concentration of nutrients and/or additives to make them more acceptable to animals, safer to use, and more capable of being mixed uniformily in a feed. (It may also be a carrier.)

Dressed, dressing. (Process) Made uniform in texture by breaking or screening of lumps from feed and/or the application of liquid(s).

Dried, drying. (Process) Materials from which water or other liquid has been removed.

Drug. (As defined by FDA as applied to feed) A substance (a) intended for use in the diagnosis, cure, mitigation, treatment, or prevention of disease in humans or other animals, or (b) a substance other than food intended to affect the structure or any function of the body of humans or other animals.

Dust. (Part) Fine, dry pulverized particles of matter usually resulting from the cleaning or grinding of grain.

Emulsifier. A material capable of causing fat or oils to remain in liquid suspension.

Evaporated, evaporating. (Process) Reduced to a denser form; concentrated as by evaporation or distillation.

Expanded, expanding. (Process) Subjected to moisture, pressure, and temperature to gelatinize the starch portion. When extruded, its volume is increased, due to abrupt reduction in pressure.

Extracted, mechanical. (Process) Having removed fat or oil from materials by heat and mechanical pressure. Similar terms: expeller extracted, hydraulic extracted, "old process."

Extracted, solvent. (Process) Having removed fat or oil from materials by organic solvents. Similar term: "new process."

Extruded. (Process) A process by which feed has been pressed, pushed, or protruded through orifices under pressure.

Feed(s). Edible material(s) consumed by animals that contribute energy and/or nutrients to the animal's diet. (Usually refers to animals rather than humans.)

Feed additive concentrate. (Part) (As defined by FDA) An article intended to be further diluted to produce a complete feed or a feed additive supplement and not suitable for offering as a supplement or for offering free choice without dilution. It contains, among other things, one or more additives in amounts in a suitable feed base such that from 10 to 100 pounds of concentrate must be diluted to produce 1 ton of a complete feed. A "feed additive concentrate" is unsafe if fed free choice or as a supplement because of danger to the health of the animal or because of the production of residues in the edible products from food-producing animals in excess of the safe levels established.

Feed additive supplement. (As defined by FDA) An article for the diet of an animal which contains one or more food additives and is intended to be: (a) further diluted and mixed to produce a complete feed; or (b) fed undiluted as a supplement to other feeds; or (c) offered free choice with other parts of the rations separately available.

Note: A "feed additive supplement" is safe for the animal and will not produce unsafe residues in the edible products from food-producing animals if fed according to directions.

Feed additive premix. (As defined by FDA) An article that must be diluted for safe use in a feed additive concentrate, a feed additive supplement, or a complete feed. It contains, among other things, one or more additives in high concentration in a suitable feed base such that up to 100 pounds must be diluted to produce 1 ton of complete feed. A feed additive premix contains additives at levels for which safety to the animal has not been demonstrated and/or which may result when fed undiluted in residues in the edible products from food-producing animals in excess of the safe levels established.

Feed grade. Suitable for animal consumption.

Feed mixture. See Formula feed.

Feedstuff. See Feed(s).

Fines. (Physical form) Any material which will pass through a screen whose openings are immediately smaller than the specified minimum crumble size or pellet diameter.

Flakes. (Physical form) An ingredient rolled or cut into flat pieces with or without prior steam conditioning.

Flaked, flaking. (Process) See Rolled.

Flour. (Part) Soft, finely ground and bolted meal obtained from the milling of cereal grains, other seeds, or products. It consists essentially of the starch and gluten of the endosperm.

Food(s). When used in reference to animals is synonymous with feed(s). See Feed(s).

Formula feed. Two or more ingredients proportioned, mixed, and processed according to specifications.

Free choice. A feeding system by which animals are given unlimited access to the separate components or groups of components constituting the diet.

Gelatinized, gelatinizing. (Process) Having had the starch granules completely ruptured by a combination of moisture, heat, and pressure, and, in some instances, by mechanical shear.

Grain. (Part) Seed from cereal plants.

GRAS. Abbreviation for the phrase "Generally Recognized As Safe." A substance which is generally recognized as safe by experts qualified to evaluate the safety of the substance for its intended use.

Grits. (Part) Coarsely ground grain from which the bran and germ have been removed, usually screened to uniform particle size.

Groats. Grain from which the hulls have been removed.

Ground, grinding. (Process) Reduced in particle size by impact, shearing, or attrition.

Heat-processed, heat-processing. (Process) Subjected to a method or preparation involving the use of elevated temperatures with or without pressure.

Hulls. (Part) Outer covering of grain or other seed.

Ingredient, feed ingredient. A component part or constituent of any combination or mixture making up a commercial feed.

Kibbled, kibbling. (Process) Cracked or crushed baked dough, or extruded feed that has been cooked prior to or during the extrusion process.

Mash. (Physical form) A mixture of ingredients in meal form. Similar term: mash feed.

Meal. (Physical form) An ingredient which has been ground or otherwise reduced in particle size.

Medicated feed. Any feed which contains drug ingredients intended or represented for the cure, mitigation, treatment, or prevention of diseases of animals other than humans or which contains drug ingredients intended to affect the structure or function of the body of animals other than humans.

Antibiotics included in a feed at growth promotion and/or feed efficiency levels are drug additives, and feeds containing such antibiotics are included in the forgoing definition of "Medicated feed."

Microingredients. Vitamins, minerals, antibiotics, drugs, and other materials normally required in small amounts and measured in milligrams, micrograms, or parts per million (ppm).

Mill by-product. (Part) A secondary product obtained in addition to the principal product in milling practice.

Mill dust. (Part) Fine feed particles of undetermined origin resulting from handling and processing feed and feed ingredients.

Mill run. (Part) The state in which a material comes from the mill, ungraded and usually uninspected.

Mineralize, mineralized. (Process) To supply, impregnate, or add inorganic mineral compounds to a feed ingredient or mixture.

Mixing. (Process) To combine by agitation two or more materials to a specific degree of dispersion.

Pearled, pearling. (Process) Dehulled grains reduced by machine brushing into smaller smooth particles.

Pellets. (Physical form) Agglomerated feed formed by compacting and forcing through die openings by a mechanical process. Similar terms: pelleted feed, hard pellet.

Pellets, soft. (Physical form) Similar terms: high molasses pellets. Pellets containing sufficient liquid to require immediate dusting and cooling.

Pelleted, pelleting. (Process) Having agglomerated feed by compacting it and forcing it through die openings.

Premix. A uniform mixture of one or more microingredients with diluent and/or carrier. Premixes are used to facilitate uniform dispersion of the microingredients in a larger mix.

Premixing. (Process) The preliminary mixing of ingredients with diluents and/or carriers.

Product. (Part) A substance produced from one or more other substances as a result of chemical or physical change.

Protein. (Part) Any of a large class of naturally occurring complex combinations of amino acids.

Pulverized, pulverizing. (Process) See Ground, grinding.

Range cake. (Physical form) See Cake.

Range cubes. (Physical form) Large pellets designed to be fed on the ground. Similar term: range wafer.

Ration. The amount of the total feed which is provided to one animal over a 24-h period.

Rolled, rolling. (Process) Having changed the shape and/or size of particles by compressing between rollers. It may entail tempering or conditioning.

Scalped, scalping. (Process) Having removed larger material by screening.

Scratch. (Physical form) Whole, cracked, or coarsely cut grain. Similar terms: scratch grain, scratch feed.

Screened, Screening. (Process) Having separated various-sized particles by passing them over and/or through screens.

Self-fed. A feeding system where animals have continuous free access to some or all component(s) of a ration, either individually or as mixtures.

Separating. (Process) Classification of particle size, shape, and/or density.

Separating, magnetic. (Process) Removing ferrous material by magnetic attraction.

Sizing. (Process) See Screened, screening.

Steamed, steaming. (Process) Having treated ingredients with steam to alter physical and/or chemical properties. Similar terms: steam cooked, steam rendered, tanked.

Supplement. A feed used with another to improve the nutritive balance or performance of the total and intended to be: (a) fed undiluted as a supplement to other feeds; or (b) offered free choice with other parts of the ration separately available; or (c) further diluted and mixed to produce a complete feed.

Tempered, tempering. (Process) See Conditioned, conditioning.

Toasted. (Process) Browned, dried, or parched by exposure to a fire or to gas or electric heat.

Trace minerals. Mineral nutrients required by animals in micro amounts only (measured in milligrams/lb or smaller amounts).

Vitamins. Organic compounds that function as parts of enzyme systems essential for the transmission of energy and the regulation of metabolism of the body.

Wafered, wafering. (Process) Having agglomerated a feed of a fibrous nature by compressing into a form usually having a diameter or cross section measurement greater than its length.

Wafers. (Physical form) A form of agglomerated feed based on fibrous ingredients in which the finished form usually has a diameter or cross section measurement greater than its length.

SUMMARY

Feedstuffs may be classified according to what their principal function in a diet may be—such as energy sources, roughage, protein supplements—or they may be grouped according to their origin, the latter method being a common method when dealing with manufactured and by-product feedstuffs. Feedstuffs vary considerably in composition, particularly those that are not standardized in a manufacturing process. Various methods are used to estimate feedstuff value. Chemical analyses and animal digestion or feeding trials are most useful if time permits. Value can be estimated by assessing physical appearance and by collecting information on where and how crops were produced. Many different feedstuffs may be subject to damage by spoilage, especially by molds or, with high-moisture feeds, by bacterial decomposition.

In order to reduce some confusion on meaning of terms, manufacturing terms, as defined by the American Feed Control Officials, are given in this chapter. This listing will be useful to the reader in later chapters.

REFERENCES

1. NRC. 1982. *United States-Canadian tables of feed composition.* 3d ed. Washington, D.C.: Nat. Academy Press.

2. Fonnesbeck, P. V., et al. 1984. *IFI tables of feed composition.* Logan, UT: International Feedstuffs Institute, Utah Agr. Expt. Std.

3. McDowell, I. R., et al. 1974. *Latin American tables of feed composition.* Gainesville, FL: Dept. of Animal Sci., Univ. of Florida.

4. Gohl, B. 1975. *Tropical feeds.* Rome: Food and Agr. Organ. of the United Nations.

5. AFCO. 1989. *Official publication 1989.* Washington, D.C.: Amer. Feed Control Officials.

6. Church, D. C., and W. G. Pond. 1988. *Basic animal nutrition and feeding.* 3d ed. New York: Wiley.

7. Church, D. C., ed. 1988. *The ruminant animal.* Englewood Cliffs, NJ: Prentice Hall.

8. Fleming, B. 1975. *Beef* 11(6):60.

9. Cardon, B. P. 1975. Personal communication.

10. Adams, R. S. 1975. *Feedstuffs* 47(22):22.

11. Church, D. C. 1979. *Digestive physiology and nutrition of ruminants. Vol. 2: Nutrition.* Corvallis, OR: O & B Books.

12. Trenholm, H. M., et al. 1984. *J. Amer. Vet. Med. Assoc.* 185:527.

13. Trenholm, H. M., et al. 1985. *J. Dairy Sci.* 68:1000.

14. Wilcox, R. A. 1988. In: *Feed additive compendium.* Minnetonka, MN: Miller.

15. Fonnesbeck, P. V., M. F. Wardeh, and L. E. Harris. 1984. *Bulletin.* 508. Logan, UT: Utah Agr. Expt. Sta.

5

Feed Laws and Labeling

The manufacture and distribution of commercial feeds, mineral supplements, premixes, or other feed supplies is controlled in the United States by regulatory agencies. All commercially produced feeds must be registered at the state level. In most states this amounts to supplying a copy of the labels to be used and paying a yearly fee. Similar agencies control commerce of this type in all advanced countries. Fortunately, in the United States most state agencies subscribe to use of the Model Feed Bill, which was developed through the joint efforts of the American Feed Control Officials and the American Feed Manufacturer's Association. Uniformity in laws and regulations from state to state greatly facilitates interstate trade of manufactured feeds.

The regulations in the Model Feed Bill cover a variety of different subjects such as appropriate definitions, registration of brand feed names, labeling, and other appropriate regulations. Of particular interest, insofar as this book and its readers are concerned, are the regulations dealing with labeling.

FEED LABELING

Labels should identify the product, inform the purchaser and/or user of the nature of the product and its intended purpose, provide instruction on how to use the product, and convey any particular cautions pertaining to the product's use. Labels are required to be attached to individual bags of feed or to be available for inspection when feed is sold in bulk lots, except for custom formula feeds. Although there are minor differences from state to state, labels are generally required to display the following information: net weight; product name and brand name, if any; the guaranteed analysis; the common or usual name of each ingredient used in the feed or collective names which describe groups of ingredients; name and address of the manufacturer or firm distributing the feed; and any precautionary statements necessary for safe and effective use of the feed.

Customer formula feeds (those made specifically for a given customer) are to be accompanied by a label, delivery slip, or other shipping document with the name and address of the manufacturer; name and address of the purchaser; date of delivery; product name and brand name, if any; net weight of each registered commercial feed used in the mixture and the net weight of each other ingredient used; adequate directions for use of feeds containing drugs or other ingredients as necessary for their safe and effective use; and such precautionary statements as necessary for safe and effective use of the feed.

With manufactured human food items, it is the accepted practice to list ingredients starting with the item making up the largest percentage of the mixture and continuing with those added in smaller quantities. This practice is, more or less, followed by feed manufacturers, although the Model Feed Bill does not specify this and most states probably do not require it. Collective feed names are used by most feed manufacturers. One reason for this is that it avoids the necessity of reregistration and preparation of new labels if use of one or more ingredients is discontinued. It also allows the manufacturer to avoid listing every specific ingredient. The commonly used groups are: animal protein products, forage products, grain products, plant protein products, processed grain by-products, roughage products, and molasses products.

With regard to the guaranteed analysis of the feed, the following items are normally required to be on the label: minimum percentage of crude protein, maximum or minimum percentage of protein equivalent from nonprotein nitrogen (NPN), minimum percentage of crude fat, and maximum percentage of crude fiber. In addition to these data, some states require that the percentage of roughage ingredients be shown if more than 5 percent is in the feed. With liquid supplements, some states require, in addition to other information given, a maximum moisture and minimum total sugar content. Total sugars are to be expressed as invert on dried molasses products or products being sold primarily for their molasses content.

With mineral feeds the label must include, in the follower order: minimum and maximum percentage of Ca, minimum percentage of P, and minimum and maximum percentage of salt (NaCl) and other minerals. Vitamins are to be labeled as specified by regulation.

There are minor differences in labeling requirements from state to state as noted. Details on differences from state to state may be found in one of the references cited (1). One hypothetical example of a fairly typical tag is shown in Figure 5–1. Note that a brand name and registration number are given as well as the guaranteed analysis, a listing of ingredients and feeding instructions, and the address of the manufacturer.

Guaranteed Analysis

The guaranteed analysis, although very limited with regard to specific requirements, is used and required for the protection of the user of the feed. In most states, registered feeds are sampled from time to time for some or all of the guaranteed items. These analyses are usually published. In cases where a manufacturer is consistently in violation of the guarantee, fines may be assessed.

The minimum defined amount of crude protein is required by all states because protein

---

SFM   **137**

Net Weight 100 Lbs.

SUPERIOR CATTLE FATTENER

GUARANTEED ANALYSIS

Minimum crude protein	11.5%
(This includes not more than 3.75% equivalent crude protein from nonprotein nitrogen.)	
Minimum crude fat	1.75%
Maximum crude fiber	7.00%

INGREDIENTS

Grain Products, Plant Protein Products, Processed Grain By-Products, Roughage Products, Dicalcium Phosphate, Calcium Carbonate, Feeding Cane Molasses, Lignin Sulfonate, Salt, Sodium Sulphate, Urea, Stabilized Vitamin A Palmitate, D-Activated Plant Sterol (Source of Vitamin D-2), Magnesium Oxide, Manganese Sulphate, Cobalt Carbonate, Ferrous Sulphate, Copper Sulphate, Zinc Oxide, Dicalcium Phosphate.

FEEDING INSTRUCTIONS

Fattening Cattle—Bring cattle to full grain feeding as quickly as feasible by increasing slightly amount fed each day. Roughage should be fed free choice at the beginning of fattening period. As grain feeding increases, roughage consumption will decrease.

Stocker Cattle—Feed at the rate of 2-6 lbs. per head per day in conjunction with roughage.

Wintering Cattle—Feed at the rate of 2-6 lbs. per head per day in conjunction with roughage.

Manufactured by
SUPERIOR FEED MILLS
General Offices - Anyplace, USA

FIGURE 5–1. An example of a feed label for a nonmedicated feed.

is normally an expensive feed ingredient and most manufacturers try to be only slightly above the guaranteed minimum. Although crude protein analysis, by itself, is not very meaningful in describing or defining how the feed may be used by the animal, the analysis is quick and repeatable and serves the intended purpose after a fashion. Other types of analyses might be preferable (2), but they are either more complicated or time-consuming or have not received widespread acceptance.

When used, the maximum percentages for added NPN are there to advise the user how much has been added. NPN compounds may be toxic if high levels are used. NPN compounds are not to be added to any feed except that intended for ruminant animals. Generally, if the feed contains more than 8.75 percent crude protein equivalent from NPN or the NPN exceeds one-third of the total crude protein, the label must give adequate directions for the safe use of feeds and a precautionary statement, "**CAUTION:** Use as directed." Several states require that any feeds containing urea have a statement reading "For ruminants only" or "Feed only to ruminants." This should be used by all states, because urea has no feeding value for nonruminant animals and may be toxic as well.

The maximum crude fiber guarantee is required with the intent that it prevent unscrupulous manufacturers from adding excessive amounts of fibrous feed ingredients which might be of little value to many animals. In many laboratories the crude fiber analytical method has been replaced by more modern methods; unfortunately, most state regulatory agencies still specify crude fiber. Not many states require a listing of "roughage" feeds if more than 5 percent is included.

Because large volumes of liquid supplements are sold each year, the tendency for states to require a guarantee of a maximum moisture and minimum sugar content is to be encouraged. There are many different liquid ingredients (see Ch. 8) that could be included but which might not contribute either to the sugar or nitrogen content. In addition, these requirements would tend to discourage manufacturers or distributors from diluting liquid supplements more than they should with water.

When required, the values for minimum and maximum of Ca have merit for mineral supplements. One reason for this is that limestone is normally one of the cheapest feed ingredients found in most feed mills. Thus the maximum Ca value would help to identify feeds diluted with excessive amounts of limestone. The same comment applies to maximum salt percentages. Phosphorus is normally one of the most expensive ingredients used in any quantity in livestock feeds. Thus minimal values are highly desirable for any feed sold on the basis of its P content.

A few states require data on maximum ash content (mineral residue left after burning in a furnace). Ash values do not provide any qualitative information, but such information would be useful in providing a quick estimate of whether soil or excessive amounts of limestone or salt had been added to a feed.

MEDICATED FEEDS

A medicated feed is defined as any animal feed that contains one or more drugs at any level and includes: (a) medicated complete feed that is intended to be the sole ration for an animal; (b) medicated supplements that are safe for direct consumption by the intended animal and can be offered in a free-choice feeding plan; and (c) medicated concentrates that are to be mixed with other feed materials to make either a supplement or a complete feed before being offered to the intended animal. Medicated concentrates are used at levels from 100 to 1,000 lb/T complete feed (1). A high percentage of commercial feeds contain some type of additive that would be classed as a drug.

In addition to the usual labeling requirements, the addition of an additive classed as a drug requires (per FDA regulations) that the word "medicated" appear directly following and below the product name. The purpose of medication must be stated, the names and amounts of the active ingredients must be listed, a warning statement must be included (when required by the FDA) listing the minimum withdrawal period required before slaughter for human food, and warnings against misuse and appropriate directions must be given for use of the feed. One example of a label is shown in Fig. 5–2.

Custom-mixed feeds are subject to the same basic legal requirements as registered feeds. The FDA requires that all medicated feed be labeled. If bagged, each bag must be labeled appropriately. One type of label that could be used for custom formulas is shown in Fig. 5–3. Other suggestions are that each batch should be given a lot number so that it can be identified at a later date.

```
┌─────────────────────────────────────────┐
│          NET WEIGHT 80 lbs.              │
│             COMPLETE                      │
│          PIG GROWER 1427                 │
│             MEDICATED                     │
│                                           │
│  For increased rate of weight gain and   │
│  improved feed effi-ciency in swine when │
│  fed in accordance with directions       │
│  for use.                                 │
│                                           │
│         ACTIVE DRUG INGREDIENT            │
│                                           │
│  Carbadox . . . . . . . . . 0.00275%     │
│                              (25 g/t)     │
│                                           │
│  WARNING: DO NOT FEED TO SWINE WEIGHING   │
│           MORE THAN 75 LBS. BODY WEIGHT.  │
│           DO NOT FEED TO SWINE WITHIN 10  │
│           WEEKS OF SLAUGHTER.             │
│                                           │
│          GUARANTEED ANALYSIS              │
│                                           │
│  Crude protein, not less than . . . 15.0%│
│  Crude fat, not less than . . . . . 2.5% │
│  Crude fiber, not more than . . . . 8.0% │
│                                           │
│             INGREDIENTS                   │
│                                           │
│  Grain Products, Processed Grain          │
│  By-products, Plant Protein Products,     │
│  Animal Protein Products, Cane Molasses,  │
│  Salt, Defluorinated Phosphate, Limestone │
│  Flour, Vitamin A Palmitate, Irradiated   │
│  Yeast (Source of Vitamin D2),            │
│  D-activated Animal Sterol (Source of     │
│  Vitamin D3), D-alpha Tocopheryl Acetate  │
│  (Source of Vitamin E), Menadione Sodium  │
│  Bisulfite (Source of Vitamin K), Vitamin │
│  B12, Riboflavin, Pantothenic Acid,       │
│  Choline Chloride, Niacin, Ethoxyquin (A  │
│  Preservative), Iron Oxide, Zinc Oxide,   │
│  Manganese Oxide, Copper Oxide.           │
│                                           │
│          FEEDING DIRECTIONS               │
│                                           │
│  Feed continuously as the sole ration.    │
│                                           │
│            manufactured by                │
│          Superior Feed Mills              │
│            Anyplace, USA                  │
└─────────────────────────────────────────┘
```

FIGURE 5-2. An example of a label used for medicated animal feed.

In the case of premixes (mixes with additives in concentrated form which will be added to other ingredients), the label must state the intended mixing ratios, the resultant drug levels, and the purpose of the final mixed medication. Any instructions and warning statements must also appear. In the case of drugs for which the FDA requires a form 1800 (see Ch. 10), the feed manufacturer must file these forms and receive FDA approval before selling such medicated feed.

A number of problems exist in the use of medicated feed. The filing of the 1800 forms and the precautions taken in labeling have been instituted to cut down on inadvertent mistakes by feed manufacturers and livestock feeders. Some drugs are toxic if used in higher concentrations than intended or are toxic for species other than those intended to consume the drug. A good example of the latter is monensin, an additive widely used for feedlot cattle, but one which is quite toxic to horses.

Feed manufacturers producing medicated feeds are expected to become familiar with Good Manufacturing Practice (GMP) regulations. The regulations have been developed and published in the Federal Register for different classes of feeds. The manufacturer is responsible for being familiar with these practices and for taking periodic samples of feed for analysis of drug concentrations.

In addition to outright mistakes that may be made in the manufacturing process (several highly publicized cases have occurred), one of the big problems is inadvertent contamination in the feed mill when a nonmedicated feed is mixed and processed in equipment following a batch of medicated feed. It is difficult to remove all traces of previous feed from the various pieces of equipment used in feed mills.

Other common problems are the use of medicated feeds in concentrations not approved or in combinations not approved, or feeding them to animals other than those on the approved list. These situations may develop as a

```
┌─────────────────────────────────────────┐
│        CUSTOMER-FORMULA                   │
│        MEDICATED LABEL                    │
│                                           │
│  Medication has been added at customer    │
│  request as checked below.  Refer to      │
│  attached label or invoice for additional │
│  description of (feed)                    │
│  _____  │
│                                           │
│        ACTIVE DRUG INGREDIENT             │
│                                           │
│  ☐ Arsanilic Acid . . . . . . . . 0.005% │
│     For increased rate of gain and        │
│     improved feed efficiency.             │
│                                           │
│  ☒ Arsanilic Acid . . . . . . . . 0.01%  │
│     For increased rate of gain and        │
│     improved feed efficiency.             │
│                                           │
│  ☐ Arsanilic Acid . . . . . . . . 0.025% │
│     For control of swine dysentery. Feed  │
│     for 5-6 days.                         │
│                                           │
│          FEEDING DIRECTIONS               │
│                                           │
│  Feed as the sole ration to swine.        │
│                                           │
│  ┌───────────────────────────────────┐   │
│  │            WARNING                 │   │
│  │  Discontinue 5 days before         │   │
│  │  slaughter.  Use as the sole       │   │
│  │  source of organic arsenic.        │   │
│  └───────────────────────────────────┘   │
└─────────────────────────────────────────┘
```

FIGURE 5-3. An example of a label that could be used for customer formula feeds.

result of requests by local veterinarians and/or nutritionists for a "special mix" of medicated feeds for their clients. If any of the parties knowingly produces and feeds an illegal mix, they are liable for legal action by the FDA.

SUMMARY

Most states in the United States subscribe to use of the Model Feed Bill, which was developed to promote uniformity in laws controlling feed manufacturing and sales and labeling of manufactured feed. Labels are required to be attached to individual bags of feed or to be available for inspection when feed is sold in bulk lots. Labels must provide information required for the particular type of feed in the state it is sold in, usually including the minimum crude protein content, the maximum crude fiber and ash (and/or Ca), and, if present, the content of nonprotein nitrogen compounds. In addition, if medicated feed is involved, the label must state the names and amounts of the active ingredients, it must include a warning statement (if required by the FDA) listing the withdrawal period required before slaughter for human food, and it must give warnings against misuse and appropriate directions for use of the feed.

REFERENCES

1. Anon. 1990. *Feed additive compendium.* Minnetonka, MN: Miller.

2. Church, D. C., and W. G. Pond. 1988. *Basic animal nutrition and feeding.* 3d ed. New York: Wiley.

6

Roughages

Plant material of one kind or another is the natural food for all grazing and browsing animals, thus it is of primary importance for domestic ruminants and horses. With species such as swine, even though they may be able to survive on a diet of herbage, productivity on such a diet is too low for market animals to be economical in our current economy. The nature of the digestive tract of poultry restricts the amount of fibrous feeds that can be fed effectively to a much lower level than with swine.

Herbage might best be defined as plant material (except seeds and roots) that can be utilized as food by herbivorous animals. It is a term used more or less interchangeably with forage, although herbage is sometimes defined as the total plant material available and **forage** as that which can be consumed by an animal. On the other hand, roughage is a term more often used by animal feeders and nutritionists. As normally used, **roughage** would include herbage or forage, but it would not be restricted specifically to plants grown to feed animals.

The reader might gain some appreciation for the importance of grazing animal species if some statistics on land area and type of vegeta-

tion are presented. Approximately one-third of the earth's surface is land—about 34 billion acres (13.7 billion ha or a little more than 53 million square miles). Of this, 3–4 percent is utilized for urban and industrial purposes, while about 10 percent is under cultivation. Non-productive lands comprise about 15 percent of the earth's land area. Forest lands, some of which may be utilized by grazing animals, cover 28–30 percent of the land. The land remaining, which includes 40 percent or more of the total area, is comprised of rangeland, which is more suitable for grazing than cultivation. Rangelands include natural grasslands, savannas, shrublands, most deserts, tundra, alpine communities, coastal marshes, and wet meadows. Thus it is obvious that production of materials useful to humans (food, fiber, clothing, and so forth) from a large majority of the earth's surface would be reduced greatly if grazing animals—both domestic and wild—were not available to utilize the vegetation to some degree.

The forage or roughage utilized in North America comes from forests, native rangelands and pastures, improved pastures, crops (hays, fodder, silages) harvested and stored specifically for animal use, and residues of crops grown for other purposes. Production and conservation of feed from these sources allows for a substantial increase in animal productivity. Harvested forage production in the United States is a substantial percentage of the total feed supply (see Table 6-1). For hays, 143–151 million T were harvested in the 1980–85 period. In addition, substantial amounts of silage were produced from corn with lesser amounts from sorghums. No current data seem to be available on production of grass-legume silages or poor-quality roughages such as straws and stovers. In the 1985 crop year, USDA publications estimate that the area harvested for hays amounted to 60.5 million acres, or about 25 percent of the total land area used for grains and hays. When expressed in terms of feeding value equivalent to corn grain (see Table 1–4, p. 4), in 1985 harvested roughage and pasture production amounted to 80 and 222 million T, respectively, as compared to 210 million T from various concentrates. Thus roughages supplied about 59% of the nutritional value of livestock feeds in the United States during that particular year.

The cultivated, or tame, grasses, when used along with appropriate management and fertilization methods, usually produce a substantial increase in forage/unit of land as compared to wild species native to many areas. In addition, with appropriate combinations of cool and warm season grasses and/or with use of temporary pastures (annuals of various types), it is often possible to nearly meet the nutritional needs of grazing animals during a major portion of the year. In the dryland range areas, management practices such as control of undesirable species, care in avoiding overgrazing, and seeding of species such as crested wheatgrass are often very effective in greatly increasing productivity of native rangeland.

Conservation of surplus forage or growing of forage specifically for livestock use also allows for a great increase in animal numbers. The conserved feed can be used during winter months when plants are dormant or covered with snow or during the warm months when rainfall is insufficient to support plant growth. At present very little forage is conserved in tropical areas of the world. It would seem that forage conservation for use during the normal dry periods experienced in most tropical areas would be a very worthwhile practice in many countries.

NATURE OF ROUGHAGES

To most livestock feeders, **roughage** is a bulky feed that has a low weight/unit of volume. This is probably the best means of classifying a feedstuff as a roughage, but any means of classifying roughages has its limitations since, due to the nature of the many different products, there is a great variability in physical and chemical composition. Most feedstuffs classed as roughages have a high crude fiber (CF) content and digestibility of components such as protein and energy is low. If we attempt, as does NRC (2), to classify all feedstuffs as roughages that have >18 percent CF and/or with low digestibility, several important exceptions are readily apparent. Corn silage is a good example; it nearly always has >18 percent CF, but the TDN content of well-eared corn silage is 70 percent or more (dry basis). Lush young grass is another example. Although its weight/unit volume may be relatively low and fiber content relatively high, its digestibility is quite high. Soybean hulls are another exception for ruminants.

Most roughages have a high content of cell wall material (see Ch. 3). The cell wall fraction (or neutral detergent fiber, NDF) may have a highly variable composition, but it contains appreciable amounts of lignin, cellulose, hemicellulose, pectin, polyuronides, silica, and other components in lesser amounts. In contrast, roughages are generally low in readily available carbohydrates as compared to cereal grains and many other feedstuffs.

The amount of lignin appears to be a critical factor with respect to digestibility. Lignin is an amorphous material found in the supportive tissues of plants; it is closely associated with the fibrous carbohydrates of the cell wall of plant tissues. Lignin tends to form

TABLE 6-1

Harvested forage production in the United States (in millions of tons)

Item	Year		
	1980	1984	1985
All hays	143.1	150.6	148.9
Alfalfa & alf. mix.	83.7	90.1	85.3
All other hays	59.4	60.5	63.7
Straws, stovers, etc.[a]	40.0±	N.A.	N.A.
Corn silage[b]	111.0	104.5	102.6
Sorghum silage[b]	8.0	6.5	6.3

[a]Data no longer available.
[b]Wet basis.
Source: USDA (1).

a lignin-cellulose-hemicellulose complex which, in turn, is highly efficient in blocking enzymatic hydrolysis of cellulose and hemicellulose. Lignin is also chemically bound to some of the plant proteins. Because of the chemical bonding and a physical masking, lignin greatly reduces digestibility of plant tissues. As a result there is a high negative correlation between lignin content and digestibility, particularly for grasses, although somewhat less for legumes.

Furthermore, the composition of lignin varies over the growing season based on analyses of its oxidation products (3). Variations are forage specific and appear to be influenced by frequency and date of harvesting. Removal of lignin with chemical methods greatly increases digestibility by rumen microorganisms and, probably, by cecal organisms.

Juvenile plant tissues contain relatively little lignin; the content gradually increases with maturity of the tissues and with increasing temperatures. In grasses, lignin typically increases with maturity (this will be illustrated later), partly because the relative amount of stem tissue increases and lignin content is nearly always higher in the stems than in the leaf tissue. When grasses are maintained in a leafy state by grazing or harvesting, there will be less change in the lignin content. Generally, grasses adapted to warm or tropical climates have higher lignin content (and higher cellulose) than do cool season grasses. Legumes (whole plant) tend to have more lignin than grasses, with the highest concentrations in the stems. Mature, dry cereal straws normally have the highest levels found in animal feeds, with the lignin content usually in the range of 10–15 percent.

The protein, mineral, and vitamin content of roughages may be highly variable both within and among roughages. Legumes may have 20 percent or more crude protein content, although a third or more may be in the form of nonprotein N. Other roughages, such as straws and chaffs, may have only 2–4 percent. Most other roughage and forage falls between these two extremes. Mineral content may also be exceedingly variable; most roughages are relatively good sources of Ca and Mg, particularly legumes. P content is apt to be moderate to low, and K content high (relative to animal needs). The trace minerals vary greatly depending on plant species, soil, and fertilization practices.

In overall nutritional quality, roughages may range from very good nutrient sources (lush young grass, legumes, high-quality silage) to very poor feeds which will not maintain an animal (straws, hulls, some browse). The nutritional value of the very poor roughages can often be improved considerably by proper supplementation or by some feed preparatory methods. The feeder must, however, use some wisdom in selecting the appropriate roughage for a given class and species of animal.

PASTURE AND GRAZED FORAGES

Many different types of vegetation are utilized by grazing animals. With respect to agricultural production, forage is usually divided into native and cultivated species, the latter being utilized to improve productivity or versatility of crop and animal production. Herbage may also be divided into the following classes:

Grasses—members of the family Gramineae (6,000+ *species*)
Cool season grasses—grasses that make their best growth in the spring and fall
Warm season grasses—grasses that grow slowly in the early spring and grow most actively in early summer, setting seed in summer or fall
Legumes—members of the family Leguminosae (14,000+ species)
Forbs—primarily broadleaf, nonwoody plants (many different species)
Browse—woody plants consumed in some degree by most ruminants and horses, particularly selective eaters such as sheep, goats, and deer

Grazing lands can be classified in various ways, but a logical classification is on the basis of temperature (subarctic, temperate, subtropical, tropical), on availability of water (wet, humid, semiarid, arid), and on seasonality of rainfall (summer, winter, aseasonal). Obviously, such regions grade into one another and the divisions are somewhat arbitrary.

Grasses

Grasses are by far the most important plants that humans are concerned with agriculturally because the grass family includes not only all of the wild and cultivated species used by grazing animals but also the cultivated cereal grains including corn and sorghum species. Because of the tremendous amount of information on the subject, the discussions presented herein will be very general in nature. For readers interested in more detail, good reference books on the subject include those edited by Heath et al. (4), Butler and Bailey (5), and Morley (6).

As a food for grazing animals, grass has many advantages. Most grass species are quite palatable when immature, and only a few are highly toxic for any appreciable part of the grazing season. Grasses of one type or another have the ability to grow in most environments in which grazing animals can survive, arctic regions being one notable exception. Furthermore, nutrients supplied in grasses during the season provide roughly the needed amounts that more or less parallel animal needs during a yearly life cycle of reproduction and production, except during midwinter in cold climates.

The digestibility of different grasses depends on their habits and local environments and on animal needs. Considerable differences may exist in the composition of grasses that fall into the cool or warm season classes. Generally, cool season grasses mature at slower rates and their quality deteriorates less rapidly than do warm season grasses. Lush, young grass is usually quite palatable, but palatability usually declines as the plants mature, and most animals object to the seed heads of many grass species. Quality differences between species of grasses become more evident with maturity. Furthermore, regrowth of grass in the fall is usually not as nutritious as spring grass, due partly to the lower concentration of soluble carbohydrates and higher amounts of lignin.

Cultivated grasses held in high esteem include perennial ryegrass (*Lolium perenne*), Italian ryegrass (*Lolium multiforum*), orchard grass (*Dactylis glomerata*), bluegrass (*Poa* spp), smooth bromegrass (*Bromus inermus*), and in dry areas various members of the wheatgrass family (*Agropyron* spp). Others considered less desirable include Bermuda grass (*Cynodon dactylon*), foxtail (*Alepecurus pratensis*), bent grass (*Agrostis* spp), tall fescue (*Festuca arundinacea*), and Reed canarygrass (*Phalaris arundinacea*). Many other species are grown in tropical areas. Tropical and subtropical species that have found appreciable uses include Buffelgrass (*Cenchrus ciliaris* L.), Rhodegrass (*Chloris gayana*), Kikuyugrass (*Pennisetum clandestinum*), Pangola digitgrass (*Digitaria decumbens*), Panicgrass (*Panicum maximum;* several strains are grown), Paragrass (*Brachiaria multica*), Napiergrass (*Pennisetum purpureum*), and Molassesgrass (*Melinis minutiflora*).

Kikuyugrass is from Hawaii; the others listed are from Africa.

The suitability of a given grass is dependent upon many factors, many of which are related to adaptation to the soils and climate of a given area. Rainfall, both total amount and seasonal distribution, and temperature are probably the most important factors determining where plants can be grown (and be productive). This is illustrated in Table 6–2. In addition to varying in growth habits and fertility requirements, grass species often vary in nutrient composition, palatability, and digestibility, the result being that suitability for use (where high production is desired) varies greatly from season to season and with stage of maturity.

In many regions some of the cereals are used for pasture, particularly winter wheat, with lesser use of barley, oats, and rye. These plants can be pastured during the winter and early spring with little effect on grain yield, provided soil conditions do not result in excessive trampling by animals. The forage of these plants is quite high in readily available carbohydrates, and crude protein is also high. Extensive use of such pasture is made in the southwestern states, particularly for pasturing calves and lambs.

Several sorghum species are also used for pasture or harvested forage. Sudan grass (*Sorghum vulgare sudanense*) is one of the more common ones used in the United States, but others, such as Johnson grass (*Sorghum halepense*), find some use. Sudan-sorghum hybrids have also been developed. These species are often utilized because they can be sown during early summer in temperate areas and will produce late summer and fall pasture. They are prone to contain high levels of glycosides which can be converted to prussic acid (which is highly toxic), particularly following drought or frost damage, so care must be used if these conditions occur while animals are grazing these species.

TABLE 6-2

Estimates of total annual dry matter production (± 50%) of grasslands in the main climatic zones of the world (tons/ha)

| Temperature | Water Supply | | | |
	Wet	Humid	Semiarid	Arid
Subarctic	4	8	—	—
Temperate	25	15	9	4
Subtropical	120	40	10	4
Tropical	150	70	12	4

Source: Rodin et al(7).

Legumes

Many different legumes are utilized by grazing animals, although the cultivated legumes comprise a much smaller group than do cultivated grasses. In overall usage, alfalfa (*Medicago sativa*), known as lucerne in most English-speaking areas other than North America, is the most common legume used for pasture, hay-crop silage, and hay in temperate climates. However, it is not very tolerant of continuous grazing, and there is often a considerable hazard of bloat for ruminants (see section on intensive grazing systems).

Other legumes that find extensive usage for pasture include clovers such as white clover (*Trifolium repens*), ladino clover (same species), red clover (*T. pratense*), Alsike clover (*T. hybridum*), crimson clover (*T. incarnatum*), sweet clover (*Melilotus* spp), subterranean clover (*T. subterraneum*), and other legumes such as birdsfoot trefoil (*Lotus corniculatus*), the lespedezas (*Lespedeza* spp), vetches (*Vici* spp), and lupines (*Lupinus* spp). Tropical legumes include leucaena or koa haole (*Leucaena leucocephala*), a shrub-tree-like plant, greenleaf desmodium (*Desmodium aparines*), Kaimi clover (*D. canum*), tropical kudzu (*Pueraria phaseoloides*), lablab (*Lablab purpureum*), Townsville clover (*Stylosanthes humilis*), and *Trifolium semipilosum*. The areas where they are grown are largely determined by suitability of soil and climatic factors.

Some legumes, particularly alfalfa, white or ladino clover, and red clover, are prone to cause bloat in grazing ruminants, especially cattle. Bloat is caused by a number of different factors, but the result is retention of excess gas in the rumen. In pasture bloat, gas is retained because rumen contents contain much foam which inhibits erucatation of the gas. Legume bloat seems to develop as a result of high levels of foam-producing compounds and low levels of foam-inhibiting compounds. Those which stimulate foam production are certain cytoplasmic proteins from the leaves and plant pectins. A reduced content of flavonals and chloroplast lipids is also associated with more bloat. Animal factors are also involved.

When these legumes are used for pasture, particularly in almost pure stands, there is a high probability that some bloat and death losses will occur. Generally, the increased animal performance is worth the added risk. Fortunately, some evidence indicates that alfalfa plants can probably be selected to have a lower content of proteins that are involved in bloat production. Perhaps legume varieties to be developed in the future will partially alleviate the problem of bloat, which is a severe one for livestock producers.

CHEMICAL COMPOSITION OF HERBAGE

The chemical composition of herbage is quite variable, being affected by many different factors. Even though this is the case, some general comments on this topic are in order so that the reader may obtain a somewhat better understanding of the nutrients contained in herbage.

Nonprotein Nitrogen

The amino acid content of herbage is quite complex. In addition to the 20 amino acids normally found in proteins, over 200 nonprotein amino and imino acids have been isolated and characterized in plants, although all of these would never be found in any given plant. The free amino acids (found in the soluble N fraction) vary with stage of maturity (they decline with maturity) and plant species as well as other factors.

Plants take up N as nitrate or ammonia. As a result of many different deficiencies of the mineral elements, there tends to be an increase in free amino acids. Saline soils also increase NPN. If N fertilizer application is liberal, and particularly if S is deficient, there is apt to be a high level of NPN in plant tissues in the form of amino acids, amides, and nitrate, and a relative deficiency of the S-containing amino acids.

With regard to nitrate, toxic symptoms may occur at levels of about 0.07 percent nitrate N in the herbage dry matter, and amounts on the order of 0.22 percent may be fatal to ruminants. However, if ruminants are adapted and fed on high-nitrate grasses continuously, toxicity is less likely because rumen microorganisms are capable of reducing nitrate to ammonia, which is well utilized.

Other factors such as duration and intensity of light, temperature, diseases, and water stress have an effect on NPN, but it tends to vary with different plant species. Grasses, in general, contain fewer nonprotein amino acids than do legumes. Some of these amino acids are toxic, and there are toxic peptides and amides as well (6).

For nonruminants, data indicate that the nonprotein amino acids have a lower nutritive value than the protein amino acids, perhaps only half the value of the latter. For ruminants, non-protein amino acids probably have very nearly the same value as protein amino acids.

Proteins

Leaf and stem proteins are usually classified on the basis of solubility. Soluble leaf proteins have been divided into two fractions. Fraction 1, also known as 18S, is the fraction highly related to bloat in ruminants. It often constitutes up to 50 percent of total soluble leaf protein and appears to be a relatively homogenous fraction of a similar nature in all plants studied. Its function is enzymatic, and it catalyzes an essential step in photosynthesis. Fraction 2 is a mixture of many different proteins. The insoluble protein of the plant is not as well characterized, but the major part is associated with lipid material in cellular membranes.

An example of the amino acid content of two grass species and two legumes is shown in Table 6–3, with data on soybean meal given for comparative purposes. Generally, grass and legume proteins are high in arginine and lysine compared to many plant proteins. Lysine is frequently a limiting amino acid for many animal species. In the samples shown in Table 6–3, the two legumes compare quite favorably with soy-

bean meal, but the grasses are lower, particularly the wheat forage. Wheat was particularly low in cystine, but it was higher in methionine than the other sources shown in this table. These forages, as a whole, compare quite favorably with the amino acid content of a high-quality source such as soybean meal. The amino acid composition of herbage is generally said to be little affected by such factors as protein content, fertilizer treatment, deficiency of nutrients, or maturity of the plant.

The NPN content of the plant may vary with different factors (see previous section), thus it must be recognized that the true protein content of herbage may differ at different times when expressed as a percentage of total N. The true protein will usually be in the range of 75–85 percent of the N, but at times it may represent considerably less than this amount. The effect of seasonal changes or maturity are illustrated in a later section.

Carbohydrates

Plant carbohydrates are usually divided into nonstructural and structural types. In nutritional terminology, the nonstructural compounds are the readily available carbohydrates—sugars, starches, fructosans. In herbage, glucose

TABLE 6-3

The amino acid composition of two grass and two legume forages

	Forage				Soybean Meal[a]
Amino Acid	Wheat[a]	Ryegrass[b]	Red Clover[b]	Alfalfa[b]	
Lysine[d]	4.68	5.78	6.14	6.35	6.85
Histidine[d]	1.47	2.26	2.47	2.49	2.09
Arginine[d]	4.88	6.06	5.97	5.91	7.78
Aspartic acid	7.84	9.53	11.17	11.26	11.20
Threonine[d]	4.34	4.78	4.81	4.89	4.17
Serine	3.95	4.30	4.36	4.60	5.46
Glutamic acid	10.88	12.35	11.88	11.77	18.68
Proline	5.86	5.28	5.07	5.13	5.00
Glycine	4.43	5.78	5.53	5.39	4.52
Alanine	6.91	6.95	5.97	6.02	4.49
Valine[d]	5.47	6.25	6.43	6.15	4.91
Isoleucine[d]	4.33	4.80	4.94	5.00	4.87
Leucine[d]	7.52	8.77	8.89	8.86	7.91
Tyrosine	3.34	4.01	4.48	4.31	4.08
Phenylalanine[d]	5.17	5.92	5.90	5.96	5.38
Cystine	0.54	1.29	0.98	1.25	1.18
Methionine[d]	2.16	2.15	1.76	1.84	1.78
Tryptophan[d]	ND[c]	1.81	1.55	2.07	ND[c]

[a]From Morey and Evans (8). Data expressed as grams/100 g of crude protein.

[b]Data from Eppendorfer (9). Data expressed as grams of amino acid/100 g of total N minus nitrite N.

[c]ND = not determined. All forage samples were in a vegetative stage.

[d]Essential amino acids.

and fructose are the principal free simple sugars, being found in a 1:1 ratio and at a level of 1–3 percent of the dry matter. Sucrose is the only other sugar found in any appreciable amount; it may often be present at about 4–5 percent. Other sugars are found only in trace amounts.

Starches and fructosans are the most common polysaccharides in this class. For the plant these compounds are a form of stored energy. The starch content of temperate grasses is usually within the range of 1–6 percent; higher levels are usually seen in leaf blades after a period of active photosynthesis following a cool night.

Legumes are characterized by sucrose and starch accumulation, with starch the primary nonstructural polysaccharide. Grasses, on the other hand, fall into two distinct groups. Grasses of tropical and subtropical origin accumulate starches in their vegetative tissues, but grasses of temperate origin tend to accumulate greater amounts of fructosans. When temperate legumes and grasses are harvested at a comparable growth stage, it appears that there is relatively little difference in total nonstructural carbohydrates. Seasonal differences have been noted, but the main change seems to be some increase in fructosan content as a result of deposition in the stems. Likewise, N fertilization appears to result in a reduced content of fructosans in grasses, particularly temperate species. Cool weather tends to increase nonstructural carbohydrates, especially starch or fructosans. Temperature also influences the molecular size of fructosans; the molecule tends to decrease in size with warmer temperatures (5).

Plant structural carbohydrates, which are all polysaccharides, range from homogenous to highly varied molecules which may be linear or highly branched and form amorphous to crystalline structures. Structural carbohydrates are grouped into three major groups: the pectic substances, which are believed to function as intercellular cement; the noncellulosic polymers (hemicelluloses), which are composed primarily of 5-carbon or 6-carbon sugars; and cellulose, a linear polymer composed of simple sugar units. The latter two are relatively insoluble and are resistant to digestion because the sugar units are chemically linked in a different manner (β 1–4 linkage) than are more available carbohydrates such as the starches.

Variations in amount of these different fractions are observed within the plant cells, between plant parts (celluloses are especially higher in stems), between different species, in type of climate adaptation, and so on. With legumes, there appears to be little change in levels of leaf and stem hemicellulose or pectin during growth, but there is a marked rise in stem cellulose. With grasses, there is generally a rise in cellulose with a lesser increase in hemicellulose in the stems. Less marked changes are seen in tropical grasses, but the cellulose level is usually considerably higher than in temperate species.

An example of changes in various plant components (primarily carbohydrates) is shown in Table 6–4 for four warm season temperate grass species. There are noticeable differences in the NDF values: high levels were recorded on the 7/23 sampling, and after that time regrowth tended to push the values down, particularly for the ryegrass and bromegrass. ADF, hemicellulose, and lignin values followed the same general trends, as did the NDF values, with the reverse being the case for cell solubles. In this example the analyzed samples were obtained from pastures that had enough grazing pressure to keep the grasses grazed closely most of the time.

The literature indicates that in leafy samples the cellulose content of grasses may be expected to be in the range of 15–30 percent, hemicellulose from 10–25 percent, and pectins from 1–2 percent. In legumes, leaf fractions may contain 4–10 percent hemicellulose, 6–12 cellulose, and 4–8 percent pectins. Stems have a similar fiber content to that of grasses (5).

Lipids

The lipid content of leaf tissues ranges from 3–10 percent, generally declining with maturity. Leaf lipids are composed of a variety of different components (see Ch. 3), the bulk of which are galactolipids and phospholipids; most of these are found in the chloroplasts. Linolenic acid usually makes up 60–75 percent of the total fatty acids, with linoleic and palmitic the next most abundant. These lipids are, thus, of most interest from a nutritional point of view. Other lipids, such as the waxes on the surface of the leaf, are believed to have little if any nutritional value.

Organic Acids

Generally, most reports on plant composition completely ignore the subject of organic acids. However, these acids, most of which are nonvolatile, are very important components of plant tissues. They have a primary role in respiration,

TABLE 6-4

Seasonal changes in carbohydrate, lignin, and cell solubles of four grass species

Species and Chemical Fraction	Sampling Date				
	4/19	5/3	7/23	9/26	10/24
Tall fescue					
NDF[a]	45.6	56.4	65.7	56.4	54.6
ADF[b]	24.6	30.2	36.5	28.7	30.8
Hemicellulose	21.9	26.2	29.2	27.7	23.8
Lignin[c]	2.8	3.8	5.5	4.2	4.3
Cell solubles[d]	53.4	43.6	34.3	43.6	45.4
Perennial ryegrass					
NDF	42.2	51.0	55.8	53.0	38.3
ADF	22.3	28.3	32.9	24.6	20.4
Hemicellulose	19.9	22.8	22.9	28.4	18.0
Lignin	3.0	3.6	6.4	4.2	3.3
Cell solubles	57.8	49.0	44.2	47.0	61.7
Smooth bromegrass					
NDF	43.9	52.8	63.1	55.4	40.3
ADF	22.8	29.5	37.7	27.1	20.7
Hemicellulose	21.1	23.4	25.4	28.3	19.6
Lignin	3.0	3.5	6.9	4.9	2.8
Cell solubles	56.1	47.2	36.9	44.6	59.7
Orchardgrass					
NDF	46.6	56.3	64.3	54.4	47.9
ADF	23.2	30.0	39.8	28.0	24.8
Hemicellulose	23.3	26.4	25.0	26.4	23.1
Lignin	3.4	4.0	6.6	4.3	3.9
Cell solubles	53.4	43.7	35.7	45.6	52.1

Source: Powell et. al. (10). Samples were randomly collected clippings from grazed pastures at various intervals.

[a]NDF — neutral detergent fiber (cellulose + hemicellulose + lignin).

[b]ADF = acid detergent fiber (cellulose + lignin).

[c]Permanganate lignin.

[d]Cell solubles = 100-NDF.

amino acid synthesis, and cation-anion balance. Organic acids accumulate in plants in concentrations ranging from 2 percent to 8 percent of dry weight. In the usual proximate analysis, they would be a component of N-free extract (carbohydrates). If using the NDF and ADF methods, organic acids would show up as cell solubles or contents.

Generally, malic, citric, quinic, shikimic, and aconitic acids are the predominant organic acids in common forage species (except for the higher fatty acids that are classed as lipids). Others that have been identified in more than trace amounts include succinic, malonic, α-ketoglutaric, and fumaric acids. In one study it was reported that the concentration of quinic, malic, and total acids in topgrowth of perennial ryegrass decreased with maturity in direct proportion to the decrease in leaf tissue. In another study it was reported that malic and *trans*-aconitic acids did not change with the stage of growth of orchard grass and smooth bromegrass, but citric acid decreased and shikimic and quinic acids increased as grasses matured.

The effect of fertilization varies with the plant species and type of fertilizer. There are also rather marked differences in different genotypes of fescue grass species in acid content and composition (70). In addition to the important role these acids may have for the plant, there is evidence that they may be an important factor in taste and palatability for grazing animals. Other organic compounds present in only small amounts in plant tissue may also be quite important in palatability of forage plants (71).

Minerals

As with the organic fractions, the mineral content of herbage is quite variable, being affected

TABLE 6-5

Range and typical mineral concentrations for pasture grasses and alfalfa plants

Mineral Element	Grasses			Alfalfa		
	Low	Typical	High	Low	Typical	High
Major elements, % of dry matter						
Ca	<0.3	0.4–0.8	>1.0	<0.60	1.2–2.3	>2.5
Mg	<0.1	0.12–0.26	>0.3	<0.1	0.3–0.4	>0.6
K	<1.0	1.2–2.8	>3.0	<0.4	1.5–2.2	>3.0
P	<0.2	0.2–0.3	>0.4	<0.15	0.2–0.3	>0.7
S	<0.1	0.15–0.25	>0.3	<0.2	0.3–0.4	>0.7
Trace elements, ppm of dry matter						
Fe	<45	50–100	>200	<30	50–200	>300
Co	<0.08	0.08–0.25	>0.30	<0.08	0.08–0.25	>0.3
Cu	<3	4–8	>10	<4	6–12	>15
Mn	<30	40–200	>250	<20	25–45	>100
Mo	<0.4	0.5–3.0	>5	<0.2	0.5–3.0	>5
Se	<0.04	0.08–0.10	>5	<0.04	0.08–0.1	>5
Zn	<15	20–80	>100	<10	12–35	>50

by soil fertility, fertilization, plant species, and various climatic factors. Compared to grasses, legumes have characteristically high concentrations of Ca, Mg, and S, and, frequently, Cu (see Table 6–5). Both have similar levels of K, as shown in the table. Legumes tend to be lower in Mn and Zn than do grasses.

Marked differences have been observed in the mineral content of many different grass species grown under similar conditions. The mineral content is usually highest in the leaves and normally decreases with stage of maturity, but there are many exceptions to this statement. Likewise, the influence of fertilizer applications on grasses at a vegetative stage (and other factors) are so diverse that it is difficult to make any general statements that cannot immediately be contradicted.

FACTORS AFFECTING HERBAGE NUTRITIVE VALUE AND CONSUMPTION

A number of factors have already been mentioned which have some effect on the nutritive content of herbage. In a given location with typical fertilization and management practices, the most important single factor is the maturity of the herbage. Early in the growing season, grasses—especially cool season species—have a very high water content, a high content of organic acids, and an excess of protein for most ruminant animals. The result is that animals may get diarrhea and, because of the low dry-matter content, may have difficulty in obtaining a maximum intake of energy, even though

energy digestibility at this stage may be quite high (70–85 percent).

As the plant matures the protein content decreases, structural carbohydrates increase along with lignin, readily available carbohydrates decrease, and digestibility of both protein and energy decreases (Table 6–6). The changes that occur will depend on the plant species and on the environment in which the plant grows. For example, if the growing season progresses rather rapidly from cool spring weather to hot summer weather, changes in plant composition will be more rapid than when the weather remains cool during plant maturation, especially in a cool season grass. In plants such as alfalfa, which has quite different growing habits than grass, rapid changes take place as the plant matures and blooms. Crude protein values given by NRC publications indicate the following concentration (percent on dry basis) for second cuttings: immature, 21.5; prebloom, 19.4; early bloom, 18.4; midbloom, 17.1; full bloom, 15.9; and mature, 13.6. Corresponding changes in TDN range from 63 to 55 percent. Some of these differences are caused by loss of leaves as the plant matures and because leaves have a higher nutrient value than the remainder of the plant. There is also a decline in concentration of Ca, K, and P and most of the various trace minerals as plants mature. Data illustrating changes with maturity are shown in Tables 6–6 through 6–9.

The decline in crude protein in grasses is illustrated in Table 6–7. Note that it declined from 17.8 percent (dry basis) at a vegetative

TABLE 6-6

Effect of stage of maturity on composition and digestibility of orchard grass

Item	Stage of Maturity			
	6-7" High Cut 5/19 Pasture	8-10" High Cut 5/31 Late Pasture	10-12" High Cut 6/14 Early Hay	12-14" High Cut 6/27 Mature Hay
Composition, % of DM				
Crude protein	24.8	15.8	13.0	12.4
Ash	9.3	6.8	7.1	7.2
Ether extract	4.0	3.5	3.9	4.2
Organic acids	6.3	6.0	5.4	5.0
Total carbohydrates[a]	49.9	63.0	64.4	63.1
Sugars	2.1	9.5	5.4	2.4
Starch	1.2	9.5	0.8	0.9
Alpha cellulose	19.5	19.8	19.1	27.7
Beta & gamma cellulose	3.4	5.4	3.8	2.5
Pentosans	15.1	15.8	16.8	18.1
Nitrogen-free-extract	35.0	45.7	44.2	41.2
Lignin	5.7	5.0	6.2	8.1
Crude fiber	26.9	28.2	31.8	35.0
Digestibility, %				
Dry matter	73	74	69	66
Crude protein	67	63	59	59
Crude fiber	81	77	71	68

[a]Total carbohydrates = (crude fiber + NFE) − (lignin + organic acids).

Source: Ely et al. (11)

stage to 6.8 percent when seeds were at the dough stage. This decline may or may not be typical in all areas, but it illustrates the general changes that occur. In addition, the digestibility of energy declines rapidly, perhaps as much as 1 percent/day in some grasses in warm climates, although a more typical decline would be about 0.5 percent decrease/day. This rapid decline will result in a reduction in animal productivity within a time span of a week or less.

TABLE 6-7

Effect of maturity on the crude protein content of grasses

Stage of Maturity	Crude Protein, % of dry weight	
	Mean of 8 Grasses[a]	Brome-grass[b]
Vegetative	17.8	19.5
Heads half emerged	12.4	16.5
Flower parts fully expanded	9.5	14.5
One-fourth heads in bloom	8.6	10.2
Seeds at milk stage	7.4	8.8
Seeds at dough stage	6.8	7.4

[a]From Phillips et al. (12). Includes Alta fescue, bromegrass, Kentucky bluegrass, orchard grass, Reed canary grass, red top, timothy, and tall oat grass.

[b]From van Riper and Smith (13).

The decrease in digestibility in grasses is largely attributable to changes in the stem and leaf sheath, which decline in digestibility at a much more rapid rate than the leaf; there is also a decrease in leaf : stem ratio with maturity. Similar changes occur in legumes but at a less rapid rate, because there is less lignification of the stems but also because the leaves change less. Legumes lose their leaves so that the leaf:stem ratio also changes with maturity.

The effect of advancing stage of maturity of legume-grass mixtures is illustrated in Table 6–8. Note that in a period of about six weeks dry matter digestibility declined about 11 percent. However, when grasses or legumes are maintained at a vegetative state, there is a less rapid change. This is illustrated in Table 6–9 with a cool season grass. Tall fescue clippings were frozen and then fed later in conventional digestion trials. Crude protein content and digestibility declined during the season, but there was much less effect on digestible energy. Further data are shown in Table 6–10 on switchgrass hay, a warm season species. Cuttings were made over a shorter time span than for the fescue shown in the previous table, but the data indicate that there is not a marked change in composition when vegetation is maintained at about

TABLE 6-8

Effect of stage of maturity of green chopped alfalfa-brome forage on digestibility, forage intake, and milk production

Stage of Maturity of Alfalfa	Harvest Date	DDM,[a] %	DM Intake, lb/day	DDM Intake, lb/day	Milk Production, lb/day
Prebud	5/17	66.8	34.0	23.0	42.5
Bud	5/24	65.0	33.2	21.6	39.5
Early bloom	5/31	63.1	32.0	20.2	31.4
Mid bloom	6/7	61.3	30.6	18.8	31.4
Full bloom	6/14	59.4	29.2	17.4	26.5
Late bloom	6/21	57.5	27.8	16.0	23.4
Mature	6/28	55.8	26.3	14.7	19.5

[a]DDM = digestible dry matter.

Source: Hibbs and Conrad (14)

TABLE 6-9

Effect of season on composition and digestibility of tall fescue

	Composition, %			Digestibility, %		
Harvest	Crude Protein	Crude Fiber	Organic Matter	Crude Protein	Crude Fiber	Energy
April	13.9	25.7	75.1	69.7	77.7	73.3
May	13.5	24.6	73.3	71.4	68.3	70.1
July	9.3	22.7	72.1	58.7	68.0	67.9
September	6.1	26.0	71.6	47.9	75.6	67.1

Source: Schubert et al. (15). Grass was clipped at a vegetative stage and stored in frozen form until fed in conventional digestion trials to sheep.

the same stage of maturity, whether the grass be a warm or cool season species.

The major factor affecting feeding value of herbage is, as indicated, the reduction in digestibility and rate of digestion, the combination of the two being reflected in lower voluntary consumption of the herbage as it matures. In ruminants these factors effectively control feed consumption and thus the amount of energy that can be consumed. Voluntary intake is also affected by a deficiency of some minerals and by N. The critical level of crude protein required in a pasture before intake is reduced by N deficiency is approximately 7.5–8 percent.

Unfortunately, there is not yet a good foolproof means of estimating voluntary intake and relating it to digestibility. Work some years ago indicated that voluntary intake of pastures was related to the quantity of dry matter soluble in acid pepsin, and a system of predicting a nutritive value index was suggested. This index was a combination of intake and digestibility. Other research involving pepsin solubility or digestion with fungal cellulase has been done (17). Even though digestibility can be predicted with reasonable accuracy using these laboratory

TABLE 6-10

Changes in composition of switchgrass hay (warm season species) with advancing maturity

	Composition, % of DM			
Cutting Date	Crude Protein	NDF	ADF	Lignin
6/23	9.4	74.9	43.7	4.7
7/16	7.5	78.1	42.7	5.2
8/9	6.2	82.5	50.3	4.9

Source: Vona et al. (16). First two cuttings were at an early head stage; the last was at an early bloom stage.

methods, it is still difficult to estimate consumption.

Further information is presented on this topic in a later section on evaluation of hay. Large differences have been observed in voluntary intake where digestibility was the same in other grasses, and, in addition, there is much variation among animals consuming the same herbage.

For many years soil fertility and fertilization practices have been known to have a pronounced effect on quantity of forage or crops produced. In addition, some alterations in plant composition may occur as a result of these factors, although the differences are much less dramatic than those changes associated with increased maturity and results given in the literature show many discrepancies in response to fertilizer. In pastures with mixed plant species, one obvious change that may occur as a result of fertilization is an alteration in the vegetative composition as some plants respond more to fertilizer than others. If a grass-legume mixture is fertilized with high levels of N, for instance, this practice is apt to kill out the legume or to stimulate the grass much more than the legume. Fertilization of grasses with N tends to increase total, nonprotein, and nitrate N of the plants. Nitrate levels usually drop off rapidly after fertilization, however. K content and, perhaps, some other minerals may increase in response to N; however, the marked increase in plant growth that may be obtained by high levels of N may be expected to result in some dilution of most mineral elements, particularly during the first few days or weeks of rapid growth after fertilization.

Digestible protein is apt to be increased and, in some instances, palatability and dry-matter intake may increase in response to fertilization with N, although not all data agree on some of these points. Fertilization studies have shown, in general, that plant concentration of most of the mineral elements may be increased by fertilization with the element in question. P use may increase palatability when used alone or in combination with N. Thus results to date indicate that soil fertility and/or fertilization practices may alter nutrient concentration and consumption of herbage.

Intensive Grazing Systems

A variety of different methods of herbage utilization have been devised in order to obtain greater pasture or animal productivity. These are generally based on continuous grazing or some type of intermittent grazing, the latter generally being systems that require more careful and intensive management and that may require considerably higher investment in fencing and other livestock equipment.

Optimal use of a continuous grazing system involves matching carrying capacity of the pasture with the appropriate number of animals. Obviously, as pasture growth varies during the growing season, this results in either a surplus during the spring or a deficiency during the summer (where it is dry, especially), or variation in the number of animals used/unit of land or in the time span over which a unit of herbage can be pastured. In actual practice there is usually too much pasture during spring and too little in periods of limited growth later in the season.

When available herbage is in excess of consumption, animals will be much more selective, especially where several to many plant species are present. Animals tend to graze repeatedly areas containing the more palatable species while leaving the less palatable plants to mature and become even more unpalatable. It is not at all uncommon for some areas to be grazed so hard that some desirable species will die out, usually resulting in the invasion of weedy plants.

Research data generally indicate that continuous grazing is as good as other methods during periods of flush growth. In less productive periods, some type of intermittent grazing usually gives greater animal production/unit of land. If feasible, time periods when a pasture is grazed should not be the same each year. For example, pasture A might be the first grazed this year, B might be second, and C might be third. In succeeding years the rotation would be changed. This practice will help to maintain a broader range of forage species. It is particularly important in dry areas.

From the point of view of both plants and animals, some type of intermittent grazing is often preferred. Continuous use is detrimental to some plants such as alfalfa or other large, erect, easily defoliated species. In addition, weedy plants tend to be unused and there is a much higher percentage of herbage which is not utilized because of trampling or fouling with dung and urine. Short, semiprostrate species are more suitable for continuous grazing over extended periods of time.

The most common form of intermittent grazing is rotational grazing. In rotational grazing the stocking rate is high and the animals are pastured for a relatively short interval on a given piece of land. For optimal use, the time probably should be no longer than 24 hours, but in practice many farmers and ranchers use considerably longer times. When the pasture is grazed down to a desirable height, the animals are then moved to another pasture and the first one is allowed to rest and grow back to a desirable pasture height.

Rotational grazing in effect restores the plant to a physiologically younger stage of growth; if done at frequent enough intervals, the plant remains in a vegetative stage in which it is much more digestible. Intermittent use also allows time for the plants to recover and to build up root reserves. Rotational grazing may not result in higher herbage production than continuous grazing, but digestible energy production is considerably higher because the plants are usually consumed at a more optimal digestibility. The high stocking rates used (35–75 cows/ha in New Zealand) means that the animals have little opportunity for selective grazing and a high percentage of the available forage will be consumed, thus discouraging the growth of clumps of unused forage and weedy plants.

The frequency of grazing or harvesting and the effect on the pasture are a function of species present and of various environmental factors. If overutilized, yield will be greatly reduced; if underutilized, yield may be increased but digestibility is likely to be reduced. In one experiment in which pasture grass was cut at frequent intervals, digestible energy was highest when cut at bi- or triweekly intervals, but total yield of digestible energy for the season was obtained with cuttings at 5-week intervals, even though the digestibility declined somewhat from maximal values. Some data indicate that maximal pasture production is achieved by close grazing followed by a relatively long interval (3–5 weeks) for regrowth. However, the effect here is dependent on the time of year and the pasture plants involved. Close grazing is generally more appropriate in the spring. This tends to increase the relative amount of legume in mixed pastures, although some favored species such as ryegrass do not tolerate close grazing at frequent intervals.

It is always a problem to make optimal utilization of forage. With rotational grazing there is more opportunity to set aside some of the pasture for harvesting as hay during periods of flush growth. However, even with rotational grazing there may be problems in getting maximal utilization of forage. High-producing animals react very promptly with a fall in production (especially dairy cows) if forced to consume overly mature, trampled, or contaminated forage. In some cases herds may be split into high and medium (or low) producers and the high producers grazed first; or, the milking cows can be followed by the dry cows and growing stock, which have lower demands. With sheep, sometimes lambs are grazed in advance of the main flock in order to allow them maximal selectivity.

Strip grazing is another variation of intermittent grazing. In practice, animals are given access to limited amounts of forage which will be consumed in a few hours. This can be controlled by the use of electric fences. Stocking rates are usually quite high so that the forage is consumed rapidly with less loss due to trampling and fouling. This method almost completely eliminates selectivity but requires intensive use of labor. Where bloat is a problem, this method facilitates control by allowing daily spraying of the strips with oil prior to grazing or use of other methods to control it.

Irrigated Pastures

In the drier areas of the plains and mountain states, irrigation has been used for many years to increase productivity of pastures. Likewise, irrigated pastures are in use in many other areas in the world. The development of more sophisticated systems such as the center pivot have greatly expanded opportunity to irrigate land formerly not suitable because of uneven terrain, provided water is available (Fig. 6–1).

As a general rule, grass-legume mixtures are favored for irrigated pastures, but there is good evidence that pure stands of legumes such as alfalfa or well-fertilized grasses such as orchard grass will also allow a high level of production. Optimal combinations of grass and legume are more difficult to maintain, but the bloat problem is usually lessened when grass is mixed in with legumes such as alfalfa and ladino clover. Birdsfoot trefoil is sometimes used where bloat is especially severe (it does not cause bloat), but it is more difficult to maintain a good

FIGURE 6–1. A central pivot irrigation system that can cover about 160 acres in one rotation.

FIGURE 6-2. Cows grazing lush improved pasture.

stand with it than with other species. The most desirable grass species depend on numerous environmental factors. The ideal species would maintain a high level of production throughout the growing season.

Irrigated pastures are usually used to best advantage with high-producing animals (Fig. 6-2). The best monetary returns are probably possible with high-producing dairy cows. Yearling steers, weaned calves, lambs, and cow and calf and ewe and lamb combinations (Fig. 6-3) also offer reasonable potential. It is not normally profitable to use irrigated pastures for dry cows and ewes or other relatively nonproductive stock.

With yearling beef steers, production of 1,000 kg of gain/ha is not too uncommon over the total grazing season, provided proper fertilization and stocking rates are maintained. As much as 1,200 kg of gain/ha may be obtained under ideal conditions. Average daily gains of yearling cattle on good pasture should be on the

order of 0.7–0.8 kg/day. With lactating dairy cows, good pasture alone should allow milk production on the order of 15–18 kg/day. On good pasture, lambs should gain on the order of 0.2–0.3 kg/day.

The high protein content of pastures, particularly grass-legume or legume stands maintained in vegetative state, results in an excess protein intake for most classes of livestock. If this type of diet is supplemented with energy in the form of grains, as would normally be done with dairy cattle, it is possible to improve the gain of growing cattle such as yearling steers and thus make more efficient use of the protein in the herbage.

PERMANENT PASTURES AND RANGELAND

Permanent pastures and rangeland account for about 405 million ha of land in the United States as compared to 141 million ha in all other harvested crops. Over half of the nutrients consumed by domestic livestock are from these grazing lands (see Ch. 1), thus they are of considerable importance to the livestock industry.

FIGURE 6-4. Five major pasture regions in the United States with type of forage that provides the majority of pasturage.

The general areas where different grasses are of major importance are illustrated in Fig. 6-4. Note that native grasses are more important in the plains and mountain states, while introduced (tame) pasture plants are of more importance in the central and eastern states, where rainfall is higher.

Permanent (Native) Pastures

In the eastern states much of the permanent pastureland is land which has at one time or other been used for crop production. Farther

FIGURE 6-3. Lambs grazing irrigated pasture in western Oregon.

FIGURE 6-5. Cattle grazing native pasture in the Flint Hills of central Kansas.

west many areas of native grass remain on which many different grass species grow. Good examples of excellent pastureland still predominantly in the native prairie grasses are the Osage Hills of Oklahoma, the Flint Hills in Kansas, and the Sand Hills in Nebraska (Fig. 6–5). Other areas still remain in other parts of the country, also.

Relatively little information is available on comparative production of native and introduced pasture grasses. That which is available indicates increased production of the introduced species; however, cultural and management practices with introduced species are generally better than that applied to native grasses. Estimates indicate that 69 percent of this type of pasture needs treatment to reestablish or improve vegetative cover, and much of the land needs improved erosion control. Available information indicates that substantial improvement could be made in most humid areas. Over 76 percent of the pasture in humid regions is located on soils with great potential for improvement. Data indicate that reseeding, liming, fertilizing, and weed control could be very effective practices that should greatly improve productivity. (4). Poor grazing management has, no doubt, contributed to the deterioration of much of this pastureland, resulting in invasion of weedy species and loss of some of the palatable and productive native species.

Dry Range Areas

A vast area of the western United States (as well as many other areas in other countries) is dry enough so that forage production is quite limited. In the United States this area encompasses deserts, arid woodlands, and large expanses of basins, plateaus, and grasslands with plant cover of grasses, broad-leaved herbs, shrubs, and noncommercial trees. These areas and the mountain meadows are the areas utilized by the livestock industry (Fig. 6–6). These areas are characterized by low precipitation, relatively low plant density, rough topography, and many shallow, rocky, saline soils.

West of the central plains, rangelands often contain many woody plants, such as some of the sage species (*Artemisia* spp) which are poorly utilized or not utilized at all by domestic livestock. In addition, toxic broadleaf plants are often a problem in many areas. The grasses and other favored plants are easily subject to overgrazing as the ecology is more fragile than in more humid climates. In addition, the growing season is often of very short duration because of lack of moisture or because of late and early frosts.

A considerable amount of research effort has gone toward improving pasture and range lands in the drier areas. Many different species have been tried in various locations. As in other situations, both total and seasonal precipitation are very limiting factors. In areas with 8–10 inches of precipitation, crested wheatgrass (*Agropyron spicatum*) is used. With up to 15 inches, western wheatgrass (*A. smithii*), intermediate wheatgrass (*A. intermedium*), and Siberian wheatgrass (*A. sibiricum*) have been used successfully. In mountain valleys, smooth brome (*Bromus inermis*) and orchard grass (*Dactylis glomerata*) find some use. Dryland alfalfas (*Medicago* spp) also find some use in limited areas.

FIGURE 6-6. A band of sheep grazing near a clear-cut in a forested area in western Oregon.

As a result of overuse in past years, much of the rangeland in the west has been invaded with undesirable plants or there has been a vast increase in poorly utilized species, such as some of the sages, at the expense of more highly preferred species. Control measures have been used extensively in some areas—herbicides, mechanical removal, fire, and biological methods. Seeding of adapted grasses—particularly species such as crested wheatgrass—has been very successful, particularly when combined with control of undesired shrubs and browse plants. Fertilization has been practiced but on a very limited scale. Development of dispersed water facilities has also resulted in improved range utilization. Insufficient water will greatly restrict the areas utilized, especially during the hot summer months.

Obviously, much more information is available on this topic. For further information, the reader is referred to texts such as Heath et al. (4).

Miscellaneous Forage Plants

Many different plants are often utilized for pasture in specific situations. For example, plants such as kale and rape are often used for pasturing sheep. The tops of root crops such as beets and turnips are frequently used as forage; in addition, turnips are grown in some areas for fall grazing by young cattle or sheep, which learn rapidly to eat the turnips.

The cereal grain plants may be used for winter pasture in many areas, and summer annuals such as Sudan grass may be used to extend the grazing season or to more nearly meet animal demands when used to supplement the usual cool and warm season grasses. In addition to these, crop residues are utilized heavily in some areas. In areas where corn is grown for grain production, cattle are often used to pasture the stalks remaining in the field after the grain is harvested. The same comment applies to straws and chaffs remaining after harvest of some of the small grains or sorghum. Crop residues of this type can often provide the major portion of the diet for beef cows after calves are weaned. Some supplementation with protein and minerals is usually required, however, for optimal performance.

Multiple Use of Grazing Land

Different herbivore species, when given a choice, will select diets which are far from identical in botanical composition. For example, cattle generally prefer grasses, although they will eat substantial amounts of forage legumes, some forbs, and limited amounts of browse. Sheep and goats are called selective eaters and, because of preference and differences in their digestive tract, eat less grass and more forbs and browse. The net result is that there is less competition among animal species than one might think. Preferences for a given forage change with season of the year and with differences in plant maturity. In East Africa, where as many as twenty-five herbivorous species graze in common, studies indicate that they tend to complement one another, provided overgrazing does not occur. The same type of studies in North America and Australia have indicated that optimum results can be achieved by having as many as four or more species grazing the same area. If grass is overconsumed, this tends to encourage growth of shrubs. Likewise, if shrubs are overconsumed, this encourages the growth of grass.

In addition to natural preferences for different plants, the terrain, temperature, and distances from water will influence areas where animals will graze. Cattle will rarely be found on slopes of 45° or more, while sheep and goats will graze on steeper slopes as will wild species such as deer and elk.

Detrimental Substances in Forage Plants

Many plants contain compounds that are toxic to grazing animals when the plant is ingested in normal amounts. With the exception of nitrates, which are normal metabolic products of plants, it is assumed by many scientists that the process of natural selection has resulted in survival of plants with toxins which inhibit consumption of the plant by various predators. Fortunately, not many grasses are highly toxic to domestic animals.

Nitrates can be a problem in some grass species (such as corn, small cereal grains, sorghum species) following heavy fertilization and especially when accompanied by a drought. Sorghum species also are prone to produce cyanogenic glycosides, which are hydrolyzed to hydrocyanic acid in the rumen. This situation is apt to occur during a drought or following frost damage.

Perennial ryegrass produces a compound, perloline, which causes a condition called ryegrass staggers, and *Phalaris* species produce a toxic alkaloid as do several other grass species. Other problems such as fescue foot occur from grazing tall fescue pastures infested with a toxic fungus, and a few species accumulate toxic levels of fluorine compounds.

In herbage other than grass, *Brassica* (cabbage family) often produce goitrogenic substances, legumes often contain compounds (isoflavones) which have estrogenic effects, many different species produce potent alkaloids, some accumulate toxic levels of oxalates, a few contain toxic amino acids, and some plants, especially legumes, may contain toxic levels of copper, molybdenum, or selenium. As a matter of fact, most plants contain compounds that may be toxic if ingested in sufficient amounts, but the level is usually low enough and the diet varied enough that they rarely cause problems. Acute toxicity is the exception rather than the rule in most cases. Nevertheless, it is a topic that deserves careful consideration, especially in situations where herbage is scarce, because animals are then apt to consume plants they usually might ignore.

HAY AND HAYMAKING

Roughages stored in the dried form are used for feeding during the time of year when grazing is not available or for feeding of confined animals. Roughages harvested in the form of long hay or bales require a relatively high labor input and present difficulties in mechanical handling during harvest and feeding. In addition, bulky feedstuffs such as hay cost more/unit of nutrients to transport. Fortunately, machinery currently available allows rather complete mechanization in operations where it is financially feasible. Continual improvement is being made in machinery for handling and feeding harvested roughages (see Fig. 6–7, 6–8, 6–9).

Hay and silage crops are grown and harvested exclusively for animal feed. Haymaking has been practiced for many centuries in Europe, perhaps as far back as 750 B.C. (4). As a result, there is a great deal of research and practical information on the subject and on hay feeding. Good review articles for further reading are available (4, 5).

The intent in haymaking is to harvest the crop at a more or less optimum stage of maturity in order to provide a maximal yield of digestible nutrients/unit of land without damage to the next crop. To make good hay the moisture content of the herbage must be reduced to a point low enough to allow storage without marked nutritional changes. Moisture content

FIGURE 6–7. *A (upper).* Newer type of machinery that can be used to mechanically handle hay. (Courtesy of the Hesston Corp.) *B (lower).* Machinery that can be used to pick up the stacks shown in *A.*

FIGURE 6–8. One example of equipment for handling large round bales. (Courtesy of the Hesston Corp.)

FIGURE 6-9. An example of equipment designed for handling and chopping hay up in large round bales. This equipment can be used to chop hay in a stationary position or to deliver it into a feed bunk as the hay is chopped. (Courtesy of the Hesston Corp.)

of green herbage may range from 60 to 85 percent or more, depending on maturity and the plant species. At a typical haymaking stage, grasses are usually within the range of 60–75 percent and legumes 70–75 percent moisture. For hay to keep satisfactorily in storage, the moisture content must be reduced to about 15 percent at the time of baling or stacking, depending on the storage conditions. If storage is satisfactory, the hay will usually continue to decrease somewhat more (2–3 percent) in moisture content.

Losses in Haymaking

It is impossible to cut, dry, and move hay into storage without losses occurring in the process. However, it may be possible to harvest more units of nutrients/unit of land than could be obtained by grazing because of trampling and feed refusals resulting from contamination by dung and urine or selective grazing of some species of plants.

The quality and quantity of field-cured hay that can be harvested depends on such factors as maturity when cut, method of handling, moisture content, and weather conditions during harvest. Losses which occur are a combination of physical loss of herbage, including leaves and incomplete recovery of harvested herbage, other less visible losses resulting from enzymic activity of the plant tissues or oxidative losses while the herbage is drying, and losses due to water damage.

Data from the literature indicate dry matter losses during field drying ranges as shown: from respiration (plant enzymes) during wilting and drying, 4–15 percent, depending on the weather; from leaf shattering, 2–5 percent for grass hays and 3–35 percent for legume hays, with as much as 15–20 percent loss in legume hays cured under the most favorable field conditions; and from leaching by rain, 5–14 percent.

Weather damage to curing hay is generally considered to be the most destructive uncontrollable factor in making quality hay. It may vary from slight loss of color from excess exposure to sunlight to extensive heating and molding resulting in a dark mess that is worthless as feed. Rain on freshly cut hay will cause little damage, but damage will be more severe as drying proceeds. Consequently, hay crops made early in the growing season are more apt to have weather damage because of longer drying times (damper ground, higher humidity), resulting in more spoilage and leaching and, in legumes, greater leaf losses. One example of a recent experiment done in Utah is shown in Table 6–11. In this case the hay was the middle cut in an area where three cuts/year are the usual for a high altitude with short growing seasons. Delaying the cut one week (from late vegetative to early bloom) resulted in an increase in NDF and statistical decreases in cell contents and soluble ash (neither shown in table). Although the effect of simulated rainfall was less than the writer thought likely, it was greater than the effect of advancing maturity. There were statistical decreases in cell contents (not shown), available carbohydrate, and total lipids (not shown), but 70 percent of the loss of cell contents was due to decreased levels of available carbohydrates. These losses resulted in statistical increases in NDF, cellulose, and lignin and, along with it, a hay with less feeding value.

Changes During Drying

Ample evidence shows that rapid drying, provided it is not accompanied by excessively hot temperatures, results in the least changes in chemical components of herbage. If drying is slow in the field, stack, or bale, appreciable changes may occur as a result of plant enzymes (respiration) and microorganisms (particularly molds), or oxidative changes. Thus machines such as crimpers (conditioners) have been developed to crush the stems of plants such as alfalfa and speed up the drying process. Available evidence indicates that losses in the field are reduced by use of this type of machinery.

Losses during drying are a reflection of the moisture content and ambient temperature. In one study it was shown that respiration losses in freshly cut immature alfalfa, which was dried at $27\,^{\circ}C$, amounted to 4.5 percent of the dry matter/day over a 3-day period. Respiration rates of more mature and wilted herbage are reduced to about half of this value, but respiration losses are extremely variable. Rapid drying by artificial methods results in relatively minor changes in composition and nutritive value.

During respiration by the plant tissues there is an appreciable loss of the soluble carbohydrates, particularly glucose, fructose, and sucrose. Variable losses of starch and fructosans have been reported, and there may also be losses in organic acids.

During drying there is generally some loss of N; this is due to action of plant protease enzymes which results in a decrease in protein N, but an increase in soluble N including peptides, amino acids, amides, and other compounds. Generally, there is also some shift in amino acids in the nonprotein fraction. However, total

TABLE 6-11

Effect of cutting date and simulated rainfall at 24 or 48 hours after cutting on composition of alfalfa hay

Forage Treatment	Dry Matter, %	Composition, % of DM				
		NDF	Cellulose	Lignin	Crude Protein	Available Carbohydrate[a]
Maturity						
Late vegetative	88.4	40.6	25.9	7.4	18.4	26.1
Early bloom	87.8	42.2	26.7	7.7	17.5	26.0
Simulated rainfall, mm						
0	88.1	39.4	24.8	7.0	18.0	27.3
5	88.6	41.3	26.1	7.6	18.0	26.3
20	88.3	41.1	26.3	7.4	17.9	26.2
Time of rainfall						
24 h after cutting	88.3	41.1	26.1	7.6	17.9	26.2
48 h after cutting	87.9	41.7	26.4	7.6	18.0	25.9

[a]Includes sugars, starches, pectins.
Source: Fonnesbeck et al. (18).

N losses are considerably less than with the readily available carbohydrates, and the changes that occur are probably inconsequential to ruminant animals. Nitrates are affected very little by drying, but the cyanogenic glucosides (which cause prussic acid poisoning) of sorghum, white clover, and some other forages lose their toxicity when the plants are dried.

With regard to the fat-soluble vitamins, slow drying results in loss of as much as 80 percent of the carotene (provitamin A) when herbage is exposed to the sun. This is very obvious to the eye as carotene losses more or less parallel the bleaching of cut herbage that occurs in the latter stages of prolonged drying. Rapid drying, particularly when the herbage is protected from sunlight, preserves most of the carotene content (for example in dehydrated hays). The vitamin D content of fresh herbage is very low. Curing in sunlight or ultraviolet light results in a marked increase in vitamin D activity as a result of synthesis of it from plant sterols, especially in the leaves, which may continue for as long as 6–8 days. With regard to vitamin E, losses generally occur during drying, but reports indicate variable amounts.

Losses in Storage

Further loss in nutritive value of hay stored under shelter is primarily due to storage with too much moisture. Excessive moisture of hay stored in the barn, stack, or bale will result in enough fermentation to cause increases in temperature which may result in browning and, sometimes, spontaneous combustion. The local environment (temperature, humidity) will affect how fast hay dries and how much moisture can be present without heating. Some evidence shows that storage of hay at 36°C with 18 percent moisture caused losses in dry matter as high as 8 percent over 9 months of storage. The losses were primarily sugars and other soluble carbohydrates. Other evidence shows that baled hays containing 16 percent moisture resulted in very little temperature rise and few microorganisms; hays with 25 percent moisture heated spontaneously to about 45°C and became moldy; wet bales with more than 40 percent moisture became very hot (60–65°C) and contained a number of thermophilic (heat-loving) fungi (19). Other data suggest that grass hay can be stored at 18 percent moisture in large round bales without much change in protein digestibility. Temperatures much above 35°C result in a

marked decrease in protein solubility in silage and would, presumably, do the same in hay (20).

Excessive heating of stored hay results in formation of brown and black hays, usually with much mold, which reduces the palatability and nutritive value. Digestibility of protein and energy of the hay is usually considerably less than for good-quality hay. Severe toxicity from consumption of molded hay sometimes occurs in animals; horses, for example, are often susceptible to moldy hay. The effect of feeding moldy hay to growing cattle is illustrated in Table 6–12. Note that digestibility, daily gain, and feed conversion were lower for cattle fed the moldy hay even though it did not produce any clinical symptoms of toxicity.

If storage of hay is not complicated by excessive moisture, hay protected from the weather changes very little in composition, and it can be stored for several years with little loss in nutritive value. Hay stored in stacks and exposed to the weather may suffer external damage, the amount depending on the weather, type and amount of precipitation, and the physical nature of the hay. In one study, grass hay was packaged in large round bales (Fig. 6–8, 6–9), compressed stacks, or small round bales. When these were stored outside from June until November, 8–13 percent of the digestible dry matter was lost in the large bales or compressed stacks and 17 percent in the small round bales. Weather damage on the large bales or stacks was limited to the outside 5–10 cm (2–4 in.). In another study, legume-grass hay in large round bales was stored in different ways. Utilization by cows was 88.8 percent if stored inside, 86.8 percent when stored outside on old automobile tires but covered with plastic, and only 65 per-

TABLE 6-12

Effect of feeding moldy hay on various parameters

Item	Good Hay	Moldy Hay
Dry matter intake, kg/d		
Hay	7.1	6.5
Total	8.8	8.2
Daily gain, kg	0.73	0.61
Feed to gain ratio	12.0	13.4
Total rumen VFA, μM/ml	88.0	72.5
Rumen ammonia, mg/dℓ	23.4	15.5
Digestibility, %		
Dry matter	63.7	53.7
Protein	76.9	53.0
Energy	63.1	54.4

Source: Mohanty et al. (21).

TABLE 6-13

Calculated yield of TDN and digestible protein from alfalfa cut at four stages of maturity in California

Item	Maturity Stage			
	Prebud	Bud	1/10 Bloom	1/2 Bloom
Season yield, kg/ha	13,260	16,430	19,130	19,260
TDN, %	66.1	60.4	57.2	54.7
TDN yield, kg/ha	8765	9926	10,940	10,533
Protein yield, kg/ha	3542	3908	3947	3652
Protein digestibility, %	78.8	74.6	72.8	70.3
Digestible protein, kg/ha	2791	2916	2873	2567

Source: Wier et al. (23).

cent when stored on tires and not covered (22). In areas where the weather and soil conditions permit, this offers one means of handling hay without transporting it to covered areas, but outside storage is not very suitable in wet areas unless the bales are protected. Feeding hay from the large packages results in appreciable wastage unless fed in some type of feeder to prevent trampling.

Time of Cutting for Hay

The stage of maturity of the herbage has just as much effect on nutritive value for hay as for pasture or silage. The marked decline in digestibility with increasing maturity of herbage has been illustrated previously in Tables 6–6 and 6–8. Two further illustrations are shown.

Data in Table 6–13, from California, show that seasonal yield, TDN, and protein production of alfalfa were greatest when cutting was at 1/10 bloom. This is not the maximal point for digestibility of either TDN or protein, but it is

the optimal time for a combination of factors. The hay producer must also consider the effect on longevity of the herbage; cutting frequently at a young stage will shorten the life of legumes such as alfalfa. Similar data to these are available from other states, and more recent research on irrigated alfalfa substantiates, in general, the conclusions drawn here.

Data from New York (Table 6–14) are shown when legume-grass mixtures were fed to dairy cows. These values clearly show the decline in hay consumption as the hay crop matured and the decline in percentage digestibility of dry matter and in the relative reduction in digestible dry-matter intake with increasing maturity. The data illustrate the principle that consumption of roughage is usually directly related to digestibility. Thus in order to have high forage intake, such as desired by lactating cows, the forage must be of high quality.

The optimal time to harvest hays may vary with different locations because of the weather, the type of herbage, and other factors. Nevertheless, it is very clear that maximal yields of dry

TABLE 6-14

Effect of time of cutting of grass-legume hay on intake and digestibility of hays by lactating cows

Cutting Date	Growth Stage	Hay Intake/Day, % of Body Wt.	DDM,[a] %	Relative DM Intake
6/3-4	vegetative	2.72	67.2	182
6/9-10	early boot	2.64	63.1	166
6/11-12	boot	2.36	65.7	154
6/14-15	late boot	2.45	62.6	153
6/16-18	early head	2.28	58.5	133
7/1	bloom	2.30	52.7	121
7/5	bloom	2.13	52.2	111
7/7-8	bloom	2.05	52.2	107
7/9-10	late bloom	1.95	51.5	100

[a]DDM = digestible dry matter

Source: Stone et al. (24). Data were compiled over several different years.

matter rarely correspond to maximal yields of digestible nutrients.

Nutritive Value of Hays

Although a substantial amount of information has been presented previously in this chapter dealing with nutritive components of herbage and hay, perhaps some additional comments are in order. Most of the following comments are applicable primarily to ruminants, as they consume about 95 percent of the hay produced in North America.

The nutritive values of hays are difficult to evaluate precisely, but there are several means of making reasonable estimates. If chemical analyses are not available, some value estimates can be made on the basis of visual appraisal. Some of the characteristics that are important are discussed briefly.

The stage of maturity is the most important factor affecting quality for any hay that has been cured reasonably well; this topic has been discussed previously in this chapter. Quality may be partially judged by leafiness, particularly in legume hays. The leaf contains about two-thirds of the total protein; consequently, when there are more leaves the protein content is higher and the fiber content lower. Color is a second factor of importance. A bright green hay color is an indication of proper curing and a high carotene content, and any reduction in normal green color is an indication of loss of quality which may be caused by rain damage or excessive bleaching by sunlight, or because the forage was far advanced in maturity. Odor of the hay gives some clue to whether the hay is moldy, musty, or putrified, conditions which reduce the palatability and nutritive value of hays. In addition, the presence of foreign material should be considered. Things such as crop residues like straw, other crops, or toxic weeds may reduce the value of hay considerably.

As a source of nutrients, hays are primarily a source of energy, although high-quality grass and legume hays may be excellent sources of protein, minerals, and vitamins. Digestibility of energy in hay is usually only moderate to medium, most hays being within the range of 50-60 percent TDN as compared to 75-90 percent for the cereal grains (see Appendix Table 1). In addition, it is well recognized that the net energy of hay (and other roughages) is relatively less as a pecentage of the digestible energy than for low-fiber feedstuffs such as the cereal grains. This is a result of a number of different factors, and it is an indication that maximal pro-

duction cannot be achieved on hay alone. However, some of the energy lost in metabolism can be used to maintain body temperature in cold weather. Consequently, hay is of greater relative value for maintenance in cold climates than comparative net energy values indicate.

Hays, generally, are satisfactory for maintenance of mature ruminants and horses; sometimes a moderate amount of supplementary protein or minerals may be needed, depending on the hay and animal involved. Hays do not allow maximal growth or lactation even when pelleted, because the amount and rapidity of digestion restricts energy intake by ruminants. This occurs because rumen digestion of cellulose and other fibrous components is relatively slow and incomplete, and all-roughage diets simply do not provide enough digestible nutrients to allow maximal production.

In addition to the nutritive properties of hays, the physical character of hay (and other roughages) is of importance to ruminant animals. This is so because the GI tract is developed to handle bulky diets, thus the absence of bulk is likely to cause problems. This is illustrated clearly in lactating cows. If the roughage portion of the diet is finely ground or pelleted, the milk fat production (percent and amount) is likely to drop drastically even though the same amount of roughage may be fed in the ground form as in long form. In feedlot animals, absence of roughage often results in indigestion and founder and in animals going off feed. Sick animals will eat much less if any concentrates, but they will often consume roughage, thus giving an idea of the need in times of stress.

Hay Analyses for Estimation of Nutritive Value

The quality of hay can be estimated by some of the factors used in grading; these include leafiness, color, odor, and the presence of foreign material or such things as mold and mildew. However, in practice hay is rarely sold on an official graded basis (as with grains) because most hay never goes through any type of central market. Hays are variable products and there has been a substantial effort to arrive at some method for quickly arriving at a quantitative basis for buying and selling. Most states now have some central laboratory which does analyses that can be used to estimate nutritive value. One example of a form used in the Pacific Northwest is given in Fig. 6–10. Samples of hay can be taken (see following section) and sent in

FORAGE ANALYTICAL SERVICE
Department of Agricultural Chemistry
Oregon State University
Corvallis, Oregon 97331

Oregon State University

TRI-STATE ALFALFA COALITION

TRI-STATE REFERENCE ALFALFA HAY TEST:
- Sample No. _____
- Sampling Date _____
- Sampled by _____
- Cutting No. _____
- County _____

RESULTS SENT TO:

Name _____
Address _____
_____
Telephone No. _____

━━━━━ **LABORATORY APPRAISAL** ━━━━━

Date Received _____   Laboratory No. _____
Percent Dry Matter _____   Percent Moisture _____

	SAMPLE 100% Dry Matter Basis	TRI-STATE REFERENCE 100% Dry Matter Basis
CHEMICAL ANALYSES:		
Crude Protein (CP)	_____	18.5%
Acid Detergent Fiber (ADF)	_____	32.0%
ESTIMATED VALUES:		
Quality Factor[1]	_____	1.00
Reference Factor[2]	_____	1.00
TDN[3]	_____	58.7%

━━━━━ **VISUAL APPRAISAL** ━━━━━
(Provided by sampler)

- COLOR (Bright-green, light green, yellow-green, brown)
- _____ % GRASS
- _____ %WEEDS
- DAMAGE (Rain, mold, frozen, dirt)
- AMOUNT (Tons, bales, loaves)
- LEAF HOLD (Attached to stems, whole leaves, not attached, crumbled leaves.)

- PROCESSING (wire, twine, round, loaves, chopped, cubed, pelleted, green chop, haylage)
- IRRIGATION METHOD (Flood, sprinkled, dry land)
- STORAGE (Covered, open)
- SAMPLING METHOD (Probe, broken bales, chopped pile, windrow, field clip.)

[1]**Quality Factor:** The estimated feeding value of the hay as compared to the reference.
QF=0.9199+0.0136 (CP)-0.0054 (ADF)

[2]**Reference Factor:** The estimated feeding value compared to the reference and adjusted for percent moisture.
RF= (QF)(DM) 0.0114

[3]**TDN:** Total digestible nutrients estimated from CP and ADF and adjusted for 3X maintenance.
TDN = 54.3208 + 0.7387 (CP) - 0.2915 (ADF)

OSJ 3866

FIGURE 6–10. One example of a form used to provide data on nutritive value of alfalfa hay.

for analysis, and the seller and buyer then have a reasonable basis for agreeing on price. Comments on analysis that might be needed from time to time follow.

Moisture. It is important to know the moisture content of hay (as well as other feeds) because moisture dilutes the nutrient concentration, and if more than expected moisture is present it results in higher than expected cost. In addition, excessive moisture (>14-15 percent) is likely to result in spoilage.

Crude Protein. The quality of hays and other roughages is highly and positively related to crude protein content. Protein is an expensive item to buy, thus it is advisable, where possible, to purchase hay on the basis of crude protein content. Hays vary greatly in protein content. For silages, it may be advisable to have analyses done on soluble protein, since the digestibility of protein may be reduced drastically if the silage has been exposed to excessive heat during the ensiling process.

Crude Fiber. Crude or acid detergent fiber content is highly and negatively correlated to the nutritive value of roughages. Thus, if analyses are available on both crude protein and fiber, the information can be used to calculate the energy value of the roughage as shown in Fig. 6–10.

Calcium. The Ca content of legume hays may vary over a wide range (see Ch. 4). Where the hay is being used for dairy cows, especially, analysis should be done for this mineral element.

Phosphorus. P is an expensive mineral element (compared to Ca) to add to feeds and, since the forage content may be quite variable, analysis should be done for P content.

Other Minerals. Analysis for other minerals may be desirable in some locations, especially if it is known that a particular element is likely to be low in a particular crop when grown on a certain soil type. Minerals that might be included are: magnesium, sulfur, zinc, and copper.

A considerable amount of effort has gone into the development of methods for rapid analysis. One instrument that may be useful for speedy on-the-spot analysis of hay is the near infrared reflectance spectrophotometer. For use with this instrument, the sample must be ground. It is then placed in a container in the instrument and infrared light is reflected off of the sample. By partitioning the reflected light and putting the results through a small computer, the machine can give reasonably good estimates (in minutes) of the nutritive properties of the hay (69). This method has the disadvantage of requiring that samples covering a wide range of chemical components must be available for calibration of the instrument. Also, it is not feasible to use this method to analyze many unknown mixtures of feedstuffs. However, for forage, it does appear to be quite feasible; thus hay could be analyzed before it was sold and especially before it was used. It is too late to do analysis, in most instances, after the feed has been fed to the animals.

Sampling Forage for Analyses

It does little good to have laboratory analyses done if the sample sent in for analysis is not reasonably representative of the forage. One type of core sampler for hay is shown in Fig. 6-11. For baled hay, it is recommended that core samples be taken diagonally from the ends of randomly selected bales. A minimum of 12 bales should be sampled from each lot (cutting, field, or the like). For stacked long hay, a minimum of 20 random samples is recommended for each lot. These samples are then composited and mixed well, and a subsample (1-2 lb) is taken to the laboratory for analysis. Samples should be stored in sealed plastic bags to avoid moisture loss.

With silage, the surface should be sampled at varying positions with a probe in upright silos or by taking grab samples while it is being unloaded. A minimum of 10 grab samples should be taken and composited. With trench silos, 10-20 grab samples should be taken on two or more surfaces. Silage samples should be stored in sealed plastic bags and refrigerated until analyzed.

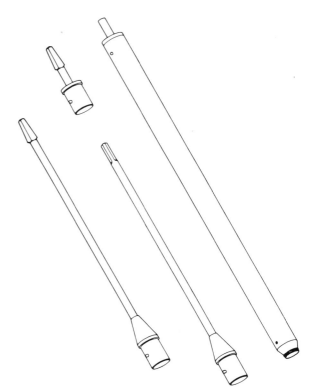

FIGURE 6-11. A core sampler used for obtaining samples of hay. Different attachments may be used for hand or power drills. (Courtesy of Scientific Systems Inc., State College, PA.)

DEHYDRATED HERBAGE

At one time in the United States, particularly in areas in the east where weather was a problem, considerable interest was shown in barn drying of hay. This is accomplished by circulating air through ducts under the hay after storage in a barn. Although a very good product can be produced, interest has declined with greater usage of silage and marked improvements in bale-handling machinery.

Dehydration of herbage with appropriate machinery is a viable industry both in the United States and some areas of northern Europe, although the production of dehydrated alfalfa has declined in recent years (see Table 8-1). In the United States, alfalfa is the primary crop that is dehydrated. However, increasing amounts are being produced from other crops such as the whole corn or sorghum plant, grasses, and grass-legume mixtures. This is partly a matter of economics, as more operating time reduces the fixed costs of dehydrating equipment.

In northern Europe there is a relatively high production of dehydrated grass or grass-clover mixtures and relatively little alfalfa production. Dried grass is used extensively in animal feeds in Europe, and a substantial percentage of U.S. alfalfa production is exported to Europe.

In the dehydration process, field-chopped herbage is fed through rotating drums heated with gas. Provided temperatures are carefully controlled, a very high-quality product can be produced. However, excessive heating will result in reduced N utilization and lower animal production.

After drying, the material is ground and usually stored in bulk under inert gas (N_2). Storage in this manner effectively stops oxidation of nutrients such as carotenes, xanthophylls, and tocopherols. To prevent oxidation of these components after removal from bulk storage, it is common practice to add antioxidants before the material is bagged. In addition, 0.5-1 percent fat is often added to reduce dustiness.

The relatively low fiber content (18-26 percent) and high protein (15-22 percent) makes dehydrated alfalfa more suitable than field-cured hay for monogastric species such as poultry and swine. Thus a high proportion of dehydrated alfalfa goes into commercial rations for these species. For poultry, the carotenes and xanthophylls serve to increase pigmentation of the skin of broilers or the yolk of eggs, a desirable feature with current consumers.

Dehydrated legumes are also a good source of protein, many of the minerals, and vitamins. For swine, particularly sows, nutrients of interest are the vitamins, Ca, and trace minerals. With regard to ruminants and horses, dehydrated alfalfa is very acceptable, but generally more expensive/unit of nutrients provided as compared to other roughage sources, and the lower fiber is of less concern than for poultry and swine. Limited data on dehydrated whole corn plants indicate that weanling calves will gain at about the same rate as they will when fed corn silage. The material in the test situation, which was finely ground and pelleted, was used less efficiently, and digestibility of energy was lower than for the silage (25).

GREEN CHOP (SOILAGE)

Green chop (soilage) is herbage that has been cut and chopped in the field and then fed fresh to livestock in confinement (Fig. 6–12). Crops used in this manner include the forage grasses,

FIGURE 6–12. Cattle consuming green chop. (Courtesy of *Beef* magazine.)

legumes, Sudan grass, corn, sorghum plants, and, at times, residues of food crops used for human consumption such as corn cannery waste, cull green beans, and so on.

A major advantage of the use of green chop with forage crops is that more digestible nutrients can be salvaged/unit of land than with other methods such as pasturing, haymaking, or ensiling. It may be feasible to harvest in this manner rather than using such crops in other ways, provided land productivity is relatively high. When herbage growth outruns animal needs, the excess can be made into hay or silage before it becomes too mature for efficient use. In addition, weather is less of a factor than in haymaking. A big disadvantage is that feeding of green chop (as opposed to grazing) requires constant attention to animal needs.

Currently, many large dairy operations and some feedlots utilize green chop from different crops in their summer feeding programs. The green chop is gradually phased in as it becomes available and then gradually phased out of the ration when it is no longer in adequate supply. This feeding method has worked out

FIGURE 6-13. One example of a field chopper used for harvesting herbage, in this case green chop.

very successfully in many livestock operations, and available machinery effectively harvests fresh cut or wilted herbage (Fig. 6–13).

Data, in general, indicate that beef steers will gain essentially the same with green chop as when pastured using intensive systems such as short-term rotations or strip grazing. Note in Table 6–15 that beef production/ha was considerably greater with green chop feeding as compared to pasture and that gains were similar. Research with lactating dairy cows (Table 6–16) indicates slightly less milk production from alfalfa green chop as compared to

TABLE 6-15

Performance of beef steers given alfalfa herbage in different forms

| | Pasture | | | |
Item	Rotation Grazing	Strip Grazing	Hay	Green Chop
Daily gain, kg	0.79	0.70	0.61	0.74
Beef production/ ha, kg	564	564	638	821
Daily feed consumed				
Alfalfa, kg	4.63[a]	4.08	8.80	6.30
Oat hay, kg	2.17	2.27	—	1.72
Feed to gain ratio	8.6[a]	9.1[a]	14.5	10.8

[a]Estimates based on digestibility of the herbage.
Source: Meyer et al. (26).

TABLE 6-16

Production data on cows during a 9-week trial when consuming alfalfa pasture, green chop, or hay

Item	Pasture	Green Chop	Hay
Milk, kg/day	24.5	23.3	22.1
Milk fat, %	2.9	3.2	3.3
Solids-not-fat, %	8.2	8.3	8.2
Dry matter consumed			
Forage, kg	13.6	13.6	14.7
Concentrate, kg	5.9	5.4	6.3
Composition of herbage			
Crude protein, %	18.2	21.0	22.7
Crude fiber, %	33.8	30.5	29.9

Source: Stiles et al. (27).

pasturing. The data also show that green chop had, on average, a higher content of crude protein and less fiber than pasture—possibly an indication of more intensive use of pasture than would result in maximal production because of reduced selectivity. Other data show that the high level of crude protein in green chop was used by cows more efficiently than that in hay or silage.

SILAGE

Silage has been used for feeding animals, primarily ruminants, for many years in Europe and extensively in other countries in the past 50-60 years. Development of appropriate machinery and ensiling methods have resulted in a large increase in use of grasses and legumes for silage making in addition to extensive use of other crops, primarily corn and sorghum in the United States. Many, many different types of high-moisture crops and crop residues can be used to make satisfactory silage. Estimates of silage production in the United States in 1984 indicate production of more than 105 million tons of corn silage and about 75 million tons of alfalfa and other mixtures.

Good silage is a very palatable product which is well utilized, and excellent results may be obtained with high-producing animals such as lactating dairy cows. Ensiling is an excellent means of preserving high-moisture crops during periods when drying is not feasible (grasses or legumes) or for crops which would deteriorate in quality if allowed to dry (corn or sorghum plants).

Ensiling itself does not result in improved nutritive values for the basic nutrients, because losses occur (see succeeding section) during ensiling. However, the fermentation that occurs usually will reduce greatly the nitrate content, if nitrate is present, and other toxic compounds, such as prussic acid, will be reduced in amount. With legume silage, bloat is less of a problem than with pasture or green chop. A big disadvantage of silage is that it is a bulky, heavy feed of low dry-matter content. Silage has a low sale value because of this, and it is not feasible to transport it any great distance.

Principles of Preservation

Silage is the material produced by a controlled anaerobic fermentation of material high in moisture. The fermentation is controlled by formation of organic acids, mainly lactic, by bacteria that grow on the herbage or by direct addition of acids or other preservatives. In any case the fermentation and storage must be in an oxygen-limiting atmosphere (anaerobic), otherwise the material decays to an inedible and frequently toxic mess.

The oxygen supply is limited by use of containers such as tower silos or oxygen-limiting sealed tower silos or by the use of bunker silos, which are normally covered with some type of plastic sheeting or materials such as hay to reduce losses. Newer methods include the use of plastic bags, which have the advantage that

FIGURE 6–15. Silage being loaded out of a large bunker silo. Silos of this type allow a high degree of mechanization in filling and unloading. (Courtesy of *Beef* magazine.)

they can be located where desired (see Figs. 6–14, 6–15, 6–16).

Preparation of silage in open stacks results in an extremely high amount of spoilage on all surfaces, and it is not a feasible method. Thorough packing of material in the silo is required to reduce the amount of oxygen and encourage a good fermentation. If sufficient acid is produced to provide a good product and if the silage is then left undisturbed, it will keep for an indefinite period of time.

Initially, when herbage is put in the silo, the dominant microorganisms are aerobes; these are replaced by anaerobes, particularly by lactic acid bacteria, a rapid process under normal conditions, so that in 2-4 days there may be

FIGURE 6–14. Examples of oxygen-limiting upright (tower) silos often used for storing low-moisture silage. (Courtesy of *Beef* magazine.)

FIGURE 6–16. A plastic bag silo. This type, although more difficult to fill, has the advantage of flexibility in location.

several hundred million lactic acid bacteria/g of silage. Although plant enzymes continue to be active while oxygen is available, most of the fermentative processes are a result of bacterial action.

The bacteria metabolize soluble carbohydrates, giving rise sequentially to different acids, as indicated in Fig. 6–17. If adequate soluble carbohydrates are present, the acids produced will reduce the pH to 4 or lower, at which point the acidity will inhibit further fermentation, depending on the dry-matter content. The concentration of lactic acid increases in well-preserved silage, eventually reaching levels of 4-8 percent in most cases, with lesser amounts of acetic and other acids such as formic, pro-

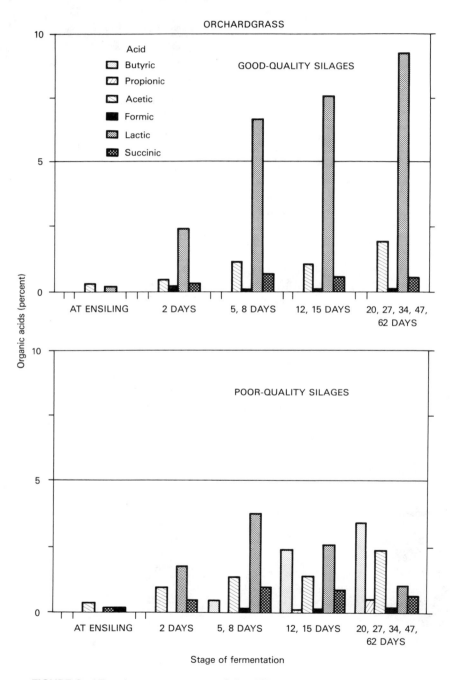

FIGURE 6–17. Average amounts of the different organic acids in good- and poor-quality orchard grass silages at different stages of the fermentation period. From Langston et al. (28).

pionic, and butyric; little butyric acid is present in well-preserved silages. Some data suggest that an increase of 1 percent in soluble carbohydrate will give an increase of 0.3 percent in lactic acid.

From the point of view of conservation of energy, lactic acid is preferred to other acids, as about 3 percent of glucose energy is lost in the conversion as compared to 22 percent if glucose is converted to butyric acid. In addition, at the high levels required for preservation, lactic acid is quite palatable, especially as compared to butyric acid.

Action of the plant enzymes and the bacteria give rise to heat. Optimum temperatures during fermentation are said to be between 27 and 38 °C (80-100 °F). Excessive heat is primarily a problem in low-moisture silages which do not compact well so that oxygen can be excluded. Thermophyllic (heat-loving) bacteria and molds may also be found under these conditions. Data from several state analytical laboratories indicate that haylage (low-moisture grass or grass-legume silage) may show very extensive heat damage; as many as half of the samples have sometimes shown excessive heating. This, in turn, results in a reduction in digestibility of the silages, particularly of the N-containing compounds. Many instances of fires and even of explosions have occurred in silos that were poorly packed or that had excessive leakage of air into the mass. Silages may also give off NO_2 gas, which can be lethal in a very short period of time in an enclosed area.

Harvesting of a forage crop is followed by rapid and extensive protein hydrolysis, which is stopped by a low pH or a high dry-matter content. Even in well-preserved silage, the NPN content may be 40 percent or more of total N. Initially, a high percentage of the NPN is present as amino acids, but continued action occurs on N-containing compounds with further solubilization and production of ammonia and other NPN compounds, primarily amines. While it has been shown that the water-soluble N in silage is highly digestible, it does not stimulate *in vitro* (laboratory) rumen cellulose digestion as readily as urea, and there is some evidence that it is utilized poorly by the animal.

As mentioned previously, silage making involves an anaerobic fermentation of wet materials. In addition to the detrimental effect of oxygen, the dry-matter content, pH, and availability of soluble carbohydrates are critical factors. If the silage material is very wet and if soluble carbohydrates are not present in sufficient supply or the plant material is highly buffered (especially legumes), then complications may arise.

For most crops a dry-matter content of 25-35 percent is near optimal for silage making. When the moisture content is high, this encourages the proliferation of clostridial bacteria, production of relatively large amounts of butyric acid, and further fermentation of NPN compounds resulting in the production of amines such as tryptamine, histamine, and others. These amines, which may be toxic, result in a foul-smelling silage. This is particularly a problem with legumes, which have lower soluble carbohydrate levels and are more highly buffered than grasses. Because of the greater buffering, it takes more acid to lower the pH to a satisfactory level in legume silage.

Grasses can be ensiled successfully at rather low dry-matter contents provided the soluble carbohydrate content is higher than normal, that is, on the order of 15 percent of the dry matter (4). Herbage with less than 10 percent soluble carbohdyrates is a doubtful proposition, especially if the dry-matter content is low. Thus very wet material requires more soluble carbohydrates and a lower pH for successful preservation.

In most areas where legumes or grass-legume mixtures are ensiled, it is a common practice to wilt the herbage before it is ensiled. Wilting raises the dry-matter content and, as a result, less acid production is required for adequate preservation of the silage. A guide for estimating the dry-matter content of green herbage is given in Table 6–17.

Losses in Silage Making

In addition to losses in the field, losses during ensilation are primarily a result of plant respira-

TABLE 6-17

Determining forage moisture content by the grab test

Condition of Forage Ball	Approximate Moisture Content, %
Holds shape, considerable juice	over 75
Holds shape, very little juice	70-75
Falls apart slowly, no free juice	60-70
Falls apart rapidly	below 60

Source: Shepherd et al. (29).

tion and microbial fermentation, spoilage on the surface and around the perimeters, and seepage from high-moisture silages. Obviously, losses may be quite variable depending upon many different factors. For example, gaseous losses are said to range from 5-30 percent of the original dry matter, but weight losses are not a good estimate of energy losses because energy is concentrated by the fermentation process. Gas losses are a reflection of plant respiration and bacterial fermentation and this, in turn, produces heat. In silos which reach 40°C, it has been calculated that this reflects a minimum loss of sugar of 4.8 percent of the dry matter. However, fermentation losses in well-preserved silage should not exceed 3-6 percent of the dry matter or an energy loss of 0.5-5 percent.

Research data on alfalfa silage indicate spoilage losses are on the order of 4-12 percent of original dry matter ensiled. Such material is not only unpalatable but may also be toxic. In sheep, listerosis is a disease attributed to consumption of spoiled silage. Some molds on silage may be quite toxic as well (see Ch. 4). Common clinical symptoms of ingesting bad silage are poor appetite and vomiting.

Seepage losses are a direct reflection of the silage moisture content. Most silages must be greater than 25 percent dry matter in order that seepage does not occur (grass or grass-legume silages in particular). With less than 25 percent dry matter, very substantial amounts of seepage may occur. Seepage moisture contains many soluble and highly digestible nutrients, and such losses should be avoided when possible. With grass-legume silages the best way to prevent seepage is to wilt the forage before ensiling.

Obviously, overall losses may be quite variable. When field losses are included, total losses may be expected to be about 15-25 percent of herbage dry matter present in the field. This is illustrated graphically in Fig. 6–18 and in tabular form in Tables 6–18 and 6–20.

Evaluation of Silage Quality

No single test is available to evaluate silage quality accurately. For those who are thoroughly familiar with silages, smell and visual appearance are relatively good methods, but they are not very quantitative. Good silage should be free from moldy and musty smells and other objectionable odors such as ammonia, butyric acid, and, especially in low-moisture silage, carmelized or tobacco odors. It should be green in color (forage silage) and not brown or black, and it should have a firm texture with no sliminess.

The pH of silage is used more commonly than any other chemical test, but by itself it is

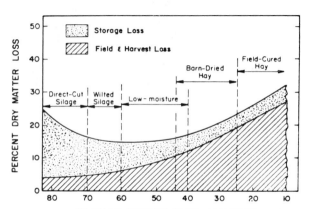

FIGURE 6–18. Estimated total field, harvest, and storage loss when legume-grass forages are harvested at varying moisture levels and by alternative harvesting methods. From Hoglund (30).

TABLE 6-18

A summary of harvesting methods for alfalfa

Method	Approx. Moisture Content, %	Approx. Harvest Loss,[a] %	Approx. Storage Loss,[b] %	Total Loss %	Approx. Hay Equivalent Factor[c]
Green chop	75–80	3.0		3.0	4:1
Direct cut silage	75–80	3.0	18.0	21.0	4:1
Wilted silage	65–70	6.0	10.0	16.0	2.7:1
Haylage	50–60	9.0	4.0	13.0	1.8:1
Baled hay	85–90	19.0	8.0	27.0	1:1

[a]Harvest loss is about average; management, weather, etc. greatly influence this %.
[b]About average loss; storage facilities, surface covers, etc., can reduce this %.
[c]Hay equivalent factors are based on dry matter and compared to 90% dry-matter hay.
Source: Fiez (31).

TABLE 6-19

Effect of dry matter of alfalfa silage on intake and utilization by sheep

Item	Dry Matter of Silage, %			
	22	40	45	80
Silage pH	4.48	4.49	4.52	5.87
Acid content, % of DM				
Lactic	5.06	4.11	3.19	0.19
Acetic	4.91	3.21	2.88	0.62
Total	10.46	7.53	6.26	1.00
Dry matter intake				
g/kg body wt$^{0.75}$	49.1	57.3	58.8	63.2
Dry matter digestibility, %	58.2	60.1	60.0	61.1
N intake, g/day	14.9	16.2	18.3	19.6
N rentention, g/day	-0.9	1.0	2.0	2.9
N digestibility, %	70.5	72.2	72.0	70.0
Water intake, g/g DM	3.5	2.4	2.4	2.2

Source: Hawkins et al. (32).

unreliable because the optimal pH for forage silage depends on the dry-matter content. Generally, a good silage should have a pH of 4.2 or less, less than 0.1 percent butyric acid, and less than 11 percent volatile N as a percentage of total N.

NUTRITIVE PROPERTIES OF SILAGES

One of the nutritive problems associated with feeding silages is that consumption of dry matter in the form of silage is nearly always lower than when the same crop is fed as hay, and this seems to apply whether the crop in question is legume, grass, or other herbage. Animal consumption of silage made from grass or legumes is usually greater as the dry matter content increases, as illustrated in Table 6–19, but not necessarily so for corn or sorghum silages. In one study it was shown that silage consumption was positively related to digestibility for legumes, but negatively for grasses other than ryegrass (33). This information would suggest that maximum intake should be achieved with silage containing just enough moisture to allow for preservation with minimum production of ammonia and acetic acid, which tend to increase at higher moisture contents.

Grass and Grass-Legume Silage

If the herbage is harvested at an optimal stage of growth, grass or legume silages are normally high in crude protein (15-20 percent) and carotene but only moderate in digestible energy. This combination may be too high in protein for efficient utilization for most ruminants, and

more nearly optimal results may be expected by supplementing grass silage with some form of energy (grains) or by diluting the protein by feeding some other form of low-protein roughage. This statement is illustrated to some extent by data in Table 6–20. In this case the grass was harvested at an early head stage past the peak in protein content, probably resulting in some reduction in consumption and liveweight gain as compared to the grass-legume silage. The corn silage had added urea, which should have provided a more optimal protein: energy ratio, and the corn silage did result in greater and more efficient gain.

TABLE 6-20

Comparison of silages made from grass, grass-legume, and corn when fed to steers

Item	Silage Source		
	Grass	Grass-Legume	Corn + Urea
Forage DM, %	25.8	18.4	24.1
Silage DM, %	27.4	24.4	27.5
Crude protein, % of DM	10.9	15.5	13.1
DM lost as seepage, spoilage, respiration, etc., %	18.4	22.6	5.1
DM digestibility, %	52.2	56.2	69.2
Silage consumption, kg/d	20.3	26.2	23.6
Silage DM consumpt., kg/d	5.6	6.4	6.5
Gain/d, kg[a]	0.56	0.89	1.05
Silage DM/kg gain, kg	10.0	7.2	6.2

[a]Silage was fed to yearling Hereford steers for 126 days. Steers received 1 kg of barley/head/d in addition.

Source: Calder et al. (34).

TABLE 6-21

Composition and digestibility of green ryegrass and material from the same field which was dried artificially or made into wilted or unwilted silage

Item	Fresh Grass	Dried Grass	Wilted Silage	Unwilted Silage
Composition of dry matter				
Organic matter, %	90.8	92.0	92.2	91.7
Total water-soluble carbohydrate, %	9.2	8.4	trace	trace
Cellulose, %	24.2	24.3	25.0	26.8
Hemicellulose, %	14.0	13.3	12.9	13.1
Crude protein, %	17.8	18.7	19.3	19.3
Gross energy, kcal/kg	4.59	4.55	4.46	4.89
Digestibility, %				
Energy	67.4	68.1	67.5	72.0
Cellulose	75.2	75.5	76.5	80.6
Hemicellulose	59.4	57.7	59.9	63.2
Crude protein	75.2	71.0	76.5	76.4

Source: Beever et al. (35). In this experiment the fresh grass was quick-frozen so that it could be fed at the same time as the other forms.

The most common procedure of harvesting grass or grass-legume silages is to cut the forage and let it wilt in the field so that the moisture content will be reduced. As pointed out previously, excessive moisture will result in high seepage losses and detrimental effects on fermentation. One example where fresh (frozen) grass, dried grass, and direct cut (unwilted) and wilted silage were fed is shown in Table 6–21. Note in this instance that drying or ensiling had little effect on digestibility, although there was a tendency for the unwilted silage to be more digestible than the other preparations. More recent data show that the organic matter in a complete dairy diet was more digestible than when the forage was provided as silage, but there was no dif-

ference in availability of protein between silage and hay rations (36).

There has been a great deal of effort put into research to improve ensiling methods for grass silage, especially in Europe, where corn and sorghum silages are less common than in North America. One of the developments has been the use of formaldehyde or formic acid or combinations of similar chemicals. The effect of adding formic acid to grass silage is shown in Table 6–22. Note that ensiling resulted (as mentioned previously) in a reduction in protein N and a marked increase in nonprotein N. Ensiling also resulted in a reduction in consumption of dry matter which was reversed by adding the formic acid. The formic acid also preserved some

TABLE 6-22

Comparison of silage made from fresh cut grass, wilted grass, and wilted grass treated with formic acid

Item	Grass	Silage Grass	Silage Wilted Grass	Silage Wilted Grass + Formic Acid
Composition data, DM basis				
Crude protein, %	14.2	14.4	14.2	15.1
Total N, g/kg DM	22.7	23.0	22.8	24.2
Protein N, g/kg DM	14.7	5.4	6.6	7.6
Water-soluble N, g/kg DM	8.0	17.6	16.2	16.6
Volatile N, g/kg DM	0.9	1.8	1.8	1.6
Water-soluble carbohydrate, %	14.0	1.0	4.7	15.1
Digestibility, %				
Organic matter	79.7	80.9	76.8	78.8
Crude protein	75.2	78.2	72.3	78.4
Consumption, g/kg BW[a]	11.2	8.5	9.7	12.3

[a]BW = body weight

Source: Donaldson and Edwards (37).

TABLE 6-23

Composition and nutritive value of 3rd cutting alfalfa harvested as hay, low-moisture and high-moisture silage

Item	Hay	Wilted Forage[a]	Low-Moisture Silage	Green Chop[a]	High-Moisture Silage
Dry matter, %	92.6	58.1	59.0	28.8	28.1
Others on DM basis					
Crude protein, %	20.6	18.1	20.4	19.8	21.6
Cellulose, %	34.0	33.3	37.4	30.3	37.9
Soluble carbohydrates, %	7.8	5.2	2.5	3.8	3.7
Total N, %	3.3	2.9	3.3	3.2	3.4
Soluble N, % of total N	31.8	37.2	51.1	32.6	67.0
NPN, % of total N	26.0	28.4	44.6	22.6	62.0
Volatile fatty acids, %					
Acetic			0.4		4.2
Propionic			0.05		0.14
Butyric			0.002		0.11
pH			4.7		4.7
Dry matter intake, g/day/kg body wt	25.3		21.8		25.8
Digestibility, %					
Dry matter	64.5		59.0		59.5
Nitrogen	77.5		63.0		72.8
Cellulose	58.8		60.4		64.3

[a]Wilted herbage was used to make low-moisture silage and the green chop was used for the high-moisture silage.

Source: Sutton and Vetter (38).

of the water-soluble carbohydrates, presumably because of a selective inhibition of microorganisms fermenting the silage (selective because there was no effect on the proteins). This has been an effective method of improving grass and grass-legume silages, provided that the addition of formic acid was not in excess. There are many other examples of this type of data.

Low-moisture silage, often called haylage, is a very palatable feed, probably because it tends to have relatively less acetic acid and less N in the form of ammonia and other NPN compounds (see Tables 6–22, 6–23). It is used to a great extent in the United States for dairy cows. This type of silage is probably best made in oxygen-limiting silos now in common use in many areas (Fig. 6–14), although other types, such as plastic silage bags, can be used with success. Note in Table 6–23 that the low-moisture silage was not consumed quite as readily as either hay or high-moisture silage and that digestibility of dry matter and N were lower than for the hay, and N was lower than for the high-moisture silage. However, it would be expected that losses from seepage and plant respiration might be reduced for low-moisture silage.

If not handled carefully, low-moisture silage is more subject to heating, resulting in brown silage which has low digestibility for the crude protein. Fires may also result where heating is excessive.

Experimental results generally show that haylage feeding will result in milk production slightly greater than with use of high-moisture silage and usually comparable to use of hay. However, in individual experiments the results may be reversed. Recent data show that maximum air exclusion (vacuum compression) resulted in a silage having the lowest pH and butyric acid and the highest lactic acid content. However, when the silage was fed as the sole diet to lactating dairy cows, intake was lower and butterfat was less than in silage having less air removed (33). It should be pointed out that data shown in a number of the tables on silage are not complete enough to make evaluations on methods to use, because information is frequently not given on amount of digestible nutrients recovered after ensiling. Thus even though one silage might be more digestible or have a higher crude protein content than another, if greater losses occur during harvest or ensiling, the method may not necessarily be a preferred one.

Corn Silage

Corn silage is the most popular silage in the United States in areas where the corn plant grows well and where adequate water is avail-

TABLE 6-24

Effect of ensiling and adding acids on consumption of frozen corn or corn silage by heifers

Item	Frozen Corn[a]		Ensiled Corn[a]	
	+ Sucrose	+ Acids	+ Sucrose	+ Acids
Dry matter consumed/d, % of BW	2.61	2.31	2.46	2.23
Gain/d, g	878	775	576	556

[a]Sucrose was added to provide energy equivalent to the acids. Lactic and acetic acids were added at a rate of 6% and 2% of silage dry matter. Urea and a mineral-vitamin mixture were added to all diets at 2% and 5% of forage dry matter.

Source: Wilkinson et al. (39).

able during the growing season. It is becoming more popular in other areas of the world because, except for sugar cane and cassava, maximum yields of digestible nutrients/unit of land can be harvested from this crop. In addition, the corn plant can also be handled mechanically at a convenient time of the year and over a period of time.

Well-made corn silage is a very palatable product with a moderate to high content of digestible energy, but it is usually low to moderate in digestible protein, particularly for the amount of energy contained. On a dry basis, corn silage will usually have 8-9 percent crude protein, 65-75 percent TDN, 0.33 percent Ca, and 0.2 percent P. Silage made from well-eared crops may have as much as 50 percent grain, particularly in silage made from mature plants, although average values are more on the order of 47 percent grain. High-yielding grain varieties of corn generally produce maximal yields of digestible nutrients. Even so, maximum growth rates or milk yields cannot be obtained from cattle without energy and protein supplementation.

Ensiling, as pointed out previously, does not usually improve the palatability of herbage.

This is illustrated with corn silage in Table 6-24 in an experiment where the harvested corn plant was frozen or ensiled. Ensiling reduced consumption of herbage dry matter, as did the addition of acids to the frozen corn, indicating that acids, by themselves, have an effect on palatability. Likewise, ensiling resulted in a reduction of liveweight gain in this instance. In another instance, where corn with low or high dry matter was frozen or ensiled (Table 6-25), ensiling resulted in a reduction in consumption of low dry matter forage but had no effect on consumption of high dry matter forage. In this case there was no depression in digestibility by ensiling the high dry matter corn. Possibly, the addition of urea may have had some effect.

There have been numerous studies to determine the optimum stage of maturity at which corn should be harvested for silage. A recent example of a research report is given in Table 6-26. In this case corn was harvested for silage at the milk or dough stage or after one, two, or five frosts. During the experiment the silages were fed to lactating dairy cows, the silage being fed at a level to equal 70 percent of ration DM intake. Based on the data presented, the authors concluded that harvest after

TABLE 6-25

Effect of ensiling on composition and consumption of corn

Item	Frozen Corn		Ensiled Corn	
	Low DM	High DM	Low DM	High DM
Dry matter, %	26.3	38.9	27.4	38.1
pH	4.6	5.6	3.7	4.0
Lactic acid, % of DM	0.9	0.7	8.7	6.4
Total N, % of DM	1.3	1.4	1.3	1.4
DM intake, g/kg $BW^{0.75}$[a]	88.2	72.1	84.2	72.0
DM digestibility, %	IM[b]	72.9	75.0	72.5
CP digestibility, %	IM[b]	68.4	69.8	67.8

[a]Data obtained with sheep. Urea was added (in solution) to all diets at a level of 1.25% of dietary DM before feeding.

[b]IM = Insufficient material to determine digestibility.

Source: Phillip and Buchannan-Smith (40).

TABLE 6-26

Effect of stage of maturity of corn silage on composition and performance of lactating dairy cows

Item Maturity: Harvest Date:	Prefrost		No. of Frosts at Harvest		
	Milk 8/30	Dough 9/7	First 9/18	Second 9/26	Fifth 10/17
Dry matter, %					
At ensiling	20.8	23.2	25.1	35.5	45.9
At feeding	23.2	25.7	28.5	34.1	45.0
NDF, % of DM	59.0	58.8	59.4	61.6	65.9
ADF, % of DM	31.5	28.5	26.0	26.2	28.1
AD lignin, % of DM	2.92	2.65	2.68	2.57	3.48
DM intake, kg/d	14.5	14.3	15.4	16.5	14.9
4% FCM, kg/d	19.6	18.7	18.7	19.7	17.6
Apparent digestibility, %					
Dry matter	64.7	64.7	64.3	63.7	61.2
Gross energy	64.9	64.9	63.7	62.6	60.6
Crude protein	52.7	49.1	53.3	52.5	48.4
DE, Mcal/kg	2.76	2.81	2.72	2.66	2.59
NEℓ, Mcal/kg	1.55	1.59	1.52	1.46	1.41

Source: St. Pierre et al. (41). Silage was fed to equal 70% of ration DM.

the second frost was optimal in this study. Dry matter was high enough to reduce seepage and runoff to minimal amounts; dry matter intake reached maximal levels at this date, and milk production was as high as for any other ration. It did not result in maximal digestibilities of those items listed in the table, but that is not an uncommon finding. In general, other studies suggest that the optimum time to harvest corn for silage is when starch deposition in kernels is complete. This stage (33-37 percent DM) is characterized by the appearance of a small black layer where the kernel attaches to the cob. Comparative values of corn silage at different dry matter contents are shown in Table 6–27 and,

Table 6–28 shows the equivalent dry matter and wet weights/acre for grain yields of different amounts.

Research in recent years has shown that some additives may improve corn silage. Treatment at ensiling time with limestone (0.5-1 percent) or other Ca salts tends to buffer the acids produced during fermentation and results in a very substantial increase in lactic acid production and, usually, an improvement in consumption and animal performance. One example of the effect of added limestone is shown in Table 6–29. Note in this case that lactic acid content was more than doubled in the limestone-treated silage. Although dry-matter consumption was

TABLE 6-27

Value of corn silage with different dry-matter content and different prices for corn silage

Price of #2 Corn, $/bu	Silage Value, $/ton[a]			
	30% DM	35% DM	40% DM	45% DM
1.00	11.54	13.46	15.38	17.30
1.50	14.50	16.92	19.33	21.25
2.00	17.46	20.37	23.28	26.19
2.50	20.42	23.82	27.23	30.63
3.00	23.39	27.28	31.18	35.08
3.50	26.35	30.74	35.13	39.52
4.00	29.31	34.19	39.08	43.96

[a]Calculated on the basis that silage has 47% grain with grain valued at indicated prices and the nongrain DM at $30/ton, air dry basis.
Source: Zimmerman (42).

TABLE 6-28

Silage yield compared to grain yields of corn with amounts of silage at different DM percentages

Corn Yield, bu/A	Corn DM, lb/A	Silage DM, lb/A	Silage Yield, T/A			
			30% DM	35% DM	40% DM	45% DM
70	3,332	7,089	11.8	10.1	8.9	7.9
80	3,808	8,102	13.5	11.6	10.1	9.0
90	4,284	9,115	15.2	13.0	11.4	10.1
100	4,760	10,128	16.9	14.5	12.7	11.3
110	5,236	11,140	18.6	15.9	13.9	12.4
120	5,712	12,153	20.3	17.4	15.2	13.5
130	6,188	13,166	21.9	18.8	16.5	14.6
140	6,664	14,179	23.6	20.3	17.7	15.8
150	7,140	15,191	25.3	21.7	19.0	16.9

Source: Zimmerman (42).

TABLE 6-29

Effect of adding 1% limestone to corn silage

Item	Corn Silage	Corn Silage + Limestone
Forage DM, %	40.1	38.6
Silage composition		
Dry matter, %	41.9	40.8
Crude protein, %	8.4	8.4
Lactic acid, %	4.4	9.3
Animal performance[a]		
DM consumed/d, kg	7.16	6.29
Daily gain, kg	0.78	0.76
DM/gain, kg	9.1	8.3
Net energy (NEg + NEm)		
Kcal/g	1.36	1.48

[a]Cattle received 400 g/d (DM basis) of a high-protein supplement.
Source: Byers (43).

not increased, daily gain was equal, feed conversion was improved, and net energy was higher for the silage treated with limestone.

Addition of urea or other NPN sources such as anhydrous ammonia has been used to increase the crude protein content of corn silage (which is low for its energy content). Two examples of cattle trials are shown in Table 6–30. Note that crude protein content of the silage was increased substantially in each study. No doubt most of the N in the silage is present as ammonia or, in lesser amounts, in NPN compounds such as amides, but the relatively low pH of silage would help to reduce losses of ammonia that otherwise might occur. When used at moderate levels (for example, 0.3 percent of wet silage), ammonia has little or no effect on consumption, as shown in the table, and it is digested and utilized about as well as the N in

urea added to a grain mix. Many other examples are available in the literature indicating that urea or ammonia are quite effective; however the value of added N to silage will depend, somewhat, on fertilization practices used on the crop, because heavy fertilization with N will increase the N content of the plant.

Corn silage can also be put up with other sources of N, for example, manures of various types have been used in many experiments. Two examples of research data are shown in Table 6–31. In the first example, 10 and 20 percent cage layer excreta were added. These increased the crude protein from 7.5 to 10.1 and 12.9 percent, respectively. However, the added manure decreased consumption and dry matter digestibility as compared to regular corn silage supplemented with equivalent amounts of soybean meal, and N retention was not improved with added cage layer manure. In the other example, urea and broiler litter were added to corn herbage at ensiling time. In this instance the addition of urea increased protein digestibility but appeared to depress consumption of silage. The added broiler litter increased silage consumption and N retention as compared to the other two silages.

A number of studies have been done on the effect of fineness of chopping of corn herbage prior to ensiling. Fine chopping will reduce the number of whole grains excreted in feces, but it is apt to result in a reduction in milk fat percentage in lactating dairy cows fed high levels of silage and is somewhat more prone to result in displaced abomasums of dairy cattle. There appears to be little effect on liveweight gain of cattle by finely chopping corn silage or by rolling sorghum grain prior to ensiling.

TABLE 6-30

Effect of adding ammonia to corn silage

Item	Michigan Data[a]		Virginia Data[b]	
	None	+ NH₃	None	+ NH₃
Silage composition				
Dry matter, %	34.6	34.4	34.9	37.4
Crude protein, %[c]	9.5	12.1	8.5	11.7
Lactic acid, %[c]	5.7	6.7	5.1	5.2
Ammonia, % of N			6.1	30.0
pH	—	4.1	3.84	4.30
Animal performance				
Milk yield, kg/d	25.2[d]	24.8[d]		
Silage DM consumed, % of BW/d	1.27	1.24	2.35[e]	2.50[e]
Digestibilities by cattle, %				
Dry matter			66.2	66.3
Crude protein			39.7	54.4
ADF			53.9	53.0

[a]From Huber et al. (44).
[b]From Carr et al. (45).
[c]Expressed as percent of dry matter.
[d]Cows were fed a standard amount of alfalfa haylage and concentrate at a standard amount/unit of milk produced.
[e]Data based on feeding heifers for two weeks.

TABLE 6-31

Effect of adding unconventional N sources to corn forage before ensiling

Item	Silage[a]			Silage[b]		
	Corn	+ 10% CLE[c]	+ 20% CLE[c]	Corn	+ 0.5% Urea	+ 15% BL[d]
Silage composition						
Dry matter, %	26.2	28.5	29.9	25.8	25.8	29.7
Crude protein, % DM	7.5	10.1	12.9	9.8	13.9	11.9
Lactic acid, % DM	11.1	17.1	17.7			
Animal performance DM consumed, g/d/kg BW^{0.75}	75.7	63.1	50.6	46.0	41.8	67.6
Digestibility						
Dry matter, %	78.0[e]	73.1	69.2	64.3	66.7	65.0
Crude protein, %	61.5[e]	56.4	66.5	57.1	71.5	59.9
Energy, DE Mcal/kg	3.10[e]	2.87	2.58			
N retention, % of intake	13.1	4.2	0.6	8.5	7.1	15.6

[a]From Buchannan-Smith et al. (46).
[b]From Harmon et al. (47).
[c]CLE = cage layer excreta.
[d]BL = broiler litter.
[e]Data obtained with lambs fed protein from soybean meal equivalent to the crude protein in the lower level of CLE.

Sorghum Silage

There are many different types of sorghum crops grow, ranging from short-stalked crops such as milo to tall forage sorghums with relatively little grain. Sorghum plants are much more resis- tant to water shortages than corn and can be grown without irrigation in areas where it is not feasible to grow corn. It seems likely that there will be a revival of sorghum usage in the drier areas in North America where ground waters used for irrigation are becoming more expensive.

TABLE 6-32
Effect of stage of maturity of forage sorghum silage on its feeding value

Component	Stage of maturity					
	Early Bloom	Bloom	Milk	Late Milk to Early Dough	Dough	Hard Dough
Forage composition						
Dry matter, %	23.2	24.6	25.3	28.6	29.6	30.8
Crude protein, %[a]	8.4	8.0	7.3	7.0	5.8	5.9
AD fiber, %[a]	35.7	37.5	36.1	33.3	34.0	34.1
Silage composition						
Dry matter, %	19.8	23.2	23.7	27.4	27.6	32.3
Crude protein, %[a]	9.2	8.3	7.7	7.2	7.1	7.4
AD fiber, %[a]	35.3	36.9	38.5	34.4	37.4	34.4
Silage digestibility, %						
Dry matter	65.2	57.8	56.9	57.7	50.3	52.1
TDN[a]	64.9	57.9	57.1	57.0	50.3	53.5
DE yield, Mcal/ha	20,867	26,439	26,720	29,225	25,348	24,152

[a]Dry-matter basis.
Source: Black et al. (48)

Sorghum plants have less grain at maturity than corn, generally containing less than 40 percent grain for the harvested plant as it goes into the silo. The result is that the energy value will normally be less than for corn silage, and yields may be expected to be less. One example of a study on the stage of maturity on nutrient value of forage sorghum is shown in Table 6–32. Note that as the forage dry matter increased, the crude protein decreased, and the same comment applies to the silage. Likewise, silage digestibility decreased with maturity. Maximum yield/ha of digestible energy occurred at the late milk to early dough stage.

Miscellaneous Silages

A wide variety of other herbaceous materials has been used to make silage. Waste from canneries processing food crops such as sweet corn, green beans, green peas, and various root or vegetative residues such as pea vines, beet tops, and cull potatoes have been used successfully. Residues of this type are often difficult to use on a fresh basis because of a variable daily supply or because they are available for only short periods of time. Ensiling is advantageous in that it tends to result in a more uniform feed and a known supply allows more efficient planning.

Silages made from the small cereal grains have been used from time to time. Data from two experiments are shown in Table 6–33 with comparisons to corn silage. Note that the crude protein content of silage from small-grain forage was higher than from corn, especially from the oat silage. In the experiment shown on the left, dry matter in the small-grain silage was apparently higher than that from corn, and this apparently stimulated greater dry matter consumption and higher daily gain, although less efficient gain. In the other experiment, daily gains were lower with the small-grain silages, especially oats. Although feed consumption was about the same for corn, barley, and wheat silages, feed efficiency was less for the cereal grain silages. Other recent comparisons have been done of silages made from oats, peas, oat-peas, or barley-peas. These cool season crops can be grown and harvested and followed by warm season crops such as pearl millet, sorghum, or Sudan grass (51). However, further work is needed to put a comparative value on silages from small cereal grains for young cattle.

A comparison between corn and wheat silage, both untreated and treated with formic acid, is shown in Table 6–34. In this instance there was little difference in the protein content of forage or silage. Digestibility of dry matter and dry matter consumption were greater for the corn silage, as was milk production by lactating dairy cows. Treatment with formic acid inhibited production of lactic acid in both silages, but it increased protein digestibility and tended to increase consumption. It had little effect on milk production.

The sunflower is currently being used more extensively because it is a plant that will tol-

TABLE 6-33

Response of growing cattle fed silages from small grain forage as compared to corn silage

Item	Silage Source[a]				Silage Source[b]			
	Corn	Barley	Wheat	Triticale	Corn	Barley	Wheat	Oats
Silage composition								
Dry matter, %	30.3	42.7	46.4	58.2	37.2	35.7	39.2	30.1
Crude protein, % of DM	8.5	11.0	11.0	10.5	8.3	9.0	11.2	12.6
AD fiber, % of DM					28.9	32.3	36.5	42.3
Animal performance								
Daily gain, kg	0.82	0.98	0.92	0.92	1.15	1.06	0.94	0.50
Daily DM intake, kg	5.58	6.42	7.24	8.30	8.68	8.87	8.52	6.64
Feed/gain ratio	7.15	6.68	8.14	9.11	7.59	8.41	9.10	13.47

[a]From Hinman (49). The complete diets were 10% alfalfa hay, 15% barley, 5% supplement, and 70% silage (DM basis).

[b]From Oltjen and Bolsen (50). Cattle were fed for 89 days on a diet (DM basis) of 84% silage, 12% of a milo-soybean meal mix, and 4% supplement.

erate colder temperatures than the soybean and will also produce in relatively arid climates. Although it is grown primarily for seed, it can be made into an acceptable silage. One example of data is shown in Table 6–35 in which sunflower silage is compared to grass-legume silage as feed for dairy cows. The crude protein content of the sunflower silage was as high as the grass-legume silage, and it allowed identical milk production, although somewhat lower milk fat percentage. Thus sunflower silage appears to be an acceptable alternative for other types of silage for high-producing animals.

In tropical areas sugar cane has been extolled as a high-potential crop of livestock feed

because as much as 20 tons/ha of TDN can be produced from it. It has been suggested that either the whole plant or the de-rined stalk could be used as feed for ruminants (54). Since sugar cane is quite high in sucrose, it would seem to be a logical candidate for silage. However, one study indicated that digestibility of sugar cane silage was low, partially because large amounts of the sugars were fermented by yeasts to ethanol (55).

Only limited studies have been reported of attempts to make silage from tropical grasses (56). Recent research (57) indicates that satisfactory grass can be made from various tropical grasses, and that, where feasible, the product

TABLE 6-34

Effect of treating corn and wheat silage with formic acid

Item	Corn		Wheat	
	Untreated	Treated[a]	Untreated	Treated[a]
Chemical composition				
Forage as ensiled				
Dry matter, %	32.3	33.1	39.7	41.3
Crude protein, % of DM	9.0	9.4	9.3	8.9
Silage composition				
Dry matter, %	33.6	33.2	42.8	40.8
Crude protein, % of DM	8.4	8.7	8.9	9.0
pH	3.5	4.1	4.1	4.6
Lactic acid, % of DM	9.1	1.7	4.3	1.3
Animal performance				
DM digestibility, %	69.5	73.1	61.4	69.9
CP digestibility, %	57.6	64.4	57.7	65.7
DM intake, % of BW[b]	2.38	2.50	2.11	2.17
FCM[c] production, kg/d	16.8	16.6	15.0	15.5

[a]Silages were treated with formic acid (82–90%) at the rate of 0.5% of the green weight of the silage.

[b]BW = body weight.

[c]FCM = fat corrected milk; cows were fed at 20% CP concentrate at a standard rate/unit of milk produced in addition to silage.

Source: Baxter et al. (52).

TABLE 6-35

Comparison of grass-legume silage with sunflower silage for lactating cows

	Silage	
Item	Grass-Legume	Sunflower
Silage composition		
Dry matter, %	25.7	25.3
Crude protein, %[a]	12.5	12.9
AD fiber, %[a]	49.7	35.8
Calcium %[a]	1.2	1.6
Phosphorus, %[a]	0.3	0.3
Cow performance		
FCM production/d, kg	17.5	17.5
Milk fat, %	3.6	3.2

[a]Composition data given on a DM basis.

Source: Thomas et al. (53).

can probably be improved by the addition of a starch source such as cassava meal or a protein-starch source such as coconut meal. Fine chopping appears to reduce pH and increase lactic acid. In general, lactic acid content of tropical grass silage is quite low, and acetic acid is probably more important in preservation. Addition of a starch source will increase lactic acid to levels more comparable to that of silages made from zone grasses.

SILAGE ADDITIVES

A wide variety of additives has been used at one time or another on an experimental basis with the intent of improving the ensiling process. The types of additives could be classed as nutrients, preservatives, fermentation aids, and biological additives. The use of urea (or ammonia) and limestone with corn and sorghum silages has already been mentioned, and there can be little doubt that both additives are effective in either increasing the crude protein or lactic acid contents, respectively, of silage. There is also evidence to indicate that addition of sulfur may be advantageous, particularly when the silage is fed to sheep.

With grass or grass-legume silages the addition of molasses or grain has long been recommended to provide a source of fermentable carbohydrates, particularly when the herbage is ensiled without wilting. More recently, it has been shown that 1 percent dried whey is an effective (but rather expensive) additive for either legume or corn silage.

Different chemicals have been used to inhibit fermentation in silage, particularly in direct cut silage of high-moisture content. The earliest use of this type of product was with a mixture of mineral acids which was pioneered in Europe. It is a very effective method, but the corrosive acids are difficult to handle and the cost is relatively high. More recently, the use of formic acid, formaldehyde, mixtures of the two, or mixtures with sulfuric acid or propionic acid have been used (examples with formic acid already cited), and there are many reports on this topic. These various acids are effective in inhibiting degradation of herbage protein and soluble carbohydrates, although results are rarely better than can be obtained by wilting (33, 58). Acid treatment also inhibits growth of fungi (molds) and reduces heating caused by fermentation. Propionic acid has also been shown to be effective in inhibiting mold growth in haylage that was too dry (58). Likewise, the addition of various hydroxides (such as NaOH) has been used with different types of silages, but there is little reason to use such chemicals on good-quality herbage, although combinations of hydroxide and molasses have given good results with crop residues (see later section).

Sodium metabisulfite is another relatively common additive. It is an effective inhibitor for most bacteria (and is usesd commonly in wine fermentations to kill wild yeasts and other microorganisms), but it has less effect on lactic acid bacteria than on some other species. Overall, experimental results do not indicate any great benefit from its use. It would be interesting to see what effect it might have if added to sugar cane silage.

Bacterial cultures, often containing *Lactobacillus* species, have been promoted extensively in recent years as silage additives. Although there are conflicting claims as to the benefit of such preparations, recent evidence suggests that such additives are not likely to improve corn or grass silages made under good conditions, one reason being that such treatments tend to increase ammonia N levels. The evidence does not suggest any reduced losses in fermentation nor improved feeding value of the silages in most instances (59, 60, 61).

DRY CROP RESIDUES

Vast quantities of low-quality roughage, primarily crop residues, are available in many areas of the world where cropland agriculture is practiced. These residues include straws and chaff from the cereal grains—rice, wheat, bar-

TABLE 6-36

Compositional differences between good and poor quality roughages

Roughage	Composition[a]								
	CP	CF	ADF	NDF	TDN	NEm	NEg	Ca	p
	%					Mcal/kg		%	
High quality									
Orchard grass pasture, early vegetative	18	25	31	55	72	1.64	1.03	0.4	0.4
Alfalfa hay, early bloom	19	25	35	40	60	1.31	0.65	1.4	0.2
Sudan grass hay, mid bloom	9	30	40	65	63	1.39	0.75	0.5	0.3
Low quality									
Grass hay, weathered	4	38	43	68	46	1.11	0.35	0.4	0.1
Grass straw	5	41	48	70	44	0.95	0.34	0.5	0.2
Oat straw	5	40	47	70	46	1.11	0.35	0.2	0.1
Wheat straw	4	42	56	85	40	0.86	0.0	0.2	0.08
Barley straw	4	42	57	82	46	0.99	0.11	0.3	0.05
Cottonseed hulls	4	48	67	86	50	1.03	0.22	0.2	0.07
Cotton gin trash	7	34			44	0.95	0.11	0.3	0.1
Corn cobs	3	36	39	88	48	1.04	0.20	0.1	0.04
Corn stover	6	35	58	87	50	1.02	0.22	0.5	0.1
Sugarcane bagasse	2	49	59	86	48	1.03	0.19	0.5	0.3
Peanut hulls	7	63	65	74	22	0.77	0.0	0.2	0.07

[a]Abbreviations are: CP, crude protein; CF, crude fiber; ADF, acid detergent fiber; NDF, neutral detergent fiber or cell walls; TDN, total digestible nutrients; NEm, net energy for maintenance; NEg, net energy for gain; Ca, calcium; P, phosphorus.

ley, and the like, grass straws, stover from corn, and sorghum, corn cobs, cottonseed hulls, cotton gin trash, hulls of various types, and other residues available in lesser amounts. In addition, there are large quantities of winter pastures which, in many places, are made up of native grasses, forbs, and browse that are utilized, especially in arid rangeland areas. In tropical and subtropical areas residues such as sugar cane bagasse, pineapple stumps, and large amounts of coarse grasses may be found in humid areas.

Data on some high- and low-quality roughages are shown in Table 6–36. Note that the outstanding characteristic of low-quality roughage is the low crude protein content. These materials are high in cellulose and other structural carbohydrates (crude fiber, ADF, NDF), highly lignified, and, in addition, may have had excessive exposure to sun and rain, the result being that usable nutrient content is low. In this particular table the relative differences in energy content are probably shown more clearly by the use of TDN values. Many of the NE values were derived using regression equations which may or may not necessarily give a true estimate of the differences involved.

Low-quality roughages are generally lower in Ca than high-quality sources, especially legumes, and they are invariably low in P. It also seems likely that the minerals present would be less digestible, although there is very little information on this topic. In addition, the content of other minerals not listed in the table would be expected to be lower.

The carotene (provitamin A) content of plant tissues is highly related to the green color of the plant. Thus for a roughage such as straw, the carotene content is nil. The content of vitamins D and E would also be extremely low, and that of the B-complex vitamins would be nil.

Use of Low-Quality Roughages

The types of low-quality roughages shown in Table 6–36 can be utilized for feeding ruminants and to a lesser extent horses. However, they are not, with rare exceptions, adequate rations for any class of animal without supplementation. The data given in Table 6–36 only partially define the problem of using such feeds for ruminants. Probably the major limitation is that such feedstuffs are low in digestibility, but also they are digested slowly in the rumen. The net result is that an animal simply cannot consume enough of some of these materials to maintain body weight. One of the limitations of the ruminant digestive tract is that feedstuffs must be digested or chewed enough so that the rumen contents will pass through the reticulo-omasal orifice. Gut fill may also be a limiting factor, but it is not likely to be as important with unprocessed roughage. The effect of quality on digestibility, consumption and rumen turnover is illustrated in Table 6–37. Note that as digestibility of the roughages declined, consumption also declined and rumen turnover rate decreased (which would inhibit consumption).

A second major factor is that these low-quality feeds do not contain enough crude protein to stimulate adequate microbial activity in the rumen. Rumen microbes need N to function and metabolize ingested feeds. Depending upon the solubility and digestibility of the proteins provided, at least 8 percent crude protein appears necessary to sustain a reasonable level of activity, although it will be affected by the nature of the dietary ingredients and the level and type of production expected from the animal. Some N from body metabolism is recycled into the rumen via saliva or through the rumen wall, but after a prolonged period of low protein intake, the amount of N recycled is very much reduced.

When low-quality roughage is going to be used as a wintering feed (Fig. 6–19), the physical limitations of digesting it, the low available energy, and the protein content pretty well restrict use as a major share of the diet to older animals (yearlings or older for cattle). Even with wintering beef cows, additional feed is required, since they will not be able to maintain their weight on most straws or similar feeds. However, these feedstuffs are worth somewhat more than net energy values indicate for main-

FIGURE 6–19. Cattle grazing on a cornstalk field after the grain has been harvested.

tenance, because some of the heat produced during rumen fermentaiton and body metabolism can be used to maintain body temperatures in cold environments.

Younger animals (weaner calves) simply cannot eat enough low-quality roughage, even when supplemented with proteins, vitamins, and minerals, to gain at generally recommended levels (1-1.25 lb/d). Limited amounts can be used for young cattle, perhaps from a quarter up to half of the diet without adverse effects, but the remainder of the diet will have to be of much higher ingredients to sustain adequate levels of production.

Low-quality roughages can be used very effectively as diluents in high concentrate rations, because some bulky feed is needed in nearly all circumstances for both ruminants and horses. Sheep do not eat straws readily; although they can be forced to consume some, it would be advisable to do so only during periods when the ewe's energy requirements are not high.

One particular problem with low-quality roughages is that the N requirements for supplemental feeds are more specific than with most other types of feedstuffs. Animals normally never achieve a high level of production when nonprotein N sources are fed with low-quality roughage (see Ch. 8 for further information on this topic). Thus it is usually desirable to feed some natural protein as a supplement to such materials.

CHEMICALLY TREATED CROP RESIDUES

Nutritionists have been interested for many years in methods of improving the utilization by animals of low-quality feedstuffs. Major emphasis in recent years has been on chemical treatments. Although many different methods

TABLE 6-37

Effect on roughage quality on consumption, digestibility, and rumen turnover rate

	Roughage		
Item	Orchard Grass Hay	Barley Straw	Corn Stover
Crude protein, %	10.1	4.2	4.1
Acid-det. fiber, %	40.7	57.0	58.6
Digestibility,[a] %			
Dry matter	60.1	53.8	48.9
Crude protein	54.1	9.5	12.5
Consumption/d,[b] kg			
Roughage dry matter	5.81	3.95	2.27
Rumen turnover rate/d	1.30	0.95	0.71

[a]Cattle were also fed 1 kg of supplement/d.
[b]Different trial, but cattle were also fed 1 kig of supplement/d.
Source: Wheeler et al. (62).

TABLE 6-38

Performance of steers fed rations containing ryegrass straw

Item	Daily Gain, kg	(lb)	Feed Conversion	Av. Daily Straw Consumption, kg	(lb)	DE of Straw,[a] %
Cubed with molasses	1.32	(2.91)	8.22	2.09	(4.6)	43.2
Sprayed with 4% dry wt of NaOH	1.43	(3.15)	7.49	2.13	(4.7)	61.9

[a]Digestible energy was determined by difference when fed with alfalfa hay to sheep.

Source: Author's unpublished data. Growing rations contained 25% straw and finishing rations contained 15% straw.

have been used—heat, steam, various alkalis and acids, combinations of steam and chemicals—the use of alkali compounds generally has resulted in the greatest improvement, especially per unit of cost involved. Treatments with alkalis such as NaOH or combinations of NaOH and others appear to produce the greatest results with minimal costs. Methods have been developed to spray concentrated solutions directly on chopped straws or other low-quality materials. The Australians use spraying on cereal forage prior to baling. Ensiling straws or corn stover with NaOH also appears to be feasible.

One example (of many that are available) of the effectiveness of NaOH is shown in Table 6-38. Note that feeding cattle diets with 15-25 percent straw that had been treated with NaOH resulted in improved daily gain and more efficient feed conversion at least partially because the digestibility of the straw was increased from 43 to 62 percent. In another instance, when treated straw was fed to lactating dairy cows, the cows were able to consume substantial amounts of treated straw with only a small effect on milk production. During the late 1970s and early 1980s some commercial mills were utilizing chemical processing methods for straws and other similar materials in Europe and some other areas. However, the costs are relatively high. The chemical cost alone for adding 4 percent NaOH to straw was about $10/ton several years ago in the United States. When chopping and/or cubing costs are added, it is not feasible in most areas in North America at this time.

There have been a number of recent papers reporting the effects of treating low-quality roughages with alkaline hydrogen peroxide. Data from one paper are shown in Table 6-39. While it is quite evident that this treatment (soaking the straw in a chemical solution and then washing and drying) is quite effective in increasing the digestibility of the ADF and cellulose, it is also highly unlikely that such a treatment could ever be financially feasible.

A more feasible method involves use of anhydrous ammonia rather than the strong alkalis. All that is required for treatment is to stack the roughage, cover it with plastic well tucked in around the edges, and release the ammonia into the stack. Reaction time required may take several weeks, depending upon ambient temperatures. Results of one study are

TABLE 6-39

Effect of treating wheat straw with alkaline hydrogen peroxide when fed to sheep

	Straw Level, % of diet			
	Low		High	
Item	Treated	Untreated	Treated	Untreated
Diet composition				
Crude protein	11.0	11.4	10.6	11.8
ADF	35.2	25.4	52.3	42.8
Cellulose	29.8	18.1	42.4	21.2
Digestibility, %				
CP	82.0	74.0	70.8	73.8
ADF	80.2	41.2	75.8	44.1
Cellulose	90.3	46.0	87.3	47.9

Source: Kerley et al. (63). Low-level diets contained about 33% straw and high-level diets about 70%. The straw was soaked for about 5 h in a solution of hydrogen peroxide, sodium hydroxide, and hydrochloric acid and then washed and dried.

TABLE 6-40
Effect of ammoniation treatments on utilization of low-quality roughages

| | Roughage Treatment | | | |
| | Untreated Fescue | | Ammoniated Fescue | |
Method	No other Treatment	+ SBM	No Other Treatment	+ Corn
Total N, % DM	1.27		2.67	
Ammonia N, %	0.02		0.39	
Hemicellulose, %	30.7		25.5	
Lignin, %	8.1		6.7	
Digestibility, % dry matter	40.1	38.8	58.6	56.2
Nitrogen consumed, g/head/d	7.92	12.84	20.55	24.36
Nitrogen absorbed, %				
of consumed	49.4	58.1	45.6	49.2
Nitrogen retained, g/head/d	0.45	0.39	−1.61	1.12
Feed consumed, $g/W_{kg}^{0.75}$				
Sheep	34.0	36.2	45.6	47.0
Cattle	39.9	49.1	65.4	68.6

Source: Buettner et al. (64).

shown in Table 6–40. In this instance when fescue was treated, there was a substantial N uptake (from 1.27 to 2.67 percent). Hemicellulose content of the fescue was reduced, as was the lignin. Digestibility of the fescue was increased substantially, but N retention (a reasonable measure of growth potential) was not improved much unless the fescue was fed with corn. Ammoniation increased consumption by cattle more than it did with sheep.

Ammoniation treatment appears to be more feasible for many individuals to use. It is a common agricultural product in most areas and is, generally, less hazardous to use than concentrated solutions of NaOH. Normally, it does not produce as marked an increase in digestibility, but some N is also added that can be used, particularly if a source of starch is fed, by rumen microorganisms. However, the ammonia is not all bound irreversibly to the straw, and some will be lost when the straw is processed or exposed to the elements.

Ammonia has also been used to preserve high-moisture (32 percent) alfalfa hay. In one study it prevented molding and raised crude protein from 18.8 to 23.8 percent, but it had no apparent effect on milk production of dairy cows (65).

There has been a considerable amount of research activity in the past ten years or so on methods and means of improving the use of either wet forages or low-quality forages. Of all the work that has been done with addition of acids and other chemicals or microbes to silage

or the treatment of crop residues with chemicals or addition of ammonia, the only ones that appear to the author to be feasible are those involving addition of N sources to silage, possibly the use of some acid-aldehyde mixtures and microbes in silage, and the use of ammonia on crop residues. For the reader desiring more information on this topic, three recent reviews are available (66, 67, 68).

SUMMARY

Roughages provide the majority of the feed consumed by herbivore species under natural conditions. In our highly developed agriculture of today, roughages are still the most important feed ingredient for these species, but roughages must be supplemented with other nutrient sources in order to allow high levels of production by fattening cattle, lactating cows and goats, or horses that have high energy expenditures. Roughages are, by definition, high in fibrous carbohydrates which are digested less completely than energy sources such as grains. The bulky nature of roughages, while necessary for the health and well-being of herbivorous species, limits feed consumption and the level of production that may be achieved. Good-quality roughages provide adequate levels of protein, minerals, and vitamins for most animal species, while poor-quality roughages must be supplemented with these nutrients if animals are forced to consume them for extended periods of time. Young animals do not have the capability of consuming as much poor-quality roughage as do older animals. However, even poor-quality roughages can be used in moderate amounts in diets for fattening cattle or for feeding horses and in large amounts for maintaining wintering cattle, sheep, and horses.

REFERENCES

1. USDA. 1987. *Agricultural statistics 1987.* Washington, D.C.: USDA.

2. NRC. 1982. *United States-Canadian tables of feed composition.* 3d ed. Washington, D.C.: Nat. Academy Press.

3. Reeves, J. B. III. 1987. *J. Dairy Sci.* 70:1583.

4. Heath, M. E., D. S. Metcalfe, and R. E. Barnes, eds. 1973. *Forages.* 3d ed. Ames, IA: Iowa State Univ. Press.

5. Butler, G. W., and R. W. Bailey, eds. 1973. *Chemistry and biochemistry of herbage. Vol. 1–3.* London: Academic Press.

6. Morley, F. H. W., ed. 1981. *Grazing animals.* New York: Elsevier Scientific Pub. Co.

7. Rodin, L. E., N. I. Bazilevich, and N. N. Rozov. 1975. In: *Productivity of world ecosystems.* Washington, D.C.: Nat. Academy Sci.

8. Morey, D. D., and J. J. Evans. 1983. *Cereal Chem.* 60:461.

9. Eppendorfer, W. H. 1977. *J. Sci. Food Agr.* 28:607.

10. Powell, K., R. L. Reid, and J. A. Balasko. 1977. *J. Animal Sci.* 46:1503.

11. Ely, R. E., et al. 1953. *J. Dairy Sci.* 36:334.

12. Phillips, T. G., et al. 1954. *Argon. J.* 46:361.

13. Van Riper, G. E., and D. Smith. 1959. *Wisc. Expt. Sta. Res. Rpt.* 4.

14. Hibbs, J. W., and H. R. Conrad. 1974. *Ohio Rpt.* 59(2):33.

15. Schubert, J. R., et al. 1958. *Proc. West. Sec. Amer. Soc. Animal Sci.* 9:LVI.

16. Vona, L. C., et al. 1984. *J. Animal Sci.* 59:1582.

17. Wheeler, J. L., and R. C. Mochrie, eds. *Forage evaluation: Concepts and techniques.* CSIRO, Armidale, NSW, Australia, and Amer. Forage and Grassland Council, Lexington, KT.

18. Fonnesbeck, P. V., et al. 1986. *Animal Feed Sci. Tech.* 16:7.

19. Gregory, P. H., et al. 1963. *J. Gen. Microbiol.* 33:147.

20. Weiss, W. P., H. R. Conrad, and W. I. Shockey. 1986. *J. Dairy Sci.* 69:1824.

21. Monhanty, G. P., et al. 1969. *J. Dairy Sci.* 52:79.

22. Baxter, H. D., et al. 1986. *J. Dairy Sci.* 69:1854.

23. Wier, W. C., L. C. Jones, and J. H. Meyer. 1960. *J. Animal Sci.* 19:5.

24. Stone, J. B., et al. 1960. *J. Dairy Sci.* 43:1275.

25. Karn, J. F., et al. 1974. *J. Animal Sci.* 38:850.

26. Meyer, J. H., G. P. Lofgreen, and N. R. Ittner. 1956. *J. Animal Sci.* 15:64.

27. Stiles, D. A., et al. 1971. *J. Dairy Sci.* 54:65.

28. Langston, C. W., et al. 1958. *USDA Tech. Bul.* 1187.

29. Shepherd, J. B., C. H. Gordon, and L. F. Campbell. 1953. *USDA Bureau Dairy Ind. Bul.* 149.

30. Hoglund, C. R. 1964. *Mich. State Univ. Agr. Econ. Publ.* 947.

31. Fiez, E. 1976. In: *Beef* 12(7):20.

32. Hawkins, D. R., H. E. Henderson, and D. B. Purser. 1970. *J. Animal Sci.* 31:617.

33. Waldo, D. R., J. E. Keys, and C. H. Gordon. 1973. *J. Dairy Sci.* 56:129.

34. Calder, F. W., J. W. G. Nicholson, and J. E. Langille. 1976. *Can. J. Animal Sci.* 56:57.

35. Beever, D. E., et al. 1971. *Brit. J. Nutr.* 26:123.

36. Prange, R. W., et al. 1984. *J. Dairy Sci.* 67:2308.

37. Donaldson, E., and R. A. Edwards. 1976. *J. Sci. Food Agr.* 27:536.

38. Sutton, A. L., and R. L. Vetter. 1971. *J. Animal Sci.* 32:1256.

39. Wilkinson, J. M., J. T. Huber, and H. E. Henderson. 1976. *J. Animal Sci.* 42:208.

40. Phillip, L. E., and J. G. Buchannan-Smith. 1982. *Can. J. Animal Sci.* 62:259.

41. St. Pierre, N. R., et al. 1987. *J. Dairy Sci.* 70:108.

42. Zimmerman, J. E. 1976. In: *Beef* 12(7):20.

43. Byers, F. M. 1980. *J. Animal Sci.* 50:1127.

44. Huber, J. T., et al. 1979. *J. Dairy Sci.* 62:965.

45. Carr, S. B., et al. 1984. *J. Dairy Sci.* 67:1474.

46. Buchannan-Smith, J. G., G. K. Macleod, and J. C. Jofriet. 1982. *Can. J. Animal Sci.* 62:163.

47. Harmon, B. W., J. P. Fontenot, and K. E. Webb, Jr. 1975. *J. Animal Sci.* 40:156.

48. Black, J. R., et al. 1980. *J. Animal Sci.* 50:617.

49. Hinman, D. D. 1982. *Univ. of Idaho Res. Rpt.* 2.

50. Oltjen, J. W., and K. K. Bolsen. 1980. *J. Animal Sci.* 51:958.

51. Jaster, E. H., C. M. Fisher, and D. A. Miller. 1985. *J. Dairy Sci.* 68:2914.

52. Baxter, H. D., M. J. Montgomery, and J. R. Owen. 1980. *J. Dairy Sci.* 63:1291.

53. Thomas, V. M., et al. 1982. *J. Dairy Sci.* 65:267.

54. Preston, T. R., and M. B. Willis. 1974. *Intensive beef production.* 2d ed. New York: Pergamon Press.

55. King, L., and R. W. Stanley. 1982. *J. Animal Sci.* 54:689.

56. Wilkinson, J. M. 1983. *World Animal Rev.* 45:37.

57. Panditharatne, S., et al. 1986. *J. Animal Sci.* 63:197.

58. Waldo, D. R. 1977. *J. Dairy Sci.* 60:306.

59. Thonney, M. L., et al. 1980. *J. Dairy Sci.* 63:587.

60. Burghardi, S. R., R. D. Goodrich, and J. C. Meiske. 1980. *J. Animal Sci.* 50:729.

61. Luther, R. M. 1987. *J. Animal Sci.* 63:1329.

62. Wheeler, W. E., D. A. Dinius, and J. B. Coombe. 1979. *J. Animal Sci.* 49:1357.

63. Kerley, M. S., et al. 1987. *J. Dairy Sci.* 70:2078.

64. Buettner, M. R., et al. 1982. *J. Animal Sci.* 54:173.

65. Weiss, W. P., V. F. Colenbrander, and V. L. Lechtenberg. 1982. *J. Dairy Sci.* 65:1212.

66. Males, J. R. 1987. *J. Animal Sci.* 65:1124.

67. Conner, M. C., and C. R. Richardson. 1987. *J. Animal Sci.* 65:1131.

68. Klopfenstein, T., et al. 1987. *J. Animal Sci.* 65:1139.

69. Marten, G. C., J. S. Shenk, and F. E. Barton II, eds. 1985. *Near infrared reflectance sprectroscopy (NIRS).* USDA Agric. Handbook 643. Washington, D.C.: USDA.

70. Boland, R. L., et al. 1976. *Crop Sci.* 16:677.

71. Aderibigbe, A. O., and D. C. Church. 1982. *J. Animal Sci.* 54:164.

7

High-Energy Feedstuffs

Feedstuffs classed as high-energy are those that are fed or added to a ration primarily for the purpose of increasing energy intake or increasing energy density of the ration. Included are the various cereal grains and many of their milling by-products, liquid feeds such as molasses and mixtures in which molasses predominates, fats and oils, and other miscellaneous plant and animal products available in lesser amounts or in restricted geographical areas. On the basis of available energy/unit of dry matter, roots and tubers are also included.

Energy from high-energy feedstuffs is supplied either by readily available carbohydrates (sugars and/or starches) or by fats and oils. Such feedstuffs are labeled high-energy, in contrast to most roughages, because the available energy—digestible, metabolizable, or net—is much greater/unit of dry matter. In other words, the animal can obtain much more energy than from a typical roughage, even though there may be very little difference in gross energy (that resulting from burning in a bomb calorimeter) between straw and starch.

High-energy feedstuffs generally have low to moderate levels of protein, although several of the high-protein meals could be included on the basis of available energy. For our purposes here, only those feedstuffs with less than 20 percent crude protein will be considered.

Depending upon the type of diet and the class of animal involved, feedstuffs in this class may make up a substantial percentage of the animal's total diet. As such, other nutrients provided by these basal feeds—amino acids, minerals, vitamins—must be considered also, but quantitatively these nutrients are normally of less concern than is the energy provided.

CEREAL GRAINS

Cereal grains are produced by plants of the grass family (*Gramineae*) grown primarily for their seeds; consequently, they provide tremendous tonnages of harvested grains for animal feed and human food. Estimated world production of wheat, corn, and coarse grains (usually meaning oats, barley, and sorghum) for the 1981–82 and 1986–87 years is shown in Table 7–1. Note that cereal production has increased in the five-year period shown in the table. Feed use for 1986–87 accounted for 48.7 percent of grain pro-

TABLE 7-1

World production and feed use of wheat, corn, and coarse grains
(in millions of tons)

Item	Crop Year 1981–82	Crop Year 1986–87	% of Production, 1986–87
Wheat			
Production	449.5	522.5	
Consumption	441.1 ±	503.0	
Feed use	84.9	94.2	+18.0
Corn			
Production	441.0	475.0	
Consumption	418.7	432.2	
Feed use	253.9	287.4	+60.5
Coarse grains[a]			
Production	766.0	833.0	
Consumption	742.6	786.5	
Feed use	444.1	710.7	+61.3
Total feed use	782.9	892.3	+48.7

[a]Primarily oats, barley, and sorghum.
Source: USDA (1).

duction. If we would include rice production for 1986–87 (465.8 million T), of which very little was used for animal feed, then feed usage would amount to 38.8 percent of grain production during that year.

In the United States, estimated feed usage for 1981, 1985, and projected use for 1986 is shown in Table 7–2 for the cereal grains and a number of other energy sources, many of which are by-products of grain milling. Note that corn accounted for 119.8 out of 159.9 million T of grain fed in 1986. This amounts to 74.9 percent of the total as compared to the world estimate of 60.5 percent. The relative amount of produc-

TABLE 7-2

Grains and by-product feeds fed to livestock in the United States (in millions of tons)

Item	Crop Year 1981	Crop Year 1985	Crop Year 1986[a]
Grains fed			
Corn	105.9	104.0	119.8
Sorghum	10.6	16.9	13.9
Oats	10.5	11.0	9.6
Barley	5.5	7.8	7.0
Wheat & rye	3.4	10.5	9.6
Total grains	135.9	150.2	159.9
Other ingredients			
Wheat millfeeds	4.58	5.35	5.77
Rice millfeeds	0.67	0.58	0.72
Dried & molasses beet pulp	1.40	1.36	1.32
Fats & oils[b]	0.66	0.77	0.76
Molasses, inedible	0.97	0.94	0.93
Miscellaneous	1.27	1.27	1.27
Total other ingredients	9.55	10.27	10.77
Grand total	145.5	160.5	170.7

[a]Partially forecasted.
[b]Values do not include amounts used in pet and fish feeds.
Source: USDA (2).

tion from the other feed grains (sorghum, oats, barley) has declined, partly because yields of corn have increased more over the past 50 years than is the case for the other grains. In any case, in other areas of the world, much less of the total production of cereal grain production is used for animal feed. With increasing costs of fuel and fertilizer and increasing human populations, it may be anticipated that relatively less of the U.S. production will be used for animal feeds in future years.

Of course, some of these "feed" grains go into human food or for the production of industrial products of a wide variety. For example, corn may be consumed as popped corn, corn flakes, corn flour, corn starch, corn syrup, whiskey, and numerous other products, but the amount used in this manner is much less than currently goes into animal feeds. Wheat and rice are grown primarily for human consumption, although moderate amounts of wheat may go into animal feed in the United States when price and supply allow it. Barley and oats, although good feeds, are becoming relatively less important because they do not usually yield as well as some of the other feed grain crops. Barley is used extensively in the brewing industry for the production of malt. Only a very small amount of oats is used off the farm. Other grains, such as millet and rye, find only limited use in North America, although they are more widely used in Europe and Asia. Sorghums are mainly an animal feed in the United States. A wheat-rye cross, triticale, is grown in limited amounts for feed. The common cereal grains are shown in Fig. 7-1.

Grain Grading and Marketing

In commercial practice in the United States, cereal grains, except for sorghums, are usually bought and sold on the basis of the archaic basis of bushel weights. This varies somewhat throughout the country, as it is more common in the West to sell by the ton, but the central markets quote prices on bushel weights.

Most of the cereal grains used for human food (and for export) pass through large terminal markets and most are sold on the basis of grades established by the U.S. Department of Agriculture, which also publishes information detailing the grade specifications (3). Grading standards, just recently revised, are published for wheat, corn, barley, oats, rye, sorghum, triticale, flax, soybeans, and mixed grain. For animal feed, an appreciable percentage of the total grains fed are probably not graded. Nevertheless, a brief discussion of this topic is pertinent to this chapter.

When a grain sample is obtained, the test weight is determined using a small device shown in Fig. 7-2. If the grain is to be graded, it is divided by use of appropriate sieves into the sample and dockage; dockage consists of weed seeds and stems, chaff, straw, grain other than the principal one, sand, dirt, and any other material that can be removed readily from the sample. The sieved sample is then evaluated on the basis of various factors. For corn, factors include weight per bushel, broken kernels and foreign material, damaged kernels, and heat-damaged kernels. The minimum or maximum limits for the different U.S. grades of the common grains are shown in Table 7-3. In addition to the grades shown for corn in the table, there may be some special grades such as weevily corn or corn of "distinctly low quality," a term that indicates more than two crotalaria seeds (Crotalaria spp.) in 1 kg of grain. Similar comments apply to the other grains, although the details are not all listed in the table.

As a result of the variability of feed grains, many large buyers, such as feedlots, may insist on discounts for light test weights, broken and damaged grain, presence of excessive foreign matter, and musty or sour odors. Moisture content will also vary greatly with high levels often found in freshly harvested grains. Most feedlots and grain elevators will discount grains having more than 15 percent moisture. This is, of course, a very legitimate practice, as the moisture is undesirable from the standpoint of keeping quality and the excess moisture is worthless unless the grain is to be stored and utilized as high-moisture grain.

Composition of Cereal Grains

Average values for some of the nutrients in cereal grains are shown in Table 7-4. Note that relatively small differences occur between the grains, and identifying them on the basis of their chemical composition would be difficult at times.

Although grains are usually said to be less variable in composition than roughages, many factors influence nutrient composition and, thus, feeding value for a given grain. For example, factors such as soil fertility and fertilization, variety, closeness of planting, weather, rainfall, insects, and disease may all affect plant growth and seed production so that average book values may not be meaningful. With wheat, for example, if a hot, dry period occurs while the grain

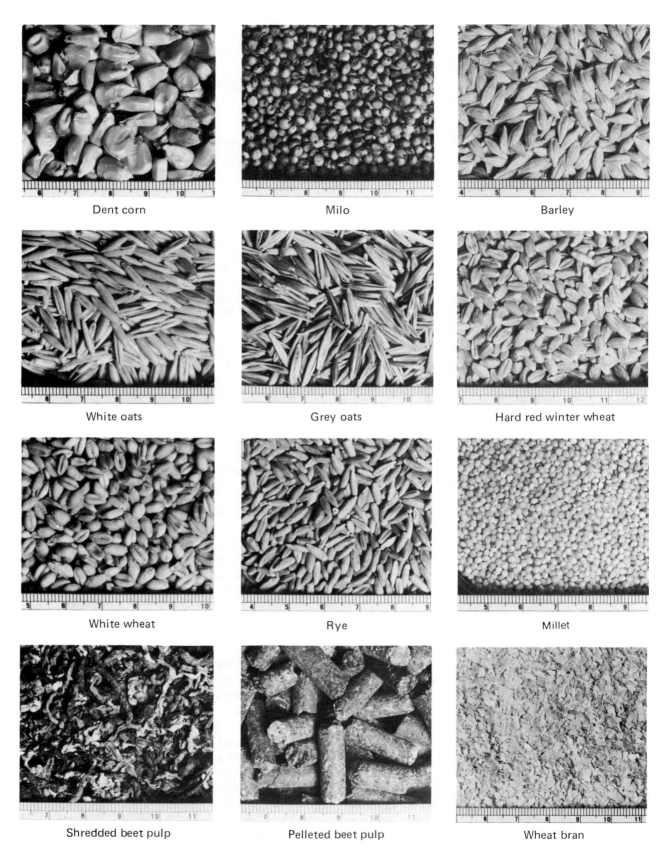

Dent corn

Milo

Barley

White oats

Grey oats

Hard red winter wheat

White wheat

Rye

Millet

Shredded beet pulp

Pelleted beet pulp

Wheat bran

FIGURE 7–1. Cereal grains and by-product feeds.

FIGURE 7–2. An apparatus used for measuring the bushel weight of grains.

is ripening, shriveled, small kernels may result. Although they may have a relatively high protein content, the starch content is apt to be much lower than usual, the weight/bushel (bulk density) will be low, and the feeding value may be appreciably lower.

Although crude protein content of feed grains is relatively low, ranging from 8-14 percent for most grains, some may be much lower than this and, particularly with wheat, some may be much higher, sometimes as high as 22 percent crude protein. Sorghum grains in particular are quite variable. Plant breeding practices are effective in increasing or decreasing the protein content.

Of the nitrogenous compounds in the seed, 85-90 percent is in the form of proteins, but the proteins, their solubility, and amino acid content vary from cereal to cereal. Most cereal grains are moderately low to deficient for monogastric species in lysine and often in tryptophan (corn) and threonine (sorghum and rice) and in methionine for poultry.

The fat content may vary greatly, ranging from less than 1 percent to greater than 6 percent, with oats usually having the most and wheat the least fat. Most of the fat is found in the seed embryo. The lipid content increases with maturity of the grain. Seed oils are high in palmitic acid and in linoleic and oleic acids; the latter two are unsaturated acids which tend to become rancid quickly, particularly after the grain is processed.

·The carbohydrates in grains, with the exception of the hulls, are primarily starch. Starch accounts for about 72 percent of the corn kernel, but is as low as 41 percent in oats (Table 7–4).

Starch is present in the endosperm (Fig. 7–4) in the form of granules that vary in size and shape in different plant species (Fig. 7–3). The starch granules increase in size but not in number with maturity. They are imbedded between a dense protein matrix and protein bodies that increase in thickness and size with maturity (4). The starch also differs somewhat in chemical composition among grains. Starch is a long-chain polymer made up of glucose molecules, and there are two primary types. Amylose is a linear, straight-chain molecule, while the other fraction, amylopectin, has many branched chains. The chain-length of amylopectin varies among species and varieties of grains. These two fractions have somewhat different chemical properties, and it may be that relative differences in amounts in different grains may have some effect on their feeding value. About 22-23 percent of the starch is amylose in corn, wheat, sorghum, barley, and oats, about 27 percent in rice, and up to 100 percent in waxy corn and sorghum, although the usual level is 21-28 percent. Other carbohydrates in grains include a variety of simple sugars and other larger carbohydrate molecules such as dextrins and pentosans, which altogether may account for 6-10 percent of the seed dry matter.

Cellulose is the principal constituent of the cell wall of the kernel and the hulls in grains such as barley and oats. While cellulose is also a glucose polymer, the linkage between the glucose molecules is much more stable and resistant to bacterial or enzymic action (see Ch. 3). The lignin content of hulls is also a factor in reducing utilization, as is the waxy covering on grains such as corn.

Hulls of seeds have a substantial effect on feeding value. Most hulls or seed coats must be broken to some extent before feeding if efficient utilization is to be achieved, particularly for cattle, which do not chew grains as thoroughly as do some other species. Because of their heavy hulls, barley and oats are sometimes known as rough grains. It might also be noted that rice hulls are almost totally indigestible; this is related to a very high silica content.

With regard to minerals, cereal grains are universally low in Ca. Although the P content is reasonably high, much of it is present in the form of phytic acid P, which has a low biological availability for monogastric animals. Trace elements are generally present only in marginal amounts.

Of the vitamins, most cereal grains are fair sources of vitamin E and low in vitamin D and

TABLE 7-3

U.S. grade and grade requirements for the feed grains

Grain, Grade	Minimum Limits, %		Damaged Kernels		Maximum Limits, %					
	Test wt/bushel lb[b]	Sound Grain	Total	Heat-Damaged	Foreign Material	Broken Kernels	Thin Barley	Other Seeds[a]	Foreign Material Other Than Wheat	Total Defects
Barley										
US No. 1	47.0	97.0	2.0	0.2	1.0	4.0	10.0	0.5		
2	45.0	94.0	4.0	0.3	2.0	8.0	15.0	1.0		
3	43.0	90.0	6.0	0.5	3.0	12.0	25.0	2.0		
4	40.0	85.0	8.0	1.0	4.0	18.0	35.0	5.0		
5	36.0	75.0	10.0	3.0	5.0	28.0	75.0	10.0		
Sample[c]	—	—	—	—	—	—	—	—		
Corn										
US No. 1	56.0		3.0	0.1	2.0					
2	54.0		5.0	0.2	3.0					
3	52.0		7.0	0.5	4.0					
4	49.0		10.0	1.0	5.0					
5	46.0		15.0	3.0	7.0					
Sample[c]	—		—	—	—					
Oats										
US No. 1	36.0	97.0		0.1	2.0			2.0		
2	33.0	94.0		0.3	3.0			3.0		
3	30.0	90.0		1.0	4.0			5.0		
4	27.0	80.0		3.0	5.0			10.0		
Sample[c]	—	—		—	—			—		

Rye						
US No. 1	56.0	2.0	0.2	3.0	1.0	
2	54.0	4.0	0.2	6.0	2.0	
3	52.0	7.0	0.5	10.0	4.0	
4	49.0	15.0	3.0	10.0	6.0	
Sample[c]	—	—	—	—	—	
Sorghum, all classes						
US No. 1	57.0	2.0	0.2	2.0	4.0[d]	
2	55.0	5.0	0.5	4.0	8.0	
3	53.0	10.0	1.0	7.0	12.0	
4	51.0	15.0	3.0	10.0	15.0	
Sample[c]	—	—	—	—	—	
Triticale						
US No. 1	48.0	2.0	0.2	2.0	5.0[e]	1.0[f]	5.0
2	45.0	4.0	0.2	4.0	8.0	2.0	8.0
3	43.0	8.0	0.5	7.0	12.0	3.0	12.0
4	41.0	15.0	3.0	10.0	20.0	4.0	20.0
Sample[c]	—	—	—	—	—	—	—

[a] Black barley in barley samples; wild oats in oat samples.

[b] Note that the legal bushel weights are those given for #1 grades; regardless of the volume taken up by a lower grade, it still requires 56 lb of weight/bu of corn, etc.

[c] Sample grades include all grain which does not meet the listed standards for the other grades. In addition to foreign odors or grain which is musty, sour or heating, other specifications may apply to specific grains. Refer to reference listed below for complete details.

[d] Foreign material, broken grains plus other grains.

[e] Plus shrunken kernels.

[f] Other than wheat or rye.

Source: USDA (3).

TABLE 7-4

Average composition of the major cereal grains, dry basis

| Item | Corn | | Wheat | | Rice with Hulls | Rye | Barley | Oats | Milo | Triticale |
	Dent	Opaque-2	Hard Winter	Soft White						
Crude protein, %	10.4	12.6	14.2	11.7	8.0	13.4	13.3	12.8	12.4	14.0
Ether extract, %	4.6	5.4	1.7	1.8	1.7	1.8	2.0	4.7	3.2	4.6
Crude fiber, %	2.5	3.2	2.3	2.1	8.8	2.6	6.3	12.2	2.7	4.0
Ash, %	1.4	1.8	2.0	1.8	5.4	2.1	2.7	3.7	2.1	2.0
NFE, %	81.3	76.9	79.8	82.6	75.6	80.1	75.7	66.6	79.6	75.4
Total sugars, %	1.9		2.9	4.1		4.5	2.5	1.5	1.5	
Starch, %	72.2		63.4	67.2		63.8	64.6	41.2	70.8	
Essential amino acids, % of DM										
Arginine	0.45	0.86	0.76	0.64	0.63	0.6	0.6	0.8	0.4	0.4
Histidine	0.18	0.44	0.39	0.30	0.10	0.3	0.3	0.2	0.3	0.2
Isoleucine	0.45	0.40	0.67	0.44	0.35	0.6	0.6	0.6	0.6	0.3
Leucine	0.99	1.06	1.20	0.86	0.60	0.8	0.9	1.0	1.6	0.4
Lysine	0.18	0.53	0.43	0.37	0.31	0.5	0.6	0.4	0.3	0.3
Phenylalanine	0.45	0.56	0.92	0.57	0.35	0.7	0.7	0.7	0.5	0.3
Threonine	0.36	0.41	0.48	0.37	0.25	0.4	0.4	0.4	0.3	0.2
Tryptophan	0.09	0.16	0.20	0.12	0.12	0.1	0.2	0.2	0.1	0.2
Valine	0.36	0.62	0.79	0.56	0.50	0.7	0.7	0.7	0.6	0.3
Methionine	0.09	0.17	0.21	0.19	0.20	0.2	0.2	0.2	0.1	0.07
Cystine	0.09	0.22	0.29	0.34	0.11	0.2	0.2	0.2	0.2	0.2
Minerals, % of DM										
Calcium	0.02	0.05	0.06	0.09	0.06	0.07	0.06	0.07	0.04	0.1
Phosphorus	0.33	0.24	0.45	0.34	0.45	0.38	0.35	0.30	0.33	0.34
Potassium	0.33	0.30	0.56	0.44	0.25	0.52	0.63	0.42	0.39	0.4
Magnesium	0.12		0.11	0.11	0.11	0.13	0.14	0.19	0.22	

Source: NRC publications.

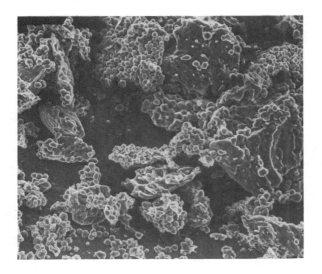

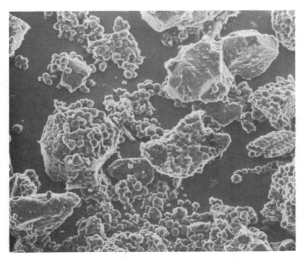

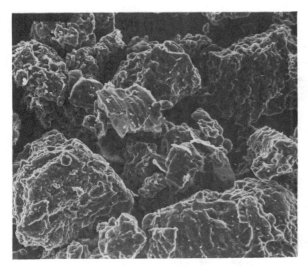

FIGURE 7-3. Electron micrographs of cereal starch from (a) ground corn, (b) milo, and (c) wheat. Note the lack of individual granules in c. (Courtesy of L. H. Harbers, Kansas State University.)

most of the B-vitamins (see Appendix Table 4). Various milling by-products may have higher levels of the B-vitamins and vitamin E. Except for yellow corn, cereal grains are also quite low in carotene.

As a general rule cereal grains are highly digestible, although the extent of digestibility will vary from animal species to species and as the quality of the grain varies. Additional information is given on this subject in a section on comparative evaluation of grains.

Additional information follows on specific cereal grains and other high-energy feeds. Cereal grain by-products that contain less than 20 percent crude protein are discussed in this chapter. Those containing more than 20 percent crude protein are discussed in Ch. 8.

Corn (*Zea mays*)

Corn (Indian corn) is usually referred to as maize in countries other than in North America. In the United States, corn is sometimes called the Golden Grain. This is because in areas where it grows well, corn will produce more digestible energy/unit of land than any other grain crop. Yields in excess of 400 bu/acre (11+ tons) of corn have been realized on small acreages. In addition to the high yield, corn is a very digestible and palatable feed, relished by all domestic animals, and it only rarely causes any nutritional problems when fed to animals.

Corn is commonly classified into 6 groups based on kernel characteristics, namely: dent, flint, flour, sweet, pop, waxy, and pod. Of these, the important commercial types are dent, sweet, and pop corn. Sweet corn, which has a high sugar content, is grown primarily for human consumption, as is pop corn. Dent corn is the main feed grain variety, and most of it is produced from double cross hybrid seed varieties (Fig. 7–4). Many different hybrids are available that have been developed for specific areas or seasonal needs, the result being that corn, as a major crop, is adaptable to a much wider geographical area than it used to be.

A diagram of a dent corn kernel is shown in Fig. 7–5. The endosperm, which is primarily starch, makes up about 85 percent; embryo and scutellum, 10 percent; and the pericarp and other parts, 5 percent. These various parts will be referred to in later sections dealing with milling by-products of the grains.

The chemical composition of corn has been studied in great detail; a very limited amount of data is presented in Table 7–4; other informa-

FIGURE 7-4. A hybrid corn field with a high yield of grain. (Courtesy of USDA.)

pigments that are of interest to the poultry industry because they contribute color to the skin of the bird and yolk of the egg. Yellow corn is generally preferred for feeding, consequently very little white corn is now produced in the United States, although it is more widely used in other countries. White corn produced is often used for preparation of corn meal for human food.

tion may be found in sources such as reference 5. With regard to protein, about 73 percent of the total protein is found in the endosperm and most of the remainder, 24 percent, is in the embryo. The protein in the embryo is of a better quality and is made up of a mixture of glutelin, globulins, albumins, and others. In the endosperm the principal protein is zein, a relatively insoluble protein that makes up about half of the total kernel protein. This protein is low in several of the essential amino acids, particularly lysine and trypotophan; the total protein of corn is deficient in these amino acids for monogastric animal species and requires supplementation for adequate performance. This is illustrated clearly in Table 7–5. In addition, the low tryptophan (which is a precursor for niacin) plus the low niacin content will lead, eventually, to a niacin deficiency and pellagra in simple-stomached animals depending on corn as a major dietary constituent. N fertilization has been shown to increase protein content (Table 7–6), but the increase is accompanied by a decrease in protein quality. This is a result of a relative increase in the zein fraction.

White and yellow corn have similar compositions, except that yellow corn has a fair content of cryptoxanthin, a precursor of vitamin A. Yellow corn also contains xanthophylls, yellow

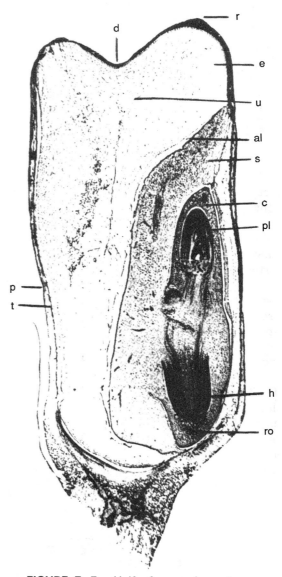

FIGURE 7-5. Half of a nearly mature dent corn kernel showing dent (d), remnant of style (r), endosperm (e), unfilled portion of immature endosperm (u), aleurone (al), scutellum (s), plumule (pl), hypocotyl and radicle (h), testa or true seed coat (t), and pericarp (p). The germ comprises the entire darker area including the scutellum (s), coleoptile (c), and root-cap (ro). (Courtesy of USDA.)

TABLE 7-5

Comparative performance of pigs fed corn, corn supplemented with adequate protein, or some of the experimental varieties of corn

Treatment	Protein, %	Daily Gain, g	Feed/Gain Ratio
Corn + soybean meal	16.0	520	2.16
Corn	9.6	91	8.94
Opaque-2 corn	9.4	310	3.32
Floury-2 corn	9.9	91	6.63
Corn + soybean meal	12.0	248	3.17
Opaque-2 + soybean meal	12.0	455	2.59
Floury-2 + soybean meal	12.0	323	3.14

Source: Pond and Maner (6).

TABLE 7-6

Effect of various fertilizer N levels on crude protein content (dry basis) of corn

Pounds N/Ac	Crude Protein, %	
	Farm 1	Farm 2
0	8.1	9.1
60	10.2	9.8
100	10.1	10.2
180	11.4	10.3
340	12.2	10.6

Source: Sunde (7).

The content of other nutrients in corn is similar to that in other cereal grains (see introduction), except that corn is particularly deficient in Ca.

Several genetic mutants of corn have been isolated and are being developed. One of these, known as opaque-2 (or high-lysine corn), is of particular interest because it has a high level of lysine and increased levels of most other essential amino acids. This change results from a reduction in zein and an increase in glutelin, a protein found in both the endosperm and the germ. The result is an improvement in the quality of the corn protein. Performance of monogastric species may be improved considerably by use of this mutant when livestock is not given supplementary protein (see Table 7-5). However, opaque-2 has not been shown to have added value for ruminants. Yields of opaque-2 are not equivalent, at this time, to regular corn, nor are prices proportionately higher, so interest of corn

producers has not resulted in a marked increase in production of this mutant.

A second mutant of interest is known as floury-2. Although it also has higher levels of lysine and some of the other essential amino acids, comparative experiments do not indicate it to be as good as the opaque-2 strain (Table 7-5). Other experimental mutants include those designated as high-fat, high-amylose, sugary-2, and brown midrib.

Harvesting of feed corn in the United States is now done with equipment that picks and shells the ear in the field (Fig. 7-6). This reduces the bulk of the finished product, and the cobs are now harvested only on a small percentage of the crop. This has resulted in changed feeding practices, particularly with hogs and cattle, as it used to be relatively common to feed ear corn to hogs and ground corn and cob meal to cattle. Other information on processing methods will be discussed in Ch. 11 or chapters on specific animals.

Spoiled and moldy feeds were mentioned in Ch. 4. Corn, of course, is subject to various molds, smuts, blights, and other problems. Relatively recent evidence indicates that some of the blights, which are severe problems in

FIGURE 7-6. A modern grain combine which, in this case, is harvesting and shelling corn in one continuous process. (Courtesy of Deere & Co., Moline, IL.)

some years, do not cause any deterioration in nutritive quality of the grain; they would, of course, result in reduced yields of grain and less forage if harvested for silage.

Grain Sorghum (*Sorghum vulgare*)

Several different sorghum varieties (all *Sorghum vulgare*) are used for seed production. These include milo, various kafirs, sorgo, sumac, hegari, darso, feterita, and cane. Other nongrain types include forage sorghums, Sudan grass, and broomcorn. Milo (Fig. 7–7) is a favorite in the United States in drier areas because it is a short plant adaptable to harvesting with grain combines. Development of hybrid varieties, primarily milo and kafir crosses, which have higher yields has increased production/unit of land greatly in recent years in the United States. On a worldwide basis, most of the sorghum seed production is in the United States, India, China, and Argentina, with lesser amounts in other countries, primarily in Africa.

FIGURE 7–7. Milo growing in Western Kansas.

The various sorghum varieties are able to withstand heat and drought better than are most grain crops. In addition, sorghum is resistant to pests such as root worm and the corn borer and is adaptable to a wide variety of soil types. Consequently, sorghum is grown in many areas where corn or other cereal crops do not do well. Sorghum yields less grain/unit of land than corn where corn thrives. The seed from all varieties of sorghum is small (2.5–3.5 × 4 mm) and relatively hard and usually requires some processing for optimum animal utilization (see Ch. 11).

Chemically, grain sorghums are similar to corn. Protein content averages about 11 percent (dry basis), but it is apt to be more variable than that of corn. Sorghum grains contain an alcohol-soluble protein, kafirin, which is similar to zein in corn. Lysine and threonine are said to be the most limiting amino acids, but some studies with turkeys and chickens indicate that methionine may be limiting (8). Content of other nutrients is similar to corn, but the starch content is somewhat lower and more variable than that of corn.

Different types of sorghum have been identified and developed by plant breeders following introduction of hybrids in the early 1960s. Those currently in use include normal, bird-resistant, waxy, and heteroyellow endosperm (hybrids) types. Some data on digestibility by sheep and cattle of the crude protein and starch from these different types is shown in Table 7–7. In nearly all cases where comparisons have been made, the brown, bird-resistant sorghums result in appreciably lower digestibility and lower animal performance than do other sorghums. The heteroyellow endosperm types generally show improved feeding values over the older, nonyellow cultivars. Waxy cultivars consistently give better feed efficiencies than do nonwaxy types. It might be noted that waxy cereal starches are

TABLE 7-7

Digestibility of crude protein and starch in different sorghum types by sheep and cattle (percent)

Sorghum Type	Sheep		Cattle	
	CP	Starch	CP	Starch
Normal	71.9	90.4	46.3	76.0
Bird-resistant	61.4	82.6	23.9	60.0
Waxy	71.6	87.3	62.1	75.7
Heterowaxy	68.4	90.4	57.7	84.4
Heteroyellow	73.4	89.0	51.8	76.9

Source: Rooney and Pflugfelder (9).

among the most digestible of all starches and that digestibility of a starch is generally inversely proportional to amylose content (9).

Most feeding studies indicate that sorghum grains are usually worth somewhat less than corn, although some data indicate an equal or higher value for swine and poultry. The presence of more protein bodies among the starch granules than in corn may affect utilization by some animal species. Fortunately, with a good job of processing, the feeding value of most sorghum grains closely approaches that of corn grain.

Other studies of interest on sorghum grains have shown that lightweight grain has a lower feeding value (and more fiber) than that of heavy grains (weight/bu). Other research on weathered grain with varying degrees of sprout damage, discoloration, or molds showed that weathered grain was less palatable to sheep, possibly because of dust, but there was little difference in digestibility between good-quality and weathered grain (10).

Barley (*Hordenum vulgare* or *H. distichon*)

Barley is widely grown in Europe and the cool, dry climates of North America and Asia. Although a small amount goes into human food and a very substantial percentage is used in the brewing industry in the form of malt, most of the barley is used for animal feeding. Even so, it accounted for only 4.4 percent of grain tonnage fed in the United States in 1986 (1).

Barley contains more total protein (11-16 percent dry basis) and higher levels of lysine, tryptophan, methionine, and cystine than corn (Table 7–4), but its feeding value for ruminants is appreciably less in most cases than that of corn or sorghum. This is in part because of its lower starch content (50–60 percent) and somewhat higher fiber content and the lower digestible energy.

Barley is a very palatable feed for horses and ruminants, particularly when steam rolled before feeding, and few digestive problems result from its use, although it is more prone to cause bloat in feedlot cattle when used as a major portion of the ration than are the other cereal grains. Barley, as the only grain source, will not allow maximum gains or optimum feed efficiency for swine, and the fiber level is too high for use of more than small amounts in poultry rations. There are also appreciable differences in chick performance on different cultivars.

Hull-less varieties of barley are roughly equivalent to wheat or corn and are thus more suitable for swine and poultry feeding; however, not much hull-less barley is produced. Pearled barley, which has had the hull and most of the bran removed, has a high feeding value, but it is used primarily as a human food.

A considerable amount of malting barley is grown. Such barleys are generally higher in protein content with heavier bushel weights than feed grain varieties (Table 7–8). The comparison between malting barley and feed grain barley shown in the table does not indicate any particular improvement in daily gain, although feed efficiency was improved slightly when the malting barley was fed to finishing cattle. Note also that there were minor differences in composition of the grain and in animal performance with barley grown under irrigated or dryland conditions. Other data from the same experiment station show that daily gain of fattening cattle decreased as the bushel weight of barley decreased. Feed efficiency was also less on the lightweight barley. This information was confirmed by another study, shown in Table 7–8.

A high-lysine barley containing 25 percent more lysine than common barley shows some promise as an energy source for nonruminant species. However, some of the high-lysine cultivars have been shown to be lower in some of the other essential amino acids (12), so the overall improvement may be less than anticipated from the higher lysine content.

Oats (*Avena sativa*)

Although oats is the third-most important cereal feed grain in the United States, it accounted for only 6 percent of feed grain use in 1986 (Table 7–2). Oats does not yield as much as the other grains and, considering the hull of the whole grain, the feeding value is relatively lower than for some of the other grains. Most of the world production is concentrated in northern Europe and North America. Only about 5 percent of the production goes into human food.

Three varieties of oats dominate the U.S. market. White oats account for most of the production and are grown primarily in the corn belt and northern plains. Red oats are grown in the south, and grey oats are grown in the Pacific Northwest.

The protein content of oats is relatively high (11–14 percent), and the amino acid distribution is the most favorable of any of the cereal

TABLE 7-8

Composition and steer performance when fed two different types of barley and steer performance when fed light, medium, and heavy barley

| | Barley Type[a] | | | |
| | 2-Row Malting | | 6-Row Feed | |
Item	Irrigated	Dryland	Irrigated	Dryland
Barley composition				
Crude protein, %	12.7	12.5	10.6	12.4
Crude fiber, %	4.5	4.4	6.7	6.9
Calcium, %	0.05	0.07	0.06	0.04
Phosphorus, %	0.45	0.47	0.38	0.31
Weight, g/ℓ	702	698	625	634
Animal performance				
Daily feed consumed, kg DM	9.9	9.3	10.0	9.9
Daily gain, kg	1.15	1.12	1.13	1.09
Feed/gain ratio	8.61	8.30	8.85	9.08

| | Weight of Barley Fed[b] | | |
Item	Light	Medium	Heavy
Barley composition			
Crude protein, %	16.1	15.3	11.1
AD fiber, %	9.0	5.8	5.5
Weight, g/ℓ	469	554	666
Steer performance			
Dry matter intake, kg	9.34	9.15	8.89
Daily gain, kg	1.62	1.72	1.69
Feed/gain ratio	5.80	5.32	5.26

[a]From Hinman (11). The finishing ration was 81% steam-rolled barley, 10% chopped alfalfa hay, 7% corn silage, and 2% vitamin-mineral supplement.

[b]From Grimson et al. (46). Barley made up 85% of the ration DM. The remainder was made up of barley silage and a vitamin-mineral mix.

grains, the ranking generally being in the order of oats first, followed by barley, wheat, corn, rice, rye, sorghum, and millet. Oats is still relatively deficient in methionine, histidine, tryptophan, and lysine. Oats is not widely used for feeding of poultry because of the hull, which makes up an average of 28 percent of the kernel. The hull may be as high as 45 percent of the total weight in lightweight oats. Because of this, oats with heavy test weights are more desirable for feeding, because there is an inverse relationship between test weight and percentage of hull.

In addition to the amount of hull, the hull itself is quite fibrous (31 percent fiber), and it is poorly digested. As a result, the fiber content of the whole grain is highest of any of the cereal grains, and the starch content is the lowest. Even when the seed is ground, it results in a very bulky feed, and including a high percentage in the ration does not allow maximal feed intake for high-producing animals. Oats is of some value for young pigs in protecting them

from stomach ulcers. The hulls contain an alcohol-soluble factor which provides the protective function. For older swine, oats is often used for finishing swine, particularly where it is desired to limit the consumption of energy so that the pig does not lay down too much back fat (see Ch. 21). For ruminants and horses, oats is a favored feed for breeding stock or in creep feeds for young animals. However, for feedlot cattle oats do not supply sufficient energy for most rapid gains.

There are hull-less varieties of oats, but they are rarely grown. Oat groats (whole seed minus the hulls) are comparable or better than corn in feeding value, but the price is not usually attractive for animal feeding.

Wheat (*Triticum* spp)

Wheat, like rice, is grown normally for the human food market, and nearly all commonly grown varieties were developed with flour mill-

FIGURE 7–8. Grain combines harvesting wheat in the Pacific Northwest.

ing qualities in mind rather than feed values. However, there are some feed grain varieties that have been developed in recent years. Wheat is a versatile crop that is adapted to a wide variety of environmental conditions. The tonnage produced on a worldwide basis rivals that produced from rice, and wheat is grown in many different areas (Fig. 7–8).

Wheat is divided into hard and soft wheats. Within each type there may be varieties that are classed as winter or spring wheats. Winter wheats are normally planted in the fall, while spring wheats are planted in the spring in areas where the winter is more severe than where winter wheats are grown. Soft wheats may be white or red. The major difference between soft and hard wheats is that hard wheats are higher in protein content (13-16 percent) and contain more gluten and gliaden proteins, which provide the sticky consistency important in bread making. White wheats contain less protein (8-11 percent) and are used more commonly for pastries, in breads which do not require the high gluten levels, or in mixtures of flour with hard wheat (all-purpose flour).

The amino acid distribution of wheat is more favorable than that of corn, especially for lysine, tryptophan, methionine, cystine, and histidine. Soft wheats generally have lower levels of the essential amino acids (as percent of dry matter), but they are still a much better source than corn of those amino acids listed for hard wheats, except for tryptophan.

Wheat is a very palatable grain for most species. As an energy source, most comparative studies indicate that it does not produce quite as rapid a gain as corn does, but it very frequently produces more efficient gain than corn does, and, in some cases, the carcasses of fattened cattle are apt to have less subcutaneous fat but equally as good marbling as corn produces when wheat is fed as a high percentage of the diet (Table 7–9). If fed in large amounts, ground wheat tends to form a pasty mass on the beaks of birds. For ruminant animals, wheat is more prone to produce acidosis than any other cereal grain. Thus it is advisable to adapt animals to wheat over a period of time, and many nutritionists advise not feeding over 50 percent of the diet to fattening cattle and less than this to fattening lambs.

Feeding "new" wheat can cause problems in poultry and other species, if comments from producers and mill operators are correct. How-

TABLE 7-9

Comparison of triticale, corn, and wheat in finishing rations for cattle

	Grain Source[a]		
Item	Corn	Wheat	Triticale
Daily feed consumed, kg	10.4	9.1	9.1
Daily gain, kg	1.33	1.25	1.13
Feed/gain ratio	7.81	7.24	8.02
Carcass marbling score	7.5	8.1	7.8
Adjusted fat thickness, cm	1.26	0.97	1.04

[a]Rations were 74% grain, 15% cottonseed hulls, 10% cottonseed meal, and 1% salt.
Source: Reddy et al. (13).

TABLE 7-10

Comparison of wheat and sprouted wheat with barley in finishing rations for cattle

	Grain Source[a]		
Item	Barley	Wheat	Sprouted Wheat
Feed consumption, kg/d	9.44	9.16	9.08
Daily gain, kg	1.32	1.30	1.29
Feed/gain ratio	7.15	7.05	7.05

[a]Rations contained the following amounts of steam-rolled grain: barley, 77% barley; wheat, 50% wheat, 27% barley; sprouted wheat, 50% wheat which was 58% sprouted, 27% barley; the remainder was made up of 10% grass-legume hay, 10% supplement, and 3% cane molasses.
Source: Preston et al. (14).

ever, research data on the topic are not available. If (and when) such problems occur, the occurrence would presumably be related to solubility of the starch granules and/or the protein matrix surrounding the granules.

In more humid areas, weather conditions often result in lodging (plants fall over and mat on the ground). If the grain is not harvested quickly, the grain may sprout; this makes it unfit for bread making and, consequently, reduces the market value. However, there does not seem to be much effect, if any, on the feeding value of wheat which has a high percentage of sprouted kernels (Table 7-10). Molding would be likely to occur under such conditions, however, and mold might reduce the feeding value in some conditions.

Triticale

Triticale is a cereal grain derived from crosses between wheat and rye. Its nutrient content (Table 7-4) is similar to that of hard wheat or rye with, perhaps, more fiber. It does not have a particularly good distribution of amino acids such as lysine, methionine, and cystine. The feeding value is similar for nonruminant species to that of wheat (6), but with some supplemental lysine, some cultivars can be equal to a corn-soy diet for pigs, according to recent data. Note in Table 7-11 that gains, feed conversion, and back fat thickness were quite similar for pigs finished on triticale + lysine or corn-soy diets. In a recent study comparing corn and triticale, these two grains were fed in a partially purified diet in which the only source of protein was from the grain (16). In this instance (which may not be characteristic of a complete diet), the DE value for the corn was 4.08 kcal/g, and for each of two triticale varieties the DE values were 3.77 and 3.56 kcal/g. Respective ME values were 3.66, 3.19, and 3.12 kcal/g. The feeding value of triticale for finishing cattle appears to be somewhat lower than that of wheat, and the efficiency appears to be lower (Table 7-9). As with some other grains, triticale is subject to ergot infestation (ergot is a toxic fungus that replaces some of the kernels). At present, triticale is not grown widely as a feed grain. Time will tell how it does.

TABLE 7-11

Comparison of corn-soy rations with triticale for finishing swine

	Ration	
Item	Corn-Soy	Triticale + Lysine
Weight gain, kg	35.9	35.2
Av. daily gain, kg	0.92	0.90
Feed/gain ratio	3.23	3.30
Av. back fat thickness, cm	2.82	2.87

Source: Hale and Utley (15).

Rye (*Secale cerale*)

Rye is an important bread grain in northern Europe. It has a composition similar to that of hard wheat with, perhaps, a slightly higher protein content. Rye is generally said to be less palatable than most other cereal grains, and it is more susceptible to ergot than is wheat. Rye is not normally fed to poultry or, if so, in only small amounts. Studies with poultry indicate that rye contains at least two detrimental factors—an appetite-depressing factor in the bran and a growth-depressing factor in all fractions of the grain (16). For swine, data indicate a value of about 80 percent of corn for young animals (6).

TABLE 7-12

Comparative value of rye and barley for lactating dairy cows

Item	Grain Source[a]		
	Barley	25% Rye	50% Rye
Dry matter consumed, kg/d			
Concentrate mix	10.9	10.3	10.4
Total	20.6	19.4	19.1
FCM production, kg/d	21.6	21.3	19.8

[a]Concentrate contained 80% grain of which 5% was oats and the remainder contained soybean meal, molasses, and minerals.
Source: Sharma et al. (17).

Rye is often said to be unpalatable and difficult to masticate for ruminants when fed in large amounts. However, studies with lactating dairy cows (Table 7–12) do not indicate any problem in feeding up to 25 percent of the concentrate mix as rye (very little ergot was found), nor was there any effect on fat-corrected milk production when fed at this level. However, a study from the same laboratory showed that daily gain and feed consumption of calves were reduced when rye made up 60 percent of the starter mix and was fed from 6 to 18 weeks of age. Roasting the rye grain restored performance to the level obtained with no rye. Other relatively recent studies with cattle suggest that rye should be restricted to perhaps 40 percent or less of the diet if depressing effects on performance are to be avoided.

Rice (*Oryza sativa*)

Rice is grown in many areas of the world. Although most of the rice is grown in areas that can be flooded during active growth of the plant, dryland varieties of rice are also grown. Rice is always grown as a food grain (for human use) and, according to the Rice Council, more than 40,000 types of rice are grown in one place or another. As a food grain, rice is not normally cheap enough to use as a feed grain (for animal use). Occasionally, rough rice (unmilled) is available at attractive prices for animal feeding. Rough rice has about 8 percent crude protein, 9 percent fiber, and 1.7 percent ether extract (Table 7–4). The hulls make up about 25 percent of the kernel weight, and they greatly reduce the energy value and are, themselves, almost totally indigestible.

Millet

Several different types of millet are grown, primarily in Asia and west Africa, for human food. They include a variety of small-grain cereal plants. In the United States, proso (*Panicum milliaceum*), a plant resembling some sorghums, is sometimes grown for a feed grain and is reported to be intermediate in feeding value between oats and corn. Others such as foxtail millet (*Setaria italica*), pearl millet (*Pennisetum glaucum* or *typhoideum*), Japanese millet (*Echinochloa crusgalli*), or finger millet (*Eleusine coracana*) are used for human food in most countries where they are grown or in other areas for forage or such things as bird seed or beer. Other than the uses mentioned, the millets are not an important source of animal feed. Recent evidence with chickens (47) indicates that ME values for pearl millet may be underestimated by as much as 21 percent, depending on which cultivar was fed.

RELATIVE FEEDING VALUES OF CEREAL GRAINS

Although a considerable amount of information has been given on the nutrient values of the cereal grains, some additional information is in order. Cereal grains are primarily a source of energy, thus energy content is the most important basis of comparison, and corn is generally used as a standard against which the others are compared. If the relative value of corn is set at 100, the value of the other grains is usually lower, as illustrated in Table 7–13. This is a reflection, in part, of the differences in crude fiber and resultant lower digestibility of those grains having higher fiber levels. This can be confirmed by removing the hulls of grains such as oats and barley. The remaining material (oat groats or pearled barley) is highly digestible. The starch of corn is also highly digestible. In addition, as fiber increases, the content of starch and other readily available carbohydrates decreases (Table 7–4). The fat content has some ef-

TABLE 7-13

Relative value as compared to corn of the other cereal grains for crude protein content and metabolizable energy as shown by NRC

Grain	Crude Protein	ME		
		Ruminants	Swine	Poultry
Corn	100	100	100	100
Barley	124	96.2	88.6	74.5
Millet, proso	118	96.2	89.0	86.5
Milo	114	98.8	96.3	96.7
Oats	122	87.1	80.9	75.0
Triticale	161	96.2	91.2	92.2
Rye	127	96.2	89.3	78.6
Wheat[a]	132	101.5	97.4	94.8

[a]Hard red winter wheat.
Source: NRC (18).

fect on energy values, of course, and it is also possible that there may be differences in utilization of the amylose and amylopectin in the different grains. Evidence also shows that starch granules in mature grains are more digestible by rumen microorganisms than for less mature kernels. Relative feeding values may be affected by various feed processing methods (not shown in Table 7–13) because some grains are improved to a greater extent than others (see Ch. 11).

Corn and milo have less protein than the other feed grains and thus are not ranked as high on a relative basis as a protein source. The quality of corn protein is also low because it is low in lysine and lower than most grains in tryptophan.

Research has gone on with feed grains for many years, but results are still reported rather

frequently. Some data from three relatively recent reports on swine are given in Table 7–14. These data are shown to illustrate the problem of comparative evaluation. In the first two experiments, pigs were fed the test grains in addition to a basal diet believed to have an excess of required nutrients other than energy. In the third experiment pigs were fed grain plus a mineral-vitamin supplement. The latter experiment would be a better estimate of the energy *and* amino acid contribution, while the former would be only a measure of energy contribution.

In the author's opinion, comparative trials should always include a "standard," such as corn. In addition, if we are dealing with complete diets, the nontest portion of the diet should be adjusted to compensate for deficiencies other than energy, since energy is the major nutrient to be concerned with. Such procedures would provide more reliable data for comparing one grain against another as an energy source. With our current knowledge of the nutrient content of grains and of animal requirements, it is not logical to feed grain by itself; neither is it logical to evaluate grains without appropriate supplementation.

MILLING BY-PRODUCTS OF CEREAL GRAINS

The milling of cereal grains for production of flour and various other food or industrial products results in the production of a number of by-products used in the feed trade. For the United States, official descriptions (names, numbers, description of the product) are published by the American Feed Control Officials, Inc. (22). Es-

TABLE 7-14

Comparative value of cereal grains for pigs

Measurement	Grains						Reference No.
	Corn	Oats	Wheat	Barley	Triticale	Milo	
Daily gain[a], g	293	259					19
Feed conversion	1.17	1.36					
Dig. energy, kcal/g	3.43	2.84					
Daily gain[a], g			251	230			20
Feed conversion			1.25	1.27			
Dig. energy, kcal/g			3.82	3.76			
Dig. energy[b], kcal/g	3.80		3.71	3.38	3.60		21
Dig. energy, kcal/g	3.84	3.18	3.86	3.52		3.82	NRC

[a]Grains were fed at an average of 1.5% of body weight in addition to a basal diet fed at 3% of body weight/day. All nutrients except energy were considered to be fed in excess of requirements.
[b]Grains were fed with only a mineral and vitamin supplement.

sentially all of these products are listed in Appendix Table 1 with data on nutrient content. Therefore, less information will be presented than has been given previously on the cereal grains. In most cases the official description will be given as a minimum.

Grains are milled either by a dry milling process or wet milling processes (in addition to grinding, rolling, and other processes that may be done to feed grains). The dry milling methods are designed primarily to grind away the hulls (as with barley and rice) or to remove the outer layers of the seed to expose the starch endosperm for flour production. Wet milling methods are intended for the production of such products as starch, sugar, syrup, or oil for human food from corn and, to a much lesser extent, sorghum grains. The type of processes involved are illustrated in Fig. 7–9. Several different by-products result that are used for animal feeds.

Wheat By-Products

With wheat, milling by-products account for about 28 percent of the intact kernel, the remainder being flour prepared for human food. Wheat millfeeds are usually classified and named on the basis of decreasing fiber as bran, middlings, mill run, shorts, red dog, and wheat germ meal. The amount of each produced depends on the type of mill and the type of wheat being milled. Formula feed manufacturers use about 90 percent of the millfeed in the United States, with the largest users being the poultry industry. Typical specifications on wheat mill-feeds are given in Table 7–15, and a brief description follows.

Wheat bran is the coarse outer covering of the wheat kernel as separated from cleaned and scoured wheat in the usual process of commercial milling. The appearance of bran is that of a flaky brown material. About 45 percent of total wheat millfeed is comprised of bran. **Wheat middlings** consist of the layer of the kernel just

inside the outer bran covering (aleurone), endosperm, and bran particles. The appearance is that of a brownish, finely ground meal. Midds usually amount to about 40 percent of total millfeed. Lysine and threonine appear to be the most limiting amino acids in the midds of hard red spring wheat. **Wheat mill run** is a blend of bran and middlings. **Shorts** consist of fine particles of bran, germ, flour, and tailings. They contain somewhat more flour than midds and have the appearance of a finely ground meal containing somewhat less brownish material than midds. **Red dog** consists of mill tailings together with some fine particles of bran, germ, and flour. There are more floury particles than in any other millfeeds. The appearance is much like grayish flour flecked with small brown bran particles; red dog accounts for only 4 percent of total millfeed. **Wheat germ** is classed as a protein supplement and will be listed and discussed in Ch. 9. Although these various milling by-products are supposed to be standardized, this is not always done, with the result that there may be more variability than indicated in Table 7–14.

Wheat millfeeds, particularly bran, are relatively bulky and laxative feeds, but they are quite palatable to animals except when used at a very high percentage (more than 40 to 50 percent) in rations for fullfed cattle, when the fine particle size may decrease consumption. They generally contain more protein than the parent grain, and protein quality is usually somewhat improved, although wheat millfeeds are apt to be relatively deficient in lysine and methionine as well as some other essential amino acids.

The bulky nature of wheat millfeeds tends to restrict intake by animals, thus maximal energy intake cannot be achieved on rations containing high levels. It might also be noted that the energy values of wheat millfeeds have not been as well defined as might be desired. The available data do indicate that ruminants utilize the energy to a greater extent than do monogastric species. Recent data with swine (Table 7–16) show that pigs did quite well when wheat midds replaced up to 30 percent (by weight) of the corn in one experiment and up to 60 percent in finishing rations in a second experiment (not shown). Maximum protein utilization was at the 20 percent level and maximum ME at the 40 percent level. Overall ME was estimated to be 2.99 kcal/g, somewhat lower than the NRC (18) value of 3.25 kcal/g. In a recent report on lactating dairy cows (24), cows were fed rations with 60 percent concentrate. When the concen-

TABLE 7–15

Usual specifications on wheat mill feeds

Wheat Mill Feeds	Min. Protein, %	Min. Fat, %	Max. Fiber, %
Bran	13.5-15	2.5	12.0
Middlings	10-14	3	9.5
Mill run	14-16	2	9.5
Shorts	14-16	3.5	7
Red dog	13.5-15	2	4

TABLE 7-16

Effect of increasing levels of wheat midds on performance of growing-finishing pigs

Item	Percentage of Midds Replacing Corn			
	0	10	20	30
Daily gain, kg	0.65	0.66	0.67	0.66
Daily feed, kg	1.82	1.85	1.85	2.00
Feed:gain	2.79	2.81	2.72	3.12
Back fat, cm	2.7	2.6	2.7	2.6

Source: Errickson et al. (23).

trate was altered to contain 20 or 40 percent wheat midds in one experiment or 40 or 60 percent in the second (with, by calculation, isocaloric diets), the cows consumed the rations with 40 percent of the concentrate as wheat midds without any change in production. However, 60 percent midds was accompanied by a reduction in milk production.

These millfeeds are also relatively good sources of most of the water-soluble vitamins, except for niacin, which is almost entirely unavailable. The Ca content is low, but the content of P, Mg, and Mn is relatively high. Most of the P is found as phytate P which is only partially available to simple-stomached animals; some data indicate that heat treatment may increase the P availability. The content of trace minerals is also usually higher than in the parent kernel.

The bulk of the wheat millfeeds is used for feeding poultry, swine, and dairy cattle. When available, bran is a favored feedstuff for all breeding classes of ruminants and for horses.

Corn Millfeeds

With dry milling methods, the primary products are corn meal, hominy, grits, or flour (foodstuffs). Feedstuffs include hominy feed, corn flour, and corn bran. **Hominy feed** is a mixture of corn bran, corn germ, and part of the starch portion of either white or yellow corn kernels or a mixture thereof as produced in the manufacture of pearl hominy, hominy grits, or corn meal for table use, and it must contain no less than 4 percent crude fat. It is also referred to as **corn grits by-product.** Hominy feed is the most important feed on a volume basis. It may be sold also as solvent-extracted hominy feed, in which case the fat content is appreciably lower. Hominy feed is an excellent energy source for both monogastric and ruminant animals and is considered equal to or superior to whole corn as an energy source.

Corn flour is the fine-sized, hard, flinty portions of ground corn containing little or none of the bran or germ. **Corn bran** is the outer coating of the corn kernel, with little or none of the starchy part or germ. **Gelatinized corn flour** is obtained from the endosperm of corn which has been gelatinized and reduced to a finely ground meal and must contain not more than 1 percent crude fiber. **Corn germ** is classified as a protein supplement because of its crude protein content.

As indicated in Fig. 7–9, different products are available from the wet milling process. When 100 kg of corn are processed with wet milling, the average yields of products are as shown (kg): pearl starch, 62.5; oil, 2.86; animal feed, 34.6. About 71 kg of syrup or 49 kg of refined corn sugar may be obtained from the starch (25). Of course, the starch, sugar, syrup, and corn oil are used as human food. Except for starch molasses and liquefied corn product, which are discussed in a section on liquid feeds, the other feedstuffs from wet milling of corn—gluten feed, gluten meal, corn germ meal, condensed fer-

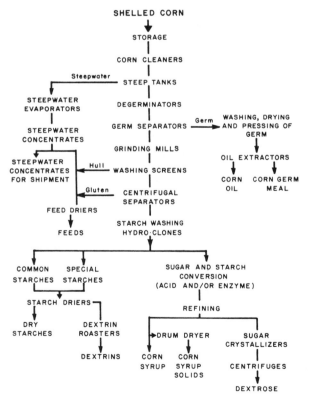

FIGURE 7–9. A schematic outline showing the processes involved in the wet milling of corn. As indicated, the wet-milling process is used primarily for starch, sugar, and syrup production. Other feed ingredients produced are by-products of the process.

mented corn extractives, and hydrolyzed corn protein—are classed as protein supplements and will be discussed in Ch. 8.

Other Cereal Millfeeds

Some sorghum grain is wet milled in the same manner as corn. Feedstuffs classed as energy feeds from the process would include **grain sorghum grits,** which consists of the hard flinty portions of sorghum containing little or no bran or germ. **Grain sorghum mill feed** is a mixture of grain sorghum bran, germ, part of the starch portion of the sorghum kernel, or a mixture thereof as produced in the manufacture of sorghum grits and refined meal and flour. It must contain not less than 5 percent crude fat and not more than 6 percent crude fiber.

By-products from barley include **barley hulls** (a roughage), **pearl barley by-product,** which is the entire by-product resulting from the manufacture of pearl barley, and **barley mill by-product,** which is the entire residue from the milling of barley flour and is composed of barley hulls and barley middlings. As with barley, oats are processed primarily to separate the hull from the groat (inner portion of the kernel). **Oat groats** are defined as cleaned oats with the hulls removed. The groat is used both for food and feed products. **Feeding oat meal** is obtained in the manufacture of rolled oat groats or rolled oats and consists of broken rolled oat groats, oat groat chips, and floury portions of the groats, with only such quantity of finely ground oat hulls as is unavoidable in the usual process of commercial milling. It must not contain more than 4 percent crude fiber. **Oat hulls** consists primarily of the outer coverings of oats, obtained in the milling of table cereals or in the groating of oats. **Oat mill by-product** is the by-product obtained in the manufacture of oat groats, consisting of oat hulls and particles of the groat and containing not more than 22 percent crude fiber. **Clipped oat by-product** is obtained in the manufacture of clipped oats. It may contain the light chaffy material broken from the end of the hulls, empty hulls, light immature oats, and dust. It must not contain an excessive amount of oat hulls.

Rice is also milled primarily to remove the hull from the kernel. **Rice bran** is the pericarp or bran layer and germ of the rice with only such quantity of hull fragments, chipped, broken, or brewers rice, and calcium carbonate as is unavoidable in the regular milling. It must not contain more than 13 percent crude fiber. **Solvent extracted rice bran** is also produced. **Rice polishing** is a by-product of rice obtained in the milling operation of brushing the grain to polish the kernel. Both of these two products are excellent feed materials comparatively high in fat (unless extracted), but the fat is oxidized easily unless it has been stabilized. Other by-products include **rice by-products fractions,** which is obtained by screening and aspirating ground rice hulls. It is used primarily as a pelleting aid and is composed of such fine particles of ground rice hulls, spongy parenchyma, and minute amounts of rice flour, rice germ, pericarp, and rice starch as will pass an 80 mesh screen. It contains not less than 5 percent crude protein, 1.5 percent crude fat, and not more than 25 percent crude fiber. **Rice hulls** are also a by-product, but they are of little if any value as a feed because of extremely low digestibility unless they are processed with steam heat and added chemicals.

With regard to rye milling, by-products include **rye mill run,** which is obtained in the usual milling of rye flour and consists principally of the mill run of the outer covering of the rye kernel and the rye germ with small quantities of rye flour and aleurone. Rye mill run must not contain more than 9.5 percent crude fiber. **Rye middlings** consist of rye feed and rye red dog combined in the proportions obtained in the usual process of milling rye flour and must not contain more than 8.5 percent crude fiber. Only very limited amounts of either are available.

Most of the millfeeds obtained from oats, barley, rice, and rye are relatively high in fiber or higher than the parent grain. The quality of the protein is not particularly appealing for monogastric species, although most millfeeds contain more protein than the original grain (hulls excluded).

Grain screenings is the name given to the foreign material obtained in the process of cleaning grains and seeds. They are likely to be extremely variable in composition and may contain broken seeds, numerous weed seeds, and other materials. When used in commerce, they must be identified as **grain screenings, mixed screenings,** and **chaff and/or dust.**

HIGH-CARBOHYDRATE LIQUID FEEDS

Molasses and Similar Liquids

Molasses is a major by-product of sugar production, the bulk of it coming from sugar cane, but other sources include sugar beets, citrus fruits, starch, and wood. Various molasses types are standardized in terms of degrees Brix. This is determined by use of a refractometer and corresponds very closely to percentage of dry matter. In commercial use, molasses (cane) is usually adjusted to about 25 percent water content. Molasses may be dried for mixing into dry diets, although at appreciably higher costs.

Cane molasses must contain not less than 43 percent sugars and a density not less than 79.5° Brix, while beet molasses must contain not less than 48 percent total sugars but with the same minimum density as for cane molasses. Citrus molasses is the partially dehydrated juices obtained from the manufacture of dried citrus pulp and must contain not less than 45 percent total sugars and a density not less than 71° Brix. Starch molasses is a by-product of the manufacture of glucose from starch derived from corn or grain sorghums in which the starch is hydrolyzed by use of enzymes and/or acid. It must contain not less than 50 percent total sugars and not less than 73 percent total solids. Hemicellulose extract is a by-product of the manufacture of pressed wood. It is the concentrated soluble material obtained from the treatment of wood at elevated temperature and pressure without use of acids, alkalis, or salts. It contains pentose and hexose sugars and must have a total carbohydrate content of not less than 55 percent. Lignin sulfonate is produced when the lignin component of wood is solublized by a combination of sulfonation and hydrolysis during the conversion of wood to wood pulp by the sulfite process. Depending on the method used, water-soluble salts of Ca, Na, or ammonium may be present. The liquor is sold as such or concentrated or dried, depending upon the intended usage.

Cane or blackstrap molasses is utilized widely as a feedstuff, particularly for ruminants. In the United States alone, more than 2.5 million T of cane and beet molasses are used annually, and large amounts are used in Europe and in other areas (semitropical or tropical) where it is produced. Worldwide about 10 million T of cane and beet molasses are produced each year. That produced contains less sugar than formerly because of more efficient extraction methods. Major exporters (1986) were Pakistan, Thailand, Indonesia, the Philippines, and Brazil. In 1979, Mexico was second and Cuba fourth in exports, but there has been a shift in production, particularly an increase by Pakistan.

Unfortunately, there is either little agreement on the typical analysis of molasses or the products are quite variable. No doubt, the composition varies from sugar mill to sugar mill. In a recent paper from the Netherlands (26), the authors quoted the following values from different molasses analyses: beet molasses, ash, 6.9–11.6 percent; crude protein, 4.7–14.0 percent; cane molasses, ash, 8.7–12.3 percent; crude protein, 4.1–6.5 percent. Digestibility values were: beet molasses, organic matter, 86–94 percent; crude protein, 34–71 percent; NFE, 91–98 percent; cane molasses, organic matter, 84–91 percent; crude protein, 0–60 percent; NFE, 87–93 percent. Comparable kinds of values can be found by comparing almost any source on nutrient content of molasses. For example, the NRC publication on beef gives TDN values of beet, cane, and citrus molasses of 79, 72, and 75 percent, respectively. The NRC on sheep gives values of 77 and 79 percent for beet and cane molasses, respectively.

Recent analyses from the Netherlands on cane and beet molasses are shown in Table 7–17. On an organic matter basis, the total sugar content was about 75 and 73 percent for beet and cane molasses, respectively. About 90 percent of total sugars in beet molasses was recovered as sucrose, and only small amounts were found as fructose or glucose. About 60 percent of total sugars in cane molasses was found to be sucrose and 30 percent fructose + glucose. However, in both products about 10 percent of total sugars were not identified. The authors state that part of this undetermined fraction is unfermentable

TABLE 7-17

Major components of cane and beet molasses

| Item, % | Molasses Source | |
	Beet	Cane
Dry matter	80.3	78.8
Ash	8.0	12.6
Crude protein	14.8	5.9
Betaine	5.2	0.1
Amino acids	7.0	2.2
Hexane extract	0.3	0.3
Crude fiber	0.1	0.3
NDF	—	—
Sugar	69.5	63.9
Sucrose	66.0	44.0
Fructose	1.0	13.0
Anhydro uronic acids	19.8	15.1
Ammonia	0.1	0.1

Source: Steg and Van Der Meer (26).

material which is not sugars, but reducing agents, possibly formed by the combination of normal reducing sugars with N compounds. With the beet molasses about 35 percent of the N was undetermined, and most of the N in cane molasses was not recovered in amino acids.

The ash content of molasses is variable, as indicated, and is largely made up of K, Ca, Cl, and sulfate salts. Cane molasses is usually a good source of most of the trace elements, but it has only moderate to low vitamin content. Part of the variability in ash (and other components) is, undoubtedly, caused by differences in sugar manufacturing procedures. Age, type and quality of sugar cane, soil fertility, and system of collection and processing also have a bearing on composition of cane molasses.

The sweet taste of molasses, whatever the source, makes it appealing to most animal species. In addition, molasses is of value in reducing dust in feeds, as a pellet binder, as a vehicle for feeding medicants or other additives, and as a liquid protein supplement when fortified with an N source (see Ch. 8). The cost is often attractive as compared with that of grains.

Most molasses products are limited in use because of milling problems (sticky consistency) or because levels exceeding 15–25 percent of the ration are apt to result in digestive disturbances, diarrhea, and inefficient animal performance. The diarrhea is largely a result of the high level of various mineral salts in most molasses products. The problem is not caused by the sugar, because pigs or ruminants can utilize comparable amounts of sugar provided in other forms. High-test molasses, which has a lower ash content, can be fed at very high levels to either pigs or cattle without any particular problem, but not much high-test molasses is available for animal feeding. Under some conditions feeding very high levels of molasses to cattle results in molasses toxicity, which resembles cerebrocortical necrosis, an induced thiamin deficiency. However, limited data on the topic suggest that the condition is caused by an abnormal metabolism of carbohydrates by brain tissue (27).

Most of the relatively recent data indicate that cane and beet molasses, if fed in limited amounts (that is, less than 10 percent of the diet), are equivalent to a good-quality grain source for replacement of energy. When fed in increasing amounts (Table 7–18), animal per-

TABLE 7-18

Performance of animals fed molasses or other liquid energy sources

Treatment	Daily Feed Consumed, kg DM	Daily Gain, kg	Milk Production, kg/d	Feed/Gain Ratio	Digestible Energy, %
Barley diet, finishing steers[a]					
Control (no molasses)	10.1	1.13		8.98	
9.6% molasses	10.4	1.12		9.08	
14.4% molasses	10.0	1.03		9.69	
High corn diet, finishing steers[b]					79.2
+10% cane molasses	9.3	1.36		6.83	83.8
+10% hemicellulose extract	9.1	1.30		7.00	79.6
+10% experimental wood mol.	9.2	1.35		6.80	84.1
Cottonseed hull roughage, lactating dairy cows[c]					
No molasses	20.0		20.8		
8% cane molasses	20.5		20.9		
8% hemicellulose ext.	20.9		20.8		
Corn, oats diet, fattening lambs[d]					
Control	1.4	0.24		5.8	
5% condensed soy solubles	1.5	0.24		6.1	
10% condensed soy solubles	1.5	0.23		6.4	
15% condensed soy solubles	1.5	0.21		7.2	

[a]From Heinemann and Hanks (28). Basal diet was 53.4% barley and 22.9% beet pulp. For treatments with molasses, the barley-beet pulp fed was reduced by 10 and 20%, respectively.
[b]From Crawford et al. (29). The basal diet contained 81% corn. When liquids were fed, they were mixed with the basal diet prior to feeding.
[c]From Vernlund et al. (30). Molasses or hemicellulose extract replaced corn meal.
[d]From Perry et al. (31). Condensed soy solubles replaced ground corn.

formance tends to decrease in level of performance and efficiency of feed utilization. There is also a fair amount of information on hemicellulose extract (two examples shown in Table 7–18) which indicates a comparable response to cane molasses when fed in restricted amounts. Much less information is available on starch and citrus molasses, but they appear to be comparable to other sources as an energy source.

Other liquid feeds containing moderate to high levels of sugars include **condensed soybean solubles,** which are a by-product of washing soy flour or flakes with water and acid. This product contains about 6–7 percent crude protein, 33 percent sucrose, and about 57 percent total soluble carbohydrates (dry basis). As shown in Table 7–18, it can be a satisfactory replacement for corn when fed at levels of up to 10 percent of the diet to lambs.

Liquefied corn product is the product resulting from steam cooking and enzymatic treatment of the corn without removing any of the component parts. It shall not contain less than 30 percent solids. On a dry-matter basis it would contain 8-9 percent crude protein. The author is not aware that much of this product is produced or used.

Other liquid products that contain relatively little soluble or fermentable carbohydrate include **extracted streptomyces solubles,** a by-product of streptomycin production. It contains about 17–19 percent crude protein (dry basis). **Condensed molasses solubles** (also called stillage), a by-product of rum or ethanol production, is available in limited amounts. It is a high-ash product with about 16–19 percent crude protein (dry basis). Both of these products can be used in limited amounts with ruminant animals (32, 33). **Citrus condensed molasses solubles,** a residue from the fermentation of alcohol, contains about 10–12 percent crude protein (dry basis). Levels of up to 20 percent of the diet can be fed to cattle without depressing gain, although feed conversion appeared to decrease; with lambs a level of 20 percent depressed gain as compared to 10 or 0 percent, and digestibility of crude protein was depressed at the 20 percent level (34).

Liquid Milk By-Products

There are several liquid by-products resulting from production of cheese and/or recovery of products from whey. These include **fresh whey, condensed whey,** and **dehydrated (dried)**

whey. Whey is the liquid fraction of milk remaining after the removal of casein and butterfat in cheese making. Most of the lactose, minerals, and water-soluble protein present in milk remain in whey. When whey is passed through an evaporator so that only water is removed, the resulting product is defined as condensed whey (or whey concentrate). When sold as condensed whey, the minimum percentage of total whey solids must be declared on the label. A typical product with 40–50 percent solids will have 10–13 percent crude protein (DM basis) and 55–70 percent lactose. Dehydrated (dried) whey is dried to the point of less than 10 percent moisture. This results in a more expensive product, but one which costs less to transport long distances. Liquid and condensed whey are subject to rapid spoilage unless steps are taken to prevent it.

Condensed whey has been used in liquid supplements for cattle and to a lesser extent in formulas for swine and poultry as a source of nutrients and to improve palatability and feed texture. Dried whey has long been used in starter feeds for poultry and baby pigs and in milk replacers for young ruminants. Liquid whey is more of a problem to utilize because of its low dry-matter content (4–5 percent). However, when it is available close at hand to livestock operations (so that transportation costs are minimal), it can be used very effectively. This is illustrated in Table 7–19. Data in the table show that high-producing cows consumed an average of 54 ℓ/d, resulting in less concentrate consumption but somewhat more total dry-matter consumption and greater milk production. Schingoethe (36) has pointed out that ruminants can consume up to 30 percent of their dry matter from liquid whey without impaired performance, although swine may develop diarrhea when more than 20 percent of diet dry matter comes from liquid whey. Small amounts of whey or other whey by-products often increase weight gains and feed efficiency and improve nutrient utilization by cattle. Whey may also prevent milk fat depression in dairy cows without reducing concentrate consumption markedly.

Other by-products of whey include **condensed whey solubles,** which is obtained by evaporating whey residue from the manufacture of lactose after removal of milk albumin and partial removal of lactose. This product contains 40–50 percent solids with about 10 percent crude protein and 60–70 percent lactose (DM basis). **Condensed whey-product** is the residue ob-

TABLE 7-19

Use of liquid (fresh) whey for high-producing dairy cows

	Dietary Treatments	
Item	Control	Fed Whey
Feed consumed/d		
Liquid whey, ℓ		54.1
Whey DM, kg		2.45
Concentrate, kg DM	16.4	14.7
Hay DM, kg	3.2	3.6
Total DM, kg	19.8	20.7
Milk yield, kg FCM/d	25.0	27.2
FCM milk/feed DM ratio	1.27	1.31

Source: Pihchasov et al. (35). The concentrate was made up primarily of sorghum, barley, corn, and wheat bran with supplemental protein, minerals, and vitamins. The concentrate, whey, and hay (med. quality vetch-oats) were fed ad libitum. Data shown are for 70–105 days of lactation.

tained by evaporating whey from which a portion of the lactose has been removed. It will contain 44–48 percent dry matter with 15–16 percent crude protein and 60–70 percent lactose and lactic acid. These two products are used in a similar manner to condensed whey.

BY-PRODUCT DRY FEEDS

Beet Pulp

Beet pulp is the residue remaining after extraction of sugar from sugar beets. In some localities feeders near the processing plants may feed wet pulp. However, a high proportion of the pulp is dried, and frequently beet molasses is added to the pulp before drying. It may be sold in shredded or pelleted form. Beet pulp is highly favored in rations for lactating cows. Its physical texture resembles that of a roughage, but the pulp is much more digestible than roughages and it is also quite palatable. Although the crude fiber content is high for a concentrate (16 percent for molasses dried), the fiber is quite digestible, partly because the lignin content is low. Relatively recent digestion data with sheep and lactation studies with cows indicate that beet pulp provides as much energy as corn when fed in complete rations in amounts up to 70 percent of the total. Usual values given for digestible energy are appreciably lower than for most cereal grains.

Citrus Pulp and Meal

Citrus by-products are prepared from the residue resulting from the manufacture of citrus juices.

The residue is shredded or ground, pressed to remove juices, and dried. Ca hydroxide may be added before pressing. Dried citrus meal is composed of the finer particles obtained by screening dried citrus pulp. The protein content is low (5–8 percent), the fiber content is moderately high (11–12 percent), and the Ca content may be high. These products are not very palatable and may be toxic to nonruminant species, although data indicate that 10 percent of the ration can be used for swine. Data on ruminant animals indicate that citrus pulp is relatively palatable, and quantities approaching 50–60 percent can be used if desired. The fiber is quite digestible, and the energy value approaches that of some of the cereal grains. However, relatively large amounts (3–4 kg/d) have been shown to cause abnormal tastes in milk fat, with no effect when 2 kg/d were fed (37).

Dried Bakery Product

This is a feed produced from reclaimed (unused or stale) bakery products or other materials such as candy, inedible flours, unsalable nuts, and the like. The materials are blended and ground to produce a feedstuff that contains 9–12 percent crude protein, 11–15 percent fat, and a low level of crude fiber. It will be variable because the ingredients will tend to vary from day to day and season to season. While relatively little is available, it is an excellent feed because the digestible energy is high, most of it being derived from starch, sucrose, and high-quality fats. It is well utilized by pigs and is a preferred ingredient in starter rations. It is also highly favored in rations for lactating dairy cows when available.

Cassava Meal

A tropical root crop (*Manihot esculenta*) which goes by names such as cassava, yucca, manioc, tapioca, or mandioca is of great potential importance as a livestock feed in tropical areas. In experimental plots it has yielded as much as 75–80 tons/ha/year. This is much more than can be produced by rice, corn, or other grains adapted to the tropics.

Although it is strictly a tropical plant, significant amounts of dehydrated cassava meal are now used in the United States and Europe for feeding livestock. Cassava root contains about 65 percent water, 1–2 percent protein, 1.5 percent fiber, 0.3 percent fat, 1.4 percent ash, and 30 percent NFE. Thus its dry matter is largely readily available carbohydrates. Dried cassava is equal in energy value to other root crops and tubers and can be used to replace all of the grain portion of the diet for growing-finishing pigs if the amount of supplemental protein is increased to compensate for the very low protein content of cassava. It can also be used as the main energy source in diets of gestating and lactating swine. The stalk and leaf portion of the plant are well utilized by ruminants, but this portion is too high in fiber for monogastrics.

Freshly harvested cassava roots and leaves may be high in hydrocyanic acid (a very toxic material). Oven drying at 70–80°C, boiling in water, or sun-drying are effective in reducing the HCN content. Principal sources of the dried product are Southeast Asian countries at this time.

ROOTS AND TUBERS

Root crops used for feeding animals, particularly in northern Europe, include turnips, mangolds, swedes, fodder beets, carrots, and parsnips. These crops frequently are dug up and left lying in the field to be consumed as desired when used as animal feed. The bulky nature of these feeds limits their use for swine or poultry, so most are fed to cattle or sheep.

Root crops are characterized by their high water (75–90 percent) moderately low fiber (5–11 percent, DM basis), and crude protein (4–12 percent) content. These crops tend to be low in Ca and P and high in K. The carbohydrates range from 50–75 percent of the dry matter and are mainly sucrose, which is highly digestible by ruminants and nonruminants. Animals (sheep, cattle) not adapted to beets or mangolds (both *Beta vulgaris*) tend to be subject to digestive upsets, probably because of the high sucrose content.

Some root crops, turnips in particular, can be used in a double cropping system. They can be planted after harvest of small grain and still get substantial production for grazing in the fall and early winter in some areas. Both cattle and sheep do quite well when grazing on turnips with some supplementary feed. They learn rapidly to eat out the root portion of the plant, which is mostly below ground.

Potatoes

Surplus or cull white potatoes (*Solanum tuberosum*) are often used for feeding cattle or sheep in areas where commercial potato production oc-

curs. Potatoes are high in digestible energy (dry basis) which is derived almost entirely from starch. Water content is 78–80 percent, crude protein content is low, and the quality of the protein is poor. The Ca content is usually low. Pigs and chickens do poorly on raw potatoes, but cooking improves digestibility of the starch so that it is comparable to corn starch. Potatoes and, particularly, potato sprouts, contain a toxic compound, solanin, which may cause problems if potatoes are fed raw or ensiled. In cattle finishing rations, cull potatoes are frequently fed at a level to provide about half of the dry-matter intake. With pigs, satisfactory performance may be obtained when growing pigs are fed cooked potatoes along with limited amounts of protein concentrates, but they are usually restricted to 30 percent or less of the total diet.

In North America the utilization of potatoes for processing has more than tripled in the past 20 years, and various by-products of potato processing are more available in some areas for feeding to livestock. It is estimated that about 35 percent of the preprocessed potato is discarded during processing. **Potato meal** is the dried raw meal of potato residue left from processing plants. **Potato slurry** is a high-moisture product remaining after processing for human food. It contains a high amount of peel. **Potato filter cake,** which represents about 20 percent of the residue from potato processing, is the residue recovered from the waste water by vacuum filtration. **Potato flakes** are residues remaining after cooking, mashing, and drying. **Potato pulp** is the by-product remaining after extraction of starch with cold water. The various raw meals have about the same relative nutritive values as raw cull potatoes. Recent studies with potato filter cake indicate that essentially all of the barley (60 percent of total diet) could be replaced with filter cake without a marked reduction in digestibility of energy by cattle. When 15 percent of the diet barley was replaced with filter cake, it stimulated energy digestibility. However, at the higher levels (45 and 60 percent), there was an apparent reduction in feed consumption (38).

Data from two different experiments with potato by-products are shown in Table 7–20. In the experiment with potato meal, it was substituted for some of the corn and soybean meal in the concentrate mix for lactating cows. This particular product had a crude protein content of 8.45 percent, a 4.72 percent lipids content, and a 65 percent starch content. For some reason the 15 percent level resulted in less dry-matter in-

TABLE 7-20

Effect of potato wastes on milk production by cows

Item	Potato Source						
	Potato Meal, % in Rations[a]			Processing Waste, % in Rations[b]			
	0	15	30	0	10	15	20
Dry matter intake, kg/d	19.8	18.6	19.5	18.2	19.0	18.3	18.7
Milk yield, kg/d	27.5	26.8	28.0	27.2	26.1	25.6	27.4
4% FCM/kg/d				24.2	22.8	22.8	23.4
Milk fat, %	3.33	3.41	3.30	3.31	3.20	3.20	3.01

[a]Data from Schneider et al. (39).
[b]Data from Onwubuemeli et al. (40).

take, but it had no statistical effect on milk yield or milk fat. In the second experiment, potato processing waste (60 percent peel and sludge, 30 percent raw potato screenings, and 10 percent cooked packaging wastes) was fed. It had a dry-matter content of 24–28 percent, a crude protein content of 4.1–6.6 percent (dry basis), and a pH of 3.6–4.2. It was substituted for high-moisture corn on a dry-matter basis. Fat content of the milk tended to decrease with use of the processing wastes, but there were no statistical differences otherwise in milk production when using this level of potato waste. Thus these two studies tend to support earlier work which indicated that small to moderate amounts of potato wastes can be utilized very well by lactating or fattening cattle, but that using as much as 40–50 percent or more of the dry matter from potato waste will likely reduce performance.

Potato by-product meal (now called **dried potato products**) is produced in some areas. It contains residues of food production such as off-color french fries, whole potatoes, peelings, potato chips, and potato pulp. These are mixed, limestone is added, and the mixture is dried with heat. Generally, the value of the various potato products is roughly comparable to that of raw or cooked cull potatoes, depending on how (or if) the product is dried. However, residues of the potato chip processing industry have much higher levels of fat, so the energy value would be increased accordingly.

Many processing plants do not dry their wastes. It is a common practice for cattle feedlot operators to collect wastes and store the waste in pits. Because of the high moisture content, substantial fermentation occurs in warm and hot weather, often resulting in high losses (60–70 percent±) of the starch originally going into the pit unless the waste is fed soon after it is available. Potatoes have also been used successfully to make silage in combination with a variety of other feedstuffs.

FATS AND OILS

Although most animals need a dietary source of the essential fatty acids (see Ch. 3), these are usually supplied in sufficient amounts in natural feedstuffs, and supplementation is not required except when low-fat energy sources are fed. However, feeding fats are frequently used in commercial feed formulas. Fats are added to rations for several reasons. Nutritionally, fats are exclusively an energy source, because they contain very little, if any, protein, minerals, or vitamins. As a source of energy, fats are unequaled and are highly digestible (especially by simple-stomached animals). Digestible fat supplies about 2.25 times as much energy as digestible starch or sugar, thus fats can be used to increase energy density of a ration. Fats often

TABLE 7-21

Estimated use of feed fats in 1986 and projected use in 1990 (in millions of pounds)

Type of Feed	1986	1990	Increase, %
Veal	100	125	25
Pet	400	450	13
Hog	100	250	150
Cattle	200	225	13
Dairy	90	250	178
Broiler	650	750	15
Turkey	500	700	15
Layer	30	50	67
Fish	30	50	67
Total	2100	2850	35

Source: Rouse (41).

tend to improve rations by reducing dustiness and increasing palatability. Fats generally increase absorption of fat-soluble nutrients such as the fat-soluble vitamins. However, they may form insoluble Ca or Mg soaps in the gut and reduce absorption of P. There is some evidence that fats will reduce bloat in ruminants. From a manufacturing point of view, the lubrication of milling machinery by added fats is often of interest. The amounts of feed fats used in 1986 and projected amounts for 1990 are shown in Table 7–21. Note that the author of the table concluded that there will be very substantial increases in fat use for both hog and dairy feeds.

Feeding fats come from a variety of sources. Animal fats are primarily from slaughterhouses or other facilities that precut meat for the restaurant or grocery trade. Some also comes from rendering plants that process inedible animal tissues. Based on a survey of 40 rendering plants in the United States in 1978 (42), the raw material used for producing feeding fats was composed of restaurant grease, 40; shop fat and bone, 21; packing house offal, 19; fallen animals (dead or sick), 9; poultry offal, 6; other materials, 4. However, the ingredients from any particular rendering plant may be appreciably different. In the feed trade, fat is supplied by renderers or by blenders or brokers. Blenders may purchase all of their fats, then process and blend them, and they normally sell their finished products under brand names and/or in formula feeds. Brokers sell fats that they purchase from renderers or refiners but do not themselves process in any way, although many brokers deliver fat in their own trucks.

In addition to the animal fats, restaurant fats or greases have become a major portion of fats recycled for feeding. These fats may be mixtures of a variety of animal or vegetable cooking fats. Another major vegetable component is acidulated vegetable soapstock. This material is primarily free fatty acids removed from crude vegetable oils as a first step in refining the oil. It is safe and well utilized and approximately 100,000 T are used annually in feeds. Other fats such as lard, high-grade tallows, and high-quality seed oils (corn, safflower, soy, cottonseed, peanut, and others) are usually too expensive to use in feed but are used in the food trade or for other industrial purposes.

Descriptions and classification of feed-grade fat sources are not uniformly applied in the feeding industry. A proposed classification is given below (41) and further recommended specifications are given in Table 7–22.

1. **Animal fat.** Includes rendered fats from beef or pork by-products. This material is mainly packing house offal

TABLE 7-22

Suggested quality specifications for feed fats

Feed Fat Categories	Quality Specifications, %					
	Min. Total Fatty Acids	Max. Free Fatty Acids	Max. Moisture	Max. Impurities	Max. Unsaponifiable	Max. Total MIU
Livestock	90	15	1	0.5	1	2
Poultry	90	15	1	0.5	1	2
Blended feed-grade animal	90	15	1	0.5	1	2
Blended animal & vegetable	90	30	1	0.5	3.5	5
Feed-grade vegetable	90	50	1.5	1.0	4.0	6

Source: Rouse (41). The following specifications apply to all fats:
- Fats must be stabilized with an acceptable feed or food-grade antioxidant added at levels recommended by the manufacturer. Fats should pass the AOM stability test at 20 h with less than 20 milliequivalents (me) peroxide.
- No cottonseed soapstock or other cottonseed by-products should be included in fats for layer, breeder, or broiler rations.
- Blended fats shall include only tallow, grease, poultry fat, and acidulated vegetable soapstock. Any other by-products should be included only with the knowledge and consent of the buyer.
- Fats must be certified that any PCB and pesticide residues are within the allowable limits established by state and/or federal agencies.
- Fats for poultry rations should be certified as being negative for the chick edema factor as measured by the Modified Liebermann-Burchard test.
- Fats shall not contain more than trace levels of any minerals, heavy metals, or other contaminants.
- The supplier should make every effort to provide a uniform fat structure in each delivery. A specification for minimum and/or maximum iodine values can be established for the type of fat purchased. Monitoring IVs can determine if product fat structure is uniform.
- Suppliers should furnish research data to support ME claims.

or supermarket trimmings from the packaging of meats. It can be identified as tallow if the titer (hardness measurement; temperature in C° at which a hydrolyzed fat solidifies) is 40 or higher or grease if under 40. A lower titer indicates higher unsaturated and/or polyunsaturated levels.

2. **Poultry fat.** Includes fats from 100 percent poultry offal.

3. **Blended feed-grade animal fat.** Includes blends of tallow, grease, poultry, and restaurant grease.

4. **Blended animal and vegetable fats.** Includes blends of feed-grade animal fat from category 3, plus vegetable fat.

5. **Feed-grade vegetable fat.** Includes vegetable oil, acidulated vegetable soapstocks, and other refinery by-products.

The official names of feeding fats (as of 1988) are: **animal fat; vegetable fat or oil; hydrolyzed fat or oil, feed grade; fat product, feed grade; corn endosperm oil; vegetable oil refinery lipid, feed grade;** and **corn syrup insolubles, feed grade.**

Although the type of fat may vary considerably depending on the source, usual specifications state that feeding fats shall contain not less than 90 percent total fatty acids, not more than 2.5 percent unsaponifiable matter, and not more than 1 percent insoluble matter. Feeding fats must also be free from toxic or undesirable substances. Moisture is detrimental because it contributes to instability of the fat and to its reactivity with metals; it is also an unneeded diluent. Occasionally, some residual solvent may be present which may be an explosion hazard. Unsaponifiable substances are largely hydrocarbons (solvents used in some processing), waxes, and tars which have little, if any, food value. Other unsaponifiable substances may include cholesterol, cholesterol esters, and some phospholipids. Of the toxic substances, the polychlorinated biphenyls (PCBs) have sometimes been a problem.

Fats are subject to oxidation with development of rancidity, which reduces palatability and may cause some digestive and nutritional problems. Thus one of the first requirements for a feeding fat is that it is stable to oxidation. Feeding fats nearly always have antioxidants added, especially if the fat is held for any length of time or if the mixed feed is not fed immediate-

ly. The use of antioxidants protects the feed sources against loss of some vitamins, also; vitamin E and A are particularly good examples.

If the proposed standards listed in Table 7–22 are finalized in this or some similar form, it will require quite a bit of policing by users or by some unbiased quality control laboratories to make them work as proposed. This is obvious when the results of the 40 samples from rendering plants are considered (Table 7–23). Some of these samples were probably quite good, but others must have fallen considerably outside the limits proposed in Table 7–22. Quality is also reflected in color and odor as well as the chemical factors listed in Table 7–22. Fats that are rancid, off-flavor, and unpalatable are not, of course, desirable feed ingredients.

Adding fat at low to moderate levels to animal rations can sometimes increase total energy intake through improved palatability, although animals usually consume enough energy to meet their demand when it is physically possible. In swine rations, 5–10 percent fat is often added to creep diets, but fat is usually used more sparingly for older market hogs. Relatively high levels may alter the character of body fat, particularly in nonruminant species because they tend to deposit dietary fatty acids relatively unchanged. In poultry rations, 2–5 percent fat is often added when fat is competitive as an energy source with the cereal grains. Amounts above 10–12 percent will usually cause a sharp reduction in feed consumption, so concentration of other nutrients may need to be increased in order to obtain the desired intake.

For ruminants, high levels of fats are used in milk replacers; depending on the purpose of the replacer, it may contain 10–30 percent added fat. Ruminants on dry feed are less tolerant of high fat levels than are monogastrics. Concen-

TABLE 7-23

Analyses of feed-grade fat from 40 rendering plants

Component	Mean	Range
Moisture and volatiles, %	0.44	0.01–1.99
Insolubles, %	0.21	0.01–2.97
Unsaponifiables, %	0.68	0.24–3.48
Total, M, I, U, %	1.33	0.48–7.33
Free fatty acids, %	6.50	0.70–36.81
Capillary melting point, °C	39.8	27.8–45.3
F.A.C. color	25	11–45
Peroxide value at 20 h	105.2	1.5–340

Source: Boehme (42).

trations of more than 7–8 percent are apt to cause digestive disturbances, diarrhea, and greatly reduced feed intake. In practice, 2–4 percent added fat is an appropriate level for finishing rations. Some fat is occasionally added to rations for lactating dairy cows, but fat would only rarely be used in other situations.

In the normal course of events, fats fed to ruminant animals are saturated by rumen microorganisms (see Ch. 3). This can be prevented by treating high-oil seeds (cottonseed, soybean, and the like) with formaldehyde or by emulsifying fat with casein and treating the emulsion with formaldehyde. The formaldehyde prevents any action by the rumen microbes on the fat but allows normal digestion in the gut if too much is not added. Using this method, milk and body fats can be altered and made more unsaturated if desired. This method does not appear to be commercially feasible at this time, but it may be something that will be used in the future.

At the present time the feeding of high-oil seeds such as soybean and cottonseed is a popular practice for dairy producers. The seeds are, of course, high in both fat and protein, and adding some to the diet will generally increase milk fat percentage somewhat (see Ch. 15). Such seeds may also be processed through extruders for feeding to monogastric species. Some processing is necessary to destroy antiquality factors for monogastric species (see Ch. 8).

One of the problems in using fat (particularly in computer-formulated rations) is that there is considerable disagreement as to the feeding value (energy content) for ruminant animals (43). Tabular values for energy content do not appear to follow any logical thought patterns. For example, in the 1984 NRC publication on nutrient requirements of beef cattle, fat is considered to be 79 percent digestible and to have energy levels as shown: TDN, 177 percent; ME, 6.41 kcal/g; NEm and NEg values of 4.75 and 3.51 kcal/g, respectively. The author's opinion is that different values should be used for preruminants or other suckling mammals than for older animals, because the young animals generally digest fats more completely and/or they are fed fats that are more digestible. A recent research report provides data on fattening cattle fed 0 or 4 percent added yellow grease (44). The results of two comparative slaughter trials and a digestion trial indicated that this fat product had the following energy values: NEm, 6.20, and NEg, 4.53 kcal/g. These appear to be more realistic values than some others quoted in tables of feedstuff composition.

GARBAGE

On a commercial scale, garbage fed to animals is primarily food waste from restaurants, hotels, food markets, and other institutions handling large amounts of food. In the United States, garbage feeding is restricted to feeding of swine near large metropolitan centers where collections can be made daily. Most of the states in the United States have laws requiring that garbage be cooked to some minimum temperature in order to prevent the spread of diseases such as salmonellesis, trichinosis, and tuberculosis. Nevertheless, occasional cases of trichinosis occur from humans eating pork which has been fed on garbage, usually from animals that were not processed through an inspected slaughterhouse.

Research data indicate that garbage can be fed successfully to market pigs if the garbage is supplemented with energy and protein sources. The high moisture content of garbage would, otherwise, result in some reduction in performance. Garbage tends to produce pork with softer fat than when cereal grains are fed, so it is a common practice to take pigs off garbage for a period of time before marketing them.

OTHER ENERGY SOURCES

Many other materials that have not been discussed in this chapter are fed to animals. However, most of them would be considered to be by-products of the food industry in one form or other or non-food-related products produced in small amounts. Many of the products are listed in a publication on by-product and unusual feedstuffs published by the California Experiment Station (45). It should be noted that good animal data are not available on many of the products often available only in localized areas.

SUMMARY

Feedgrains—corn, barley, sorghum, oats, triticale, millet—are the primary sources of high-energy feed for farm livestock. The grains and various milling by-products of the grains provide a readily digested source of starch with lesser amounts of other carbohydrates. In general, the feedgrains are moderate in protein content, low in Ca, moderate in P, and variable in vitamins and trace minerals. Molasses of various types are also available as are other liquid by-products in lesser amounts. These find ready use in commercial feed formulas or in liquid supplements.

Although there is some competition between animals and humans when grains are fed to animals, the use of such high-energy feeds allows animals to produce at considerably higher levels and with greater efficiency than they could otherwise do if dependent on forage or other high-fiber feeds for their energy supply.

Other energy sources available in substantial amounts include the various milling by-products of flour milling, primarily from wheat, but with lesser amounts from rice, barley, sorghum, and rye. Corn milling by-products are also available in substantial amounts, though some are classed as protein supplements. Although the by-product feedstuffs are sometimes standardized for protein and/or fiber content, they are still rather variable. Molasses, primarily a by-product of sugar production, is used in relatively large amounts. It is also available from citrus juice production as well as from some wood processing. Liquids such as molasses have multiple uses in formula feeds or as liquid protein supplements when fortified with N. Other by-product feeds include beet pulp, citrus pulp and meal, and dried bakery product. Some roots and tubers are fed directly to animals. In addition, wastes from food production with potatoes are very useful energy sources. Inedible (for humans) fats and oils are used in many modern finishing rations for swine, poultry, and cattle. Garbage and a host of other by-products of food processing are available in limited amounts in localized areas.

REFERENCES

1. USDA. 1987. *World grain situation and outlook.* Foreign Agr. Ser. Cir. Series FG–2–87 (November). Washington, D.C.: USDA.

2. USDA. 1987. *Feed situation and outlook report.* Econ. Res. Ser. FDS–304 (November). Washington, D.C.: USDA.

3. USDA. 1987. *The official United States standards for grain.* Washington, D.C.: Federal Grain Inspection Service.

4. Subramanyam, M., C. W. Deyoe, and L. H. Harbers. 1980. *Nutr. Rept. Internat.* 22:657;667.

5. Kent, N. 1983. *Technology of cereals.* Oxford, UK: Pergammon Press.

6. Pond, W. G., and J. H. Maner. 1984. *Swine production and nutrition.* Westport, CT: AVI.

7. Sunde, M. L. 1971. *Hatch* (February). Madison: University of Wisconsin Poultry Dept.

8. Luis, E., and T. Sullivan. 1984. *Poultry Sci.* 61:321.

9. Rooney, L. W., and R. L. Pflugfelder. 1987. *J. Animal Sci.* 63:1607.

10. Lichtenwalner, R. E., et al. 1979. *J. Animal Sci.* 49:183.

11. Hinman, D. D. 1979. *Proc. West. Sec. Amer. Soc. Animal Sci.* 30:49.

12. Misir, R., W. C. Sauer, and R. Cichon. 1984. *J. Animal Sci.* 59:1011.

13. Reddy, S. G., M. L. Chen, and D. R. Rao. 1975. *J. Animal Sci.* 40:940.

14. Preston, R. L., D. C. Rule, and W. E. McReynolds. 1980. *Proc. West. Sec. Amer. Soc. Animal Sci.* 31:269.

15. Hale, O. H., and P. R. Utley. 1985. *J. Animal Sci.* 60:1272.

16. Misir, R., and R. R. Marquardt. 1978. *Can. J. Animal Sci.* 58:717.

17. Sharma, H. R., et al. 1981. *J. Dairy Sci.* 64:441.

18. NRC. 1982. *United States-Canadian tables of feed composition.* 3d ed. Washington, D.C.: Nat. Academy Press.

19. DeGoey, L. W., and R. C. Ewan. 1975. *J. Animal Sci.* 40:1052.

20. Wu, J. F., and R. C. Ewan. 1979. *J. Animal Sci.* 49:1470.

21. Cornejo, S., et al. 1973. *J. Animal Sci.* 36:87.

22. AFCO. 1988. *Official Publication. Amer. Feed Control Officials.* Washington, D.C.: AFCO.

23. Erickson, J. P., et al. 1985. *J. Animal Sci.* 60:1012.

24. Adeola, O., et al. 1986. *J. Animal Sci.* 63:1854.

25. Anon. 1972. *Millfeed manual.* Chicago, IL: Miller's National Federation.

26. Steg, A., and J. M. Van Der Meer. 1985. *Animal Feed Sci. Tech.* 13:83.

27. Lora, J., et al. 1978. *Tropical Animal Prod.* 3:19.

28. Heinemann, W. W., and E. M. Hanks. 1977. *J. Animal Sci.* 45:13.

29. Crawford, D. F., W. B. Anthony, and R. R. Harris. 1978. *J. Animal Sci.* 46:32.

30. Vernlund, D. S., et al. 1980. *J. Dairy Sci.* 63:2037.

31. Perry, T. W., et al. 1976. *J. Animal Sci.* 42:1104.

32. Randel, P. F., and B. Vallejo. 1982. *J. Agr. Univ. P.R.* 66:11; Vallejo, B., and P. F. Randel. 1982. *J. Agr. Univ. P.R.* 66:44.

33. Potter, S. G., et al. 1985. *J. Animal Sci.* 60:839.

34. Chen, M. C., et al. 1981. *J. Animal Sci.* 53:253.

35. Pihchasov, Y., et al. 1982. *J. Dairy Sci.* 65:28.

36. Schingoethe, D. J. 1976. *J. Dairy Sci.* 59:556.

37. Bartsch, D. B., and R. B. Wickes. 1979. *Australian J. Exp. Agr. Animal Husb.* 19:658.

38. Stanhope, D. L., et al. 1980. *J. Animal Sci.* 51:202.

39. Schneider, P. L., et al. 1985. *J. Dairy Sci.* 68:1738.

40. Onwubuemeli, C., et al. 1985. *J. Dairy Sci.* 68:1207.

41. Rouse, R. H. 1986. In: *Feed Mgmt.* 38(2):18.

42. Boehme, W. R. 1978. Personal communication. Des Plaines, IL: Fats & Proteins Res. Foundation.

43. Church, D. C. (ed.). 1979. *Digestive physiology and nutrition of ruminants. Vol. 2: Nutrition.* 2d ed. Corvallis, OR: O & B Books.

44. Zinn, R. A. 1988. *J. Animal Sci.* 66:213.

45. Bath, D. L., et al. 1980. *By-products and unusual feedstuffs in livestock rations.* West. Regional Ext. Pub. 39, Davis, CA: Univ. of California.

46. Grimson, R. E., et al. 1987. *Can. J. Animal Sci.* 67:43.

47. Fancher, B. I., L. S. Jensen, and R. L. Smith. 1987. *Poultry Sci.* 66:1693.

8

Supplementary Protein Sources

INTRODUCTION

Protein is a critical nutrient (that is, one likely to be low or deficient), particularly for young, rapidly growing animals and for mature animals such as high-producing dairy cows. Optimal use of protein is a must in any practical feeding system, because protein supplements are usually much more expensive than energy feeds and wasteful usage increases the cost of production in almost all instances.

As pointed out in Ch. 3, the need for protein differs with different species. For monogastric species and young suckling ruminants (preruminants), a diet must supply the essential amino acids, thus quality is important because protein quality is a measure of the ability of a protein to supply needed amino acids in the diet. For ruminant species the dietary need is a combination of needs to nourish the microorganisms and needs for an adequate supply of digestible essential amino acids in the gut. High-producing ruminants pass appreciable amounts of some ingested proteins into the intestines without it being metabolized in the rumen; protein quality is more important under these circumstances

than for animals producing at low levels and consuming much less feed. This topic is discussed in more detail later in the chapter.

Most energy supplements (except for fat, starch, or refined sugar) supply some protein, but usually not enough to meet total needs except for adult animals in a maintenance situation. Thus supplementary protein sources are often needed in rations for all species of animals.

Protein supplements are arbitrarily defined (by NRC) as those feedstuffs which have 20 percent or more crude protein (dry basis). Many proteins from animal, marine, plant, or microbial sources are available as well as nonprotein N sources such as urea and biuret, which come from chemical manufacturing processes. Some commentary will be presented on most of the more common sources.

The selection of a given protein to use in a feed formula is affected by several different considerations. One of the principal items, of course, is availability and cost in the area. Many protein sources are available in limited supply in some localities, while others are available on a nationwide or worldwide basis.

A second and quite important factor for

monogastric species is the content and availability of amino acids. The content is reasonably well defined, but much less information has been published on availability. Data on digestibility of N are available on all common protein supplements. Such information is not complete, because it does not provide information on availability of critical amino acids. This type of information must be collected using other techniques to measure absorption from the small gut with the use of animals with intestinal cannulas and/or catheters implanted in blood vessels draining the small gut. Obviously, not much information of this type is available, especially under practical conditions.

Likewise, digestibility data on N sources such as urea are of little value. This is so because such compounds are highly soluble and are probably completely absorbed, thus yielding high digestibility values. However, excretion of urea via the urine will also be high, showing that it is not utilized by the animal as well as digestibility data indicate.

At the present time most nutritionists (and computer programs) simply match up analytical data on critical amino acids with amino acid needs as listed in feeding standards. If information were available on true availability of amino acids, listed requirements for various amino acids would undoubtedly be lower than now shown.

A third and quite important factor is the presence of undesirable or toxic compounds in protein supplements. This is particularly a problem with plant sources, but it may also be a problem with some animal proteins. This topic will be discussed in more detail in a later section.

Last, but not always least, is the content of other nutrients. Many protein sources are an excellent source of P, which often needs to be added to rations in some form or other. The various vitamins and trace minerals may also be worthy of consideration if there is difficulty in making a decision on which protein source to use.

COMMERCIAL PROTEIN SOURCES

The major protein sources manufactured and utilized in the feed trade or sold directly to livestock enterprises are listed in Table 8–1. These data show clearly that soybean meal is the predominant protein source, providing 69 percent of the tonnage in 1986 of those sources

listed in this table. Tankage and meat meal, corn gluten feed and meal, distillers dried grains, and cottonseed meal followed in order of tonnage for that particular year. It is obvious that cottonseed meal use has declined. Part of the decline may be due to production of less cotton, but part of it is also due to a change in usage because whole cottonseed has become a favored feed ingredient in dairy cow rations. Peanut meal use has declined while sunflower has increased tenfold in the past 10 years. Other oilseed meals not listed in this table (statistics not readily available) include safflower meal and rapeseed meal. Gluten feed and meal production has increased appreciably, reflecting a greater use of corn for wet milling use. Likewise, the use of distillers dried grains has increased markedly. No doubt part of the increase reflects increased production of ethanol; however, in the past it was common for feedlots to be located quite close to distilleries so that the wet distillers grains could be used with only a short haul to the feedlot. Thus the increased use may partly represent a shift in usage. Note that the production of alfalfa meal (most of it is dehydrated) has declined to about half of that produced 10 years ago. There are also several animal protein sources not listed in this table. Important sources would include feather and hair meals and several products produced from poultry slaughtering plants and hatcheries. In addition, there are many other minor plant and animal products that are not listed but which will be named and described to some extent later on in this chapter. Overall, we are producing about 24 percent more tonnage of these protein sources (listed in the table) than was the case in 1976.

PLANT PROTEIN SOURCES

Oilseed Meals

Oilseed meals are produced from a variety of crops (see Table 8–1) that have seeds which are high in oil. The oils all have important nutritional or industrial uses. Soybeans, peanuts, and sunflowers are grown primarily for their seed, and all produce edible oils used in the human food trade. Cottonseed is strictly a by-product of cotton production, but its oil is widely used in food and for other uses. Flax used to be grown to provide the fibers for linen cloth production and for the oil from the seed which is used as a drying oil in paint and for other industrial uses. Demand for linen cloth is much less than

TABLE 8-1

Processed protein sources used as feed in the United States (in thousands of metric tons)

Source	Crop Year 1976	1981	1986[a]
Oilseed meals			
Soybean[b]	14,056	16,070	18,461
Cottonseed	1,556	1,812	1,018
Linseed	114	100	115
Peanut	203	107	93
Sunflower	23	181	236
Total of oilseed	15,952	18,270	19,923
Other plant sources			
Gluten feed and meal	1,038	1,298	1,960
Brewers dried grains	297	194	145
Distillers dried grains	374	681	1,190
Alfalfa meal[c]	1,202	898	622
Total	2,911	3,071	3,971
Animal protein meals			
Tankage & meat meal	2,200	2,261	2,440
Fish meal & solubles	414	480	386
Dried milk products	160	165	91
Total	2,774	2,906	2,917
Grand total	21,637	24,247	26,757

[a]Partially forecast.
[b]Includes use in edible soy products and shipments to U.S. territories.
[c]Not always listed as a protein supplement.
Source: USDA (1).

it was before the days of synthetic fibers, and production of other types of paints and varnishes has reduced the need for linseed oil.

As a group the oilseed meals are high in crude protein (Table 8–2); protein levels of those meals shown in the table are all 40 percent or more except safflower meal with hulls. The crude protein content is standardized before marketing by dilution with hulls or other material. A high percentage of the N is present as true protein (90 percent±), which is usually highly digestible and of moderate to good biological value, although of usually lower value than good animal protein sources. As an average about 9 percent of the crude protein of oilseed meals is from nucleic acid protein as compared to 8.8 percent in fish meal, 3.5 percent in meat and bone meal, and 14–20 percent in yeast. This source of N is of questionable value even for ruminant species.

Most meals are low in cystine and methionine and have a variable and usually low lysine content (Table 8–3; Appendix Table 3); soybean meal is an exception in lysine content. The energy content varies greatly, depending on processing methods. Note in Table 8–2 that the Ca content is usually low. Most meals are high in P content, although half or more is present as phytin P, a form poorly utilized by monogastrics. These meals contain low to moderate levels of the B-vitamins and are low in carotene and vitamin E.

The oilseed meals are processed to remove the oil with three primary methods at present. The methods are designated as screw press (or expeller), direct solvent, and prepress solvent. In the expeller process the seed, after cracking and drying, is cooked for 15-20 minutes, then extruded through dies with the use of a variable-pitch screw. This results in rather high temperatures which may cause reduced solubility as well as reduced biological value of the protein. Usually only a moderate amount of heating for short periods of time is necessary to inactivate some of the antinutritional factors (see later section). If longer or excessive levels of heat are involved, reactions involving carbohydrates (glucose) and amino acids may occur (browning reaction) which result in formation of linkages between glucose and some amino acids. When this reac-

TABLE 8-2

Data on different types of protein sources (dry-matter basis)*

Source	Typical Dry Matter %	Crude Protein %	Ether Extract %	ADF %	TDN %	Minerals Ash %	Ca %	p %	Mg %
Plant sources									
20–30% CP range									
Beans, cull navy	90	25.0	1.6	6	83	4.6	0.17	0.60	0.15
Brewers dried grains	92	26.0	7.2	23	66	4.1	0.29	0.54	0.15
Coconut meal, solv. extd.	92	23.1	2.7	24	74	7.3	0.18	0.66	0.39
Corn distillers solubles, dried	93	28.9	5.7	6	88	7.2	0.38	1.47	0.69
Corn gluten feed	90	27.5	2.8	10	82	8.6	0.45	0.89	0.32
Malt sprouts	92	28.0	1.6	20	68	6.7	0.26	0.84	0.23
Safflower meal, mech. extd. (w/hulls)	91	22.8	7.6	45	57	4.2	0.28	0.79	0.36
Wheat germ meal	90	28.1	10.2	5	95	5.8	0.06	1.16	0.28
30%+ CP									
Alfalfa seed screenings	90	34.4	10.9	15	86	5.6			
Brewers dried yeast	93	48.3	0.8	4	78	7.7	0.14	1.54	0.25
Corn gluten meal	90	48.0	2.4	5	87	3.9	0.15	0.45	0.05
Cottonseed meal, 41% solv. extd.	92	44.8	2.3	20	75	6.9	0.17	1.31	0.61
Linseed meal, solv. extd.	90	40.7	1.1	13	82	6.4	0.43	0.95	0.66
Rapeseed meal, solv. extd.	92	44.0	1.2	13	71	7.8	0.72	1.01	0.50
Soybean meal, solv. extd. 44%	89	49.6	1.4	10	81	6.8	0.36	0.75	0.30
Sunflower meal, solv. extd.	93	50.3	1.2	30	65	6.3	0.40	1.10	0.81
Animal sources									
Blood meal	89	89.6	1.1	—	68	4.9	0.31	0.25	0.25
Feather meal	90	87.4	2.9	1	63	3.8	0.20	0.75	0.21
Meat meal, 55%	93	59.3	7.8	2	73	26.9	8.19	4.31	0.29
Meat and bone meal, 50%	93	54.0	9.2	2	70	35.6	9.93	4.75	1.22
Marine sources									
Crab meal	95	31.6	2.3	9	27	31.0	18.95	1.57	0.92
Fish meal, herring	93	77.4	10.7	1	75	11.2	2.15	1.07	0.19
Fish solubles, dried	94	69.9	9.9	1	79	15.8	1.36	1.80	0.29
Milk sources									
Buttermilk, dried	93	34.2	5.6	—	86	10.8	1.07	0.73	0.10
Skim milk, dried	94	36.0	1.1	—	86	8.5	1.25	1.03	0.11

*Most values are from NRC publications

tion occurs, the aminio acid(s) become less available to the animal because the linkage cannot be hydrolyzed completely in the intestinal tract. The result is that the biological value of the protein decreases markedly. Amino acids of concern are lysine and, to a lesser degree, arginine, histidine, and tryptophan. A similar reaction occurs with gossypol (in cottonseed) and lysine. Fortunately, these problems are well recognized by the oilseed processors, with the result that most meals are of higher or more uniform quality than formerly.

TABLE 8-3
Crude protein and essential amino acid content of several important protein supplements*

Item	Dried Skim Milk	Meat Meal	Fish Meal, Herring	Corn Gluten Meal, Solv. Extd.	Cottonseed Meal, Solv. Extd.	Safflower Meal w/o Hulls, Solv. Extd.	Soybean Meal, Solv. Extd.	Yeast, Dried Brewers
Dry matter, %	94.3	88.5	93.0	90.0	91.0	90.0	89.1	93.7
Crude protein	36.0	55.0	77.4	48.0	45.5	46.5	52.4	47.8
Essential amino acids								
Arginine	1.23	3.0	4.5	1.6	4.6	4.1	3.8	2.3
Cystine	0.48	0.4	0.9	0.7	0.7	0.8	0.8	0.5
Histidine	0.96	0.9	1.6	1.0	1.1	1.1	1.4	1.2
Isoleucine	2.45	1.7	3.5	2.6	1.3	1.9	2.8	2.2
Leucine	3.51	3.2	5.7	7.3	2.4	2.8	4.3	3.4
Lysine	2.73	2.6	6.2	0.9	1.7	1.4	3.4	3.2
Methionine	0.96	0.8	2.3	1.1	0.5	0.8	0.7	0.7
Phenylalanine	1.60	1.8	3.1	3.2	2.2	2.1	2.8	1.9
Threonine	1.49	1.8	3.2	1.6	1.3	1.5	2.2	2.2
Tryptophan	0.45	0.5	0.9	0.2	0.5	0.7	0.7	0.5
Valine	2.34	2.2	4.1	2.4	1.9	2.6	2.8	2.5

*Composition on dry basis. Data from NRC publications.

Solvent-extracted meals are extracted with hexane or other solvents, usually at low temperatures. When low temperatures are used, usually the meal will be heated or toasted after the solvent is removed. The heating is necessary for some meals to inactivate antiquality factors. A combination method, called prepress-solvent extraction, is often used. The seed oils are partially removed with a modifier expeller process and then extracted with solvents. In the case of cottonseed meal, the solvent and prepress solvent methods each account for about 40 percent of total seed processing. The maximum amount of fat can be removed with the prepress solvent method while the least amount of fat is removed with the expeller process. N solubility is also higher with the solvent method than with the other two methods.

In addition to the high-protein meals (40 percent± CP), a number of protein supplements are available in the 20-30 percent CP range (Table 8–2, Appendix Tables 2, 3). Feedstuffs in this range include grain legumes (peas, beans), several milling by-products such as corn gluten feed, germ meals, distillery and brewery by-products, and other feeds such as coconut meal (or copra), an important source in some tropical countries. As a group, these lower protein meals tend to have protein that is usually less digestible (Table 8–2) and of lower biological value than the high-protein meals. In addition, the fiber content is often higher and the energy value is lower than for the oilseed meals. Photos of some of the common meals are shown in Fig. 8–1.

Soybean Meal

Whole soybeans (*Glycine max*) contain 15–21 percent oil, which is usually removed by solvent extraction during preparation of the meal. The meal is toasted, a process which improves the biological value of its protein; the protein content is standardized at 44 or 50 percent (as fed basis) by dilution with soybean hulls. Soybean meal is produced in large and ever increasing amounts in the United States and is a highly favored feed ingredient because it is quite palatable, highly digestible, of high energy value (Table 8–2), and results in excellent performance when used for different animal species. Methionine is the most limiting amino acid for monogastric species (Table 8–3), and the B-vitamin content is low. In overall value soybean meal is the best plant protein source available in any quantity, and it is the standard protein source in many rations used for broilers and swine.

As with most other oilseeds (and plant high-protein seeds), soybeans have a number of toxic, stimulatory, or inhibitory substances. Raw soybeans are of lower nutritional value than heat-treated soybeans or soybean meal. For example, chicks show a growth depression on a ra-

Soybean meal

Cottonseed meal

Linseed meal

Meat meal

Fish meal

Feather meal

Brewers dried yeast

Malt sprouts

Urea

FIGURE 8-1. Examples of common protein supplements.

tion with raw beans for the first 8-12 weeks of life, but eventually they gain weight at a rate equal to those fed heated beans. Sheep, swine, and calves are also affected by inhibitors in raw beans. Hens produced eggs just as fertile as those they produce when on treated beans, but the eggs have more blood spots in the yolks. Raw soybeans cause the pancreas of affected animals to become enlarged, and fat absorption is reduced. Heat treatment, particularly pressure cooking, is effective in removing most of the inhibitory effect. The inhibitory factor(s) depress utilization of methionine and cystine or both, but addition of these amino acids to the ration does not restore performance to that of birds fed heat-treated beans. Addition of antibiotics enhances performance of animals fed raw soybeans.

Soybeans also contain at least four proteins which inhibit trypsin (or chymotrypsin) activity (antitrypsin factor). The presence of this factor (not restricted to soybeans) reduces protein digestibility, which is accompanied by increased excretion of N and S. Heat treatment inactivates this factor. A goitrogenic material is found in soybean meal, and its long-term use at high levels may result in goiter in some animal species, particularly if iodine content of the ration is low. Other antiquality factors include saponins and proteins that cause agglutination of red blood cells in the laboratory. The latter is readily inactivated by pepsin, and both are inactivated by heat treatment. Soybeans also contain genistein, a plant estrogen, which may account, in some cases, for part of the high growth-inducing properties of the meal. Some meals also contain relatively high levels of phytic acid, which may interfere with Zn utilization.

Dehulled, solvent-extracted soybean meal is sometimes used in animal feeds. The dehulling process results in a higher protein content with less fiber. Some unextracted soybeans are fed after appropriate heat processing (110 °C for 3 minutes) and grinding. The product is known in the feed trade as **full-fat soybean meal** and officially as **ground extruded whole soybeans**. It contains about 38 percent CP, 18 percent fat, and 5 percent fiber and has a higher energy value because of the high oil content. Heating-extruding equipment has been developed for on-the-farm processing, and its use appears feasible in relatively small operations. Such meal has found some favor in dairy cow rations and, in moderate amounts, in rations for swine and poultry. Heat-treated soybeans can be used to replace all of the soybean meal in corn-soy rations for growing-finishing pigs.

Soy flour is the finely powdered material resulting after screening the ground, dehulled, extracted meal. It is often used as a partial replacement for milk proteins in milk replacers. For the food trade, **soy protein concentrate** is prepared from dehulled beans that have been fat-extracted and leached with water to remove water-soluble nonprotein constituents. It must have not less than 70 percent CP (dry basis). It is used as a protein extender in food products and is used to produce texturized products resembling meat because it can be spun into fibers.

Examples of recent feeding trials comparing soybean meal to other proteins are shown in Table 8–4 for swine and poultry and in Table 8–5 for ruminants. Note that soybean meal always produced very acceptable performance, although some of the data indicate that combinations with other proteins might, in some cases, allow slightly improved production (gain, efficiency, or lactation).

Cottonseed Meal

The cotton plant (*Gossypium* spp) will grow in hot areas, thus cottonseed meal (CSM) is available in many areas where soybeans do not grow, particularly in some areas in South America, northern Africa, and Asia. CSM protein is of good, although variable, quality as a result of variations in processing procedures. Most meals are standardized (in the United States) at 41 percent CP (as fed), but meals may be found, at times, with 44 and 48 percent CP.

The protein of CSM is low in cystine, methionine, and lysine, and the meal is low in Ca and carotene. Although palatable for ruminants, CSM is less well liked by swine and poultry. Nevertheless, it finds widespread use in animal feeds, although its use is more limited by various antinutritional factors than that of soybean meal.

The cotton seed contains a yellow pigment, gossypol, which is relatively toxic to monogastric species, particularly young pigs and chicks. A high percentage of the gossypol in the seed is free (readily removed), but heat processing results in the formation of various complexes including a gossypol-lysine complex. Prepress solvent meals tend to have the highest levels of bound gossypol, while the screw press meals tend to have the highest levels of free gossypol. Research evidence indicates that free gossypol is the toxic form. It is generally agreed that free

TABLE 8-4

Recent examples of comparative feeding trials with swine and poultry fed different protein sources

Comparison	Daily Gain	Feed Consumed/d	Feed to Gain Ratio	Reference No.
Growing-finishing pigs, 25–95 kg				
Soybean meal[a]	0.68 kg	2.11 kg	3.08	2
4% blood meal	0.71	2.11	2.98	
6% blood meal	0.69	2.05	2.96	
8% blood meal	0.60	1.90	3.21	
Soybean meal	0.74	2.55	3.40	2
Blood-meat meal	0.72	2.40	3.33	
Soybean-blood meal	0.73	2.33	3.16	
Soybean-meat meal	0.76	2.45	3.22	
Growing-finishing pigs, 18–98 kg				
Soybean meal	0.85	2.35	2.79	3
SBM + glandless cottonseed				
Ground	0.82	2.27	2.27	
Extruded	0.82	2.79	2.78	
Young pigs (25 d-old fed for 4 weeks)				
Soybean meal	408 g	639 g	1.57	4
1/3 yeast[b]	418	630	1.51	
2/3 yeast	399	609	1.53	
All yeast	373	599	1.61	

Comparison	Daily Gain		Gain/feed	Reference No.
Young chicks, fed for 2 weeks[c]				
Dehulled soybean meal	226 g/2 wk		0.75	5
Extruded soybeans	241		0.80	
Extruded red beans	178		0.68	
1/3 beans, 2/3 soybeans	221		0.78	
2/3 beans, 1/3 soybeans	228		0.75	
Turkey poults, fed from 7 to 42 d of age				
Soybean meal	1.79 kg total gain		0.66	6
Soybean-fish meal[d]	1.87		0.65	
Soybean-rapeseed meal[d]	1.79		0.63	
Rapeseed-fish meal[d]	1.89		0.63	

[a]Basal diet contained 17.5% soybean meal; blood meal (new process) at the designated levels replaced an equivalent amount of protein, and corn was increased accordingly.

[b]Soybean meal was replaced by a combination of yeast and corn.

[c]The red beans (*Phaseolus vulgaris*) were extruded, as were the mixtures of beans and soybeans. For the data shown here, methionine was added to all diets.

[d]Herring meal was fed at 0, 60 or 120 g/kg and rapeseed meal at levels of 0, 150, 300 or 450 g/kg in all possible combinations. Only the overall means are shown.

gossypol levels (total ration) of less than 40, 100, and 100 ppm are not problems for layers, broilers, and swine, respectively. Toxicity for swine and poultry can be reduced or eliminated by addition of iron salts such as ferrous sulfate. Recommended levels are 1-2 ppm of additional Fe for each ppm of free gossypol for broilers and about 4:1 for layers. Older research evidence indicated that gossypol might be inactivated in the rumen of ruminant animals. However, more recent research (25) indicates that levels of 24 g/d of free gossypol for high-producing dairy cows resulted in toxicity (reduced blood hemoglobin, erythrocyte fragility, increased total protein of plasma, elevated respiration rates at hot ambient temperatures). Although gossypol was detected in liver and plasma, it was not found in milk from the cows fed high levels of CSM. Reduced feed intake also occurred. Feeding large amounts of whole cottonseed also results in small amounts of gossypol in serum and liver tissue and small amounts of cyclopropene fatty acids in tissue lipids and milk fat (26). These experiments suggest that some of the gossypol

TABLE 8-5

Recent examples of comparative feeding trials with lambs, beef cattle, or lactating dairy cows fed different protein sources

Comparison	Daily Gain	Feed Consumed/d	Feed to Gain Ratio	Reference No.
Finishing lambs, high sorghum ration				
Cottonseed meal	289 g	1.48 kg	5.29	7
Soybean meal	290	1.38	4.76	
Guar meal	200	1.22	6.10	
Blood meal	250	1.37	5.48	
Feather meal	250	1.39	5.56	
Urea	260	1.41	5.42	
Finishing lambs, sorghum-cottonseed hull ration				
Cottonseed meal	227	1.84	8.11	8
Sunflower meal	256	1.91	7.46	
Cottonseed-sunflower	246	1.96	7.97	
Finishing lambs, high roughage pellet				
Alfalfa-barley pellet	210	1.95	9.29	9
+ 10% cull beans	200	1.89	9.45	
+ 20% cull beans	160	1.79	11.19	
Finishing lambs, high corn-corncob ration				
Soybean meal	289	1.86	6.6	10
Blood meal	250	1.90	7.6	
Meat & bone meal	210	1.65	7.9	
Dehy. alfalfa	250	2.06	8.2	
Finishing lambs, high-roughage pellet				
Cottonseed meal	390	2.35	6.0	11
Liquefied fish-urea	370	2.26	6.1	
Urea	380	2.29	5.9	
Growing cattle, high corn silage ration				
Urea	0.79 kg	5.93 kg	7.6	12
Soybean meal	0.94	6.33	6.8	
Blood meal	0.95	6.35	6.7	
Meat & bone meal	0.89	6.20	7.0	
Dehy. alfalfa	0.94	6.69	7.1	
Finishing steers, high corn ration				
Urea	1.27	7.76	6.13	10
Soybean meal	1.33	8.13	6.13	
Wet corn gluten feed	1.38	8.80	6.37	
Dry corn gluten feed	1.35	9.46	7.01	
Finishing cattle, high corn ration[a]				
Soybean meal	1.25	7.97	6.4	10
Blood meal	1.33	8.29	6.2	
Meat & bone meal	1.36	8.41	6.2	
Finishing cattle, med. grain ration				
Cottonseed meal-urea	1.72	9.9	5.8	13
Cottonseed-feather meal	1.72	10.1	5.8	
Feather meal-urea	1.72	9.4	5.5	
Finishing cattle, high-moisture corn, corn silage[b]				
Soybean meal	0.98	6.32	6.4	14
Soybean-feather meal	0.99	6.29	6.4	
Soybean-hair meal	0.99	6.67	6.7	

TABLE 8-5

(cont.)

Comparison	Daily Gain	Feed Consumed/d	Feed to Gain Ratio	Reference No.
Finishing cattle, ground shelled corn, corn cobs				
Soybean meal-urea	1.05	7.2	6.9	15
Crambe meal-urea	1.03	7.1	6.9	

Lactating dairy cows	DM consumed per d, kg	FCM/d kg	Milk fat, %	
Corn silage, alfalfa-grass hay, concentrate				
Soybean meal[c]	17.8	20.7	3.96	16
Sunflower meal[c]	17.9	20.5	3.87	
Corn silage, alfalfa hay, concentrate				
Basal ration[d]	17.3	22.3	3.52	17
+ whole cottonseed[d]				
(1.9 kg/d)	18.1	25.1	3.57	
Control[e]	18.0	24.1	3.66	17
Whole cottonseed[e]	18.4	25.4	3.70	
Energy equivalent[e]	18.5	24.4	3.60	
Urea-treated corn silage, alfalfa-grass hay, concentrate				
Soybean meal[f]	19.3	21.2	3.8	18
Tower rapeseed meal[f]	19.1	23.1	3.9	
Turret rapeseed meal[f]	18.7	20.7	3.9	
Hay-concentrate diet				
Cottonseed meal	21.0	36.7	3.52	19
Rapeseed meal (low glucosinolate)	20.8	38.5	3.54	
Corn silage, alfalfa silage, ensiled gr. corn				
Soybean meal	20.1	26.2	3.45	20
Wet brewers grains	20.1	28.9	3.22	
Dried brewers grains	22.3	29.4	3.09	
Corn silage, alfalfa cubes, concentrate				
Soybean meal	19.7	33.3	3.74	21
75% ESB, 25% CGM[g]	19.2	29.4	3.58	
50% ESB, 50% CGM[g]	18.8	29.3	3.59	
25% ESB, 75% CGM[g]	19.6	32.0	3.81	
Corn silage, alfalfa hay, conc. (complete diet)[h]				
Soybean meal	19.3	27.2	2.98	22
Heated soybean meal	20.1	29.0	2.89	
Extruded soybeans	20.5	28.5	2.63	
Corn silage, corn grain rations				
Soybean meal	24.2	31.6	3.48	23
+ dehy. alfalfa	23.8	31.0	3.58	
+ dehy. alfalfa + urea	24.0	30.7	3.63	
Corn silage, alfalfa hay, concentrate				
Gr. corn, soybean meal	20.1	29.9	3.06	24
Corn, soybean meal,				
+ chickpeas	20.0	30.4	3.09	
Chickpeas	20.6	31.1	3.28	

[a]All rations contained 0.2% urea.

[b]Feather or hair meal supplied half the supplemental protein in rations where fed.

[c]When sunflower meal was fed, the concentrate contained more rolled oats and less corn to equalize the fiber content.

[d]When fed, whole cottonseed replaced an equivalent amount of concentrate. Trial was for 56 d.

TABLE 8-5

(cont.)

eCows were fed in a Latin Square arrangement of treatments so that each cow was fed each ration for a 4-week period. The control ration was the same as the previous experiment (d). When whole cottonseed was fed, it replaced 20% of the concentrate fed. For the energy equivalent ration, additional concentrate was fed so that the energy (ME) was equivalent to the whole cottonseed ration.

fRapeseed meal replaced soybean meal and straw. Tower RSM is a newer variety low in glucosinolates (20.5 vs. 36.2 μmol/g for Turret). Cows were fed for an 8-week period.

gA different concentrate was fed to those cows getting extruded soybeans (ESB) and corn gluten meal (CGM); it had added fat to compensate for the higher level of fat in the ESB.

hAll protein supplements were fed with and without methionine. Data shown here are without methionine.

must pass through the rumen without being metabolized by rumen microorganisms as was previously thought to be the case.

Although gossypol can be removed by extraction with a mixture of hexane, acetone, and water, such extraction is not used in practice. Gossypol is produced by glands in the seed that can be reduced in size or removed by genetic changes in the plant. Meals from glandless seeds have resulted in good performance with poultry, although not with young pigs. Low gossypol and/or biologically tested meals are available in some areas. The biologically tested meals are tested by feeding to hens, but this, obviously, increases the cost.

CSM also creates problems with egg quality if fed in high levels. The gossypol tends to produce green egg yolks. In addition, a fatty acid (sterculic acid) found in CSM can cause egg whites to turn pink during storage. Obviously, either condition would be undesirable. If fed to poultry, direct solvent or prepress solvent meals are recommended because of these factors. As a result of the presence of the antiquality factors mentioned, the feeding of CSM to monogastric species is usually limited to a portion of the protein supplement fed.

The feeding of whole cottonseed to lactating dairy cows has become popular in recent years. Evidence (see Table 8-5) indicates that it may be somewhat stimulatory for milk production, usually for milk fat percentage, but also for FCM production. Other examples where CSM has been compared to other protein supplements for ruminants are shown in Table 8-5.

Sunflower Meal

Sunflowers (*Helianthus annuus*) are produced for oil and seeds, primarily in northern Europe and Russia and, in recent years, in Canada and the northern states of the United States. This plant will grow in cooler and drier climates than will soybean or cotton plants. The meal, although high in protein (50 percent± if dehulled, dry basis), is deficient in lysine, but

otherwise the quality of the meal is comparable to that of soybean meal. However, the relatively high fiber content (Table 8-2) discourages use in poultry and swine feeds; when used for these species, the amount fed should be restricted because of the fiber, particularly for younger animals, or the dehulled meal should be used.

Studies with sunflower meal with ruminants indicate that it produces performance comparable to that with soybean or cottonseed meal (Table 8-5). It has also been suggested that whole sunflower seeds are an efficient way of providing nutrients for lactating dairy goats without the risk of producing acidosis and enterotoxemia (because of the high fiber content).

Peanut Meal

Peanut meal (called groundnut meal in England) is available in substantial amounts in many countries because peanuts (*Arachis hypogaea*) are produced for human food in many warmer areas. The protein content varies from 45-55 percent, and the quality is influenced by the processing as well as the amount of hulls in the meal. Peanut meals are quite deficient in lysine, and the protein is low in digestibility, possibly because of tannins found in the skins. In addition, peanuts may frequently be contaminated with molds such as *Aspergillus flavus*, a fungus that produces a potent toxin of particular concern with young animals. Peanut meal is quite palatable to swine, and research with swine has indicated a value equivalent to soybean meal if fed with feeds not low in lysine or methionine. No recent information appears to be available on ruminants or poultry.

Safflower Meal

Safflower (*Carthamus tictorius*) is a plant grown in increasing (but limited) amounts for its oil. The plant also has the advantage that it does not require as much water as many other oilseed plants. The meal is high in fiber and low in protein unless the hulls are removed. The hulls make up about 40 percent of the seed and 60 percent of the meal, which contains 18–22 percent CP. Partial removal of hulls results in a meal with about 46 percent CP and 21 percent ADF. The protein is deficient in S-containing amino acids and lysine. Research studies with both swine and poultry indicate that its use should be restricted to provide only part of the supplementary protein. For ruminants, the high fiber is no problem, and it is utilized well by both sheep and cattle (Table 8–5).

Linseed Meal

Linseed meal is made from flax seed (*Linum usitatissimum*), which is now produced primarily for the drying oils it contains, although the flax plant was used extensively in the past to produce fibers used to weave linen cloth. Linseed meal accounts for only a small part of the total plant proteins produced in North America (Table 8–1). The CP content is relatively low (35 percent) and it is deficient in lysine, but it contains selenium in higher amounts than most feeds owing to the fact that most of the flax in the United States is grown on soils relatively high in Se. The meal may contain a cyanogenic glycoside (produces toxic hydrogen cyanide) in small amounts as well as an antipyridoxine factor. Linseed meal is favored in rations for ruminants and horses and, sometimes, for sow diets, but it is rarely used for poultry because of its poor amino acid distribution, its high fiber, and its laxative nature. In addition, it is usually priced higher/unit of protein than some of the other oilseed meals.

Rapeseed Meal

Rapeseed meal may be produced from a Polish type rapeseed (*Brasica campestris*) or the Argentine type (*B. napus*). Rape is a crop which will grow in colder climates than the soybean or cotton plants, thus it is of interest in areas such as northern Europe and Asia, Canada, the northern states in the United States, and in colder areas of South America (27).

Solvent-extracted meals run about 41–43 percent CP (dry basis) and have a good distribution of amino acids. Rapeseed meal contains less lysine than soybean meal but more methionine and, in general, is probably less palatable than soybean meal. Some meals contain a high level of tannic acid, which may depress growth of young animals.

In common with other members of the *Brassica* species, rapeseed contains goitrogenic compounds which are attributed to a group of compounds called glucosinolates. Although the glucosinolates themselves are biologically inactive, they can be hydrolyzed by enzymes in the seed to produce isothiocyanates, thiocyanates, nitriles, and various derivatives of these chemicals. Fortunately, selected cultivars of both species have been developed that contain lower levels of the glucosinolates. Recent feeding trials with dairy cows and calves indicate that the low-glucosinolate meals do not cause any problems other than a slight increase in thiocyanate in milk (18, 28). One example of data from a trial with turkey poults is shown in Table 8–4, and the two from lactation trials are shown in Table 8–5. Thus if rapeseed meal is to be used in substantial amounts to replace other protein supplements, the low-glucosinolate meals should be used. Rapeseed meals with less than 3 mg of glucosinolates/g of solid may now be labeled Canola meal in the United States, an official change in terminology since the last edition of this book.

Sesame Meal

Sesame meal is produced as a by-product of extracting oil from sesame seed (*Sesame indicum*). The plant is grown primarily in India and China, although production is increasing in California. The meal contains 38–48 percent CP (dry basis) which is low in lysine but which has good levels of methionine. It can be used in limited amounts in diets for simple-stomached animals. The meal apparently contains enough phytic acid to interfere with Zn utilization under some conditions.

Miscellaneous Oilseed Meals

A few other oilseed meals are available in very limited amounts in some areas. These would include **babassu meal, castor seed meal, crambe meal** (one example given on crambe meal is in Table 8–5), **hempseed meal, meadowfoam meal,** and **mustard seed meal.** On the basis of quantity produced, these meals are not important at this time, although several of them show some promise in particular climatic and soil conditions. Several of them, such as castor meal, crambe meal, and meadowfoam meal, contain antinutritional factors which either require special processing or feeding methods that restrict their use for most animal species.

General Comments

Some of the good points and limitations of the various oilseed meals have been discussed. The reader should be aware that these protein sources can be used in moderation in rations for nearly all animals. As a general rule, one-quarter to one-third of a basal protein concentrate can often be replaced with less common meals without any marked effect on animal production and often at a reduced cost of production.

MILLFEED PROTEIN SOURCES

Corn millfeeds with 20 percent or more CP include corn gluten feed, corn gluten meal and condensed fermented corn extractives (corn solubles) produced from wet milling methods, and corn germ meal that comes from either wet or dry methods. Similar products are produced from milling sorghum grain, although in much smaller quantities. Small amounts of germ meal are produced from wheat or other grains milled for flour.

Corn gluten meal is marketed at levels of about 41 or 60 percent CP (as fed). It is the residue remaining after removal of the larger part of the starch and germ and separation of the bran. **Gluten feed** contains gluten meal (corn bran with or without the fermented extractives) and usually has a protein level of 21–23 percent (as fed). The **fermented extractives** are condensed material derived from steeping corn in water prior to milling. The water content is about 50 percent and the protein 21–23 percent. The **germ meal** has the best overall balance of amino acids.

The protein in these different products resembles somewhat that in the parent grain in that lysine or tryptophan are usually the most limiting amino acids but, on the other hand, the S-containing amino acids are found in higher concentrations (Table 8–3). Gluten meal is used in rations for all farm livestock, and the 60 percent meal with added xanthophylls is used in poultry feed as a source of protein but also for the pigments (for skin or yolk color). The gluten feed, because of its high fiber content, is not often used for poultry or growing pigs. The water content of the solubles limits its use in dry feeds.

There has been quite a bit of research interest in these products recently. One example of comparative trials is given with finishing steers and one with lactating cows in Table 8–5. Two other papers might be mentioned (29, 30), both of which present data which show that corn gluten feed makes a satisfactory supplement to either fescue hay or native grass hay. The protein in corn gluten feed or meal is not as soluble as the protein in some products such as soybean meal.

Similar products produced from sorghum grains include **grain sorghum gluten feed, grain sorghum gluten meal,** and **grain sorghum germ cake** or **germ meal.**

DISTILLERY AND BREWERY BY-PRODUCTS

Over 1 percent of the corn crop in the United States is used for manufacturing beers and distilled liquors, and most of the residue, minus part of the starch, is returned as animal feed. In manufacturing of bourbon whiskey, a mash must contain a minimum of 51 percent corn, but more typical ingredients include 75 percent corn, 12 percent rye, and 13 percent malted barley (31). The grains are cooked with water and cooled, and the barley malt is added to provide a source of enzymes to produce maltose and dextrin. Yeast is then added and the mixture is fermented. Following fermentation and distillation, the solids are recovered in different ways and dried. Feedstuffs produced include condensed and dried distillers solubles, distillers dried grains, and distillers dried grain with solubles. **Distillers dried grains** account for the largest volume of distillery by-products. If official terminology is used in naming the grains, they may be listed as corn distillers grains, rye distillers grains, and so on, according to the predominant grain in the mix. Other protein supplements may also be available from the distilling industry. These would include **molasses distillers condensed** or **dried solubles** and **potato distillers dried residue.**

Analytical data on some of these products are given in Table 8–2 and in Appendix Table 1. The distillers dried grains are mainly differentiated by the relatively high fiber content (11–13 percent), but all have a protein content on the order of 27–29 percent due to the presence of yeast. The energy value is medium to high, and the B-vitamin content is high. The grains are relatively deficient in lysine and phenylalanine, but the solubles have a more balanced amino acid distribution. With regard to the minerals, the P content is relatively high, as is the S content. Some trace minerals, such as Se, are found in relatively high concentrations.

Protein sources from the beer industry include brewers dried grains, dried spent hops, malt sprouts, and brewers yeast. The **malt sprouts** are dried rootlets which are removed in the preparation of malted barley. **Brewers dried grains** are the dried residue of barley malt and other grains that have been used to provide maltose and dextrins for fermenting. **Brewers yeast** is surplus yeast used to ferment the wort, the liquid drawn off from the malt-grain mixture. **Dried spent hops** are obtained by drying the material filtered from hopped wort. **Brewers grains meal** is scalped brewers dried grains containing not less than 35 percent CP and not more than 10 percent moisture. **Converted cereal extractives** may be produced from effluents resulting from the production of malt, wort, ale, or beer.

Protein levels of the grains and malt sprouts range from 26–29 percent, and the quality is good. Lysine appears to be the most limiting amino acid in the dried grains and methionine for malt sprouts; tryptophan is relatively high in all brewery by-products. Brewers yeast has about 45 percent CP with high levels of lysine and tryptophan. The B-vitamin content is high, as it is in most fermentation by-products.

Use of brewers grains and malt sprouts is limited in monogastric rations because of the relatively high fiber level (18–19 and 14–16 percent, respectively). Brewers grains and distillers grains, as well as other fermentation by-products, have been touted as a good source of so-called unidentified growth factors. Whether there are, indeed, unidentified factors or an optimal combination of different nutrients remains to be seen, but they do produce favorable production responses in many circumstances (Table 8–5). The dried grains, in particular, have proteins that are resistant to degradation by rumen microorganisms. Research results show a good response when the dried grains are fed to animals needing higher levels of some amino acids. Wet brewers and distillers grains are often fed to cattle, but high moisture content requires that they be used regularly and close to the source of supply. Recent evidence (32) shows that ammonia can be used as a preservative for wet distillers grains without any detrimental effect on milk production by cows. This would, no doubt, be cheaper than drying.

OTHER PLANT PROTEIN SOURCES

Coconut or **copra meal,** the residue remaining after extraction and drying of the meat of the coconut (*Cocus nucifera*), is available in many tropical areas of the world. The protein content is low (20-26 percent, dry basis), it is relatively deficient in lysine and methionine, and it may be quite variable in digestibility and quality because of variations in processing methods. It is also subject to molding while drying. Coconut meal can be used to supply some of the supplementary protein for swine and poultry, but results with both poultry and swine have indicated a drop in performance when the meal has been used as a major protein source.

Palm kernel meal, a meal remaining after extraction of palm oil from seeds of *Elaeis guineenis,* apparently has some promise as a low-protein meal. It should be noted that the better-quality palm oil used as a feedstuff is extracted from the husk of the fruit rather than from the seeds.

Cull beans and **peas** of a number of different species are sometimes available for animal feeding, although they are usually grown primarily for human food. Those available include kidney beans, pinto beans, navy beans (*Phaseolus vulgaris*), broad or horse beans (*Vici faba*), lima beans (*P. lunatus*), and various types of peas such as the common green pea (*Pisum sativum*), chick-pea or garbanzo (*Cicer arietinum*), cowpea or black-eyed pea (*Vigna sinensis*), pigeon pea (*Cajanus indicus*), winged pea (*Lotus tetragonolobus*), and Austrian field pea (*Pisum* spp).

Pea and bean seeds generally contain 20-28 percent CP that tends to be deficient in S-containing amino acids as well as tryptophan. Pea seeds that have had adequate testing with animals generally are quite satisfactory when fed without processing (other than grinding) and will allow very satisfactory performance with all species. One example of use of chick-peas with lactating dairy cows is shown in Table 8–5.

Bean seeds, on the other hand, often contain antinutritional factors such as toxins or trypsin inhibitors. Because of the toxins and poor protein quality, use in feed for monogastric species should be limited, and some type of heat processing is highly desirable. Recent data (62) indicate that steaming at 100 °C for 75 min was adequate when cull beans were fed to pigs. Those steamed only 45 min resulted in reduced feed intake, diarrhea, and lower digestibility. Most beans can be used efficiently in ruminant rations, provided they are fed in moderate amounts (Table 8–5). Some of these grain legumes hold promise as complete energy-protein feeds for swine and poultry in tropical areas of the world. Considerable research is being carried out to identify high-yield varieties and to develop economical methods of removing or inactivating inhibitors and toxins.

Legume seed screenings (from seed production of alfalfa, clover, and the like) are often available in limited amounts in restricted areas. Limited research indicates that they are quite satisfactory as feeds for ruminants. Little research has been reported for other species. Crude protein content is usually on the order of 22–25 percent.

PROTEIN SUPPLEMENTS OF ANIMAL ORIGIN

Protein concentrates derived from animal tissues have been used for many years and are highly prized for supplemental sources. Because these products come from animal sources, the amino acid distribution is generally similar to dietary needs. However, it must be recognized that quality may be quite variable because products with essentially the same label may come from many different sources. In addition, quality may be affected markedly by processing methods and use of appropriate temperatures in cooking and drying the meals.

Meat Meal, Meat and Bone Meal

AFCO listings for animal products include **meat meal, meat and bone meal, meat meal tankage,** and **meat and bone meal tankage.** The only difference in the specifications between meal and tankage is that the meals shall not contain added dried blood. Meat meal is differentiated from meat and bone meal (or tankage) on the basis of P content. If the product contains more than 4.4 percent P, it shall be labeled as meat and bone. For all products (mentioned above) there are specifications that not more than 14 percent of the material shall be indigestible by pepsin and that not more than 11 percent of the CP shall be pepsin indigestible. These products are made from carcass trimmings, condemned carcasses, condemned livers, inedible offal (such as lungs), and bones. They are not supposed to include hair, hoof, horn, hide trimmings, manure, and stomach contents except in such amounts as may occur unavoidably in good factory practice.

In practice, tankage is the unground material produced by dry rendering, and meat meal is the material remaining after grinding (33). Nearly all of the tankage and other similar products goes to blenders, who then incorporate the different ingredients into meals which are standardized on the basis of protein and ash content. This results in much more uniform products to the feeder. These meals are usually standardized to have 45, 50, or 53-55 percent CP (as fed), usually by the addition of dried blood or dried meat solubles.

Most large meat packers process and produce meat meal and meat and bone meal. In addition, such products may be produced by rendering plants which utilize dead animals (from farms and feedlots), meat and bone wastage from wholesale meat houses, grocery stores, hotels, and so on. Products from rendering plants of this type are apt to be more variable in quality and in protein and ash content.

Data on animal experiments indicate that the protein is 81-87 percent digestible and that the limiting amino acids for swine with cereal diets are lysine, methionine, and threonine (34) and methionine and cystine for poultry (35). In meals with higher protein content, isoleucine may be limiting also, as this amino acid is quite deficient in blood meal. The protein quality is generally considered to be lower than that of fish meals or soybean meal (35).

In addition to protein, these meals have about 8 percent fat which is, of course, high in digestible energy. The ash content generally ranges from about 28-36 percent in blended meals, and about 7-10 percent of the meal will be Ca and 3.8-5 percent will be P; K, Mg, and Na also are present in substantial amounts. Consequently, meat meals may be an important dietary source of these minerals. On the other hand, the mineral content may limit usage in some cases. Meat meals (as with most animal products), fish meals, and fermentation products are a good to excellent source of vitamin B_{12}.

Blood Meal

Blood meal is produced from dried, ground blood. Drying is done by methods referred to as drum, ring, and flash. Flash drying, a relatively new process, results in a more uniform product than the other methods, and a meal that has a high available lysine content. The protein content of blood meal is about 85 percent and, except for isoleucine, it is an excellent source of other amino acids. Recent data on young pigs indicate that the better methods of drying produce a blood meal with about 7 percent available lysine (34). The meal is low in minerals (except Fe) and fiber as well.

Miscellaneous Mammalian Products

Other products available include **dried meat solubles,** which is obtained by drying the defatted water extract of the clean, wholesome parts of slaughtered animals prepared by steaming or hot water extraction. It must contain no less than 70 percent CP. **Dried liver meal** is sometimes available. A high proportion is derived from livers condemned because of abscesses, infection with liver flukes, worms of various types, or for other reasons. **Glandular meal** is produced by drying liver and other glandular tissues from slaughtered mammals. If a significant portion of the water-soluble material has been removed, it may be called **extracted glandular meal. Fleshings hydrolysate** is obtained by acid hydrolysis of the flesh from fresh or salted hides. It is defatted, strained, and neutralized. If evaporated to 50 percent solids, it is referred to as **condensed fleshings hydrolysate. Hydrolyzed hair** is produced in limited amounts. It must be cooked under pressure for relatively long periods to hydrolyze the hair protein. When prepared in this manner, it will contain a minimum of 80 percent CP, which is well utilized by ruminants (Table 8–5). **Animal by-product meal** is the dry product from animal tissues prepared for feeding when processed by steam or dry rendering. It must be designated according to its protein content. **Hydrolyzed leather meal** is also available in some areas. A considerable amount of steam cooking is required to produce a digestible product.

Miscellaneous Poultry Products

Hydrolyzed poultry feathers are produced in relatively large amounts. They must be cooked under steam pressure for 30-45 minutes to produce a digestible product in which the CP must be 75 percent digestible by pepsin. Feather meal may contain 85-90 percent CP, but it is deficient in cystine, methionine, lysine, histidine, and tryptophan for poultry (35), so care must be used in selecting other protein sources to complement the amino acid content. It is a satisfactory protein source for ruminant animals (Table 8–5).

Poultry by-product meal is made from ground, rendered, clean parts of the carcass (except feathers) of slaughtered poultry, such as heads, feet, undeveloped eggs, and intestines. It must contain not more than 16 percent ash and not more than 4 percent acid-insoluble ash. The CP content is on the order of 58 percent (as fed). It has proven to be a very satisfactory protein source for chickens.

Poultry hatchery by-product is a mixture of egg shells, infertile and unhatched eggs, and culled chicks which have been cooked, dried, and ground with or without removal of part of the fat. **Hydrolyzed poultry by-products aggregate** is the product resulting from heat treatment of all by-products of slaughter. The produce may, if acid-treated, be neutralized. It provides a satisfactory protein source for broilers if supplemented with methionine and lysine. **Dried poultry waste** is the dried excreta collected from caged layers. It contains 25-28 percent CP (dry basis) of which about one-third is true protein, and the remainder is nonprotein compounds such as uric acid (excreted by birds in urine). This product is not suitable for monogastric species because of the NPN and the high ash content (25-30 percent), but it can be used in some situations for ruminants, particularly in wintering or maintenance rations. **Poultry litter,** primarily from broiler operations, usually has enough CP to qualify as a protein source. There is a considerable amount of information on its use in ruminant diets for both sheep and cattle. It has been fed as is, ensiled with or without other products (such as corn forage), or fed after sun drying or dehydration. Overall, it is a rather cheap source of N for growing calves or for maintenance feeding of ewes or wintering beef cows. Neither dried poultry waste nor litter are permitted to be fed to lactating dairy cows.

MILK PRODUCTS

Dried whole milk, although considered to be almost the perfect food for young suckling mammals, is nearly always too expensive for use as an animal feed. When used as animal feed, **dried skim milk** is used primarily in milk replacers and, to a lesser degree, in solid starter rations for young pigs and ruminants and in some pet foods.

The quality of dried milk can be impaired by overheating during the drying process (drum drying), therefore spray dried milk is preferred.

Poor-quality milk, when used in milk replacers, is apt to lead to diarrhea and digestive disturbances.

From a nutritional point of view, dried skim milk is apt to be deficient in fat-soluble vitamins and, depending on the animal species, in Mg, Mn, Fe, and Cu. Normally, other minerals and vitamins will be supplied in adequate amounts for young animals.

Condensed or **dried buttermilk** is often available, and it qualifies as a protein concentrate, since the CP content is about 34 percent (dry basis). It has a comparable feeding value to skim milk except for having a slightly higher energy content. **Cheese rind** (cooked cheese trimmings) is available in some areas and is said to have a good feeding value. It has about 60 percent CP. **Dried whey protein concentrate** (25 percent minimum CP) is also available in some areas.

Other milk products are available but usually are not economical for feeding animals except for whey, which does not qualify as a protein concentrate because its CP content is below 20 percent. **Casein,** the solid residue obtained by acid or rennet coagulation of defatted milk, is available, as are **dried hydrolyzed casein, dried milk albumin,** or **dried milk protein.**

MARINE PROTEIN SOURCES

Fish Meals

Fish protein sources are primarily of two types—those from fish caught for making meal and those made from fish residues remaining after processing for human food or other industrial purposes. Anchovy (*Engraulis* spp), herring (*Clupea* spp), and menhaden (*Brevootia tyrannus*) provide a majority of the meals made from whole fish. These fish have a high body oil content, much of which is removed in preparation of the finished meal. In addition to these sources, residues from any species processed for human food may be used to make fish meal. Some of the processing residue may be fed directly as is (or ground) to mink, foxes, and other species raised for fur, and limited amounts may be used in making up diets for pets.

Fish meal is defined as the clean, dried, ground tissue of undecomposed whole fish or fish cuttings, with or without extraction of part of the oil. It must not contain more than 10 percent moisture and, if it contains more than 3 percent salt, the amount of salt must be specified.

In no case must the salt content exceed 7 percent. Fish meal may be processed using several different methods. The oil content is objectionable if fed in relatively large amounts to poultry or swine (because of fishy flavor in the meat), thus it is preferable if most of it is removed. In addition, fish oils oxidize readily, thus it is common for most processors to add antioxidants to prevent oxidation, overheating, and molding. Unfortunately, the quality of the meal may still be variable if it is not well processed.

Good-quality fish meals are excellent sources of proteins and essential amino acids (Tables 8–2, 8–3). The protein content is high and highly digestible. Fish meals are especially high in essential amino acids, including lysine, which are deficient in the cereal grains. In addition, fish meal is usually a good source of the B-vitamins and most of the mineral elements. As a result, fish meal is a highly favored ingredient for swine and poultry feeds (Table 8–4), although the cost is usually higher than for other protein sources except milk. Some fish meal is used in ruminant rations in Europe and South America, but very little is used elsewhere because of the cost. Some use of fat-extracted meals appears feasible in milk replacers.

Other Marine Protein Sources

Although fish meals make up the majority of marine protein feeds, a variety of other products may be found on the market in some places. **Fish residue meal** is prepared from the residue from the manufacture of glue from nonoily fish. **Fish protein concentrate, feed grade,** is prepared from the residues used to prepare fish protein concentrate for human food. **Fish liver and glandular meal** is made up of viscera of the fish; at least 50 percent of the dry weight must be from fish liver. **Condensed fish solubles** are obtained by condensing the stickwater so that the product contains at least 30 percent CP (as fed), while **dried fish solubles** must be dried and contain at least 60 percent CP. Fish solubles are considered to contain protein of high quality, to be a good to excellent source of water-soluble B-vitamins, and to contain "unidentified growth factors."

Fish by-products are comprised of the nonrendered portions of fish. **Dried fish protein digest** is the dried enzymatic digest of fish or fish cuttings using the enzyme hydrolysis process. It must be free of bones, scales, and undigested solids with at least 80 percent CP and not more than 10 percent moisture. **Condensed**

fish protein digest is the condensed enzymatic digest of fish or fish cuttings with at least 30 percent CP. **Fish digest residue** is the undecomposed residue (bones, scales, and the like) of the enzymatic digest.

In addition to the products mentioned, the Scandinavians have developed a product labeled as **fish silage.** Fish are ground and treated with acids (mineral acids and/or formic acid). The combination of the body enzymes and acids reduces the material to a relatively liquid product which will keep at ambient temperatures for some period of time. Although this product would probably be more suitable for non-ruminants, it can be used as a feed for ruminants (36, 37). **Liquefied fish,** prepared from ground fish or fish residues which are liquefied by fish enzymes, pasteurized briefly, strained to remove the bones, and acidified to a pH of about 4, is another promising way to use fish without the need for dehydration. Liquefied fish has been used in liquid protein supplements or in complete diets for ruminants with no problems (Table 8–5). Both methods (ensiling, liquefication) offer a way to utilize nutritious products without going to the high expense of drying.

Shrimp and **crab meals** prepared from processing residues are also on the market at times. Although shrimp meal is said to be about equivalent to tankage for swine, crab meal is unpalatable to swine. Crab meal does not show much promise for ruminants. Both of these meals contain a fair amount of chitin (a major component making up the animal's exoskeleton) which has a CP content of about 40 percent. Chitin is composed of a glucose polymer with N-acetyl groups on the second carbon atom of the glucose. Although the glucose molecules are linked in the same manner as in cellulose, rumen microbes do not appear to produce chitinase, the enzyme required to hydrolyze chitin (38). This enzyme would be expected to be found primarily in the GI tract of species that feed on insects or marine animals with exoskeletons. The relative values of these meals probably depend on the amount of nonchitinous residue in the meal.

MISCELLANEOUS PROTEIN SOURCES

As the world protein supply becomes more critical, efforts are underway to identify and develop additional sources for use in livestock feeding. Potential sources include animal wastes, plant extracts, and single-cell organisms such as algae, bacteria, fungi, and yeasts. Some discussion of these sources follows.

Poultry wastes have been mentioned previously. In areas with a high poultry population, **broiler litters** have fairly widespread usage for wintering adult cattle or as a supplement or in silage (see Ch. 6) for growing calves or for feeding to ewes during some stages of their reproductive cycle. **Cage layer wastes** have also been used (after air drying) to feed sheep or goats, and the commercially dried product, **dried poultry waste,** is marketed in a number of areas. Wastes from cattle do not contain enough N to qualify as a protein source. However, they show some promise as a N source when making silage. They have also been mixed fresh with other feed ingredients and fed to cattle, they have been included in silage (see Ch. 6), and they have been screened to remove solids and the fluid portion has sometimes been mixed with other ingredients and fed to cattle. There is less interest in feeding wastes from swine, although some experimental data are available.

There is interest in preparing **leaf protein concentrates** from crops such as alfalfa because of its high yield of protein/unit of land. Such concentrates will (when dried) contain 40-47 percent CP of high quality, even though some concentrates have antitrypsin activity. The dehydrated product has been shown to be an effective protein substitute for soybean meal for fattening lambs, and the presscake (residue after extracting leaf juices) is said to be equal to alfalfa hay when used in limited amounts for fattening cattle (39).

Single-Cell Proteins

Single-cell protein (SCP) could be developed into a very large source of supply for animal feeds. Some individuals have gone so far as to suggest that SCP sources will provide the principal protein source for domestic animals (worldwide basis) in the not-too-distant future, depending upon world population growth and the availability of feed proteins from plant sources. This could develop, because microbes can be used to ferment some of the vast amounts of waste materials such as straws; wood and wood processing wastes; food, cannery, and food processing wastes; and residues from alcohol production or from human and animal excreta.

Producing and harvesting microbial proteins is not without costs, unfortunately. In nearly all instances where a high rate of production would be achieved, the SCP will be found in rather dilute solutions, usually less than 5 percent solids. Methods used for concentration include filtration, precipitation, coagulation, centrifugation, and use of semipermeable membranes for concentration. Such materials must either be dried to about 10 percent moisture, then condensed and acidified to inhibit spoilage, or be fed in the fresh state. Removal of the amount of water necessary for storage would, in most instances, not be economical.

Algae is a potential feed source. Preliminary results with cultivated freshwater algae indicate a potential for about 10 times as much protein/unit of land area as from soybeans. Algae contains about 50 percent protein, 6-7 percent fiber, 4-6 percent fat, and 6 percent ash. Because of its bitter taste and protein of low biological value, it should not be used at levels exceeding 10 percent of the diet of growing swine. A major problem, of course, is how to harvest and dry a product of this type.

Yeast products have been available to the feed trade for many years. They are described as dried yeast (nonfermentative, that is, inactivated with heat), live yeast, and irradiated yeast. Those available include **brewers dried yeast** and **brewers liquid yeast** (both *Saccharomyces* spp) which must contain a minimum of 35 percent CP (dry basis). Other nonfermentative yeasts include **grain distillers dried yeast, molasses distillers dried yeast,** and **primary dried yeast** or **dried yeast** (all *Saccharomyces* spp). **Torula dried yeast** (*Torulopsis* spp) is also available as a feed ingredient. The yeast products just mentioned must contain a minimum of 40 percent CP. Yeasts contain protein of high quality and are high in most B-vitamins, although there are differences between brewers and Torula yeast in vitamin content. The costs are also relatively high, so not much yeast is used in most animal feeds. In moderate amounts it is a very satisfactory protein supplement (Table 8–4).

Live yeast (active) products include **active dry yeast, yeast culture** (a dried product), and **molasses yeast condensed solubles,** which is a condensate of broth remaining after removal of bakers yeast cells propagated on molasses.

Irradiated yeast or **irradiated dried yeast** is prepared from yeast which has been subjected to ultraviolet light to increase the concentration of vitamin D_2, which is a satisfactory form of the vitamin for domestic animals except poultry, which utilize D_3 much more efficiently than D_2. This is a common source of the vitamin in many feedstuffs.

Bacterial SCP sources (which may include fungi) are only just beginning to come on the market. In Europe, a long-researched microbial product known as **Pruteen** is available for commercial use in the European Economic Community (40). This SCP source is derived from microorganisms selected to utilize methanol (wood alcohol). It is said to contain 71 percent CP and 13 percent fat. Numerous research reports have shown that it can be used to replace a high proportion of the dried skim milk normally used in milk replacers for young calves or lambs (41). In the United States, Coor's Brewery markets a product grown on effluent from their brewery. It is designated as **Brewers SCP**. ITT Rayonier did, for a time, market a dried SCP product (with added fat) designated as **Raypro**™. It was produced from aerobic microbes grown on effluent from a paper-pulp mill operation. It contained about 50 percent CP (dry) and about 10-13 percent fat. Limited data on this product show that it was a satisfactory replacement for some of the standard protein sources in complete rations for fattening beef cattle or lactating dairy cows (42). Other preparations from pulp mills, but dried in different ways, have been shown to be satisfactory feeds for sheep or cattle (43). Microbes can be used to ferment solubles in processing waters, thus reducing microbial growth in streams, lakes, or oceans; consequently, with only costs for drying, a valuable source of protein can be brought on the market.

NONPROTEIN NITROGEN (NPN)

NPN includes any compounds that contain N but are not present in the polypeptide form of protein which can be precipitated from a solution. Organic NPN compounds include ammonia, urea, amides, amines, amino acids, and some peptides. Inorganic NPN compounds include a variety of salts such as ammonium chloride, ammonium phosphates, and ammonium sulfate.

Although some feedstuffs, particularly some forages and silages, contain substantial amounts of organic NPN, from a practical point of view, NPN in formula feeds refers to added materials, primarily urea or, to a lesser extent, such compounds as biuret and ammonium phosphates, or in silage or dry roughage to ammonia. There is adequate research evidence to show that a number of other compounds could be used, but they are too costly to use for feeding to animals at the present time. In most areas, urea is the least costly source of crude protein. This simple fact accounts for the tremendous interest in its use in feeds for ruminants.

NPN, especially urea, is primarily of interest for feeding to animals with a functioning rumen. The reason for this is that urea is hydrolyzed rapidly to ammonia and carbon dioxide, and the ammonia is then incorporated into amino acids and microbial proteins by rumen bacteria which are utilized later by the host. Thus the animal itself does not utilize urea directly. In simple-stomached species the only microorganisms that can synthesize protein from urea are found in the lower intestinal tract at a point where absorption of amino acids, peptides, and proteins is believed to be rather low or nonexistent. Research with pigs, poultry, horses, and other species indicates only slight utilization of N from urea.

Limitations on Urea Usage

A variety of factors must be considered in utilizing urea in feeds. One of the more important facts is that urea is not a satisfactory source of N to feed to animals fed primarily on poor-quality roughage. This is illustrated by data in Table 8–6. Note that when steers were fed cottonseed hulls, they responded fairly well to urea supplementation, but rate of gain was increased by adding fish meal or soybean meal. When fed

barley straw or corn stalks, performance was quite low. With wintering beef cows, winter losses were not reduced by adding urea to a basal supplement with 15 percent CP. Neither did biuret or the addition of methionine hydroxy analog (a substitute for methionine) improve performance. Many other examples of a similar nature could be gleaned from the literature to illustrate this point. Although some divergence in responses can be found in the literature, the writer believes that the illustrations presented are representative of typical responses. Other examples were also given in Table 8–5, in which cattle were fed corn cobs or corn silage as the principal roughage. Urea did not allow the same level of production as supplements with natural proteins.

There have been hundreds of research reports dealing with the utilization of urea since it was first tried in the early 1940s. While it is true that most cellulose-digesting rumen microorganisms require ammonia and also true that *in vitro* (laboratory) rumen studies show that urea as the only added N source will stimulate very adequate cellulose digestion, this is not the case for the live animal. Under laboratory conditions where fermentations are usually carried out in nonpermeable containers (glass), the urea and/or ammonia remain in solution and are available to the microorganisms. In the rumen the ammonia can be absorbed through the rumen wall or pass into the lower stomach. In

TABLE 8-6
Response of cattle fed nonprotein N with low-quality roughage

| Item | Daily Gain, kg | Feed Consumed, kg | | Reference No. |
		Roughage	Supplement	
Steers fed cottonseed hulls				44
Urea	0.51	7.92	0.36	
80% urea, 20% fish meal	0.59	7.94	0.48	
80% urea, 20% soybean meal	0.71	8.44	0.96	
Steers fed chopped barley straw				
80% urea, 20% SBM	0.20	4.72	0.21	
Steers fed corn stalks				
80% urea, 20% soybean meal	−0.08	2.98	0.24	
	Winter loss, kg			
Beef cows wintered on native pasture				45
15% CP, natural protein	90.0		1.34	
30% CP, natural protein	76.0		1.31	
Biuret[a]	86.1		1.40	
Urea[a]	91.2		1.24	
Biuret + MHA[a]	88.5		1.32	
Urea + MHA[a]	98.5		1.02	

[a]Supplements formulated to be 30% CP with half of the CP from the source identified in the table. MHA = methionine hydroxide analog. Cows were fed for an 88-d period.

either case it is no longer available to the bacteria, although some of it eventually will be recycled back to the rumen through saliva or, under some conditions, through the rumen wall. Ammonia is absorbed from the rumen more rapidly as the pH rises toward 7 or higher. At acid pHs of 6 or lower, absorption is slow or nil. If enough starch is fed to the animal to reduce the pH to this range, then utilization of urea by the live animal is very satisfactory. Sugars, such as those in molasses, will not support maximum urea utilization.

Urea Toxicity

Urea may also be toxic or lethal, depending on the size and timing of the dose (feed consumption). Clinical symptoms may show up as soon as 30 min after ingestion of the feed. They include uneasiness, staggering, and kicking at the flank, at which point affected animals tend to go down. Labored breathing, incoordination, tetany, slobbering, and bloating have been observed. Fatally affected animals are prone to regurgitate rumen contents just before death. The reaction tends to be an all or none type, that is, the animal either dies or recovers with little if any aftereffect. Fatal levels of urea are affected by adaptation of the animal to urea, how long it has been without food, the type of diet, and other things. Generally, an intake in a period of about 30 min of about 40-50 g/100 kg of body weight may be lethal. The toxicity occurs because urea is hydrolyzed rapidly in the rumen to ammonia and carbon dioxide. If the rumen fluid is alkaline (urea and ammonia make it more alkaline), ammonia will be absorbed rapidly, resulting in an overload on the liver, which would normally remove most of it. Ammonia builds up in the peripheral blood, resulting in the symptoms observed. There is really no feasible means of treatment. Provided animals are observed before the late stages of toxicity, they can be treated with vinegar (or other acids). One recommendation is to administer one gallon of vinegar and one gallon of water/100 lb of body weight. The point is that if several animals are affected, not enough vinegar would be available soon enough to prevent death if it would otherwise occur. Prevention of urea (or ammonia) toxicity amounts to good feeding practices, to careful mixing of feeds containing urea, and to adapting animals gradually to feeds containing large amounts (that is, liquid supplements or dry protein supplements with high percentages of urea).

Where livestock management is good and feed is formulated and mixed properly, urea can provide a substantial amount of the supplemental N required for feedlot animals, dairy cows, and other ruminants. In practical rations, current recommendations are that not more than one-third of the total N be supplied by urea or other NPN compounds. In complete feeds, urea should be restricted to 2 percent or less. More than this may be unpalatable and cause reduced feed intake. Some recent data indicate that feeding urea-based rations may result in meals of shorter duration, although the cows tended to eat more frequently than when fed rations without urea. Note in Ch. 5 that most states require labeling of feed tags with maximal amounts of urea or other NPN compounds as a protective measure for the buyer.

Methods for Improving Urea Utilization

A considerable amount of research effort has been expended to improve utilization of urea when used as a protein concentrate or to increase its versatility in feeding. Several different examples of use of urea or anhydrous ammonia in silage were given in Ch. 6. This appears to be one of the most cost-effective means of increasing the CP content of forages without increasing the likelihood of any problems with feeding NPN.

At least two extruded urea-grain mixtures are on the market—**Starea** and **Golden-Pro.** If extrusion is carried out under the correct conditions of heat, moisture, and pressure, the process results in a product which releases ammonia at a slower rate than urea in the rumen. Most studies indicate satisfactory results when such products are used for feeding dairy cows, young calves, or wintering beef cows. Results are normally better than with grain-urea mixes and approach or equal the value of soybean meal (in most but not all experimental studies).

Urea has been used also with other feed ingredients. A mixture of dehydrated alfalfa meal, urea, dicalcium phosphate, sodium sulfate, and sodium propionate formulated to contain 100 percent CP has produced very satisfactory results with high-producing dairy cows. It is called **Dehy-100.** Urea solutions absorbed on **flaked soybean hulls** also appears to be a satisfactory means of feeding to dairy cows (46). Pressure cooking **urea with cassava meal** is a possible means of expanding use of urea in tropical areas (47). In Europe, it is apparently fairly common to absorb **urea solutions** (50 percent urea-water) **on whole grains** for feeding to cattle or sheep. In addition, there have been efforts to produce treated urea products which release ammonia at a slower rate than untreated urea (**Slo-release**). Although some of the products do release urea at a slower rate, animal performance on low-quality roughage has not been improved much, if at all. Studies from the same laboratory indicate that release rate is not the problem. In one experiment when urea was administered directly into the rumen over a 24-h period or during a 6-h or 1-h period, there was no effect on N retention by the animals. Thus it may be that other factors have more influence on utilization of ammonia from urea than the speed of urea hydrolysis in the rumen.

Ammoniated Liquid Feeds

Two liquids containing ammonia are worthy of note for use with ruminants. **Ammonium lignin sulfonate** is produced by the paper manufacturing industry when wood is reacted under conditions of heat and pressure with sulfur dioxide and ammonium bisulfite (other sulfonates are produced using Na or Ca bisulfite). The liquids are partially evaporated, resulting in a product with about 50-55 percent solids, 25-30 percent sugar or sugar acids, and 15-25 percent CP. When used at levels approved by FDA (4 percent of finished feed or 11 percent of a sulfonate-molasses mixture), it appears to be a satisfactory feed ingredient.

Fermented ammoniated condensed whey is another product of interest. It is produced from whey by fermenting with *Lactobacillus bulgaricus* (which metabolizes lactose to lactic acid) accompanied by continual neutralization with ammonia. The resulting product contains about 68 percent ammonium lactate with a crude protein equivalent of 69 percent (dry basis) with about 64 percent DM. Research results from various experiment stations indicate that the product is utilized more effectively than urea and that it appears to be quite comparable to soybean meal for dairy cattle. Certainly, it also provides another means of utilizing large amounts of surplus whey.

Other NPN Compounds

Biuret, a condensation product of urea, has been used to some extent as an NPN feed ingredient (Table 8–6). It usually gives a better response when fed with low-quality roughage than does urea. However, it is more costly and not as readi-

ly available on the market. Biuret is also less soluble and is much less likely than urea to cause toxicity. It is not approved for use with lactating dairy cows because biuret will show up in the milk.

A wide variety of other N-containing salts could be used as NPN sources in place of urea. **Urea phosphate** and **isobutylidendiurea** appear to be well utilized. In addition, many different ammonium salts have been used experimentally. These include the **chloride, bicarbonate, acetate, propionate, lactate,** and **sulfate** salts as well as the **mono-** and **diammonium phosphates** (the latter two are not very palatable). Available evidence indicates that most of these compounds are less likely to be toxic than urea, but most of them are not used because of cost. Ammonium chloride is frequently used as a preventative/treatment for urinary calculi, and the mono- and diammonium phosphates are used at times to supply both N and P.

The only other NPN compound of practical interest for ruminants is **methionine hydroxy analog.** It is used as a source of methionine for poultry because the compound can be converted to methionine by the liver. There has been limited use in dairy rations, because some evidence indicates that it has been effective to a limited extent in increasing milk fat percentage in early lactation and it is less likely to be degraded in the rumen than is free methionine. **Lysine** is, of course, often added to poultry diets, since it can be produced commercially at a reasonable cost.

LIQUID SUPPLEMENTS

Liquid supplements (LS) have been used for some time (50 years±), primarily for cattle, to a much lesser extent for sheep, and with very limited use for horses. In the early days LS were primarily molasses with minor amounts of additives. Most manufacturers still use some molasses, but many other liquids are available from the production of sugar, paper, and cheese and from many different products involving fermentations of one kind or another. The increased use of these many different liquids may have been caused by several factors, including an increasing cost of cane molasses and reduced availability of beet molasses, poor results with cattle fed low-quality roughage and LS primarily of molasses-urea, and, last but not necessarily least, tougher environmental regulations prohibiting indiscriminate dumping of many wastes down the sewer and into the nation's water supply.

If they are consumed regularly and used with reasonable efficiency, LS offer a great deal of convenience for supplying needed nutrients to cattle and sheep on winter ranges. Lickwheel feeders have been developed to restrict consumption (one example is shown in Fig. 8–2). Generally, LS are formulated on the basis of a desired consumption of 1–1.5 kg (2–3 lb) for cattle and 50–100 g/d (2–4 oz) for sheep. Unfortunately, it is difficult to obtain a uniform daily consumption because it will vary with the weather, palatability of the liquid, availability and kind of feed, and other factors. Sheep are slower to learn to use lickwheel feeders than are cattle, possibly because they have less of a preference for sweets. Studies in Australia involving the use of tritium-labeled water in molasses indicated that about half of the sheep never did consume LS (tritium can be detected in very low concentrations in the blood), and consumption by those that did consume the supplement was quite variable.

LS are also used for feeding in drylot situations to beef and dairy cattle and to sheep. As a result, formulas may vary depending on the intended purpose. Most companies manufacturing LS provide custom mixes with additional ingredients or modification of their basic formula if desired by the user.

The other major use of LS is for addition to complete feeds for finishing beef cattle or for dairy cattle or for use as a top-dressing for all or part of the remainder of the ration. In these circumstances the amount consumed is controlled by the feeder, so it is then a matter of cost or convenience if LS are used. LS serve as a very useful vehicle for including small amounts of additives in rations in these circumstances, because more uniform mixing is always likely when micro ingredients are diluted before addition to the major part of a ration.

Energy Sources

LS are usually based on use of one or more of the various types of molasses (usually cane or beet in the United States) diluted with water and other liquids and with various materials in suspension. In addition to molasses, other liquid energy sources (discussed in Ch. 7) that find increasing use in LS include hemicellulose extract, lignin sulfonate, hydrolyzed grain, whey, condensed whey, condensed whey product, condensed whey solubles, condensed distillers or brewers solubles, liquid streptomyces solubles, blended feeding fats, and, in some cases, propylene glycol; the latter compound is metabolized for energy but also acts as a preservative and also depresses the freezing point.

Nitrogen Sources

Most commonly, some urea is used in most LS, but its use is lower and less frequent than was the case several years ago. Urea is usually added as a saturated urea solution (ca. 50 percent urea in water). Protein equivalents in LS may range up to 80 percent or more, although most advertised LS are in the range of 30–35 percent CP. Other liquid N sources which qualify as protein supplements include fermented ammoniated whey, ammonium lignin sulfonate, condensed fermented corn extractives, condensed extracted glutamic acid fermentation product (also listed sometimes as condensed beet fermentation solubles, Dynaferm, or Manaferm), condensed molasses fermentation solubles, liquid brewers yeast, condensed fish solubles, or liquefied fish waste. In addition to these various liquids, dry products can be suspended in limited amounts in the supplement with the aid of suspending agents such as bentonite, xanthan gum, or alginates. Dry protein sources which have been used include dry poultry waste, feather or hair meal, fish meal, blood meal, corn gluten meal, and meat and bone meal.

Other Additives in Liquid Supplements

Phosphoric acid has been used extensively in LS. In addition to supplying P, the acid serves to

FIGURE 8–2. One example of a lickwheel feeder for liquid supplements.

reduce viscosity, an important factor in cold climates, and serves to limit intake as well because of the lower pH of the mixture. Ammonium polyphosphates are also used as P sources (as well as a source of NPN); some companies also use monosodium phosphate and dicalcium phosphate as P sources (48).

Other minerals such as Mg and S may often be added. Although it may be desirable to add Ca, most Ca salts have a low solubility in aqueous solutions; if large amounts are added, they must be in suspension. Mineral compounds added by some companies include limestone, salt, potassium chloride, magnesium oxide, ammonium sulfate, copper sulfate, sodium bicarbonate, sodium sesquicarbonate, sodium carbonate, and calcium phosphate (48).

Depending on the intended use, average vitamin A fortification is about 30,000 IU/lb (10,000–100,000 range). Vitamin D is added at average levels of about 9,000 IU/lb (1,500–40,000 range) and vitamin E at levels of about 12 IU/lb (4–67 range). A variety of trace minerals may be added, depending on local needs.

Nonnutritive additives added to LS may include various antibiotics, hormones such as melengestrol acetate, antioxidants, ethanol, and flavoring agents. Emulsifiers and other agents such as clays or gums to aid in keeping ingredients in suspension would normally be used if dry ingredients are added.

The basic liquids in the LS will have a controlling effect on how much material can be put into solution or into suspension. Recommended restrictions by one of the major LS producers in the country are as follows: total solids, 60–80 percent; Ca, 10 percent; P, 2.5 percent; salt, 10 percent; fat, 30 percent; K, 6 percent; Mg, 5 per-

cent; S, 6 percent; Na bicarb, 7.5 percent; and crude protein, 90 percent (48). Obviously, not all of the maximums could apply in any given batch.

Research Reports on LS

Although LS have been (and probably still are) used widely for supplementing cattle consuming poor-quality forage (winter range, crop residues, or harvested roughage), urea as the principal N source does not give the response of a dry supplement such as soybean meal in stimulating added consumption or improved digestibility of the total ration. A fairly typical response between the two types of CP sources is illustrated in Table 8–7. Note that SBM stimulated greater consumption of wheat straw and greater digestibility than the urea-based LS. Likewise, when fed to cows on winter range (Table 8–8), urea in either dry or liquid form and biuret in a LS resulted in greater winter weight loss than did a dry supplement with no urea. These results are reasonably typical of most of the reports in the literature. Animals do respond when fed most NPN sources as a supplement to poor-quality roughage, but not to the extent that they will if fed a dry supplement. A response is more likely with medium-quality roughages such as cottonseed hulls or grass hay than with the very poor quality roughages.

The amount of urea in a LS will influence consumption. This is illustrated by two experiments shown in Table 8–9. In the first experiment, increasing urea from 1.35 to 4 percent increased consumption of both supplement and straw. A further increase to 9.8 percent urea decreased supplement but not straw consumption. In the second experiment, steers were first

TABLE 8-7

Comparison of straw consumption and energy digestibility when cattle were fed soybean meal or a molasses-urea LS

	Supplement			
	Soybean Meal		Molasses-Urea	
Supplement Level[a]	Straw Consumed[a]	Energy Digestibility, %	Straw Consumed[a]	Energy Digestibility, %
0	43.3	38	43.3	38
1	63.1	55	44.3	43
2	69.6	48	48.4	41
3	72.6	49	50.8	43
4	70.4	52	51.4	38

[a]Expressed as g/kg body weight$^{0.75}$.
Source: Church and Santos (49).

TABLE 8-8

Supplement consumption and winter weight loss of cows fed various nitrogen supplements on winter range

Supplement	Supplement Consumed, kg/d	Winter Weight Loss, kg
Dry supplements		
SBM-sorghum grain	1.18	−72
SBM-sorghum-urea	1.33	−92
SBM-sorghum-biuret	1.23	−92
Liquid supplements		
Molasses-urea	1.55	−96
Molasses-biuret	3.08	−117

Source: Rush and Totusek (50).

fed a supplement with 6 percent urea. When urea was subsequently increased to 9.8 percent, consumption of supplement decreased to about half. This is probably one reason most commercial supplements are formulated to contain about 30 percent CP when using a substantial amount of urea.

The addition of preformed (natural) protein sources to LS has, in a limited number of cases, resulted in some improvement in animal performance when low-quality roughages were fed.

Some data on this topic are shown in Table 8–9 when part of the CP was made up of liquefied fish, feather meal, or pulp mill single-cell protein. Note in each experiment shown that there was some modest improvement in daily gain of young cattle fed ryegrass straw and LS with the preformed protein.

Two other examples are shown in Table 8–10 in which cows with calves or yearling heifers were fed supplements on winter range. They received a dry (NC) supplement with a low CP level or a dry supplement with 29 percent CP compared to liquids containing part of the N from corn steep liquor or fermented ammoniated condensed whey. In this experiment the LS with the two liquid N sources allowed performance at least equal to the 29 percent CP dry supplement, thus providing additional data showing that preformed proteins are needed for adequate performance of cattle consuming low-quality roughage.

A number of reports are available in which a variety of different liquid N sources have been incorporated into complete diets. For example, in one case cattle were fed corn silage, shelled corn, and 10 percent LS (54). The liquids fed were ammonium lignin sulfonate-molasses, condensed cane solubles-molasses-urea, condensed

TABLE 8-9

Effect of level of urea or addition of native proteins on performance of cattle self-fed liquid supplements

Item	Feed Consumption		Av. Daily Gain, kg
	Liquid, kg/d	Straw, kg/d	
10-d trial, individually fed steers[a]			
1.35% urea, 7.5% CP	1.69	3.1	
4.03% urea, 15% CP	2.24	3.5	
9.8% urea, 30% CP	1.1	3.5	
60-d trial, group-fed steers, 20% CP[a]			
6% urea	1.45	3.2	0.18
5.3% urea, 13.3% LF[b]	1.81	3.1	0.23
60-d trial, group-fed steers, 30% CP[a]			
9.8% urea	0.69	3.2	0.23
8.6% urea, 20% LF[b]	0.91	3.5	0.37
88-d trial, group-fed steers, 30% CP[c]			
9.8% urea	0.85	5.2	0.55
8.6% urea, 3.9% FM[d]	1.10	5.3	0.61
8.6% urea, 7.9% SCP[e]	0.60	5.6	0.59

[a]From Kellems et al. (51).
[b]LF = liquefied fish.
[c]From Kellems (52). The basal roughage was ryegrass straw in each experiment.
[d]FM = feather meal.
[e]SCP = pulp mill single-cell protein.

TABLE 8-10

Response of cattle to liquid supplements based on corn steep liquor (CSL) or fermented ammoniated condensed whey (FACW)

Item	Supplement[a]			
	NC	PC	CSL	FACW
Cows (fall calving) with calves, 85 days				
CP content of supplement, %	12.9	29.0	16.8	16.0
Supplement intake, kg/head[b]	2.4	2.3	2.1	2.2
CSM intake, kg/hd	—	—	0.8	0.8
Total CP intake, kg/hd	0.31	0.67	0.68	0.68
Change in cow wt., kg	− 54.4	− 20.8	− 25.0	− 22.5
Change in calf wt., kg	31.7	37.7	34.9	36.0
Heifers, yearlings, 85 days				
Suppl. intake, kg/hd	0.8	0.7	0.7	0.8
CSM intake, kg/hd	—	—	0.2	0.2
Total CP, kg/hd	0.10	0.20	0.20	0.21
Weight change, kg	− 22.4	− 4.8	8.0	4.2

[a]NC = negative control; PC = positive control. NC supplement was made up of 11.5% CSM, 41.8% gr. corn, 41.8% gr. sorghum, plus minerals and vitamins. PC supplement was 66.7% CSM, 30.6% gr. corn, plus min. and vitamins. CSL was 69.9% CSL, 27.4% cane molasses, 1.1% H_2SO_4, plus min. and vitamins; FACW was 37.2% FACW, 60% cane molasses, 1% H_2SO_4, plus min. and vitamins. Cattle were fed individually 6 days/week.

[b]CSM was fed at a level so that the CP intake of cattle on the LS was equal to that in the NC.

Source: Wagner et al. (53).

beet solubles-molasses-urea, or molasses-urea. No differences were found in daily gain of the cattle. Dry-matter consumption was lower by cattle fed the condensed beet solubles and highest for those fed the molasses-urea, however the feed/gain ratio was the best for those fed the beet solubles and cane solubles. In another case the addition of fish solubles increased the growth rate of steers fed a mixture of ground ear corn and LS (55).

The addition of preformed proteins may affect palatability of LS; certainly they will affect consumption over a short period of time. It has been demonstrated that small additions of SCP from pulp mills, feather meal, hair meal, and liquefied fish waste all stimulated greater consumption than urea when fed to cattle given LS and ryegrass straw (56). No doubt other additives such as phosphoric acid may also have some effect on consumption.

Current Usage of LS

It is obvious from the preceding discussions that a wide variety of materials could be used to satisfy nutrient specifications in LS. There is some indication that more and more commercial products are routinely formulated to contain preformed proteins of one type or another. This is an encouraging step and one which will without doubt result in more efficient use of LS by livestock feeders using them to supplement poor-quality roughage of one kind or another.

A recent innovation with LS is the use of so-called "pumpable dry" supplements. This term is used to describe a product with about 70 percent solids which would appear as a thick slurry. Some pumpable dry products have suspending agents giving them thixotropic characteristics (they tend to gel when at rest but take on liquid characteristics when agitated or stirred). Some that are not thixotropic products use suspending agents such as xanthan gum. According to trade sources, pumpable dry products are currently being used to mix with other feed ingredients in complete rations rather than being used for self-feeding, as is often done with typical LS.

PROTEIN SOLUBILITY AND DEGRADABILITY BY MICROORGANISMS AS RELATED TO RUMINANTS

Proteins can be evaluated (and rated) for monogastric species on the basis of digestibility of the protein and its ability to supply a satisfactory balance of essential amino acids for the animal's needs. With ruminant animals, if optimal utilization is desired, the needs can be more complex because of microbial fermentation taking place in the forestomach. For optimal protein efficiency, it would be desirable to be able to quantitate and express in feeding standards the needs for rumen microorganisms *and* for the host animal separately for all of the likely production situations. Although several systems have been proposed, there appear to be too many variables and unknowns to make them workable except in very specific situations.

Proteins provided by rumen microorganisms provide an adequate supply to the tissues in most instances for animals producing at moderate levels. However, for young, rapidly growing animals and for high-producing dairy cows, this does not appear to be the case. That is, these two classes of ruminants probably require a greater supply of some amino acids than are supplied by the microorganisms. This has been shown by infusing either intact proteins or different amino acids into the abomasum or duodenum. In such conditions it can be shown that wool growth can be increased and that milk production or growth of young animals can be increased under experimental conditions.

For animals that have a higher than normal need for some of the limiting amino acids, the optimal situation for highly efficient N utilization would be to supply adequate N for the rumen microbes (primarily ammonia for rumen bacteria) and to have any excess dietary protein be digested and absorbed in the gut. If this is to be accomplished, some of the protein in the feed must escape degradation by the microorganisms but be digested in the gut. Proteins that are digestible yet not degraded in the rumen are sometimes referred to as bypass proteins. This term should, more logically, be applied only to proteins that go through the esophageal groove (primarily milk) and do, in truth, bypass the rumen. Proteins escape degradation in the rumen if (a) they pass out too rapidly or (b) rumen microorganisms cannot metabolize them. More recently the term "escape proteins" has been applied to those proteins which are not degraded in the rumen.

Protein reaching the lower GI tract is a combination of microbial protein synthesized in the rumen and that from the feed which escapes degradation. The latter is highly affected by a number of factors which include solubility of the various N fractions in the feed, the particle size of ingested material (small particles pass out of the rumen at a faster rate, thus allowing less digestion in the rumen), the speed of digestion in the rumen (affected by particle size and resistance to digestion), and the level of feeding

(a high level of feeding pushes feed through the system at a faster rate, thus reducing potential digestion).

There is a considerable interest by nutritionists, feeders, and milling companies in applying information on protein utilization to improve protein efficiency by ruminant animals and to allow more efficient use of added NPN. However, it must be realized that there is a great variation in solubility and utilization of different N fractions within and among various feedstuffs. With forages and silages, about 31 ± 15 percent of the N will be in NPN form, which is metabolized very rapidly by rumen microorganisms. About 32 ± 16 percent is insoluble leaf protein which is metabolized at a slower rate. Insoluble protein from other plant parts accounts for 12 ± 5 percent that is slowly metabolized, and about 18 ± 4 percent is unavailable to the microorganisms, a high proportion being bound to lignin-fiber complexes (57). In some animal products, proteins such as keratins (high in hair, feathers, connective tissues) are almost totally indigestible unless they are cooked enough with moist heat to partially hydrolyze these proteins.

Although a variety of methods have been tried to measure solubility (extraction with hot or cold water, rumen fluid, buffers, alkaline or acid solutions; pepsin digestibility; suspension of the product in nylon or dacron bags in the rumen of rumen-fistulated animals), from the preceding information it is obvious that one of the first criteria would be that NPN compounds should be quantitated separately from proteins. This is so because most ruminant nutritionists believe that essentially all of the soluble NPN is metabolized in the rumen. Note in Table 8–12 that many common feedstuffs have large proportions of the total N present as NPN. Most feedstuffs contain rapidly degradable protein, more slowly degradable protein, unavailable protein, and other N-containing compounds that are not protein. Furthermore, there is evidence to show that some proteins insoluble in buffers may be degraded rapidly and that some soluble proteins show a slow rate of degradation. Also, protein solubility is quite different in different types of solutions. Consequently, methods of defining solubility and relating it to rumen utilization need further improvement.

The solubility of proteins in forages is generally greatest in lush, young plants and decreases with age. Drying, particularly with heat, generally results in a reduction in solubility of cytoplasmic proteins which is associated

TABLE 8-11

Soluble proteins and acid detergent fiber-bound protein in various feedstuffs

Feedstuff	Typical Crude Protein Content, %	% of Crude Protein	
		Soluble in Buffer Solution	Bound to ADF
High-solubility feeds			
Corn solubles + germ meal and bran	29	63	3
Corn gluten feed	22	55	3
Rye middlings	18	48	2
Wheat middlings	18	37	2
Wheat flour	15	40	0.2
Intermediate-solubility feeds			
Oats	13	31	5
Corn gluten feed w/corn germ	24	32	3
Cotton waste product	22	24	2
Hominy	11	24	3
Soybean meal	52	24	2
Soybean mill feed	15	22	14–20
Distillers dried grains w/sol.	29	19	15
Low-solubility feeds			
Cottonseed meal	44	12	3
Corn	10	15	5
Brewers dried grains	29	6	13
Corn gluten meal	66	4	11
Beet pulp	8	3	11
Distillers dried grains	27	6	19
Forages and silages			
Alfalfa hay	15–25	30	10
Alfalfa, dehy.	17–25	25–30	10–30
Alfalfa silage[a]	17–25	30–60	15–40
Corn silage[a]	9	30–40	10–30

[a]Higher-moisture silages tend to have greater soluble NPN while low DM silages may have greater heat damage.

Source: Sniffen et al. (58).

with denaturation of the proteins. Solubility may be reduced intentionally by heating feed ingredients, resulting in coagulation or denaturation. Heat treatment appears to reduce rumen degradation partly by blocking reactive sites for microbial enzymes and partly by reducing solubility. If excessive heat is applied to the point of causing browning (Maillard reaction), solubility is reduced by the formation of complexes between amino groups and carbohydrate. Such products may be totally indigestible, although not necessarily insoluble. Such products can be detected by increasing amounts of N in the acid-detergent fiber fraction. Solubility may also be reduced intentionally by treating feedstuffs with formic acid, formaldehyde, tannins, acids, bases, or ethanol. If the amount added is not overdone, these chemicals will inhibit rumen degradation, yet allow an adequate level of digestion in the gut. Solubility, as determined using buffer solutions, of N in a wide range of feedstuffs is shown in Table 8–11. Note that it ranges from 3 percent in beet pulp to a high of 63 percent in a corn solubles-germ meal-bran mix. If urea were included, it would be 100 percent. Note also that the amount of N bound to ADF tends to increase as percentage solubility decreases. Either value may be quite variable depending on previous treatment of the feedstuff, especially when it has been subjected to heat. Another example of solubility of feed proteins when done with a bicarbonate-phosphate buffer is shown in Table 8–12. In this case soluble N ranged from a low of 4.1 for brewers dried grains to a high of 53.1 percent for oats. However, except for oats and peanut meal, most of the soluble material was classed as soluble NPN. Except for oats and dried corn silage, the majority of the N was insoluble in this buffer system.

A major reason for discussing this topic is that there is much interest in learning under

TABLE 8-12

Nitrogen fractions in various feedstuffs as determined by solubility in bicarbonate-phosphate buffer

Feedstuffs	Total Crude Protein, % of DM	Crude Protein Fractions, % of Total N			
		Insoluble	Soluble	Soluble True Protein	Soluble NPN
Corn grain	9.9	88.9	11.1	3.4	7.7
Brewers dried grains	27.9	95.9	4.1	1.2	2.9
Corn gluten feed	24.0	60.8	39.2	0.2	39.0
Beet pulp	10.2	73.5	26.5	0.7	25.8
Corn gluten meal	69.0	95.8	4.2	0.5	3.8
Oat grain	14.0	46.9	53.1	43.3	9.8
Distillers grains w/sol.	25.1	88.8	11.3	1.1	10.2
Soybean meal, sol. extd.	54.8	79.7	20.4	9.1	11.3
Rapeseed meal, sol. extd.	42.3	67.6	32.4	9.4	23.0
Peanut meal, sol. extd.	47.5	67.1	32.9	24.3	8.6
Dried corn silage	7.9	47.8	52.2	4.0	48.2
Guinea grass hay, mature	7.1	61.2	38.8	3.3	35.5
Timothy hay, mature	8.1	74.2	25.8	0.8	25.1
Tall fescue hay, mature	11.3	74.1	25.9	0.5	25.4
Rice straw	3.9	59.2	40.8	6.6	34.2
Corn stover	4.4	57.1	42.9	3.0	39.9

Source: Krishnamoorthy et al. (59).

what conditions soluble N sources such as urea can best be utilized and when proteins undegradable in the rumen should be fed. There is a reasonable amount of literature on the topic, but it does not present a clear picture at this time because results with diets of differing N solubility have been contradictory. In some cases animals fed diets with low N solubility have given greater yields of milk or improved gain or improved N retention, but in others there has been no response. One example with growing calves is shown in Table 8–13. In this instance it was observed that inclusion of blood meal or meat meal (both rather insoluble) resulted in somewhat improved feed efficiency and more gain/unit of N than did a urea or soybean meal-urea based ration. Other examples are given in Ch. 13, 14, and 15. However, at this time in the writer's view we are not yet in a position to take full advantage of known differences in protein solubility and rumen degradability.

Information on proteins that escape rumen degradation but that are digested in the small intestine is even more scarce. French work, based on a number of studies with cattle and sheep, suggests that about 65 percent of insoluble N escapes rumen degradation. Their calculated values for digestibility of undegraded protein which was digestible in the gut ranged from 8-46 percent of dietary N with a mean of 28 percent for 31 feedstuffs, most of which were forages (61).

SUMMARY

Concentrated sources of protein are necessary in modern-day agriculture to supplement other ration ingredients for high-producing animals.

TABLE 8-13

Effect of feeding growing calves diets with different nitrogen solubility

Item	N Source[a]			
	Urea	SBM-Urea	BM-Urea	MM-Urea
Daily gain, kg	0.72	0.81	0.91	0.85
Daily feed, kg	6.20	6.32	6.47	6.06
Feed/gain	8.36	7.82	7.12	7.10
Gain/protein		0.64	1.37	1.38

[a]SBM = soybean meal, BM = blood meal, MM = meat meal.
Source: Stock et al. (60).

A wide variety of sources are available from plants, milling by-products, the brewing and distilling industries, animal and marine sources, as well as various miscellaneous sources. For ruminants, a number of nonprotein N sources are available that can be utilized with good efficiency in some situations. Protein sources vary greatly in content of total N, essential amino acids, digestibility, and solubility. Many plant sources contain antinutritional factors, most of which can be inactivated with heat or by use of various solutions or solvents. Ruminant animals are, generally, more flexible in that they can utilize moderate to large amounts of most protein sources. Use is more restricted with swine and poultry because of fiber or antinutritional factors and because essential amino acids are more critical. Liquid supplements have been developed to the point that they can be used in many situations, but recent evidence indicates that they can be improved when fed with low-quality roughage if some native protein is added rather than depending on NPN sources. Solubility and rumen degradability of proteins appears to be an important factor in efficient N utilization by ruminants, but further research is required for utilization in most practical situations.

REFERENCES

1. USDA. 1987. *Feed situation and outlook report.* Econ. Res. Serv. FDS-304 (November). Washington, D.C.: USDA.
2. Wahlstrom, R. C., and G. W. Libal. 1977. *J. Animal Sci.* 44:778.
3. La Rue, D. C., et al. 1987. *J. Animal Sci.* 64:1051.
4. Slagle, S. P., and D. R. Zimmerman. 1979. *J. Animal Sci.* 49:1252.
5. Myer, R. O., C. N. Coon, and J. A. Froseth. 1982. *Poultry Sci.* 61:2117.
6. Salmon, R. E. 1982. *Poultry Sci.* 61:2126.
7. Huston, J. E., and M. Shelton. 1971. *J. Animal Sci.* 32:334.
8. Richardson, C. R., et al. 1981. *J. Animal Sci.* 53:557.
9. Doyle, J. J., and C. V. Hulet. 1978. *Proc. West. Sec. Amer. Soc. Animal Sci.* 32:96.
10. Loerch, S. C., and L. L. Berger. 1981. *J. Animal Sci.* 53:1198.
11. Shqueir, A. A., R. L. Kellems, and D. C. Church. 1981. *Proc. West Sec. Amer. Soc. Animal Sci.* 32:96.
12. Firkins, J. L., L. L. Berger, and G. C. Fahey, Jr. 1985. *J. Animal Sci.* 60:847.
13. Church, D. C., D. A. Daugherty, and W. H. Kennick. 1982. *J. Animal Sci.* 54:337.
14. Wray, M. I., et al. 1979. *J. Animal Sci.* 48:748.
15. Perry, T. W., et al. 1979. *J. Animal Sci.* 48:758.
16. Schingoethe, D. J., et al. 1977. *J. Dairy Sci.* 60:591.
17. Anderson, M. J., et al. 1979. *J. Dairy Sci.* 62:1098.
18. Papas, A., J. R. Ingalls, and L. D. Campbell. 1979. © *J. Nutr.* 109:1129, American Institute of Nutrition.
19. DePeters, E. U., and D. L. Bath. 1986. *J. Dairy Sci.* 69:148.
20. Polan, C. E., et al. 1985. *J. Dairy Sci.* 68:2016.
21. Annextad, R. J., et al. 1987. *J. Dairy Sci.* 70:814.
22. Schingoethe, D. J., et al. 1988. *J. Dairy Sci.* 71:173.
23. Price, S. G., L. D. Satter, and N. A. Jorgensen. 1988. *J. Dairy Sci.* 71:727.
24. Hadsell, D. L., and J. L. Sommerfeldt. 1988. *J. Dairy Sci.* 71:762.
25. Lindsey, T. O., G. E. Hawkins, and L. D. Guthrie. 1980. *J. Dairy Sci.* 63:562.
26. Hawkins, G. E., et al. 1985. *J. Dairy Sci.* 68:2608.
27. Bell, J. M. 1984. *J. Animal Sci.* 58:996.
28. Laarveld, B., R. P. Brockman, and D. A. Christensen. 1981. *Can. J. Animal Sci.* 62:131.
29. Cordes, C. S., et al. 1988. *J. Animal Sci.* 66:522.
30. Fleck, A. T., et al. 1988. *J. Animal Sci.* 66:750.
31. Anon. Undated. *Distillers feeds research.* Cincinnati, OH: Distillers Feed Research Council.
32. Johnson, C. O. L. E., and J. T. Huber. 1987. *J. Dairy Sci.* 70:1417.
33. Boehme, W. R. 1975. Personal communication. Des Plaines, IL: Fats and Proteins Research Foundation, Inc.
34. Parsons, M. J., P. K. Ku, and E. R. Miller. 1985. *J. Animal Sci.* 60:1447.
35. Church, D. C., and W. G. Pond. 1988. *Basic animal nutrition and feeding.* 3d ed. New York: Wiley; Scott, M. L., M. C. Nesheim, and R. J. Young. 1982. *Nutrition of the chicken.* 3d ed. Ithaca, NY: M. L. Scott & Assoc.
36. Raa, J., and A. Gildberg. 1982. *CRC Crit. Rev., Food Sci. Nutr.* 16:383.
37. Chirase, N. K., M. Kolopita, and J. R. Males. 1985. *J. Animal Sci.* 61:661.
38. Ortega, E., and D. C. Church. 1979. *Proc. West. Sec. Amer. Soc. Animal Sci.* 30:302.
39. Zinn, R. A. 1988. *J. Animal Sci.* 66:151.
40. Phelps, A. 1982. *Feedstuffs* 54(2):17.
41. Hinks, C. E. 1978. *J. Sci. Fd. Agric.* 29:99.

42. Church, D. C., J. C. Steinberg, and B. N. L. Khaw. 1982. *Feedstuffs* 54(3):30.

43. Kellems, R. O., M. S. Aseltine, and D. C. Church. 1981. *J. Animal Sci.* 53:1601.

44. Oltjen, R. R., D. A. Dinius, and H. K. Goering. 1977. *J. Animal Sci.* 45:1442.

45. Rush, I. G., R. R. Johnson, and R. Totusek. 1976. *J. Animal Sci.* 42:1297.

46. Peyton, S. C., and H. R. Conrad. 1979. *J. Dairy Sci.* 61:1742.

47. Schultz, T. A., E. Schultz, and C. F. Chicco. 1972. *J. Animal Sci.* 35:865.

48. Jimenez, A. A. 1986. *Feedstuffs.* 58(8):12.

49. Church, D. C., and A. Santos, 1981. *J. Animal Sci.* 53:1609.

50. Rush, I. G., and R. Totusek. 1976. *J. Animal Sci.* 42:497.

51. Kellems, R. O., E. Ortega-Rivas, and D. C. Church. 1981. Unpublished data. Corvallis, OR: Dept. of Animal Sci., Oregon State Univ.

52. Kellems, R. O. 1982. Unpublished data. Corvallis, OR: Oregon State Univ. Dept. of Animal Sci.

53. Wagner, J. J., K. A. Lusby, and G. W. Horn. 1983. *J. Animal Sci.* 57:542.

54. Wahlberg, M. L., and E. H. Cash. 1979. *J. Animal Sci.* 49:1431.

55. Velloso, L., et al. 1971. *J. Animal Sci.* 32:764.

56. Ortega-Rivas, E., and D. C. Church. 1981. Unpublished data. Corvallis, OR: Oregon State Univ. Dept of Animal Sci.

57. Van Soest, P. J. 1982. *Nutritional ecology of the ruminant.* Ithaca, NY: Cornell Univ. Press.

58. Sniffen, C. J., et al. 1980. *Feedstuffs* 52(20):25.

59. Krishnamoorthy, U., et al. 1982. *J. Dairy Sci.* 65:217.

60. Stock, R., et al. 1981. *J. Animal Sci.* 53:1109.

61. Verite, R., M. Journet, and R. Jarrige. 1979. *Livestock Prod. Sci.* 6:349.

62. Rodriguez, J. P., and H. S. Bayley. 1987. *Can. J. Animal Sci.* 67:803.

9

Mineral and Vitamin Supplements

MINERAL SUPPLEMENTS

Minerals make up only a relatively small amount of the diet of animals. Nevertheless, they are vital to the animal and in most situations some diet supplementation is required to satisfy the requirements of high-producing animals. Of course, all of the required mineral elements are needed in an animal's diet (or water supply), but needed supplementary minerals will vary according to the animal species, age, type, and level of production and diet, which, in turn, will be affected by the mineral content of water, soils, and crops in the area where grown and of the fertilization practices used.

Generally, those minerals of concern include common salt (NaCl), Ca (calcium), P (phosphorus), Mg (magnesium), and, sometimes, K (potassium) and S (sulfur) of the macrominerals. With regard to the trace elements, Cu (copper), Fe (iron), I (iodine), Mn (manganese), Se (selenium), and Zn (zinc) are often deficient for domestic animals, and Co (cobalt) may be deficient for ruminant species. With rare exceptions, the other required mineral elements (see Ch. 3) are not normally a problem.

Adequate mineral concentrations and balance between minerals are also important items. Thus excessive amounts of one mineral may interfere with utilization of one or more other elements. For example, excessive Ca may cause problems with P, Mg, and Zn, and excessive aluminum may interfere with P. Other similar interactions are known, and there are, without doubt, interactions among other mineral elements that have not been identified. Even if no interaction occurs, minerals may be outright toxic, so maximal levels are of some concern in many situations (1). This is one reason why state and federal regulations often specify maximum concentrations in labeling laws for formula feeds (Ch. 5).

Mineral supplements must be provided from compounds that are available to the animal. The amount that may be dissolved and absorbed may vary with different compounds. For example, ferric oxide (Fe_2O_3) is almost insoluble and, therefore, of very little use to the animal. An appreciable amount of information is available on this topic. For further information the author would suggest other references cited at the end of the chapter (2, 3).

Whenever possible or practicable the mineral requirements should be met by selection or combination of available feedstuffs which supply energy or protein. Most energy and N sources—fat and urea being two marked exceptions—provide minerals in addition to the basic organic nutrients. Although considerable opportunity exists to provide most of the mineral needs from basal feedstuffs, the flexibility needed in formulating rations often requires concentrated sources of one or more mineral elements, particularly for high-producing animals. Some of these sources are discussed in subsequent sections. Mineral sources used commercially are listed in Table 9–1, with those used most commonly identified by an asterisk.

The choice of a mineral supplement is governed by the cost/unit of the element or elements required; the chemical form in which the mineral is combined; its physical form, especially its fineness of division; and its freedom from harmful impurities. These factors are generally of more importance for minerals required in large amounts and usually of less consequence for the trace minerals. Note also that the mineral concentration is not always constant in any given source unless the source is highly purified. Figure 9–1 is included to provide some idea of the appearance of some of the mineral supplements.

Common Salt (NaCl)

Common salt, which is practically pure sodium chloride, is the most common mineral supplement added to any livestock ration. It is unique

Trace-mineralized salt   Sodium phosphate   Limestone

Bone meal   Magnesium oxide   Defluorinated rock phosphate

FIGURE 9–1. Examples of common mineral supplements.

TABLE 9-1

Sources of mineral supplements used in feed supplements or complete feeds or in mineralized salt

Name, Principal Element	Name, Principal Element
Macro Minerals	**Trace Minerals**[a]
Calcium	Cobalt
Calcium carbonate*	Cobalt acetate
Calcium chloride	Cobalt carbonate*
Calcium gluconate	Cobalt chloride
Calcium hydroxide	Cobalt oxide
Calcium oxide	Cobalt sulfate*
Chalk, precipitated	Cobalt-choline-citrate complex
Dolomitic limestone*	
Limestone*	Copper
Oyster or clam shells*	Copper carbonate
	Copper chloride
Calcium-Phosphorous	Copper gluconate
Bone charcoal	Copper hydroxide
Bone charcoal, spent	Copper orthophosphate
Bone meal, steamed*	Copper oxide*
Dicalcium phosphate*	Copper pyrophosphate
Monocalcium phosphate	Copper sulfate*
Rock phosphate	
Rock phosphate, defluorinated*	Iodine
Rock phosphate, soft	Calcium iodobenhenate
Tricalcium phosphate	Calcium periodate*
	Diiodosalicylic acid
Magnesium	Ethylenediamine dihydroiodide*
Dolomitic limestone*	Iodized salt*
Magnesium carbonate	Potassium iodate*
Magnesium hydroxide	Potassium iodide*
Magnesium oxide*	Sodium iodate
Magnesium sulfate*	Sodium iodide
	Thymol iodide
Phosphorous	
Diammonium phosphate*	Iron
Monoammonium phosphate	Ferric ammonium citrate
Phosphoric acid, feed grade*	Ferric chloride
Sodium phosphate, dibasic	Ferric phosphate
Sodium phosphate, monobasic*	Ferric pyrophosphate
Sodium phosphate, tribasic	Ferrous chloride
Sodium tripolyphosphate*	Ferrous fumarate
Triammonium phosphate	Ferrous gluconate
	Ferrous sulfate*
Potassium	Iron carbonate*
Potassium bicarbonate	Iron oxide (coloring agent)*
Potassium carbonate	Reduced iron
Potassium chloride*	
Potassium sulfate	Manganese
	Manganese acetate
Sodium	Manganese carbonate
Sodium bicarbonate*	Manganese chloride
Sodium chloride*	Manganese citrate
Sodium phosphates	Manganese gluconate
Sodium sulfate	Manganese orthophosphate
	Manganese oxide*
Chlorine	Manganese phosphate (dibasic)
Potassium chloride	Manganese sulfate*
Sodium chloride*	

(continued)

TABLE 9-1 *(cont.)*

Name, Principal Element	Name, Principal Element
Sulfur	Selenium
Ammonium sulfate	Sodium selenate
Elemental sulfur (ruminants)*	Sodium selenite
Macro mineral sulfates*	Zinc
Organic sulfur in proteins*	Zinc acetate
	Zinc carbonate
	Zinc chloride
	Zinc oxide*
	Zinc sulfate*

*Sources used most commonly in commercial feeds. All of these materials are generally recognized as safe except for the two selenium salts.

ªTrace minerals such as fluorine, molybdenum, nickel, or others are not commonly needed in feed supplements.

in that it is quite palatable and attractive to animals and they can be relied upon to consume enough and usually more than enough to meet their needs. In addition, salt is often used as a carrier for other required elements or other materials such as pesticides, medicines, or antibloating drugs. Mixtures which contain about 40 percent salt will usually be consumed at adequate levels to achieve satisfactory consumption of other elements.

Salt is usually required for good animal production, particularly for lactating animals and those species which sweat profusely. It is a common practice to add 0.5–1 percent salt to most commercial formulas for ruminants and horses, and some supplemental concentrates may contain 1–3 percent salt. Poultry and pig feeds usually contain from 0.25–0.5 percent salt. In most cases this amount of salt is more than required but less than will be consumed free choice.

Salt is often fed ad libitum, particularly to ruminants and horses, because their requirements are probably higher than that of swine or poultry and different feeding methods lend themselves to this practice. Salt may be fed in loose form or as compressed blocks (Fig. 9–2). The blocks tend to restrict consumption if access is limited, but they are often convenient to use and are more resistant to losses from rain and moisture condensation. Where rainful is high, loose salt needs protection (Fig. 9–3).

Excess salt may be a problem for all species, but it is particularly so for swine and poultry, because they are much more susceptible to toxicity than are other domestic species, especially if water consumption is restricted in some manner. In areas where the soil and/or water are quite saline, it may not be necessary

to feed salt, nor will the consumption be very high if it is available.

When salt is mixed in feed, it should be fairly fine in texture, noncaking, and free-flowing. Iodized salt is regular feed-grade salt to which iodine has been added to supply a minimum of 0.007 percent iodine. If KI is used, a stabilizer is usually added to preserve the iodine content. If other compounds such as potassium iodate (KIO_3) or diiodosalicylic acid are used, then a stabilizer is unnecessary.

Trace-mineralized salt is available in most areas and is usually compounded so that sources of Co, Cu, Fe, I, Mn, and Zn are added. S and Mg may sometimes be added, as may be Se, but the latter mineral is closely restricted by the Food and Drug Administration (FDA) (discussed later). In most instances there are sound reasons for feeding trace-mineralized salts. In rare instances it might cause a problem if local soil and

FIGURE 9–2. Cattle consuming salt from a compressed block.

FIGURE 9-3. One example of a salt-mineral feeder which turns with the wind and thus offers some protection from the weather.

forage are particularly high in some element such as Cu.

In addition to the trace minerals, various medicines or drugs are frequently added to salt. Ethylenediamine dihydroiodide (EDDI) is often added to mineralized salt. It is a therapeutic agent for prevention and treatment of footrot and lumpy jaw in cattle as well as a source (poor) of iodine. Antibloating compounds may be combined with salt or other mixtures. Phenothiazine or other drugs used to control stomach worms are often added to salt fed to sheep.

Calcium and Phosphorus

Supplementary Ca and P are generally needed in many animal diets because the demands for them are higher than demands for most minerals for skeletal growth, lactation, or egg production and because many feedstuffs are borderline to deficient in these minerals. P is usually more apt to be deficient in the diets of herbivorous animals, since more forage is relatively lower in P than in Ca. Animals on high-cereal diets are more likely to be deficient in Ca because grains and similar feedstuffs are usually a relatively good source of P but quite low in Ca.

Most nonplant sources of Ca are well util-

ized by different animal species. Although net digestibility may be low, particularly in older animals, there is little difference between Ca sources provided particle size and other physical factors are similar. However, this situation does not apply to P because sources may differ greatly in availability. In plants, about half of the P is bound to phytic acid, and P in the product, phytin, is utilized poorly by nonruminant species. The usual recommendation is to consider only half of plant P available for these animal species, although ruminants utilize phytin P very well because of metabolism of phytin by rumen microorganisms.

Marked differences also exist in the biological availability of some inorganic P sources. Phosphoric acid and the mono-, di-, and tricalcium phosphates are well utilized, but sources such as Curacao Island and colloidal (soft) phosphates are utilized less well by most animals. Some sources derived from rock phosphates must be defluorinated, otherwise long-term consumption may produce chronic fluorine toxicity. Ca and P sources are listed in Table 9-1, and some descriptions of a few of the common sources are given in following paragraphs. Analytical data of some common mineral supplements are given in Appendix Table 5.

Dicalcium phosphate is one of the more common supplements for both Ca and P. The commercial sources are generally prepared from bones that have been treated first in a caustic solution, then in a HCl solution, and then precipitated with lime and dried. The other form is manufactured by adding Ca compounds to phosphoric acid and precipitating the dicalcium phosphate. These forms of dicalcium phosphate are excellent sources of both Ca and P, as they are readily soluble in the digestive tract and are low in fluorine. They contain 18-21 percent P and 25-28 percent Ca. Although a considerable amount of work has been done to determine the availability of P from some of these sources, the information is still inadequate (4).

Other products prepared from bone include steamed bone meal, bone charcoal, spent bone charcoal, and bone ash. The steamed bone meal is prepared from bones by cooking under steam, grinding, and drying. Bone charcoal (bone black) is obtained by charring bones in closed retorts. Spent bone charcoal is the product resulting from repeated charring of bone charcoal after use in clarifying sugar solutions in the manufacturing of table sugar, and bone ash is the ash obtained by burning with free access to air. The

Ca and P content vary somewhat in these products, but they are all good sources of these elements. Much smaller amounts of other required elements are also present in most bone products.

Other Ca and P sources include monocalcium and tricalcium phosphates, salts which are prepared from mixtures of Ca oxide and phosphoric acid. The mono salt contains about 20 percent Ca and 21 percent P and tricalcium salt about 38 percent Ca and 18 percent P. Defluorinated phosphate is also a low-fluorine product prepared from Ca phosphates and must have less than 1 part of F to 100 parts of P.

Feed-grade phosphoric acid is a solution of phosphoric acid and water and is used extensively in liquid supplements for ruminants. In addition to being a good source of P, it has the property of reducing the viscosity of molasses. It must not contain more than 100 ppm of F, 3.2 ppm of arsenic, and 1.3 ppm of heavy metals.

Ammonium phosphates are prepared by treating phosphoric acid with ammonia. The monoammonium form must contain at least 9 percent N and 25 percent P with limits on F, arsenic, and heavy metals such as lead. It is more palatable than the diammonium form which must have at least 17 percent N and 20 percent P. These products are restricted to ruminant feeds (when used as a source of N) in an amount that supplies not more than 2 percent of crude protein equivalent in the total daily ration. Rumen microorganisms can utilize the N as well as the P. In some situations it may be desirable to add P without Ca or ammonia. When it is not feasible to use phosphoric acid, mono- or disodium phosphate may be useful sources.

Rock phosphates of a variety of different types are also available. Those of domestic origin are usually relatively high in F, so their use must be restricted to prevent F toxicity. Soft rock phosphate, also known as colloidal phosphate, is not utilized well by some species.

Other Ca sources used extensively are usually some form of Ca carbonate, which is the principal Ca salt in limestone, oyster shells, calcite, chalk, or dolomitic limestone. Ca sulfate (gypsum) is sometimes added to ruminant rations containing nonprotein N to provide needed S. These different Ca sources are well utilized, and the Ca content of the carbonates runs from about 33 to 38 percent except for dolomitic limestone, which must contain at least 10 percent Mg.

Other Major Minerals

A supplementary source of Mg is frequently required in animal rations. As mentioned previously, dolomitic limestone must have 10 percent or more Mg, however it is not highly available to some species and Mg oxide is usually the preferred source. Mg carbonate or sulfate are also used. K is required for ruminants on high-concentrate rations as well as in some other situations. The chloride, bicarbonate, or carbonate are the usual sources used. S may be needed in some situations for ruminants. It can be supplied as elemental S or as any of a variety of sulfate salts.

Trace Minerals

The trace minerals most commonly added to animal diets include cobalt, copper, iodine, iron, manganese, selenium, and zinc; various sources are listed in Table 9–1. With regard to Fe, a considerable amount of iron oxide is used primarily as a coloring agent in things such as trace-mineralized salt, but the Fe is only slightly soluble and, as a result, it is a poor nutritional source of Fe. Other compounds commonly added include iron carbonate and ferrous sulfate. Cu is probably most commonly added as the sulfate, but the oxide, carbonate, and hydroxide are used sometimes. Experimental evidence indicates that small Cu "needles" can be given to cattle in a capsule and that they will lodge in the abomasum and provide a relatively long-term supply of Cu. Mn is usually required in poultry diets. The oxide and the sulfate are most often used in feeds. Co is, of course, required only by rumen microorganisms (to synthesize vitamin B_{12}). When added to feed, it is most often added as the carbonate or sulfate. Co "bullets" (small heat-treated cylinders of various metallic compounds) are utilized extensively in Co-deficient areas in Australia and New Zealand. The bullet is administered with a balling gun and, if successfully administered, gets positioned in the ventral sac of the rumen, where it will last for a year or more and provide a steady supply of the metal. Iodine is most commonly fed in the form of iodized salt, but it is also fed in various forms as indicated previously. Zn is needed frequently in swine, poultry, and ruminant diets. The oxide is the most common compound used.

If any of the trace minerals are added to premixes, the minimum amount must be specified according to most regulations. Selenium (Se) is the only trace mineral closely regulated in the

United States by the FDA. This is so because there is evidence that high levels can be carcinogenic; there is also evidence that low levels may be anticarcinogenic. At any rate, although evidence has been available since the late 1950s that Se is a required nutrient, the FDA did not approve it in some animal feeds until 1974 and for others it was much later. The current (early 1990) regulations are as given. Se may be added at a level of 0.1 ppm in complete diets for broilers, for chicken layers and breeders, and for ducks. A level of 0.2 ppm is approved for turkeys. For swine, a level of 0.3 ppm is permitted for pigs up to 50 lb in weight and 0.1 ppm for swine over this weight. Se can be added to sheep, beef, and dairy complete feeds at a level of 0.3 ppm. For horses, 1-2 mg/head (hd/d) is approved with a maximum of 3 mg/hd/d for up to three months and then a level of 1 mg/hd/d with the specification that meat from such horses is not to be used for human food. In all cases Se must be provided in a premix that is produced by a registered manufacturer, and all premixes must carry this statement: "Caution: Follow label directions. The addition to feed of higher levels of this premix containing selenium is not permitted." If Se is added to a salt-mineral mix, the FDA limits are 90 and 120 ppm, respectively, for sheep and cattle.

Some interest remains in utilization of chelated trace elements. Chelates are compounds in which the mineral atom is bound to an organic complex (hemoglobin for example). Feeding of chelated minerals has been promoted based on the contention that chelates will prevent the formation of insoluble complexes in the GI tract and reduce the amount of the particular mineral that will be required in the diet. Limited evidence indicates that this works sometimes (with Zn in poultry diets) but not in all cases. Usually, the cost/unit of mineral is appreciably higher than that of using more common forms. Chelates are also promoted for use in premixes containing vitamins or other compounds that may oxidize readily. Chelation reduces this type of reaction. One method of chelation is with soluble proteins. **Metal proteinate** is the product resulting from the chelation of a soluble salt with amino acids and/or partially hydrolyzed protein. It must be declared as an ingredient as the specific metal proteinate, for example, copper proteinate. **Metal polysaccharide complex** is the product resulting from complexing of a soluble salt with a polysaccharide solution declared as an ingredient as the specific metal complex. Several different products are on the market, but the author is not familiar with the amount used in the feed trade, and little research evidence has been forthcoming.

VARIATION IN CONTENT AND UTILIZATION OF MINERALS IN NATURAL FEEDSTUFFS

The reader may remember that data were given earlier on the variation in chemical composition of forage samples coming into an analytical laboratory (Table 4-3, p. 44). Another example is presented on minerals in corn and soybean meal in Table 9-2. In this example, values quoted in the NRC on beef (6) are listed and the analytical values and range in values are shown. With regard to corn, the NRC and the mean analytical values for the macrominerals were reasonably close, although P was lower than might be expected. With the trace minerals, Cu analytical values were lower than indicated and Zn values were quite a bit higher than suggested by NRC. With soybean meal, analytical means for Ca, Mg, Fe, and Zn were appreciably higher than NRC, and K and Cu were appreciably lower. These data show clearly that trying to get by on minimal levels for several months might cause some problems to livestock feeders if they depend only on book values which may not pertain to their area or to the crops they feed.

In addition to the problem of using incorrect values for mineral content of feedstuffs, there is a great scarcity of information on how much of the minerals in the feed will be absorbed by the animal. Certainly, it will not be 100 percent from natural feedstuffs, although it might or might not approach that level for some of the manufactured mineral sources. A random check of the literature shows that Ca in legumes is generally less available than that from a good supplement such as bone meal or dicalcium phosphate (7). Data of Ward et al. (8) indicated that 20–33 percent of Ca in alfalfa is in the form of oxalate and is apparently unavailable to ruminants. Other information shows that Cu is more available from silage than from hay and that feeding forages highly fertilized with N will result in reduced utilization of Mg and increased use of Ca by sheep. Unfortunately, there is just not much information on this topic. Even in studies with mineral supplements, it is difficult to obtain information showing how much of a given source was absorbed unless the use of radioactive isotopes can be incorporated into the

TABLE 9-2

The variation in mineral content of corn grain and soybean meal (dry-matter basis) samples from Iowa

Mineral	Mineral Concentration		
	NRC[a]	Iowa Samples[b]	
		Mean	Range
Corn grain			
Ca, %	0.02	<0.01	<0.01-0.18
K, %	0.37	0.34	0.27-0.42
Mg, %	0.13	0.17	0.14-0.21
Na, %	0.02	<0.01	<0.01-0.03
P, %	0.35	0.30	0.18-0.41
Cu, ppm	4	2.3	0.3-8.0
Fe, ppm	26	33.1	21.9-94.8
Mn, ppm	6	5.2	1.7-21.1
Se, ppm	—	0.21	0.04-0.66
Zn, ppm	16	58.7	16.9-147.7
Soybean meal, 44%			
Ca, %	0.33	0.55	0.33-0.82
K, %	2.14	1.92	1.21-2.37
Mg, %	0.30	0.48	0.45-0.53
Na, %	0.03	<0.01	<0.01-0.03
P, %	0.71	0.75	0.63-0.85
Cu, ppm	30	16.2	11.8-21.6
Fe, ppm	142	213.6	132.3-326.3
Mn, ppm	32	36.3	30.6-41.2
Se, ppm	0.14	0.71	0.28-0.93
Zn, ppm	61	91.5	59.8-168.3

[a]From NRC beef (6).
[b]Values represent data on 49 corn and 16 soybean meal samples collected on farms in Iowa.
Source: Ewan (5).

study. One reason for this is that there is a great deal of recycling of the mineral elements within the body, particularly of those excreted primarily in the feces. Oral administration of isotopes shows that the majority of Cl, K, Na, S, and iodine are excreted via the urine. A majority of the (normal) dose of all of the other minerals is excreted via the feces. Depending on the mineral, excretion may occur in the rumen, abomasum, or glandular stomach, via bile or pancreatic juice, or through the intestinal wall (small and/or large). In any case, unless samples can be obtained at various sites in the GI tract, it is difficult to determine how much of an element is truly absorbed.

Problems with Commercial Mineral Sources

There is often a problem that mineral mixes, particularly those intended to supply the trace minerals, may not be satisfactory supplements to the usual feedstuffs. There is also evidence that special premixes (prepared for specific feedlot use) may not always be as close to the target as they should be. Data illustrating these problems are presented in Table 9–3. These data were put together by Owens (9), who used a base diet with the major components of corn, milo, or wheat, alfalfa hay, and corn silage, supplemented as needed by soybean meal and cottonseed meal (except for the wheat ration). Based on the NRC requirements for 600-lb steers (6) (these specifications are not necessarily exactly right for all animals) and on NRC mineral composition for these feed ingredients (6), Owens calculated what the maximum shortage of the various trace minerals might be (shown in the table) and then showed how specialized mixes prepared by nutritionists might meet these requirements or how commercial trace-mineralized salts would fill the need when fed at levels recommended by the manufacturers. As is evident from the table,

TABLE 9-3

Mineral concentrations of typical feedlot rations, deficits for 600-pound steers, and amounts provided by some premixes and trace-mineralized salts

Item	Mineral, ppm						
	Co	Cu	I	Fe	Mn	Se	Zn
Diet base[a]							
Corn	0.08	6.20	0.0	45	9	0.07	19
Milo	0.19	11.80	0.03	65	19	0.40	21
Wheat	0.15	5.70	0.0	43	31	0.39	39
Requirement							
NRC 1984 Beef	0.1	8.0	0.5	50	40	0.2	30
Max. shortage	0.02	2.3	0.5	7	31	0.13	11
Mineral content of mixes prepared by nutritionists							
A	2.1	11.30	1.0	19	10*	0*	43
B	6.0	0.6	1.5	9	15*	0*	30
C	0.3	5.3	0.4*	0*	6*	0*	24
D	1.2	18.7	1.2	73	37	0*	88
E	0.6	7.0	0.8	30	8*	0*	52
F	0.1	6.0	0.4*	10	40	0.2	60
G	0.2	7.8	0.2*	25	25*	0*	67
Mineral content of commercial trace-mineralized salts[b]							
H	0.2	3.3	0.7	20	25*	0*	1*
I	0.5	2.5	0.5	13	20*	0*	25
J	0.5	1.0*	0.4*	33	3*	0*	1*
K	0.1	0.5*	0.1*	4*	5*	0*	6*
L	0.02	0.1*	0.3*	10	0*	0*	0*

[a]Diets calculated on the basis that alfalfa and corn silage made up 5% each of the dry matter, and cottonseed meal and soybean meal were added at a level of 3% of the dry matter to the corn and milo diets, but not to the wheat diet (which is already high enough in CP).
[b]The amount of minerals that should be present according to the manufacturer's recommendations to add levels of 0.5 to 1%.
*Potentially deficient ration.
Source: Owens (9).

some of the mineral mixes were below and some were above the suggested target amounts. One of the mixes put out by nutritionists was off only very slightly on its iodine content and one had no Se, but the others were off on two or three minerals. With the commercial trace-mineralized salts, all five mixes were on or above the Co target; two out of five were adequate for Cu and iodine, one was low in Fe, all five were low in Mn and Se, and only one of five was above the target for Zn. If this situation is representative of what exists around the country, it shows that livestock feeders must be more careful in the future to be reasonably certain that the mineral needs of their animals are taken care of. The cost is so small in comparison to the likely benefits that feeders should consider careful selection of mineral sources as potentially critical to success.

VITAMIN SOURCES

Almost all feedstuffs contain some of the various vitamins. However, vitamin concentration in plant or animal tissues varies tremendously. In plant tissues, vitamin concentration is affected by harvesting, processing, and storage conditions as well as by plant species and plant part (seed, leaf, stalk). In animal tissues, the liver and kidney are generally good sources of most of the vitamins. Yeasts and other microorganisms are also excellent sources, particularly of the B-vitamins.

As a rule, vitamins are easily destroyed by heat (especially in conjunction with exposure to air), sunlight, oxidizing conditions, or storage conditions that allow mold growth. Thus if any question arises of adequacy of a diet, it is frequently better to err on the positive side than to have a diet that is deficient. It is now a common practice to provide premixes in diets of poultry and swine to be sure that deficiencies do not occur.

As a general rule, vitamins that are likely to be limiting in natural diets include vitamins A, D, E, riboflavin, pantothenic acid, niacin, choline, and cobalamin (B_{12}), depending on the species and class of animal with which we are concerned. Biotin may also be a problem with both swine and poultry under some conditions. Vitamin K would normally be synthesized in adequate amounts in the gut, but it may also be needed, because synthesis may be inhibited by some feed additives.

With regard to ruminant species, normally vitamin A is most likely to be deficient, particularly for animals that have not had access to green feed for some period of time. There is also a fair amount of recent evidence indicating that β-carotene may be an important factor affecting fertility in high-producing dairy cows—

a situation which would not be remedied by normal vitamin A supplementation. It is also a fairly standard practice to supplement dairy cows and, sometimes, feedlot cattle with vitamins D and E. There is increasing evidence that niacin may be a factor in ketosis. In some situations an induced thiamin deficiency (polioencephalomalacia) develops, most often in feedlot cattle. It apparently is brought about by either excessive levels of thiaminase enzymes (which inactivate thiamin) or by thiamin analogs (which compete with thiamin). Thus it is a common practice to supplement ruminant diets with more vitamins than was common in earlier years with less productive animals.

Sources used for supplementing rations with vitamins are listed in Table 9–4, and the vitamin content of a limited list of feedstuffs is shown in Appendix Table 4. Appendix Table 5A lists the various vitamins used commonly in feed formulation and the typical concentrations available from manufacturers and in premixes.

TABLE 9-4

Recognized supplementary sources of vitamins for use in feedstuffs

Name and IFN Number		Status under Food Additives Amendment
Ascorbic Acid 7-00-433	Crystalline ascorbic acid— commercial feed grade	Reg. 582.5013
Betaine Hydrochloride 8-00-722	Crystalline chloride of betaine— commercial feed grade	Effective date extended
Biotin 7-00-723	Biotin—commercial feed grade	Reg. 582.5159
Calcium Pantothenate 7-01-079	Crystalline calcium pantothenate— commercial feed grade	Reg. 582.5212
Carotene 7-01-134	The refined crystalline carotene fraction of plants	Reg. 582.5245
Choline Chloride 7-01-228	Choline chloride—commercial feed grade	Reg. 582.5252
Choline Pantothenate 7-01-229	Crystalline choline pantothenate— commercial feed grade	GRAS[a]
Choline Xanthate 7-01-230	Choline xanthate—commercial feed grade	Reg. 573.300
Erythorbic Acid 7-09-823	Acid or sodium salt	GRAS[a]
Folic Acid 7-02-066	Crystalline folic acid—commercial feed grade	GRAS[a]
Herring Oil 7-08-048	The oil extracted from whole or parts of herring	Not a food additive
Inositol 7-09-354	Vitamin B complex vitamin; Lipotropic. Chemical name Cyclohexanehexol. Also referred to as i-inositol or meso-inositol.	Reg. 582.5370
Menadione Dimethylpyrimidinal Bisulphite 7-08-102	Crystalline meandione—dimethylpyrimidinal bisulphite—commercial feed grade	Reg. 573.620

(continued)

TABLE 9-4 *(cont.)*

Name and IFN Number		Status under Food Additives Amendment
Menadione Sodium Bisulphite 7-03-077	The addition product of menadione and sodium bisulphite containing not less than 50% menadione	GRAS[a]
Menadione Sodium Bisulfite Complex 7-03-078	The addition product of menadione and sodium bisulfite containing not less than 30% menadione	GRAS[a]
Menhaden Oil 7-08-049	The oil extracted from whole menhaden	Not a food additive
Niacin; Nicotinic Acid 7-03-219	Crystalline nicotinic acid—commercial feed grade	Reg. 582.5530
Niacinamide; Nicotinamide 7-03-215	Crystalline amide of nicotinic acid—commercial feed grade	Reg. 582.5535
Pyridoxine Hydrochloride 7-03-822	Crystalline chloride of pyridoxine—commercial feed grade	Reg. 582.5676
p-Aminobenzoic Acid 7-03-513	p-Aminobenzoic acid—commercial feed grade	GRAS[a]
Riboflavin 7-03-920	Crystalline riboflavin—commercial feed grade	Reg. 582.6595
Salmon Oil 7-08-050	The oil extracted from a cannery refuse of salmon	Not a food additive
Salmon Liver Oil 7-02-013	The oil extracted from salmon livers	Not a food additive
Sardine Oil 7-02-016	The oil extracted from whole fish or cannery refuse of the packing of sardines	Not a food additive
Shark Liver Oil 7-02-019	The oil extracted from shark liver	Not a food additive
Thiamin, Thiamin Hydrochloride	Crystalline chloride of thiamin—commercial feed grade	Reg. 582.5875
Thiamin Mononitrate 7-04-829	Crystalline mononitrate of thiamin—commercial feed grade	Reg. 582.5878
α-Tocopherol 7-00-001	α-Tocopheral—commercial feed grade	Reg. 582.5890
Tuna Oil 7-02-024	The oil extracted from cannery refuse of tuna	Not a food additive
Vitamin A Acetate 7-05-142	Vitamin A acetate—commercial feed grade	Reg. 582.5933
Vitamin A Palmitate 7-05-143	Vitamin A palmitate—commercial feed grade	Reg. 582.5936
Vitamin A Propionate 7-26-311	Retinol or esters of retinol formed from edible fatty acids	GRAS[a]
Wheat Germ Oil 7-05-207	The oil extracted or expressed from wheat germ	Not a food additive

[a]GRAS—Abbreviation for the phrase "generally recognized as safe by experts qualified to evaluate the safety of the substance for its intended use."

Fat-Soluble Vitamins

The best feed sources of carotene are green and yellow plants; generally, the more intense the green color, the higher the carotene content. Commercially, dehydrated alfalfa leaf and alfalfa meals or sun-cured alfalfa are normally used as sources of carotene (as well as other nutrients). More concentrated sources of carotene such as carrot oil or alfalfa extracts are also available, as are dry products in which carotene has been absorbed on a millfeed product for use in feeds. Carotene products in vegetable or animal oils are also available.

Vitamin A, itself, is not found in plants, but only in animal tissues. In animal products the liver, kidney, and liver oils from fish such as cod and shark are highly concentrated sources. Although fish liver oils are still used commercially, they have been replaced to a large

TABLE 9-5

Influence of pelleting, initial vitamin A concentration, and urea content on the supplement vitamin A content prior to storage

Initial Vit. A Conc., IU/lb	Feed Form		Loss by Pelleting, %
	Meal	Pellet	
3000			
0% urea	4.0±0.2	3.0±0.1	25
3.5% urea	9.0±0.3	7.0±0.1	22
7.0% urea	12.0±0.1	7.0±0.2	42
30,000			
0% urea	23.8±0.2	15.5±0.3	35
3.5% urea	24.2±0.5	14.5±0.5	40
7.0% urea	24.5±1.5	14.8±0.2	40
300,000			
0% urea	260±4.0	164±5.0	37
3.5% urea	293±0.5	177±5.0	40
7.0% urea	235±2.5	154±4.5	34

Values indicate vitamin A content expressed in thousands of IU/lb on a 90% DM basis.
Source: Shields et al. (10).

extent with vitamin A that is produced synthetically or concentrated from fish liver oil by molecular distillation. For addition to feed, vitamin A is normally sold in a dry, gelatin-coated form to which antioxidants have been added. The chemical form normally sold is the ester (a combination of an alcohol and an acid), usually as vitamin A acetate, propionate, or palmitate.

Vitamin A preparations normally are quite stable and can be added to most feed mixes or liquid supplements without much loss of vitamin activity during normal storage periods. However, there is probably more loss during processing and storage than normally realized. A common practice such as grinding a feed makes it susceptible to loss of vitamin activity because of the heat involved and because ground feed is more exposed to oxygen. One example of the effect of pelleting is shown in Table 9–5. Note that pelleting reduced vitamin A content in this particular study by about 30–40%. Other factors that may reduce vitamin A content of stored feeds include time in storage, temperature, the presence of ultraviolet light, and trace mineral content of the diet. In addition, moisture or hygroscopic compounds such as choline chloride or urea or the initial concentration of the microingredients may reduce vitamin content. It is now a common practice to add antioxidants to premixes to avoid vitamin destruction. Modern methods of preparation of vitamin A (use of emulsifying agents, antioxidants, gelatin, and sugar in spray-dried, beaded, or prilled products)

all help to reduce losses in storage (10). At any rate, the cost of adding vitamin A to rations is low enough that there is no economic reason not to add it when any likelihood of a need exists.

Important dietary sources of vitamin D are sun-cured forages, fish liver oils, and synthetic vitamin D produced by irradiating yeast, plant, or animal sterols with ultraviolet light. Although animals may obtain all the vitamin D they need as a result of ultraviolet light acting on sterols in the skin, most if not all commercial feeds have vitamin D added.

Four-footed animals are able to convert vitamin D_2 to D_3 (see Ch. 3), whereas poultry utilize D_2 very inefficiently. When intended for use with poultry, vitamin D is standardized in International Chick Units (based on preparations containing crystalline D_3). Use of D_3 (rather than D_2) in feeds for animals other than poultry is more efficient, resulting in lower dietary requirements. Vitamin D_3 is found naturally in animal products, but vitamin D produced from irradiation of plant or yeast products is in the D_2 form. D_3 not originating from fish products is usually derived from irradiated animal sterols.

In addition to the fish liver oils which may be fortified or concentrated, D-activated animal sterol is available; it may be dissolved in oil or absorbed on flour or other fine powders suitable for feeding. Vitamin D_2 supplements may also be purchased, as may irradiated yeast products.

Vitamin D is relatively stable in mixed feeds. However, when mixed directly with such materials as limestone, oxidizing compounds, and some organic ingredients, it is subject to rapid losses.

Vitamin E (primarily α-tocopherol) is present in most common feedstuffs, but it is found in highest concentrations in the germ or germ oil of plants and in moderate concentrations in green plants or hays, or in dehydrated alfalfa meal. Commercially, the germ oil is used extensively, although synthetically produced concentrates of vitamin E are available. Vitamin E is an antioxidant, thus it is lost rapidly in any situation resulting in oxidizing conditions (heat, light, high trace mineral content of feed, and so on).

Vitamin K is widely distributed in green plant material. There are a number of different compounds which have vitamin K activity, but menadione, a naturally occurring compound, is usually the normal reference standard. It is fat-soluble and may be stored in relatively high concentrations in animal tissues or in seeds such as soybeans. Two common water-soluble forms, menadione sodium bisulfite and menadione dimethylpyrimidinol bisulfite, are often used as feed supplements. Both have good stability in feeds.

Water-Soluble Vitamins

Animal and fish products, green forages, yeast, fermentation products, milk by-products, oilseed meals, and some seed parts are usually good sources of the water-soluble vitamins. The bran layers of cereal grains are fair to moderate sources, and roots and tubers are poor to fair sources. Cobalamin (B_{12}) is the only required vitamin that is not found in plants. It is produced exclusively by microorganisms. Thus good sources are yeast or similar products. Animal and fish products, particularly liver, are good sources. Animal manures contain B_{12}, also.

Commercially, some of the crystalline vitamins or mixtures used for humans are prepared from liver, yeast, or other fermentation products, but a number are produced at competitive prices from synthetic processes. Water-soluble vitamins produced synthetically include: thiamin hydrochloride, riboflavin, nicotinic acid or nicotinamide, pyridoxine, ascorbic acid, choline chloride, and pantothenic acid. These sources may be used when especially high vitamin content is needed in some particular

situation. Supplementary sources of the vitamins are listed in Table 9–4, and some of the synthetic products and their vitamin content are listed in Appendix Table 6.

SUMMARY

Mineral supplements, which are concentrated sources of needed minerals, are available for all of the required elements needed for domestic animals. Of the Ca supplements, it is generally agreed that those normally used are more completely available than are natural feed sources such as the legume hays. Ca sources include quite a variety of materials, and most of them are quite inexpensive. P is usually a much more costly mineral to provide and, often, is found in association with Ca (for example, in bone meal and other bone products and a number of the Ca-P salts prepared from rock phosphates). Most of the P sources are utilized efficiently, with the exception of some of the colloidal clays. Rock phosphates may be too high in fluorine to be used as a mineral supplement because of potential fluorine toxicity unless they are defluorinated. Defluorinated phosphate and dicalcium phosphate are the most common supplements. K is easily provided from carbonates, bicarbonates, chlorides, or sulfates. Mg can be provided easily by the oxide, sulfate, or dolomitic limestone. Na and Cl can be provided easily and cheaply by common salt. S can be provided to ruminants in any of many different forms, including elemental S, but nonruminants need an organic source such as methionine. Numerous different salts are available as sources of the different trace minerals. Iodine presents a problem in that ordinary KI is partially volatile and, if used, stabilizers must be added.

With regard to the vitamins, natural sources such as germ meals, brans, high-quality dehydrated grass or legume products, and various other products such as yeast and liver meals are often used as supplementary sources. In addition, relatively pure sources of a number of the vitamins are available in feed-grade purity and at prices that enable them to be used routinely where needed. A number of these vitamins are produced synthetically. Some natural sources such as fish liver oils are still used in moderate amounts as sources of vitamins A, D, and E, but vitamin K is primarily added, where needed, as a synthetic product.

REFERENCES

1. Ammerman, C. B., et al. 1980. *Mineral tolerance of domestic animals.* Washington, D.C.: Nat. Acad. Sci.

2. Church, D. C., ed. 1988. *The ruminant animal.* Englewood Cliffs, NJ: Prentice Hall.

3. Underwood, E. J. 1981. *The mineral nutrition of livestock.* 2d ed. Farnham Royal, England: Commonwealth Agr. Bureaux.

4. Miller, W. J., et al. 1987. *J. Dairy Sci.* 70:1885.

5. Ewan, R. C. 1986. *Report* AS-580-K. Ames, IA: Iowa State Univ. Dept. Animal Sci.

6. NRC. 1984. *Nutrient requirements of beef.* 6th rev. ed. Washington, D.C.: Nat. Academy Press.

7. Church, D. C., ed. 1979. *Digestive physiology and nutrition of ruminants. Vol. 2: Nutrition.* 2d ed. Corvallis, OR: O & B Books.

8. Ward, G., L. H. Harbers, and J. J. Blaha. 1979. *J. Dairy Sci.* 62:715.

9. Owens, F. N. 1988. *Beef* 24(7):29.

10. Shields, R. G., et al. 1982. Feedstuffs 54(47):22.

10

Feed Additives

INTRODUCTION

A feed additive is defined by AFCO as "an ingredient or combination of ingredients added to the basic feed mix or parts thereof to fulfill a specific need. Usually used in micro quantities and requires careful handling and mixing" (1). In practice, feed additives are defined as feed ingredients of a nonnutritive nature which will stimulate growth or other types of performance or improve the efficiency of feed utilization or which may be beneficial in some manner to the health or metabolism of the animal. The official federal definition is somewhat different (and ambiguous); it is outlined in Public Law 65.929 for those interested in further detail.

Many of the commonly used feed additives are classified as drugs. Drugs are defined by the FDA as "A substance (a) intended for use in the diagnosis, cure, mitigation, treatment or prevention of disease in man or other animals or (b) a substance other than food intended to affect the structure or any function of the body of man or other animals"(3). It is obvious that this is a very broad definition.

Of the various groups of additives classed as drugs, the major groups include many different antibiotics, nitrofurans and sulfa compounds (synthetic antibacterial compounds), coccidiostats, wormers (antihelmintics as well as other types), and hormone-like compounds. These are discussed in some detail in a later section.

Feed additives have been used extensively in the United States and in many other countries following the discovery and commercial production of antibiotics and sulfa drugs in the late 1940s and thereafter. The simple reasons for use were early observations that low levels of the additives, fed more or less continuously, often resulted in a marked improvement in the health and growth or feed efficiency of young animals such as chicks, baby pigs, or calves. In more recent years a trend has developed (particularly in Europe) for government regulatory agencies and law-making bodies to restrict usage of additives for a variety of reasons. For example, it has been claimed but not proven that usage of some additives with animals results in the development of resistant strains of microorganisms that might be more pathogenic to humans or that might be resistant to antimicrobial agents used in treating diseases in humans.

While it is undoubtedly true that feed additives are misused from time to time, it is also true that they have been extremely beneficial to livestock producers under our modern methods of production. Development of more intense systems of management and concentration of animals such as broilers, laying hens, growing-finishing pigs, and fattening cattle and sheep have been possible only with the use of a number of the additives to help control various diseases and/or parasites. Further information is given on this in later sections.

USE OF FEED ADDITIVES CLASSED AS DRUGS

In the United States the use and regulations of additives classed as drugs is controlled by the FDA (or more specifically, within the FDA, the Center for Veterinary Medicine). The responsibility of the FDA is to determine that drugs and medicated feed are properly labeled for their intended use and that animal feeds and food derived from animals are safe to eat. The federal law plainly states that no animal drug can be used in feed until there has been extensive research proving to the FDA that the drug is both safe and effective. In the process of developing a new drug for use with animals, the manufacturer must go through extensive testing. They must establish the safety for the target species, effectiveness of the drug, environmental impact, safety to humans, and chemistry and manufacturing specifications for labeling of the drug. Some of these data may be collected while using a permit for investigational new animal drugs (INAD) which allows some compounds to be tested under practical conditions and, providing there are no significant problems with tissue residues, for the animals to be marketed. General marketing of a new drug can be done only after approval of a new animal drug application (NADA).

Medicated Feed Requirements

The FDA's medicated feed requirements focus on those medicated feed mixers who use human risk drug sources. A human risk drug source is a drug premix that requires a form FD-1900 for its use. Medicated feed mixers who choose not to use human risk drug sources are subject to less demanding regulation and are exempt from mandatory FDA inspections, establishment registration, and drug assay requirements. Ob-

viously, there is some incentive not to use the human risk drugs as defined by the FDA.

All animal drugs used in medicated feeds are divided into one of two classes, called Category I or Category II. These drugs are listed in Table 10–1. As of February 1989, there were 31 drugs or drug combinations in Category I and 74 drugs or drug combinations in Category II. Category I drugs are the safest to use, have the least potential for unsafe residues, and require no withdrawal period before slaughter of meat-producing animals. Category II drugs are those (a) for which a withdrawal period is required at the lowest use level for at least one species for which they are approved, or (b) that are regulated on a "no-residue" basis or with a "zero" tolerance because of a carcinogenic concern, regardless of whether a withdrawal period is required.

Manufacturers normally provide drugs (or other microingredients) to feed mixers in rather concentrated mixes because it is impossible to add only a few grams per ton of feed and have it distributed with any accuracy. Thus drugs, vitamins, and other additives are diluted in packages that might range from 5 to 100 lb for addition to other feeds. This practice ensures more safety and/or accuracy for the feed mixer.

With regard to medicated feeds, they are classified as Type A, B, or C. A Type A medicated product contains a drug(s) at a potency higher than permitted in Type B feed levels (see Category I and II levels, Table 10–1). In other words, it is a concentrated premix of the product(s) that will be added to other feed with resultant dilution of the drug(s). Type B is a medicated feed for further mixing that contains drug(s) and that is intended solely for manufacture into another Type B or Type C medicated feed. It is produced from a drug component, a Type A medicated article, or another Type B medicated feed. A Type C medicated feed is one not intended for further mixing. It may be fed as a complete feed or it may be fed top-dressed or offered free choice in conjunction with other animal feed to supplement the animals' total daily ration. It is produced by substantially diluting a drug component, a Type A medicated article, or a Type B or C medicated feed with ingredients to a level of use that is covered by an approved new animal drug application.

Any feed mixer must be registered with the FDA before mixing any Type A feeds containing Category II animal drugs into animal feed. Feed mills that use any Category I animal drug source, or that use a Category II, Type B animal

TABLE 10-1

Category I and II animal drugs for use in Type B feeds

Drug	Maximum Potency[a] g/lb	Maximum Potency[a] %	Drug	Maximum Potency[a] g/lb	Maximum Potency[a] %
Category I Drugs			**(Category II Drugs (cont.)**		
Aklomide	22.75	5.0	Lincomycin	10.0	2.2
Ammonium chloride	113.4	25.0	Melengestrol acetate	2g/T	0.00022
Amprolium with			Morantel tartrate	66.0	14.52
Ethopabate	22.75	5	Neomycin	7.0	1.54
Bacitracin methylene			Neomycin	7.0	1.54
disalicylate	25.0	5.5	Oxytetracycline	10.0	2.2
Bacitracin zinc	5.0	1.1	Nicarbazin	5.675	1.25
Bambermycins	0.4	0.09	Nitarsone	8.5	1.87
Buquinolate	9.8	2.2	Nitrofurazone	10.0	2.2
Chlortetracycline	40.0	8.8	Nitromide	11.35	2.5
Coumaphos	6.0	1.3	Sulfanitran	13.6	3.0
Decoquinate	2.72	0.6	Nitromide	11.35	2.5
Dichlorvos	33.0	7.3	Sulfanitran	5.65	1.24
Erythromycin			Roxarsone	2.275	0.5
(thiocyanate salt)	9.25	2.04	Novobiocin	17.5	3.85
Fenbendazole	4.54	1.0	Phenothiazine	66.5	14.6
Iodinated casein	20.0	4.4	Piperazine	165	40.25
Lasalocid	40.0	8.8	Pyrantel tartrate	4.8	1.1
Monensin	40.0	8.8	Robenidine	1.5	0.33
Narasin	7.2	1.6	Ronnel	27.2	6.0
Nequinate	1.83	0.4	Roxarsone	2.275	0.5
Niclosamide	225	49.5	Roxarsone	2.275	0.5
Nystatin	5.0	1.1	Aklomide	11.35	2.5
Oleandomycin	1.125	0.25	Roxarsone	2.275	0.5
Oxytetracycline	20.0	4.4	Clopidol	11.35	2.5
Penicillin	10.0	2.2	Bacitracin	5.0	1.1
Penicillin	1.5	0.33	methylene		
Streptomycin	7.5	1.65	disalicylate		
Polaxalene	54.48	12.0	Roxarsone	2.275	0.5
Salinomycin	6.0	1.3	Monensin	5.5	1.2
Tiamulin	3.5	0.8	Sulfadimethoxine	5.675	1.25
Tylosin	10	2.2	Ormetoprim (5/3)	3.405	0.75
Virginiamycin	10	2.2	Sulfadimethoxine	85.1	18.75
Zoalene	11.35	2.5	Ormetoprim (5/1)	17.0	3.75
			Sulfaethoxypyridazine	50.0	11.0
Category II Drugs			Sulfamerazine	18.6	4.0
Amprolium	11.35	2.5	Sulfamethazine	10.0	2.2
Apramycin	7.5	1.65	Chlortetracycline	10.0	2.2
Arsanilate sodium	4.5	1.0	Penicillin	5.0	1.1
Arsanilic acid	4.5	1.0	Sulfamethazine	10.0	2.2
Butynorate	17.0	3.74	Chlortetracycline	10.0	2.2
Butynorate	63.45	14.0	Sulfamethazine	10.0	2.2
Piperazine	49.85	11.0	Tylosin	10.0	2.2
Phenothiazine	263.32	58.0	Sulfanitran	13.6	3.0
Carbadox	2.5	0.55	Aklomide	11.2	2.5
Carbarsone	16.0	3.74	Sulfanitran	13.6	3.0
Clopidol	11.4	2.5	Aklomide	11.2	2.5
Dimetridazole	9.1	2.0	Roxarsone	2.715	0.6
Famphur	5.5	1.21	Sulfanitran	13.6	3.0
Fenbendazole	8.87	1.96	Aklomide	11.2	2.5
Furazolidone	10.0	2.2	Roxarsone	2.27	0.5
Halofuginone			Sulfaquinoxaline	11.2	2.5
hydrobromide	0.136	0.3	Sulfathiazole	10.0	2.2
Hygromycin B	0.6	0.13	Chlortetracycline	10.0	2.2
Ipronidazole	2.84	0.63	Penicillin	5.0	1.1
Levamisole	113.5	25.0	Thiabendazole	45.5	10.0

[a]The maximum amount of Category I drugs that may be used in Type B feeds is 200 times the amount permitted for continuous use in a complete feed. That for Category II drugs is 100 times that approved for continuous use.

Source: Published in the Federal Register (2) and compiled by Anon. (3).

TABLE 10-2

Drugs approved for use as feed additives in the United States

Drug Name	Animal	Approved Dose Level[a]		Claims[b]	Withdrawal Time
		g/Ton of Feed	Other Measure of Dose		
Antibiotics					
Apramycin	Swine	150	for 14 d	DR	
Bacitracin methylene disalicylate	Feedlot cattle		70 mg/hd/d or 250 mg/hd/d for 5 d	LA	
	Swine	10–250		GP, FE, DR	
	Chickens, turkeys	4–200		GP, FE, EP, NE	
	Pheasants	4–50		GP, FE	
	Quail	5–20		GP, FE	
Bacitracin zinc	Feedlot cattle	35–70		GP, FE	
	Swine	10–50		GP, FE	
	Chickens, turkeys	4–50		GP, FE	
	Pheasants	4–50		GP, FE	
	Quail	5–20		GP, FE	
Banbermycins	Swine growing, finishing	2–4		GP, FE	
	Broilers, growing turkeys	1–4		GP, FE	
Chlortetracycline	Calves		0.1–0.5 mg/lb BW	GP, FE, DR	
	Beef cattle, non-lactating dairy cattle		70–750 mg/hd/d	GP, FE, LA, DR, FR, RD, AP	48 h at 350 mg/hd/d or higher
	Beef		5 mg/lb BW for 60 d	AP	
	Dairy cows		0.1 mg/lb BW/d	DR, FR, RD	
	Sheep	20–50		GP, FE	
	Breeding sheep		80 mg/hd/d	Vibrionic abortion	
	Swine	10–400		GP, FE, BE, leptospirosis	
	Horses to 1 yr of age		85 mg/hd/d	GP, FE	
	Mink	20–50		GP, FE, pelt size	
	Chickens, turkeys	10–500		GP, FE, RD, EH, BC	
	Ducks	200–400		FC	
Erythromycin	Chickens, turkeys layer and breeder	92.5–185		RD	24–48 h
Hygromycin B	Swine	12		GW	15 d
	Chickens	8–12		GW	3 d

TABLE 10-2
(cont.)

Drug Name	Animal	Approved Dose Level[a]		Claims[b]	Withdrawal Time
		g/Ton of Feed	Other Measure of Dose		
Lasalocid sodium	Cattle				
	Feedlot	10–30		GP, FE	
	Pasture except for lactating d. cows		60–200 mg/hd/d	GP	
	Sheep	20–30	15–70 mg/hd/d	GP	
	Broilers, fryers	68–113		CC	
Lincomycin	Swine	20–200		DR, GP	6 d
	Broilers	2–4		GP, FE, NE	5 d
Monensin	Cattle, feedlot	5–30	w/complete feed or	GP	
	pasture	5–30	25–400 w/supplement	GP	
	Chick. broilers & replacements	90–110		CC	
	Turkeys	54–90		CC	
Neomycin	Cattle, sheep, goats	70–140		DR, BE, ET (sheep)	Cattle 30 d, sheep 20 d
	Young animals on milk replacer		200–400 mg/gal MR	BE, DR	20 d
	Swine, horses, mink	70–140		BE, DR	
	Poultry	70–140		BE	
Novobiocin	Mink	200–350		BP, FE	14 d
	Chickens, turkeys	350	200 mg/T wet feed for 5–7 d	Breast blisters	4 d
	Ducks		for 5–7 d	Fowl cholera	
Nystatin	Chickens, turkeys	50	continuously or 100 g/T for 7–10 d	Crop mycosis and mycotic diarrhea	
Oxytetracycline	Cattle				
	Calves, 0–12 wk starter feeds or milk replacer	50–100	0.5–1 mg/lb BW/d	GP, FE	5 d if fed in MR or 2 g/hd in dry feed
	Feedlot		0.5–5 mg/lb BW/d or 25–75 mg/hd/d	DR, FE	
	Beef		75 mg/hd/d	GP, FE	
			75–100 mg/hd/d	LA, DR, RD	
	Dairy cows		75–100 mg/hd/d	MP, BT, DR	
	Sheep	10–20		GP, FE	
		20–100		DR, ET	

Drug	Animal	Level (g/ton unless noted)		Purpose	Withdrawal
Penicillin, procane	Swine	7.5–500		GP, FE, BE	5 d at 500 g/T
	Mink	25–100		GP, FE, DR	
	Rabbits	10		GP, FE	
	Chickens	5–500		FE, RD, GP, CC, BC	3 d at 200 g/T
	Turkeys	5–200		EP, FE, BC	3 d at 200 g/T
	Swine	10–50		GP, FE	
	Chickens, turkeys	2.4–100		GP, FE, RD, BE, BC	
	Pheasants, quail	2.4–50		GP, FE	
Salinomycin	Broilers	40–60		CC	
Streptomycin	Swine	7.5–75		GP, FE, DR	
	Chickens, turkeys	12–180		EP, BC, RD, IS	
Tiamulin	Swine	10–35		GP, FE, DR	2 d
Tylosin	Beef cattle	8–10		LA	2 d
	Swine				
	Starter feed	10–100		GP, FE, DR	
	Grower feed	10–40		GP, FE, DR	
	Chickens	4–50 or 800–1,000 for 5 d		GP, FE	
Virginiamycin	Swine	5–100		Chronic RD	
	Poultry			GP, FE, DR	
	Broilers, replacements	5–20		GP, FE, NE, CC	
	Turkeys	10–20		GP, FE	
Arsenicals					
Arsanilic acid or sodium arsanilate	Swine	45–90		GP, FE, DR	5 d
Nitarsone	Chickens, turkeys	90		GP, FE	5 d
Roxarsone	Chickens, turkeys	170		BH	5 d
	Swine	22.5–67.5		GP, FE, DR	5 d
Coccidiostats					
Amprolium	Calves	5 mg/kg BW for 21 d or 10 mg/kg for 5 d		CC	24 h
	Chickens	72.5–113.5		CC	
	Turkeys	113.5–227		CC	
	Pheasants	159		CC	
Butynorate	Chickens, turkeys	340–680		CC	
Clopidol	Broilers, replacements	113.5–227		CC	
Decoquinate	Cattle, goats	0.5/kg BW/d		CC	28 d
	Broilers	27.25		CC	
Halofuginone hydrobromide	Broilers	2.72		CC	4 d

183

TABLE 10-2
(cont.)

Drug Name	Animal	Approved Dose Level[a]		Claims[b]	Withdrawal Time
		g/Ton of Feed	Other Measure of Dose		
Nicarbazin	Chickens	90.5–181		CC	4 d
Robenidine HCl	Broilers	30		CC	5 d
Nitrofurans					
Furazolidone	Sows, pigs	100–300		DR, BE, GP	5 d
	Chickens, turkeys	7.5–200		GP, FE, CC, BC, TT	5 d
Nitarsone	Chickens, turkeys	170		BH	
Nitrofurazone	Broilers, replacements and turkeys	50		CC	5 d
	Swine	500		BE	
	Mink	100		DR	5 d
Sulfa Drugs					
Sulfamethazine	Swine	100		BE	15 d
Sulfadimethoxine	Chickens, turkeys	72.5		FC, bact. infect.	10 d
Sulfaquinoxaline	Rabbits	159		CC	7 d
Sulfathiazole	Swine	100		BE	
Other Antimicrobials					
Carbadox	Swine	10–50		GP, FE, DR, BE	10 wk
Dimetridazole	Turkeys	136–725		GP, FE, BH	5 d
Ipronidazole	Turkeys	56.7–227		GP, FE, BH	4–5 d
Drugs for Gastrointestinal, lung, or kidney worms					
Coumaphos	Cattle	27.2–36.3		GW	
	Chicken over 8 wk of age		0.091 g/100 lb BW for 6 d	GW	
Dichlorovos	Swine	348–499		GW	
Fenbendazole	Swine		3 mg/kg BW/d for 3 d	GW	13 d
	Cattle		5 mg/kg BW/d	GW	48 h
Levamisole HCl	Beef cattle, young dairy cattle	72.5–725		GW, lung worms	
	Swine	725		GW, lung worms	72 h
Morantel tartrate	Cattle		0.44 g/100 lb BW	GW	14 d
Phenothiazine	Cattle, except lact. d. cows		0.25 g/100 lb BW or 2 g/hd/d in feed or salt	GW	

Drug	Animal	Amount (g/T)[a]	Level or dosage[a]	Claims[b]	Withdrawal
Piperizine	Sheep, goats		12.5–25 g/d or 1g/hd/d in feed or salt	GW	
	Swine		5–30 g for 1 d	GW	
	Horses, mules		2 g/hd/d for 21 d	GW	
	Chickens, turkeys		0.5–1 g/bird for 1 d	Cecal worms	
	Swine		0.1–0.2% in water or 0.2–0.4% in feed for 1 d	GW	
	Chickens, turkeys		0.2–0.4% in feed or 0.1–0.2% in water for 1 d	GW	
Pyrantel tartrate	Swine	96–800		GW	
Thiabendazole	Cattle		3–5 g/100 lb BW	GW	3 d
	Sheep, goats		2–3 g/100 lb BW	GW	30 d
	Swine	45–908		GW	30 d
	Pheasants	454	for two weeks	GW	21 d
Miscellaneous Drugs					
Larvadex	Chickens			FP	
Methoprene	Cattle	454	22.7–45.4 mg/100 lb BW/month	FP	3 d
Poloxalene	Cattle		1–2 g/100 lb BW/d	BT	
Propylene glycol	Dairy cows		0.25–0.5 lb/hd/d prior to or after calving	KT	
Rabon	Cattle		0.07 g/100 lb BW/d	FP	
	Swine		0.05 g/100 lb BW/d	FP	
	Horses		0.07 g/100 lb BW/d	FP	
	Mink		3 mg/kg BW/d	FP	
Hormonelike Compounds					
Melengestrol acetate	Beef heifers		0.025–0.50 mg/hd/d	GP, FE, ES	48 h

[a] Quantities are given in grams (g) per ton (T) of feed or in amounts/unit of body weight (BW).

[b] The claims are for improvement of such things as growth, GP; feed efficiency, FE; egg production, EP; egg hatchability, EH; improved pigmentation, IP; milk production, MP; or for control or treatment of diseases or problems listed: AP, anaplasmosis; BC, blue comb (nonspecific infectious enteritis); BE, bacterial enteritis; BH, blackhead; CC, coccidiosis; DR, diarrhea; ES, estrus suppression; ET, enterotoxemia; FP, fly prevention; FR, foot rot; FT, fowl typhoid; GW, gastrointestinal worms; IS, infectious sinusitis; KT, ketosis; LA, liver abscesses; NE, necrotic enteritis; RD, respiratory diseases.

Source: Original data are from the Federal Register (2) and were excerpted from Anon. (3). *Note:* Many compounds are approved for use in various combinations that are not listed here. Approved use levels vary according to the specific purposes. The claims listed may not be complete in all cases, nor are many of the warnings listed here.

TABLE 10-3

Summary of antibiotic responses in pigs of different weights

Initial Weight, lb	Growth Response, %	Feed Utilization Response, %
Runt pigs	82	11
Normal pigs		
<25	19.6	4.1
25-30	15.6	-0.9
30-35	15.0	2.6
35-40	14.3	7.8
40-50	10.5	4.2
>50	8.7	4.1

Source: Adapted from Wallace (4).

drug source, are not required to register. Individuals mixing medicated feed for feeding only to their own animals are subject to the same rules as commercial feed mills. Labeling of medicated feeds is under strict control. It is discussed briefly in Ch. 5.

Antibiotics

Antibiotics are compounds produced by microorganisms; these compounds have the properties of inhibiting the growth or metabolism of (some, not all) other microorganisms and, in some instances, they may be toxic to warm-blooded animals. Most antibiotic names end in "cin" or "mycin." All antibiotics used commercially for growth promotion are produced by fermentation processes using fungi or bacteria. Those compounds currently aproved for use with farm animals are listed in Table 10-2 along with data on which compound is approved

for a given species, the range of antibiotic concentration approved, claims by the manufacturer and, if required, any withdrawal time before slaughter.

Antibiotics have, in general, been effective as production improvers when fed at low levels to young, growing animals, as is illustrated in Tables 10–3 and 10–4. Their use tends to result in an increased feed intake which may account for some of the improvement usually found in feed efficiency. Growth is nearly always increased, particularly when the animal is exposed to adverse environmental conditions. Weekly intramuscular injections (cattle) may work just as well as daily oral intake, but it is not a feasible method of administration except for dairy animals.

The response in growth and feed efficiency is apt to be variable among animal species and from time to time and place to place. For example, there is little or no response in new animal facilities, in very clean surroundings, or in germ-free animals raised under aseptic conditions. Generally, the most pronounced responses in young animals occur in situations where organisms such as *E. coli* or other organisms causing diarrhea are in high concentrations, because antibiotics, as a rule, will help to reduce the incidence or severity of several types of diarrhea. Antibiotic-fed animals are less apt to go off feed. In addition, evidence indicates that antibiotics may have a sparing effect on dietary needs for some amino acids and B-complex vitamins for young chicks, pigs, or rats, the beneficial response being greater when diets contain submarginal or minimal levels of these nutrients.

Antibiotics may be useful for a number of other purposes, for example, in the prevention and control of a wide variety of animal and poul-

TABLE 10-4

Effect of feeding low levels of antibiotics to beef cattle

Item	Growing-Wintering		Finishing	
	Controls	+ Antibiotic	Controls	+ Antibiotic
Daily gain, kg	0.56	0.61	1.16	1.24
Feed/unit gain	12.70	12.02	9.85	9.37
Number of animals	5353		2354	
Number of days on feed	112		117	
Improvement in gain, %	8.9		6.7	
Improvement in efficiency, %	5.4		4.9	

Source: Wallace (4). Antibiotics were fed continuously, most at 70 mg/hd/d. Antibiotics involved were chlortetracycline, oxytetracycline, and bacitracin.

try diseases. Various antibiotics are approved at low levels of continuous use for reducing the incidence of enterotoxemia in lambs, liver abscesses in fattening cattle, or diarrhea in young mammals deprived of colostrum. With poultry, some of the claims include reduction in respiratory disease, nonspecific enteritis (blue comb), and infectious sinusitis, as well as improved egg production and hatchability.

Antibiotics are often used at therapeutic levels in the treatment or control of many common diseases or control of gastrointestinal worms. When used at higher levels for therapeutic treatments (usually for only a few days), antibiotics have been very useful for treating or preventing stresses associated with transportation and adjustment to new conditions with cattle, for treatment of diseases such as anaplasmosis in cattle, bacterial enteritis in swine, and respiratory diseases, diarrhea, fowl cholera, fowl typhoid, and breast blisters in poultry. In most instances the higher levels are not approved for long-term usage.

Two antibiotics approved in recent years for cattle, monensin and lasalocid, are unusual in that they give a good response in both growing and mature animals. Technically, they would be classed as rumen additives. Although the mode of action is not completely worked out, these antibiotics result in a shift in the rumen volatile fatty acid production to relatively more propionic acid and a reduction in methane production, which in turn results in more efficient gain of growing animals and some improved efficiency and increased growth or gain in cattle (both young and adult) on pasture or forage. An example of the performance of growing-finishing cattle fed monensin and lasalocid is given in Table 10–5.

In the case of monensin and lasalocid, approval was first received for use as coccidiostats for use with poultry (they can also serve the same function in cattle or sheep). Although a few antibiotics do act on coccidia, most of the coccidiostats shown in Table 10–2 are synthetic compounds. Presumably, this normal difference accounts for the way these two compounds were named. It might be noted in passing that both of these antibiotics are quite toxic to horses.

Obtaining approval for new drugs to be used as feed additives has been more difficult in recent years. More investigative effort and much more expense has been involved, the result being that not many have been approved.

TABLE 10-5

Effect of feeding of monensin and lasalocid on performance of cattle

Treatment	Feed Consumed, kg/d	Daily Gain, kg/d	Feed to Gain Ratio
Feedlot cattle[a]			
Controls	8.27	1.09	8.09
Monensin	7.73	1.10	7.43
Controls	8.89	1.14	8.01
Monensin	8.65	1.18	7.43
Implant	9.61	1.28	7.63
Monensin + implant	8.97	1.32	6.85
Pasture cattle[a]			
Controls		0.61	
Monensin		0.69	
Feedlot cattle[b]			
Controls	8.68	0.99	8.75
Lasalocid, 30 g/T	8.27	1.02	8.09
Lasalocid, 45 g/T	8.09	1.04	7.79
Monensin, 30 g/T	8.09	1.03	7.93

[a]Data excerpted from a review (5) that contains a compilation of many different experiments done in many different places.
[b]Data from Berger et al. (6) from cattle (48/treatment) fed a 60% high-moisture corn, 30% corn silage diet (dry basis).

For example, with antibiotics, only apramycin and tiamulin have been approved for use with swine, nystatin for use with chickens and turkeys (for treating crop mycosis and mycotic diarrhea), and salinomycin (a coccidiostat) for use with broilers. There has been some slight expansion in approved use of lasalocid for cattle since the second edition of this book appeared in 1984. There have been some other changes in approvals of different species for compounds other than antibiotics, some alterations in approved levels, removal of some drugs from the list, but the addition of only a few compounds.

The reader may note (Table 10–2) that very few additives have been approved for horses, rabbits, sheep, goats, and species such as ducks, pheasants, and quail. No approvals are given for geese or pets such as cats and dogs. The primary reason for this is the cost of obtaining approval in relation to potential sales volumes. The approval procedure must be done with each species and at different levels that are recommended. Thus if projected sales do not indicate sufficient volume to justify the costs, no approval will be requested. Many of the antibiotics approved for cattle have been tested with sheep and they may be quite effective for a specific purpose, but few ever get approved for sheep and even fewer for species other than cattle, swine, chickens, and turkeys.

With cattle, most of the antibiotics (in feed) are used for baby calves and growing-finishing animals. Although there is approved use of chlortetracycline and oxytetracycline for lactating dairy cows, experimental data have indicated little if any advantage from long-term feeding of low levels.

With regard to poultry, the trend is to use one or more antibiotics in nearly all broiler feeds. Most of the antibiotics (Table 10–2) can be used for layers with the exception of high levels of chlortetracycline and erythromycin, and normal levels of lincomycin, novobiocin, and virginiamycin. Note that approval must be obtained for using different combinations of antibiotics or antibiotics and other controlled drugs by the manufacturers of at least one of the drugs. Far more drug combinations have been approved for use with chickens and turkeys than for all other animals combined. Also note that it is illegal to feed antibiotics at different levels or in different combinations (with other antibiotics or other controlled drugs) than those which have been approved.

With swine (Table 10–2) there are restrictions based on age or weight, but probably less so than for poultry. A fairly large number of antibiotics have been approved for use with swine.

Arsenicals

Arsenicals, which are all synthetic compounds, include a number of drugs used in turkey, chicken, and swine rations (see Table 10–2). These drugs were developed as a means of controlling parasites, but it was soon discovered that some of the compounds stimulated growth in the same manner as do antibiotics, and in fact sometimes it was additive to that of antibiotic stimulation. Note (Table 10–2) that several of the arsenicals have claims of improved growth production as well as improved feed efficiency for chickens, turkeys, or swine and for control of blackhead in poultry and diarrhea in swine. There have been other claims in earlier years, but they have been withdrawn as data on most of the older additives have been reworked and updated with added research.

Arsenicals have the disadvantage that they may accumulate in body tissues, particularly the liver. At the levels fed, they are not considered to be toxic, but all have a 5-day withdrawal period before animals are to be slaughtered for human food.

Coccidiostats

Coccidiostats include a wide variety of compounds ranging from a number of synthetic drugs to several of the antibiotics. These drugs are of considerable importance to the poultry producer because close confinement methods used in modern facilities accentuate the possibility of coccidiosis outbreaks. In addition, there is evidence that coccidiosis is becoming more of a problem with sheep and cattle kept under close confinement. In addition to the drugs listed under the heading of coccidiostats in Table 10–2, several antibiotics—lasalocid, monensin, oxytetracycline, salinomycin, and virginiamycin—have claims for prevention or treatment of coccidiosis. Also, some of the nitrofurans and sulfa drugs are effective against coccidiosis.

Nitrofurans

The nitrofurans are antibacterial compounds and are effective against a relatively large number of microbial diseases. Continued use of nitrofurans has not as yet developed bacterial resistance as is the case for some antibiotics. The nitrofurans are often used in combination with other drugs, especially with swine and poultry.

Sulfas

The first sulfa drug was synthesized in the 1930s, and some of the early ones were used extensively against some human diseases that were very difficult to treat at the time. Unfortunately, most sulfas present problems with tissue residues, and some of the injectibles are even worse, resulting in tissue residues in edible cuts of meat. The result is that there has been a gradual withdrawal of sulfa drugs as feed additives; fortunately, most of the problems alleviated by sulfas can be treated successfully with other drugs that cause fewer problems.

Drugs for Control of Gastrointestinal Parasites

Gastrointestinal and other types of worms (lung, kidney, and others) are a problem with all domestic species. Fortunately, a number of com-

TABLE 10-6
Additional special-purpose additives

Name	Classification under Food Additives Amendment	Limitations or Restrictions
Aluminum sulfate	Antigelling agent for molasses	None
Aniseed[a]	Spice, seasoning, essential oils	None[b]
Attapulgite clay[a]	Anticaking agent and pelleting aid; suspension aid in liquid feed supplement	Not to exceed 2% in finished feed or 1.5% in supplement
Ball clay	Anticaking agent and pelleting aid	Not to exceed 2.5% in finished feed
Calcium silicate	Anticaking agent	Not to exceed 2%
Calcium stearate	Anticaking agent	In accordance with good manufacturing practices
Capsicum; red pepper[a]	Spice, seasoning	None[b]
Diatomaceous earth	Inert carrier and anticaking agent	Not to exceed 2% of total ration
Disodium EDTA	To solubilize trace minerals in aqueous solutions	Not to exceed 0.024% in finished feed
Ethyl cellulose	Binder or filler in dry vitamin preparations	Specified in Reg. 121.230
Fennel[a]	Spice, seasoning, essential oils, etc.	None[b]
Fenugreek seed[a]	Spice, seasoning, essential oils, etc.	None[b]
Ginger[a]	Spice, seasoning, essential oils, etc.	None[b]
Glycyrrhizin ammoniated	Spice, seasoning, essential oils, etc.	None[b]
Iron ammonium citrate	Anticaking agent in salt	Not to exceed 0.0025% in finished salt
Kaolin[a]	Anticaking agent	Not to exceed 2.5% in finished feed
Lecithin[a]	Stabilizer	None[b]
Methyl glucoside coconut oil ester	Surfactant in molasses	Not to exceed 0.032% in molasses
Monosodium glutamate[a]	Spices, seasoning	None[b]
Montmorillonite clays[a]	Anticaking aid, pelleting aid, and nonnutritive carrier	Not to exceed 2% of the finished material
Mineral oil	To reduce dustiness of feed or mineral supplements, to serve as lubricant in the preparation of pellets, cubes, or blocks, to improve resistance to moisture of such pellets, cubes, and blocks, and to prevent segregation of trace minerals in mineralized salt.	Not to exceed 3% in mineral supplements
Petrolatum or a combination of mineral oil and petrolatum		Not to exceed 0.06% in finished feeds
Paraffin	Dust control agent	Not to exceed 3% in mineral supplements or 0.06% in finished feeds
Petroleum jelly	Dust control agent in mineral mixes	Not to exceed 3% in mineral mixes or 0.06% in finished feed

(continued)

TABLE 10-6
(cont.)

Name	Classification under Food Additives Amendment	Limitations or Restrictions
Phosphoric acid	Misc. and/or general purpose	None[b]
Polyethylene glycol (400) mono and dioleates	Processing aid when present as a result of its addition to molasses	Not to exceed 0.025% in the molasses
Polyoxy-ethylene glycol (400) mono & dioleate	Emulsifier	Calf milk replacers
Polysorbate 80	Emulsifier	Calf milk replacers
Polysorbate 60	Emulsifier	Calf milk replacers, mineral premixes
Propylene glycol alginate	Emulsifier, stabilizer, or thickener	None except in those specific foods listed in 121.1015[b]
Pyrophyllite	Anticaking aid, blending agent, pelleting aid, or carrier	Not to exceed 2% in finished feed
Saccharin Sodium[a]	Nonnutritive sweetener	None[b]
Sodium carboxymethyl cellulose[a]	Stabilizer	Not to exceed 2% in finished feed
Sodium silico aluminate[a]	Anticaking agent	Not to exceed 2% in finished feed
Sodium stearoyl-2-lactylate	Emulsifier and stabilizer	None[b]
Sorbitan monostearate with or without polysorbate 60	Emulsifier in mineral premixes and dietary supplements for animal feed	None
Tagetes (Aztec marigold) meal and extract	To enhance the yellow color of chicken skin and eggs	Sufficiently supplemented with xanthophyll and other carotenoids to accomplish the desired effect
Tetrasodium pyrophosphate	Dispersant	Not to exceed 1% of the finished product
Titanium dioxide	Color additive	Not to exceed 1% of the finished material
Urea formaldehyde[a]	Coating for feed-grade urea for ruminant animal feed	Not to exceed 0.0013%
Yellow prussiate of soda	Anticaking agent in salt	

[a] Generally recognized as safe.

[b] No quantitative restrictions, although use must conform to good manufacturing practices.

Source: Feed Industry Red Book (7).

pounds have been developed that can be used to control these pests. In most cases these additives are used in the feed or water for only a few days.

Hormonelike Production Improvers

Only one hormonelike production improver remains on the approved list. Melengestrol acetate (a synthetic progestogen) has found rather extensive use with beef heifers. It acts to suppress estrus, resulting in more efficient and more rapid gain.

Although not feed additives, several products are available for use as subcutaneous implants (in the ear). These include hexestrol (used outside the United States), zeranol (Ralgro™), said to be an anabolic agent, Synovex™, a combination of estrogen and progesterone, Rapid Gain™, a combination of testosterone and estrogen, and Steer-oid™, a combination of progesterone and estradiol. Most of these products also appear to work well for feedlot lambs, although much lower dosages are required. A high percentage of growing-finishing cattle are treated with one or another of these implants.

In ruminants the various natural or synthetic hormones appear to produce a response which results from increased N retention accompanied by an increased intake of feed. The result is, usually, an increased growth rate, an improvement in feed efficiency, and, frequently, a reduced deposition of body fat which may, at times, result in a lower carcass grade for animals fed to the same weight as nontreated animals.

There is ample evidence at this time (1990) that injections of natural growth hormone (somatotropin) can be used to increase milk production of dairy cows substantially. The hormone, which would normally be in very short supply, can be produced from bacteria by modern gene splicing techniques (as are insulin and some other drugs or "natural" products). Growth hormone will, in all likelihood, be administered daily in small intramuscular injections. Thus it does not qualify as a feed additive, but it is mentioned here so that the reader will be informed of its potential use. As of this date it has not yet been approved for use on a production basis.

Other Special-Purpose Additives

In addition to the many different compounds discussed as drugs in Category I or II (and the brief discussion of implants), there are many others that are used in manufactured feeds, sup-

plements, liquids, mineral or vitamin premixes, or in other special-purpose products (Table 10–6). Many of these products are used to improve the handling or processing properties of feedstuffs or ration ingredients, to alter their flavor, to prevent some ingredient from settling out of a liquid, to control dust, and so forth. Because these compounds are not considered to be drugs, they are not regulated at the feed mill level by the FDA. There are some limits to how much can be used and in what types of feed they can be used, and all users are expected to follow accepted "good manufacturing practices" which apply to feed mills or other manufacturers producing and using these chemicals.

SUMMARY

Feed additives are a most important part of modern-day animal production, especially in any situation where animals are housed in large numbers in limited spaces. Many of the additives used are classed as drugs, and all drugs used in animal production are under some degree of control by the Food and Drug Administration (in the United States), which must approve a feed additive for use before it can be used at the commercial level on a routine basis.

Antibiotics are among the most widely used feed additives and, it should be pointed out, many of these antibiotics result in more rapid growth, improved feed efficiency, and improved general health, primarily in young animals, when fed continuously at low levels. They may be used at intermediate levels for some types of disease control or at high levels for therapeutic use for short periods of time. Other antibiotics may be effective against problem organisms such as coccidia (a protozoan) or gastrointestinal parasites. Arsenicals, nitrofurans, coccidiostats, sulfa drugs, and other special-purpose additives have been developed for use with domestic animals. In some cases there may be problems with tissue residues (particularly with arsenicals or sulfas), and the animal producer may be required to withdraw the drug for a period of time before the animal is slaughtered for human food. Two hormonelike products are approved for use with some species. Other than use to suppress estrus in beef heifers, the primary use of hormones or hormonelike compounds is as subcutaneous implants (not as a feed additive) with finishing cattle or sheep. However, it is likely that growth hormone, produced from bacterial sources, will be approved for use as an injectible with lactating dairy cows in the near future.

REFERENCES

1. AFCO. 1988. *Official publication 1988*. Washington, D.C.: Assoc. Amer. Feed Control Officials.

2. Superintendent of Documents. *Federal register*. Washington, D.C.: Government Printing Office.

3. Anon. 1989. *Feed additive compendium*. Minnetonka, MN: Miller, and Alexandria, VA: The Animal Health Institute.

4. Wallace, H. D. 1970. *J. Animal Sci.* 31:1118.

5. Goodrich, R. D., et al. 1984. *J. Animal Sci.* 58:1484.

6. Berger, L. L., S. C. Ricke, and G. C. Fahey, Jr. 1981. *J. Animal Sci.* 53:1440.

7. Anon. 1988. *Feed industry red book*. Eden Prairie, MN: Communications Marketing.

11

Feed Preparation and Processing

INTRODUCTION

Feed represents a major cost in any intensive system of animal production. Even with sheep, which typically consume more forage (as a percentage of their diet) than do other domestic species, feed may represent 55 percent or more of total production costs. A value of 75-80 percent might be more appropriate for poultry. Thus it is imperative to supply an adequate diet (in terms of nutrient content) and to prepare and present the ration in a manner that will encourage consumption without excessive feed wastage.

Feed processing methods may involve mechanical, chemical, and/or thermal methods. Microbial fermentation may also be involved. Feeds may be processed to alter the physical form or particle size, to prevent spoilage, to isolate specific parts of a seed or plant, to improve palatability, or to detoxify poisons or antinutritional factors of one type or another. In some cases feed may be processed primarily to improve the capability of machinery to handle it, for example, chopping or grinding of baled hay.

Generally, feed preparatory methods become more important as the level of feeding increases and when maximum production is desired. This is so because heavily fed animals become more selective and are more inclined to sort out less palatable ingredients or to refuse and/or waste feed if the physical texture is not to their liking.

With ruminants, digestibility generally decreases as the level of feeding increases. This occurs primarily because feed does not remain in the GI tract long enough for maximal effect of the various digestive processes. Appropriate processing methods may, then, partially counteract the normal decline in digestibility.

Some large feedlots must purchase and store large amounts of grain (Fig. 11–1) so that they will have an adequate supply. It will, then, be processed as needed. Feed preparation becomes more important as animal production units become more concentrated, larger in size, and more mechanized. This applies particularly to roughage, because many roughages must be processed to some degree if they are to be used with equipment that is now available and (where complete rations are fed) chopped,

FIGURE 11–1. Milo grain stored outside at a large feedlot in Arizona. It is not obvious in the picture, but this large pile of grain is covered with wire netting to keep birds away from it.

pelleted, or ground roughages are much easier to mix with other ingredients.

The methods that will be discussed in this chapter are those used for processing feed grains or roughages or for preserving high-moisture grains. Methods used in milling grains for flour, processing oil seeds or processing pet foods will not be discussed.

GRAIN PROCESSING METHODS

Grain processing methods may be divided conveniently into dry and wet methods or into cold and hot methods. Heat is an essential part of some of the methods, but it is not utilized at all in others. Likewise, added moisture is essential in some methods but may even be detrimental in others. Examples of grains processed in different ways are shown in Fig. 11–2, and various methods are listed and discussed in following sections.

Cold Processing Methods

Roller Mill Cracking and Grinding.
Roller mills act on grain by compressing it between two corrugated rolls that can be screwed together to produce smaller and smaller particles (Figs. 11–3, 11–4). With grains like corn, wheat, or milo, the product can range in size from cracked grain to a rather fine powder. With the coarse grains—barley and oats—the product may range in size from a flattened kernel to a relatively fine-ground product, but the hulls will not be ground as well as with other types of grinding mills. Roller mills produce a less dusty feed than a hammer mill. If not ground too fine-

ly, the physical texture is very acceptable to most species. Roller mills are not used with roughage.

Grinding

Grinding is by far the most common method of feed processing and, other than soaking, is the cheapest and most simple process. A variety of equipment is available on the market, and all of it allows some control of the particle size of the finished product. The hammer mill is probably the most common food processing equipment used in North America. Hammer mills (Fig. 11–5) process feed with the aid of rotating metal bars (hammers) that blow the ground product through a metal screen. The size of the product is controlled by changing the screen size. These mills will grind anything from a coarse roughage to any type of grain, and the product size will vary from particles similar to cracked grain to a fine powder. There may be quite a bit of dust lost in the process, and the finished product is usually more dusty than grain ground with a roller mill or other type of grinding equipment.

Grinding generally improves digestibility of all small, hard seeds. Coarsely ground grains are preferred for ruminants because they dislike finely ground meals, particularly when the meals are dusty. Finer grinding is more common for poultry and swine. Grinding is just as satisfactory as other more expensive methods when grain intake is relatively low.

Soaked Grain

Grain soaked for 12–24 h in water has long been used by livestock feeders, particularly when they wish to pamper prize animals a bit. The soaking, sometimes with heat, softens the grain, which swells during the process, making a palatable product that should be rolled before it is used in finishing rations. Most research results do not show any marked improvement in feed efficiency as compared to other methods of processing. Space requirements, problems in handling, and potential souring (during warm weather) have discouraged large-scale use.

Reconstitution

Reconstitution is a process somewhat similar to soaking; it involves adding water to mature, dry grain to raise the moisture content to 25–30 percent and storage of the wet grain in an oxygen-limiting silo for 14–21 days prior to feeding. This

Steam-rolled corn   Coarsely cracked corn   Finely cracked corn

Popped, rolled barley   Steam-rolled barley   Ground Barley

Popped, rolled corn   Popped, rolled wheat   Popped, rolled milo

FIGURE 11–2. Cereal grains processed in different ways.

FIGURE 11–3. *Above.* One type of a roller mill used for processing grain. *Below.* The large corrugated rolls that physically crush the grain are shown. (Courtesy of Automatic Equipment Mfg. Co., Pender, NE.)

FIGURE 11–4. One example of feed processing equipment which will roll grain, mix it with other feed ingredients, and deliver the final mix into a bin or delivery vehicle. (Courtesy of Automatic Equipment Mfg. Co., Pender, NE.)

procedure has worked well with sorghum and corn grains, resulting in improved gain and feed conversion by beef cattle fed high-concentrate rations when whole grain was used, but it does not work well if grain is ground prior to reconstitution. Some fermentation takes place during the holding period, obviously. A major disadvantage is that storage is needed for a considerable amount of feed and, if sorghum grain is used, it should be rolled before feeding.

High-Moisture Grain

This term refers to grain harvested at a high moisture content (ca. 20–35 percent) and stored in a silo (or under plastic) to preserve the grain. Unless stored in such a manner or treated with chemicals, the grain will heat and mold if the weather is not cold. High-moisture grain may be ground or rolled before ensiling or before feeding. This is a particularly useful procedure when weather conditions do not allow normal drying in the field, and it obviates the need to dry the grain artificially with expensive fuel. Storage

costs may be relatively high, but high-moisture grain produces good feedlot results, comparable to some of the better processing methods discussed. Feed conversion, particularly, is improved over that of dry grain. Wet grains are more difficult to dispose of on the market, of course, than are dry grains.

Acid Preservation of High-Moisture Grains

With higher fuel costs, increased interest has developed in recent years in eliminating artificial drying of newly harvested cereal grains. Data with barley or corn for pigs and research with corn or sorghum grains for beef cattle show promise with the use of acids to preserve high-moisture grains. Thorough mixing of 1–1.5 percent propionic acid, mixtures of acetic and propionic acids, or formic and propionic acids into high-moisture whole corn or other cereal grains retards molding and spoilage without affecting animal performance appreciably, compared with that obtained with dried grains.

Hot Processing Methods

Methods used in recent years for heat processing grains and other products (such as oilseed meals, pet food, and so on) include steam rolling and flaking, extruding, pelleting, popping, micronizing, and roasting. Pressure cooking and exploding are methods that have been tried at the feedlot level, however, cost of the equipment and maintenance problems have discouraged

FIGURE 11–5. One example of a portable grinder (hammermill)-mixer which is available for on-the-farm use. (Courtesy of Ford New Holland, Inc., New Holland, PA.)

continued use. Information available to the author indicates that micronizing and roasting are not being used at the present time, and popping is on its way out. Comments on some of these methods follow.

Steam-Rolled and Steam-Flaked Grains

Steam rolling is a process that has been used for many years, partly to kill weed seeds (in the early days). The steaming is accomplished by passing steam up through a tower above the roller mill (Fig. 11–6). Grains are subjected to steam for only a short time in the usual procedure (3–5 min) prior to rolling—usually just enough to soften the seed, but not long enough to modify the starch granules to any degree. Most results indicate little if any improvement in animal performance as compared to dry rolling, but use of steam does allow production of larger particles and fewer fines, thus resulting in an improved physical texture (as compared to the result of dry rolling), which is an advantage when feeding very high levels of grains.

Steam-flaked grains are prepared in a similar manner except that the grain is subjected to high-moisture steam for a longer time (15–30 min), usually sufficient to raise the moisture content to 18–20 percent, and the grain is then rolled between corrugated rolls to produce a rather flat flake. Feedlot data with cattle indicate that the best response is produced with thin flakes, which allow more efficient rupture of starch granules and produce a more desirable physical texture in the finished product. Corn, barley, and sorghum usually give a good response in terms of increased gain; although feed efficiency is improved with corn

FIGURE 11–6. A high-capacity roller mill used in a large cattle feedlot.

and sorghum, steam flaked barley shows little improvement over steam rolled barley.

Pelleting

Pelleting is accomplished by grinding the feed and then forcing it through a thick, spinning die

FIGURE 11-7. One type of pellet mill widely used for pelleting concentrates. A quick change dye is shown at the left. Roughages can be pelleted, but production is reduced and costs are appreciably higher than for other feedstuffs.

with the use of rollers, which compress the feed into the holes in the pellet die. Feedstuffs are usually, but not always, steamed to some extent prior to pelleting. Pellets can be made in different diameters, lengths, and hardnesses, and they have been available commercially for more than fifty years. All domestic animals generally like the physical nature of pellets, particularly as compared to meals, and a high percentage of poultry and swine feeds are pelleted. However, results with ruminants on high-grain diets have not been particularly favorable because of decreased feed intake, even though feed efficiency is usually improved over other methods. Pelleting the ration fines frequently is desirable because the fines often will be refused otherwise. Supplemental feeds such as protein concentrates are often pelleted so that they can then be fed on the ground or in windy areas with much less loss. An example of a pellet mill is shown in Fig. 11-7.

Extruding

Extruded grains or other feeds are prepared by passing the feed through a machine with a spiral screw which forces the feed through a tapered head (Fig. 11-8). In the process the feed is ground and heated, producing a ribbonlike product. Results with cattle fed high-grain rations are similar to those with other processing methods. Some extruders are being used to process whole soybean seeds or other oilseeds for feeding to domestic animals. The heating is sufficient to get rid of most of the antinutritional factors found in soybeans or other types of field beans (see Ch. 8). Extruders are also used extensively for processing pet and human foods and for making fat-extracted oilseeds into oilseed meals.

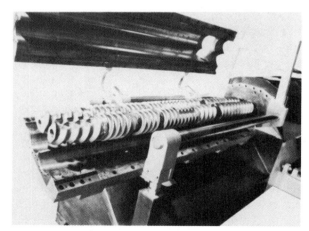

FIGURE 11-8. The spiral screws that are the unique part of an extruder used for processing pet feeds, some fish foods, oilseed meals, and numerous human foods. (Courtesy of Wenger Mgf. Inc., Sabetha, KS.)

Popping, Micronizing, Roasting

Most readers are familiar with popped corn, which is produced by action of dry heat, causing a sudden expansion that ruptures the endosperm of the grain. This process increases gut and rumen starch utilization, but results in a low-density feed. Consequently, the popped feed usually is rolled before feeding to reduce bulk. Micronizing is essentially the same as popping except that heat is provided in the form of infrared energy. Roasting is accomplished by passing the grain through a flame, resulting in heating and some expansion of the grain, which produces a palatable product, but the process has not found much favor among livestock feeders.

ROUGHAGE PROCESSING

Baled Roughage

Baling is still one of the most common methods of handling roughage, particularly where it is apt to be sold or transported some distance. Baling has a considerable advantage over loose hay stacked in the field or roughage in other less dense forms insofar as transportation is concerned. Although baled hay can now be handled mechanically for the most part, it still requires considerably more hand labor than many other feedstuffs. Furthermore, considerable waste may occur in feeding, depending on how it is fed (feed bunks, on the ground) and on the level of feeding. Heavily fed animals such as dairy cows may be quite selective, so that coarse stems will not be consumed. Thus a high loss nearly always occurs in feeding baled hays. Consumption is not adequate for high levels of performance when baled hay provides the only feed for cattle.

Chopped and Ground Roughage

Chopping or grinding puts roughage in a physical form that can be handled readily by mechanical equipment (Fig. 11–9, 11–10). Processing of this type also tends to provide a more uniform product for consumption and usually reduces feed refusal and waste. However, additional expense is incurred by grinding, and loss of dust may be appreciable from grinding with a hammer mill. The dust loss is sometimes reduced in commercial mills or feedlots by spraying fat on bales before they are ground. Ground hays are, as a rule, quite dusty and may not be consumed readily. Adding molasses, fat, or water will usually improve in-

FIGURE 11–9. An example of a simple hay chopping machine.

FIGURE 11–10. An example of a tub grinder, a type that is quite useful for grinding roughages coarsely.

take. Chopping produces a physical texture of a more desirable nature for ruminants or horses than does grinding, but chopped hay does not lend itself as well to incorporation into mixed feeds as does ground hay.

Pelleting

Pelleted roughages are usually consumed readily by ruminants, horses, and rabbits because the particle size and physical texture are of a desirable nature, provided very large pellets are not fed to small animals. Roughages such as long hay must be ground before pelleting, a slow, costly process compared to similar treatment of grains. Thus cost of processing is a bigger item than for most other feed processing methods. Pelleting usually gives the greatest relative increase in performance for low-quality roughages.

FIGURE 11-11. The effect of baling (left), grinding in a hammermill (center), or grinding and pelleting (right) on the volume of alfalfa hay after processing. Each pile contains 5 lb of hay.

This appears to result from an increase in density with more rapid passage through the GI tract and not to any great improvement in digestibility. Pelleted roughages are also metabolized somewhat differently by ruminants; as a result of more rapid passage out of the rumen, less cellulose is digested and relatively less acetic acid is produced with relatively greater digestion in the intestines. Utilization of metabolizable energy is usually more efficient.

Pelleted high-quality roughages will produce performance (gain in weight) in young cattle or lambs almost comparable to high-grain feeding. However, it should be noted that feeding finely ground, pelleted rations for long periods of time may be detrimental to rumen physiology. Animals fed in this manner will develop hyperkeratosis of the rumen papillae, which indicates reduced absorption. Rumen contents are generally higher in density and more apt to be foamy. An example is shown in Fig. 11-11 of the change in density achieved with grinding and pelleting of hay.

Cubed Roughages

Cubing is a process in which hay is forced through dies that produce a square product (about 3 cm in size) of varying lengths and hardnesses. Grinding before cubing is not required with field-cubed hays, but water is usually sprayed on dry hay as it is cubed. Field cubers have been developed and stationary cubers are also used to cube hay from stacks or bales, usually after grinding. Alfalfa hay produces good cubes that are less likely to break up than are cubes of grass hays.

Research data indicate that cubes will produce satisfactory performance in cattle provided the cubes are not too hard. Cubes are used for

dairy cattle more than with other animals. However, the volume of usage has not risen to the levels thought likely several years ago.

Dried, Dehydrated Roughages

Discussion of this topic will be very limited. However, it should be pointed out that a substantial amount of dehydrated alfalfa meal is produced in the United States (see Table 9-1), and some dehydrated alfalfa is produced in Europe. In northern Europe, where alfalfa does not thrive, grass forage is dried in limited volumes. Equipment such as that illustrated in Fig. 11-12 is used for such purposes.

Dehydrated alfalfa, bermuda grass, or others are harvested at an early stage of growth (prebud for alfalfa) when the protein content is high and the fiber content relatively low. Such products also have a high content of carotene and xanthophylls. The cost is also relatively high, thus dehydrated forage is usually used in limited amounts in poultry or swine rations as a source of carotene, vitamins, or "unidentified growth factors." Only limited use is made of dehydrated forage for other species. A substantial portion of the dehydrated alfalfa produced in the United States is exported.

EFFECT OF PROCESSING ON NUTRITIVE VALUE

A high percentage of feedstuffs used for nongrazing animals is processed to some degree by use of heat and grinding and, to a lesser extent, by pelleting. These methods may result in substantial alteration of the nutritive value of feeds, and, because there is quite a volume of literature on the subject, particular attention will be focused on these methods.

Heating

Heat may be used to dry plant or animal materials to a point that will allow storage without refrigeration, use of preservatives, or ensiling; to sterilize some products; to alter the chemistry of proteins or carbohydrates; or to detoxify some plant toxins.

With regard to proteins (see Ch. 8), it has been known for many years that excessive heating in the presence of sugars may result in browning (Maillard reaction). As a consequence of this reaction, lysine (and possibly some other amino acids) reacts with the sugars and, as a

FIGURE 11-12. One example of a commercial dryer used for drying and dehydrating feeds.

result, the lysine becomes partially unavailable to the animal. This reaction is mainly a problem with plant proteins or milk and milk by-products (most other animal sources have little or no carbohydrate present).

Data generally indicate that heating of fish or animal proteins makes them less efficient in promoting growth. With plant sources, heating of the cereal grains to a moderate degree and for short periods of time may result in a slight improvement in protein utilization for ruminants but little if any improvement for nonruminants. However, with legume seeds, heating results in an improvement in protein quality, partly by degrading antiquality factors which are present (see Ch. 8). Heating of soybeans also increases the metabolizable energy value, and it will reduce solubility of the soy protein, resulting in less degradation in the rumen.

With cereal grains ample evidence exists to show that heat, especially in the presence of moisture, results in partial gelatinization of the starch. Especially for ruminants on high-grain diets, this results in more efficient utilization of the cereal grains, particularly if the heating and processing results in mechanical rupture of the starch granules (1).

With regard to the vitamins, any treatment that increases exposure to air (oxygen) or which results in prolonged exposure to heat or light will normally result in some deterioration of most of the vitamins. The fat-soluble vitamins and thiamin, pantothenic acid, folic acid, and biotin are particularly susceptible to destruction by heat. In studies with dehydrated alfalfa, it has been shown that high temperatures result in the conversion of $trans$-β-carotene to compounds with much less vitamin A activity. Xanthophylls, which are important as skin pigments for poultry, are also much reduced if temperatures are excessive. Additional information shows that natural plant antioxidants in alfalfa (in addition to vitamin E) are reduced with high-temperature drying (2).

With regard to minerals, there is some evidence that heat processing may slightly alter the availability of some trace minerals, probably as a result of changes in natural chelating agents in the original feedstuffs. With fats, it is well known that excessive heating will result in production of acreolins, which are toxic to most animals. In most instances excessive heating is also likely to be conducive to increased rancidity.

Grinding and Pelleting

Grinding results in a substantial reduction in particle size and exposure of much more surface area to action of chemicals as well as to the digestive juices. Digestibility is usually increased, but storage of ground grains or other feedstuffs results in destruction of those nutrients which are readily oxidized, especially in the presence of trace minerals such as iron and manganese or unsaturated fats.

Pelleting has been shown to be quite advantageous for swine and poultry in many instances (see later sections). With some feedstuffs the improved performance may be due to the increased density of the diet, thus allowing greater consumption. When unpalatable ingredients are a factor, pelleting tends to mask the flavor and promote greater consumption. In addition, the heat involved in pelleting is believed to be a factor in inactivating heat-labile toxins in feeds. With corn there may be some improvement in utilization of amino acids by swine. Various studies have shown that larger amounts of feedstuffs such as dehydrated alfalfa, rye, wheat bran, wheat germ meal, rapeseed meal, or field peas can be used in poultry rations when they are pelleted without any appreciable effect on performance (3).

Even regrinding of the pellets still allows the same response with feedstuffs such as wheat middlings, while the effect is less apparent with the cereal grains. Some of the improvement with wheat middlings from pelleting is believed to be due to improved protein availability and, possibly, enhanced availability of phosphorus as well as the reduction in bulk. However, pelleting corn-soy diets appears to be of relatively little value for poultry. It may improve performance if protein is adequate, but it may depress production in some cases with marginal levels of protein or lysine, suggesting reduced availability of protein as a result of heat and pelleting. With some feeds the reduction in bulk may be less of a factor than chemical changes brought about by the heat of pelleting or rupturing of cells by mechanical means. Poultry can, apparently, eat reground pelleted mash more easily than the original mash (3).

FEED PROCESSING FOR NONRUMINANT SPECIES

A discussion of feed processing for different species is given in this chapter. In addition, some comparative research data have been cited. Additional information will be presented by most authors in Ch. 13–25 when discussing specific classes or species of domestic animals.

Swine

With respect to cereal grains or roughages such as alfalfa hay, grinding and pelleting are the most common feed processing methods used for swine. As with other animals, grinding will usually increase digestibility; the improvement is probably greater with older pigs or hand-fed pigs, which masticate food less well than do young pigs or self-fed pigs.

Rather fine grinding (0.16 cm hammer mill screen) results in an improvement in feed conversion compared to coarse grinding (Table 11–1), but pigs fed finely ground rations are prone to develop stomach and esophageal ulcers. Thus most swine nutritionists recommend a medium degree of fineness. Rate of gain is not affected appreciably by fineness of grinding.

Pelleting generally results in a very slight improvement in gain and an improvement in feed efficiency with corn-based diets (Table 11–2). As a rule, feed intake may decrease slightly and feed wastage is normally reduced as compared to meal diets. With the high-fiber grains (oats, barley) there is generally less improvement from pelleting than with other cereal grains. As with most animals, pigs usually show a preference for rations in pelleted form. Pelleting is of less value for older hogs which do not need to produce at maximal rates.

Other feed preparatory methods have been used for swine but have not found much acceptance. With barley, soaking and treatment with amylase enzymes results in some improved efficiency, but the improvement usually does not justify the expense. Treating whole barley by spraying with an aqueous NaOH solution to

TABLE 11-1

Effect of fineness of grinding on pig performance

	Hammer Mill Screen Size, cm		
Item	0.16	1.27	2.54
Experiment I			
Av. daily gain, kg	0.65	0.63	0.63
Feed conversion	3.19	3.56	3.67
Experiment II			
Av. daily gain, kg	0.70	0.71	
Feed conversion	3.52	3.74	

Source: Pickett et al. (4).

TABLE 11-2

Effect of pelleting corn-based diets on pig performance

Item	Daily Gain, kg	Daily Feed, kg	Feed Conversion
Growing pigs[a]			
Meal	0.725	2.02	2.78
Pellets	0.745	1.86	2.50
Advantage of pellets, %	+2.8	−7.9	+10.1
Finishing pigs[a]			
Meal	0.845	3.10	3.68
Pellets	0.905	3.00	3.32
Advantage of pellets, %	+7.1	−3.2	+9.8
Total period[b]			
Meal	0.69	2.52	3.71
Pellets	0.72	2.43	3.42
Advantage of pellets, %	+4.3	−3.6	+7.8

[a]Data from Becker (5) and Perry (6).
[b]Data from Baird (7).

avoid milling is not an effective method for swine (8). Steam flaking and reconstitution may improve digestibility for pigs, but they have little effect on gain. Feeding diets in liquid or paste form is also used (see Ch. 21), but not to the extent predicted a few years ago.

Roughage processing for swine is very simple because alfalfa is generally the only roughage fed in North America. Except in instances where high levels might be fed to restrict caloric intake, only small amounts of dehydrated alfalfa or ground, sun-cured hay are fed, usually incorporated into the complete diet, which is often pelleted.

Horses

Relatively little recent information is available on this topic as related to horses (9). The few reports available suggest that ground or rolled grains are probably utilized more efficiently by young animals and working horses than are whole grains. Rolled or cracked grains would have the advantage of being less dusty and would be favored in this respect.

With respect to roughages, the limited research data show that horses will eat more alfalfa hay when cubed or pelleted as compared to baled hay. Chopping appears to have no particular advantage. Grass hays and other products such as grass seed screenings are often fed

to horses. Pellets, in general, are well accepted by horses, and this is a feasible way to feed some finely ground feedstuffs which are not particularly palatable to horses. Limited data indicate that horses can be fed complete diets in pelleted form.

Poultry

Poultry feeds are nearly all fed as a rather finely ground mash, pellets, or crumbles, a product that has been pelleted and then put through rollers to partially break up the pellets. In producing crumbles the feed can be pelleted in a larger size than would be used normally for poultry, resulting in a savings in the cost of pelleting as compared to the production of very small pellets.

It has been estimated that as much as 70 percent of poultry feeds is fed in pelleted or crumblized form. Some of the advantages and disadvantages of feeding pelleted, steam-heated feed have been mentioned previously. In addition, with poultry, there tends to be an increased incidence of cannibalism and feather picking and an increased consumption of water when pelleted feeds are used. If wet litters are a problem in broiler production, pelleting would appear to worsen the condition.

Data illustrated in Tables 11-3, 11-4, and 11-5 show that broiler chicks or turkey poults gain more and have improved feed conversions when fed pelleted feed, crumbles, or reground crumbles as compared to performance of birds on mash diets. This type of improvement has resulted in a widespread use of pellets or crumbles for broilers and turkeys. Fortunately, the cost of pelleting rations of this type is low as compared to costs of pelleting high-fiber feedstuffs. Australian data (56) show that feeding crumbled pellets, as opposed to mash, resulted in an increased digestibility by chicks of 2.1 percent for a barley-based diet versus 4.5 percent for corn or wheat.

If the data in Table 11-6 are representative of most diets for laying hens, there is no great advantage in pelleting rations containing high levels of cereal grains. For layers the advantages would more likely be in use of higher levels of fibrous grains such as barley, less dense feedstuffs such as wheat bran or shorts, or other feedstuffs that are not particularly palatable for poultry.

With regard to roughage, the same comments apply as to swine because very little roughage is included in poultry diets. Small

TABLE 11-3

Performance of broiler chicks fed mash, crumbles, and reground crumbles

Item	Mash	Crumbles	Reground Crumbles
Corn-soy diet			
Av. weight, g	407	471	461
Feed/gain	2.06	1.90	1.96
Corn-soy + 30% wheat bran			
Av. weight, g	388	417	413
Feed/gain	2.16	2.00	1.97

Source: Summers (10).

TABLE 11-4

Influence of amount of corn or barley in mash or pellet form on broiler performance

Grain Component, %		Form	Body Weight, lb	Feed Conversion	Water Consumption, lb
Corn	Barley				
100	0	mash	2.76	2.73	10.8
100	0	pellets	2.92	2.56	12.0
50	50	mash	2.70	2.88	11.5
50	50	pellets	2.82	2.60	13.5
0	100	mash	2.50	3.27	12.9
0	100	pellets	2.77	2.82	15.8

Source: Arscott et al. (11).

TABLE 11-5

Influence of amount of corn or barley in mash or pellet form on turkey poults (0-8 wk)

Grain Component, %		Form	Body Weight, lb	Feed Conversion
Corn	Barley			
100	0	mash	4.20	2.07
100	0	pellets	4.40	2.02
50	50	mash	3.94	2.14
50	50	pellets	4.38	2.11
0	100	mash	3.94	2.33
0	100	pellets	4.31	2.24

Source: Harper (12).

TABLE 11-6

Effect of pelleting corn or barley rations for White Leghorn layers

Gain Component	Form	Egg Production, %	Feed Intake, lb	Feed/Doz Eggs, lb	Body Weight Gain, lb
Corn	mash	67.3	68.1	4.00	0.65
	pellets	70.8	74.2	4.15	0.82
Barley	mash	70.8	74.1	4.14	0.48
	pellets	69.6	77.2	4.38	0.75

Source: Arscott et al. (13).

amounts of dehydrated alfalfa or ground, sun-cured alfalfa are used in most instances. Ground, good-quality dehydrated grass may be used in some areas.

GRAIN PROCESSING
FOR BEEF CATTLE

Feedlot Cattle

Processing of cereal grains for feedlot cattle is done primarily to improve efficiency of utilization by means of improved digestibility and/or greater consumption because grain is already in a physical form that can be handled easily with mechanical equipment. Improvement in utilization can usually be obtained by a number of methods discussed previously, provided that the hull or waxy seed coat is broken up, thus allowing easier and more rapid access of rumen micro-organisms and digestive juices to the interior of the kernel. Some physical disruption of the starch granules of the endosperm and, normal-ly, partial gelatinization of the starch by heat treatment, soaking, or the like is also required for maximal efficiency. Heat treatment often im-proves protein utilization of cereal grains for ruminants.

Some processing methods may also provide a more favorable particle size, particularly for the smaller grains. Optimal particle size and density facilitate more timely passage through the rumen. In addition, particle size and freedom from dust are important factors affecting palat-ability.

As indicated, grain (or roughage) process-ing is expected to give greater returns/unit of cost when intake of grain is high. Usually, as the percentage of roughage in the diet increases, the physical nature of the concentrate becomes less important, although processing may still in-fluence digestibility and efficiency. Animals on a maintenance diet would not likely return the added costs. In beef feedlot rations typically in use at this time in the United States, grain and other concentrates in finishing rations for cat-tle may account for 70–90 percent of total in-take. With this type of ration the need and benefits of grain processing can be shown in most instances.

Data from about fifty different feeding trials with cattle fed corn or sorghum processed with different methods were summarized by Hale (14) on research done before 1980. Although the data were lumped together for many different experiments (not always an in-formative process), the data indicate that various methods (dry-rolled, steam-flaked, high-moisture and ensiled, and reconstituted) had little effect on daily gain of cattle fed corn. It did appear that flaking resulted in some reduction in feed consumed and an improved efficiency as compared to the other methods. Whole corn was used as efficiently as rolled, but less efficiently than flaked, early harvested (high-moisture), or reconstituted. With regard to sorghum, any of the methods resulted in improvement in daily gain as compared to dry-rolled grain, with some reduction in feed consumption and improved feed efficiency.

Some more recent data on processed grain are shown in Table 11–7, although it should be pointed out that not much work has been re-ported in the past decade compared to the previous one. It is rather surprising that very little information is available on steam-flaked barley in comparison with other methods. That which is available indicates that steam flaking will improve consumption and early gain with no appreciable effect on efficiency as compared to dry-rolled grain.

The example shown in Table 11–7 on wheat is fairly typical in that processing did not have any effect on daily gain of cattle fed wheat, but dry-rolling resulted in efficiency as high as any of the other methods and it was considerably better than feeding whole wheat. The one com-parison of sorghum grain that was reconstituted shows that this method did improve daily gain and efficiency, information typical of that reported earlier. Four examples are shown where corn was processed in different ways. In each case it is apparent that some type of proc-essing improved the feeding value of whole corn both in gain per day and feed efficiency and with rations in which the grain content ranged from 50 to 80+ percent. The evidence suggests that almost any method of breaking up the kernel will result in some improvement. Most of the papers listed in Table 11–7 give data on starch or organic matter digestibility. In each case where it was given, starch digestion was im-proved by heat treatments or flaking of corn and, for sorghum, it was improved by using high-moisture or reconstituted grain.

Other Feeding Situations
with Beef Cattle

Varying amounts of grain may be fed to grow-ing beef cattle (stockers, feeders), but only limited amounts are fed to adult cattle. In either

TABLE 11-7

Performance of feedlot cattle fed grains processed in different ways

Grain, Method	Feed Consumed/d, Dry Basis	Av. Daily Gain, kg	Feed:Gain Ratio	Reference No.
Barley, dry-rolled	9.44	1.31	7.22	14
Steam-flaked	10.31	1.41	7.32	
Barley, dry rolled	8.96	1.67	5.41	57
Steam-flaked	9.29	1.69	5.51	
Wheat (hard, red winter)[a]				15
Whole	11.53	1.35	8.50	
Dry-rolled	9.72	1.32	7.34	
High-moisture	9.81	1.32	7.39	
Steam-flaked	9.90	1.33	7.45	
Extruded	9.99	1.30	7.71	
Corn vs. sorghum (80% grain)				16
Corn, dry-rolled	8.87	1.48	5.99	
Sorghum				
Dry-rolled	9.00	1.42	6.34	
High-moisture, ensiled	9.87	1.42	6.95	
Reconstituted	9.00	1.52	5.92	
Sorghum, reconstituted (80% grain)				16
At 23.5% moisture	9.39	1.39	6.76	
At 31.5% moisture	8.81	1.37	6.43	
Corn (5–15% hay)				17
Whole	7.37	1.22	6.06	
Cracked	7.81	1.31	5.97	
Fine ground	7.87	1.33	6.00	
50:50 whole-cracked	7.54	1.33	5.75	
50:50 whole-fine gr.	7.82	1.33	5.95	
Corn (66.8–68.4% corn)				18
Whole	7.20	1.18	6.09	
75:25 whole-flaked	7.35	1.23	5.95	
50:50 whole-flaked	6.95	1.12	6.17	
25:75 whole-flaked	7.01	1.19	5.89	
Steam-flaked	6.30	1.05	5.97	
Corn (67% of ration)				19
Whole, shelled	7.01	1.25	5.62	
Whole, steamed	7.59	1.31	5.79	
Steam-flaked	6.71	1.33	5.06	
Corn (50.6% of ration)				20
Dry-rolled	6.77	1.19	5.71	
Steam-flaked	6.41	1.21	5.32	

[a]Data expressed on an air-dry basis.

case, grinding or dry rolling appear to be satisfactory methods, and there is little justification for resorting to more expensive processing (see Ch. 13, 14). Some processing is normally justified when grain is fed, because cattle do not masticate most grains efficiently. In one experiment cattle excreted in feces 7, 48, and 40 percent, respectively, of the oats, barley, and wheat fed in rations containing about two-thirds grain; dry rolling increased grain digestibility from 77 to 81 percent for oats, 52 to 85 percent for barley, and 63 to 88 percent for wheat (21).

ROUGHAGE PROCESSING FOR BEEF CATTLE

As pointed out in the section on roughage processing methods, roughage is frequently chopped or coarsely ground to facilitate mixing with other ration ingredients. Roughage may also be processed in this manner to reduce wastage or selectivity. Other than information on chemical treatments or addition of ammonia, there has been very little material published on roughage processing in the past 10 years.

A limited amount of older data are shown in Table 11–8. These data generally show that chopping and grinding do not have much effect on daily gain or feed efficiency (unless waste is reduced). Pelleting or cubing will almost always result in increased gain and feed consumption along with improved efficiency, but feed efficiency values may be biased, as pointed out in the footnote in Table 11–8. Unless waste is reduced, normally cubing or pelleting may not be enough more efficient to pay added costs for growing cattle. Cubed or pelleted roughage is sometimes used as supplementary feed for wintering animals. When it is necessary to feed on the ground, wastage will be reduced considerably.

Pellet size is probably not as critical with cattle as with some other species. However, young animals may have difficulty in consuming cubes (usually at least 1 in. square), especially if they are quite hard. In one study with calves

TABLE 11-8

Effect of roughage processing on performance of growing-finishing cattle

Item	Gain, kg/d	Dry Matter Intake, kg/d	Feed Conversion[a]	Reference No.
Coastal bermuda grass				
Long	0.33	4.67[b]	17.0[b]	22
Ground	0.50	6.07[b]	13.9	
Pelleted	0.66	6.53	11.3	
Meadow hay				
Chopped	0.18	4.49	26.8	23
Wafered	0.14	4.58	33.7	
Pelleted	0.32	5.58	17.3	
Alfalfa hay				
Baled	0.29	4.31	15.1	24
Chopped	0.28	4.22	15.1	
Pelleted	0.78	6.49	8.3	
Alfalfa hay				
Baled	0.67	6.14	9.1	25
Cubed	0.86	6.65	7.8	
Haylage	0.77	6.79	8.9	
Concentrate-wheat straw				
15% straw, loose	1.05	10.4	9.9	26
15% straw, pelleted	1.16	10.4	9.0	
30% straw, loose	1.05	12.1	11.5	
30% straw, pelleted	0.98	9.9	10.1	
Concentrate, alfalfa cubes				
Chopped & cubed hay	1.15	5.85C, 3.27B[b,c]	8.6[b]	27
Field-cubed hay	1.15	6.12C, 3.22B	8.8	
0.5%[d] barley	1.14	8.35C, 1.72B	9.5	
1.0%[d] barley	1.15	6.08C, 3.31B	8.8	
1.5%[d] barley	1.16	3.49C, 4.72B	7.8	

[a]Feed conversion values for animals fed cubes or pellets with all roughage or high roughage tend to bias the results because rumen and/or gut fill will nearly always be greater in animals fed roughage compressed in such a manner. More realistic values on comparative weight gains would be obtained by adjusting live weights using the carcass weight divided by an average dressing percentage or by using empty body weight.
[b]As fed basis.
[c]C = daily consumption of cubes, B = daily consumption of barley which was fed at about 0.5, 1, or 1.5% of body weight/d.
[d]Cattle were also fed limited amounts of corn silage.

7–14 weeks of age, there was little effect of size (9–18 mm in diameter) or density of grass pellets when calves could also consume hay. Consumption of high-density pellets was reduced, but the calves ate more hay to compensate (28).

FEED PROCESSING FOR DAIRY COWS

Feed processing may result in somewhat different responses in dairy cows than for growing or finishing cattle or lambs. Generally, feeding lactating cows high-grain rations (more than 60 percent grain), particularly heat-treated grains or all of their roughage in ground, pelleted, or cubed form, results in reduced rumen acetate

production and lower milk fat percentages (Table 11–9). Total milk fat production may not be decreased because milk production may be increased. However, when milk is sold on the basis of its fat percentage (a wasteful method), then use of heat-treated grains or pelleted roughages may need to be restricted.

As a rule it is generally accepted that processing of grain by grinding or rolling is about all that needs to be done for dairy cows, although pelleting the concentrate will speed up consumption considerably when cows are fed some portion of their concentrate in the milking parlor, particularly when eating time is limited. In one study (29), eating rate was in the order (highest to lowest) of pelleted, coarse cracked corn with

TABLE 11-9

Effect of feed processing on milk production of lactating dairy cows

Ration, Process	Feed/d, kg	Milk/d, kg		Milk Fat, %	Reference No.
		Total	4% FCM		
Processed Concentrates					
Alfalfa, 40%, concentrate, 60%					30
Whole corn	14.6	14.1	13.7	3.81	
vs. corn meal	14.2	16.0	13.8	3.09	
Corn meal	13.4	15.2	14.5	3.68	
vs. cracked corn	13.3	14.3	14.1	3.90	
53-55% concentrate (80% sorghum)					31
Finely ground grain	20.0	28.4	25.6	3.42	
Reconstituted grain	20.3	28.0	25.1	3.34	
Concentrates as					32
Meal	13.2	17.8	15.0	2.98	
Pelleted w/o steam	12.9	17.9	13.7	2.47	
Pelleted w/steam	13.0	17.4	13.4	2.53	
Processed Concentrates and Roughage					
Ration form, % concentrate					33
Milled, 60%	15.7	24.5	22.7	3.51	
Cubed, 60%	17.2	21.5	17.3	2.72	
50%	19.4	23.8	20.0	2.90	
40%	19.2	22.6	19.4	3.06	
Alfalfa, high-barley concentrate					34
Pelleted conc., baled hay	25.9	30.1	31.0	4.19	
Cubed ration[a]	24.7	28.6	25.1	3.28	
Pelleted concentrate, cubed hay[b]	22.9	29.3	26.5	3.40	
Processed Roughage					
Alfalfa hay fed as					35
Baled	17.6	30.4	28.2	3.48	
Baled + corn silage	17.2	27.3	24.4	3.32	
Cubes	20.3	32.7	30.7	3.60	
Cubes + corn silage	21.3	31.8	29.8	3.54	
Alfalfa hay fed as					36
Baled		20.2	18.7	3.7	
Ground		19.9	18.2	3.6	
Pelleted		19.1	16.1	3.1	

[a]Alfalfa hay was baled in the field and then ground and cubed in a stationary cuber.
[b]Alfalfa hay was field-cubed and fed with pelleted concentrate.

pelleted premix, crumbled pellet, and concentrate in meal form.

Pelleting complete diets for dairy cows is generally advantageous only when the roughage level is high and when the quality of roughage is moderate to low. Cubing or pelleting roughage will often result in somewhat greater consumption of feed, but milk production may or may not be improved. Some data on effect of feed processing are shown in Table 11–9. Further comments will be found in Ch. 15.

FEED PROCESSING FOR SHEEP AND GOATS

It is not feasible to spend much money on processing feed for mature sheep or goats. The convenience and reduced waste related to use of chopped hay may make chopping feasible, but the cost of pelleting or cubing roughage is usually prohibitive. Pelleted feeds are sometimes used where ewe bands are fed on the range or in winter lambing quarters for short periods of time. The savings in feed plus the fact that feed bunks are not needed allow it to be done. When grains are fed, anything more than coarse grinding, cracking, or rolling is of doubtful benefit. Very limited studies with lactating dairy goats also show that ground or pelleted alfalfa did not result in any greater milk production than did feeding long hay.

In the feedlot, not much if any benefit is obtained by processing cereal grains (Table 11–10) for lambs. However, it may be feasible to pellet complete rations when they contain appreciable amounts of roughage (see Ch. 19). Lambs do very well on high-roughage pellets and they will, in fact, finish to a satisfactory degree (USDA grades) when fed nothing but alfalfa pellets. Maximal gains will usually be achieved by using 15-25 percent grain along with alfalfa hay; feed conversion will be improved proportionately as the grain is increased.

When lambs are fed pelleted roughages (good-quality grass hay, legume hays), several research studies have shown clearly that consumption will be increased considerably as compared to when they are fed ground or chopped hay. In one study lambs ate 40 percent more of a grass pellet than comparable chopped grass. When given a choice of chopped and pelleted grass hay, the lambs ate about 90 percent pellets (40). Pelleting (with sheep as well as other ruminants) of roughage results in more rapid passage out of the rumen and proportionately more digestion in the intestines. This may result in somewhat lower digestibility of energy, but it also results in less degradation of protein in the rumen and greater protein absorption (41). The overall result of feeding pelleted forage to lambs is that energy is utilized more efficiently when it is pelleted than when fed in other forms (long, ground, chopped) (42), but this situation

TABLE 11-10

Effect of feed processing on feedlot performance of lambs

Rations	Gain, g/d	Feed Intake, kg/d	Feed Conversion	Reference No.
Chopped alfalfa	136	1.41	10.31	37
Pelleted alfalfa	177	1.68	9.43	
Chopped alfalfa + 30% barley	141	1.27	9.16	
Pelleted alfalfa + 30% barley	163	1.45	8.97	
Alfalfa hay-corn (50:50)				
Long hay				
ground corn	141	1.30	9.18	38
pelleted corn	145	1.25	8.54	
Ground hay				
ground corn	145	1.34	9.38	
pelleted corn	154	1.20	7.79	
Pelleted hay				
ground corn	177	1.42	8.02	
pelleted corn	177	1.37	7.83	
Pelleted complete ration	186	1.43	7.88	
Pelleted complete, then reground	168	1.39	8.36	
Shelled corn	241	1.48	6.24	39
Extruded corn	241	1.41	5.91	

is applicable (in economic terms) to young, fast-growing animals rather than to mature sheep which do not need the higher level of energy intake. It should be pointed out that lambs fed pelleted or heat-processed feeds are apt to have softer fat than if fed otherwise. Presumably, this is a reflection of differences in volatile acids produced in the rumen as a result of processing.

HIGH-MOISTURE GRAIN

As pointed out in Ch. 7, grains must be dried to a moisture content of less than 15 percent to avoid spoilage in storage. In some areas it is not possible to get grains dry enough to store without resorting to drying with a source of heat. In addition, harvesting grains at an earlier date may avoid losses to bad weather or, in the case of sorghum grains, large amounts of damage from birds in some areas.

Early-harvested corn or sorghum may be expected to have a moisture content of 25-30 percent. While corn or sorghum can be harvested without difficulty at this moisture content, it is then necessary to dry, ensile, or treat it with chemicals if the grains are stored. Early harvesting has other advantages in that it requires less energy to grind or roll grains and they are, generally, quite palatable to livestock. The protein and starch fractions are more soluble and more completely digested or are digested at a more rapid rate by ruminant animals. A major disadvantage is that high-moisture grains cannot be sold and transported any distance without spoilage, and large amounts of storage facilities are required if a season's supply of grain is laid in at harvest time.

A rather limited practice in some sorghum growing areas is to harvest the whole sorghum head, chop it, and ensile it. While there is essentially no information in the scientific

TABLE 11-11
Utilization of high-moisture (HM) or chemically treated grains for feeding ruminants

Item	Feed Consumed/d, kg DM	Daily Gain, kg	Feed Conversion		Reference No.
			Poststorage DM	Prestorage DM	
Beef Finishing Trials					
Corn, corn silage, supplement[a,b]					43
Dried corn	6.73	1.15	6.39	5.83	
vs. Acid-treated HM corn	6.72	1.16	5.97	5.77	
Dried corn	6.56	1.15	6.17	5.70	
vs. HM corn treated with ammonium isobutyrate	6.24	1.17	5.50	5.33	
HM corn, high corn silage					44
Ensiled, ground corn[c]	6.36	1.08		5.93	
Urea-treated whole corn	6.24	1.02		6.14	
Corn, corn silage, supplement					45
Whole shelled	9.62	1.07		9.0	
Whole HM	9.03	1.00		9.1	
Rolled HM	9.08	1.14		8.0	
NaOH treated[d]					
Whole shelled	9.40	0.95		9.9	
Whole HM	9.40	0.93		10.1	
Corn, supplement					46
Whole, shelled	6.8	1.41		4.8	
HM corn					
Whole, acid-treated	6.7	1.38		4.8	
Rolled, acid-treated	6.4	1.33		4.7	
HM corn:dry-rolled grain sorghum (80% grain)					47
100:0	10.65	1.64		6.49	
75:25	10.61	1.66		6.39	
50:50	10.84	1.66		6.53	
0:100	11.07	1.58		7.01	

TABLE 11-11 (cont.)

Item	DM Consumed, kg/d		Milk Production		Butterfat %	Reference No.
	Grain	Total	kg/d	FCM/d		
Dairy Feeding Trials						
Barley trials						
Dry barley	11.3	18.7	23.2	20.8	3.37	48
Dry barley, acid treated	11.2	18.7	22.8	21.1	3.53	
HM barley						
Acid-treated	11.1	18.0	21.8	19.8	3.49	49
Ensiled	10.9	17.7	22.1	20.4	3.53	
Corn, corn silage						
Dried corn	9.8	17.1	25.2	19.6	2.64	49
HM corn, ground, ensiled	9.3	17.2	24.1	20.6	3.09	
Alfalfa, concentrate, 70-30% ±						
Rolled rye grain		19.4	25.0	22.2	3.29	50
NaOH-treated rye		20.9	26.0	23.6	3.38	
Corn, corn silage, alfalfa hay						
Dry rolled corn		24.0	22.6	21.8	3.76	51
vs. HM corn, rolled, ensiled		23.4	22.2	21.3	3.74	
Dry rolled corn		19.9	27.4	26.0	3.67	
vs. HM corn, rolled +1% acid		18.9	27.8	26.1	3.59	
Dry rolled corn		21.0	23.2	22.3	3.75	
vs. HM ear corn, gr., + acid		21.0	23.1	22.1	3.75	

[a]These data represent 6 trials on acid-treated corn and 4 on AIB-treated corn.
[b]Values on feed consumption are expressed as grain DM consumed/d.
[c]When fed, urea was added to equalize that added to the other treatment (3.7%).
[d]NaOH added equivalent to 3% of DM of corn.

literature on the product (sorghum head silage), information in field day reports and trade magazines indicates that it is a useful method of harvesting and storing sorghum grains.

Examples of recent research data using high-moisture grains for feeding beef cattle are shown in Tables 11–7 and 11–11 and for dairy cattle in Table 11–11. In general, the data indicate that high-moisture grains (sometimes called early-harvested grains) are not likely to increase rate of gain of beef cattle, but efficiency generally is improved *provided* that the grains are ground or rolled prior to storage or before feeding. Results with dairy cattle indicate that high-moisture barley and corn were about equivalent to the dry-rolled grains (on an equal DM basis).

Although use of high-moisture corn or sorghum grains may be somewhat more efficient in some cases, it must be remembered that any fermentation will result in some energy losses as well as some change in protein solubility; it may enhance the B-vitamin content. One example of losses associated with ensiling corn grain is shown in Table 11–12. Note that the

dry-matter loss amounted to about 4 percent, with an additional loss of 3 percent of the grain that was considered to be spoiled and not usable as feed. In another example (50), it was calculated that 7.5–13.6 percent of dry matter from high-moisture corn was lost during storage. In most experiments only the weight of the feed going onto the scales is used to calculate consumption and efficiency; thus if losses even approached these levels, the data would not look

TABLE 11-12

Storage loss from ensiling high-moisture corn

Nutrient	Recovery after Ensiling, %[a]
Dry matter	96.0 ± 1.9
Crude protein	97.2 ± 2.1
Crude fiber	95.5 ± 4.1
Ether extract	100.5 ± 2.6
N-free extract	95.9 ± 1.9
Ash	82.4 ± 2.0

[a]In addition to these losses, 3% of the ensiled corn was classified as spoiled grain.
Source: Chandler et al. (49).

FIGURE 11–13. Loading out ensiled high-moisture corn. Many feedlots are making extensive use of high-moisture grains. In this photo, the corn is covered with a layer of silage which reduces moisture loss and spoilage.

as good for the high-moisture feeds. The amount of fermentation, leaching, and spoilage loss would vary considerably with the type of silo (or plastic bag) used, its size, location, and so on. Whether these values are typical or not is not known, but losses are undoubtedly more than most feeders realize. One example of a large trench silo used on a commercial beef feedlot is shown in Fig. 11–13.

In addition to ensiling, grains may be preserved by various chemicals. Propionic acid or mixtures of propionic acid with formaldehyde or other similar compounds, ammonium isobutyrate, or the like have been proven to be effective means of preventing mold and/or bacterial growth. Data in Table 11–10 show that acid-treated grains produce performance in beef or dairy cattle that is comparable to other methods of preservation. There has also been quite a bit of interest (particularly in Europe) in using NaOH or urea solutions on wet grains. Urea used at a level of about 1 percent of the grain has proven effective in inhibiting bacterial

and fungal growth in grains with enough moisture to cause spoilage. Urea also has the advantage of providing a source of N that rumen microorganisms can utilize. NaOH will also inhibit spoilage of high-moisture feed grains, and several reports show that it will increase digestibility of whole grains fed to cattle and, at the same time, increase somewhat the digestibility of the fibrous components of the diet (presumably because of higher rumen pH). However, other reports indicate that increases in digestibility were no greater than if the grains were cracked or rolled and that the cost of mechanical processing was less. Two examples of using NaOH-treated grains are shown in Table 11–11. With beef cattle, feeding NaOH-treated grains did not result in improved performance, while feeding NaOH-treated rye resulted in some apparent increase in milk production of dairy cows.

A limited number of feeding trials have been done using high-moisture or reconstituted corn or sorghum for feeding swine. Results indicate a slight improvement in use of high-tannin sorghums, but otherwise not much effect.

ECONOMICS OF FEED PROCESSING AND GRAIN PRESERVATION

The relatively higher energy costs experienced in the past 15 years or so have increased interest in minimizing feed processing costs or in obtaining the maximum return/unit of cost for processing or preservation. Current fuel costs are higher in proportion to grain costs than when most of the various methods discussed previously were developed. Costs in Mcal of fossil fuel (oil, coal, gas) per ton of processed feed have been estimated and are shown in Table 11-13. It is quite obvious that grinding is the cheapest method available for minimal processing when measuring fuel costs. Note that the greatest use of fuel is required to dry very wet materials such as green forage (alfalfa) or raw beet pulp.

Data presented in Table 11-14 confirm that any grain processing more elaborate than grinding or rolling normally does not result in any marked increase in daily gain of cattle and

that the primary benefit may be some improvement in feed efficiency. Of course, good processing can stimulate feed consumption just as poor processing may depress feed consumption, and many reports show appreciable differences in gain (see earlier tables). Wastage may be reduced by good processing and feed bunk management.

The relative values of different grain processing methods for feedlot cattle have been calculated by Schake and Bull (53) based on daily gains and efficiencies shown in Table 11-14, which was compiled from a number of experimental trials done in Texas. Flaking, reconstitution, or high-moisture storage all resulted in some improvement in feed efficiency when compared to feeding dry-ground or rolled grain. However, because of higher costs for equipment, power, storage (high-moisture grain requires that all grain be purchased at one time), and the like, the most efficient methods did not necessarily result in the greatest net value/ton of grain. Under their specified conditions, reconstitution or steam-flaking had the greatest net values.

EFFECT OF PROCESSING ON DENSITY

Frequent references have been made to the effect processing methods have on the density of feedstuffs. Density, which is a measure of weight/unit of volume, is sometimes referred to as bulk density in contrast to caloric density, which is a measure of useable energy/unit of weight. In view of the importance of density, it is desirable to present some data and a few comments. Values on selected feedstuffs are shown in Table 11-15.

In feedstuffs such as unprocessed roughage and grains, density is inversely related to fiber

TABLE 11-13

Fossil fuel energy use for some feed processing methods

Process	Fuel Energy Used per Ton, Mcal
Drying corn	240
Adding propionic acid	200
Grinding corn	40
Pelleting corn	80
Steam-flaking corn	120
Dehydrating & pelleting alfalfa	1800
Dried beet pulp	1750

Source: Ward (52).

TABLE 11-14

Daily gain and feed conversion values of cattle fed corn or sorghum processed in different ways

Method	Corn			Sorghum		
	Gain	Feed:Gain		Gain	Feed:Gain	
		lb	%[a]		lb	%[a]
Dry ground or rolled	2.62	5.79	—	2.50	6.09	—
Steam-flaked	2.68	5.36	7.46	2.65	5.60	8.11
Reconstituted	2.61	5.33	7.97	2.54	5.34	12.32
High-moisture						
Ground, ensiled	2.57	5.14	11.14	2.64	5.52	9.35
Acid-treated	2.68	5.56	3.97	2.45	5.60	8.11

[a]Percent improvement in feed conversion of grain dry matter compared to dry processing.
Source: Schake and Bull (53).

TABLE 11-15

Density of some selected feedstuffs

Feedstuff	lb/cu ft	g/ℓ[a]	Feedstuff	lb/cu ft	g/ℓ[a]
Alfalfa			**Cereal by-products** (continued)		
Long hay	2-3	40	Rice grits	42-45	695
Chopped hay	4-5	70	Rye bran	15-20	280
Ground hay	8-10	145	Rye middlings	42	670
Dehydrated meal	18-22	320	Rye shorts	32-33	520
Pelleted hay	41-43	670	Wheat bran	11-16	215
			Wheat midds	18-25	345
Other roughage			Wheat red dog	22-28	400
Bagasse	7-10	135	Wheat flour	32-42	590
Corn cobs, gr	17	270	**Protein supplements**		
Cottonseed hulls	12	190	Blood flour	30	480
Oat hulls, gr	11-12	185	Blood meal	39	625
Soybean hulls, gr	20	320	Corn gluten feed	26-33	470
Cereal grains			Corn gluten meal	32-43	600
Barley, whole	38-43	650	Cottonseed meal	37-40	615
Barley, gr	24-26	400	Feather meal	34	645
Barley, rolled	21-24	360	Fish meal	30-34	510
Corn, whole, shelled	45	720	Flax seed	33-45	625
coarsely cracked	35	560	Meat meal	37	590
finely cracked	37-38	600	Shrimp meal	25	400
roasted	39	625	Soybeans, whole	46-48	750
steam-flaked	34	545	Soybeans, gr	25-34	470
popped, rolled	19	305	Soy. meal, expeller	36-40	610
corn & cob meal	36	575	Soy. meal, sol. 44%	35-38	585
Kafir	40-46	690	Soy. meal, sol. 50%	41-42	665
Millet, whole	38-40	625	Sunflower seed	26-38	510
Milo, whole	40-45	680	Tankage	49	785
finely gr	37	590			
dry-rolled	31	495	**Miscellaneous**		
steam-flaked	18	290	Beans, dry, lima	45	720
whole, reconstituted	40	640	Beet pulp, dried	11-16	215
popped, rolled	16	255	Brewers dried grains	14-15	230
Oats, whole	25-35	480	Buttermilk, cond.	31	495
rolled	19-24	345	Citrus pulp, dried	20-21	330
crimped	19-25	350	Corn dist. dried grains	18-19	295
ground	20-25	360	Corn dist. dried sol.	25-26	410
Rice, rough	32-36	545	Malt sprouts	13-16	230
polished	30	480	Molasses, 79.5° Brix	88	1,410
Rye, whole	43-45	705	Sugar	54-56	880
ground	39	625	Peas, dried	48-50	785
Wheat, whole	45-52	775	Tallow, melted	54	865
ground	38-39	615	Urea	34-42	610
coarse cracked	35-38	585	Whey, dried	35-46	650
finely cracked	38-41	630	Yeast, dried	41	655
steam-flaked	31-33	510			
			Mineral Supplements		
Cereal by-products			Bentonite	51	815
Corn bran	13	210	Bone meal	50-53	830
Corn hominy feed	25-28	425	Ca carbonate	75	1,200
Grain screen, light	22-24	370	Limestone	68	1,090
Oat groats	46-47	745	Oyster shell, gr	53	850
Oat middlings	38	610	Salt, coarse	62-70	1,055
Rice bran	20-21	345	Salt, fine	70-80	1,200

[a]Values given as grams/liter; where a range in weight is given in lb/cubic foot, the mean is used to calculate density in g/ℓ, and values have been rounded off to the nearest 5 units.

Source: Most values taken from Anonymous (54); other values are from various research papers and the author's unpublished data.

content. Hays, which have higher fiber content than most other feedstuffs, have a much lower density than the grains and other concentrates. This is partly because of the physical nature of the hay and not entirely because of the fiber content. Grinding will always increase the density of hay and usually that of other roughages. Pelleting and cubing result in a marked increase in the density of hay, although there should be little if any change in fiber content.

With grains, grinding is more apt to result in a decrease in density. Pelleting and cubing grains will increase density, but not nearly as much as they will with roughage. Other processing methods such as flaking, popping, and roasting result in reduced density of feed grains.

Some increase in density of feedstuffs, particularly roughages, is advantageous in transportation, milling, and handling during feeding operations. Nutritional benefits are less clear except for the marked increase in consumption of pelleted and cubed roughages by ruminants. With processing methods that result in a marked expansion and reduced density of grains (such as popping), data on feedlot cattle indicate that consumption will be reduced unless these processed grains are rolled (and made more dense) before feeding. However, digestibility appears to be altered very little, if any.

Caloric density is used extensively in ration formulation. There are appropriate values beyond which feed intake may either decrease (high values) or energy intake will decrease (low values). However, the relationships between caloric density and bulk density have not been well defined. For example, the digestibility of pelleted alfalfa may actually be less than that for ground or long hay, but the intake by ruminants will nearly always be considerably higher when the hay is pelleted, and the gain will be increased considerably.

When dealing with complete rations, it seems obvious that there is probably an optimum density range for a given feeding situation. It seems reasonable to this author that density probably could be substituted for maximum and/or minimum fiber specifications when formulating least-cost rations with computerized methods (see Ch. 12).

OXIDIZED FEED

A chapter on feed processing is probably a good spot to mention the subject of oxidized feed, because processed feed is more subject to oxidation and deterioration than grains (or roughage) that have not been ground, rolled, chopped, pelleted, or otherwise disturbed. Feeds that have been ground or otherwise broken up have more unprotected surfaces exposed to oxygen or other chemicals, which may cause problems. Feeds, particularly complete feeds, with added fats or metal ions are more subject to oxidation than a ground grain or hay might be. Thus the sooner a mixed feed is used, the better off the feeder is likely to be, because the feed will not improve with age.

In the oxidation process, free radicals formed by unsaturated fatty acids react with oxygen to form peroxides that serve as the entry point into a multitude of reactions producing numerous by-products which may result in decomposition of the feed. Aldehydes, ketones, acids, esters, and polymerized fats are direct products of the oxidation process, and they result in reduced energy values, off-tastes, and off-odors. Peroxides can intitiate the oxidation and destruction of the fat-soluble vitamins or other susceptible feed constituents such as xanthophylls or aroma and flavor constituents. In situations where animals may be forced to consume oxidized feed for some period of time, they may develop such problems as steatitis in swine and cats, exudative diathesis, muscular dystrophy, and necrotic tissues in various species (sheep, swine, cattle, poultry), or poor fertility and reduced hatchability in poultry. Less severe problems, which may not be readily detactable, include such things as reduced rate of gain and lower body weight and poor feed efficiency, which have been observed in studies with broilers and growing pigs, or inadequate egg yolk pigmentation in hens' eggs because of oxidation of xanthophylls in the feed (55).

Normally, feeding fats have antioxidants added to them (see Ch. 7). Other feed ingredients such as dehydrated alfalfa may also have added antioxidants, as may some complete feeds which the manufacturer might anticipate would not be used immediately. Antioxidants often used in the feed trade include ethoxyquin and butylated hydroxy tolalene.

SUMMARY

Feed processing is an important aspect of animal production for confined animals, especially those expected to produce at high levels. Various methods are available for processing feed grains. At the present time, grinding and pelleting are used extensively for preparing feeds for broilers, turkeys, growing-finishing swine, rabbits, and to a lesser extent other classes or species of animals. Dairy cows may be fed some pelleted concentrates while being milked, some portion of the ration may be pelleted for finishing beef cattle, and protein supplements may be pelleted or cubed when fed to range cattle. Only minimal amounts of pelleted feeds would normally be fed to other animals.

Grinding or rolling of grains are satisfactory methods for lactating dairy cows or for beef cattle fed moderate to low levels of grain. Likewise, such methods are satisfactory for adult swine or horses. Although whole corn is used with reasonable efficiency by finishing beef cattle, other grains should be processed in some manner to improve efficiency of use. Utilization of reconstituted corn or sorghum or high-moisture (early-harvested) grains usually results in improved efficiency when fed to finishing beef cattle, but economics of using a particular process will depend on relative costs of fuel and feed and on the size of the operation. High-moisture feeds are not, generally, used much by large beef feedlots.

Hay processing is less complex. Grinding or chopping will usually reduce wastage and selectivity, but may not increase consumption. Feeding large amounts of finely ground, pelleted, or cubed roughage may be expected to result in reduced butterfat percentage of milk from lactating dairy cows. Pelleting or cubing of roughage will increase consumption, particularly of lower-quality roughage, but it is a relatively expensive process because of power and time requirements for processing.

REFERENCES

1. Theurer, C. B. 1987. *J. Animal Sci.* 63:1649.
2. Kohler, G. O., A. L. Livingston, and R. M. Saunders. 1973. In: *Effect of processing on the nutritional value of feeds.* Washington, D.C.: Nat. Acad. Sci.
3. Slinger, S. L. 1973. In: *Effect of processing on the nutritional value of feeds.* Washington, D.C.: Nat. Acad. Sci.
4. Pickett, R. A., et al. 1969. *J. Animal Sci.* 28:837.
5. Becker, D. E. 1966. *Merck Agr. Memo.* Vol. 11, No. 1. Rahway, NJ: Merck & Co.
6. Perry, T. W. 1973. In: *Effect of processing on the nutritional value of feeds.* Washington, D.C.: Nat. Acad. Sci.
7. Baird, D. M. 1973. *J. Animal Sci.* 36:516.
8. Patterson, D. C. 1984. *Animal Prod.* 38:271.
9. Ott, E. A. 1973. In: *Effect of processing on the nutritional value of feeds.* Washington, D.C.: Nat. Acad. Sci.
10. Summers, J. C. 1974. *Can. Poult. Rev.* 93:44.
11. Arscott, G. H., et al. 1958. *Poultry Sci.* 37:117.
12. Harper, J. A. 1959. *Proc. 17th Oregon Animal Ind. Conf.,* Corvallis, OR: Oregon State Univ.
13. Arscott, G. H., et al. 1962. *Oregon Agr. Expt. Sta. Tech. Bul.* 64.
14. Hale, W. H. 1980. In: *Digestive physiology and nutrition of ruminants. Vol. 3: Practical nutrition.* 2d ed. Corvallis, OR: O & B Books.
15. Prasad, D. A., et al. 1975. *J. Animal Sci.* 41:578.
16. Stock, R. A., et al. 1987. *J. Animal Sci.* 65:548.
17. Turgeon, O. A., Jr., D. R. Brink, and R. A. Britton. 1983. *J. Animal Sci.* 57:739.
18. Lee, R. W., M. L. Galyean, and G. P. Lofgreen. 1982. *J. Animal Sci.* 55:475.
19. Ramirez, R. G., et al. 1985. *J. Animal Sci.* 61:1.
20. Zinn, R. A. 1987. *J. Animal Sci.* 65:256.
21. Toland, P. C. 1976. *Australian J. Expt. Agr. & Animal Husb.* 16:71.
22. Cullison, A. E. 1961. *J. Animal Sci.* 20:478.
23. Wallace, J. D., R. J. Raleigh, and W. A. Sawyer. 1961. *J. Animal Sci.* 20:778.
24. Webb, R. J., and C. F. Cmarik. 1957. *Univ. of Illinois Rpt. 15-40-329,* Dixon Springs Sta., IL.
25. Kercher, C. J., W. Smith, and L. Paules. 1971. *Proc. West. Sec. Amer. Soc. Animal Sci.* 22:33.
26. Levy, D., et al. 1972. *Animal Prod.* 15:157.
27. Kercher, C. J., et al. 1978. *Proc. West. Sec. Amer. Soc. Animal Sci.* 29:410.
28. Tetlow, R. M., and R. J. Wilkins. 1978. *Animal Prod.* 27:293.
29. Kertz, A. F., B. L. Darcy, and I. R. Prewitt. 1981. *J. Dairy Sci.* 64:2388.
30. Moe, P. W., J. F. Tyrrell, and N. W. Hooven. 1973. *J. Dairy Sci.* 56:1298.
31. Bush, L. J., et al. 1979. *J. Dairy Sci.* 62:1094.
32. Carpenter, J. R., R. W. Stanley, and K. Morita. 1972. *J. Dairy Sci.* 55:1750.
33. Dobie, J. B., et al. 1974. *Feedstuffs* 46(6):30.
34. Murdock, R. F., and A. S. Hodgson. 1977. *J. Dairy Sci.* 60:1921.
35. Anderson, M. J., et al. 1975. *J. Dairy Sci.* 58:72.
36. NRC. 1973. *Effect of processing on the nutritional value of feeds.* Washington, D.C.: Nat. Acad. Sci.
37. Weir, W. C., et al. 1959. *J. Animal Sci.* 18:805.

38. Fontenot, J. P., and H. A. Hopkins. 1965. *J. Animal Sci.* 24:62.

39. Jordan, R. M. 1965. *J. Animal Sci.* 24:754.

40. Greenhalgh, J. F. D., and G. W. Reid. 1974. *Animal Prod.* 19:77.

41. Beever, D. E., et al. 1981. *Brit. J. Nutr.* 46:357.

42. Thomson, D. J., and S. B. Cammell. 1979. *Brit. J. Nutr.* 41:297.

43. Ware, D. R., H. L. Self, and M. P. Hoffman. 1977. *J. Animal Sci.* 44:722.

44. Mowat, D. N., P. McCaughey, and G. K. Macleod. 1981. *Can. J. Animal Sci.* 61:703.

45. Anderson, G. D., L. L. Berger, and G. C. Fahey, Jr. 1981. *J. Animal Sci.* 52:144.

46. Macleod, G. K., D. N. Mowat, and R. A. Curtis. 1976. *Can. J. Animal Sci.* 56:43.

47. Stock, R. A., et al. 1987. *J. Animal Sci.* 65:290.

48. Ingalls, J. R., K. W. Clark, and H. R. Sharma. 1974. *Can. J. Animal Sci.* 54:205.

49. Chandler, P. T., C. N. Miller, and E. Jahn. 1975. *J. Dairy Sci.* 58:682.

50. Sharma, H. R., J. R. Ingalls, and J. A. McKirdy. 1983. *Animal Feed Sci. Tech.* 10:77.

51. Voelker, H. H., et al. 1985. *J. Dairy Sci.* 68:2602.

52. Ward, G. W. 1981. Unpublished data. Ft. Collins, CO: Colorado State Univ.

53. Schake, L. M., and K. L. Bull. 1980. *Texas Agr. Expt. Sta. Tech. Rpt.* 81–1.

54. Anon. 1982. *Feedstuffs* 54(30):136.

55. Calabotta, D. F., and W. D. Shermer. 1985. *Feedstuffs* 57(48):24; Arnold, R. L. 1985. *Feedstuffs* 57(42):30.

56. Farrell, D. J., E. Thomson, and A. Choice. 1983. *Animal Feed Sci. Tech.* 9:99.

57. Grimson, R. E., et al. 1987. *Can. J. Animal Sci.* 67:43.

12

Ration Formulation

D. C. Church and Hugo Varela-Alvarez

INTRODUCTION

Ration (or diet) formulation is a topic that should be mastered to some degree by anyone concerned with feeding livestock. For a nutritionist or feed formulator, it is an absolute necessity. The previous statement may require some qualification with the increasing availability of personal and office computers which have the necessary programs to do all of the manipulations without the operator needing to know much about the mathematical problems involved.

In ration formulation the objective is to utilize knowledge about nutrients, feedstuffs, and animals in the development of nutritionally adequate rations that will be eaten in sufficient amounts to provide the level of production desired at a reasonable cost. Obviously, a blend of knowledge is required for optimum results. Fortunately, the mathematics required are not complex, and the reader will be led through a series of processes which will enable him or her to formulate rather complex rations by the time this chapter is completed. It should be emphasized that it is necessary to master each step as presented.

INFORMATION NEEDED

Before any mathematical manipulations can begin, several different types of information are needed for an organized approach to ration formulation for any given situation. These are discussed in the following sections.

Nutrient Requirements of the Animal

In order to develop a satisfactory diet, we must have some knowledge of the limiting nutrients needed by an animal in a specific situation and of the amounts of nutrients required in the diet. In the United States, the National Research Council (NRC) publications are the generally accepted standards used for domestic animals (and for others, as well). These publications represent the opinions of different committees that have organized the publications. The NRC publications provide a generally satisfactory starting point, and tables delineating these requirements are given in the Appendix. Similar feeding standards have been developed in other countries.

218

Assuming that the NRC standards are to be used as is, the first step in formulating a ration is to look up and tabulate the nutrient levels needed in the particular situation. Depending on the situation, it is not usually necessary to be concerned with all known nutrients, because some are always more critical than others; that is, some nutrients are more likely to be deficient in the usual feed ingredients than are other nutrients. For example, if it were desired to formulate a protein supplement for cows on the range, protein would be the first consideration, with other considerations being the energy content and one or two of the macrominerals such as P and Ca. Most other nutrients would probably be disregarded, with the possible exception of vitamin A. This can be done because past experience indicates that other vitamins and minerals are not likely to be as limiting as those mentioned; in addition, the animals in question will be consuming an appreciable percentage of their total diet from roughage sources. However, if a broiler ration is to be formulated where the chick has access only to the feed the ration provides, then it is necessary to be concerned with a much more detailed list of nutrients, because all required nutrients must be contained in the diet formulated and because the nutrient requirements of the chick are more demanding (numerous vitamins, amino acids, some minerals) than those of the range cow. In any case, the various nutrients of concern should be tabulated on a form such as that shown in Fig. 12–1.

Feedstuffs

The next step is to list available feedstuffs that are suitable for the particular animal in question. In many cases only a limited number of locally grown feeds are available at competitive prices. Although a long list of by-product and supplementary feeds might be contrived, this is usually unnecessary when we are concerned with ration formulation at the farm or ranch level and are primarily concerned with utilization of homegrown products. Commercial feed mills would normally have a much wider variety of available feedstuffs. If a relatively long list is required, use of a form similar to Fig. 12–1 will facilitate summarization of the needed data.

The contribution of critical nutrients by each feed should be listed. Analytical data on roughages and grains are preferred where they are available from a local laboratory on the actual feedstuffs to be used. If no information of this type is available, the average composition data can be used from NRC tables or from other sources.

The list of feeds it is necessary to consider can be reduced greatly by careful consideration. Is this feed suitable and economical for its intended use? For each species and class of animal some feeds are more useful than others. For adult ruminants we would usually want to include urea where protein is of concern, but on the basis of present regulations urea is not permitted in rations for any of the monogastric species or for milk replacer formulas. Meat and fish meals, on the other hand, may be favored feeds for poultry and pigs, but they are usually too high in price for ruminant feeds. Remember, also, that a given feed may have different feeding values for different animal species.

Furthermore, we must consider whether the feed should be processed and, if so, in what manner and at what cost? What effect will the processing have on animal production? Is it a palatable feed or will the mixture be palatable? Does it present problems in handling, mixing, or storage? Are feed additives required and, if so, what additives and at what concentrations?

Obviously, it takes a fund of knowledge and experience to answer these questions. The ability to answer them correctly is a must for a practicing nutritionist. For our purposes here, the beginner can ignore such questions as posed in the last paragraph, as time and experience will help provide the answers which cannot be covered in this chapter. Other chapters on the different animal species will illustrate and answer some of these questions.

Type of Ration

The type of ration has a great deal to do with its needed composition and nutrient content. That is, is it a complete feed, is it a finishing grain mix to feed along with roughage, or is it a supplemental feed formulated primarily for its protein, vitamin, or mineral content? If a complete feed, is it intended to be fed on a restricted or free-choice basis? If the feed is for herbivorous animals such as ruminants, it would be normal to first evaluate roughage as the base feed and then determine what nutrients are needed to supplement the roughage. Sometimes, roughage may be added only as a diluent to rations for fattening animals to control intake or produce a desired physical texture for the ration.

Feed Formulation Worksheet

Date _____

Prepared by _____

Animal: (species, weight, purpose, expected performance) _____

Animal Requirements:

Dry matter (as g, kg or lb/day) _____

Protein (as g, kg or lb/day or as % of ration) _____

Energy (as g, kg or lb TDN/day or as % of ration
or as Mcal of DE, ME, NE or NEm, NEg, NEℓ per day or
per unit of ration) _____

Ca (as g/day or as % of ration) _____

P (as g/day or as % of ration) _____

Nutrient Composition of Feedstuffs   ☐ as fed   ☐ dry basis

Feed ingredient	DM, %	Protein, % Crude Digest.	Energy	Ca, %	P, %	Other*	Cost lb	ton

Ration ingredients	Lb/ ton	% dry basis	Lb, as fed basis	% as fed	Protein	Energy	Ca	P	Others	Cost

*Fat, fiber and ash values are usually required for commercial mills because of legal restrictions (see Ch. 4); depending on the species and age, we might wish to include Mg,S and K of the macro minerals and several of the trace minerals in some areas; vitamins A, D, E and K, and riboflavin, niacin, pantothenic acid, folic acid and B_{12}; and amino acids such as lysine, arginine, methionine, cystine, glycine and tryptophan.

FIGURE 12–1. An illustration of one type of ration formulation worksheet.

Expected Feed Consumption

Complete rations should be designed so that animals will consume a desired amount, because the required concentration of a nutrient in a ration depends on consumption. For example, if we want a steer to consume 500 g of protein per day, the feed needs to contain only 10 percent protein if the steer eats 5 kg of feed; if it will eat only 4 kg, then 12.5 percent protein is needed to achieve the desired protein intake.

Energy concentration greatly affects feed intake, as do other factors such as physical (bulk) density, deficiency of some nutrients, or presence of unpalatable ingredients. Pelleted hay, for example, will usually be consumed in much larger amounts by ruminants than will long hay, thus the concentration of some nutrients can be reduced when pelleted hay is fed.

Some information on this topic is presented in the various appendix tables. Additional information is also presented in the chapters on individual species.

GUIDELINES AND RULES OF THUMB FOR RATION FORMULATION

Note in the tables on feed composition (Appendix Tables 1–5) that feed data may be given either on the basis of dry feed (oven dry basis) or on an as-fed (air dry) basis, depending on which publication the information was taken from. When it is desirable to formulate rations to rather exact specifications or when part of the ration ingredients contain a considerable amount of water (silage, for example), then it is preferable to formulate rations on a dry basis. For the feedstuffs listed in the appendix tables for swine and poultry, bear in mind that these are given on an as-fed basis. Therefore, if formulation is to be done on a dry basis, some recalculation will be required before ration formulation is commenced. If laboratory data are available on dry matter, then these should be used; if not, then use appropriate values from the appendix tables or other sources. For example, if the usual dry-matter content is 90 percent and it is desired to convert the nutrient concentration from an as-fed (or air dry) to a dry basis, divide the nutrient content by 0.9. If there is difficulty in remembering whether to multiply or divide by dry-matter percentage, just keep in mind, when converting from as-fed to dry basis, that the resulting values must be higher than those started with. The reason for this, of course, is that removal of water increases the concentration of the remaining ingredients. However, after the ration is formulated, be sure to convert it to an as-fed basis. Feed mills mix rations in the amounts given in formulas and the percentage composition on a dry basis will nearly always be different than on an as-fed basis. This simple procedure is illustrated later in this chapter. It might be noted that some people (in research or commercial formulators) prefer to formulate all rations (even those containing wet feeds) on a 90 percent DM basis. The logic of this practice escapes the writer.

Formulation can be done on the basis of daily needs, although in practice this is seldom done for most animals. Rather, it is more common to formulate on the basis of a given weight unit—100 lb, 100 kg, 1000 lb, or one ton. Use of percentage units is the simplist means, because the final values can be converted easily to any final weight unit.

If formulas are worked out to exact specifications, fractional units (g, lb, kg) may result, which are undesirable in commercial feed mill usage. Where pound units are used to make up ton batches, these should be rounded off to at least 10-lb increments, except for ingredients included in the ration in very small amounts (urea, minerals, antibiotics, and the like). As a rule, the errors caused by this procedure will be small.

An important rule of thumb is that **simple nutrient needs can be met adequately by simple feed formulas.** Thus when nutrient needs are simple, complex formulas do not guarantee improved performance. Also, the more complex the nutrient specifications, the more complex a formula is required to meet all specifications without having an excess of some nutrient(s). One individual feedstuff rarely will suffice to supply all needed nutrients without one or more being in excess. For example, if it is desired to feed a roughage to cows to supply 12 percent CP, the feeding of alfalfa hay, which usually has 15 percent or more protein, will be wasteful of protein, although it may have other nutrient properties of considerable value. Therefore, the alfalfa could be diluted with some other roughage which has a lower protein content, such as grass straw, without having excess protein consumption. In some instances it may be cheaper to use the feed with excess nutrients rather than dilute it with another ingredient. Suppose that alfalfa is the only hay available in an isolated farming area. It might actually cost less to feed the alfalfa hay, under some price situations, rather than to bring in another roughage over long distances.

Commercial concentrate mixes frequently contain a wide variety of feedstuffs, even in situations where nutrient requirements are relatively simple. There are two reasons why a variety may be included. First, it is felt that a variety of feedstuffs in a mixture may be more palatable for heavily fed animals; perhaps this is true where the same mix is fed for a long period of time. The second reason is that a mixture of several energy or protein sources may provide some insurance against trace nutrient deficiencies. This may or may not be true, depending on the feed ingredients chosen for the mixture.

As seasonal changes occur in availability or costs of feeds, many times it is desirable to alter formulas, particularly for the feed grains and protein concentrates. Some substitution can take place with relatively little effect; for example, corn, sorghum, and wheat have about the same energy value for most animals. For ruminants, barley and oats can be substituted more liberally than for most monogastric species. If drastic changes are in order, then formulas should be recalculated.

With respect to protein sources, most nutritionists suggest using protein (either crude or digestible) for ruminants on the basis of least cost per unit of protein. Factors other than protein content may affect value (plant hormones, Se in linseed meal), but these are poorly quantified. Some meals may not be very palatable, so some judgment and knowledge of the specific feedstuff is required when liberal substitution is practiced. For monogastric species, the amino acid content of protein substitutes must be evaluated, as well as other factors such as gossypol content of cottonseed meal.

Attention should be called to a few other simple guidelines. Salt (NaCl) can be supplied for herbivorous species by providing it ad libitum in a separate container from other feed. In complete feeds or concentrate mixtures, usually 0.25-0.5 percent salt is included for poultry and swine and 0.5-1 percent for ruminants. Likewise, trace-mineralized salt can be used as a supplementary source of some trace minerals, and mineral supplements are commonly used to supply sources of additional Ca, P, and Mg. When fat is added, it is the usual practice to add not more than 5 percent for swine and poultry and more on the order of 2-3 percent in finishing rations for cattle and, sometimes,

in rations for dairy cattle. Feeds with high levels of fat do not store well because they are apt to become rancid unless antioxidants have been added to the fat. With molasses or other similar liquid feeds, the amount commonly added in mixed feeds is usually restricted to 7-8 percent because of handling and mixing problems and because, in stored feed, more than this is apt to set up into a firm mass that does not lend itself to good feeding practices.

When a tentative formula is finished, check it over to determine if needed nutrients are present in desired concentrations. Evaluate the ration with respect to any excesses and specify what (if any) nutrients or feedstuffs will be needed in addition (for example, salt or salt-minerals fed free choice) and compute the cost for the ration.

MATHEMATICS OF RATION FORMULATION

Unless we are concerned with least-cost formulation, nothing more than very simple algebra is required to put together some rather complicated diets. Most beginners have trouble with it, but it is not difficult provided the various steps are learned thoroughly. Various techniques that are useful for hand formulation are illustrated in the following sections.

Pearson's Square

Pearson's square is a simple procedure that was originally devised for use in blending milk products to a known fat percentage. Use of the square allows blending of two feedstuffs (or two mixtures) with different nutrient concentrations into a mixture with a desired concentration. To solve a problem with Pearson's square, the desired solution is placed in the center (X) and feed source A, with its usual level of protein or energy (or any other nutrient needing a solution), is then added. If we are working for a solution of crude protein (CP), the CP level must be either higher or lower than X. Then a second feed source (or a mixture of several) with its typical CP level is placed in the B position. To solve,

the difference (+ or −) between X and A goes in the D position, and, likewise, the difference between B and X goes in the C position. The answer is expressed as parts. Add up the total parts and the amounts of A and B needed to provide the desired solution (X) can be expressed as parts of the whole or as percentages, as illustrated in the following example. Suppose we have a protein concentrate, such as cottonseed meal (CSM) with 40 percent CP, and a grain with 10 percent CP, and we wish to have a blend with 18 percent CP.

Using this square:

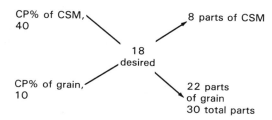

The answer is

8 parts of CSM and 22 parts of grain; or

if expressed as percent,

CSM in mix = $8 \div 30 \times 100 = 26.67\%$
Grain in mix = $22 \div 30 \times 100 = 73.33\%$

Check for CP:

26.67 (CSM) $\times$ 40% = 10.67
73.33 (grain) $\times$ 10% = 7.33
for a total of 18.00

As shown in the illustration, compare the CP percentage of each feed on the left with the desired percentage in the middle of the square. The **lesser value is subtracted from the greater value and the answer,** in parts of a mixture (rather than in percent), **is recorded diagonally.** It would usually be best to calculate the percentage of the final mixture. Although this is not necessary in this illustration, working with percentages is easier than working with fractions. The same procedure can be used for energy, minerals, and so on, but remember that **one feed** (or mixture) **must have a value higher and the other must be lower than the desired solution.** Furthermore, calories or ppm can be used as well as percentage. Further illustrations of the use of Pearson's square will be given later in the chapter.

As a matter of information, the check run on CP in the example illustrates the use of a weighted average. Where there are two or more ration ingredients with different nutrient concentrations, the total is obtained by multiplying the amount of each ration ingredient by its nutrient concentration and summing the answers for all ingredients.

Algebraic Solution

Some individuals would prefer to solve the simple problems of ration formulation using algebraic solutions from equations with two unknowns. For the same problem as with the Pearson's square, the approach would be as follows:

X = lb of CSM in mix
Y = lb of grain in mix
$X + Y = 100$ lb of mix
$0.40X + 0.10Y = 18$ (lb of CP in final mix)

To solve this problem, it is necessary to multiply the equation ($X + Y = 100$) by a unit that will allow one of the unknowns in the second equation to factor out. Thus if we multiply by 0.1 we have $0.10X + 0.10Y = 10$. The problem is then solved as shown:

Unknown equation, $0.40X + 0.10Y = 18$
Subtract from it $0.10X + 0.10Y = 10,$
and the answer is $0.30X = 8,$
so one can compute $X = 8 \div 0.3 = 26.67,$
and thus $Y = 100 - 26.67$
                           $= 73.33$

The answer, obviously, is the same as with Pearson's square.

Double Pearson's Square

In many situations we might want to have exact amounts of two major nutrients, such as CP and energy. We can accomplish this by going through three squares, as shown below. Suppose we want a final mix with 12 percent CP and 74 percent TDN. We have corn with 10 and 80, CSM with 40 and 68, and alfalfa hay with 15 and 55 percent CP and TDN, respectively. We must first go through two squares and get a mix exact for one of the nutrients—in this example we will do CP first, but it makes no difference which goes first. We must have one mix with 12 percent CP and greater than 74 percent TDN and one mix with 12 percent CP and less than 74 percent TDN. For this we must have a minimum of three feedstuffs, and we could use four if desired. Proceed as shown.

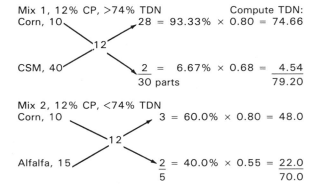

Mix 1, 12% CP, >74% TDN

Corn, 10

CSM, 40

12

28 = 93.33% × 0.80 = 74.66

2 = 6.67% × 0.68 = 4.54

30 parts

79.20

Compute TDN:

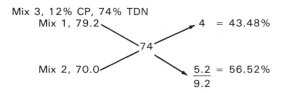

Mix 2, 12% CP, <74% TDN

Corn, 10

Alfalfa, 15

12

3 = 60.0% × 0.80 = 48.0

2 = 40.0% × 0.55 = 22.0

5

70.0

Then solve for TDN:

Mix 3, 12% CP, 74% TDN

Mix 1, 79.2

Mix 2, 70.0

74

4 = 43.48%

5.2 = 56.52%

9.2

Calculate the ingredient composition as follows:

Corn in Mix 1, 93.33
  43.48% of Mix 1 in Mix 3) = 40.58 ⎫
Corn in Mix 2, 60.00   ⎬ 74.49
  (53.52% of Mix 2 in Mix 3) = 33.91 ⎭
CSM in Mix 1, 6.67
  (43.48% of Mix 1 in Mix 3) =   2.90
Alfalfa in Mix 2, 40.0
  (56.52% of Mix 2 in Mix 3) =   22.61
                                     100.00

Check TDN =
  (0.7449 × 80 + 0.029 × 68 + 0.2261 × 55)
    = 59.59 +   1.97 + 12.44 = 74.00

As the reader can see, this procedure works very well to produce a mix with exact specifications on two nutrients. However, if we want to add a third nutrient, it could require as many as 9 squares, although it would not necessarily need this many. Therefore, diets that have exact requirements for more than two major nutrients are tedious to formulate by hand. Minor nutrients can be handled with slack space (see later section).

If we want to use algebra to solve this problem with corn, alfalfa, and CSM, the solution would be the same. We can arrive at a solution for two nutrients with only two feeds (sometimes), but the answer will be in weight units rather than percent. For example, if we want a mix to supply 12 lb of protein and 74 lb of TDN using only corn and CSM, the algebraic solution would be as shown (where X is corn and Y is CSM):

For CP, $0.1X + 0.40Y = 12$
For TDN, $0.8X + 0.68Y = 74$

Now, divide all elements of the first equation by 0.1 and the second by 0.8 and the equations become:

CP, $X + 4Y = 120$
TDN, $X + 0.85Y = 92.5$

Subtract the second equation from the first and the answer is:

$$3.15Y = 27.5$$
$$Y = 8.73$$

X can be solved by substituting the value of Y in one of the original equations, thus with the first equation,

$$0.1X + (0.4 × 8.73) = 12$$
$$0.1X + 3.492 = 12$$
$$0.1X = 8.508$$
$$X = 85.08$$

Thus the answer is 8.73 lb of CSM and 85.08 lb of corn. Unless there are some coincidental values, it is not possible to formulate a mixture with exact values for two nutrients using only two feeds. In this example, with the amounts of CSM and corn shown, we have 12 lb of protein and 74 lb of TDN, but the percentage of protein in the mix is 12.79 (12.0 ÷ 93.81) and that for TDN is 78.88 (74.0 ÷ 93.81). In other illustrations the Pearson's square will be used because it is the authors' opinion that fewer mistakes are made by most students using the square and it certainly is just as fast, if not faster.

Required Ingredients

In a number of situations there is some need to specify exact or minimal amounts of specific feedstuffs or quantities of supplements, additives, or the like. Suppose, for example, that we want a pig ration with 3 percent fish meal and 10 percent ground wheat grain in a final mix with 18 percent CP and 3500 kcal of DE/kg of feed. Corresponding values are (as-fed basis) for fish meal (herring) 70.6 and 3650 and wheat 12.7 and 3520. Now, what we must do is calculate how much of the required nutrients is provided by the required ingredients and what concentration is needed in the remaining portion of the mix, as shown below:

Ingredient	Fish Meal	Wheat Grain
Amount required, %	3.0	10.0
Composition		
CP, %	70.6	12.7
DE, kcal/kg	3650	3520
Nutrients supplied/		
100 kg		
CP, kg	2.12	1.27
DE, kcal	10,950	35,200
Total CP, kg		3.39
Total DE, kcal		46,150

To calculate the amount needed in the remaining part of the diet, proceed as follows:

	DP, kg	DE, kcal
Amount required/100 kg	18	350,000
Supplied by fish and wheat	3.39	46,150
Still needed in 87 kg	14.61	303,850

Thus the concentration of CP required is $14.60 \div 87 = 16.78$ percent, and for DE, it is $303,850 \div 87 = 3492.5$ kcal/kg. Knowing the concentrations required for these two nutrients, we could proceed to formulate the remainder of the ration.

Slack Space

The use of slack or reserved space is quite convenient and, indeed, necessary if we want to adjust amounts of nutrients such as some of the minerals (Ca, P) or amino acids without changing specifications for other nutrients or required feed ingredients. Usually, 1 to 2 percent of the total is quite adequate for slack. If all of it isn't needed for adjustment, then a normal ingredient such as salt could be added. One brief example will be given here and another in a later example of a complete ration being formulated.

If, for example, we have reserved 1 percent slack and we have formulated a ration to exact amounts of CP and DE, but we want 0.6 percent Ca and 0.35 percent P and we only have 0.4 percent Ca and 0.30 percent P, we could solve this problem in the following manner. The amount of Ca still needed is 0.2 percent (= 0.2 lb/100) and for P, it is 0.05 percent (= 0.05 lb/100). If we pick dicalcium phosphate to supply the P, it contains 23.3 percent Ca and 18.2 percent P. The amount needed to supply 0.05 lb of P is equal to 0.27 lb of dical (0.05 ÷ 0.182). Now, this amount will also supply 0.06 lb of Ca (0.27 × 0.233 = 0.06). We needed 0.2 lb of Ca; with the addition of the dical, we still need 0.14 lb (0.2 − 0.06 = 0.14). We could supply this with limestone (35.8 percent Ca). It would require about 0.39 lb (0.14 ÷ 0.358) of limestone.

Thus we have added 0.27 lb of dicalcium phosphate and 0.39 lb of limestone for a total of 0.66 lb. We could use up the remaining slack space by adding salt if we want the other ingredients to remain unchanged.

Slack space is easy to use and allows adjustment to exact amounts of nutrients required in relatively small quantities. We haven't altered the composition otherwise. Granted that replacement of a small amount of a major ingredient with less than 1 percent of the total diet wouldn't alter nutrient content greatly. Nonetheless, formulation to exact levels should be the desired objective, and, in commerce, certain minimums or maximums may be legal requirements.

RATION EXAMPLE

We will now go through the steps of formulating a ration for growing pigs (30-120 lb) using the various procedures already illustrated.

Step 1. Determine dietary requirements on a dry-matter basis from NRC (given in the appendix tables). For our example they are: 16 percent CP, 1670 kcal DE/lb, 0.60 percent Ca, 0.50 percent P, 0.74 percent lysine, and 0.50 percent methionine. There are specifications on other nutrients, but these are all that we will be concerned with in this example.

Step 2. Determine any other ration restrictions. It is a common practice with both swine and poultry rations to add a vitamin-trace mineral package (premix) as a needed supplement or in the form of insurance. We will add this at the rate of 10 lb/ton or 0.5 percent. We will also specify the addition of 5 percent dehydrated alfalfa (15 percent CP), 10 percent wheat (hard red spring), and 1.5 percent fish meal (herring). For the remainder of the diet, we will choose from corn, wheat middlings, soybean meal, and tallow. Thus our required ingredients and their nutrient compositions are shown in the following table:

Required	%	DM, %	Composition, DM basis, % or kcal[†]					
			CP	DE[†]	Ca	P	Ly	Meth
Slack	1.0		—	—	—	—	—	—
Vit-min premix	0.5		—	—	—	—	—	—
Alf. meal	5	93.1	16.3	736	1.32	0.24	0.64	0.21
Fish meal	1.5	92.0	76.7	1730	3.20	2.39	7.94	2.17
Wheat	10.0	89.1	14.6	1735	0.06	0.47	0.40	0.20
Total of nutrients from required, lb or kcal/100 lb								
	18.5		3.42	23,625[†]	0.124	0.095	0.191	0.128

Step 3. Calculate the nutrient concentration needed for the remainder (81.5 percent) of the ration:

	Composition, DM basis, % or kcal[†]					
	CP	DE[†]	Ca	P	Ly	Meth
Required in diet	16.0	167,000	0.60	0.50	0.74	0.50
Still needed in 81.5 lb	12.58	143,375	0.476	0.405	0.549	0.372
Concentration required/lb	15.44	1759.3	0.584	0.497	0.674	0.456

Step 4. Assemble the needed data on other feed ingredients:

	DM	Composition of other ingredients, % or kcal,[†] dry basis					
		CP	DE[†]	Ca	P	Ly	Meth
Corn	89.0	10.0	1684	0.02	0.35	0.20	0.10
Wheat middlings	89.0	20.2	1575	0.09	0.58	0.67	0.11
Soybean meal (44%)	90.0	44.0	1871	0.30	0.70	3.00	0.89
Tallow	98.0	—	3690	—	—	—	—

Step 5. Use the square (or algebra) to formulate a final mix that is exact for needed CP and DE:

Mix 1, 15.44% CP, <1759 kcal DE

Calculate DE:

Corn = 84.0% × 1684 = 1415 (rounded)
Soybean = 16.0% × 1871 = 299
                          1714

Mix 2, 15.44% CP, >1759 kcal DE

Calculate DE:

Wheat midds = 76.44% × 1575 = 1204
Tallow = 23.56% × 3690 = 869
                        2073

Mix 3, 1759 kcal DE

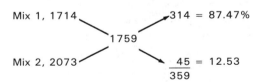

Step 6. Calculate the ingredient composition:

Required	%
Slack	1.5
Premix	0.5
Alfalfa meal	5.0
Fish meal	1.5
Wheat	10.0
Corn	59.88 = 81.5(0.840 × 0.8747)*

*Values are lb of total diet supplied by these 4 ingredients: % of Mix 1 × % of Mix 1 in Mix 3, etc.

Wheat midds $7.80 = 81.5(0.7644 \times 0.1253)$
Soybean meal $11.41 = 81.5(0.16 \times 0.8747)$
Tallow $2.41 = 81.5(0.2356 \times 0.1253)$

Step 7. Check to see that CP (16.01) and DE (1669.7) are correct. The slight discrepancies between the amounts required and the final values are caused by rounding errors.

Step 8. Compute the amounts of other nutrients specified (lb/100):

	Ca	P	Ly	Meth
In required ingredients	0.124	0.095	0.191	0.128
In remaining 81.5 lb	0.053	0.329	0.514	0.171
Total	0.177	0.424	0.705	0.299
Still needed	0.323	0.046	0.055	0.261

Step 9. Determine how to meet the remaining specifications. We can meet P needs by adding 0.25 percent of dicalcium phosphate (0.046 ÷ 0.182, or the lb of P needed divided by the amount supplied by dical). The dical supplied 0.058 lb of Ca, but we still need 0.265 lb of Ca (0.323 − 0.058) which can be provided by 0.74 lb of limestone (0.265 ÷ 0.358).

Because rather pure sources of lysine and methionine are available commercially, we could complete the lysine by using the commercial product (76.9 percent L-lysine). This would require 0.07 lb (0.055 ÷ 0.769). For methionine, we could use methionine hydroxy analog. The

product is at 93 percent purity and it is generally rated at about 80 percent the value of methionine, so this material has a replacement value of 74.4 percent (0.8 × 0.93). It would require about 0.35 lb (0.261 ÷ 0.744) for our diet. In place of using purified amino acid sources we could go back and revise the diet by increasing feedstuffs which are higher in these amino acids; a logical place to start would be to eliminate most if not all of the alfalfa meal and/or to increase the fish meal to perhaps 3 percent or more. As you have seen, normally there is more than one way to get a final solution on most problems.

Step 10. Convert final formula to an as-fed basis. The final diet is shown on a dry basis (in the following table). Of course, we don't mix feed or feed it to animals on a dry-weight basis. Therefore, we must convert it to the as-fed basis. This requires that the amounts of ingredients be divided by the decimal of the dry-matter content, summing up the total weights and calculating a final percentage for the as-fed ration.

Final Pig Grower Ration

Ingredient	%	DM, %	As-Fed Weight[a]	As Fed, %[b]
Alfalfa meal	5	93.1	5.37	4.82
Fish meal	1.5	92.0	1.63	1.46
Wheat	10.0	89.1	11.24	10.09
Corn	59.88	89.0	67.28	60.38
Wheat middlings	7.80	89.0	8.76	7.86
Soybean M	11.41	90.0	12.68	11.38
Tallow	2.41	98.0	2.46	2.21
Vit-min premix	0.50	100	0.50	0.45
Limestone	0.74	100	0.74	0.66
Dicalcium phos.	0.25	100	0.25	0.22
Meth. hydrox. analog	0.35	100	0.35	0.31
Lysine	0.07	100	0.07	0.06
Remainder	0.09[c]	100	0.09	0.08
			111.42	100.00

[a]For alfalfa = 5 ÷ 0.931 = 5.37
[b]For alfalfa = 5.37 ÷ 1.1142 = 4.82
[c]Add salt

COST FACTORS IN RATION FORMULATION

In the examples presented so far in this chapter, cost has not been considered. However, in the normal course of events, cost of feedstuffs is an important factor that must be considered in ration formulation. Only in a few instances—show animals, some hobby situations, or for racing animals—is cost not a primary factor.

Effect of Differences in DM

Feeds, of course, are purchased on an as-fed basis, so some calculations are always involved to get comparative costs on a dry basis. If the buyer ignores the moisture content of feed, water in feed may be an expensive purchase. It is always best to calculate costs on a dry-weight basis or relative to a standard DM content such as 90 percent DM.

Suppose that corn with 89 percent DM costs 7 cents/lb. What is corn of 75 percent DM worth, assuming utilization of nutrients on a dry basis is comparable? This is easily calculated by the method shown:

$$(0.75 \div 0.89) \times 7\cent = 5.9\cent \text{ or } 8.4\% \text{ less}$$

Although it is often not a common practice to buy feed grains or other products such as soybeans on a standard moisture content, it would be a fair practice which would not be difficult to do. Various devices are on the market which can determine moisture content quickly. As now practiced, not buying on moisture content may encourage some unscrupulous producers to add water before selling. Likewise, it certainly does not pay producers to overdry grain in areas where drying is necessary.

Data shown in Table 12–1 could be used for a standardized bushel weight and moisture

TABLE 12-1

Base data for a standardized bushel for feed grains in the United States

	Legal Weight, lb	Base Moisture,[a] %	Dry Matter, %	Dry Matter, lb
Corn	56	15.5	84.5	47.32
Soybeans	60	13.0	87.0	52.20
Sorghum	56	14.0	86.0	48.16
Wheat	60	13.5	85.5	51.90

[a]These are the accepted values used by the grain trade when buying and selling these products.
Source: Hill (1).

TABLE 12-2

Equivalent bushels at base moisture from 1000 bushels of grain at selected moisture contents

Moisture Content, %	Feedstuff[a]			
	Soybeans	Wheat	Sorghum	Corn
10.0	1034	1040	1047	1065
11.0	1023	1029	1035	1053
12.0	1011	1017	1023	1041
12.5	1006	1012	1017	1036
13.0	**1000**	1006	1012	1030
13.5	994	**1000**	1006	1024
14.0	989	994	**1000**	1018
14.5	983	988	994	1012
15.0	977	983	988	1006
15.5	971	977	983	**1000**
16.0	966	971	977	994
16.5	960	965	971	988
17.0	954	960	965	982
17.5	948	954	959	976
18.0	943	948	953	970
19.0	931	936	942	959
20.0	920	925	930	947

[a]Boldfacing denotes base moisture content generally used for pricing in the market. Refer to note at bottom of Table 12–1.
Source: Hill (1).

content. The values for equivalent bushel weights shown in Table 12–2 show quite clearly that one bushel is not always equal to another bushel! Assuming that the grain is of the same grade (for variables other than moisture content), grain with less moisture has a greater value than grain with more moisture. As it stands now, the old maxim of "let the buyer beware" is very applicable to buying and selling grains. Note that grains are bought on a weight basis. However, except for sorghum, central markets quote prices on a bushel weight basis, an archaic practice.

Evaluation on Basis of Replacement Costs

One way to evaluate feedstuffs with different CP or energy concentrations is to calculate how much money would be saved (or spent) by using a similar feed with higher or lower nutrient concentration. If, for example, a 7 percent CP corn costs 6 cents/lb and you want a 12 percent CP ration with corn and cottonseed meal and the CSM is valued at 9 cents/lb, what is 9 percent CP corn worth? The answer can be obtained by putting these ingredients through Pearson's square, as follows:

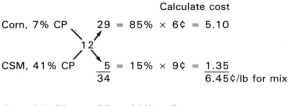

Calculate cost

Corn, 7% CP $\quad$ 29 = 85% × 6¢ = 5.10

CSM, 41% CP $\quad$ 5 = 15% × 9¢ = 1.35
$\qquad\qquad\qquad$ 34 $\qquad\qquad\qquad$ 6.45¢/lb for mix

Corn, 9% CP $\quad$ 29 = 91% × ?

CSM, 41% CP $\quad$ 3 = 9% × 9¢ = 0.81
$\qquad\qquad\qquad$ 32

Thus if 9 percent corn is substituted, 54 cents is saved per 100 lb by using less CSM (1.35 − 0.81). The second mixture should be worth the same as the first and the corn should be worth 6.45 cents − 0.81 or 5.64 cents. Because more corn was used in the second mix, the price/lb is 5.64 ÷ 0.91 = 6.198 cents/lb. On a ton basis, the 7 percent corn would be worth $120 and the 9 percent corn worth $124 when CSM sells for $180. In this particular example each additional 1 percent CP in corn is worth $2/ton.

With the use of these simple procedures, it is obvious that some feed ingredients can be selected that have a lower cost than others. Evaluating feeds on the basis of cost of only CP or energy is not a very complete method, although feeds can be ranked easily on cost of one nutrient. A combined value is not obtained for both protein and energy, nor is there a good means of evaluating other nutrients such as P, which may be relatively expensive to provide from concentrated supplements, thus other methods can be more informative.

MATHEMATICAL PROGRAMMING*

Mathematical programming is widely used in the United States, by both private and public institutions, to formulate rations for livestock. The rapid development and distribution of desktop computers with the appropriate programs has greatly improved the opportunity for even modest-sized livestock producers or small feed mills to do their own programming.

With the Pearson's square and the simultaneous equations methods, the mix obtained is of a predetermined CP percentage or a predetermined energy level. The amounts of the in-

*This section has been taken from *Basic Animal Nutrition and Feeding,* 3d ed., by D. C. Church and W. G. Pond. It is reproduced here by permission of the publisher, John Wiley & Sons, Inc., New York, NY. Copyright © 1988 by John Wiley & Sons, Inc.

gredients considered for the mix are therefore fixed. In reality, the percentage of protein required or the amount of energy in a diet is considered a minimum, and therefore the final mix should have "at least" the required amount of the nutrient. Sometimes the specified nutrient is required within a range, that is, at least some minimum quantity, but less than a maximum quantity. These two methods, the Pearson's square and the simultaneous equations, cannot handle inequalities or ranges, and both methods are independent of price. When price is considered, optimization is done by trial and error.

In cases of multiple nutrient requirements, multiple feed sources, price consideration, and requirements being greater than and/or less than some level, diet formulation should be done by mathematical programming. This technique, when properly used, helps to achieve both a nutritionally balanced diet and economic optimization, because it allows for simultaneous consideration of economical and nutritional parameters.

Nutritionists should have a good knowledge of diet specifications, should be familiar with formulation and interpretation of results, and should think of the solution process, that is, the mathematical manipulation, as a "black box." Nutritionists (or students) need not be concerned with the mechanics of the mathematical solution of the linear programming matrix. Diet formulation by mathematical programming should be treated as an interactive process, in which the nutritionist should verify, interpret, and reformulate, if necessary, all diet formulas.

With the availability of microcomputers, mathematical programming can be performed quite easily if the programming is done properly. We use the term "programming" as the planning of "economic" activities for the sake of optimization, subject to some constraints. There exist a large number of computer programs for the solution of mathematical programming problems, so a detailed explanation of the mathematics involved is not given here. Further information may be found in other sources (2–4).

Least-Cost Formulation

A great percentage of production cost is due to feed, thus diet formulation using least-cost techniques has been used extensively during the past 20 years. For any of the mathematical programming techniques to work, formulation of the problem should be done properly. Once the formulation of the problem is stated, then we can use any linear programming package to solve the diet formulation. Once we have a solution, it is one of the functions of the nutritionist to verify whether the solution conforms with nutritional knowledge.

EXAMPLE

To illustrate the problem statement for a least-cost formulation, the following steps of this technique are presented. Let us formulate a diet for growing pigs (20–35 kg).

Step 1. DETERMINE THE ANIMAL'S DIETARY REQUIREMENTS from the NRC tables (given in the Appendix). They are 16 percent CP, 3380 kcal DE/kg, 0.60 percent Ca, 0.50 percent P, 0.70 percent lysine, 0.45 percent methionine. There are other nutrient specifications, but for this example only these requirements will be utilized.

Step 2. DETERMINE ANY OTHER RATION RESTRICTIONS. It is a common practice with both swine and poultry rations to add a vitamin-trace mineral package (premix) as a needed supplement. We will add the premix at a rate of 5 kg/ton or 0.5 percent. We will also specify the addition of 5 percent dehydrated alfalfa (16.3 percent CP), 10 percent wheat (hard red spring), and 1.5 percent fish meal (herring). For the remainder of the diet, we will choose from corn, wheat middlings, soybean meal, tallow, dicalcium phosphate, limestone, L-lysine, methionine hydroxy analog, and salt. Our required in-

gredients, price per ton, and their nutrient compositions are presented in Table 12–3. Note that in the case of amino acid supplements the amount of protein content is equal to the amount of the amino acid (or sum of amino acids) supplied.

Step 3. STATE THE PROBLEM IN EQUATION FORM, as follows: Let X_1, X_2, X_3, X_4, X_5, X_6, X_7, X_8, X_9, X_{10}, X_{11}, X_{12}, and X_{13} be the nonnegative quantities of the vitamin-mineral premix, alfalfa meal, fish meal, wheat, corn, wheat middlings, soybean meal, tallow, dicalcium phosphate, limestone, L-lysine, methionine hydroxy analog, and salt, respectively. They will be mixed to yield 100 units of a minimum-cost diet that will satisfy all the specified nutritional requirements. The mix will also consider the constraints on the first four ingredients.

Using the crude protein content of the different feedstuffs under consideration, we can say that there are $0X_1$ units of protein in X_1 units of vitamin-mineral premix, $0.175X_2$ units in X_2 units of alfalfa meal, $0.723X_3$ units in X_3 units of fish meal, $0.141X_4$ units in X_4 units of wheat, $0.088X_5$ units in X_5 units of corn, $0.16X_6$ units in X_6 units of wheat middlings, $0.44X_7$ units in X_7 units of soybean meal, $0X_8$ units in X_8 units of tallow, $0X_9$ units in X_9 units of dicalcium phosphate, $0X_{10}$ units in X_{10} units of limestone, $0.769X_{11}$ in X_{11} units of L-lysine, $0.744X_{12}$ units in X_{12} units of methionine hydroxy analog, and $0X_{13}$ units in X_{13} units of salt. Expressing it in an equation form we have:

TABLE 12-3
Feedstuff composition on an as-fed basis

Ingredient	Feed Reference Number	DM, %	$ /T [a]	CP, %	DE, Mcal/ kg	Ca, %	P, %	LYS, %	METH, %
Vit-min premix		100	900						
Alfalfa meal	1–00–023	92	137	17.5	2270	1.44	0.22	0.73	0.20
Fish meal	5–02–000	93	310	72.3	2500	2.29	1.70	5.70	2.10
Wheat	4–05–268	87	120	14.1	3220	0.05	0.37	0.31	0.20
Corn	4–02–935	89	77	8.8	3325	0.02	0.28	0.24	0.20
Wheat middlings	4–05–205	88	83	16.0	2940	0.12	0.90	0.69	0.20
Soybean meal	5–04–604	89	209	44.0	3090	0.29	0.65	2.93	0.70
Tallow	4–00–409	99	220	—	7900	—	—	—	—
Dical. phos.	6–01–080	100	292	—	—	23.70	18.84	—	—
Limestone	6–02–632	100	72	—	—	36.07	0.02	—	—
L-Lysine		100	4080	76.9	—	—	—	76.9	
Meth. hydroxy analog		100	3420	74.4	—	—	—	—	74.4
Salt		100	66	—	—	—	—	—	—

[a] 1 ton = 1000 kg.

$$0X_1 + 0.175X_2 + 0.723X_3 + 0.141X_4$$
$$+ 0.088X_5 + 0.16X_6 + 0.44X_7 + 0X_8 + 0X_9$$
$$+ 0X_{10} + 0.769X_{11} + 0.744X_{12} + 0X_{13} \geq 16$$

This equation states that the sum of the contribution of protein by each ingredient should be greater than or equal to 16, which is the minimum requirement of CP in this diet. This also implies that

$$X_1 + X_2 + X_3 + X_4 + X_5 + X_6 + X_7 + X_8$$
$$+ X_9 + X_{10} + X_{11} + X_{12} + X_{13} = 100$$

That is, that the sum of all ingredients should be equal to 100 units, thus having a diet with a minimum of 16 percent CP. The equation that includes the sum of all ingredients would be called the "Amount" equation.

The difference between mathematical programming and simultaneous equations is that in mathematical programming we work with equalities and inequalities at the same time, while in simultaneous equations all are equalities. By handling inequalities, mathematical programming allows us to handle ranges for ingredients or nutritional specifications.

The rest of the equations (constraints) for the nutritional requirements are as follows:

Energy: $0X_1 + 2270X_2 + 2500X_3 + 3220X_4$
$$+ 3325X_5 + 2940X_6 + 3090X_7$$
$$+ 7900X_8 + 0X_9 + 0X_{10} + 0X_{11}$$
$$+ 0X_{12} + 0X_{13} \geq 338,000$$

The figure 338,000 comes from the fact that the specified requirement for energy is 3380 kcal DE/kg. Because we are formulating a 100 kg diet, then the total content of energy will be at least $3380 \times 100 = 338,000$ kcal DE.

Ca: $0X_1 + 0.0144X_2 + 0.0229X_3 + 0.0005X_4$
$$+ 0.0002X_5 + 0.0012X_6 + 0.0029X_7$$
$$+ 0X_8 + 0.237X_9 + 0.3507_{10} + 0X_{11}$$
$$+ 0X_{12} + 0X_{13} \geq 0.6$$

P: $0X_1 + 0.0022X_2 + 0.017X_3 + 0.0037X_4$
$$+ 0.0028X_5 + 0.009X_6 + 0.0065X_7 + 0X_8$$
$$+ 0.1884X_9 + 0.002X_{10} + 0X_{11} + 0X_{12}$$
$$+ 0X_{13} \geq 0.5$$

Lysine: $0X_1 + 0.0073X_2 + 0.057X_3$
$$+ 0.0031X_4 + 0.0024X_5 + 0.0069X_6$$
$$+ 0.0293X_7 + 0X_8 + 0X_9 + 0X_{10}$$
$$+ 0.769X_{11} + 0X_{12} + 0X_{13} \geq 0.7$$

Methionine: $0X_1 + 0.002X_2 + 0.021X_3$
$$+ 0.002X_4 + 0.002X_5 + 0.002X_6$$

$$+ 0.007X_7 + 0X_8 + 0X_9 + 0X_{10}$$
$$+ 0X_{11} + 0.744X_{12} + 0X_{13} \geq 0.45$$

Step 4. SET THE RESTRICTIONS FOR INDIVIDUAL FEEDSTUFFS.

Vitamin-mineral premix	$X_1 = 0.5$
Alfalfa meal	$X_2 = 5$
Fish meal	$X_3 = 1.5$
Wheat	$X_4 = 10$

Step 5. SET UP THE OBJECTIVE FUNCTION. Set up the objective function. Construct the equation dealing with the price of the diet. Price in dollars/ton or any other unit does not affect the results. As long as the prices for each ingredient are in the same units ($/kg, $/ton, $/cwt), the cost of the resulting diet formula will be correct. We add all the prices and state the minimum-cost diet as the objective function in the following way:

$$900X_1 + 137X_2 + 310X_3 + 120X_4 + 77X_5$$
$$+ 83X_6 + 209X_7 + 220X_8 + 292X_9 + 72X_{10}$$
$$+ 4080X_{11} + 3420X_{12} + 66X_{13}$$
$$= \text{minimum price}$$

Step 6. UTILIZING ANY APPROPRIATE LINEAR PROGRAMMING SOFTWARE, RUN THE DIET FORMULATED. The final setup will be as follows:

Minimize price: $900X_1 + 137X_2 + 310X_3$
$$+ 120X_4 + 77X_5 + 83X_6$$
$$+ 209X_7 + 220X_8 + 292X_9$$
$$+ 72X_{10} + 4080X_{11}$$
$$+ 3420X_{12} + 66X_{13}$$

such that:

$$X_1 + X_2 + X_3 + X_4 + X_5 + X_6 + X_7 + X_8$$
$$+ X_9 + X_{10} + X_{11} + X_{12} + X_{13}$$
$$= 100 \quad \text{(Amount)}$$

$$0X_1 + 0.175X_2 + 0.723X_3 + 0.141X_4$$
$$+ 0.088X_5 + 0.16X_6 + 0.44X_7 + 0X_8 + 0X_9$$
$$+ 0X_{10} + 0.769X_{11} + 0.744X_{12} + 0X_{13}$$
$$\geq 16 \quad \text{(Protein)}$$

$$0X_1 + 2270X_2 + 2500X_3 + 3220X_4 + 3325X_5$$
$$+ 2940X_6 + 3090X_7 + 7900X_8 + 0X_9 + 0X_{10}$$
$$+ 0X_{11} + 0X_{12} + 0X_{13} \geq 338000 \quad \text{(Energy)}$$

$$0X_1 + 0.0144X_2 + 0.0229X_3 + 0.0005X_4$$
$$+ 0.0002X_5 + 0.0012X_6 + 0.0029X_7 + 0X_8$$
$$+ 0.237X_9 + 0.3607X_{10} + 0X_{11} + 0X_{12} + 0X_{13}$$
$$\geq 0.6 \quad \text{(Ca)}$$

$$0X_1 + 0.0022X_2 + 0.017X_3 + 0.0037X_4$$
$$+ 0.0028X_5 + 0.009X_6 + 0.0065X_7 + 0X_8$$

$$+ 0.1884X_9 + 0.002X_{10} + 0X_{11} + 0X_{12} + 0X_{13}$$
$$\geq 0.5 \quad (P)$$

$$0X_1 + 0.0073X_2 + 0.057X_3 + 0.0031X_4$$
$$+ 0.0024X_5 + 0.0069X_6 + 0.0293X_7 + 0X_8$$
$$+ 0X_9 + 0X_{10} + 0.769X_{11} + 0X_{12} + 0X_{13}$$
$$\geq 0.7 \quad (Lysine)$$

$$0X_1 + 0.002X_2 + 0.021X_3 + 0.002X_4$$
$$+ 0.002X_5 + 0.002X_6 + 0.007X_7 + 0X_8 + 0X_9$$
$$+ 0X_{10} + 0X_{11} + 0.744X_{12} + 0X_{13}$$
$$\geq 0.45 \quad (Methionine)$$

$X_1 = 0.5$ (vitamin-mineral premix)
$X_2 = 5$ (alfalfa meal)
$X_3 = 1.5$ (fish meal)
$X_4 = 10$ (wheat)

Step 7. FROM THE RESULT OF THIS RUN (Run 1 in Table 12–4), VERIFY WHETHER THE DIET IS APPROPRIATE. We can see that in this case we have too much wheat middlings and no salt. The reader should note that this was done on purpose to illustrate the need for verification. We should specify an upper limit of 20 percent wheat middlings, and include salt within a range of 0.2 and 0.5 percent in our diet. Therefore, we have to include the following additional equations (constraints) to our initial formulation:

$X_6 \leq 20$ upper limit for wheat middlings
$X_{13} \geq 0.2$ lower limit for salt
$X_{13} \leq 0.5$ upper limit for salt

Then, we run the program again.

After verifying the new diet (Run 2, Table 12–4), we may decide that this ration is acceptable. Notice that because of the new constraints, this new diet has a higher price than the first one ($127.8827 vs. $125.2653), but it will be *the lowest-cost diet given those constraints.* Also, in the second run we obtained a lower tallow and limestone content as well as an increase in soybean meal. With the *proper mathematical formulation and interactive interpretation of the results,* we can arrive at a satisfactory formulated diet that is lowest in cost for a particular set of requirements and constraints.

Most linear programming software packages will give us, in addition to the properly balanced diet, a table with feedstuffs opportunity prices or "shadow prices," that is, a list of those feedstuffs not included in the diet and the price at which each would be included within the constraints specified. This information will help us in determining which are the "bargain" prices if we want to buy other feedstuffs. The opportunity prices (shadow prices) for the diet of Run 1 in Table 12–4 are presented in Table 12–5.

TABLE 12-4

Diet composition and analysis (as fed)

		Run 1	Run 2
X_1	Vitamin-mineral premix	0.5000	0.5000
X_2	Alfalfa meal	5.0000	5.0000
X_3	Fish meal (herring)	1.5000	1.5000
X_4	Wheat (hard red spring)	10.0000	10.0000
X_5	Corn	—	41.8823
X_6	Wheat middlings	67.9875	20.0000
X_7	Soybean meal (44%)	3.4641	12.6562
X_8	Tallow	10.1408	6.7764
X_9	Dicalcium phosphate	—	0.2482
X_{10}	Limestone	1.1007	1.0001
X_{11}	L-Lysine	—	—
X_{12}	Methionine Hydroxy Analog	0.3068	0.2368
X_{13}	Salt	—	0.2000
	Amount, kg	100.0000	100.0000
	Price/ton	125.2653	127.8827
	DE, Kcal/kg	3380.0000	3380.0000
	Protein, %	16.0000	16.0000
	Ca, %	0.6000	0.6000
	P, %	0.7081	0.5000
	Lysine, %	0.7236	0.7623
	Methionine, %	0.4500	0.4500

TABLE 12-5

Opportunity prices for the Run 1 diet

	Feedstuffs Not Included in Diet	Price, $/ton	Feedstuff Would Be Used If Price Is Less Than $/ton
X_5	Corn	77	73.207
X_9	Dicalcium phosphate	292	12.400
X_{11}	L-lysine	4080	165.292

MAXIMUM-PROFIT FORMULATION

With maximum-profit formulation, both the nutritional requirements and the animal performance are considered. The formulation contains all known feeding and nutrition inputs and animal production outputs. In this method we utilize feedstuffs based on cost and composition, animal performance (kg of milk, or daily gain) as a function of nutrients, and total animal product output. The animal product output is treated as an income, and price of feed as an expense. The objective is to maximize profit. This type of formulation requires knowledge of the maximum daily dry-matter intake (DMI) of the animal, production response to nutrient intake, and daily nutrient requirements for maintenance.

EXAMPLE

To illustrate this technique, a diet will be formulated to achieve maximum profit while supporting an optimum level of milk production in a cow with a good dairy potential. The cow has a weight of 600 kg and is in her first lactation.

In this case, minimum daily requirements for maintenance and growth for the lactating cow are obtained from the NRC tables. These requirements are: net energy for lactation (NEℓ), 12.36 Mcal/d; crude protein, 0.881 kg/d; Ca, 0.0264 kg/d; P, 0.0204 kg/d. We will also specify salt within a range of 0.05 to 0.1 kg/d.

The optimum level of milk production and maximization of returns are interdependent; we want to maximize the amount of money that is left after we subtract feed price from milk sales, so the solution will include the amounts of each feedstuff that should enter into the formula and also the optimal amount of milk to be produced. Requirements for production are dependent on amount of milk produced and milk butterfat. In this case we will be working with fat corrected milk (FCM) at 3.5 percent butterfat.

In dairy cows, milk production response to NEℓ intake is quadratic (5), as described in Fig.

12–2. The procedure for incorporating that selected curvilinear milk production response into our mathematical programming setup is to linearize portions of that curve, and then specify them as inequalities. These linearized values are presented in Table 12–6.

For the formulation of this diet, the objective function will be to maximize the difference between the income from milk and the expense of feed. Because the diet is being formulated on a dry-matter basis we have to convert the prices of the feedstuffs from an as-fed to a dry-matter basis. The price per kg of X_1 will be $90/ton divided by dry-matter percent of X_1 then divided by 1000 (1000 kg/ton)—that is, $(90 \div 0.89) \div 1000 = 0.1011$. Using the prices (dry-matter basis) presented in Table 12–7, and using $0.25 per kg of milk as the selling price, the objective function will look like this:

$$
\begin{aligned}
\text{Maximize profit:}\quad & 0.25\text{MILK} - 0.1056X_1 \\
& - 0.0865X_2 - 0.292X_3 \\
& - 0.072X_4 - 0.2348X_5 \\
& - 0.1419X_6 - 0.1348X_7 \\
& - 0.1254X_8 - 0.066X_9
\end{aligned}
$$

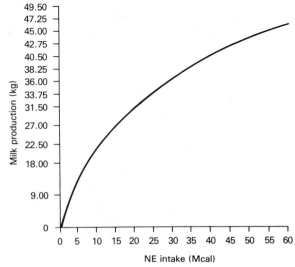

FIGURE 12-2. Milk production response to NEℓ intake.

TABLE 12-6

Linear representation of milk production response to net energy for lactation (NE$_l$)

Portion	Milk Production Portion, kg	Amount of Milk, kg	NE Lactation /kg Milk, Mcal
P_1	0.00– 9.00	9.00	0.33
P_2	9.00–18.00	9.00	0.51
P_3	18.00–22.50	4.50	0.77
P_4	22.50–27.00	4.50	1.10
P_5	27.00–31.50	4.50	1.21
P_6	31.50–33.75	2.25	1.34
P_7	33.75–36.00	2.25	1.70
P_8	36.00–38.25	2.25	2.38
P_9	38.25–48.25	10.00	3.22

TABLE 12-7

Feed composition on a dry-matter basis

	Feedstuff	Reference Number	As DM, %	Fed $/ ton[a]	$/kg	NEl Mcal /kg	MEm, Mcal /kg	NEg, Mcal /kg	CP, %	Ca, %	P, %
X_1	Barley	4-07-939	89.0	94	0.1056	1.89	2.12	1.45	10.7	0.05	0.36
X_2	Corn	4-02-931	89.0	77	0.0865	2.42	2.24	1.55	10.0	0.02	0.35
X_3	Dical. Phos.	6-01-080	100.0	292	0.2920	—	—	—	—	23.70	18.84
X_4	Limestone	6-02-632	100.0	72	0.0720	—	—	—	—	36.07	0.02
X_5	Soybean meal	5-04-604	89.0	209	0.2348	2.07	2.09	1.43	51.5	0.36	0.75
X_6	Cottonseed	5-01-608	93.0	132	0.1419	2.66	2.41	1.69	24.9	0.15	0.73
X_7	Alfalfa hay	1-00-063	89.0	120	0.1348	1.21	1.24	0.68	16.0	1.35	0.22
X_8	Corn silage	3-08-154	27.9	35	0.1254	1.70	1.56	0.99	8.0	0.27	0.20
X_9	Salt		100.0	66	0.0660	—	—	—	—	—	—

[a] 1 ton = 1000 kg.

In this equation, "MILK" is the optimum amount of milk to be produced per cow per day.

The amount of energy supplied by the feed minus the energy required for production must be greater than or equal to the energy required for maintenance and growth. The equation for energy (NEl) will be as follows:

$$1.89X_1 + 2.42X_2 + 2.07X_5 + 2.66X_6 + 1.21X_7$$
$$+ 1.70X_8 - 0.33P_1 - 0.41P_2 - 0.77P_3$$
$$- 1.1P_4 - 1.21P_5 - 1.34P_6 - 1.7P_7 - 2.38P_8$$
$$- 3.22P_9 \geq 12.36$$

The next point to consider will be to estimate total milk production. Total milk production will be the variable "MILK." Therefore, if from total milk production we subtract the milk from each portion of production, the results must be equal to zero:

$$MILK - P_1 - P_2 - P_3 - P_4 - P_5 - P_6 - P_7$$
$$- P_8 - P_9 = 0$$

This equation ensures that the amount of "MILK" is restricted by the milk produced under each portion of production, otherwise the amount could go very high because the object is to maximize profit.

To set the limits on each portion of production, as presented in Table 12–6, the following equation must be set:

$P_1 \leq$	9.00	1st portion
$P_2 \leq$	9.00	2nd portion
$P_3 \leq$	4.50	3rd portion
$P_4 \leq$	4.50	4th portion
$P_5 \leq$	4.50	5th portion
$P_6 \leq$	2.25	6th portion
$P_7 \leq$	2.25	7th portion
$P_8 \leq$	2.25	8th portion
$P_9 \leq$	10.00	9th portion

If we assume that the production requirements for protein, Ca, and P are linear, that is, directly porportional to the amount of milk, then these equations can be written in such a way that the amount of protein (or Ca or P) supplied by the feedstuffs minus the amount of protein required for production (protein per kg of milk times "MILK") is greater than or equal to the requirement of protein for cow maintenance and growth. According to the NRC tables, a cow needs 0.074, 0.0026, and 0.0019 kg of CP, Ca, and P per kg of milk (3.5 percent FCM), respectively.

Maximum dry-matter intake equations can be set directly, that is, the sum of all feedstuffs being less than certain maximum dry-matter intake, or we can set the equation dependent on production, similar to the way we have set the energy equation. Here we will set it in the former way:

$$X_1 + X_2 + X_3 + X_4 + X_5 + X_6 + X_7 + X_8 + X_9 \leq \text{MDMI}$$

In this equation MDMI is the maximum dry-matter intake. The figure used here is 3.7 percent of the body weight of the animal, that is, $600 \times 0.037 = 22.2$ kg dry matter.

The rest of the equations are set in the same way as in the least-cost formulation problem. The final maximum-profit formulation will be as follows:

Maximize profit: $0.25\text{MILK} - 0.1056X_1$
$- 0.0865X_2 - 0.292X_3$
$- 0.072X_4 - 0.2348X_5$
$- 0.1419X_6 - 0.1348X_7$
$- 0.1254X_8 - 0.066X_9$

such that

$$X_1 + X_2 + X_3 + X_4 + X_5 + X_6 + X_7 + X_8 + X_9 \leq 22.2 \quad \text{(dry-matter intake)}$$

$$1.89X_1 + 2.42X_2 + 2.07X_5 + 2.66X_6 + 1.21X_7 + 1.70X_8 - 0.33P_1 - 0.51P_2 - 0.77P_3 - 1.1P_4 - 1.21P_5 - 1.34P_6 - 1.7P_7 - 2.38P_8 - 3.22P_9 \geq 12.36 \quad \text{(energy)}$$

$$0.107X_1 + 0.1X_2 + 0X_3 + 0X_4 + 0.515X_5 + 0.249X_6 + 0.16X_7 + 0.08X_8 + 0X_9 - 0.074\text{MILK} \geq 0.881 \quad \text{(protein)}$$

$$0.0005X_1 + 0.0002X_2 + 0.237X_3 + 0.3607X_4 + 0.0036X_5 + 0.0015X_6 + 0.0135X_7 + 0.0027X_8 + 0X_9 - 0.0026\text{MILK} \geq 0.0264 \quad \text{(Ca)}$$

$$0.0036X_1 + 0.0031X_2 + 0.1884X_3 + 0.002X_4 + 0.0075X_5 + 0.0073X_6 + 0.0022X_7 + 0.002X_8 + 0X_9 - 0.0019\text{MILK} \geq 0.0204 \quad (P)$$

$$\text{MILK} - P_1 - P_2 - P_3 - P_4 - P_5 - P_6 - P_7 - P_8 - P_9 = 0$$

$P_1 \leq$	9.00	(1st portion)
$P_2 \leq$	9.00	(2nd portion)
$P_3 \leq$	4.50	(3rd portion)
$P_4 \leq$	4.50	(4th portion)
$P_5 \leq$	4.50	(5th portion)
$P_6 \leq$	2.25	(6th portion)
$P_7 \leq$	2.25	(7th portion)
$P_8 \leq$	2.25	(8th portion)
$P_9 \leq$	10.00	(9th portion)
$X_9 \geq$	0.05	(lower limit of salt)
$X_9 \leq$	0.10	(upper limit of salt)

As with the least-cost formulation, maximum-profit formulation has to be run with a linear programming software package and the result should be interpreted and modified accordingly. After running this formulation for the first time the diet does not contain any forage (Run 1, Table 12–8). We will explain how to correct this in the next section.

The reader should note that when diets are formulated on a dry-matter basis, the formulation also should include the prices on a dry-matter basis. Failure to use prices on a dry-matter basis will give erroneous results that do not satisfy the maximum-profit property. When the result is obtained it should be converted to an as-fed basis.

Under a maximum-profit formulation we obtain a ration together with the optimum level of production for maximum profit. The reader should note that the *mathematical statement of the diet and the revision of the results* are important components for an appropriate diet formulation.

PROPORTIONS IN MATHEMATICAL PROGRAMMING FORMULATION

In diet formulations the nutritionist wants to fulfill not only the quantity of a given nutritional requirement of an animal, but also to specify the proportion in which some feedstuff must be in the diet, or the porportions in which two nutrients should be present in the diet. Examples of these are the proportion of forage to concentrate and the proportion of Ca to P in dairy rations.

EXAMPLE

We shall reformulate the previous diet in such a way that the forage to concentrate ratio is be-

TABLE 12-8
Diet composition and analysis

	Feedstuff	Run 1		Run 2	
		Dry Matter	As Fed	Dry Matter	As Fed
X_1	Barley, kg	0.000	0.000	0.000	0.000
X_2	Corn, kg	10.085	11.331	6.772	7.610
X_3	Dicalcium phosphate, kg	0.000	0.000	0.030	0.030
X_4	Limestone, kg	0.316	0.316	0.217	0.217
X_5	Soybean meal, kg	0.000	0.000	2.921	3.282
X_6	Cottonseed, kg	11.749	12.634	3.330	3.581
X_7	Alfalfa hay, kg	0.000	0.000	0.000	0.000
X_8	Corn silage, kg	0.000	0.000	8.880	31.828
X_9	Salt, kg	0.050	0.050	0.050	0.050
	Profit, $/cow/d	7.748		6.709	
	Optimum milk, kg/d	41.257		38.379	
	Feed, kg/cow/d	22.200	24.331	22.200	46.600
	Energy, NEℓ, Mcal	55.658		46.389	
	CP, kg	3.934		3.721	
	Ca, kg	0.134		0.126	
	P, kg	0.121		0.093	
	Cottonseed in concentrate, %	52.925		25.000	
	Forage: concentrate	0:100		40:60	

tween 40:60 and 50:50; also, we shall include an upper limit for whole cottonseed such that it cannot exceed 25 percent of the concentrate.

To specify that the diet requires a forage to concentrate ratio between 40:60 and 50:50, we first write an expression that specifies the *forage*, that is, $X_7 + X_8$; then, we represent the *total diet* by the expression

$$X_1 + X_2 + X_3 + X_4 + X_5 + X_6 + X_7 + X_8 + X_9$$

The ratio between the first and second expressions (forage and total diet) gives us the proportion of forage in the diet. The lower ratio (40:60) can be represented as follows:

$$\frac{X_7 + X_8}{X_1 + X_2 + X_3 + X_4 + X_5 + X_6 + X_7 + X_8 + X_9} > 0.4$$

Multiplying both sides by $(X_1 + X_2 + X_3 + X_4 + X_5 + X_6 + X_7 + X_8 + X_9)$, we get

$$X_7 + X_8 \geq 0.4(X_1 + X_2 + X_3 + X_4 + X_5 + X_6 + X_7 + X_8 + X_9)$$

Performing the multiplication on the right-hand side and then subtracting from the left side, we obtain

$$-0.4X_1 - 0.4X_2 - 0.4X_3 - 0.4X_4 - 0.4X_5 - 0.4X_6 + 0.6X_7 + 0.6X_8 - 0.4X_9$$
$$\geq 0 \quad (\text{forage} \geq 40\%)$$

This linear equation then can be used in mathematical programming to specify the lower limit. With the following equation for the upper limit, the diet will have the range of 40–50 percent forage in the final form:

$$-0.5X_1 - 0.5X_2 - 0.5X_3 - 0.5X_4 - 0.5X_5 - 0.5X_6 + 0.5X_7 + 0.5X_8 - 0.5X_9$$
$$\leq 0 \quad (\text{forage} \leq 50\%)$$

With these manipulations we can set specified percentages of any nutrient in a diet whose total amount is determined by the formulation—that is, it is a part of the optimal solution. This formulation is used to set ratios of an individual or a group of feedstuffs with respect to the total or part of the diet, and to set ratios of individual nutrients with respect to the diet or any other nutrient. These manipulations are necessary because ratios (proportions) and percentages are not additive and, therefore, not linear. Linearity is essential for solving linear programming problems.

To specify that the whole cottonseed (X_6) must be less than 25 percent of the concentrate, we take the ratio of X_6 and the total concentrate $(X_1 + X_2 + X_3 + X_4 + X_5 + X_6 + X_9)$ and make it less than 0.25:

$$\frac{X_6}{X_1 + X_2 + X_3 + X_4 + X_5 + X_6 + X_9} \leq 0.25$$

Multiplying both sides of this expression by the

total concentrate ($X_1 + X_2 + X_3 + X_4 + X_5 + X_6 + X_9$) and then subtracting the right-hand side from X_6, we obtain

$$-0.25X_1 - 0.25X_2 - 0.25X_3 - 0.25X_4 \\ - 0.25X_5 + 0.75X_6 - 0.25X_9 \leq 0$$

After adding this equation and the two forages to concentrate equations to our original maximum-profit formulation, we obtain a new result (Run 2, Table 12–8). The diet in Run 2 complies with the constraints that the forage to concentrate ratio should be between 40:60 and 50:50, and that whole cottonseed should be less than 25 percent of the concentrate.

This procedure can be used with the simultaneous equations method. Two things should be taken into consideration when using the simultaneous equations procedure: (a) the equations should have the "=" sign; (b) ranges are not possible, and therefore, the ratio should be set at some fixed point.

Formulating with NEm and NEg Values

The NRC uses a system for expressing net energy requirements (NE) and feed values for beef cattle which separates the NE requirements for maintenance (NEm) from those for gain (NEg) and gives different energy values for feedstuffs used for these two functions (6). NEg is applied only if the total energy intake is above that required for maintenance. NEm and NEg are not independent of each other. To handle this dependency with linear equations, some mathematical manipulations are necessary. Let us illustrate how to formulate the energy requirement for beef cattle with the NEm-NEg system, using the following example.

EXAMPLE

Using the feedstuffs in Table 12–7, let us formulate a minimum-cost diet for a growing steer with the following daily requirement: a minimum 9.4 kg dry-matter intake, 6.89 Mcal NEm, 5.33 Mcal NEg, 0.87 kg CP, 0.021–0.042 kg of Ca, 0.02 kg of P, and a minimum of 45 percent forage. We would also specify that salt must be included within a range of 0.03 and 0.06 kg.

The equation to specify crude protein is as follows:

$$0.107X_1 + 0.1X_2 + 0.515X_5 + 0.249X_6 \\ + 0.16X_7 + 0.08X_8 \geq 0.87$$

Dividing both sides by 0.87 we obtain

$$\frac{0.107}{0.87}X_1 + \frac{0.10}{0.87}X_2 + \frac{0.515}{0.87}X_5 + \frac{0.249}{0.87}X_6$$
$$+ \frac{0.16}{0.87}X_7 + \frac{0.08}{0.87}X_8 \geq \frac{0.87}{0.87}$$

Let us examine the coefficient of each feedstuff: $0.107 \div 0.87$ for X_1 is the inverse of the amount of X_1 necessary to supply the 0.87 kg of protein required—that is, $0.87 \div 0.107 = 8.1308$ kg of X_1 are necessary to supply **all** the required protein; $0.44 \div 0.87$ is the inverse of the amount of X_2 necessary to supply the 0.87 kg of protein required—that is, $0.87 \div 0.10 = 8.7$ kg of X_2 are necessary to supply **all** the required protein; and so on with X_5, X_6, X_7, and X_8.

Based on this, we can construct an equation to specify NE requirement in which X_1, X_2, X_3, X_4, X_5, X_6, X_7, X_8, and X_9 have coefficients equal to the inverse of the total amount of each feedstuff required to supply **both** NEm and NEg.

The amount of X_1 necessary to supply all the NE requirement for maintenance is the amount of NEm required divided by the amount of NEm/kg in X_1 ($6.89 \div 2.12 = 3.25$ kg); the amount of X_1 necessary to supply all the NE requirement for gain is the amount of NEg required divided by the amount of NEg/kg in X_1 ($5.33 \div 1.45 = 3.6759$ kg). Therefore, the total amount of X_1 required to supply all the requirement of NEm and NEg will be: $3.25 + 3.6759 = 6.9259$ kg. The inverse of this number will be $1 \div 6.9259 = 0.144586$. If a feedstuff does not have a NEm and NEg value, such as dicalcium phosphate, the inverse value is taken as zero ("0"). Table 12–9 presents the amounts of each ingredient necessary to supply NEm and NEg, and the inverse value that will be used as the coefficient for the equation to specify the NE (NEm and NEg) requirement. The equation to specify the requirement of both NEm and NEg will be as follows:

$$0.144586X_1 + 0.153501X_2 + 0.142371X_5 \\ + 0.166313X_6 + 0.074656X_7 + 0.102036X_8 \geq 1$$

This procedure is tedious if done by hand, but a fast and accurate one if done by computer. Formulating a diet under the Lofgreen-Garrett system with this approach is a simple and accurate method.

For our example the equation to specify dry-matter intake will be as follows:

$$X_1 + X_2 + X_3 + X_4 + X_5 + X_6 + X_7 + X_8 \\ + X_9 \geq 9.4$$

TABLE 12-9

Amounts required to supply NEm and NEg and inverse of total NEm + NEg

Feedstuff	Amount Required to Supply **all**			Inverse NEm + NEg
	NEm	NEg	NEm + NEg	
X_1	3.2500	3.6759	6.9259	0.144586
X_2	3.0759	3.4387	6.5146	0.153501
X_3	—	—	—	0.000000
X_4	—	—	—	0.000000
X_5	3.2967	3.7173	7.0240	0.142371
X_6	2.8589	3.1538	6.0127	0.166313
X_7	5.5564	7.8382	13.3946	0.074656
X_8	4.4167	5.3838	9.8005	0.102036
X_9	—	—	—	0.000000

To specify the minimum 45 percent forage, we will divide the total forage ($X_7 + X_8$) by the total intake ($X_1 + X_2 + X_3 + X_4 + X_5 + X_6 + X_7 + X_8 + X_9$) and make it greater than or equal to 0.45:

$$(X_7 + X_8)/(X_1 + X_2 + X_3 + X_4 + X_5 + X_6 + X_7 + X_8 + X_9) \geq 0.45$$

Multiplying both sides of this expression by total dry-matter intake and subtracting the right-hand side from ($X_7 + X_8$), we get

$$-0.45X_1 - 0.45X_2 - 0.45X_3 - 0.45X_4 - 0.45X_5 - 0.45X_6 + 0.55X_7 + 0.55X_8 - 0.45X_9 \geq 0$$

The final formulation to produce a diet that is minimum cost for our example will be as follows:

Minimum price = $0.1056X_1 + 0.0865X_2 + 0.292X_3 + 0.072X_4 + 0.2348X_5 + 0.1419X_6 + 0.1348X_7 + 0.1254X_8 + 0.066X_9$

such that

$X_1 + X_2 + X_3 + X_4 + X_5 + X_6 + X_7 + X_8 + X_9$
≥ 9.4 (dry-matter intake)

$0.107X_1 + 0.1X_2 + 0.515X_5 + 0.249X_6 + 0.16X_7 + 0.08X_8 \geq 0.87$ (protein)

$0.144586X_1 + 0.153501X_2 + 0.142371X_5 + 0.166313X_6 + 0.074656X_7 + 0.102036X_8$
≥ 1 (NE)

$-0.45X_1 - 0.45X_2 - 0.45X_3 - 0.45X_4 - 0.45X_5 - 0.45X_6 + 0.55X_7 + 0.55X_8 - 0.45X_9$
≥ 0 (minimum 40% forage)

$0.0005X_1 + 0.0002X_2 + 0.237X_3 + 0.3607X_4 + 0.0036X_5 + 0.0015X_6 + 0.0135X_7 + 0.0027X_8$
≥ 0.021 (lower limit of Ca)

$0.0005X_1 + 0.0002X_2 + 0.237X_3 + 0.3607X_4 + 0.0036X_5 + 0.0015X_6 + 0.0135X_7 + 0.0027X_8$
≤ 0.042 (upper limit of Ca)

$0.0036X_1 + 0.0031X_2 + 0.1884X_3 + 0.002X_4 + 0.0075X_5 + 0.0073X_6 + 0.0022X_7 + 0.002X_8$
≥ 0.02 (P)

$X_9 \geq 0.03$ (lower limit of salt)
$X_9 \leq 0.06$ (upper limit of salt)

The results of this formulation after running it with a linear programming program are presented in Table 12–10.

EXACTNESS IN RATION FORMULATION

In practice, most rations for farm animals are milled and mixed with little or no analysis of individual batches of ingredients, even though the nutrient content of a new batch may differ from that of previous batches. The result is that the finished ration is not likely to have precisely its expected nutrient content, and it may be higher or lower in quality than it is supposed to be. It might also be noted that the long detailed lists of nutrients which may be obtained from computer printouts, sometimes expressed to the 1/1000 of a pound, tend to give the impression of far greater precision than actually exists.

The commercial feed mill that sells mixed diets with this uncertainty in composition may have a substantial percentage of batches that fall outside legal limits, thus rendering the miller liable to prosecution by regulatory agencies. The miller can respond by formulating to a higher average standard than is claimed or gain greater control by analyzing ingredients before use.

As a general rule, milling by-products of cereals and many commercial protein supple-

TABLE 12-10

Diet composition and analysis

	Feedstuff	Dry Matter	As Fed
X_1	Barley, kg	0.000	0.000
X_2	Corn, kg	5.038	5.661
X_3	Dicalcium phosphate, kg	0.000	0.000
X_4	Limestone, kg	0.072	0.072
X_5	Soybean meal, kg	0.000	0.000
X_6	Cottonseed, kg	0.000	0.000
X_7	Alfalfa hay, kg	0.347	0.390
X_8	Corn silage, kg	3.883	13.918
X_9	Salt, kg	0.060	0.060
	Minimum price $	0.979	
	Feed, kg/day	9.400	20.100
	Energy, total NEm, Mcal	17.774	
	total NEg, Mcal	11.890	
	available NEg, Mcal	7.280	
	CP, kg	0.870	
	Ca, kg	0.042	
	P, kg	0.024	
	Forage, %	45.000	

ments are standardized by the processors, so they tend to vary less in crude protein content than feedstuffs such as cereal grains and roughage sources. Consequently, if variation in nutrient content is to be reduced, analyses must be done on the major ration ingredients which are most likely to vary from batch to batch.

Least-cost ration formulation implies that a ration will be produced which will result in least cost to the feeder, however this concept is misleading for several reasons. As illustrated previously, there are problems in knowing what the nutrient concentration is in the diverse variety of feedstuffs utilized today, not to mention the problems in evaluating animal utilization of nutrients from different sources of feedstuffs.

It is true that least-cost formulas can be obtained from computers if feedstuff composition is accurately known, but there is no guarantee that such formulas will result in least-cost animal production. A diet which maximizes profit must consider the effects of the nutrient levels on animal performance, costs of the nutrients, costs of the livestock operation, and returns from production.

From the nutritionist's point of view, it is not a simple matter to establish a fixed nutrient requirement for animals, because of differences in breeds, variation between animals of similar genetic background, differences in utilization of nutrients from different sources, and many other environmental factors. Theoretically, as a limit-

ing nutrient is added to a ration, animal performance will increase up to a point where the animal has all of the nutrient it can use and further additions will not improve response at all.

FORMULATING PREMIXES

In nutritional use a premix refers to a small amount of a total mixture. Commercial premixes are made of antibiotics, vitamins, trace minerals, and various drugs and medicines which may be used in livestock feed. In nearly all instances the amount of material to be added is very small, perhaps as little as a few grams per ton of finished feed. Quantities as small as this are difficult to mix uniformly into large batches, thus the reason for the larger premixes. In addition, many small feed mills do not wish to be bothered with weighing out micro amounts of these different ingredients and they would prefer to use the premixes; fewer errors probably result, also, from use of the premixes.

Premixes are often made up so that they come in packages of 5–50 lb which will be added to one or more tons of feed. They are mixtures of the microingredients mixed with some type of carrier, which may be soybean meal, ground grain, wheat middlings, or other mill feeds. Sometimes about 2 percent stabilized fat will be added to reduce loss of the microingredients as dust in any future mill operations. Normally, the vitamins are not mixed in with the mineral premixes because a high concentration of mineral elements is apt to result in oxidation and destruction of vitamin activity.

Preparation of a Vitamin A-Antibiotic Premix for Cattle

Suppose we want to formulate a premix to be used at 10 lb/ton in a complete finishing ration for cattle which should have 1000 IU of vitamin A/lb and 5 mg/lb of antibiotic. This means we need 10 g of antibiotic (5 mg × 2000 = 10 g) and 2 million IU of vitamin A (1000 IU × 2000 lb). Antibiotics may come in different concentrations varying from pure sources (usually expensive) to much more dilute concentrations (see Appendix Table 7). For our purposes here it will be specified that the product has 50 g/lb. Likewise, vitamin A may be purchased in different concentrations. In this example, a source with 650,000 IU/g will be used. Consequently, for the premix 3.08 g (rounded to 3.1) of vitamin A concentrate and 0.20 lb of antibiotic (or 0.2 × 453.6 g/lb = 90.7 g) for a total of 93.8 g will be needed; the remainder of the 10 lb (4536 g), or 4442.2 g,

will be made up of soybean meal. In practice, probably enough of this for several tons of feed would be made up at one time. If 100 lb of premix are wanted, enough for 10 tons, it is merely a matter of multiplying the different ingredients by 10 in this instance.

Vitamin and Mineral Premixes for Broilers

For many poultry rations it is sometimes common to ignore most of the vitamins likely to be present in feedstuffs or, in some instances, to formulate premixes on the assumption that about half of the vitamins in the feed will be available at the time of feeding. An example of a premix used for broilers getting typical corn-soy rations is shown. It is made up in a concentration so that 5 lb will be added to each ton of finished feed. Since this total is to be in 5 lb (or 2268 g), we need, in grams, 2268 − 456.21 = 1811.79 g of carrier. This amounts to 79.88 percent of the 5 lb of premix. If premix is needed for more than 1 ton, it is simply a matter of increasing the amount.

Vitamin	Amount/ 5 lb	Concentration in Source	Amount Source Needed in Premix
Vitamin A	3 mil IU	650,000 IU/g	4.62 g
D	1 mil ICU[a]	200,000 ICU/g	5.0 g
E	1000 IU	275 IU/g	3.64 g
K	500 mg	pure	0.50 g
Riboflavin	3 g	0.50 g/g	6.0 g
d-pantothenic acid	5 g	0.41 g/g	12.2 g
Niacin	20 g	pure	20.0 g
Choline	173.6 g	0.434 g/g	400.0 g
B_{12}	5 mg	1.32 mg/g	3.8 g
Folacin	200 mg	0.45 g/g	0.45 g
			456.21 g

[a]International chick units.

Mineral Element	Amount/ 5 lb	Source	Element in Feed-Grade Salts, %	Amount of Source Needed in Premix, g
Mn	54.4 g	$MnSO_4$	28	194.6
Fe	18.16 g	$FeSO_4$	21	86.5
Cu	1.82	$CuSO_4$	25	7.3
I	1.09	KI	69	1.6
Zn	2.50	$ZnSO_4$	36	6.9
				296.9

With mineral premixes, which are usually used for the trace minerals, the procedure is similar. A mixture that might be used for broilers is shown, along with the amount, source, concentration in the source, and amount needed for a 5-lb premix.

The total amount of these mineral salts, 296.9 g, would then be diluted to 5 lb (2268 g) with some appropriate carrier (see bottom of p. 240).

USE OF FIBER OR PHYSICAL DENSITY IN FORMULATION

Limitations on fiber are often used in formulation, particularly for dairy cows (minimums). Maximum values may be used for other species. For cows, this is done because of the well-known effect of low-fiber rations on milk fat depression (see Ch. 15). In the opinion of the writer, this is not a very effective nor versatile means of achieving the objective of presenting a ration having an optimal bulk density to the animal—an important factor in maintaining good rumen function over a prolonged period of time. For example, if we have hay available from the same source as long (baled or stacked), chopped, ground, cubed, or pelleted, then the fiber concentration should be the same in each product, provided no losses occur in harvesting or processing. Obviously, pelleted hay does not produce the same production response as long hay because of much greater consumption and more rapid passage through the rumen (see Ch. 11). Furthermore, the fiber restrictions do not always give the same type of response when used with dry roughages as opposed to wet roughages (for example, silage) or with different types of roughage. Thus the fiber limitation is limited to a restricted usage rather than as a versatile means of defining ration characteristics. In addition, processing of grains will alter bulk density (see Ch. 11) although it may not always affect digestibility.

In the opinion of the author, nutritionists who use fiber (crude or ADF) and concentrate limitations for dairy cows to help define a ration are really trying to come up with a measure of physical density. Consequently, it seems logical that utilization of some measure of bulk density, particularly in computer formulation, should allow a more complete characterization of a ration.

Physical density data have been included for some feedstuffs listed in Table 11–15 of Ch. 11. Such data are not readily available on many roughages, partly because such measurements are more tedious to collect and more variable than for concentrates.

Mertens (7) has presented data which suggest that NDF (neutral detergent fiber) is a reasonably good measure of density when the roughage in the ration was ground. In contrast to the other fiber values, NDF contains all of the normal fibrous components (lignin, cellulose, hemicellulose). NDF is also highly correlated to digestibility (negatively), rumination (positively), and intake (negatively). A graph showing response of dairy cows to different NDF levels is shown in Fig. 12–3. However, this procedure may not resolve the problem of changes in density which occur with different types of feed processing, with roughages fed in different physical forms, or when different roughages are substituted in the ration.

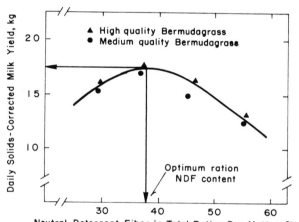

FIGURE 12–3. Determination of the optimal neutral detergent fiber content of the total ration resulting in maximum solids-corrected milk production using the quadratic regression equation. Courtesy of D. R. Mertens (2).

The effect of feeding beef cattle diets with different densities is shown in Table 12–11. In this instance the concentrate portion of the ration remained the same, and density was altered by varying the proportions of cottonseed hulls and ryegrass straw—each presumably containing about the same level of TDN. It is obvious from the table that decreasing the density resulted in less DM consumption, consumption of a greater volume of feed, and less intake of TDN. These data are too limited to extrapolate to other situations, but the method seems to be one that could be used with minimal effort in computer programs.

TABLE 12-11

Consumption by beef cattle of diets varying in bulk density

Diet	Density of Diet, kg/bu[a]	Consumption by Cattle		
		DM, % of BW	Volume, bu/1000 lb of BW	TDN, kg/1000 lb of BW
1	12.8	3.52	1.25	11.4
2	10.7	3.42	1.46	11.2
3	9.2	3.21	1.59	10.5
4	8.0	2.91	1.65	9.5
5	7.1	2.56	1.63	8.4

[a]Density is expressed as kg/bushel. It was altered by changing the proportions of cottonseed hulls and chopped ryegrass straw, presumably without altering caloric density of the diets. Cattle were fed each diet individually for a two-week period.

Source: Kellems and Church (8).

FACTORS AFFECTING NUTRIENT NEEDS OR FEED UTILIZATION

Now that the reader has been exposed to the methods used to formulate rations by hand, it is appropriate to call attention to various factors which may alter nutrient needs or utilization of feed. Unfortunately, a number of these are not, at this time, built into feeding standards. Nevertheless, the reader should be aware of them.

Animal Variation

Animals of similar breeding do not always have the same nutrient needs, even though it is economically feasible to treat them as if they do. Previous exposure to various stresses (disease, injury) may have altered their capabilities. Hormone stimulus (thyroid, growth, and sex hormones) can easily alter metabolism as well as produce differences in physical activity. In addition, some individuals are more susceptible to a given stress than others. In animal research there are many documented instances that show marked differences in nutrient requirements. Thus it is well to remember that closely related animals may differ in nutrient requirements just as they differ in taste preferences, hair color, or temperament. The consequence (for ration formulation) is that our objectives should be to satisfy the needs of most of the animals. A few will receive more of one or more nutrients than needed; most should get what they need; and a few may be underfed on one or more nutrients. Only in the case of outstanding animals (such as superior dairy cows) is it feasible to feed on an individual basis so that none is underfed.

Miscellaneous Factors

In many instances experienced nutritionists may modify specified requirements in a given situation on the basis of experience under similar conditions with a given class and species of animal. This is often needed, particularly for animals (especially ruminants) grown under nonstandard conditions and fed markedly different ration ingredients. In contrast, poultry (and many swine) are produced under rather standard conditions regardless of the area and, in addition, basic rations are rather similar regardless of where the birds are grown. Consequently, it is much more difficult to refine the dietary requirements of ruminants and horses to the degree that can be accomplished with poultry or swine.

Nutrient requirements of healthy animals may be altered by a considerable number of genetic and environmental factors. Some of these which have been identified include:

Genetic: species, breed, strain.

Production related: age, sex, pregnancy, lactation (or egg production) and level of lactation, growth and rate of growth, desired carcass fatness, and composition of milk produced.

Other environmental: disease, nutrient deficiencies, climatic factors such as temperature and humidity, muddy lots, wind, rain, and other miscellaneous stresses.

Although they may not always alter the requirement for absorbed nutrients, factors such as level of feed consumption, energetic and physical density of the diet, feed additives, growth stimulators, and feed processing methods may greatly affect efficiency or completeness of digestion and metabolism of absorbed nutrients. Thus if we are basing animal needs on chemical composition or digestibility, these factors usually alter efficiency and have the same final effect as if they altered nutrient requirements. For example, if we feed lambs a pelleted hay-grain diet, consumption will be increased greatly, as compared to a nonpelleted diet, and the lambs will gain more per day even if they are on a diet with a lower concentration of digestible protein and energy.

The NRC publications generally are developed to make allowances for some differences related to species, occasionally for breeds, and for body size, sex, age, pregnancy, lactation and milk fat percentage, level of egg production, and rate of growth. Information is not, at this time, sufficient to include the marked effect of the environmental factors in the nutrient requirement tables.

SUMMARY

Formulation of a satisfactory ration for a given situation represents the summation and utilization of information on animal requirements and nutritive value and palatability of feedstuffs. While a variety of different methods can be used to formulate acceptable rations for livestock, the result should be a ration that is acceptable to the animal, one that will produce the desired results (level of production) and one that will be economical for the livestock feeder.

Hand methods of ration formulation are quite satisfactory for formulating rations in which exact amounts are required for two major nutrients. More complex formulas can be put together using reserved feedstuffs or slack space for minor ingredients. Very complex rations involving minimums of a number of different nutrients are, generally, better done with linear programming methods using computers. The reader should remember that exact mathematical methods do not guarantee exactness in actual formulas because tables of nutrient composition of feedstuffs may not always be representative of the feedstuffs that will be combined into a formula that will be fed to the animals.

REFERENCES

1. Hill, L. B. 1982. *Feedstuffs* 54(23):30.
2. Cooper, L., and D. Steinberg. 1974. *Methods and applications of linear programming.* Philadelphia, PA: W.B. Saunders Co.
3. Hadley, G. 1962. *Linear programming.* Reading, MA: Addison-Wesley.
4. Varela-Alvarez, H. 1978. *Description of an introductory course in operations research for animal science students.* M.A. Paper, University Park, PA: Dept. of Statistics, Penn. State Univ.
5. Dean, G. W., et al. 1972. *Giannini Foundation Monograph #31,* Berkeley, CA: Cal. Agr. Exp. Sta.
6. NRC 1984. *Nutrient requirements of beef cattle.* 6th rev. ed. Washington, D.C. Nat. Acad. Press.
7. Mertens, D. R. 1980. *Proc. Distillers Feed Conf.* 35:35.
8. Kellems, R. O., and D. C. Church. 1981. *Proc. West. Sec. Amer. Soc. Animal Sci.* 32:26.

13

Nutritional Management of the Beef Cow Herd

John K. Ward and Terry J. Klopfenstein

INTRODUCTION

Nutritional management of the beef cow herd involves grazing to the extent possible and supplemental feeding of harvested feeds when necessary. Grazing has several advantages over harvested forage: it is usually more economical, it is less labor and management intensive, and it allows the animal to select higher-quality forage, thus improving performance. The major disadvantage of grazing is that it requires more land due to trampling losses and animal selectivity of plant parts of higher quality.

The extent to which the cow herd can be grazed is dependent upon a number of factors, such as rainfall, temperature, soils, and topography, and the interaction of these conditions. In the United States and over most of the world, less than half of the land area produces forage useful for grazing by cattle. The quantity and quality of forage produced varies greatly and changes on a seasonal basis (Fig. 13–1).

In warmer climates such as that of the southern United States, grazing of pastures may approach year-round availability. In the more

temperate zone across the central states, pasture grazing is restricted to 5 or 6 months, while in northern areas it may be further reduced to 4–5 months. Grasses that grow in warmer climates tend to produce higher quantities and lower quality of forage, while those that grow in cooler climates tend to produce less quantity but higher quality of forage.

In all regions forages other than traditional pastures may be available for grazing. These are largely fibrous materials associated

FIGURE 13–1. Hereford cow-calf pairs grazing smooth bromegrass.

FIGURE 13-2. Spring calving cows in mid-gestation grazing grain sorghum stubble.

mainly with cereal grain production such as cornstalks, grain sorghum stubble (Fig. 13–2), and residues of other crops left in the field after harvest. They are available in large quantities on a localized basis and have a wide range of energy and protein levels, feeding value, and digestibility.

The management challenge to the cow herd operator is to develop an optimum feeding-management plan based on breed or breed combinations of cattle, reproductive and productive nutritive requirements, and adjustment of the calving season to complement forage resources. It is usually biologically more efficient to supply nutrients directly to the calf, but it may be more economically efficient to have the cow convert low-cost, low-quality forage (which the calf otherwise could not use) into milk for the calf (1). Fitting the various components of cow-herd management into a system to optimize beef calf-yearling production (Fig. 13–3) is the goal of producers.

FIGURE 13-3. Crossbred 550-lb steer calves at weaning.

NUTRIENTS

Energy

The most important nutrient from a quantitative standpoint is energy. Although not as costly per unit, it is the most costly portion of the ration. Compounds such as starch, cellulose, protein, and fat can supply energy, but the most common form in forages is cellulose. Forage cell walls are made up primarily of cellulose, thus they become the primary energy source for the cow herd. Immature forages, including pasture grasses and legumes, are more digestible because their cell walls are not as lignified as those of more mature plants. Forages for either grazing or to be used as harvested feeds need enough growth and development to provide adequate yields while maintaining reasonable forage quality. Dry-matter yields will go up as the plant matures; however, quality will decline, with nutrient yield per acre usually being higher in early cut hay or grazed grasses and legumes (see Ch. 6). Mature nonlactating cows in mid-gestation use nearly all of their energy requirements for maintenance. As fetal development requirements increase and lactation begins following parturition, energy requirements for production increase. Superior milk-producing cows in early lactation may require as much additional energy for production as is required for maintenance (see Appendix Table 12). Lower-quality forages are frequently used to supply energy for maintenance, but as production requirements increase, even high-quality forages may not be an adequate energy source.

Protein

Protein is the second-most important nutrient from a quantitative standpoint. It is more expensive than a unit of energy but needs to be supplied in adequate amounts and with the proper degree of rumen degradation. Adequate levels of rumen ammonia are necessary for maximum fiber (cellulose) digestion and for the bacterial and protozoal growth that is the protein synthesis process in the rumen. Growth, reproduction, milk production, and animal maintenance all have specific protein and amino acid requirements. Diet protein levels provide some indication of meeting the animal's needs, but to optimize protein nutrition several factors need to be considered.

Diet protein must supply ammonia in the rumen sufficient to maximize bacterial breakdown of fiber without having excess ammonia produced which will be absorbed and excreted in the urine as urea. Certain branched-chain fatty acids of protein origin enhance bacterial and protozoal protein synthesis. Once these requirements for ammonia and branched-chain fatty acids in the rumen have been met, for most efficient use of dietary protein, the remainder should bypass (escape rumen degradation) and be enzymatically broken down to amino acids in the small intestine. Heat treatment systems (or other protein-altering regimes) have been used to process protein sources, thus reducing rumen degradation. The combination of bacterial, protozoal, and bypass protein needs to provide the proper balance of amino acids postruminally for absorption via the portal blood system for tissue utilization. The use of nonprotein-nitrogen (NPN) compounds such as urea in diets for the cow herd should be limited to feed combinations that fail to provide adequate rumen ammonia levels (see Ch. 8). The rate of ammonia release from urea is very rapid and will likely exceed microbial utilization rates on high-roughage rations unless the urea supplement is being consumed several times per day. Diets high in forage, because of slower rates of digestibility, fail to provide sufficient energy to optimize rumen ammonia utilization due to high rumen ammonia peaks associated with urea hydrolysis. Optimum protein feeding in functional ruminants should provide adequate rumen ammonia for maximum fiber digestion without excessive ammonia loss, with sufficient amounts and balance of amino acids in the small intestine from the combination of microbial and bypass proteins.

MINERALS AND VITAMINS

Calcium (Ca)

Mature ruminants on high-quality forage diets would not be deficient in Ca, but forage of low quality, such as straw, will not supply sufficient Ca due to low intakes and digestibility. Legume forages provide Ca in excess of ruminant requirements. As the starch level in feed increases due to grain feeding, such as with corn silage, Ca levels may not be adequate for growth or milk production. Diets providing energy for high levels of production will likely need to be supplemented with a Ca source such as limestone.

Phosphorus (P)

P is frequently deficient in diets fed to nonlactating cows. Forages of lower quality which may supply adequate energy for maintenance, such as crop residues, weathered grass, or mature grass hay, may not meet P requirements. P is involved in reproduction, with deficiencies resulting in delayed estrus or failure to come into estrus and delayed breeding or nonbreeding. Symptoms of a deficiency include loss of appetite, weight loss, lower milk production, and the chewing of objects such as bones, posts, rocks, or soil. Cattle on diets of high-quality forage such as pasture grass or legumes, high-quality hay or silage, or combinations of high-quality forage plus grain will usually meet their P requirements. Supplementation of P may be through mineral mixes fed in meal form, blocks, or liquids. Because this nutrient is rather expensive, it is important to restrict intake to the level required by using salt or other methods to avoid excessive consumption. Sources include dicalcium phosphate, bone meal, or defluorinated rock phosphate compounds.

Salt

Salt should be available in loose or block form at all times. Intake of salt will be highly variable depending on such factors as type of forage, forage composition, and climate. Daily intake will vary from 1 to 4 ounces (25–100 g). Salt may be incorporated into a complete ration, fed separately, or added to supplements. It can be used at higher levels (up to 20–25 percent) to control intake of ad libitum-fed supplements.

Potassium (K)

K is used in the body as the principal cation (that is, positively charged ion) of intracellular fluid. Although normally present in adequate quantities in high-quality forages, it has been shown to be deficient in diets consisting of weathered grass for gestating beef cows (2). The requirement for mature gestating cows appears to be 0.5–0.7 percent of a diet consumed in normal amounts (3). The most common supplemental sources are potassium chloride, sulfate, or carbonate. Plant protein supplements such as soybean or cottonseed meal are also good sources of K.

Sulfur (S)

Common feedstuffs contain adequate amounts of S for microbial amino acid synthesis. If urea or other NPN compounds are fed, supplementation of S may be desired to maintain a N:S ratio of between 10:1 and 15:1 (3). Ammonium sulfate is a common source of S.

Magnesium (Mg)

A deficiency of Mg is most common with cows in early lactation, however, metabolic disturbances have been known to occur in growing cattle on lush pastures. The condition in cows commonly known as "grass tetany" or "grass staggers" affects the central nervous system and may cause convulsions and death. The onset is rapid and without previous signs of difficulty. It is most common on cool-season grasses in cool, wet weather and on soils high in K that have been heavily fertilized with N. Pastures lacking residual growth allowing cows to consume new growth freely are the most apt to cause hypo-magnesium. Impaired Mg absorption and low blood Mg levels are the immediate causes of grass tetany (4). The requirement level appears to be in the range of 0.2–0.3 percent of the diet (5). Prevention involves avoiding grazing pastures that may cause the condition, or supplementing Mg. Mg consumption should be in the 20 g/d range to avoid tetany in lactating cows. It may be added to grain, protein, or mineral supplements in the form of magnesium oxide, but with a palatability problem that can sometimes be overcome by mixing it with other feed ingredients.

Microminerals

Additional minerals of concern in ruminant diets include cobalt, copper, iodine, zinc, molybdenum, and selenium. All have specific metabolic functions, such as the inclusion of cobalt in vitamin B_{12} and iodine in thyroid activity. Requirements are not well established. Interrelationships exist with other minerals and vitamins which affect absorption and metabolism. Overfeeding of specific minerals may cause an imbalance resulting in lowered performance of cattle. Deficiencies have been linked to reproductive problems and excesses to a variety of problems including white muscle, heart failure, and paralysis (6).

Vitamins

Vitamin A of the fat-soluble vitamins is the most likely to be deficient. Green forages such as grass or high-quality hay will likely supply adequate vitamin A. Mature forages that have been weathered, such as winter range or crop residues, will be low or devoid of vitamin A activity. The liver can store a quantity of vitamin A sufficient to avoid a deficiency for several weeks, but winter-long feeding of forages low in vitamin A precursors (carotenes) may result in a deficiency. Calves from deficient cows may be born dead or blind, and cows may exhibit reproductive problems such as retained placenta with subsequent rebreeding problems. Vitamin A can be supplied in supplements from synthetic sources, green forages, or hay (particularly legumes), or it can be given as an intramuscular injection. Vitamin D may be deficient in feedstuffs. Lack of vitamin D or an imbalance of Ca and/or P can cause bone formation problems. Sunlight, sun-cured hay, or vitamin D supplements will provide vitamin D. The water-soluble vitamins are usually adequate from dietary sources and/or microbial synthesis.

NUTRITION OF THE BREEDING HERD

Developing Replacement Heifers

Replacement heifer development (Fig. 13–4) is a continuing process usually divided into the following segments: (a) preweaning, (b) postweaning, prebreeding, and (c) postbreeding, precalving. Early puberty and conception are desirable in replacement heifers to facilitate a short and early calving season. Many breeders will calve first-calf heifers at an average age of 23 months to allow the needed extra 3–4 weeks to return to breeding condition and move into the cow herd calving schedule. Factors involved in early breeding are body weight and heifer age, with breed or breed combinations affecting puberty.

FIGURE 13–4. Hereford and Hereford x Angus replacement heifer calves.

Preweaning

Adequate size and development of the replacement heifer at weaning are essential in moving her into the cow herd as an early calver capable of calving with minimal assistance and with the potential for early rebreeding. Replacements need to wean at 450–500 lb (Table 13-1, 13-2) to avoid the need for high-energy rations post-weaning prebreeding. A replacement weaned at 205 d of age has approximately 200 d prior to conception in order to calve at 23 months of age. Heifers weighing less than 450 lb at weaning would need to gain 1.25–1.5 lb daily to achieve puberty and breed to calve at 23 months. Smaller mature-size cattle tend to put on too much condition if daily gains exceed 1.1–1.2 lb daily. Calf weaning weight is affected by milk production of the dam, along with quantity and quality of forage available to the calf and,

TABLE 13-1

Weight needed to reach puberty by breeds

Breed	Weight, lb
Hereford	600–650
Angus	575–650
Shorthorn	575–650
HxA or AxH	600–625
Charolais crosses	675–725
Simmental crosses	650–700
Limousin crosses	650–700
South Devon crosses	625–675
Tarentaise crosses	600–650
Pinzgauer crosses	600–650
Brown Swiss crosses	600–650
Gelbvieh crosses	600–650
Brahman crosses	700–750

Source: Deutscher (7).

possibly, creep feeding. Creep feeding can add 25–75 lb to weaning weight; however, overconditioned heifers at weaning, due to creep feeding, have been shown to have lower milk production as cows. Older heifer calves out of mature cows have the greatest potential to be selected as replacement heifers. Replacement heifers should achieve adequate weaning weight and puberty without having to be fed large quantities of high-energy feeds.

Postweaning, Prebreeding

The replacement heifer [depending upon breed(s) and breeding date] should be developed to achieve puberty preferably at least one estrus period prior to artificial insemination (AI) or bull exposure. Heifers of predominantly English breeds or breed crosses weaning at 450 lb or more and wintered at 1.0–1.2 lb/d gain will weigh 650–700 lb at breeding time and should have over 80 percent conception during the first 21 d of the breeding season. These gains can be achieved on a diet containing 60–65 percent TDN or 6.4–7.3 Mcal of NE along with adequate protein, minerals, and vitamins. Harvested forages do not supply adequate energy, and added grain or corn silage will be necessary to properly develop heifers (Fig. 13–5).

Breeding to First Calving

Heifers developed for early breeding should gain an additional 300 lb during gestation. A precalving weight of 950–1000 lb will allow for easier calving and a more rapid return to estrus when compared to heifers of lesser size and body condition. Large-breed heifers may need heavier weights and more rapid growth to breed early

TABLE 13-2

Breed, age, weight sequence for replacement heifers to first calving

Breed	Age, d	Weight, lb	Average Daily Gain, lb	Approximate Energy Level Needed	
				TDN, %	NE, Mcal
Angus-Hereford	205	475	2.0	77.0	6.94
	400	675	1.0	62.0	8.23
	700	975	1.1	54.1	9.5
Large breed exotic cross	205	500	2.1	77.0	7.43
	400	725	1.1	60.0	8.81
	700	1050	1.1	54.1	10.4

Source: NRC (3).

FIGURE 13-5. Calves grazing corn-stalks receiving pelleted protein supplement.

FIGURE 13-6. Gestating replacement heifers on fall pasture gaining about one pound per day.

and calve with minimal assistance. Gains during gestation of one lb/d can be achieved on high-quality forage without additional grain feeding (Fig. 13-6).

First Calving to Rebreeding

Although factors such as breed, weather, and calving difficulty are involved in rebreeding, the major item seems to be nutrition. Heifers must be in good body condition to cycle and rebreed early in the breeding season. Body condition scoring may provide an indication of predicted breeding success. Using a scale of 1-9 with 1 being very thin and 9 very fat (Table 13-3), it appears that optimum rebreeding will occur if cows have a score of 5-6. This is also illustrated in Fig. 13-7.

There appears to be general agreement on the need for good body condition (8, 9, 10). Work reported by Whittier indicates that replacements in good condition going into the last trimester of pregnancy will cycle and rebreed satisfactorily as long as recommended weight gain occurs at any time during that period and remains adequate from postpartum to rebreeding (10). Feeding at recommended NRC levels (Table 13-4) postpartum until breeding was equal or superior to feeding higher levels (130 percent) the first 45 d followed by lower levels (70 percent) or reversing this feeding

---

TABLE 13-3

Body condition scoring system

Score	Description
1	Severely emaciated. All ribs and bone structure easily visible and physically weak. Animal has difficulty standing or walking. No external fat present by sight or touch.
2	Emaciated. Similar to 1 but not weakened.
3	Very thin. No palpable or visible fat on ribs or brisket. Individual muscles in the hind quarter are easily visible and spinus processes are very apparent.
4	Thin. Ribs and pin bones are easily visible and fat is not apparent by palpation on ribs or pin bones. Individual muscles in the hind quarter are apparent.
5	Moderate. Ribs are less apparent than in 4 and have less than .5 cm of fat on them. Last two or three ribs can be felt easily. No fat in the brisket. At least 1 cm of fat can be palpated on pin bones. Individual muscles in hind quarter are not apparent.
6	Good smooth appearance throughout. Some fat deposition in brisket. Individual ribs are not visible. About 1 cm of fat on the pin bones and on the last two to three ribs.
7	Very good. Brisket is full, tailhead and pin bones have protruding deposits of fat on them. Back appears square due to fat. Indentation over spinal processes due to fat on each side. Between 1 and 2 cm of fat on last two to three ribs.
8	Obese. Back is very square. Brisket is distended with fat. Large protruding deposits of fat on tailhead and pin bones. Neck is thick. Between 3 and 4 cm of fat on last two to three ribs. Large indentation over spinal processes.
9	Very obese. Description of 8 taken to greater extremes.

Source: Wagner et al. (12).

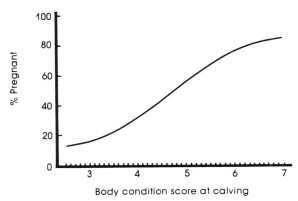

FIGURE 13-7. Body condition score at calving and subsequent rebreeding (11).

system. Underfeeding for short periods of time was compensated for by later feeding higher levels than recommended. Postpartum weight gain of about 0.5 lb/d is adequate for heifers in good body condition prepartum. Heifers that lose weight postpartum will cycle late and have poor conception rates (Tables 13-4, 13-5, 13-6).

Postcalving, Cow Herd Nutrition

Commercial cow herds contain two-year-old heifers in their first lactation to "running age" cows from 3 years of age and older with cows

TABLE 13-4

Reproductive performance of beef heifers as affected by pre- and postpartum nutrition

Treatment[a]	Calving to Estrus, d	Calving to Conception, d
1	110	118
2	95	99
3	102	106

[a]1 = 130% NRC for 45 d then 70% for 45 d.
  2 = 100% NRC for 90 d.
  3 = 70% NRC for 45 d then 130% for 45 d.
Source: Whittier et al. (10).

TABLE 13-5

Weight change and reproductive performance of first-calf heifers fed to maintain postcalving weight or gain one lb/d

Item	Maintain	Gain
No. of cows	16	14
Postcalving weight, lb	827	794
Weight at breeding, lb	800	869
Weight change, lb	−27	75
No. pregnant	7	12
% pregnant	44	86
Estimated days to pregnancy	100	80

Source: Morrison et al. (8).

TABLE 13-6

The effect of postpartum nutrition on the reproductive performance of fall-calving beef cows

Item	Postpartum Nutrition Levels	
	Moderate	Low
No. of cows	214	200
Days postpartum to first estrus	52.1	67.1
Conception, %	94.9	80.0
Adjusted 210-d calf weight	465	450

Source: Hancock et al. (13).

beyond 10 years of age subject to culling due to age or physical unsoundness. Although approximately 40 percent of the herd will be below 5 years of age and thus still growing, they are usually managed together with older cows as one group. This results in cow condition differences with 2-, 3-, and 4-year-old cows usually somewhat underfed and thinner, with 5–10-year-old cows overfed and often carrying unneeded body condition. The relationship between reproductive efficiency and pre- and postparturition nutrition is well established (Tables 13-4, 13-5, 13-6). Return to estrus was shorter and date of conception earlier when cows were fed 100 percent of recommended requirements pre- and postpartum. Nutrient restriction either before or after parturition delayed return to estrus and conception. The open period for cows is only 82 d for a 365-d calving interval. For early return to estrus, the lactating cow must be in good body condition (score 5–6) and maintaining or gaining weight. Cows of average or lower milk-producing ability tend to have higher precalving and postcalving condition scores and may meet their nutritive requirements on pasture or good-quality grass or legume hay. Cows of superior milking ability tend to have lower body condition scores and may not be able to meet their requirements without a supplemental source of nutrients.

Nutritive requirements for lactation (Table 13-7) are greater than for any other phase of production. Requirements are affected by cow age, milk production potential, cow size, and stage of lactation (Fig. 13-8). The highest nutritive need occurs in early lactation, when milk flow is greatest. This time corresponds to prebreeding, and the breeding season; early conception is the primary objective.

TABLE 13-7

Total digestible nutrients and crude protein requirements by month for spring calving, mature, 1100-lb gestating or 1000-lb lactating cow of superior milking ability

Cow Weight, lb	Production Stage	Total Digestible Nutrients, %	Crude Protein, %
1100	Nonlactating, mid-gestation (Oct–Dec)	48.8	7.0
1100	Nonlactating, late gestation (Jan–March)	53.2	7.8
1000	Early lactation (April–June)	67.0	12.3
1000	Late lactation (July–September)	62.2	9.5

Source: Adapted from NRC (3).

In order to meet energy and protein needs of young superior milking cows and/or first-calf heifers, rations need to supply 60–65 percent TDN and 10–12 percent protein. High-quality pasture that is readily available is the only forage source that can supply these requirements. When feeding harvested feeds, it will be necessary to use a high-energy feed such as corn silage in order to raise ration TDN above 60 percent. A combination of corn silage and alfalfa or other sources of protein could be used (Table 13–8). Nutrition levels pre- and postcalving are closely related to those of return to estrus and conception. Young or thin cows are particularly susceptible to rebreeding problems. Nutritional status of the cow herd has been difficult to measure; however, body condition scoring (Table 13–3) has become an accepted means of predicting satisfactory reproduction.

Feeding and Nutritional Management

Feed continues to be the major cost item in cow-calf production. The economic efficiency of cow herds or individual animals within a herd can be estimated with the following formula (14):

$$\text{Economic efficiency} = \frac{\text{lb calf weaned} \times \text{weaning percentage} \times \text{price}}{\underset{(60\%)}{\text{feed costs}} + \underset{(20\%)}{\text{interest costs}} + \underset{(10\%)}{\text{labor costs}} + \underset{(10\%)}{\text{other costs}}}$$

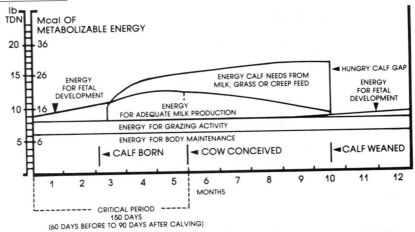

FIGURE 13–8. Estimated energy requirements of a mature 1100-lb beef cow with average milking ability during a 12-month reproductive cycle based on a 60-day calving season and a 500-lb calf at 205 days of age. Adapted by the author from Texas A&M University publication B 1044 (Fig. 2) and data from NRC (3).

TABLE 13-8

Rations for developing replacement heifers, gestating replacements, and lactating first-calf heifers

Ration 1.   600-lb Heifers Gaining 1–1.3 lb/d

Feed	Dry	As Fed	Protein	TDN	C A	P
Alfalfa hay	7.6	8.4	1.2	4.2	0.10	0.02
Corn silage	6.9	19.6	0.6	4.8	0.02	0.01
Dical phosphorus	0.03	0.03	—	—	0.01	0.01
	14.53	28.03	1.8	9.0	0.13	0.04

Ration 2.   600-lb Heifers Gaining 1–1.3 lb/d

Feed	Dry	As Fed	Protein	TDN	C A	P
Prairie hay	11.1	12.4	1.0	6.1	0.05	0.02
Corn	2.0	2.3	0.2	1.8	—	0.01
32% protein supp.	0.8	0.9	0.3	0.6	0.02	0.01
	13.9	15.6	1.5	8.5	0.07	0.04

Ration 3.   Gestating 1–2-Year-Olds, 0.5 lb Gain (plus fetal gain)

Feed	Dry	As Fed	Protein	TDN	C A	P
Alfalfa hay	14.3	15.8	2.6	8.4	0.20	0.03
Prairie hay	4.8	5.3	0.4	2.6	0.02	0.01
	19.1	21.1	3.0	11.0	0.22	0.04

Ration 4.   Lactating 2–3-Year-Olds, Average Milk, 0.5 lb Gain

Feed	Dry	As Fed	Protein	TDN	C A	P
Corn silage	11.2	32.0	0.9	7.7	0.03	0.02
Alfalfa hay	9.0	9.9	1.4	5.0	0.21	0.03
Dical phosphorus	0.1	0.1	—	—	0.02	0.02
	20.3	42.0	2.3	12.7	0.26	0.07

Producers must adapt their feeding and nutritional management program to complement the stage of animal production, available feeds, form in which feeds can be fed, equipment, and time schedule. Feeds available may change from year to year, and there may be wide variations in quality of forages (Fig. 13-9). Supplements may be fed when necessary to maintain optimum production and reproduction levels. Methods of feeding will vary with feeds available, weather, facilities, equipment, and labor.

The system of production used will affect feeding and nutritional management. The single most important factor is the time of calving, particularly where winters are more severe. Most cow herds are on a spring calving system with a 45–90 d breeding season starting about June 1. In a well-managed herd, 75–80 percent of the cows will calve between March 10 and April 10. Variations in breeding and calving require feeding and management adaptations. The suc-

FIGURE 13-9. Ammoniated wheat straw fed as the only forage source to cows in mid-late gestation.

cess of a nutrition-management program is measured primarily in terms of early conception, successful calving, and weight of calf weaned per cow exposed in the breeding pasture. Pregnan-

TABLE 13-9

Predicted probabilities of estrus and pregnancy for certain values of the variables selected by the logistic regression model[a]

Condition Score at Calving[b]	Calving Difficulty Score[c]	Change in Condition Score Postpartum[b]	Milk Category[d]	Predicted Probability	
				Estrus	Pregnancy
4.0	1.0	1.0	1	0.25	0.31
4.0	1.0	1.0	−1	0.49	0.52
5.0	1.0	1.0	1	0.77	0.68
5.0	1.0	1.0	−1	0.90	0.83
5.0	1.0	−1.0	1	0.25	0.25
5.0	1.0	−1.0	−1	0.48	0.45
5.0	3.0	1.0	1	0.46	0.34
5.0	3.0	1.0	−1	0.70	0.56
6.0	1.0	0.5	1	0.95	0.86
6.0	1.0	0.5	−1	0.98	0.94
6.0	1.0	−0.5	1	0.85	0.72
6.0	1.0	−0.5	−1	0.94	0.86
6.0	2.0	0.5	1	0.91	0.76
6.0	2.0	0.5	−1	0.97	0.87

[a]Predicted probability = (natural logarithm of a) ÷ (1 + natural logarithm of a) where a = Intercept + RC × condition score at calving + RC × change in condition score postpartum + RC × milk category + RC × calving difficulty score.

[b]1 = emaciated to 9 = obese.

[c]1 = unassisted to 3 = mechanical assistance.

[d]−1 = below and 1 = above, the mean level of milk production at 60 d.

Source: Goehring et al. (16).

cy probability as affected by cow condition, calving difficulty, postpartum condition change, and milk production is shown in Table 13–9.

Supplementation

Energy is most apt to be limiting when harvested feeds are being fed during seasons when pasture is not available. This problem becomes more acute when cow requirements are high due to factors such as cold weather, stage of reproduction, and lactation. The primary constituent of the cow's ration will be forage, with a range in quality from cereal straws at 40–45, grass hay 50–55, legume hay 52–57, and corn silage 65–70 percent TDN. First-calf heifers or superior milking cows have a peak TDN requirement of 65–67 percent, while mature cows in mid-gestation require only 48–50 percent (Appendix Table 12). To meet the energy needs of first-calf heifers or superior milking cows in early lactation, it will be necessary to add grain or a more highly digestible fiber such as soybean hulls to the ration.

The negative associative effect of starch on fiber digestion is an important factor in energy supplementation. The addition of small amounts of starch to a forage-type ration has, in some instances, slightly increased fiber digestibility. As additional starch is added to the diet, the rumen microbial population adapts by increasing starch-digesting bacteria and decreasing fiber-digesting bacteria. Athough fiber digestibility decreases, digestible dry-matter intake will rise as additional starch is added to the ration.

When it is necessary to supplement energy in a lactating cow ration, the effect of that energy source on fiber digestibility should be considered. Soybean hulls or corn bran may be available and will not significantly lower fiber digestibility of the forage. If grains are more economically priced, they can be used with some sacrifice of fiber utilization. Soyhulls and corn grain produced similar gains when added to a grass or cornstalk ration for steers or heifers (15). Producing higher-quality harvested forages by early cutting and better preservation should continue to be the goal of the cow-calf producer rather than relying on the addition of grain to high-roughage diets.

Energy will likely be adequate for lactating cows on pasture in early to mid-vegetative stages of growth (Fig. 13–10). As the pasture season progresses and forage quality decreases, the cow's requirements also decrease. Late summer grass may fail to meet the cow's energy requirement; however, she should be pregnant by that time and be carrying sufficient body condition so that a limited energy deficiency is not

FIGURE 13-10. Three-year-old cows with their second calf.

a major problem. If postweaning nutrition is adequate, a body condition score of 5.0–6.0 should be acceptable for a cow in late lactation.

Protein is frequently deficient in the forage available for the cow herd. Growing pastures (grass or legume-grass mixtures) will normally be adequate sources of protein during all stages of production. As plants mature, the protein level they provide drops below cow requirements. Although cow-calf performance can be enhanced by protein supplementation on mature grasses, it is seldom done due to limited response, cost, and labor required. Mature grasses will have dropped to 6–8 percent protein by weaning time, with the cow's requirement 7–8 percent as a dry cow in mid-gestation. As quality deteriorates due to weathering and selective grazing, the cow will respond to supplemental protein. Mature grass, low-quality hay, and crop residues are usually deficient in protein, with normal ranges of 3–8 percent. Since these feeds are used primarily in mid-gestation for the spring-calving cow, need for supplemental protein is not great; however, these feeds should be supplemented with protein as needed and when economic response will justify it.

Fall-winter grazing of crop residues such as cornstalks or grain sorghum stubble provides an adequate source of both energy and protein until the more palatable parts of the plant have been selectively grazed or lost due to trampling or weather (17). If cows are rotated to fresh fields for grazing, they will not need supplementation as long as adequate forage is available. Daily gains of 1–2 lb are common on fresh row-crop residues (18). Grain availability, particularly in cornstalks, is normally in the 3–5 bushel/acre range and may be much higher. The supply of grain may approach ad libitum consumption early in the grazing season. The quantity of supplemental protein needed may vary from none

early in the grazing period to 0.5 lb/hd/d as available grain decreases and forage quality drops.

Protein supplements fall into two categories, natural and NPN sources (see Ch. 8). The need for rumen ammonia can be met by any rumen-degradable source; however, NPN sources such as urea may be too rapidly broken down for efficient use of nitrogen. The best combination of supplemental protein would furnish adequate rumen ammonia for maximum fiber digestion with the remainder of the protein bypassing the rumen but being digested in the small intestine with a desirable amino acid profile. Adequate rumen ammonia is necessary for maximizing intake digestibility of forage (19). Supplements need to supply adequate rumen ammonia if the remainder of the ration is too low in protein or has protein resistant to rumen degradation. A combination of urea with a high-bypass protein source may be most efficient. Calculations based on metabolizable protein are useful. Sources of natural proteins with a low to medium degree of bypass include soybean meal, cottonseed meal, peanut meal, and linseed meal (20). These proteins, depending upon processing techniques, will usually have less than 40 percent bypass. Because they are readily rumen-degradable, they do not make a good combination with urea because of the high rumen ammonia peak associated with rapid breakdown. Sources with higher bypass such as blood meal, feather meal, corn gluten meal, and distillers grains (see Ch. 8) make excellent ingredients to combine with urea because they do not contribute greatly to rumen ammonia levels. The blood amino acid profile is a combination of microbial amino acids and bypass amino acids, thus it becomes much more important to have bypass sources of high biological value or that are complementary to the microbial amino acid profile.

Methods of Supplementing Protein

Traditional supplementation of the range cow with protein occurred as range cube feeding on a daily or two- or three-times-weekly basis. Factors to consider are cost, convenience, and nutritional adequacy. In most instances a protein deficiency in the nonlactating cow can be corrected by improving forage quality of the ration. If weathered grass or crop residues are the main or only forage source available, it may be economically feasible to feed a protein supplement. Legume hay is frequently the cheapest source of protein available and will also supply additional energy, minerals, and possibly vitamin A.

Protein blocks or tubs varying in size from 33 to 50 lb can be used for self-feeding a protein source. These sources may contain a wide variety of ingredients but frequently have ¼ to ⅓ of the protein equivalent supplied by urea. Producers need to determine the cost/lb of protein equivalent, calculate the usefulness of urea in the supplement, check consumption levels to avoid overconsumption, and be aware of the potential for urea toxicity if improperly managed. Urea containing supplements need to be provided daily to minimize chances for overconsumption and to avoid high rumen ammonia peaks associated with large amounts of readily degradable nitrogen sources. Lick tanks with a molasses-based liquid supplement are filled directly from the dealer's truck with cattle allowed free access to the supplement (Fig. 13–11). Concerns similar to those mentioned for block feeding exist. The primary advantage for self-fed supplements is the saving in labor.

Cow performance is usually better on natural supplements than when using supplements with a high crude protein equivalent from an NPN source with liquid supplement (16, 21, 22). Overconsumption of a urea-based supplement could cause toxicity and results in inefficient use of nitrogen. Overconsumption of natural protein supplements also results in inefficient use of nitrogen; however, excess protein can be deaminated and used as an energy source.

Fall Calving

Many cow-calf producers have part or all of their herd in a fall calving program with calves dropped primarily in August, September, and October. The major advantage of fall calving is better weather with fewer calf losses. The primary disadvantage is the need for high-quality harvested forage due to limited availability of growing pasture. Fall-calved cows have similar requirements compared to spring-calved cows but they may have higher energy needs if cold weather is a problem. Producers with fall pasture, crop residue grazing, and adequate facilities may adopt fall calving with options including early weaning of calves at 4–5 months of age and movement of calves directly into the feedlot rather than returning them to summer pasture.

Grazing

The beef cow herd should be grazed when possible to lower inputs and costs of production. Year-round grazing may be possible in the southern United States with increased use of stockpiled and/or harvested forage further north. All pastures in the United States are seasonal; however, northern states may have less than 5 months of good pasture grazing. Intensive pasture rotation (short-duration grazing) can be used to increase production/acre. Various systems have been devised which involve higher initial stocking rates and more intensive management. These systems are particularly effective on monocultures of grass which can be managed to take advantage of quality and quantity parameters of grass growth. Although requiring additional investments in fencing and water supply, various forms of intensive grazing are being used throughout the country. Use of cool- and warm-season grasses along with row-crop residues can extend the grazing season from May to December or later, if snow cover is not

FIGURE 13–11. Spring calving cows in mid-gestation grazing cornstalks with a liquid supplement.

severe, in much of the Midwest (17). Crop residues can extend the grazing season and are most important in the row-crop areas producing corn and grain sorghum. These crops can supply 1½ animal unit months of grazing/acre if fully utilized (22).

SUMMARY

Many factors interact in nutritional management of the beef cow herd, including cow size, milk producing ability, cow age, cow breed, stage of gestation, stage of lactation, date of calving, weather, feedstuff quality, feedstuff availability, feedstuff cost, and grazing opportunities. All of these factors must be considered in planning a program for the cow herd. In addition to the more traditional questions involving nutrition-management of the cow herd, tomorrow's producer will need to be aware of other factors that affect the profitability of the operation. Some of these include: (a) use of the computer for record keeping, enterprise analysis, and modeling, (b) modifying breeding and management programs to meet the needs of feedlot operators and packers, and (c) being aware of the trends in the industry relating to supply and demand for beef, consumer desires, and export needs. The challenge to cow-calf producers is to develop a program to take advantage of whatever factors are in their favor or that they can manipulate to achieve a more efficient operation than that of their competitors in the cow-calf enterprise.

REFERENCES

1. Gosey, J. 1986. Matching cattle to forage resources. *Proc. NE Forage and Grasslands Council*: 5.
2. Clanton, D. C. 1980. *Proc. Third Inter. Min. Conf.* Miami, FL.
3. NRC. 1984. *Nutrient requirements of beef cattle.* Washington, D.C.: Nat. Acad. Press.
4. Goodrich, R. D., et al. 1978. *Natl. Feed Ingred. Assoc.* Des Moines, IA.
5. Greene, L. W. 1983. *J. Animal Sci.* 57:503.
6. Church, D. C., ed. 1988. *The ruminant animal. Digestive physiology and nutrient metabolism.* Englewood Cliffs, NJ: Prentice Hall.
7. Deutscher, G. H. 1975. *South Dakota Cow-Calf Field Day Proc.* AS-75:72.
8. Morrison, D. G., J. I. Feazel, and C. P. Bagley. 1985. *Louisiana Livestock Report.*
9. Wetteman, R. P., et al. 1986. *Oklahoma Animal Sci. Res. Rpt.* MP 118:314.
10. Whittier, J. C., et al. 1986. *Nebraska Beef Rpt.* MP 50.
11. Selk, G. E., et al. 1988. *J. Animal Sci.* 66:3153.
12. Wagner, J. J., et al. 1988. *J. Animal Sci.* 66:603.
13. Hancock, K. L., et al. 1985. *Okla. Animal Sci. Res. Rept.* MP 117:180.
14. Doornbos, D. E. 1986. *Montana Agricultural Research,* Spring-Summer:22.
15. Anderson, S. J., J. K. Merrill, and T. J. Klopfenstein. 1988. *J. Animal Sci.* 66:2959.
16. Goehring, T., et al. 1987. Cattlemen's day. *K-State Report of Progress* 514:55.
17. Lamm, W. D., and J. K. Ward. 1981. *J. Animal Sci.* 52:954.
18. Ward, J. K. 1978. *J. Animal Sci.* 46:831.
19. Guthrie, M. J., and D. G. Wagner. 1988. *J. Animal Sci.* 66:1529.
20. Stock, R., et al. 1981. *J. Animal Sci.* 53:1109.
21. Clanton, D. C. 1970. *Proc. Texas Nutrition Conference* 25:131.
22. Lamm, W. D., J. K. Ward, and G. C. White. 1977. *J. Animal Sci.* 45:1231.

14

Feeding Growing-Finishing Beef Cattle

Terry J. Klopfenstein, Rick Stock, and John K. Ward

INTRODUCTION

There are an almost infinite number of ways to feed beef cattle from weaning to market. Cool- and/or warm-season grasses are available in most of the United States in the summer, and a variety of pastures are available in southern areas in the winter. Crop residues, hay, and silages are available in the northern areas. However, in the United States, much of the animal's postweaning gain is the result of grain feeding (Fig. 14–1). Grain supplies in the Corn Belt states are in surplus and usually represent an economical energy supply for cattle.

The combinations of forage and grain that can be used to feed cattle are numerous. Also, the variation in cattle types in the United States has increased dramatically in the past few years. We have extremes from heifers weighing 800–1000 lb at low choice grade to steers weighing 1300–1400 lb (Table 14–1) at the same grade and degree of fatness. The packing industry has moved rapidly to boxed beef with an acceptable carcass range of 600–800 lb.

The feeding system interacts with cattle type to produce various carcass weights at low

FIGURE 14–1. A confinement feeding facility which has some advantages during periods of severe winter weather.

choice grade. Cattle with similar growth potential that are grown on roughages prior to finishing on grain are older at market time (low choice grade) and may have heavier carcasses (Table 14–2). This is because they have developed further along their growth curve and have had the opportunity to make more skeletal and muscle growth prior to fattening.

While variation in mature size of beef cattle has increased, feed efficiency of cattle taken

258

TABLE 14-1

Expected live weights at low choice grade

Breed Type	Weight Range (lb)		Feeder-Grade Frame Type
Small-frame British breeds	800–1000	640–800	Small
Average-frame British breeds	1000–1100	800–880	Medium
Large-frame British breeds	1100–1200	880–960	Medium
Average-frame European breeds & Holsteins	1200–1300	960–1040	Large
Large-frame European breeds	1300–1500	1040–1200	Large

Source: Thomas (1).

TABLE 14-2

Effect of frame score on steer performance in Kansas futurities

	Frame Score							
	1	2	3	4	5	6	7	8
Number of steers	22	127	305	526	593	483	203	56
Yearling hip height, in.	37–39	39–41	41–43	43–45	45–47	47–49	49–51	51–53
Starting weight, lb	496	536	576	602	641	683	706	752
Average daily gain, lb	2.58	2.75	2.84	3.08	3.24	3.37	3.43	3.50
Quality grade[a]	7.3	7.2	7	6.8	6.7	6.5	6.4	6.1
Carcass weight, lb	571	605	634	672	716	757	777	801
Dressing percent	61.3	61.3	61.1	61.1	61.2	61.2	61.1	61.0
Fat thickness, in.	0.42	0.44	0.44	0.42	0.39	0.37	0.32	0.31
Rib-eye area, in.^{2}	11.9	11.9	12.1	12.8	13.4	13.7	13.9	14.3
Yield grade	2.5	2.6	2.6	2.5	2.4	2.4	2.2	2.2
Days fed	172	166	165	162	163	165	167	162

[a]6 = USDA high good, 7 = USDA low choice.

Source: Lambert (2).

to the same degree of fatness probably has not. Efficiencies of feed conversion are primarily affected by composition of gain rather than mature weight. Therefore, the current trend to try to produce uniform cattle is not really necessary. The important point is to match the feeding system to the cattle type so as to produce cattle with acceptable weights at the low choice grade. As a generalization, as frame size decreases

(mature weight potential), more roughage should be fed to the animal to avoid overfinish at an acceptable carcass weight (Table 14–3).

The more difficult market requirement to meet is low choice grade combined with yield grade 1 or 2. The correlation of external fat to marbling is quite high. We feed grain to cattle to fatten them. The desirable fat is marbling (intramuscular fat), while outside fat is waste-

TABLE 14-3

Steer performance and efficiency as affected by added gain

	Days on Feed		
	218	249	279
Av. daily gain (ADG), lb	2.45	2.39	2.32
Adjusted ADG, lb[a]	2.44	2.46 (2.58)	2.42 (2.28)
TDN/gain	6.10	6.27 (7.39)	6.41 (7.47)
Final adjusted wt., lb	1008	1088	1151
Dressing, %	60.2	61.1	61.7
Quality grade	11.6	12.1	12.3
Yield grade	3.2	3.7	3.9
Fat cover, in.	0.56	0.65	0.72

[a]Adjusted to equal dressing percentage.

Source: USMARC (3).

ful. We can make cattle as lean as desired without growth promotants or repartitioning agents, simply by feeding more roughage and less grain. However, no magic method exists for consistently producing low choice, yield grade 2 cattle. Until genetic changes occur or a specific repartitioning agent is developed to produce low choice, yield grade 2 cattle, we can only feed for the average, which is choice 2s and 3s with the majority as 3s.

Packers usually discount carcasses that grade select with a yield grade of 4 and 5. The goal of the cattle feeder is to minimize these discounts and cost of gain. Fat is more expensive to produce than muscle, because of the water content of the muscle. Therefore, cost of gain increases with increasing time on grain feed as the cattle fatten. Cattle were 20 percent less efficient when fed to increase fat cover from 0.56 to 0.65 inches (Table 14–3). Quality and yield grade increased with greater fat cover. Cattle should be marketed on a timely basis to avoid overfinishing and declining feed efficiency. The relative discounts for the select grade and yield grades 4 and 5 will affect marketing decisions.

The beef industry is also facing a critical economic challenge. Profitability has been variable at best and often low or nonexistent. One problem is competition from lower-cost meats, primarily poultry and pork. While promotion may sell more beef, especially in the short run, it seems that cost of production must be reduced if the beef enterprise is to remain competitive and profitable. The ultimate goal of beef production systems is to produce product suitable to meet market demand, utilizing available resources and at a price sufficient to encourage further production and consumption.

MAJOR GROWING-FINISHING SYSTEMS

Cattle, because of their ability to utilize fiber, are competitive with other species only when fed forage. The trend of the beef industry has been the opposite direction in the past 30+ years with more grain fed (including that in corn silage). It seems that the beef industry has two primary directions it can take. We will refer to them as high-grain and high-forage systems of production.

High-Grain or High-Forage Systems

In the high-grain system, calves would be placed on high-grain rations after an adjustment period of approximately 30 d after weaning. This system would likely be restricted to exotic cross steers and/or bulls. It is important to note here that these animals will reach the necessary fatness to grade choice 50–200 lb lighter than the same animals grown in a high-forage system. This is an advantage for these rapidly gaining, large, mature-weight animals, because their carcass weights will not be too large for the packer and therefore will not be discounted. A disadvantage is that less beef is marketed per cow and therefore the cost of keeping the cow must be covered with fewer pounds of beef. The primary advantage to the high-grain system is the rapid and efficient rate of gain, which reduces interest and yardage costs. Using some corn silage in this system does not really help the economics, because the price of silage should be based on the price of the grain in the silage.

A high-forage system has the obvious disadvantages of higher interest costs and relatively higher yardage costs when the animals are fed forage in the feedlot. To compensate for this, feed cost must be reduced considerably. The following are some principles which we need to be aware of in designing high-forage systems:

A. Animal harvesting (grazing) is economical. The high cost of fuel, equipment, and labor indicates that this will be more of a factor in the future.

B. Crop residues are always cheaper to produce than conventional forages because the cost of production (land, fertilizer, and the like) is charged against the grain. Admittedly, harvesting costs may be high for crop residues, but conventional forages must be harvested as well and the cost may be nearly as great.

C. Grasses should primarily be grazed, not harvested. Some harvesting may be needed to provide winter forage and to meet supplemental needs.

D. There will be a premium on lean growth in beef cattle, not for fat.

E. Beef cattle must be finished on grain to have an acceptable amount of fat (quality) to meet present U.S. market demands and receive a reasonable market price.

F. Cattle make excellent compensatory gain during the early stages of finishing following high-forage feeding.

Because carcasses are discounted heavily unless they are in an acceptable weight range, cattle used in the high-forage system would likely be heifers and British breed steers. About 40 percent of the cattle fed in feedlots are heifers. In addition, many British breed steers are produced from first- and second-calf cows even if exotic terminal cross sires are to be used later. Therefore, one would expect that over half of the beef animals produced in the future will be of a frame size that will fit the high-forage system.

As winter rates of gain increase, summer gains decrease (Table 14–4). Increasing the length of the growing phase increases carcass weights at similar finish. Cost of gain is lowest for the high-grain system; however, compensatory gain enhances the competitiveness of the high-forage production system. An economic accounting model was developed to aid the understanding of biological and economic relationships and to study the impact of variation in resource costs on returns through different

TABLE 14-4

Performance and carcass characteristics of cattle from different production systems—two years' data

Item	System 1 Grain	System 2 Corn Silage Grain	System 3 LQ Residue Grain	System 3 MQ Residue Grain	System 4 LQ Residue Grass Grain	System 4 MQ Residue Grass Grain	SE[a]
Winter phase							
Initial wt., lb		508	492	495	491	488	4
Days		133	137	137	137	137	
Gain, lb/d[b]		2.04	0.44	0.89	0.50	0.96	0.02
Summer grass—grazing phase							
Initial wt., lb					554	612	10
Final wt., lb					756	788	11
Days					143	143	
Gain, lb/day[c]					1.42	1.24	0.05
Grain finishing phase							
Initial wt., lb	514	781	549	610	756	788	9
Final wt., lb[d]	1024	1027	1054	1030	1087	1112	29
Days	197	94	156	132	121	107	29
Gain, lb/d[e]	2.64	2.80	3.31	3.26	2.84	3.04	0.23
DMI, lb/d[f]	15.3	18.8	19.3	19.8	20.4	22.1	0.9
DMI, % of BW[g]	1.99	2.08	2.42	2.42	2.22	2.31	
Feed/Gain[h]	5.81	6.71	5.85	6.06	7.25	7.14	
Carcass characteristics							
Total retail product, lb[i]	464	467	479	469	475	502	9
Ribeye area in.^{2}	11.2	11.3	11.5	11.2	11.2	11.1	0.2
Yield grade[j]	3.0	3.0	2.9	3.0	3.1	3.3	0.1
Quality grade[k]	5.4	5.8	5.6	5.4	4.8	5.1	0.1
Percent choice[l]	59.3	74.7	74.7	71.8	40.1	62.4	7.9

Finishing performance data, excluding initial weight, are expressed on an equal fat basis (steers, 0.44 in.; heifers, 0.62 in.; 12th rib fat). Carcass data are expressed on an equal fat basis (0.53 in. 12th rib fat). Corrections to a common fatness were made using subclass linear regressions. LQ and MQ denote Low Quality and Medium Quality, respectively.

[a]Standard error.
[b]System 2 vs. 3, 4 (P < 0.01). For systems 3 and 4, main effect of winter growth rate (LQ vs. MQ, P < 0.01).
[c]Means differ (P = 0.01).
[d]System 3 vs. 4 (P = 0.07).
[e]System 1 vs. 3, 4 (P = 0.08).
[f]System 1 vs. 3, 4 (P = 0.01). System 3 vs. 4 (P = 0.07).
[g]System 1 vs. 3, 4 (P = 0.01). System 2 vs. 3, 4 (P = 0.02).
[h]System 3 vs. 4 (P = 0.03). Feed/Gain calculated as reciprocal of Gain/Feed. Statistics were done on Gain/Feed.
[i]System 1 vs. 3, 4 (P = 0.06). System 2 vs. 3, 4 (P = 0.12). Winter growth rate × grass grazing interaction for Systems 3 and 4 (P = 0.05).
[j]Main effect of winter growth rate for systems 3 and 4 (LA vs. MA, P = 0.05). System 3 vs. 4 (P = 0.01).
[k]High good = 4; low choice = 5. System 2 vs. 3, 4 (P < 0.01). System 3 vs. 4 (P < 0.01).
[l]System 3 vs. 4 (P = 0.01).
Source: Turgeon et al. (4).

production systems. The model compared production costs and breakevens of cattle finished immediately after weaning (high-grain system) to those of cattle grown on forage diets prior to finishing. Two experiments were conducted to establish a biological basis for the model. One experiment was designed to compare intensive versus extensive growing-finishing systems. A second experiment was designed to evaluate the effect of wintering rate of gain on total system performance (4).

Intensive versus Extensive Systems

Three successive spring-born calf crops from 136 British breed cows and Charolais bulls were weaned at an average age of 187 d and utilized to evaluate the two systems. After an initial 30-d period to allow adjustment to weaning, the cattle were randomly allotted to either an intensive system, where they were placed directly into the feedlot for finishing on a high-grain diet (Figs. 14–2, 14–3), or to an extensive system, where they were grown on high-forage diets prior to finishing. Cattle in the intensive system were adjusted to a high-grain diet over 21 d and then finished an additional 185 d. Cattle in the extensive system were wintered on crop residues (165 d), grazed in the summer (115 d), and then finished in the feedlot (122 d) in the same manner as cattle in the intensive system.

Wintering Systems

Eighty mixed British breed steers (587 lb) were used each year for 2 years to evaluate winter-

FIGURE 14–2. Cattle using shades in a large commercial feedlot in the southwestern United States. (Courtesy of D. C. Church.)

FIGURE 14–3. A conveyor-auger feed distribution system which can be used for automated feeding in small feedlots.

ing systems (20 hd/system/year). This experiment had two objectives: to determine what level of performance could be expected with the different wintering systems, and to establish three different levels of wintering gain in order to evaluate the effect of wintering rate of gain on subsequent performance. For the second objective only three of the four systems were continued beyond the end of the wintering phase each year.

Across both years, six different wintering systems were evaluated utilizing harvested crop residues supplemented with different levels of escape protein and alfalfa hay, as well as cornstalk grazing supplemented with harvested crop residue and protein supplement or alfalfa hay (5). In addition to these six wintering systems, performance from two other systems was included in the model: (A) cornstalk grazing supplemented with supplemental protein, and (B) all alfalfa hay.

Within this experiment, three rates of wintering gain (0.62, 0.84, and 1.1 lb/d, average of 2 years' data) were established to evaluate the effect of wintering performance on subsequent performance. After wintering (106 d), cattle were grazed on pasture (116 d) and then finished in the feedlot (112 d).

Increased wintering gain decreased summer gain so that upon entering the feedlot, cattle weighed the same. Therefore, any increase in wintering cost decreased the economic feasibility of the system. Variable costs such as corn price, interest rate, and purchase price affected both systems similarly, while fixed costs such as wintering yardage and finishing yardage affected systems differently. Increases in wintering yardage favored intensive systems while increases in finishing yardage favored extensive systems. The greatest benefit of extensive systems is increased total product per animal unit. This increased product dilutes the cost of the feeder calf, which yields a lower breakeven price. Cattle finished after being grown on high-forage diets finished at a faster rate but consumed almost as much feed as those that were finished immediately after weaning. Extensive systems produced beef at lower cost per unit product except in times of very low cost grain relative to other inputs (interest, feeder cattle, and so on) or high wintering costs (Table 14–5).

The opportunities to use forages in beef growing-finishing systems are numerous, and the economic benefits can accrue to those who are innovative enough to design and manage them. Because of the diversity of such systems, we will not further discuss grazing systems. The following discussion will focus on the situation when cattle are placed in a feedlot.

FEEDLOT SITUATIONS

Receiving Diets

Prior to entering the feedlot, calves or yearlings normally would have been fed primarily roughage; therefore, receiving diets should be forage-based. The cattle are usually stressed when arriving at the feedlot because of transportation, lack of feed, handling, and weaning. Good nutrition as soon as possible after arrival is important to health maintenance and a good start in the feedlot.

Feed intake is a most important factor for incoming cattle. It is necessary to avoid feeds that are unpalatable or which the animal is not familiar with, such as silages and moldy and coarse roughages. Protein supplements containing urea and protein sources such as blood meal or fish meal should also be minimized. Because intake may be low the first few days after arrival, the concentration of several nutrients—energy, protein, and K—should be increased (6).

Energy can be supplied by grains, but the possibility of acidosis exists. Highly digestible fibers such as soybean hulls, corn bran, and corn gluten feed make excellent components in receiving diets because they supply energy essentially equal to grains without presenting the danger of acidosis. They are also very palatable as long as dust is controlled.

Protein is necessary for meeting the ruminal microbial needs and the needs of the body for amino acids. Rumen-degradable protein should be fed to a point, but high-bypass (escape)

TABLE 14-5

Cattle performance affected by winter rate of gain

Item	Winter Gain		
	Low	Med	High
Weight, lb			
Initial	525	513	527
End of winter[a]	592	602	642
End of pasture	755	744	762
Final[a,b]	1159	1163	1193
Daily gain, lb			
Winter[a]	0.62	0.84	1.09
Pasture[a]	1.41	1.24	1.03
Finish	3.62	3.74	3.84
Finishing daily feed, lb	26.35	26.41	27.20
Feed/gain[c]	7.30	7.09	7.09
Carcass data			
Hot car. wt, lb	719	721	740
Fat, in.	0.49	0.45	0.43
Quality grade[d]	7.24	7.27	7.24
Yield grade	2.71	2.78	2.80

[a]Linear effect (P < 0.05).
[b]Based on carcass weight adjusted to a 62% dress.
[c]Feed/gain was analyzed as gain/feed. Reported feed/gain is reciprocal of feed/gain.
[d]Low choice = 7.17, average choice = 7.5.
Source: Lewis et al. (5).

protein sources offer good opportunities to get amino acids to the animal (see later discussion on this topic).

Step-up Diets

The phrase "putting cattle on feed" refers to the process of changing from a predominately forage to a predominately grain diet in the feedlot, because not only is the ration changing but other physical and environmental stresses are occurring. This is perhaps the most critical period nutritionally for finishing cattle. The microbial population is shifting from one of fiber digesters to one of starch digesters. Ruminal pH may drop dramatically, and both acute and subacute acidosis may be experienced by the animal. Feed intake usually increases but also may vary markedly from day to day. Finally, and perhaps most important, the animals shift from control of intake by distention to control by chemostatic factors.

There are numerous methods used to put cattle on feed. The most common in feedlots is the use of 3 or 4 step-up rations. Commonly, these step-up rations contain about 35, 55, and 75 percent concentrate (grain plus supplement), with the final finishing diet about 90 percent concentrate. These levels of concentrate are guides and not intended as absolute numbers. The ration with 35 percent concentrate is commonly referred to as the receiving diet, but in some cases step-up 1 and the receiving diets may be different, with the receiving diet frequently an unchopped high-quality hay.

Cattle are most efficient (in energy utilization) in the feedlot when fed the finishing diet. Therefore, it is economically desirable to move the cattle to the finishing diet as rapidly as possible. Four to five days on each step-up ration is about the minimum feasible time. With problem cattle, the receiving diet may be fed up to 10–14 d, until consumption meets expectations and health problems have been solved. Problem cattle may need 7–10 d per step-up ration.

The change to the next-higher-concentrate diet is usually made abruptly on a given day. It is critically important that the bunks not be clean (or slick) the day of ration changes. If the cattle are hungry, they will overconsume the next-higher-concentrate diet and will likely develop some degree of acidosis. In some feedlots the change is made at the second feeding for the day.

As cattle move through the series of step-up diets to the final finishing diet, their eating pattern changes (Fig. 14–4). On the receiving diet and the first step-up diet (55 percent concentrate), the cattle consume much of the feed soon after feeding in a meal-eating pattern. Usually, when the second step-up diet is fed (75 percent concentrate), the cattle consume the diet rapidly and in some excess. They usually experience mild acidosis, and the intake pattern changes the second day on this diet. Then cattle consume the diet at a slower rate and often consume a smaller total amount. Intake may increase gradually to day 5. When switched to the 90 percent finishing diet, the cattle may again eat too rapidly and in some excess. They will likely experience mild acidosis again. The following day the cattle will nibble instead of eating meals, thus spreading the intake over the day. This is the animal's response to acidosis and effectively minimizes the reoccurrence of acidosis.

During the process of being put on feed the animals must learn to nibble instead of eating meals, to minimize acidosis. They also must learn to respond to chemostatic intake control mechanisms. As nutritionists and feedlot managers, it is our job to help the animals through this learning period and minimize the chances of acute acidosis, which may have long-term detrimental effects on cattle performance (burned cattle). Observation of the cattle and proper bunk reading is critical during this period.

The same process of putting cattle on feed can be achieved by varying the diet each day. For example, the cattle may be fed 6–8 lb of concentrate/d during the receiving period. When they are ready to be moved to higher concentrate levels, 1 lb of concentrate can be added to the diet per animal each day with a proportionate amount of roughage removed. When the animals are consuming 14–16 lb of concentrate/d, it may be advisable to increase at the rate of 0.5 lb concentrate/d thereafter until the animals leave some grain in the bunk. At that point the cattle are on feed. This method requires close observation and daily judgment about the porportion of concentrate and roughage to feed. If the diet change is well managed, cattle may be placed on feed with very minimal acidosis. However, such flexible feeding is not easily dictated by computer programs and does not fit into the highly structured systems used in most feedlots.

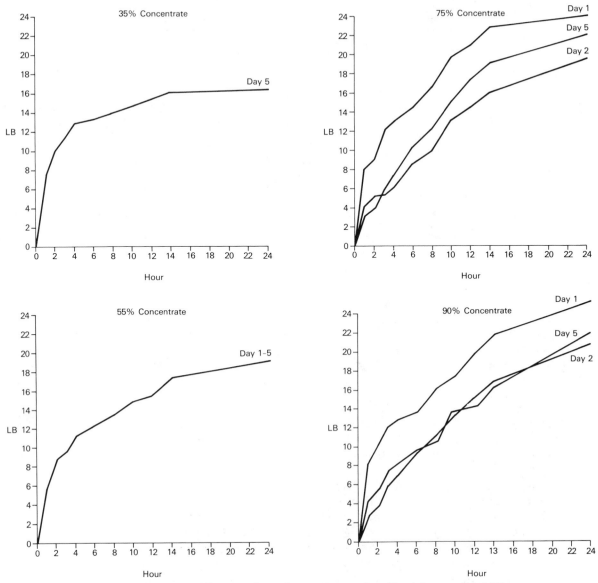

FIGURE 14-4. Changes in eating patterns of cattle going on feed (7).

Roughage in Finishing Diets

Roughages have important functions in growing diets, receiving diets, and step-up diets as sources of nutrients. However, the use of roughages in the final finishing diet is primarily to control digestive disturbances by making the diet less dense and not as a source of nutrients. These digestive disturbances include subacute acidosis, liver abscesses, bloat, and rumen parakeratosis. Advanced stages of rumen parakeratosis include sloughing of papilli, hemorrhaging, and matted and abscessed papilli. Absorption of the primary energy sub-

strates (volatile fatty acids) will be reduced markedly.

There are several reasons why we want to minimize roughage in the finishing diet. Roughages are difficult to handle mechanically and may cause added expenses related to hauling, chopping, and mixing compared to concentrates. Usually, net energy can be supplied in the feed bunk more cheaply from grain than from roughage. The emphasis in feedlots is to maximize rate of gain and to minimize interest and yardage costs.

The alternative to feeding roughage in the finishing diet is the feeding of an all-concentrate

TABLE 14-6

Effect of various levels of roughage

	% Roughage		
	15	5	0
No. head	14	14	14
Initial wt, lb	705	695	705
Final wt, lb	1123	1146	1090
Adjusted daily gain[a], lb	3.14	3.34	2.89
Adjusted feed/lb gain, lb	8.34	6.98	7.44
Daily feed consumption, lb	26.2	23.3	21.5
Carcass grade score[b]	17	16.7	16.7
Dressing percent[a]	60.4	60	60.4
Condemned livers, %	7.14	21.4	57.1

[a]Daily gains calculated by adjusting final weight in order to give equal dressing percent for hot carcass weight. Sixty-two percent was yield for calculating final live weight from hot carcass weight.

[b]16 = high good, 17 = low choice.

Source: Woods et al. (8). 134 day feed trial.

diet. Cattle fed 0, 5, or 15 percent roughage will eat more feed and gain more rapidly when fed the 5 percent diet (Table 14–6). Feed efficiency will be improved by feeding both 5 and 15 percent roughage. This suggests that the roughage was utilized with greater efficiency than the grain was; however, this is not possible. Digestibility data indicate that fiber digestion in the rumen of cattle fed finishing diets is near zero because of negative associative effects, likely due to low ruminal pH. The most likely explanation for the response in efficiency, intake, and gain is that the roughage controlls digestive disturbances mentioned previously. It may be expensive to include in the diet, but roughage acts as insurance against digestive disturbances which can lead to depressed cattle performance. A good target level of roughage in the finishing diet is 10 percent of the dry matter as good-quality roughage such as alfalfa hay or corn silage. Several factors might lead one to decrease this amount of roughage: (A) use of lower-quality roughage so that the same amount of fiber is used; (B) use of ionophores which appear to reduce the incidence of acidosis; (C) excellent management of bunk reading, feed mixing, feed delivery, and feedlot conditions, or (D) short-fed cattle.

Some factors may also lead us to recommend higher levels of roughage. These include: (A) poor management; (B) inexpensive roughage; (C) heifers that are cycling; (D) changing weather conditions [such as cold fronts in the winter or very hot days followed by cool nights] that might cause cattle to overeat; and (E) long feeding period, such as that for calves.

Because of the universal use of ionophores, it is quite possible that the need for roughage in the finishing diet has changed. Recent research with all-concentrate diets containing an ionophore suggests that no roughage is needed. This has been demonstrated by improved feed conversions for the all-concentrate fed cattle compared to those fed roughage. The need for roughage likely interacts with the grain source. Those grain sources with rapid rates of digestion may still require some roughage. Conversely, grains with slow rates of digestion, such as grain sorghum, may benefit the most from lower roughage levels.

The use of buffers such as sodium bicarbonate in diets to counteract the effects of acidosis has been moderately effective, particularly early in the feeding period (9). Cattle being put on feed rapidly with highly fermentable rations show the greatest response.

Roughage in the finishing diet likely affects rate of passage, perhaps through the intestinal tract as well as from the rumen. The rate of passage when cattle are fed all-concentrate diets is quite slow. Roughage stimulates the rate of passage. A rapid rate of passage would be expected to reduce rumen residence time and acidosis, and would shift the site of starch digestion toward the small intestine. This would be advantageous for rapidly digested grains. Conversely, the slow rate of passage with no roughage would benefit a slowly digested grain such as grain sorghum by increasing total tract residence time and overall digestibility.

For cattle fed 80–120 d, all-concentrate

FIGURE 14–5. A heifer showing stiff forelegs and foundered front feet, both conditions typical aftereffects of acidosis. (Courtesy of D. C. Church.)

diets are probably the most efficiently utilized, unless wheat or barley are fed. However, there is a greater risk of acidosis involved with feeding all-concentrate diets. Roughage in the finishing diet is management insurance. As with most insurance, there is a cost involved. The cost benefit ratio must be weighed against the other aspects of feedlot management such as customer retention.

Acidosis

The most important nutritional consideration for cattle on finishing diets is acidosis (Fig. 14–5). Many nutritionists and feedlot managers might disagree, but we believe that many of their management techniques are in fact aimed at controlling acidosis. Cattle seldom die from acidosis in the feedlot, however reduced performance may be very expensive.

Acidosis results from the accumulation of organic acids in the rumen due to rapid fermentation of carbohydrates. This is almost always the result of consumption of starch (in grain) in a relatively short time period. Acute acidosis is the result of excess consumption (probably in excess of 2 percent of body weight) of grain in 1 to 2 h. Rumen pH drops below 5.5 and lactic acid accumulates. Rumen pH may drop as low as 4.5, rumen stasis occurs, and severe damage to rumen papilli may follow. In severe cases, ulceration of the rumen wall may occur. When enough acid is absorbed into the bloodstream, metabolic acidosis occurs and death may result. Diarrhea usually results if the animals survive.

More commonly, cattle experience subacute acidosis. Rumen pH drops below 5.6, but prob-

ably not much below that point, and lactate may not accumulate. The cattle adjust to the low pH by reducing feed intake. It is our experience that cattle attempt to adjust eating patterns to maintain rumen pH at 5.6 or above.

Reduced feed intake is the most common signal for subacute acidosis. While other factors, such as water availability, may influence feed intake, any time cattle are on finishing rations and feed intakes are below normal, one should look for causes of subacute acidosis. These might include starch fermentability of the grain, roughage level in the diet, poor feed bunk management, and adverse feedlot conditions.

Occasionally, cattle will gradually increase intake until they experience subacute acidosis followed by 1 or 2 days of low feed intakes. It is common for many cattle to exhibit this type of intake cycle. If there are 200 cattle in a pen, individual cycles may be canceled and pen intakes appear to be consistent while intake of individual animals may be erratic. Conversely, the cattle may cycle together because of a common trigger of the cycle, such as a weather change or a mistake in bunk reading or other management factors. The intake of the whole pen may cycle up and down in a yo-yo effect. Both situations are indications of subacute acidosis, but the second is much more obvious to the feedlot manager.

Grains vary in the fermentability of the starch in them (Table 14–7). Wheat is fermented very rapidly and commonly leads to subacute acidosis and low feed intakes. Many cattle growers assume the low intakes are due to the flour in the wheat when it is dry rolled, but it is probably due to subacute acidosis rather than palatability. Similarly, high-moisture grains have rapid rates of starch digestion. Many cat-

TABLE 14-7

Grains categorized by rate of starch breakdown in the rumen

FAST
Wheat
Barley
High-moisture corn (bunker silo)
*   Steam-flaked corn, high-moisture corn (stored whole, fed whole)
Dry-rolled corn, reconstituted grain sorghum, steam-flaked grain sorghum
Dry whole corn
Dry-rolled grain sorghum
SLOW

Source: Stock et al. (10).

tle growers assume that cattle consume less high-moisture grain than dry grain because of the moisture in the grain. Their solution is to add dry roughage and dry grain to the diet. While both of these factors reduce diet dry-matter content, they also reduce acidosis. Subacute acidosis is usually the primary problem with feeding high levels of high-moisture grains.

Some feed processing methods also increase the rate of starch digestion and may lead to subacute acidosis. Examples are flaking and fine grinding. Therefore, grain type and processing as well as roughage level influence the propensity to acidosis in finishing diets.

Bunk Reading

Bunk reading is one of the most important management considerations in the feedlot in attempting to minimize subacute acidosis. Most feedlot cattle are fed 2–3 times/d. The most critical bunk reading is the first one of the day. Pens of cattle with empty bunks should be fed first. Later reading can modify the amount projected for feeding for the day.

The goal in bunk reading is to have the last mouthful of feed consumed as the feed truck is dumping additional feed in the bunk, but it is seldom this simple. If the bunk is empty or slick from the cattle licking it, the cattle will be hungry and may overconsume feed during the first 1–2 h and create subacute acidosis. Con-

FIGURE 14–6. A typical feed bunk arrangement used by many large commercial feedlots. (Courtesy of D. C. Church.)

versely, if too much feed is left in the bunk, it will become stale and may spoil if it contains high-moisture ingredients. Spoiled, moldy, stale feed will inhibit intake and may interfere with proper bunk reading, because it may appear that feed is remaining (Fig. 14–6). It is feed that the animals will or should not consume, however. In these cases the spoiled feed should be removed from the bunk.

GRAINS AND GRAIN PROCESSING

High-Moisture Grains

Grains fed to cattle may vary in rate (Table 14–8), site, and extent of starch digestion within the animal's digestive tract. Any grain processing method that reduces particle size and/or causes disruption and gelatinization of the starch granules will increase the amount of that starch being digested in the rumen, thus increasing the possibility of acidosis. Although digestion of starch in the small intestine is more efficient (20–25 percent) than digestion by the rumen microbes, the capacity of the small intestine to digest starch is limited. Grains with low ruminal starch digestibilities may also have lower small intestinal starch digestibilities and lower total tract starch digestibilities. Grain sorghum is digested slowly in the rumen, has a lower total tract digestibility, and has a relative feeding value of 85–95 percent that of corn. Feeding a mixture of rapidly digested grains (wheat, barley, high-moisture corn) and slowly digested grains (grain sorghum, dry corn) may reduce the incidence of acidosis and improve overall starch utilization.

Cattle fed a combination of 67–75 percent high-moisture corn (HMC) with 33–25 percent dry-rolled grain sorghum (DRGS) or dry corn, gained 2.7 percent faster and 4.6 percent more efficiently than predicted from the performance of cattle fed either grain alone (Tables 14–9, 14–10), demonstrating that a complementary effect occurs when feeding HMC and dry grain. Dry-matter intake was decreased slightly when mixtures of grain were fed. In general, the greatest improvement in animal performance occurred during the step-up period (21–28 d) when cattle were adjusting from a high-roughage diet to a high-grain diet. Subacute acidosis appears to have been the major problem with cattle fed HMC alone, because they showed a reduced feed intake and a subsequent reduction in gain and feed efficiency.

TABLE 14-8

Effect of feeding mixtures of high-moisture corn and dry-rolled grain sorghum on starch intake, flow, and digestibility

Item	High-Moisture Corn: Dry-Rolled Grain Sorghum			
	100:0	67:33	33:67	0:100
Intake,[a] g/d	3893	3981	4402	4439
Duodenal digesta flow,[a,b] g/d	407	596	1300	2293
Ileal digesta flow,[a,b] g/d	156	280	456	768
Ruminal digestion,[a,b] %	89.9	85.0	68.8	45.7
Small intestinal digestion, %				
Of intake[a]	6.3	7.9	20.9	37.3
Of entering small intestine	67.8	53.7	45.5	54.3
Total tract digestion,[a,b] %	95.3	93.5	92.4	87.0

[a]Linear effect ($P < 0.01$).
[b]Quadractic effect ($P < 0.10$).
Source: Sindt et al. (11).

The complementary effects appear to be different when cattle are fed a combination of HMC and DRGS versus HMC and dry corn. Cattle fed 100 percent DRGS consumed 7.0 percent more feed, gained 5.6 percent more slowly, and were 13.7 percent less efficient than cattle fed HMC. Cattle fed a combination of 67–75 percent HMC and 33–25 percent DRGS gained at least as fast and efficiently as cattle fed 100 percent HMC. The complementary effect was 2.6 percent for gain and 4.8 percent for feed efficiency. When cattle were fed a combination of 50 percent HMC and 50 percent DRGS, the complementary effect was 3.6 percent for gain and 4.8 percent for feed efficiency. At the present time, we do not have enough pens of cattle fed 25 percent HMC and 75 percent DRGS to describe the complementary effect at that point. Cattle fed a combination of HMC and DRGS consistently consumed less feed than expected, although the magnitude of difference (1.3–1.6 percent) was small.

Cattle fed 100 percent HMC or 100 percent dry corn gained and converted feed to gain similarly (Table 14–10). Cattle fed a combination of 67–75 percent HMC and 33–25 percent dry corn gained 2.9 percent faster and 4.3 percent more efficiently than cattle fed either HMC or dry corn alone. The complementary effect of HMC and dry corn was reduced when a combination of 50 percent HMC and 50 percent dry corn was fed. The complementary effect was 1.9 percent for gain and 1.7 percent for feed efficiency. When a combination of 25–33 percent HMC and 75–67 percent dry corn was fed, cattle consumed more feed resulting in faster gains, but feed conversion was similar to expected values.

The slope of the expected gain and feed/gain lines are quite different in Figs. 14–7 and 14–8. However, the magnitude of the complementary effect of 23–33 percent dry corn or DRGS is quite similar. The high feed intake and low feed efficiency of the cattle fed 100 percent DRGS may explain a major portion of this difference. Complementary effects appear to be maintained with higher levels of DRGS, but they are reduced with higher levels of dry corn.

TABLE 14-9

Performance of cattle fed high-moisture corn-dry grain combinations — 144 pens of cattle[a]

Item	High-Moisture Corn, %				
	100	75-67	50	33-25	0
Daily feed, lb	20.59	20.59	20.99	21.43	21.65
Complementary effect, %		−1.45	−0.62	+0.46	
Daily gain, lb	3.16	3.22	3.20	3.18	3.07
Complementary effect, %		2.72	2.81	2.83	
Feed/gain	6.47	6.32	6.51	6.65	6.99
Complementary effect, %		−4.56	−3.28	−2.64	

[a]Nine Nebraska trials. Dry grain sources were dry-rolled grain sorghum, dry whole corn, or dry-rolled corn.

TABLE 14-10
Finishing steers fed high-moisture corn, dry-rolled corn, or dry-rolled grain sorghum either alone or in combination

Item	HMC 100%	HMC: DRC			HMC: DRGS		
		75:25	50:50	0:100	75:25	50:50	0:100
Daily feed,[a,b] lb	23.46	22.95	23.05	23.33	23.37	23.88	24.38
Daily gain, lb	3.61	3.70	3.68	3.66	3.66	3.66	3.48
Feed/gain[a,b,c]	6.45	6.17	6.25	6.37	6.37	6.49	6.94
Complementary effect		4.2	2.6		3.1	3.0	

HMC = high-moisture corn ground and stored in a bunker; DRC = dry-rolled corn; DRGS = dry-rolled grain sorghum.

[a]Corn vs. grain sorghum ($P < 0.05$).

[b]Linear effect of mixture ($P < 0.10$).

[c]Quadratic effect of mixture ($P < 0.15$).

Source: Sindt et al. (11).

Wheat-Grain Sorghum, Corn Blends

Although feed intake is reduced when wheat is fed, efficiency of feed conversion is often increased because of the higher digestibility of wheat as compared to other feed grains. Several studies have shown that wheat is best utilized when fed in combination with other grains.

Researchers in Kansas reported that the feeding value of wheat was improved when it was fed in combination with corn or grain sorghum (Table 14–11) but not when it was fed with barley. Because wheat and barley are digested rapidly in the rumen, there should be minimal complementary effects. Research in Nebraska showed that feeding a combination of 67 or 33 percent wheat with 33 or 67 percent dry-rolled corn resulted in a 6.0 and 2.8 percent complementary effect in feed efficiency, respectively (Table 14–12). Starches present in corn and grain sorghum are digested more slowly in the rumen than the starch in wheat, thus acidosis is less of a problem. Also, because a portion of the starch in corn and grain sorghum may escape digestion in the rumen and be digested in the small intestine, feeding mixtures of wheat with corn or grain sorghum may improve the efficiency of starch digestion.

Steam-Flaked Corn and Whole-Shelled Corn

Other research is shown in which combinations of steam-flaked corn and whole shelled corn were fed to cattle (15). In trial 1 (Table 14–13) cattle

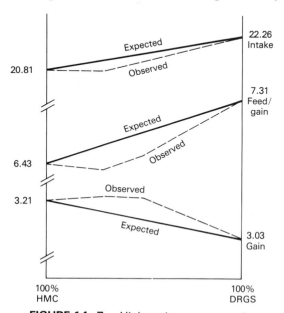

FIGURE 14–7. High-moisture corn-grain sorghum effects on feed intake, feed efficiency, and daily gain of feedlot cattle (7).

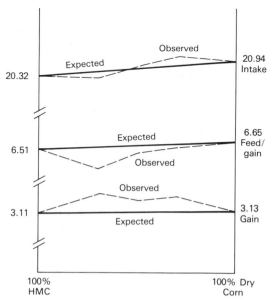

FIGURE 14–8. High-moisture corn versus dry corn effects on feed intake, feed efficiency, and daily gain of feedlot cattle.

TABLE 14-11

Relative performance from wheat rations

Grain	Average Daily Gain, %		Average Air-Dry Intake, %		Pounds Concentrate Replaced by 1 Pound Wheat		Number of Comparisons	
	Wheat Alone	Wheat Mixed	Wheat Alone	Wheat Mixed	Wheat Alone	Wheat Mixed	Wheat Alone	Wheat Mixed
Corn	97	102	91	96	1.09	1.17	30	12
Sorghum	90	98	84	91	1.15	1.24	3	7
Barley	98	98	92	97	1.10	1.04	18	11
Rye	104		98		1.06		3	

Source: Brethour (12).

TABLE 14-12

Performance of cattle fed a combination of dry-rolled wheat and dry-rolled corn

Item	Dry-Rolled Wheat:Dry-Rolled Corn			
	100:0	67:33	33:67	0:100
Daily feed,[a] lb	18.71	19.29	20.55	21.24
Daily gain,[a,b] lb	2.66	2.87	2.91	2.90
Feed/gain[a,b]	6.99	6.66	6.99	7.29
Complementary effect, %		6	2.8	

[a]Linear effect (P < .05).
[b]Quadratic effect (P < .05).
Source: Kreikemeier et al. (13).

TABLE 14-13

Performance of steers fed mixtures of whole-shelled and steam-flaked corn

Item	Steam-Flaked Corn:Whole-Shelled Corn				
	100:0	75:25	50:50	25:75	0:100
Trial 1					
Daily feed, lb	13.86[a]	15.42[b]	15.29[b]	16.17[b]	15.84[b]
Daily gain, lb	2.31[a]	2.62[b]	2.46[a,b]	2.71[b]	2.60[a,b]
Feed/gain	5.97	5.89	6.17	5.95	6.09
Trial 2					
Daily feed, lb	16.10	16.70	16.79	16.48	16.37
Daily gain, lb	2.60[a]	2.68[a]	2.47[a,b]	2.35[b,c]	2.33[c]
Feed/gain	6.17	6.20	6.55	6.95	6.96

[a,b,c]Means in the same row with different superscripts differ (P < 0.05).
Source: Lee et al. (14).

fed 75 percent steam-flaked corn and 25 percent whole-shelled corn gained faster and consumed more feed than cattle fed 100 percent steam-flaked corn. Feed conversions were similar. The reduced feed intake may have been the result of subacute acidosis. In trial 2, cattle performance was similar, between 75:25 and 100:0 steam-flaked corn:whole-shelled corn. A consistent finding in both experiments was that cattle fed a combination of 75 percent steam-flaked corn and 25 percent whole-shelled corn performed as well as cattle fed 100 percent steam-flaked corn. Such mixtures not only maintained animal performance, but also reduced feed processing costs and conserved energy by reducing the need for steam flaking.

Feeding combinations of rapidly digesting grains (HMC, wheat) with slowly digesting grains (grain sorghum) results in a positive complementary effect in feed efficiency in the feedlot. This improvement is partially explained by less acidosis, increased ruminal digestion of grain sorghum, and increased total tract starch digestion. Cost of gain may be reduced due to the use of a lower-priced grain and/or improved feed efficiency of the grain combination.

Grain Comparisons

Most of the total dollars spent for feedlot rations is for grain. Therefore, it is critically important to purchase the grain as economically as possible. In order to do this, it is imperative to know the precise energy values of the grains or alternative energy sources (see Ch. 11).

It should be obvious from the previous discussion on mixtures of grains and rates of starch digestion that there is no one value for a specific grain. The value depends on the level the grain is fed in the diet and the other ingredients in the diet such as roughage level and other grain sources. It might be a very expensive mistake to assume a given value for a grain. For example, grain sorghum had 91 percent the value of HMC when each was fed as the only grain in the diet. When fed as 25 or 50 percent of the diet, the grain sorghum appeared to have over 100 percent the value of HMC.

In a similar manner, wheat appears to have greater value than corn when fed in combination with other grains. The most important consideration is the rate of starch digestion, as discussed previously. The greatest benefits come from combining grains with the greatest differences in rate of starch digestion.

Negative Associative Effects

One of the greatest nutritional problems we face in the feedlot is the negative effect of grain on forage utilization. This negative effect is likely a result of low rumen pH caused by rapid digestion of the starch in the grain. Most feedlot rations contain both forage and grain and, therefore, negative associative effects occur. Feedlot growing rations, step-up rations, and finishing rations may have large negative associative effects. The function of roughage in finishing rations and in step-up rations has been discussed previously. These functions are essentially nonnutritive in nature. The negative associative effects we want to minimize are associated with the growing rations.

Growing rations in corn-growing areas are commonly based on corn silage. Good corn silage is usually a 50:50 mixture of grain and forage. This is precisely the type of ration where negative associative effects occur. Adding some grain to the silage further accentuates the problem.

In a summary of 2 years of data, calves fed corn silage followed by high-grain finishing were less efficient, and cost of gain was higher than for calves finished immediately after weaning on a high-grain diet (Table 14–4). The authors feel this was probably caused by the poor use of energy in corn silage because of the large negative effect of the grain on fiber digestion. Mixtures of grains and other forages such as alfalfa likely have similar problems.

Cattle grown on corn silage were not much larger at low choice grade than calves finished immediately on high-grain diets. This suggests that corn silage (and similar diets based on hay and grain) are really low-energy finishing diets, not growing diets. Consider that corn silage is half grain and that the grain is more digestible than the forage. Therefore, 60 percent or more of the energy in corn silage is from grain. Many nutritionists have drawn incorrect conclusions about growing cattle because their "growing" rations were based on corn silage or hay and grain. Growing rations are really those based primarily on roughages that give rates of gain less than 2 lb/d.

Because of negative associative effects and the necessity to obtain rapid rates of gain, we conclude that calves should not be grown in feedlots. This leaves two alternatives. They can be finished (as calves) or they can be grown in a high-forage system (outside of the feedlot) such as that described previously.

Limit-fed high-grain diets have become popular in feedlots. These diets have been developed because grains are cheaper sources of energy in feedlots than roughages. It is necessary to ensure that sufficient bunk space is available when limit feeding, and nutrients other than energy should be calculated to supply NRC needs on a daily basis rather than a percentage basis. It is possible that less negative associative effect is observed on limit-fed diets, but this has not been quantitated. Cattle can be successfully grown on limit-fed high-grain diets. However, the same basic criticisms exist as for corn silage and hay grain diets. It seems more logical to just finish the cattle than to attempt to "grow" or "stretch" them.

PROTEIN SUPPLEMENTATION

Concepts of protein metabolism in the rumen have changed appreciably in recent years. Some of these changes increase the possibility for reducing supplemental protein costs. Three important areas seem to have potential for savings: use of urea in finishing rations, use of urea in corn silage rations, and use of high-bypass proteins in growing rations.

High-Grain Finishing Rations

Cattle will gain essentially as rapidly and as efficiently on urea-supplemented finishing (high-grain) rations as on similar soybean meal-supplemented rations (Table 14–14). About 75 percent of the protein in a finishing ration is supplied by the grain, and grain proteins are high-bypass proteins, as will be discussed later. In addition, the energy available from starch digestion allows the rumen microorganisms to produce ample amounts of protein from urea (via ammonia). Some concern has been expressed about protein solubility in HMC. Research in Nebraska has shown that urea works as well with HMC as with dry corn (Table 14–14).

Corn Silage Rations

Many calves or yearlings are grown, back-grounded, warmed-up, or "stretched" on high-corn silage rations. Corn silage is lower in protein, especially bypass protein, and requires more supplemental protein than does corn grain. One should expect some reduction in performance when a urea supplement is used, compared to performance with soybean meal. However, this depends on the size and kind of cattle, since size and kind affects protein requirement. The heavier and fleshier the cattle, the less reduction due to urea. Over a period of years we have had a reduction of 0.2 lb/d in gain with calves fed urea (Table 14–15). Over the past 10 years the monthly price of soybean meal (per pound) averaged 2.4 times that of corn. When corn silage price is based on corn price, and soybean meal is two times the price of corn grain, urea gives a small savings at 2.5 times the price of grain. There is potential for more savings using an all-urea supplement (Table 14–15). A savings of $4–5/hd is possible when putting 300 lb on a calf with corn silage.

High-Bypass Proteins

The greatest potential for savings, especially in rations where feeders want to use natural protein, is with the use of high-bypass proteins. Many feed companies are now using the bypass protein concept in supplement formulation, although some might argue that insufficient research data are available to be able to apply the concept in practical feeding situations.

Bypass protein is that protein which escapes (or bypasses) digestion in the rumen (see Ch. 8). This protein is then digested in the lower tract of the animal and absorbed as amino acids to be used for productive functions. The animal has two sources of protein to use for these functions: bypass protein and microbial protein. We must always be aware of the significant role that microbial protein plays in meeting the animal's needs. In many cases, such as that of finishing cattle, the microbial protein is sufficient to meet the animal's needs. When the microbial protein is inadequate, the only way to supply additional protein to the animal is with bypass protein. Therefore, the value of a protein source for ruminants is highly dependent upon its bypass value. Most proteins are bypassed to some extent, but some are bypassed more than others. Protein broken down in the rumen supplies ammonia, which can be supplied cheaper by urea.

Growing calves and lactating cows have high protein requirements and usually require some bypass protein to maximize productivity. The growing calf probably offers the best opportunity for use of high-bypass protein sources.

Accurate evaluation of protein is absolutely necessary before systems of meeting ruminant protein requirements can be used with confidence. Estimates of the bypass values for protein sources can be made from laboratory analyses or by directly measuring bypass of a protein source with intestinally fistulated animals. We feel these values are useful as supporting evidence, but that measuring animal growth or production is the best way to obtain these bypass values.

Current estimates of the value of the protein in several sources are presented in Table 14–16 and in Appendix Table 2. The protein in grain, especially corn and milo, is bypassed to a great extent and, therefore, the grain by-products are high in bypass protein. Heating reduces rumen degradation of proteins and, therefore, the drying of dehydrated alfalfa, blood meal, and meat meal causes them to be high-bypass protein sources. Our research has been conducted with flash-dried blood meal. The value for old process blood meal (200 percent) is calculated and based on differences in amino acid availabilities in nonruminants. Meat meal is somewhat more variable than blood meal but is often an economical bypass protein source. Dehydrated alfalfa is probably least predictable, and because much of the 17 percent dehy contains sun-cured pellets, the authors estimate its

TABLE 14-14

Urea vs. soybean meal in high-moisture corn rations

	Treatment							
	Urea		SBM		HMC 10.5% CP		HMC 12% CP	
Item	10.5% CP	12% CP	10.5% CP	12% CP	HMC (23%)	HMC (29%)	HMC (23%)	HMC (29%)
	(lb)	(lb)	(lb)	(lb)	(lb)	(lb)	(lb)	(lb)
Initial wt.	648	652	650	642	742	737	736	740
Adjusted final wt.[a]	1034	1029	1039	1052	1019	1009	1016	1006
Daily feed (DM)	22.16	21.71	22.41	22.31	20.4	19.9	20.3	20.1
Daily gain	2.99	2.95	3.03	3.12	2.31	2.23	2.29	2.20
Feed/gain	7.57	7.57	7.60	7.35	8.98	8.76	8.78	9.17
Quality grade[b]	11.54	11.71	11.90	11.46	11.92	12.05	11.96	12.23
Abscessed livers,[c] %	46[0.77]	42[0.83]	39[0.86]	47[0.74]	22[0.39]	35[0.56]	49[0.79]	36[0.64]

[a]Final weight adjusted to 62% dress from hot carcass weight.

[b]11 = high good; 12 = low choice.

[c]Number in brackets denotes average severity of abscess: 1 = one small abscess; 3 = abscessed.

Source: Schnidler and Farlin (15).

TABLE 14-15

Value of all urea supplements in corn silage rations[a]

Item	SBM	Urea
Daily gain, lb	1.75	1.56
Silage[b]/gain, lb	7.06	7.84
Supplement/gain, lb	0.79	0.87
SBM at 2 times corn price ($86/ton corn)[c]	$172	$103[d,e]
SBM at 2 1/2 times corn price	$215	$140[d,e]

[a]Summary of nine Nebraska trials, 405 hd fed each supplement.
[b]Dry basis.
[c]Corn at $2.40/bu = $68/ton of silage dry matter.
[d]Breakeven price for urea supplement.
[e]13% urea plus 87% corn = $101 (urea at $200/ton).

TABLE 14-16

All-natural beef supplements

Normal 32%		Bypass 32%		Bypass 64%	
SBM	55%	Dehy 17	72%	Dehy 20	39%
Dehy 17	41%	Meat meal	15%	Meat meal	34%
Min	4%	Dehy 20	8%	Blood meal	14%
		Urea	3.2%	Urea	9.7%
		Min	1.8%	Min	3.3%
$188/ton		$142/ton		$193/ton	

Source: Klopfenstein et al. (29). Prices: SBM, $227; Dehy 17, $123; meat meal, $218; Dehy 20, $128; blood meal (old process), $185; urea, $220.

value equal to that of soybean meal. Twenty percent protein dehy (or higher) should not contain sun-cured alfalfa and has generally given the authors good results (1.5 × SBM).

Results from a digestion study (21) indicate no differences in dry-matter or total tract N digestion as affected by urea, soybean meal (SBM), blood meal (BM), corn gluten meal (CGM), or feather meal (FthM) supplementation. These data indicate that feather meal protein is as digestible as the other protein sources. Performance of steers in a growth trial indicated that calves consuming BM, FthM, or BM + FthM gained faster than steers fed urea. The improved protein efficiency for BM + FthM compared to either fed alone may be due to sulfur amino acids supplied by the FthM and lysine and/or other amino acids, supplied by blood meal. Combinations of two slowly degraded protein sources (blood meal and corn gluten meal) improved performance of steers above the weighted average of the two individual sources. This may be due to an improved amino acid pattern reaching the lower tract.

The advantages of using the bypass protein system are that the amount of natural protein fed is reduced and the use of urea is increased.

This results in lower cost of supplementation and performance is maintained. Assuming that the animal's protein requirement was met with an all-natural supplement, performance could not be increased, it could only be done at a lower cost.

What should a cattle producer expect from a commercial bypass protein supplement? It should be sold at a lower cost. The cost/ton may be as high or higher than a conventional all-natural supplement, but if it is higher in crude protein, the feeding rate will be lower. Therefore, the cost per head per day should be lower. If the supplement is not cheaper, the feed company is taking all the benefit of the bypass protein. A bypass supplement should be recommended for growing calves and perhaps for lactating cows, but not for finishing (high-grain) cattle. The producer should expect gains similar to those with previous all-natural supplements and should be wary of claims for increased gain.

Three computer-formulated rations are shown in Table 14-16. An all-natural 32 percent protein supplement using SBM is shown which had ingredient costs of $188/ton. A comparable supplement using bypass sources cost $142/ton. If our assumptions are correct, the two sup-

TABLE 14-17

Protein sources and alfalfa silage as supplements to corn-stalklage-based growing diets

	Stalklage[a]			Stalklage + alfalfa[a]		
	Soybean	Bypass 2x	Bypass 2.5x	Soybean	Bypass 2x	Bypass 2.5x
Initial wt, lb	480	452	470	453	473	474
Daily gain, lb	0.63	0.70	0.60	0.48	0.67	0.58
Daily feed intake, lb DM	10.63	10.74	10.44	10.32	10.54	10.72
Feed/gain	16.98	15.32	17.28	21.63	15.82	18.45

[a]2 pens, 10 head each per treatment fed 119 days (Jan. 6 to May 5, 1983).
[b]Rate of gain was different ($P < 0.05$) for roughage source and different ($P < 0.01$) between soybean and by-pass 2x protein supplements when both roughages are combined.
Source: Guyer et al. (30).

plements are equal in feeding value. At 64 percent supplement using bypass sources cost $193/ ton. Using half the amount of supplement to meet the same supplemental protein needs as the 32 percent SBM supplement would cut the cost to the beef producer nearly in half.

An experiment was conducted to validate this concept (Table 14–17). Calves were fed corn stalklage and supplements of SBM or a combination of blood meal and corn gluten meal. The two bypass supplements were calculated assuming 2 or 2.5x the bypass of SBM. Results verify that the bypass of 2.5x that of SBM was accurate (equal gains). The 2x supplement gave significantly better gains, indicating that the other two supplements did not meet the protein requirement. The cost of protein supplementation with the bypass supplements was half that of SBM.

The application of the bypass protein concept offers economy to the cattle producer with essentially no risk of reduced performance. Those feed companies that have been using this concept for the past few years indicate excellent results. This as much as the research conducted assures us that the concept is valid.

FEED ADDITIVES

One of the best methods to reduce feed costs is through the use of feed additives. The primary nonnutritional feed additives used by the beef feedlot industry are ionophores, antibiotics, and estrus suppressants (see Ch. 10).

Ionophores

At present, monensin (Rumensin™, Eli Lilly and Company) and lasalocid (Bovatec™, Hoffman-LaRoche) are the only ionophores approved to be fed to beef cattle. They are primarily used to improve feed efficiency, however, they may also elicit a small increase in daily gain. In general, ionophores improve efficiency 6–8 percent and daily gain 1–5 percent, the magnitude of the response depending on the dosage of each ionophore.

When starting cattle on feed, ionophore step-up programs have been shown to be useful. Feeding 10–15 g/T of monensin during the grain adaptation period and then switching to 25–30 g/T has been shown to increase feed intake and gain of cattle. Much of the depression in feed intake appears to be a palatability problem associated with monensin. Contrary to many nutritionists' thinking, the depression in feed intake may be a benefit to the cattle. During grain adaptation, feed intake patterns may be erratic because of problems with subacute acidosis. In one case cattle fed 30 g/T had a lower but more consistent intake pattern throughout the grain adaptation period. Thus ionophores may provide a tool to reduce subacute acidosis in the feedlot.

Antibiotics

Antibiotics are primarily fed to finishing cattle for the control of liver abscesses. Severe liver abscesses may reduce gain and feed efficiency by as much as 10 percent. When high-grain diets are fed, cattle that are borderline with subacute acidosis and have a few small abscesses gain faster and more efficiently than cattle that are not stressed and have no liver abscesses. However, managing to allow for a slight amount of acidosis is difficult.

Antibiotics may also reduce the incidence of grain bloat, but the data are limited. Antibiotics have been shown to improve grain and feed efficiency, but this response may be primarily due to a reduction of liver abscesses. Combination feeding of ionophores and antibiotics has proven beneficial and is a widely utilized practice.

Melengestrol Acetate (MGA)

The use of MGA to inhibit ovulation and estrus results in an increase in feed intake and a subsequent improvement in gain and feed efficiency. The suppression of estrus also reduces injuries due to riding as well as reducing energy losses of the animals from riding and chasing. The reported response to MGA is variable and may depend on the age of the heifers being fed, the number of sources of heifers fed together, the amount of space per heifer, implant effects, and the number of days on a high-concentrate diet. MGA is approved to be fed in combination with an ionophore, but not with both an ionophore and an antibiotic. Thus feedlot managers must decide which combination they wish to use.

SUMMARY

Growing-finishing systems for cattle production are influenced by many factors. Interactions exist between size, frame, breed, age, and sex condition of the cattle. Available feedstuffs, facilities, and economics may alter systems of production. Nutritional considerations include composition and complementary characteristics of grains, supplements, and forages. Research is providing new insights into starch utilization, negative associative effects between starch and fiber digestion, and metabolizable protein requirements and availability. The manager of a growing-finishing system must be able to integrate the components of production to optimize animal performance and profitability.

REFERENCES

1. Thomas, V. M. 1987. *Beef cattle production.* Philadelphia: Lea & Febiger.
2. Lambert, C. 1984. *Kansas State U. Rept. of Progress* 448:118.
3. USMARC. 1976. *Germ Plasm Evaluation Program, Prog. Rpt.* 4.
4. Turgeon, A., et al. 1985. *Nebr. Beef Cattle Rpt.* MP 48:20.
5. Lewis, M., et al. 1989. *Nebr. Beef Cattle Rpt.* MP 54:34.
6. Cole, N. A., and D. P. Hutcheson. 1988. *J. Animal Sci.* 66:1764.
7. Fulton, W. R., et al. 1979. *J. Animal Sci.* 49:775.
8. Woods, W., et al. 1969. *Nebr. Beef Cattle Rpt.* EC 69–218:14.
9. Trenkle, A., and R. Arnold. 1978. *Iowa State A.S. Leaflet* R 277.
10. Stock, R., et al. 1985. *Nebr. Beef Cattle Rpt.* MP 48:32.
11. Sindt, M., et al. 1987. *Nebr. Beef Cattle Rpt.* MP 52:9.
12. Brethour, J. R. 1966. *Kansas Agr. Exp. Sta. Bul.* 487.
13. Kreikemeier, K., et al. 1987. *Nebr. Beef Cattle Rpt.* MP 52:12.
14. Lee, R. W., et al. 1982. *J. Animal Sci.* 55:475.
15. Schnidler, G. E., and S. D. Farlin. 1979. *Nebr. Beef Cattle Rpt.* EC 79–218:8.
16. Klopfenstein, T. J. 1985. *Prof. Animal Scientist* 1:27.
17. Guyer, P. G., et al. 1984. *Nebr. Beef Cattle Rpt.* MP 44:24.

15

Feeding Dairy Cows

David J. Schingoethe

INTRODUCTION

Milk and milk products are an important part of the American diet, with annual per capita consumption of dairy products requiring about 270 kg of milk. Dairy products supply about 75 percent of our dietary Ca and are also an important dietary source of protein, vitamins, other minerals, and energy. In some countries per capita consumption of dairy products is 50–100 percent higher than in the United States. Even when one averages in those countries that consume much less milk, world consumption of dairy products is more than 100 kg per capita.

In order to meet these needs for human food, the approximately 10 million U.S. dairy cows each produce an average of 6,400 kg per year, most of it in dairies that are highly mechanized (Fig. 15–1). A number of herds average more than 11,000 kg per cow, and some cows have produced nearly 25,000 kg of milk annually. Approximately 385 million metric tons of milk are produced annually in the world, mostly in the temperate zones.

The sale of milk and milk products accounts for nearly 13 percent of all farm cash

FIGURE 15–1. The interior of a modern milking parlor.

receipts in the United States, while sales of veal calves, dairy beef, and other dairy cattle account for another 3 percent of the nation's farm income. On the expenditure side of the dairy farm ledger, feed cost is an important consideration, because feeds usually account for 50 percent of

TABLE 15-1

Daily protein, energy, calcium, and phosphorus needs of a 650-kg cow at maintenance, late gestation, and when producing 50 kg of milk daily

Nutrient	Status		
	Maintenance	Late Gestation	Peak Lactation[a]
Protein, kg	0.428	1.120	4.628
NEℓ, Mcal	10.30	13.39	44.8
Calcium, g	26	43	174
Phosphorus, g	19	26	110

[a]Requirements for maintenance plus production of 50 kg milk containing 3.5% fat.
Source: Based on NRC for dairy cattle (9).

the cost of operating the dairy farm enterprise. In order to achieve profitable milk production, it is important to feed dairy cows sufficient amounts of nutritionally balanced diets at reasonable costs.

Dairy cows need to consume a lot of feed to achieve the levels of production expected today; however, the nutrient needs of dairy cows vary tremendously throughout the lactation and dry period cycle, as illustrated by the example in Table 15–1. At peak production, a dairy cow may require 3–10 times as much protein and energy as she required during late gestation. This is further complicated by the fact that the cow's appetite usually lags behind her nutrient requirements. The challenge for a dairy feeding program is to meet the cow's nutrient needs while minimizing body weight loss, minimizing digestive upsets, and maintaining health.

THE LACTATION AND GESTATION CYCLE

Figure 15–2 illustrates the relationships between milk production, dry-matter intake, and body weight changes typically observed during the normal lactation and gestation cycle. Milk production increases rapidly and reaches peak (maximum) production 6–8 weeks after calving. However, appetite lags behind production such that maximum daily dry-matter intake often does not occur until 12–15 weeks postpartum. As a result, most cows are in negative energy balance for 8–10 weeks and possibly as long as 20 or more weeks for some high producers. The cow makes up these nutrient deficits by "borrowing from her body stores." Cows in good condition often lose 90–135 kg of body weight during early lactation, which is sufficient to support 700–900 kg of milk production. If that source of nutrients is not available, peak production and

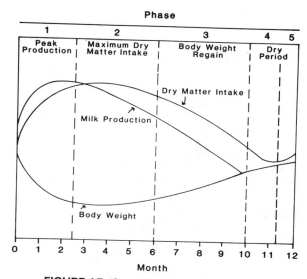

FIGURE 15–2. Milk yield, dry-matter intake, and body weights of cows during phases of the lactation-dry period cycle.

total lactational production will likely be less than optimal.

After optimal dry-matter intake is achieved, intake tends to follow production requirements and decreases as production decreases. There is still a lag in intake, only now the cow tends to consume more than she needs during later lactation. This allows her to regain the body weight lost in early lactation. The cow should regain most of this body weight during late lactation for optimal energetic efficiency, with most of the weight gain during the dry period being accounted for by fetal growth.

A PHASE FEEDING PROGRAM

The lactation and gestation cycle can be divided into five phases, as illustrated in Fig. 15–2, based on particular nutritional considerations at various times. Phase 1, which is approximately the first 10 weeks of lactation, is when peak production occurs, but body stores are being utilized to make up for deficits in nutrient intake. Phase 2, which starts approximately 10 weeks postpartum for most cows and may continue for 10–20 weeks, corresponds with maximum dry-matter intake and is the period in which intake is in balance with requirements. In later lactation, phase 3 is entered as intake exceeds nutrient requirements for production. This is the main period for restoring body reserves for the next lactation.

The exact timing and relative length of these three phases of lactation may be altered if one is injecting cows with bovine somatotropin (bST) or other similar compounds which may alter the lactation curve. Production increases rapidly after the initiation of bST injections regardless of when they are started in the lactation cycle, but appetite lags behind the increased production and may not increase until 5–8 weeks after starting bST administration.

Phases 4 and 5 are in the dry period. This time may be considered as only one phase by some authors, but this author chooses to divide it into two phases. Phase 4, which may be most of the dry period, is a period for any final regaining of body weight and for regeneration of secretory tissue in the udder for the next lactation. Phase 5 is the last 1–3 weeks prepartum. During this time segment, one should start increasing grain intake as a means of preparing the rumen for the increased nutritional intakes which will soon follow upon parturition.

Feeding programs for the various phases of the lactation and gestation cycle will be discussed in following sections. The discussion will start with the dry period, or late gestation for bred heifers, and then proceed through lactation.

Dry Period and Bred Heifers

Cows need a short dry period as rest while preparing for the next lactation. A 60-d dry period results in the highest production during the next lactation for most cows (Table 15-2). Dry periods shorter than 40 d do not allow enough time for udder regeneration, and the result is reduced milk production in the succeeding lactation. Dry periods longer than 70 d do not promote increased milk production but may result in excess body condition and complications resulting from excess body condition.

The dry period is a time for cows to regenerate new secretory tissue in the udder as

TABLE 15-2

Effect of dry period length on milk production in the next lactation

Days Dry		Differences from Herdmates for Milk, kg/lactation
5–20		−585
21–30		−285
31–40		−71
41–50		+86
51–60	Recommended	+135
61–70		+142
71–80		+72
81–90		+29
More than 90		−49

Source: Butcher (1).

well as to replace lost body condition. Several changes occur in the udder during the dry period: active involution, steady state involution, and lactogenesis plus colostrogenesis. Milk continues to be secreted for several days after drying off before active involution takes over. During active involution, which is completed by 30 d into the dry period, milk-secreting tissue is reabsorbed. The second stage, steady state involution, can exist indefinitely, and the mammary gland remains in a collapsed state. The third stage, lactogenesis plus colostrogenesis, begins 15–20 d prepartum and involves the onset of lactation and the secretion of colostrum (14). The first and third stages suggest that the dry period should be at least 45–50 d in length.

Emphasis in dry cow feeding programs has shifted from one of putting body condition on during the dry period to one of maintaining the condition a cow carries when dried off. This change in emphasis is the result of USDA research which demonstrated that cows convert feed energy to body tissue more efficiently during lactation than during the dry period (7). Thus the cow should be in ideal calving condition when she goes dry. Then, weight gain during the dry period will be mostly accounted for by growth of the fetus. Approximately 2/3 of the fetal growth occurs during the last 2 months of gestation, which could account for 25–35 kg of weight gain. Of course, if a cow is still thin at drying off, one will want to replenish body stores as well as provide for fetal growth.

FIGURE 15-3. An excessively fat cow shown just prior to parturition.

Fat Cows. A cow should be fed enough during the dry period to maintain or get into good condition but not become excessively fat (Fig. 15-3). Cows consuming excess energy from grain and/or corn silage are more likely to develop a disorder called fat cow syndrome, which is characterized by high blood lipids and fatty livers. Such cows are more likely than the average to have calving difficulties, displaced abomasums, ketosis, and other health problems. Cows fed hay and/or haylage are less likely to have problems than cows receiving free-choice corn silage. If corn silage must be fed, limit dry cows to 9.5–11 kg/d of corn silage, plus 0.5 kg/d of protein supplement such as soybean meal, and provide a Ca-P supplement free choice. In all cases, dry cows should be separated from the milking herd to avoid excess energy intake.

Bred Heifers. Nutrient requirements of bred heifers during late gestation are slightly greater than are requirements of dry cows of similar size, because they are still growing. Bred heifers will likely need some grain along with forages during the last 3–4 months of gestation in order to continue growing, provide nutrients for the fetus, and not become thin. Good-quality forages can provide all of the nutrient needs of bred heifers during early gestation. But if forages are not of good quality, or if heifers are exposed to severe weather conditions, additional grain may be needed to maintain optimal growth rates. As with dry cows, heifers should be in good condition but not excessively fat at calving. Heifers are usually fed in groups of similar ages or sizes (Fig. 15-4).

Dry Cow Rations. The pregnant dry cow requires more protein, energy, Ca, and P than when not pregnant or lactating, but not nearly as many nutrients as when lactating (Table 15-1). The nutrient content of dry cow rations and example rations are listed in Table 15-3. A dry cow's nutrient requirements can often be met with only forages and no grain. Neither legume-grass hay nor corn silage alone meet all of the requirements; however, a combination of the two needs only vitamins and a small amount of P to meet requirements.

The dry cow ration can be quite simple but should include the following considerations. Include a minimum of 1 percent of body weight as long-stem, dry forage. Preferably this should be grass hay, because legumes contain excessive amounts of Ca and are low in P, a dietary combination which may increase the incidence of milk fever. Free-choice feeding of corn silage should be avoided, because it leads to excessive energy intake and increases the likelihood of displaced abomasum and fat cow syndrome. Grain should be limited to the amount needed to meet energy and protein needs. Ca intake should be kept under 100 g/d while providing adequate amounts of P (35–40 g/d for larger breeds). Higher amounts of Ca, especially if the diet is deficient in P, will increase the incidence of milk fever.

Additional Se (selenium) (3–5 mg) may be needed in areas where crops are deficient in Se. A Se deficiency, especially if vitamin E intake is not large, may result in retained placenta. Most stored feeds contain adequate but not excessive amounts of vitamin E, but usually only green forages contain greater amounts. Injecting Se and vitamin E or feeding supplemental amounts of these two nutrients during the last

FIGURE 15-4. Healthy heifers being group fed in drylot.

TABLE 15-3

Recommended nutrient content of diets for dry cows and approximate nutrient content of two forages (100% dry-matter basis)

	Dry Cow Requirement[a]	Alfalfa-Grass	Corn Silage	1/2 Alfalfa-Grass, 1/2 Corn Silage
Crude protein, %	12	16(+)[b]	8(−)	12(+)
TDN	56	50(−)	70(+)	60(+)
Net energy, Mcal/kg	1.25	1.15(−)	1.54(+)	1.34(+)
Acid detergent fiber, %	27	34(+)	28(+)	31(+)
Calcium, %	0.39	1.01(+)	0.27(−)	0.64(+)
Phosphorus, %	0.24	0.25(+)	0.20(−)	0.23(−)
Vitamin A, IU/kg	4000			
Vitamin D, IU/kg	1200			
Vitamin E, IU/kg	15			

[a]Based on NRC for dairy cattle (9).
[b]Plus (+) values are at or above requirements; negative (−) values are below.

3 weeks of the dry period may effectively provide this need and reduce the incidence of retained placentas. Most dairyfarmers provide supplemental amounts of vitamins A and D as well as trace minerals to all of their cattle as insurance against any possible deficiencies. But high mineral intake should be avoided, especially Na-based buffer mixtures, and salt intake should be limited to 28 g daily. High salt intake can aggravate the fluid retention problems of edema which is a problem with some cows, especially first-calf heifers.

Approaching Parturition (Phase 5).
The last couple of weeks before parturition is the time to make several nutritional changes to help the cow prepare for parturition and the ensuing lactation. Most of these nutritional changes are aimed at adapting the ruminal microflora to the higher-energy diets that will be needed postpartum to meet the greatly increased nutrient requirements. This adjustment is often best achieved by including small amounts of all ingredients of the lactating ration and gradually increasing the amounts of grain fed so that by parturition the cow is consuming 0.5–1 percent of her body weight as grain mix. Such a "steaming up" approach may also minimize the chance for milk fever, because most grain mixes have a more desirable Ca to P ratio than do legume forages, and this approach may minimize the chance for ketosis during lactation by helping the cow adapt to higher-energy diets more rapidly in early lactation.

It is advisable to start switching to some forage that the cow will receive after calving, but continue to provide at least 0.5–1 percent of her body weight as long-stem hay. This will help provide sufficient bulk in the diet to minimize the likelihood of displaced abomasum. It is important to make these ration changes as gradually as possible, because abrupt changes are likely to cause digestive upsets and throw cows off-feed. Most cows will experience a sharp decrease in total dry-matter intake 24–48 h before calving, so stabilizing the rumen is important to avoid displaced abomasum, acidosis, and off-feed.

This late prepartum period is a time to take steps to minimize several problems likely to occur around parturition. In milk fever-prone cows, one may consider lowering the Ca intake to 13–18 g daily for several days prepartum. This will help activate the Ca-mobilizing hormonal system to increase Ca absorption from the gut and Ca mobilization from the bones. For cows that are fat (body scores of 4 and 5), ketotic-prone, and high producers, one may consider feeding 6 g/d of supplemental niacin starting the last couple weeks prepartum and continuing during the first 8 weeks of lactation. In Se-deficient areas, supplemental Se-vitamin E should be fed or injected during the last 2–3 weeks prepartum.

Peak Milk Production

The most critical period for a dairy cow is from parturition until peak milk production. Each one-kilogram increase in milk production usually means an additional 200 kg of milk production during the lactation. However, since appetite lags behind nutritional requirements, phase 1 (peak milk production) is a period of negative nutrient balance.

The objective during this phase of lactation is to increase feed intake as rapidly as possible so as to minimize the nutritional deficit, but not introduce ration changes so rapidly as to cause digestive upsets and off-feed. Once the stress of calving has passed, grain intake can usually increase 0.5–0.7 kg/d. Or, if total mixed rations are fed, the concentrate to forage ratio can be gradually increased to a maximum of 60:40. At higher concentrate ratios it may be difficult to maintain a minimum of 18–19 percent acid detergent fiber.

A successful phase 1 feeding program will maximize peak milk yield, utilize body weight as an energy source, minimize ketosis, and return cows to a positive energy balance by 8–10 weeks postpartum. This is the period of lactation that requires the best in nutritional management. During this phase, positive responses to feed additives, special feed treatments, and special ration formulations are most likely to occur. Some examples of nutritional considerations are listed in following sections.

Cows can compensate for much of their deficit in energy intake by "borrowing" the remaining needed energy from body fat; however, they cannot borrow very much protein. Thus most of their protein must be supplied in the diet. When energy intake equals energy requirements, a diet containing 16–17 percent crude protein will likely meet protein requirements for most cows. However, in early lactation, 18–20 percent crude protein may be needed to meet protein requirements when energy intake is not supplying all of the cow's energy needs.

Early lactation cows will also likely benefit from bypass (escape) proteins (see Ch. 8 and 14). The protein requirement of cows producing up to 5 kg milk/100 kg body weight can usually be met by rumen microbial protein synthesis plus normal amounts of bypass protein. Cows producing more than this amount of milk will likely benefit from bypass proteins and/or ruminally protected amino acids. Nonprotein nitrogen (NPN) supplements will not be efficiently used by these cows, although NPN utilization can be improved by increasing the amount of fermentable carbohydrates in the diet.

Increasing the energy density also helps the early lactation cow more nearly meet her energy requirements. This can be achieved to a certain extent by increasing the concentrate to forage ratio. However, higher starch-lower fiber diets are more apt to cause acidosis, digestive upsets, and milk fat depression. Supplemental dietary fat may allow one to increase energy density of the diet while maintaining adequate fiber intake. There are limits to how much fat can be fed (see later section), but cows can easily consume an additional 0.5–0.7 kg fat, which will increase energy density of the diet. Ca content of the diet should be increased to more than 0.9 percent and Mg to about 0.3 percent of ration dry matter when feeding added fat.

Buffers such as $NaHCO_3$ (sodium bicarbonate) alone or in combination with MgO (magnesium oxide) may be helpful during early lactation. Cows fed ensiled forages, especially if of small particle size, and high amounts of soluble carbohydrates will likely benefit from 100–200 g/d of $NaHCO_3$ or its equivalent. The primary benefit is from maintaining ruminal pH, which minimizes acidosis, reduces digestive upsets, and results in increased dry-matter intake.

Niacin supplementation, which may have already started during the late dry period, should be continued with high-producing cows. Feed intake will likely increase faster than without niacin supplementation, and the chances of ketosis are reduced.

Providing at least 2.25 kg of dry hay in the daily ration helps maintain normal rumination and digestion, especially during early lactation. If chopped or ground forages are used, strive to maintain a particle length of at least 2.5–4 cm. Cornell research demonstrated few cases of displaced abomasums in cows fed long-stem hay, a slight increase when fed legume silages, and the most cases of displaced abomasums in cows fed corn silage as the only forage (3).

Maximum Dry-Matter Intake

In order to maintain peak milk production, maximum dry-matter intake should be achieved as early in lactation as possible. This will minimize the negative nutrient balance experienced in early lactation and shift cows from negative to positive energy balance earlier. Conception rates are greater for cows in positive energy balance than cows in negative energy balance, which is an important consideration, because cows are usually being bred during this phase of lactation. Body weights should stabilize and weight gains should actually start occurring during this phase.

Maximum dry-matter intake may reach 3.5–4 percent of body weight for most cows but can vary with production and individual cow appetites (Table 15–4). Dry-matter intakes are usually higher for higher-producing cows, and some cows seem to have the ability to consume more than 5 percent of their body weight.

TABLE 15-4

Dry-matter requirements to fulfill nutrient allowances for maintenance, milk production, and normal body weight gain during mid and late lactation (DM intake, percent of body wt)

	Body Weight, kg				
4% FCM	400	500	600	700	800
10	2.7	2.4	2.2	2.0	1.9
20	3.6	3.2	2.9	2.6	2.4
30	4.4	3.9	3.5	3.2	2.9
40	5.5	4.6	4.0	3.6	3.3
50	—	5.4	4.7	4.1	3.7
60	—	—	5.4	4.8	4.3

Source: Adapted from NRC for dairy cattle (9).

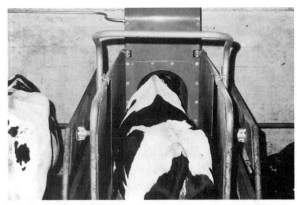

FIGURE 15-5. A magnet feeder that allows individual animals to be fed additional concentrate when in pens with other cows.

The percent protein needed in the diet during this period may likely be lower than what was needed in early lactation because the cow is now getting all of her needed energy as well as her needed protein supplied by the diet. Increased microbial protein synthesis stimulated by the greater dry-matter intake, coupled with lower dietary protein percentages, means that these cows are less likely to benefit from bypass protein than they would have benefited in early lactation. However, one should strive to maintain a balance between degradable crude protein and carbohydrates for optimal nutrient utilization.

While a cow is less likely to go off-feed during this phase than in early lactation, one should still strive to prevent conditions that may precipitate digestive upsets or result in less than optimal intake. Adequate fiber intake is still important, and grain intake should not exceed 2.5 percent of body weight. Frequent feeding, especially if fed as total mixed rations, minimizes digestive upsets and maximizes dry-matter intake. If all or some grain is fed through electronic grain feeders (Fig. 15-5), limit the grain available per meal to 2.25–3.25 kg. Dry-matter content of the diet may limit dry-matter intake if the total ration is too wet. Dry-matter intake may be limited by gut fill if the feeds are more than 45–50 percent moisture.

Late Lactation

Late lactation should be the easiest phase to manage because the cow is pregnant, nutrient intake normally exceeds requirements, and milk production is declining. This is the time to replace the weight lost during early lactation so that the cow is in good condition at drying off, but one should also maintain milk persistency

as much as possible. Keep in mind that young cows are still growing and thus need additional nutrients for growth as well as for weight regain. The usual guidelines for estimating nutrient requirements for growth are 20 percent of maintenance requirements for two-year-olds and 10 percent maintenance for three-year-olds.

During this phase, one has an opportunity to minimize feed costs by increasing the forage to concentrate ratio to match nutrient needs based on milk production and body condition and by utilizing NPN. A lower protein content is likely needed because the protein to energy ratio needed for weight gain is less than the ratio needed for milk production. NPN sources may be well utilized for a portion of the crude protein needs of these cows, while bypass proteins will be less cost-effective than in earlier lactation when production was higher.

SPECIAL NUTRIENT CONSIDERATIONS

There are certain nutritional factors to consider when feeding dairy cows. Some of these factors apply in all cases, whereas others may be of concern only during certain phases, such as during early lactation.

Energy

One of the greatest challenges to a dairy producer is to get cows to consume sufficient amounts of energy, especially during early lactation. Energy intake may be increased by increasing energy density of the diet (by providing a greater proportion in the form of fat), by increasing the amounts of readily fermentable carbohydrates in the diet (by increasing the concentrate to forage ratio in the total diet), or, in some instances, by using individual feeders to supplement intake.

Added Fat. One kilogram of fat contains approximately 2.25 times as much energy as contained in one kilogram of carbohydrates, thus the energy density of the diet can be increased by replacing portions of the carbohydrates (grains) in the diet with fat. This may allow an increase in energy intake while avoiding excessive starch or deficient fiber intakes.

Cows can consume more fat than is usually present in forages and grain mixes, but they cannot consume an unlimited amount. Most forages and grains contain 2–4 percent fat. The amount of fat can be increased to 5–7 percent of total diet dry matter without adversely affecting feed intake or nutrient utilization. However, diets containing more than 8–10 percent fat may reduce feed intake, reduce fiber digestibility, and cause digestive upsets. This is because many fatty acids are inhibitory to rumen microorganisms, especially fiber digesters, and ruminants can't digest as much fat in the intestinal tract as nonruminants can. Unsaturated fatty acids are generally a greater problem than are saturated fatty acids.

The optimal energetic efficiency for milk production is when fat provides 15–17 percent of the dietary metabolizable energy, which can be supplied by 5–8 percent of the total ration dry matter as fat (10). Adding 0.5–0.7 kg of fat to a cow's daily diet already containing 2–4 percent fat from forages and concentrates will provide this level. The energy in this amount of added fat is sufficient to produce 3.5–4.9 kg of milk, or 2.4–3.3 kg more milk than would have been produced from the 0.5–0.7 kg of carbohydrates the fat may replace. Researchers have observed increases in milk production of 2–12 percent from feeding added fat.

High-producing cows during the first 2–5 months of lactation will benefit most from added fat. This generally means cows producing more than 30 kg of milk daily. Herds with averages higher than 7500 kg per cow per year will likely benefit from added fat for the high-producing cows. Low producers and cows in the last half of lactation are not likely to respond to additional energy in their diet unless they are presently receiving a poor-quality diet in restricted amounts. Cows under heat stress may also benefit from added dietary fat.

Production increases from feeding added fat are not always as great as some would expect, but the added energy intake may result in other benefits. The writer has observed in a number of studies (in which various sources of added fat were fed during the first 3–4 months of lactation) that cows fed added fat usually attain peak daily milk yields a couple of weeks later than do other cows, but they then maintain their production with greater persistency. Field reports also indicate that cows fed added fat have less weight loss in early lactation, which may result in improved reproductive efficiency and fewer cases of ketosis; however, research data have not given definite support to such claims.

Fat Sources. Several acceptable fat sources for feeding lactating cows are listed in Table 15–5. Not all sources of fat are suitable feeds for milking cows. For instance, while soybeans, sunflower seeds, and cottonseeds are acceptable fat sources, free oils such as soybean oil, sunflower oil, cottonseed oil, corn oil, and fish oil should not be used because they affect rumen fermentation adversely, resulting in reduced fiber digestion and lowered milk fat tests. Fat sources listed in Table 15–5 are essentially inert in the rumen in that they do not significantly alter rumen fermentation. Oilseeds such as cottonseed, soybeans, and sunflower seeds also provide some protein and fiber, which can be considered when formulating diets.

Cottonseed, especially if it still includes the lint, contains relatively high amounts of protein and digestible fiber to go along with the fat. Thus it is a popular feed in areas where it is available at reasonable cost. Some researchers have observed increased milk fat tests when feeding cottonseed; however, no change in milk fat is more common. Feed handling may be a consideration with cottonseed because it does not flow well, which creates problems with some feed handling equipment. It is best stored in a dry flat area and fed through some type of total mixed ration feeding system.

Soybeans and sunflower seeds can be fed whole without processing, although they are often rolled prior to feeding. Soybeans usually benefit from heat treatment, while heating is not necessary with most other oilseeds. Soybeans contain several antinutritional factors which are destroyed by heat (see Ch. 8). These factors, such as soybean trypsin inhibitors, may interfere with intestinal digestion of proteins in cows consuming more than 1.8–2.3 kg of unheated soybeans daily. Heated soybeans may be stored longer than ground unheated soybeans because they are less likely to develop rancidi-

TABLE 15-5

Fat sources for lactating cows

	Composition (% of dry matter)			Recommended Amounts to Feed, kg/cow/day
Source	Fat	Crude Protein	Acid Detergent Fiber	
Oilseeds				
Cottonseeds	23	23	35	2–3
Soybeans	19	41	6	2–3.6[a]
Sunflower seeds	30–40	19	34	1.5–2.2
Fat supplements				
Tallow	99	—	—	0.5–0.7
Hydrolyzed animal-vegetable blend	99	—	—	0.5–0.7
Ca salts of fatty acids	85	—	—	0.6–0.8
Prilled fat	99	—	—	0.5–0.7

[a]Greater than 2.3 kg only if the soybeans are heated.

ty. Heated soybeans are often more palatable and may have greater protein bypass properties than unheated soybeans.

Some fat supplements, such as tallow as well as some animal and vegetable fat products, are more difficult to handle on the farm because they are not dry and free-flowing at normal handling temperatures. Ca salts (soaps) and prilled fats are dry, free-flowing products that can be handled conveniently in most feeding systems. These products are formulated for maximum rumen bypass and utilization for milk production, although data are limited which compare the effectiveness of these products relative to other high-fat products.

Fatty acid composition of the fat source should be a consideration also. Highly unsaturated fat sources such as vegetable oils are more likely to interfere with ruminal fermentation and cause milk fat depression. Hydrogenated vegetable fats as well as animal sources of fats are more saturated and thus less likely to cause problems with cows.

Extensive hydrogenation of unsaturated fatty acids normally occurs in the rumen, explaining why the fatty acid composition of milk fats and carcass fats of cattle remain virtually unaffected by the fatty acid composition of dietary fats. However, when cows are fed highly unsaturated fats such as soybeans and sunflower seeds, the milk fat becomes slightly more unsaturated (2). This slight alteration of the milk fat composition may offer some marketing advantages for dairy products, such as allowing the manufacture of butter that is more spreadable at refrigerated temperatures than butter from normal milk. However, if the unsaturated fatty acids completely escape ruminal hydrogenation, the milk may develop undesirable oxidized flavors.

Considerations with Added Fat. There are several possible concerns when feeding added fat. Milk protein percentages are usually reduced 0.1–0.2 percentage units, a problem that researchers have not yet solved (10). Milk fat percentages are usually unaffected, but they may be reduced slightly unless dietary Ca is increased to more than 0.9 percent of dry matter. Palatability is sometimes a problem with some fat sources, and feed handling presents problems with some products.

Several other nutritional adjustments should be made when feeding added fat. Boost the Ca content to more than a 0.9 percent of the diet dry matter. Ca complexes with fatty acids, forming soaps. This helps minimize the undesirable effects of fatty acids on fiber digestion in the rumen, but also means that some Ca may be lost in the feces as soaps. The Mg content of the diet should be increased slightly to more than 0.3 percent of dry matter to maintain a balance between Ca and Mg. Crude protein content may need to be increased slightly to maintain the proper protein to energy balance for optimal milk production. For instance, if a 16 percent protein diet is adequate without added fat, a 17 percent protein diet may be needed with added fat. Providing the extra protein in a bypass form rather than in a highly soluble form may be a good way to ensure that the protein is utilized efficiently. This is because the fat replaces nonstructural carbohydrates, which may result in a loss of energy to the rumen microbes and reduce ruminal microbial protein synthesis.

Carbohydrates. Most of the cow's energy is provided by carbohydrates, but the form of carbohydrates and carbohydrate digestibility vary substantially among various feed sources. Structural (fibrous) carbohydrates such as cellulose and hemicellulose are digested in the rumen, whereas the noncarbohydrate lignin is virtually undigestible. Nonstructural carbohydrates such as starches and sugars are readily digested in the rumen as well as in the intestinal tract, although some grain sources of starch are fermented more rapidly in the rumen than are other sources. It is necessary to maintain a sufficient amount of structural carbohydrates in the diet for normal rumen function, and fine-tuning the ratio of ruminally degradable carbohydrates and crude protein can increase ruminal microbial protein synthesis and energy utilization by the cow.

Some researchers have suggested that neutral detergent fiber (NDF) is related to dry-matter intake and that one should formulate diets for an optimal amount of NDF in order to optimize dry-matter intake (9). Theoretically, this principle is probably correct; however, the digestibility of NDF, which contains all of the fibrous components, varies substantially among various types of feed sources. Thus one cannot be confident that a certain percent of NDF will always allow maximum dry-matter intake. In general, at higher proportions of NDF (probably greater than 36 percent NDF with most forages), energy intake will likely be limited by gut fill, while at lower proportions (24–26 percent NDF) chemostatic factors may limit intake and insufficient fiber may be available for normal rumen function. Acid detergent fiber (ADF) should generally be at least 19 percent of dry matter to avoid milk fat depression, although some research studies with 16–17 percent ADF observed no milk fat depression. This amount of fiber can usually be supplied by a minimum consumption of 1–1.5 percent of body weight as forage dry matter. Fiber physical form is also a factor because ground, finely chopped, or pelleted forages are more likely to cause ruminal

upsets and milk fat depression than are longer feed particles. From a practical standpoint, the above items generally mean that the concentrate to forage ratio should not be greater than 60:40. If corn silage comprises all or most of the forage, 50–55 percent concentrate may be maximum because of the higher nonstructural carbohydrate content of the corn silage.

Feed grains are the primary dietary source of nonstructual carbohydrates, so increasing the amount of grain in the diet generally increases the amount of readily digestible carbohydrates and, hence, available energy for the cow. However, not all grain sources are equal in providing fermentable energy in the rumen. For instance, corn starch is usually fermented less rapidly in the rumen than is starch from grains such as barley, oats, and wheat (5). Sugars such as those found in dried whey or molasses are fermented even more rapidly. Increasing the rate of carbohydrate fermentation in the rumen stimulates ruminal microbial protein synthesis, which can improve protein utilization by the animal and reduce the need for bypass proteins.

Processing of feed grains can also influence digestibility and utilization. For instance, high-moisture corn is usually more digestible than dry corn (15). Ground, cracked, or rolled grains are usually more readily utilized than are whole grains, and processing such as steam flaking may improve digestibility (8).

The interrelationships between carbohydrate and crude protein degradation in the rumen are important for optimal nutrient utilization and production by the cow. Ideally, one desires a balance between carbohydrate and crude protein degradation rates in the rumen that will allow optimal microbial protein synthesis and volatile fatty acid production. Even with very high producing cows, it is still most advantageous to utilize the rumen to the fullest extent and to bypass the rumen with protein and energy sources only after ruminal production can no longer be increased.

Protein

Requirements for protein increase even more dramatically at the onset of lactation than the increase in energy requirements because milk solids contain about 27 percent protein (9). Only small amounts of protein can be borrowed from blood, liver, and muscles for milk protein synthesis, thus virtually all of the required protein must be supplied by the diet. Protein requirement is really a requirement for amino acids by animal tissues. The amino acids are supplied by the digestion of microbial protein and feed protein that escapes microbial breakdown in the rumen.

In the typical dairy cow a sizable portion of the dietary crude protein is broken down or degraded by rumen microbial digestion to ammonia. For the ruminally degraded crude protein to be of any value to the animal, the ammonia must be converted to microbial protein which in turn can be digested in the gastrointestinal tract (see Ch. 8). The relative proportion of ruminally degradable crude protein in the typical dairy cow diet is approximately 60 percent, but this proportion varies with feed intake, organic matter digestibility, feed type, protein level, and feeding system.

Bypass Proteins. Optimal protein utilization by the animal can best be achieved by supplying sufficient amounts of degradable crude protein and fermentable energy for maximum microbial protein synthesis and by supplying the remainder of the protein needs with high-quality bypass (undegradable) protein. The amount of microbial protein synthesized varies with the factors listed above but is likely limited to about 2–3 kg daily. The remainder of the required protein must be derived from bypass pro-

tein. High-producing cows (in general cows producing more than 5 kg of milk/100 kg of body weight) will likely benefit from diets formulated to contain greater than normal proportions of bypass protein.

All feed proteins are not degraded to the same extent in the rumen, as illustrated in Table 15–6. For instance, proteins in brewers grains, distillers grains, corn gluten meal, and heated soybeans are degraded less readily in the rumen than are most feed proteins. The protein in high-moisture corn is more degradable than that in dry corn, and the protein in grass or legume silage is more degradable than the protein in hay from the same forage. Crude protein from NPN sources such as urea is 100 percent degradable in the rumen.

Because proteins in various feed ingredients vary in animal degradability, it may be possible to formulate rations based on ruminal degradability or undegradability. However, our technology is not sufficiently refined to do this accurately. Values such as those presented in Table 15–6 are based on *in vitro* and *in situ* data which may not be precisely correlated with *in vivo* results. Also, variabilities associated with those data are generally very large. Despite these shortcomings, research data support the general concept that high-producing cows will produce more milk if fed diets containing less

TABLE 15-6

Approximate rumen undegradability of protein in some common feeds

Feed	No. of Determinations	Undegradability ± SD, % of Crude Protein
Alfalfa, hay	12	28 ± 7
Alfalfa, silage	6	23 ± 8
Barley	16	27 ± 10
Brewers dried grains	9	49 ± 13
Corn	11	52 ± 18
Corn gluten meal	3	55 ± 8
Corn silage	3	31 ± 6
Cottonseed meal	21	43 ± 11
Distillers dried grains with solubles	4	47 ± 18
Fish meal	26	60 ± 16
Linseed meal	5	35 ± 10
Meat and bone meal	5	49 ± 18
Oats	4	17 ± 3
Rapeseed meal	10	28 ± 9
Soybean meal	39	35 ± 12
Soybeans, unheated	2	26 ± 11
Soybeans, heated	2	49 ± 19
Sunflower meal	9	26 ± 5
Wheat	4	22 ± 6

Source: Adapted from NRC for dairy cattle (9).

degradable protein. A number of research studies indicated a 5–8 percent increase in production during the first 120 d postpartum in cows fed bypass proteins (11), although not all studies were positive and some studies demonstrated greater increases than others.

There are several points to consider in the use of bypass proteins to assure that a positive response is obtained.

a. Don't bypass the rumen at the expense of rumen microbial production. If this occurs, the amount of microbial protein may be reduced to the same extent as the increased bypass protein with no net gain to the cow.

b. Some bypass proteins may be undigestible and therefore unusable in the lower digestive tract as well as in the rumen. Heat-damaged proteins and some by-product proteins may be in this category.

c. The quality (blend of amino acids) of the bypass protein should be at least as good as or better than the quality of rumen microbial protein. Several of the bypass proteins used in cattle feeds are very deficient in some of the dietary essential amino acids. Even if the protein is digested, little is gained unless the supply of the amino acid(s) limiting production is increased. In some cases, treating proteins of known good quality such as additional heat treatment of soybean meal or heated soybeans may give a greater milk production response than substitution with a poorer-quality protein that is naturally less degradable in the rumen.

Bypass Amino Acids. Supplementing the diet with ruminally protected amino acids can be another means to increase the amount of amino acids presented to the gastrointestinal tract for absorption and, ultimately, to increase milk production. However, to be successful with this approach, one must supplement with the most limiting amino acid(s). It is sometimes difficult to determine which amino acids are most limiting, because the amino acid composition of the portion of feed protein that escapes ruminal degradation and the proportion of microbial protein to escape protein are seldom known with any degree of certainty. With many diets, methionine, lysine, or one of several other dietary essential amino acids may be most limiting. Supplementing with a ruminally protected form of the limiting amino acid(s) may increase production (12); however, the response to the first limiting amino acid may be small if the second limiting amino acid soon becomes first limiting. One may obtain a greater production response by supplementing with two to four amino acids that are likely to be limiting than by supplementing with only one amino acid. However, cost of such a supplement relative to feeding more of a quality feed protein may be a consideration. Technological advancements may make the use of supplemental ruminally protected amino acids a feasible alternative in the future.

Vitamins

Vitamins A and D. Vitamin supplementation of diets usually has no direct affect on milk production, but there are situations in which supplementation of certain vitamins may be considered. Most nutritionists recommend providing supplemental vitamins A and D to ensure adequacy of the diet for the animal's health, even though no response in production is likely to occur. Supplemental vitamin A may be needed when cows are fed low-quality forages or low amounts of forage, primarily corn silage and a low-carotene concentrate mixture, or only feeds that have been stored for several months or longer.

Some reports suggest that β-carotene, the precursor to vitamin A, has a role in reproduction independent of other forms of vitamin A (9). However, conflicting research results indicate that additional studies are needed to clarify the physiological role of β-carotene before its supplementation can be recommended.

Supplemental vitamin D is unnecessary when animals consume sun-cured forage or are exposed to ultraviolet light or sunlight (9). In cows consuming adequate amounts of Ca, vitamin D supplementation permitted a positive Ca balance earlier in lactation. Continuous high doses of vitamin D (for example, 70,000 IU of vitamin D/kg of concentrate) or massive doses (for example, 20 million IU of vitamin D/d) starting 3–5 before the expected calving date may help reduce the incidence of parturient paresis. However, one should be cautious when using such procedures because continuing the massive doses of vitamin D beyond 7 d can cause toxicosis.

Vitamin E. Most feeds, even when stored for several months, contain sufficient amounts of vitamin E, although supplementation may be warranted under certain conditions. Vitamin E supplementation may be necessary if oxidized flavor of milk becomes a problem. This problem is most likely to occur when diets contain only stored feeds and/or when diets contain supplemental fats. If milk flavor problems occur, 400–1000 IU of additional vitamin E/hd/d may be needed to correct the problem (9).

Recent research indicated that vitamin E and Se can help lower the incidence of mastitis (13). The vitamin E supplementation may be most helpful during the dry period, but supplementation during lactation may also be helpful. Se supplementation may also be helpful if diets contain less than 0.3 ppm of Se. The specific mechanism(s) in the mammary gland is not definitely known, although it is known that vitamin E and Se are involved in the protection of cells against oxidative damage caused by free radicals.

Water-Soluble (B) Vitamins. The B-vitamins are usually synthesized by rumen microorganisms in more than adequate amounts to meet the cow's needs. Thus supplementation with B-vitamins or microbial products such as yeast to supply B-vitamins is usually unnecessary and will not show any benefit. However, recent evidence indicates that supplementation with certain B-vitamins may occasionally be beneficial.

Because niacin is involved intimately with energy metabolism, niacin supplementation may increase milk production by moderating effects of ketosis on energy-stressed high-producing cows. Niacin supplementation is most effective if initiated either before or immediately after calving and continued for 4–10 weeks. A level of 6 g/hd/d effectively reduced the incidence of ketosis; feeding 12 g of niacin daily for several days to ketotic cows decreased blood and milk ketones and improved milk production. Several studies showed small positive responses in milk production and fat tests when feeding 6 g of niacin daily with all-natural proteins to early lactation cows (9). There were no benefits from such feeding in mid- to late-lactation cows, and cows fed NPN did not respond.

Choline supplementation will not affect milk production when diets contain adequate forage, but it may slightly increase milk fat percentages when diets are low in fiber (9). However, to improve animal performance, it may be necessary to provide the choline post-ruminally.

Vitamin B_{12} and/or Co supplementation will not likely be beneficial unless diets are deficient in Co (9). Cyanocobalamin, which contributes 10–20 percent of the vitamin B_{12} activity synthesized by rumen microorganisms, tends to be highest in the rumen of grazing animals and lowest in animals fed high-concentrate diets.

Minerals

Supplemental amounts of Ca, P, and salt (NaCl) are needed in most rations, with supplemental amounts of some trace minerals possibly needed also, depending on regional soil deficiencies. These can often be supplied by 1–1.5 percent of a Ca-P supplement and 0.5–1 percent trace mineral salt in the concentrate mix, plus making these available for free-choice consumption. The source of Ca-P supplement can vary with the forages fed, which likely dictates the amounts of supplemental Ca and P needed. For instance, legume-based diets need primarily supplemental P which can be supplied by a product such as dicalcium phosphate, monosodium phosphate, or monoammonium phosphate. In contrast, diets based on corn silage likely need large amounts of both Ca and P. The use of a trace-mineralized salt instead of merely NaCl often provides an inexpensive insurance that minerals needed in trace amounts are supplied.

Calcium and Phosphorous. Requirements of Ca and P increase substantially with the onset of lactation as milk contains substantial amounts of both minerals. The inability of a cow to adjust rapidly to this increased Ca demand can result in milk fever. Dietary manipulations during the dry period to minimize the risk of milk fever were discussed previously. Diets for lactating cows should be formulated with the intent of meeting the cow's requirements of these two minerals; however, considerable resorption of Ca and P from bones can occur to make up for short-term deficits. In fact, many cows may be in a negative Ca and P balance during the first 3–5 months of lactation. Ca requirements may also increase slightly with high-fat diets because of increased fecal Ca losses, as mentioned earlier.

The nutritional availability (true digestibility) of Ca may vary with different sources, so one may want to take this into account when formulating diets (9). Ca from inorganic sources may be more available than that from organic sources. Of various organic sources,

Ca from alfalfa—especially mature alfalfa—may be used less efficiently than that from other sources as a result of the relative indigestibility of Ca-containing crystals such as Ca oxalate. The nutritional availability for ruminants of various supplemental P sources varies somewhat (9), although these variations usually are not of great concern in formulating diets.

Sodium and Chlorine. Substantial amounts of Na and Cl are secreted in milk, thus making it essential to supply sufficient amounts in the diet. It is recommended that diets for lactating cows contain 0.18 percent Na and 0.25 percent Cl, which is about 80 percent higher than the concentrations recommended for dry cows (9). If most of the supplemental Na is supplied by NaCl, more than adequate amounts of Cl will be provided. However, if substantial amounts of the dietary Na comes from other sources, such as $NaHCO_3$, it may be necessary to evaluate the Cl status of the diet.

Other Minerals. Forages generally contain more K than the estimated 0.8 percent of dietary dry matter required by lactating cows (9). However, stress, especially heat stress, increases the K requirement, possibly due to greater losses of K through sweat. While K deficiency was previously considered unlikely to occur, it is more likely to occur today because of several changes in rations in recent years which have tended to reduce the amount of K fed. Although most forages contain more K than required by cattle, a major forage source, corn silage, is low in K, some fiber sources such as cottonseed hulls and corn cobs are low in K, and many concentrates are deficient in K. Thus feeding programs which include larger amounts of concentrates, more corn silage, and complete feeds using low-K fiber sources are likely to be bordering on K deficiency.

Iodine and Se are two trace minerals that are likely to be deficient in feeds grown in many areas of the world. Lactating cows require more I than do nonlactating cows because 10 percent or more of the intake is normally excreted in milk (9). Iodine is usually supplied as iodized salt to ensure adequate intake of 0.6 ppm I in diets; I compounds sometimes are used to prevent foot rot. However, excessive consumption of I may lead to dramatically increased I content of milk, because excretion of I via milk is one of the cow's means of getting rid of excess I. Supplementation of Se may be necessary to elevate dietary Se to 0.1–0.3 ppm.

Buffers. Cows fed acidic diets especially during the first few months of lactation may benefit from added buffers in their diets. Times when buffers may help include when animals are being fed high corn silage diets or wet diets (more than 50 percent moisture), during heavy grain feeding (more than 2 percent of body weight), during heat stress, when the particle size of forages and grains is too small, when off-feed is a problem such as during early lactation, or when milk fat tests are depressed. Under such conditions, adding buffers often improves feed intake, fiber digestibility, and microbial protein synthesis; increases the acetate to propionate ratio; and minimizes off-feed problems. $NaHCO_3$ at the rate of 0.75–1 percent of dietary dry matter or 1.25 percent of a 3 to 1 mixture of $NaHCO_3$ and MgO are effective buffers, as well as are similar mixes of similar buffering compounds.

Water

An abundant supply of fresh water should always be available for cattle to ensure optimal production. Water is supplied by free drinking water, water in the feed consumed, and metabolic water produced by oxidation of organic nutrients. The amount of water a cow needs is influenced by milk production, ambient temperature, humidity, salt intake, dry-matter intake, and other factors (9). With large groups of cows, several watering stations may be needed, because cows may not drink sufficient amounts of water if they have to stand in line very long to wait for a drink.

OPTIMIZING FEED INTAKE DURING LACTATION

Water content of feed may be a factor to consider when attempting to achieve optimal intake. This is usually not important for diets containing primarily hay and concentrates, but it can become a limitation for diets containing mostly ensiled or fresh forages, coupled with other high-moisture feeds such as high-moisture corn, wet brewers grains, and liquid whey. Moisture's effect on dry-matter intake is less when present in the form of fresh forages than it is in the form of silage or other fermented feeds. Limited data indicate that total dry-matter intake decreases as the moisture content of the diet exceeds 50 percent from ensiled feeds (9). This response may be caused partially by chemicals in the feed rather than by moisture per se.

FIGURE 15-6. Group-fed cows on a large dairy in southern California. Under these conditions the cows have a shaded area for rest and go inside only for milking and, sometimes, for calving.

The number of times cattle are fed daily may influence total dry-matter intake. A minimum of four daily feed offerings, alternating between forages and concentrates, appears to be the most desirable method of feeding ration components individually (4). Frequent feeding of total mixed rations does not necessarily increase dry-matter intake, however, more frequent feeding may help stabilize rumen fermentation, which may prevent drops in milk fat percentages and can minimize digestive upsets which may otherwise reduce feed intake.

High-producing cows should have access to their feeds for at least 18–20 h per day for maximum feed intake. When cows have access to their feeds, they will consume their daily intake in 12–22 meals. Feeding in groups, the most common practice in the United States, facilitates ready access to food (Fig. 15-6). Feeding more than 4.5 kg of concentrate mix/meal may cause acidosis. Many of the electronic grain feeders currently marketed are programmed to limit the amount of concentrate consumed by a cow within a short period of time, thus helping to maintain rumen stability under situations where concentrate mixes are fed separate from forages.

EXAMPLE RATIONS

Several example rations for lactating cows are listed in Table 15-7. These rations are formulated to approximately meet the nutritional needs of a 600-kg cow producing 40 kg of 3.5 percent fat-corrected milk daily. Such a cow requires a high protein and energy diet; and it is often difficult to meet those requirements and still maintain adequate fiber in the diet. It would be much easier to meet the nutritional needs of lower-producing cows. While there are numerous feed ingredients available in various areas, several feed sources predominant in many areas were used in these examples to illustrate a couple of points.

TABLE 15-7

Example ration formulas for lactating cows

	Ration, % of DM						
Ingredient	1	2	3	4	5	6	7
Alfalfa	50.0	55.0	—	27.4	50.0	25.0	45.0
Corn silage	—	—	60.0	27.4	—	25.0	—
High-moisture corn	41.2	—	17.2	32.9	—	29.3	35.3
Barley	—	38.0	—	—	42.0	—	—
Cottonseed meal	—	—	—	—	7.1	—	8.3
Cottonseeds	—	—	—	—	—	—	10.0
Soybean meal	7.7	6.0	20.9	11.1	—	8.7	—
Heated soybeans	—	—	—	—	—	10.0	—
Dicalcium phosphate	0.3	0.5	0.5	0.7	0.4	0.4	0.3
Monsodium phosphate	0.3	—	—	—	—	—	—
Limestone	—	—	0.9	—	—	1.0	0.5
Trace min. salt	0.5	0.5	0.5	0.5	0.5	0.5	0.5
MgO	—	—	—	—	—	0.1	0.1
Composition							
CP	17.0	17.0	17.0	17.0	17.0	18.0	18.0
NEℓ	1.67	1.65	1.71	1.69	1.63	1.73	1.70
ADF	17.5	20.0	19.4	18.3	20.8	17.6	20.2
Ca	0.80	0.86	0.64	0.64	0.83	0.90	0.91
P	0.42	0.42	0.43	0.44	0.42	0.41	0.42

Two somewhat extreme ration examples are ration 1, which contains only alfalfa as the forage, and ration 3, which contains only corn silage as the forage. Because corn silage contains more energy/kg than does alfalfa, a higher forage to concentrate ratio could be maintained and still provide slightly more energy than the alfalfa-based diet. However, because corn silage contains less crude protein and Ca than does alfalfa, corn silage-based diets need much more protein and mineral supplementation.

Rations 6 and 7 were included as examples containing added fat from heated soybeans or cottonseed. Note that the protein content was raised slightly because the energy densities were also elevated slightly, and the Ca and Mg contents were raised.

SUMMARY

Nutrient needs of dairy cows vary immensely between the dry period and peak lactation. Requirements for the former can often be met with forages alone, while the latter may require a considerable amount of high-energy feed sources such as feed grains and added fat sources, and bypass proteins of good amino acid quality. A challenge is to formulate a diet that contains sufficient fiber to maintain normal rumen fermentation so as to prevent digestive upsets and to prevent milk fat depression. A successful feeding program will meet a cow's nutritional needs for high production while minimizing body weight loss during early lactation, not causing digestive upsets, and maintaining health.

REFERENCES

1. Butcher, K. R. 1974. *DHI Record Briefs*. North Carolina State Univ. 10:1.

2. Casper, D. P., et al. 1988. *J. Dairy Sci.* 71:1267.

3. Coppock, C. E. 1974. *J. Dairy Sci.* 51:926.

4. Gibson, J. P. 1984. *Animal Prod.* 38:181.

5. Herrera-Saldana, R., and J. T. Huber. 1987. *J. Dairy Sci.* 70 (Suppl. 1):114 (Abstr.).

6. Mertens, D. R. 1985. In: *Proc. 46th Minn. Nutr. Conf.* 209. St. Paul, Univ. Minn.

7. Moe, P. W., W. P. Flatt, and H. F. Tyrrell. 1971. *J. Dairy Sci.* 54:548.

8. NRC. 1984. *Nutrient requirements of beef cattle.* Washington, DC: Nat. Acad. Press.

9. NRC. 1988. *Nutrient requirements of dairy cattle.* Washington, DC: Nat. Acad. Press.

10. Palmquist, D. L., and T. C. Jenkins. 1980. *J. Dairy Sci.* 63:1.

11. Schingoethe, D. J. 1984. Application of rumen bypass proteins in ruminent diets. *Animal Nutr. Res. Highlights* (April). St. Louis, MO: Amer. Soybean Assn.

12. Schingoethe, D. J., et al. 1988. *J. Dairy Sci.* 71:173.

13. Smith, K. L., et al. 1984. *J. Dairy Sci.* 67:1293.

14. Smith, K. L., and D. A. Todhunter. 1982. In: *Proc. 21st Ann. Mtg.,* p. 97. Arlington, VA: Natl. Mastitis Council.

15. Tyrrell, H. F., and G. A. Varga. 1990. *J. Dairy Sci.* 73: (in press).

16

Feeding Dairy Calves and Heifers

J. L. Morrill

INTRODUCTION

Dairy calves and heifers must be fed properly in order for them to produce according to their inherited potential. The degree of success of the calf raising program, of which nutrition is a major part, impacts on herd productivity in two major ways. For one thing, proper development of the individual animal to be retained for use is essential for good production. Also, a program that allows more animals to be raised to productive age allows more rigid selection of those animals to be kept. For example, assume that, in a 100-cow herd, 45 heifer calves are born each year and 25 cows are culled. If herd size is maintained at 100, there is a potential for culling 44 percent of the heifers (20 not needed/45 born). If losses from death, failure to breed, and all other reasons are 20 percent (a number often exceeded), then only 11 heifers (24 percent) of the 45 can be culled, thus decreasing the probability of having superior replacement animals.

A good nutrition and health program will produce heifers able to produce to their potential, beginning at about 24 months of age, and will be economical. This chapter will be concerned with feeding dairy heifers intended for herd replacements in a typical commercial dairy where profit is an important consideration. In some herds, where the main objective is producing show cattle and economics of milk production is a less important factor, different programs may be used.

NUTRITION OF THE NEWBORN CALF

The calf, like other young mammals, is born without antibodies (immunoglobulins, designated Ig) which provide immunity against diseases. Antibodies are concentrated in colostrum and can be absorbed by the calf for only a short time after birth. Ig absorption will be significantly reduced by 12 h after birth, and by 24 h absorption will be very low. Therefore, it is extremely important that the calf consume colostrum as soon as possible after birth. Not all calves will consume sufficient colostrum to provide adequate protection without help, thus it is a good idea to give the calf colostrum from a nipple bottle or esophageal feeder (Fig. 16–1). About 2 quarts should be given to an average-

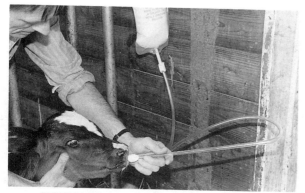

FIGURE 16–1. Administration of colostrum using an esophageal feeder. (Courtesy of E. P. Call.)

size Holstein calf as soon as possible after birth and again about 8 h later.

Ig content of colostrum produced by a cow increases as the cow gets older and is exposed to a wider variety of disease, and it is decreased by premilking. Commercial vaccines are available to increase Ig content of colostrum by vaccinating the cow a few weeks before freshening. In this way, stimulation of production of antibodies specific against certain bacterial and viral antigens can be accomplished.

If a heifer is brought into a herd just before calving, she may not have been exposed to some strains of microorganisms that exist in the new surroundings. In that case the newborn calf would not receive protection against disease organisms that it would encounter. This may be a frequent problem in cases where heifers are raised away from the lactating cows and are brought into the herd just before calving, in which case using colostrum from older cows would be desirable.

The antibody content of colostrum is correlated to specific gravity; therefore, colostrum quality can be estimated by measuring its specific gravity. Two commercial devices available from dairy supply stores for estimating colostrum quality are the Colostrometer and the Colostrodoser.

Some high-quality colostrum should be frozen for use when, for any reasons, good quality colostrum is not available from the dam. Freezing the colostrum in small (1 quart) amounts will make it easier to thaw. Because immunoglobulins are proteins, they can be denatured by excessive heat and should be thawed in warm (not hot) water. In one study colostrum was not damaged by thawing in a microwave oven (3), but one should not assume

those results would hold true with a different oven or for a different period of time.

Ig content of blood from a calf at about 24 h of age will be a good indication of Ig intake soon after birth. By measuring blood Ig concentration at 1 day of age, the newborn calf program can be monitored. Tests such as the zinc turbidity test (11) will be specific for antibodies. Because plasma protein at 1 day of age is highly correlated with Ig concentration, estimating plasma protein concentration with a refractometer is an easy way to determine whether calves are receiving adequate colostrum.

Transition milk is that milk produced by the cow from the second milking after freshening until normal at about 4 d after freshening. Either colostrum or transition milk should be fed to the calf on the second and third day of life, and longer if possible. Although Igs are not absorbed into the bloodstream at this time, they will be useful in the lumen of the intestines by helping to prevent attachment of bacteria to the mucosal surface of the intestines. If bacteria are able to attach, they will multiply and produce toxins that are absorbed by the calf.

NUTRITION OF THE CALF BEFORE WEANING

At birth the four-compartmented stomach of the calf is very different from the stomach of the mature cow. The rumen is underdeveloped, lacking the size, absorptive ability, or microbial population found in the rumen of the older animal (Fig. 16–2). In the newborn the large abomasum is useful because the primary food of the very young calf will be milk, which goes directly to the abomasum when the esophageal groove is closed. Dry feed is necessary for development of rumen size and musculature, papillary development, and establishment of bacteria, protozoa, and other microorganisms. Consumption of dry feed is responsible for rumen development, thus it follows that stimulation of dry feed intake will hasten the time when the calf can depend on digestion in the rumen to make major nutritional contributions. After weaning, the cost of feed, labor required, and frequency of loose feces are all reduced. Thus it should be obvious that stimulation of dry feed intake is an important part of nutrition of the calf before weaning. This is not an easy task, because the very young calf does not readily eat dry feed.

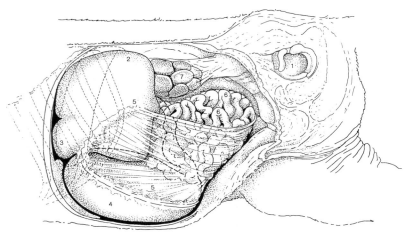

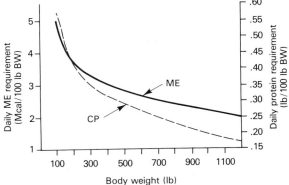

FIGURE 16–2. Topography of the abdominal organs in a newborn calf (left lateral view). The left abdominal wall and the left hindlimb have been removed. 1. Left acetabulum, 2. Rumen, 3. Reticulum, 4. Abomasum, 5. Greater omentum, 6. Small intestine, 7. Left kidney. From Dyce, Sack, Wensing: *Textbook of Veterinary Anatomy.* Philadelphia: W. B. Saunders, 1987. Used by permission.

Figure 16–3 shows the amount of protein and energy required at various ages from birth to 2 years of age, expressed as the amount per unit of body weight. From this it can be seen that the calf requires a very concentrated ration early in life and that the concentration can decrease as the heifer matures. Milk, having lots of protein and energy, is well suited to meet the requirements of the very young calf for these nutrients (Table 16–1). It is interesting to compare the protein and energy requirements of the lactating cow during the different stages of lactation (they are high early in lactation and decrease as lactation progresses) to the requirements of the growing heifer, as expressed in Fig. 16–3.

The young calf is quite limited in its ability to digest nutrients fed in liquid form and thus go to the abomasum through the closed esophageal groove, bypassing the rumen (Table 16–2). Milk has a number of characteristics that make it a good feed for calves. Over the years, development of milk replacers has resulted in products that contain significant amounts of milk products.

FIGURE 16–3. Daily energy and protein requirements of growing dairy heifers.

Liquid Feed for the Young Calf

Milk is usually fed at 8–10 percent of body weight daily. Larger amounts will result in faster growth, but less dry feed will be consumed, rumen development will be slower, and incidence of loose feces will be higher. Furthermore, this weight advantage gained from more liberal feeding of milk will not exist when the

TABLE 16-1

Composition of colostrum, transition milk, and milk from Holstein cows

	No. of Milking					
	1[a]	*2*	*3*	*4*	*5 + 6*	*27 + 28*
Specific gravity	1.056	1.040	1.035	1.033	1.033	1.032
Total solids, %	23.9	17.9	14.1	13.9	13.6	12.9
Fat, %	6.7	5.4	3.9	4.4	4.3	4.0
Solids not fat, %	16.7	12.2	9.8	9.4	9.5	8.8
Protein, %	14.0	8.4	5.1	4.2	4.1	3.1
Lactose, %	2.7	3.9	4.4	4.6	4.7	5.0
Ash, %	1.11	0.95	0.87	0.82	0.81	0.74

[a]First milking after parturition.
Source: Parrish, D. B., et al. 1950. *J. Dairy Sci.* 33:457.

TABLE 16-2

Ability of young calf to digest nutrients fed in liquid form

Nutrient	Enzyme Status
Protein	Adequate for milk proteins; other proteins less well digested
Carbohydrate	
Starch	No salivary amylase, pancreatic amylase low during first few weeks of life
Disaccharides	Adequate lactase, no sucrase, maltase low
Fat	Pregastric (salivary) esterase and pancreatic lipase adequate for large amounts of milk fat and other animal fats; unsaturated fats not well tolerated

FIGURE 16-4. Calf facilities used on a large calf rearing ranch. (Courtesy of Steve Marks, Calico Ranches, Inc.)

calf is older, compared to the weight of calves fed lower amounts of milk but the right kinds and amounts of dry feed. In several experiments calves grew as well when fed milk once daily, but twice daily feeding has the advantage of forcing the feeder to observe the condition of the calf at least twice daily. Incidence of sickness and death among calves is sometimes high, and early detection of poor appetite or other abnormalities is more likely if calves are fed twice daily.

Especially in cold weather, the temperature of milk or milk replacer should be close to body temperature when fed to calves. In warm weather some dairy producers feed milk soon after removal from a refrigerator. To facilitate mixing, warm water should be used to reconstitute milk replacer.

Milk or milk replacer can be fed from an open bucket, a nipple bottle or nipple bucket (Fig. 16-4), or some type of automatic feeder. If the calf is nursing from a nipple, the esophageal groove is more likely to close and less milk will go into the rumen. Nipple bottles or nipple pails are harder to clean than are open pails, and they may be a cause of digestive upsets if not properly cleaned. The open pail is more likely to be cleaned properly and has the added advantage that, if used, the calf can be stimulated to eat dry feed by putting a small amount of starter in the bucket as the calf finishes drinking milk or milk replacer.

Extra colostrum and transition milk should be stored and fed to calves. The desirable

method of storage is by freezing if space is available, otherwise, these products can be preserved by fermentation. For fermentation preservation, the colostrum should be stored in plastic containers or containers with plastic liners, and mixed daily. Colostrum that obviously is not normal or that contains antibiotics should not be used. Preservatives such as formaldehyde have been used and may be helpful but are not necessary if good management is used. Sodium bicarbonate added at the rate of 0.5 lb/100 lb of fermented colostrum before feeding will help encourage consumption of fermented colostrum. Because colostrum contains more dry matter than milk does, feeding colostrum at the same rate as milk may cause scours. To prevent this, colostrum (either fresh, frozen, or fermented) should be diluted with water at a rate to approach the composition of normal milk before being fed to calves. When using true colostrum (the first milking after freshening), it should be diluted with an equal amount of water. For a typical mixture of colostrum and transition milk, a blend of 2 parts of the mixture and 1 part of water is suggested. Colostrum fed to calves during the first day after birth, or milk at any time, should not be diluted.

Many dairy producers feed mastitic milk to calves and Kesler concluded, from published research, that mastitic milk could be fed successfully provided that certain restrictions were maintained (5). If used, mastitic milk should appear normal and should not contain large amounts of antibiotics. It is desirable that calves not be able to contact other calves before weaning, and that is especially true if they are fed mastitic milk. On some large farms all milk is pasteurized before it is fed to calves.

Milk Replacers

Before using saleable milk or milk replacer to feed calves, proper use should be made of all extra colostrum, transition milk, and mastitic milk. Depending on the amount of mastitic milk available, how long bull calves are kept, and when calves are weaned, saleable milk or milk replacer may not be needed. Only a good milk replacer should be used and then only if there is a definite economic advantage in doing so. To make a comparison, price of both milk and the milk replacer should be compared on a dry-matter basis. Assuming that milk is 13 percent dry matter and milk replacer is 95 percent dry matter, dividing the price of milk by 0.13 and the price of milk replacer by 0.95 will give the price per pound of dry matter for each. The value of a pound of milk dry matter compared to a pound of milk replacer dry matter would depend on the quality and composition of each, but as a start it will be helpful to remember that Holstein milk contains about 26 percent protein and 30 percent fat on a dry-matter basis. Most milk replacers for herd replacements contain about 23 percent protein and 10.5–19 percent fat on a dry-matter basis. Typical formulas for some milk replacers are shown in Table 16–3.

Quality of milk replacer components is critical and is not reflected by routine laboratory analysis. Reputation of the company should be considered, but it should be remembered that most companies produce different quality milk replacers. Final evaluation of the nutritional value of milk replacers is difficult without actually feeding the product to calves. The replacer should contain at least 22 percent protein and 10 percent fat (7). For best results, all protein should come from milk sources. Table 16–4 classifies some of the commonly used protein sources, and Table 16–5 shows results when three different types of protein were used in milk replacers.

The fat used in milk replacers should be from an animal source, or, if it is from a plant source, it should be saturated. The most com-

TABLE 16-3

Typical composition of some milk replacers (%)

Item	1[a]	2	3	4	5	6
Dry skim milk	18	20	2	3	11	15
Dry whey	13	32	37	32	27	37
Whey protein concentrate	17	18	4	3	10	17
Delactosed whey	10	10	10	10	5	0
Dry buttermilk	0	0	0	0	10	0
Sodium caseinate	0	0	0	0	0	1
Fat source[b]	0	2	0	0	0	8
Fat source[c]	40	16	30	40	35	20
Soy protein isolate	0	0	0	10	0	0
Soy protein concentrate	0	0	15	0	0	0
Supplements[d]	2	2	2	2	2	2

[a]1 = high-quality ''all-milk'' replacer; 2 = lower-quality ''all-milk'' replacer; 3 and 4 = replacer containing soy protein; 5 and 6 = veal milk replacers.
[b]Contains liquid fat and emulsifiers.
[c]Dry product containing 10% protein, 50% fat.
[d]Vitamin and mineral supplements, amino acid supplements, antioxidants, flavoring compounds, etc.

TABLE 16-4

Milk replacer protein sources classified by degree of acceptability for the young calf[a]

High	Medium	Low
Dried skim milk	Delactosed whey	Soy flour
Dried whey	Soy protein concentrate	Dried meat solubles
Whey protein concentrate	Soy protein isolate	Fish meal
Dried buttermilk	Fish protein concentrate	Single-cell protein
Casein	Hydrolyzed fish protein	Distillers solubles
Demineralized whey	concentrate	

[a]There is considerable variation in some of these prodcuts, and in some cases a different classification would be appropriate.

TABLE 16-5

Weight gain and nitrogen balance of calves fed three different milk replacers

Protein Source	Weight Gain, lb		Nitrogen Retained, %	
	3 wk	6 wk	3 wk	6 wk
All milk	17.6	55.0	47.0	61.5
Soy protein concentrate[a]	9.2	34.1	30.3	51.1
Soy flour[b]	2.2	22.0	22.5	38.2

[a]Commercial soy protein concentrate supplied 75% of the protein.
[b]Commercial soy flour supplied 75% of the protein.
Source: Dawson, D. P., et al., 1988. *J. Dairy Sci.* 71:1301.

monly used sources are lard oil, choice white grease, tallow, and coconut fat. The fat should be properly protected with antioxidants, and adequate emulsifiers should be included. Soybean lecithin is used both as a source of energy and as an emulsifier.

Lactose is the only carbohydrate that can be used in milk replacers without problems or potential problems unless special steps are taken, such as use of dietary enzymes. Complete absence or deficiencies of sucrase, maltase, and amylase result in the very young calf being unable to digest significant amounts of sucrose, maltose, dextrins, or starch. Even glucose, which requires no digestion, has the potential problem of being fermented to alcohol by yeast in the abomasum. Fortunately, lactose is available in large amounts in the form of dried whey.

The NRC recommends 1700, 270, and 18 IU of vitamins A, D, and E per pound of milk replacer, respectively (7). Some research suggests that the recommended amount of vitamin E is low and should be about 150 IU per pound (10). Most manufacturers add more vitamins A and D than the amounts suggested by the NRC.

Acidified milk replacers were first used to retard spoilage in ad libitum feeding systems where reconstituted milk replacers were prepared daily or less frequently. Some research results and field observations suggested that acidification was beneficial even when preservation was not a factor, but in other studies there has not been an advantage to acidification. Types of ingredients used, whether the replacer causes a curd to form in the abomasum, frequency of feeding, and degree of acidification are factors that would affect the response to acidification.

Use of antibiotics in milk replacers will increase dry feed consumption and weight gains of calves but will not decrease morbidity or mortality. In addition to economic considerations, decisions concerning use of antibiotics must also involve consideration of the potential for development of antibiotic-resistant strains of microorganisms. Probiotics (beneficial microorganisms) have potential for being useful, especially in the diet of a calf with a digestive tract disturbance. However, there is a paucity of published research identifying which probiotics are actually beneficial. Adequate numbers of viable microorganisms of the right strain must be delivered to the right place in the digestive tract if the product is to be useful.

Most calves readily consume milk replacers containing good-quality ingredients. Therefore, from the standpoint of the nutrition of the calf, commercial feed flavors are not needed but may be used as a marketing tool (they may have more effect on the buyer than on the calf). Rapid mixing of the powder in water is important, a process made easier by an instantizing process often used during manufacture of the milk replacer.

Dry Feed and Water

Except when a prestarter is used, the calf starter will be the first dry feed consumed by the calf. Because the very young calf does not readily consume dry feed and because dry feed is so important for rumen development, palatability of the starter is the most important feature. For this reason, certain ingredients such as oats and molasses are often used, even though they may not be an economical source of protein, energy, or other nutrients. The NRC recommends 1.41 Mcal of ME per pound and at least 3 percent ether extract in starters (7). Other recommendations are (percentages): protein, 18; Ca, 0.6; P, 0.4; Mg, 0.4; K, 0.65; Na, 0.1; Cl, 0.2; and S, 0.2. Recommended amounts of trace minerals (ppm) are: Fe, 50; Co, 0.1; Cu, 10; Mn, 40; Zn, 40; I, 0.25; and Se, 0.3. Recommended amounts of vitamins (IU per lb) are A, 1000; D, 140; and E, 11. Other evidence indicates that to increase ef-

TABLE 16-6

Example of an acceptable calf starter

Ingredient	%
Corn, cracked	51.5
Oats, rolled	20.0
Soybean meal	19.5
Molasses, liquid	7.1
Limestone, ground	1.0
Sodium bicarbonate	0.5
Salt, trace mineral	0.25
Dicalcium phosphate	0.15
Vitamin supplement	*

*Should supply 1000 IU of vitamin A, 140 IU of vitamin D, and 25 IU of vitamin E/lb of starter.

TABLE 16-7

Composition of prestarter (pelleted 3/16 inch diameter)

Ingredient	%
Whey, dried	46
Fat source[a]	23
Skim milk, dried	19
Sodium caseinate	12
Additives[b]	+

[a]Fat 60%, protein 7%.
[b]Includes antibiotic, preservatives, vitamins, minerals, and flavoring compounds.

ficiency of the immune system, the amount of vitamin E should be at least 25 IU per lb, and probably more (9).

An example of a satisfactory calf starter is shown in Table 16–6. The starter should be fed as a coarsely ground, cracked, or rolled mixture or as a pellet. Calves do not like a finely ground texture. A soft pellet (but not one that crumbles easily) about 3/16 inches in diameter is desirable.

If desired, hay can be ground and incorporated into a pelleted mixture at 20–25 percent of the total, or the hay can be fed separately. Hay should be available to calves from the time they are moved from their dams, because adequate fiber is essential for proper health of rumen papillae. Calves crave roughage and if other forms are not available they will consume bedding. It is much better that they consume high-quality feed than soiled bedding.

A prestarter may be used to stimulate calves to consume dry feed, thus allowing early weaning. A prestarter is a dry feed specifically formulated to be palatable to very young calves. Prestarters contain milk solids to take advantage of the natural affinity of the calf for milk, and they are fed in small amounts as the only dry concentrate until the calf is regularly eating about 0.5 lb per day. Then starter is added to the daily allotment of prestarter, in small amounts at first and increasing as the consumption by the calf increases. When the consumption of the mixture of prestarter and starter reaches a certain point (2–3 lb/d), feeding of prestarter is terminated and starter is made available ad libitum. An example of a prestarter formula is shown in Table 16–7.

Calves fed milk or milk replacer from an open bucket can be stimulated to eat dry feed by putting a small amount of starter in the bucket at about the time the calf finishes drinking the milk. In attempting to lick the last amount of milk, the calf will get the starter into its mouth and thus develop an appetite for that type of feed. If using a pelleted prestarter or a pelleted starter that does not break apart in milk, the feed can be put directly into the milk.

Calves should have clean water available at all times. Having water available results in increased growth and dry feed consumption (4) and eliminates the problem of water intoxication, characterized by bloody urine, which sometimes occurs when calves that have not had access to water are allowed to consume as much water as desired.

Weaning Calves

Most dairy calves are weaned between 6 and 11 weeks of age. With proper management, calves can be weaned earlier and still perform well, resulting in earlier rumen development and a reduction of feed cost, digestive upsets, and labor (1, 6). Age and size should also be taken into consideration, but the most imporant criterion is dry feed consumption. The healthy calf that is eating dry feed at the rate of 1.5 percent of body weight, in addition to milk, can be weaned successfully. With proper management this will usually be between 3 and 4 weeks of age, with some weaned earlier and some later than this age. To be successful with this approach, good management is necessary. A palatable, nutritious starter must be used, and the housing provided should reduce environmental stress. At the time of weaning the dry feed provided should not be changed, nor should the calves be moved or subjected to stresses, such as dehorning.

NUTRITION FROM WEANING TO FRESHENING

Weaning to Three Months of Age

During the period from weaning to 3 months of age the calf requires a ration high enough in energy that concentrates are always needed. In most cases, self-feeding concentrates during this time is most logical. Excessive energy intake is prevented by changing from a starter to a grower ration at the proper time. The calf should remain in an individual pen or hutch for a few days after weaning, until the sucking desire has diminished. The dry feed provided should not be changed at weaning time, so the calf will be able to increase dry feed consumption rapidly to compensate for loss of nutrients from milk. Except in very large dairy herds, calves of this age that differ in size and aggressiveness will often be penned together, and if they are fed a limited amount of concentrate some will not get their share. By allowing self-feeding, all calves can consume to their appetite. When consumption reaches the desired maximum on calf starter, the calf is moved to a pen with a self-feeder containing a suitable grower (Table 16–8).

During this time the roughage should be self-fed, and good-quality hay is usually the roughage of choice. Silage is neither desirable nor practical to feed during this time. Excellent-quality pasture could be used but rarely is available and a poor-quality or parasite-infested pasture may be worse than none at all. A good-quality mixed legume-grass hay is desirable for calves of this age.

Three Months to Freshening

Unfortunately, the period from 3 m of age to freshening is often a time in the life of dairy

TABLE 16-8

Example of acceptable calf grower (for calves fed a mixed legume-nonlegume hay)

Item	%
Corn, sorghum grain, or barley	64.7
Oats, rolled	10.0
Soybean meal	20.3
Molasses, liquid	3.0
Limestone, ground	1.5
Salt, trace mineral	.5
Vitamins A, D, and E	*

*To provide 1000 IU of vitamin A, 140 IU of vitamin D, and 25 IU of vitamin E/lb of grower.

animals when they are neglected, resulting in lower production or delayed freshening. Providing proper nutrition is made difficult during this time by the fact that often heifers within a pen are not uniform in size or aggressiveness, yet concentrate is fed in limited amounts. Much of this problem can be overcome by feeding a total mixed ration. When developing the feeding program for heifers, the following facts should be considered:

A. Heifers reach puberty at a certain size, rather than at a certain age, thus underfeeding can result in delayed conception and subsequently delayed milk production.

B. Overfeeding heifers will reduce milk-producing ability because of displacement of secretory tissue with adipose tissue in the udder. This is more critical if overfeeding occurs before puberty.

C. Decreased energy intake at breeding time decreases conception rate.

D. If properly fed before and after freshening, heifers will not produce more milk if freshened at a later age, compared to freshening at 24 months of age (Fig. 16–5). Also, by proper selection of bulls to breed heifers to, calving difficulties can be minimal.

E. Heifers should be fed enough grain during the last 2 weeks before parturition so that the rumen microorganisms will be adapted and grain intake can be increased rapidly after freshening.

After 3 months of age, heifers can make use of hay, pasture, or some silage. If concentrate mixture is fed separately, a simple mixture will be satisfactory, and often this can be one or more of the mixtures fed to lactating cows.

When formulating rations, a desirable growth rate should be established. Table 16–9 was developed from various sources and incorporates the suggestions of Waldo and coworkers (12). Using data from this table and NRC requirements (7), examples of satisfactory rations are shown in Table 16–10. In practice, least-cost programming should be used to formulate balanced rations that are most economical in a given location. Too often, heifers are pastured on poor-quality pasture or are fed poor-quality

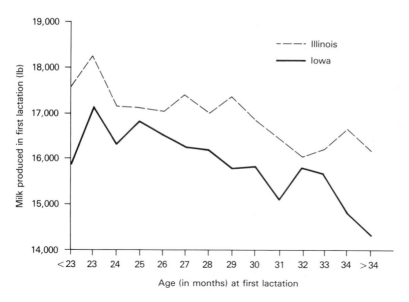

FIGURE 16-5. Effect of age at first lactation on milk produced during first lactation in Illinois and Iowa Dairy Herd Improvement Association herds.

roughage without proper supplementation. The benefit of using good-quality roughage is apparent from the data in Table 16-11.

FEEDING BULL CALVES

Because of the widespread use of artificial insemination in the dairy industry, only a few of the dairy bull calves born are used for breeding purposes, leaving many more that are available to be used for meat production. Most of these will be marketed as either veal or dairy steers. Those bull calves that result from special mating for the purpose of producing a bull to be used in the artificial insemination industry are very valuable, and proper care of these calves is especially critical. In most cases the calves are raised on the farm where they are born and are sent to a bull stud after several months of age. Rapid growth is desirable so that the bull can begin producing semen at an early age, but overconditioning is not desirable. Because of the value of the calf and the fact that the cost of feeding is less critical, feeding programs for these calves are less conservative. Thus only milk or high-

quality milk replacer is usually used, and special attention is paid to details concerning provision of top-quality calf starter, grower, and roughage. Silages are not usually fed to calves intended for breeding use. Except for those things mentioned, the nutrition program can be the same as for heifer calves.

Dairy Steers

Holstein and Brown Swiss steers are desirable animals to be fed and marketed as beef. In some cases these steers are used to harvest feed that otherwise would be wasted, such as corn or sorghum stalks, wheat pasture, or other excess pasture, then fed a high-grain diet during a finishing period in a feedlot. In those cases, early rapid growth may not be especially valuable and an early weaning program followed by high-forage diets that do not support maximum growth may be the most economical. The particular program may be planned to make maximum use of the kinds of feedstuffs mentioned, which are seasonal in availability.

In other cases the calves may be destined to remain in feedlots and be fed high-concentrate

TABLE 16-9
Desirable weights for dairy heifers (pounds)

Age	Ayrshire	Brown Swiss	Guernsey	Holstein	Jersey
6 wk	105	130	95	130	85
3 mo	165	205	150	205	130
6 mo	280	345	250	345	225
12 mo	500	625	450	625	405
15 mo	615	760	550	760	490
24 mo	1000	1240	900	1240	800

TABLE 16-10

Examples of rations for dairy heifers at indicated size and gain in pounds per day, dry-matter basis (as-fed basis in parentheses)

Feedstuffs	Body Weight and Desired Daily Gain, lb				
	400		800		1000
	1.4	1.6	1.4	1.6	1.6
Alfalfa hay	6.0 (6.7)	3.0 (3.4)	6 (6.7)	—	7.5 (8.4)
Bromegrass hay	—	3.0 (3.4)	—	12 (13.5)	7.5 (8.4)
Corn silage	—		6 (17.1)	—	
Corn grain	4.4 (4.9)	4.5 (5.1)	3.2 (3.6)	4.7 (5.3)	6.1 (6.9)
Soybean meal	—	0.3 (0.34)	0.17 (0.19)	1.2 (1.2)	—
Salt	0.05 (0.05)	0.05 (0.05)	0.05 (0.05)	0.05 (0.05)	0.06 (0.06)
Limestone	—	0.03 (0.03)	—	0.06 (0.06)	0.06 (0.06)
Dicalcium phosphate	0.07 (0.07)		0.03 (0.03)	—	—
Other	*	*	*	*	*

*Should provide vitamins A, D, and E and trace minerals as required, depending on amounts of those nutrients in the forage. A coccidiostat and/or other additives may be beneficial.

TABLE 16-11

Amount of concentrate mixture (lb) required for different sized heifers, at different levels of hay consumption[a]

Body Weight, lb	Hay Consumption, % of Body Weight				
	2.5	2.0	1.5	1.0	0.5
200	2.1	2.8	3.5	4.1	4.8
400	2.1	3.5	4.8	6.2	7.5
600	2.1	4.1	6.0	8.0	10.0
800	1.2	3.9	6.5	9.1	11.6
1000	0.7	3.8	6.9	10.0	13.1
1200	0	2.9	6.6	10.4	14.1

[a]Assumptions:
1. Daily gain of 1.6 lb
2. Concentrate mixture contains 1.37 Mcal ME/lb
3. Energy content of hay (Mcal ME/lb) as follows:
  200 and 400 lb heifers—0.93 (for example, mid-bloom alfalfa)
  600 and 800 lb heifers—0.89 (for example, full-bloom alfalfa)
  1000 and 1200 lb heifers—0.85 (for example, mature alfalfa)

diets (refer to Ch. 14). In these cases self-feeding of grain along with some roughage, or full-feeding of a high-concentrate, lower-fiber diet may be desirable. Some producers market Holstein steers at less than 12 months of age, weighing around 1000–1100 lb, that have been self-fed high-concentrate diets throughout life. If properly fed, these steers produce meat that is lean and tender.

Veal Calves

Veal is meat from calves that have been fed only liquid feed (colostrum, then milk replacer) until slaughtered. The amount of milk replacer fed is carefully adjusted to be near maximum con-

sumption at all times. The resulting carcass is lean, tender, and light in color. Intake of iron is restricted to the minimum amount required, especially near the end of the feeding period, to prevent production of dark-colored meat. If dark in color, the carcass will not be classified as veal and will not bring the premium price paid for true veal. Although several variations exist, most veal calves are fed in individual elevated crates or pens in climate-controlled buildings. Because they are not fed dry feed, the rumen does not develop normally. The large amounts of milk replacer fed (Table 16–12) make it especially important that the quality of products be high. Thus veal milk replacers contain only milk protein or high-quality replacements, and

TABLE 16-12
Nutrient requirements of veal calves

Body Weight, lb	Daily Gain, lb	Dry-Matter Intake, lb	ME, Mcal	Protein, lb	Ca, lb	P, lb
100	0.8	1.2	2.88	0.26	0.018	0.010
150	1.8	2.5	4.76	0.55	0.032	0.019
200	2.6	4.0	7.62	0.88	0.041	0.023
250	2.8	5.0	9.52	1.16	0.046	0.027
300	2.6	5.6	10.67	1.23	0.050	0.031

Source: NRC (7).

TABLE 16-13
Feeding schedule for veal calves[a]

Age days	Type of Milk Replacer	Amount Fed,[b] lb	Solids in Replacer,[b] %
1–10	Starter	4–7.5	6.2–6.7
11–42	Starter	8–12	7–13.5
43–63	Grower	13–15	13.9–14.6
64–105	Finisher	15.5–17	15.3–17.6

[a]A simplified presentation for illustration only. Many variations of this schedule exist.
[b]Value gradually increases during the indicated time period.

they are high in fat. Some examples of milk replacers for vealers are shown in Table 16–3, and an example of a feeding schedule is in Table 16–13.

Consideration based on welfare of the calves, and price and availability of some milk replacer ingredients (both those that have been extensively used as well as new ones), are stimulating interest and research in alternative feeding and management practices such as group housing, self-feeding of milk replacers, and provision of some type of dietary fiber.

SUMMARY

Calves are born without immunity, a developed rumen, or appetite for dry feed. Adequate consumption of quality colostrum soon after birth is imperative. Consumption of dry feed stimulates rumen development and determines length that milk or milk replacer must be fed. Therefore, palatable, nutritious dry feeds are very important for the young calf unless it is in-

tended for veal production. Milk is unsurpassed as the liquid feed of choice, but satisfactory milk replacers are available for use if milk is unavailable or if milk replacer is economically justified. If milk replacers are used, only high-quality products should be used. Calves intended for herd replacements can be successfully weaned when consuming dry feed at the rate of 1.5 percent of body weight daily. A high-quality starter and good-quality hay should be available free choice until about 9–10 weeks of age, at which time the calf can be switched to calf grower.

The nutrition program for replacement heifers should provide for continuous moderate growth to reach 80 percent of desirable mature weight at 24 months of age. Heifers should be fed adequately to provide for conception by 15 months of age, but care should be exercised to prevent overcondition, especially before puberty. A heifer should freshen with adequate stores of energy, but not be too fat, and her rumen should be adapted to the feed she will be fed after freshening.

REFERENCES

1. Anderson, K. L., T. G. Nagaraja, and J. L. Morrill. 1987. *J. Dairy Sci.* 70:1000.

2. Dawson, D. P., et al. 1988. *J. Dairy Sci.* 71:1301.

3. Jones, L. R., A. W. Taylor, and H. C. Hines. 1987. *J. Dairy Sci.* 70:1941.

4. Kertz, A. F., L. F. Reutzel, and J. H. Mahoney. 1984. *J. Dairy Sci.* 67:2964.

5. Kesler, E. M. 1981. *J. Dairy Sci.* 64:719.

6. Klein, R. D., et al. 1987. *J. Dairy Sci.* 70:2095.

7. NRC. 1989. *Nutrient requirements of dairy cattle.* Washington, D.C.: Nat. Acad. Press.
8. Parrish, D. B., et al. 1950. *J. Dairy Sci.* 33:457.
9. Reddy, P. G., et al. 1987. *J. Dairy Sci.* 70:993.
10. Reddy, P. G., J. L. Morrill, and R. A. Frey. 1987. *J. Dairy Sci.* 70:123.
11. Reinhold, J. G. 1960. *Advances Clin. Chem.* 3:83.
12. Waldo, D. R., A. V. Capuco, and C. E. Rexroad, Jr. 1988. *Proc. of Southwest Nutrition Conf.* Arizona State Univ., Tempe.

17

Nutrition of the Ewe

Hudson A. Glimp

INTRODUCTION

Books, and many chapters in books, have been written on the subject of ewe nutrition. The NRC in the United States (1) and the Agricultural Research Council (ARC) in Great Britain (2) have thoroughly reviewed the world research studies and established the nutrient requirements of the ewe for various stages of production and different levels of productivity. These authoritative resources represent the current understanding of the needs of the ewe for specific nutrients such as energy, protein, minerals, and vitamins in order to meet clearly defined production objectives. It is not the purpose of this chapter to restate what has been clearly and concisely stated in these publications. Instead, it is hoped that we can develop an understanding of how these fundamental principles apply to production systems in the various ecosystems in which sheep production may be a viable enterprise.

The major justification for the existence of sheep is their ability to convert certain feed, management, and other resources more efficiently than other livestock species into products

of economic value, namely, meat, wool, and milk. The relative importance of these three end-products depends on the relative demand and economic return within a given region and the efficiency of production compared to that of competing end-products. In some situations, available feed resources may dictate production levels of these end-products. In other cases, specialized or unique product demands may dictate the relative importance of meat, wool, or milk.

Ultimately, the production of sheep is controlled by their economic efficiency in converting available feed resources into products that have adequate consumer demand and economic value to be competitive with other similar products (disregarding price substitutes). In the case of lamb, production costs must be competitive with beef production, or the land will be used for beef production. With wool, the competitors may be other natural fibers such as cotton, or synthetic fibers. The end-products must not only be cost-competitive, but they must meet consumer demands for quality, satisfaction, and safety. To further complicate the situation, consumer demands may be quite different in different regions of the world. As examples, American consumers prefer larger lambs than do European consumers, and the type of fabric traditionally worn within a society and the current fashion trends will affect the prices of different grades of wool. All of these factors restrict the generalizations that can be made about sheep production systems, and thus sheep nutrition.

PRODUCTION OBJECTIVES

The extent to which a production system will produce certain levels of meat, wool, and milk will be dictated to a large extent by the breeds of sheep selected, the ability of the breeds to produce within the ecosystems, the available feed resources, the extent to which nutrient supplementation may be economically feasible to overcome resource limitations, and management capabilities.

Sheep are expected to produce in a wide range of environments throughout the world. Many different breeds are available for use, ranging from breeds best known for their wool production, to breeds that produce only modest amounts of wool but superior lamb carcasses or more lambs per lambing, to breeds that have no wool. The husbandry practices are almost as widely variable as the breeds available.

Available Feed Resources

Throughout the world the common denominator in sheep production is pasture and forages. Productivity of the pasture or rangeland or forage crop will largely dictate the maximum levels of productivity the sheep producer can achieve. These vary from subsistence production levels on the African desert, to commercial milk sheep production systems in Mediterranean countries, to intensive lamb production systems where meat production is the primary goal in Great Britain, central Europe, and the United States. In all cases end-product production objectives are closely related to the forage production capabilities of the land.

Arid Rangelands

The majority of the world's sheep are located in arid to semiarid ecosystems. Examples of these ecosystems would be the arid rangelands of Australia, Africa (Fig. 17–1), South America, Asia, and the southwestern United States. The extremely low rainfall in many of these regions

FIGURE 17–1. Persian Blackhead sheep grazing desert range in East Africa. Many breeds in this area are fat-tailed, where fat is stored during lush periods for mobilizing during dry periods.

will only marginally provide enough nutrients to support reproduction. In these situations, wool production is economically more important to the sheep enterprise. There are still large areas of Australia, southern Argentina, and other world regions that support large flocks of wethers for wool production. This is not necessarily by choice but by necessity, because the feed resources are not sufficient to support the nutrient needs of reproduction and lamb growth. Rainfall in these areas is generally less than 200 mm per year and not sufficiently concentrated or predictable on an annual basis to support seasonal forage growth. Because expected production outputs are low, these production systems are extensive, external inputs to the system are minimized, and sheep numbers are generally large enough to offset low outputs per animal unit.

Arid to semiarid rangelands in the 200–400 mm/year rainfall range generally involve production systems that include lamb production. Without supplementation at strategic periods of the production cycle, outputs generally range from 0.7 to 1.1 lambs/ewe/year. Lambs are generally sold at 20–30 kg live weight unless supplemental feed or forage is provided. Much of the southwestern United States fits this description, where lambs are generally sold as feeder lambs. With the lower income from lamb, wool is more important to the economy of the sheep enterprise. The ewe flock is largely of Rambouillet origin, with fine wool production approaching the economic return from lambs in the lower potential regions of the area. The extensive nature of the production systems, combined with generally higher feed costs than most regions of the United States, prevents supplementation of nutrients from being economi-

FIGURE 17–2. Ewes and lambs on sagebrush-grassland range in Idaho. Feed resources are limited except in the spring growing season.

cally viable in most years and production situations.

Rangelands and Crop Residues

A major exception to these generalizations is the transhumant herded production systems that have been used in the intermountain western United States (Figs. 17–2, 17–3). Producers have a home base that is often close to higher-quality harvested feeds, generally in irrigated valleys. Hay and grain from these croplands will be fed during late gestation and early lactation. Lambing is generally in the spring to take advantage of spring growth of high desert rangelands, which will be grazed by ewes and lambs until early summer. Ewes and lambs are then herded

FIGURE 17–3. Sheep under herder control on the U.S. Sheep Experiment Station alpine summer range in Montana. Herding is necessary for predator control and is required on western public rangelands in the United States.

onto summer alpine grazing in mountains at 7000–10,000 feet elevation. Ewes and lambs will be moved out of the mountains in late summer or early fall, at which time the lambs are normally sold at weights ranging from 40–55 kg, depending on the age of lambs and quality of the summer forage. Ewes will then return to fall range of medium to low quality.

In many locations, ewes are grazed on crop residues such as alfalfa aftermath, corn stubble, sugar beet tops, or other forage crops through the breeding season. Following breeding from October to December, the ewes will often be moved to winter desert range, where they will stay until 4–6 weeks prior to lambing. The late gestation-early lactation period, usually from 8–10 weeks duration, is largely a confinement or semiconfinement feeding system.

This type of production system may be described as opportunistic in that ewes are utilizing forage resources from several ecosystems at different times of the year. These systems utilize public lands, which means herders are required to control grazing patterns and protect sheep from predators. Production inputs are higher, which means outputs must be higher. Progressive producers are producing 1.3–1.6 lambs per ewe at market weights previously indicated. Wool production from the ewe flock, dpending on breeds used, ranges from 4–6 kg per ewe, with 50–60 percent clean wool yield.

Browse and Grassland Areas

The third broad rangelands category can be described as either improved rangelands or mixed browse and grassland areas. In the United States these rangelands tend to be on the fringes of the arid to semiarid rangelands. Rainfall would generally be in the 400–700 mm range and would normally be predictable enough to provide seasonal forage growth. Crop production from wheat, barley, and sorghum grains would be the normal practice on the higher-potential lands in this region. Sheep and other livestock production may be the only agricultural enterprise in the lower-potential or less productive areas. Many of the sheep enterprises are, however, secondary to crop production and are integrated into the total farming system to utilize crop residues, wheat pasture grazing, root crops, and the like.

The best example of the mixed browse and grassland region in the United States is the Edwards Plateau region of Texas (Fig. 17–4). The land is marginal to not suitable for crop produc-

FIGURE 17–4. Sheep and goats grazing together in mixed browse-grassland areas of the Edwards Plateau in Texas.

tion. Grass species tend to be mixed shortgrass and tall grass prairie species. Much of the area has been invaded by various species of shrubs and trees. Grazing systems are extensive and utilize cattle and sheep, and goats if browse is adequate or a problem. Over two-thirds of the nation's Angora and Spanish or meat goats, 10 percent of the nation's sheep, and a large number of beef cattle are located in the Edwards Plateau region. Where crop farming is part of the system, sheep production systems tend to be more intensive (Fig. 17–5). The region will also incorporate a lot of the feeder lambs produced in the arid regions for further growth on pasture and forage crops prior to their finishing in feedlots in years when production is adequate. Rambouillet and Merino-type ewes are normally used in this region. A portion of the ewes may be mated to Suffolk sires for crossbred lamb production.

The wheat production region in the southern great plains is another example of this ecosystem. Sheep production is closely tied to

FIGURE 17–5. Integrated crop-sheep production systems. Land not suited to crops or rotated to pasture will be utilized by sheep along with crop residues and farm-grown feeds.

wheat production in this area. Lamb production systems normally produce fall-born lambs from Rambouillet or Dorset × Rambouillet crossbred ewes. Lambing is scheduled to coincide with the availability of wheat pasture grazing, with lambs being weaned and marketed in the spring when grazing must cease for the wheat to produce a grain crop. A large number of feeder lambs from the arid rangelands of west Texas and New Mexico will be grazed on wheat pasture in the fall and winter months in this region. A good percentage of these feeder lambs will be finished on wheat pasture with minimum nutrient supplementation.

The northern Great Plains of the United States, much of which also fits in this ecosystem, tends to be shortgrass prairie grasslands. Sheep production systems tend to be extensive in nature, although spring shed lambing may be practiced. These production systems normally produce feeder lambs, although in good rainfall years many of these lambs will be at or near slaughter weight and finish when marketed. The ewes in this region are generally of Rambouillet origin. Many producers still breed one-third to one-half of their ewes to Rambouillet rams for replacement production, and the remainder of the ewes will be mated to meat-type sires for market lamb production. Supplemental feeding is normally restricted to the winter months when hay is fed to the ewe flock during gestation. Supplemental grain would be fed to ewes only during late gestation and early lactation, before spring pasture growth. The only producers that would supplement the pasture with creep feed for lambs would be those that plan to produce finished lambs for slaughter. These systems would be in the higher rainfall areas of this ecosystem and would have improved pastures and forage crops for use in their sheep production systems.

High-Potential Grazing Land

The fourth broad category of production systems in the United States is located in the more temperate, high-potential ecozones (Figs. 17–6, 17–7). These are areas with rainfall in excess of 700 mm/year, or areas associated with irrigated crop and pastureland in the more arid zones. Pastures tend to be improved varieties of adapted grasses and legumes and other forage crops. Most sheep enterprises are secondary to crop production and are closely integrated with crop production to utilize crop residues for grazing and hay and feed grains produced in the

FIGURE 17–6. Pastoral sheep production in New Zealand. Highly productive pastures, hardy sheep breeds, and good managers make New Zealand one of the most productive pastoral regions of the world.

system for ewe and lamb feeds to produce market lambs for slaughter. Small feedlots may be associated with some operations to permit the purchase of feeder lambs to finish for slaughter.

Some producers in this category are approaching or exceeding 200 percent lamb crops. Ewe flocks tend to be crossbred females, with many including one-quarter to one-half Finnsheep breeding. Ewes are generally mated to terminal sire breeds to produce market lambs at slaughter weight. High production goals make nutrition more critical in these systems. Farm flock producers tend to lamb in the winter to utilize farm labor that may not be available during the crop production season. A few producers in this category are attempting to lamb more than once per year. The critical elements in these systems are skilled management, appropriate genetic resources capable of both out-of-season breeding and at least two lambs/ewe/lambing, and adequate feed resources to support these production demands (Fig. 17–8).

FIGURE 17–7. Feeder lambs grazing clover-grass pasture in Kentucky. Intensive pasture production systems are appropriate for sheep in many high-potential areas of the world.

FIGURE 17–8. Confinement sheep production, though limited in use, may be appropriate where land costs are high and feed costs are reasonable. Productivity must be high and lamb markets must be strong to make this a feasible method of production.

NUTRITIONAL STATUS

For optimum production, the sheep producer must realize that nutritional status of the ewe may be critical at all stages of the production cycle. Lack of understanding on this point has caused much confusion among sheep producers and even research scientists. Body composition at a given point in the production cycle may influence both production response at that point and response to varying levels of nutrition. Our inability to measure body composition of the live animal has been a problem for both researchers and sheep producers. Many researchers have overcome this problem by using animals with uniform body condition for a given study, and slaughtering samples of the animals initially and after the study period. This provides more precise answers for research, but is laborious, expensive, and impractical for the sheep producer. New technologies are being developed that may overcome this problem by presenting a rapid, reliable, and inexpensive method of estimating composition of the live animal. When this occurs, both research scientists and sheep producers can plan nutritional regimens with greater confidence in expected biological and economic responses.

Assessing Body Condition

Although our measurements of body composition of the live animal are imprecise, we must work with the best system available at this time. Researchers, educators, and progressive producers have developed a subjective scoring system that permits fairly reliable assessment of body condition. Although some people use scores of 1 through 10, most use scores of 1 through 5, with lower-scoring animals being the least fat and highest-scoring animals being the fattest. The scale used is immaterial, as the most critical element is consistency in scoring from sheep to sheep.

Evaluation of fatness is made by palpation of fat thickness immediately behind the last rib in the lumbar region. Dr. J. J. Robinson, in the second edition of this book, provided excellent graphic examples of condition scores 1 through 5, which are shown as Fig. 17–9. Dr. Robinson's illustration shows a condition score of 1 as being an extremely emaciated individual, with no detectable fatty tissue between skin and bone. With a score of 2, the spinous process is still prominent and only a slight amount of fat can be palpated over the rib and loin eye. A condition score of 3–3.5 is considered as medium fat thickness, and the normal desired body condition for the ewe at mating. A condition score of 5 is entirely too fat, requires a waste of nutrients to achieve, and may cause production problems. An experienced person will find that condition scoring is easy, and she or he will develop confidence in the ability to further refine the score to decimal points, such as 2.25, 3.5, and so on.

Estimating body condition can be helpful in planning feeding programs at critical stages of production. Ewes can be grouped according to condition score and managed accordingly. For example, flushing ewes prior to breeding would probably be beneficial in ewes with a condition score of less than 3.0, but it is not likely to improve ovulation and conception rates among ewes with condition scores above 3.5. Sorting ewes is probably even more critical in the last 4–6 weeks before lambing. The target condition score at parturition for ewes carrying twins should be near 4.0, and at least 3.5 for ewes carrying singles. Condition scores much below these may result in weak lambs and reduced milk production. Condition scores much above 4.0 may create problems such as dystocia, excessive fat in udders, and increased incidence of pregnancy toxemia.

Body Weight Targets

Another good measure of ewe nutritional status is target weights. A mature ewe, 3–7 years of age, should be expected to be at her mature weight with a condition score of 3.5 at mating

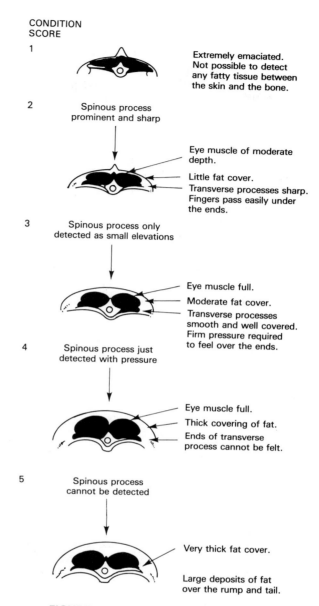

FIGURE 17–9. The physical characteristics used in defining body condition of ewes.

time. Ewe lambs that are expected to lamb at 12 months of age should be a minimum of 65 percent of mature weight at mating at 7 months of age and 75 percent of mature weight at lambing. Ewes should be at 80 percent of mature weight when mated at 19 months of age, and at 95 percent of mature weight when lambing at 2 years of age. These lambing weights should be at least 10 percent higher for ewes carrying twins than for ewes with singles. Younger ewes at less than mature weight are still growing and will obviously have to be fed to meet their growth needs as well as their gestation and lactation requirements.

Changes in Nutritional Status

Many variations from the ideal can occur in terms of nutritional status, but certain generalizations are appropriate. Based on a review of research studies on the subject, one can generalize with the statement that each point in the condition score on a scale of 1 to 5 represents approximately 1.0–2.5 percent body fat reserves above the minimum amount of body fat required for survival. In other words a condition score of 1.0 would indicate body fat reserves of 2 percent or less, which is about the minimum required for survival. A condition score of 3.0–3.5, which is considered desirable at mating, would indicate body fat reserves of 6–8 percent. For optimum productivity, body fat reserves should approach 9–10 percent at lambing time, depending on gestation of singles versus two or more lambs.

In reality, arid range conditions, for example, will not support these desired levels of body condition. Under range conditions in a normal production cycle, body condition scores of 2.5–3.0 at mating (5–7 percent body fat reserves) are not normally reached. Body fat reserves are more likely to be near 6 or 7 percent at lambing, and approaching 3 or 4 percent at weaning. With nutrient resources providing only these levels of body condition, it is easy to understand why highly productive ewes that would produce two or more lambs would be considered undesirable under arid range conditions. At the same time, improved pastures and farm-produced supplemental feedstuffs that can support the desired body condition would be wasted on less than highly productive ewes.

NUTRITION AND PRODUCTION GOALS

In most production situations, nutritional status may be the dominant factor that determines whether or not a flock reaches its production potential. Short-term deviations from optimum may occur without affecting production, but these must be corrected if future effects on productivity are to be avoided. The producer must have a clear understanding of feed resources and the economics of supplementing potential nutrient deficiencies before establishing production goals. The nutritional limits on production will affect decisions such as breeds to use, lambing season, grazing management systems, market weight goals for lambs, and many other management decisions.

The lambing season is normally timed to coincide with the onset of high-quality forage production. Peak nutrient demands on the system will be during late gestation and early lactation for the ewe and during the first 4–5 months after birth for the lamb. Since the lamb is largely dependent on the ewe for nutrients during the first 2 months of life, this period becomes even more critical for ewe nutrition. Deviations from this schedule are clearly possible, and may even be economically desirable because of market considerations and other factors, but the producer must be aware of the nutritional consequences of these deviations.

Although it is clearly understood that no single set of standards or conditions are applicable to all production situations, we must establish a base or standard for discussion purposes. Once this is done, then deviations from this standard can be discussed more objectively. Figure 17–10 attempts to describe optimum body weight changes and expected body condition for a 70-kg ewe through an annual production cycle.

It is relatively easy to define the nutrient needs of confined sheep to meet expected body weight and composition changes. These can be derived from the nutrient requirement tables provided by the NRC (1) or the ARC (2) and the nutrient content of available feedstuffs. The nutrient needs of pasture and range sheep are higher due to energy expended in harvesting and due to greater exposure to environmental effects on nutrient needs.

Replacement Ewe Lambs

The most critical factor affecting nutrient needs of ewe lambs is whether or not they are to be bred to lamb at 1 year of age. Arid rangelands will not support growth rates adequate to mate ewes at 7 months of age. Range ewe lambs should be separated from the flock and managed on pasture that will support growth rates that will allow them to reach approximately 65 percent of mature weight at 1 year of age, 80 percent of mature weight when mated at 18 months, and 90–95 percent of mature weight when lambed at 24 months. Growth rates should not permit excessive fattening, as fat cells may invade mammary tissue and depress subsequent milk production. At the same time, growth rates that are below those required to meet these target weights may result in ewes that do not conceive first until 2.5 years of age.

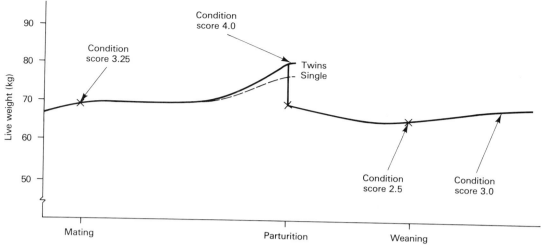

FIGURE 17-10. Suggested optimum body weight and condition scores for a 70-kg mature ewe.

Producers with improved pasture and confinement or semiconfinement nutrition programs should plan to mate ewe lambs at 7 months of age. Research has shown that ewes lambing first at 12 months have significantly higher lifetime production, even excluding the first year of production. These ewe lambs should be managed to reach a minimum of 65 percent of mature weight at 7 months of age at mating and 80 percent of mature weight at lambing. Ewe lambs must be fed and managed separately from mature ewes throughout this period to provide nutrients necessary for growth as well as gestation and lactation. The NRC, for example, has estimated that the 11-month-old ewe lamb in the last months of gestation would require 20–25 percent more energy and 40 percent more crude protein than the nonpregnant ewe lamb expected to mate first at 18 months (1). These higher nutrient needs must follow through lactation and to the next breeding at 18 months. High-quality pastures, especially those containing 25 percent or more legumes or high-protein forbs may meet nutrient needs. The important point to realize is that significant weight losses during lactation in ewe lambs will result in lambs of inferior quality and ewes that may not recover sufficiently to mate at 18 months, either of which negates the benefits of lambing ewe lambs at 12 months of age. If pasture quality is not adequate, then supplemental nutrients must be provided if this management practice is to be successful.

Maintenance

Figure 17–10 shows that the mature ewe can be fed a maintenance diet for 4–5 months, or 30–40 percent of the year. Assuming a 35-d breeding season, the ewe flock can be managed on a maintenance diet for the next 60–75 d. If the ewe is on a once-yearly lambing schedule and the lambs are weaned at 120 d postpartum, then the postweaning period can be essentially a maintenance program for the next 4–6 weeks. Earlier weaning may result in a longer maintenance period if ewe weight losses were not too great during early lactation. With the exception of mid-winter and extremely arid conditions, pasture is generally adequate to meet the maintenance requirements of the nongestating, nonlactating ewe.

Flushing

Flushing, or improving nutrition during the 3–4 weeks prior to mating as a method of increasing ovulation rate and conception rate, is poorly understood by many people associated with sheep production. Further, research results have been conflicting on the efficacy of this management practice. A lack of understanding of target weight and body condition objectives accounts for most of this confusion. Ewes that are at or near their normal mature weight and that have a condition score of 3.0–3.5 at 3–4 weeks prior to mating are not likely to respond to flushing. Ewes at 5–10 percent below normal mature weight and with condition scores of 2.5 or less will likely respond to flushing. The greater the deviation below normal, the longer the flushing period should be. Ewes with condition scores of greater than 3.5 may actually show a negative response to flushing, especially if high ambient temperatures can be a problem during the breeding season. Range producers with fall pastures that are dry mature grasses and forbs and low in energy and protein may benefit from flushing if the ewes have not had an adequate opportunity to fully recover from lactation. Producers with improved, high-quality pastures may find that the greater challenge is to keep the ewe from becoming too fat during the postweaning to mating period.

A general misconception is that flushing requires supplemental grain or protein. Progressive producers will identify pastures that are suitable for premating and mating management and schedule grazing so that the ewes can be flushed, or moved to an improved plane of nutrition on these pastures. This could also be accomplished by feeding supplemental forage crops such as alfalfa aftermath grazing after frost has stopped alfalfa growth. This is a popular practice in the western United States. Range lambing operations, or those that are operating in arid range ecosystems where excessive twinning may be undesirable, should recognize that flushing may also be undesirable as long as body condition scores are approaching 2.5. This level of body condition may depress maximum ovulation rate, but should be more than adequate to support ovulation, conception, and implantation. Body condition scores at 2.0 or lower are likely to depress ovulation, conception, and implantation rates, resulting in significant decreases in the percent of ewes lambing.

Early Pregnancy

There is growing evidence that the nutritional status of the ewe is critical from conception until the completion of implantation at approximately 40 d. Prior to implantation the embryo is completely dependent on placenta fluids for nourishment. Severe undernutrition or stress may deplete these fluids, either in volume or in content of essential nutrients. Deficiencies of Se and vitamin E can lead to embryonic death loss during this period. Ewes in poor condition and young ewes are most susceptible to undernutrition at this stage.

A very high plane of nutrition may also cause problems, especially in combination with environmental factors such as heat stress. Research has shown that fat ewes exposed to 85° F for as little as 12 h may suffer embryo loss during the preimplantation phase. Excessive intake of legumes high in estrogen can potentially cause early embryonic deaths. In extreme conditions, excessive fat may interfere with migration of the egg from the ovary through the oviduct.

Mid-Pregnancy

The period from approximately day 40 through day 110–115 of pregnancy is generally considered a maintenance period in terms of ewe nutrition, but this period can become critical if extreme deviations from maintenance are permitted. Range operations that lamb in the spring often find nutrient limitations such that even maintenance is difficult during this period. Nutritional status of the ewe entering this period is also critical in terms of what can happen during mid-pregnancy. Ewes in normal body condition at day 40 with a single pregnancy can probably lose up to 5–7 percent of body weight without significant negative effects. Ewes carrying two or more fetuses should be kept close to normal body condition and weight. The major winter range deficiencies are normally protein and energy, with phosphorus deficiency also a potential problem.

A high plane of nutrition that permits significant fat deposition can also potentially cause problems later in pregnancy, especially with pregnancy toxemia and dystocia. Pregnancy toxemia is most often a problem that occurs in improved pasture systems where the ewes are permitted to gain too much weight during mid-pregnancy and then are not maintained at this nutritional level during late pregnancy, most often in winter lambing systems.

Late Pregnancy

Approximately two-thirds of fetal growth occurs in the last 6 weeks of gestation. The protein level of ewe diets is more critical at this time due to the high protein content of fetal tissue and colostrum. Energy is also important to the ewe's need to increase fat reserves for lactation. The ewe should be entering this period with a condition score of 3.0 to 3.5, and should be expected to gain 12–15 percent of body weight with a single fetus and up to 20 percent of body weight with twins.

The critical point is the nutritional status of the ewe entering the last 6 weeks of pregnancy. If the ewe lost up to 5 percent of body weight during the mid-pregnancy period, then an adequate plane of nutrition is very critical for ewe recovery and fat deposition and fetal growth. This is often the case in western U.S. spring lambing systems where the winter desert range may be marginal for ewe maintenance needs. In improved pasture production systems, ewe nutrition during the maintenance or mid-gestation phase should be adequate, thus requiring only limited supplementation to achieve the desired late gestation body weight gains.

Close to 75 percent of the total energy in fetal tissue is protein, and colostrum contains approximately 20 percent protein. The extent to which protein supplementation is required at this time is dependent on energy intake. If energy intake is marginal or inadequate, supplemental protein may be degraded for the ewe to meet energy needs. For ewes that are fed adequate energy levels to meet ewe and fetal growth objectives, it is likely that most feed-stuffs commonly used would meet the ewe and fetal growth protein needs. Most sheep producers in the United States feed high-quality alfalfa or grass-legume mix hay during late gestation, which should be more than adequate to meet protein needs.

Inadequate nutrition levels during late gestation can affect fetal growth and subsequent birth weight and can also cause reductions in milk production and subsequent lamb growth rate. Ewe nutrition levels that result in lamb birth weights much below 3 kg will result in lower lamb survival. The lamb at birth also needs adequate tissue energy reserves to minimize the stresses associated with birth and potential environmental stresses such as extreme low temperatures. Undernutrition of the ewe can affect colostrum production and potentially cause delayed onset of lactation as well as affect the level of milk production. Because extensive range production systems are often hard-pressed to provide optimum nutrition levels at this stage, and the economics of nutrient supplementation are marginal at best, the desirability of less prolific breeds for these situations is further emphasized. Where supplemental pasture or forage crops or feed grains are available, then these should be incorporated into the system and production goals can be increased.

Overnutrition causing excessive fatness in the ewe can also cause problems, especially if this occurs prior to the last 3–4 weeks of pregnancy and is not maintained until parturition. The most common manifestation of problems caused by excessive ewe condition is pregnancy toxemia. Pregnancy toxemia most commonly occurs in fatter ewes carrying multiple fetuses. With multiple fetuses, stomach capacity is reduced, which will accentuate problems of sudden changes in nutrition. A sudden reduction in feed supply is the most common factor causing the onset of pregnancy toxemia. The problem can also be triggered by sudden changes in the diet, such as drastic increases in the intake of concentrates that may cause acidosis.

From an operational standpoint, the best management practice for the producer would be to sort the ewe flock into two or three groups at the beginning of the late gestation phase on the basis of body condition score and feed accordingly. Ideal conditions would be to divide the ewe flock into three groups. The first group would include younger ewes that are still growing plus older, thinner ewes that may require extra feed. The second group would be those that are in more appropriate body condition. The third group, if any are in the flock, might be those carrying excessive body condition that would require special feeding and management.

The technology is rapidly becoming available for sorting ewes carrying singles versus multiple fetuses. Commercial availability of this technology will greatly enhance nutritional management of ewes during gestation. Even range producers could afford to provide supplemental feed to those ewes carrying multiple fetuses if they could be identified and separated from those carrying singles.

Milk Production

Lambs are allowed to nurse in a majority of the world's sheep production systems. Commercial milk production, particularly for the manufacture of cheese, is important in many southern European, central and eastern European, and Middle East countries (Fig. 17–11). Sheep milk may contribute directly to the human diet in many countries of northern Africa and the Middle East. In most of the cases where sheep are milked, the ewe still provides milk for lamb growth for the first 4–6 weeks of lactation.

Several factors may affect lactation in the ewe. Number of lambs suckled has probably the greatest influence on milk production of any nonnutritional factor. Ewes suckling twins will produce 30–50 percent more milk than ewes suckling singles, and ewes suckling triplets will generally produce slightly more milk than ewes suckling twins. Lambs suckling as singles, however, generally grow faster than lambs suckling as twins. In general, lambs suckling as singles provide the most reliable measure of the contribution of milk, genetic potential, and other

FIGURE 17–11. A sheep milking unit in Spain. Milk production from sheep for cheese production is widespread in Europe, North Africa, and the Middle East.

factors on lamb growth, while ewes suckling twins will provide the most reliable measure of ewe milk production potential.

Age at first lambing and parity will both have significant effects on level of milk production. Level of milk production generally increases from the first through the third lactation, is generally stable from the third through sixth lactations, then will begin to decline with increasing age. Ewes lambing first at 1 year of age will have lower milk production than those lambing first at 2 years of age, but subsequent lactations should equal or exceed those lambing first at an older age.

There are substantial genetic influences on milk production level and composition in sheep. Breed differences of as much as 300 percent in weight of milk produced may exist among world sheep breeds. The percent of nutrients such as fats and total solids tends to decline as weight of milk produced increases, although the total nutrients produced will likely increase with increasing weight of milk produced. With the exception of the breeds of sheep that are milked commercially, there has been almost no direct selection for increased milk production in sheep. Increasing milk production of breeds that are emphasizing increased prolificacy will likely receive increased attention from geneticists in the future. Increasing both number of lambs reared and milk production level will clearly increase nutrient needs in these highly productive ewes.

Nutritional status prior to lactation can have a significant influence on level of milk production. The ewe will mobilize surplus energy intake into deposited fat during late gestation, then utilize these fat reserves for milk produc-

tion during the first 6–8 weeks of lactation. Undernutrition during late gestation may also affect lamb birth weight and vigor, which may indirectly affect milk production due to the reduced ability of the lamb to challenge its mother's ability to produce milk. Ability of a ewe to produce milk is, therefore, a function of her genetic potential to produce milk, the provision of adequate nutrients to support milk production, and the ability of the lamb or lambs to consume the milk the ewe produces. As with other livestock species, if the milk that is produced is not removed from the udder, then milk production will adjust downward to the level that is removed.

The two most critical nutrients to support milk production are energy and protein. Due to the high fat content of sheep's milk (4–7 percent) and the high level of milk sugars in sheep's milk, energy is the major limiting nutrient affecting milk synthesis. During early lactation it is difficult for high-milk-producing ewes to consume adequate energy levels, hence the importance of body fat reserves when entering the lactation period. Protein intake is also quite critical and can be a limiting factor to milk production. At a given energy intake level there is a minimum protein intake level required to support milk production, and the ratio of protein to energy generally increases as milk production level increases. Excess protein, however, will be used as an energy source rather than to increase protein level in the milk. The use of labile body protein for the production of milk appears to be quite small, which means that most protein in milk must come from ingested feed sources. The source of protein may also be critical to the amount needed for milk production. Research has generally shown that when protein is the limiting factor, the source of protein is less critical than the level in the diet. As milk yield increases and if the energy intake level is not limiting, there may be additional milk production responses to protein sources such as blood meal or fish meal that are not readily degraded in the rumen.

Ca and P, both notably at high levels in milk, are probably the most critical minerals to the lactating ewe. K and Mg may also be critical, especially on fertilized pastures. High K levels tend to interfere with Mg absorption, resulting in a condition known as hypomagnesemia or grass tetany. Fertilizing lush growing pastures with K should be avoided, or if such fertilizing is done, the ewe's diet must be supplemented with a source of Mg.

The question to the producer is the adequacy of the available forage and other nutrient sources to meet the nutrient needs of the ewe during lactation. Research and experience have generally shown that growing forages are adequate in protein and energy to support moderate lactation levels. Ability of pasture to meet the nutrient needs of the ewe for lactation is a function of nutrient content of the forages, herbage availability for grazing, the palatability of the available herbage, and the intake limits of the ewe. In some situations with lush pastures, low dry-matter content may limit the ability of the ewe to consume adequate amounts, even though the nutrient content of the dry matter may be more than adequate. Pastures containing at least 25 percent high-quality legumes such as clover or alfalfa or high-quality, palatable growing forbs will generally meet the protein needs of high-producing ewes. High-milk-producing ewes will usually need either substantial body fat reserves or supplemental energy to maintain high levels of milk production on pasture.

PASTURE AND FEEDING OPTIONS FOR EWES

The ewe is very adaptable in her ability to utilize a wide variety of feedstuffs. These may range from very high quality grass and legume forages on improved pastures, to forbs and browse of varying quality in extensive range conditions, to harvested hays, silages, and concentrates in confinement. The expected level of production of the ewe should be near the level of production the land can support, rather than at a level such that a producer expects to supplement forage-nutrient deficiencies throughout the year. The production cycle of the ewe should also be planned to coincide with the forage production cycle, so that peak nutrient needs are in synchrony to the extent possible with peak nutrient availability.

Extensive Rangelands

The nutrient resources on arid to semiarid rangelands are generally quite limited, and the extensive nature of most sheep operations will not economically justify much use of supplemental nutrients. The options for the producer are, therefore, to limit production objectives to the available nutrient resources or to remove the sheep to improved feed conditions at strategic times during the year. Both of these are common practices in various parts of the world. The

management of wethers for wool production is an example of limiting range production objectives to the limited forage resources. The movement of sheep in the western United States from arid desert range to alpine grasslands to crop residues is an example of optimizing forage use in several ecosystems resulting in increased productivity of the sheep.

The vegetation on extensive rangelands is generally characterized by shrubs, limited trees, annual and perennial grasses, and annual herbs and forbs. Several shrubs are edible and nutritious for sheep and can be an important component of the diet during parts of the year, generally during winter maintenance periods. Annual forbs can be a major component of the diet during their vegetative growth, with many forbs being highly palatable and high in protein content. Grasses, particularly shorter growing and prostrate growing grasses, are preferred by sheep during their vegetative growth period. Sheep are selective grazers, particularly during periods of abundant growth of highly nutritious grasses and forbs. As available herbage and herbage quality decline, sheep are forced to become less selective in their grazing habits.

Little can be done economically to improve extensive range systems. The major problem is often excessive invasion of unpalatable shrubs, which can be reduced or controlled through burning. Research at the U.S. Sheep Experiment Station has shown that burning of dense sagebrush stands can increase edible forage production by as much as 400 percent. In the Karoo region of Australia, plantings of spineless cactus and saltbush (*Atriplex mummularia*) are used for supplemental feed. Other options are to feed supplementary hay or grain at strategic times of the year, normally during late gestation and early lactation. Supplementary feed costs relative to production increases generally limit the benefits of supplementary hay or grain in extensive range areas.

Semiarid Rangelands

The semiarid rangelands, usually in areas that receive 400–700 mm of annual rainfall, are usually located in ecosystems where the better lands may be in wheat or other small grain production, but large areas may be too steep or the soils too shallow or rocky for farming. Sheep and cattle may often be grazed in common in these areas. Most of these areas are also characterized by one or more periods of the year in which rainfall is adequate to support plant growth. However, the use of improved pastures is generally limited to improved strains of native varieties which are adapted to the local conditions.

Although pasture production may be reasonably good during certain times of the year, forage quality may limit the producer's ability to maximize lamb and wool production. The most popular form of strategic supplementation is generally through wheat or other small grain grazing or use of supplementary forage crops such as hybrid sorghum-Sudan grass in the more temperate areas. Hay and/or grain supplementation may be necessary during winter months.

Improved or Cultivated Pastures

Improved pastures are generally associated with more intensive integrated crop-livestock production systems. Portions of the farm may not be suitable for cropping and thus be in pasture, or a rotation cropping system may include a period of pasture or forage crop in the land rotation scheme. Sheep production schemes in these areas must be more intensive and productive to be competitive economically for land use. A livestock production system has much to offer to a crop farming system, in particular the manure and opportunities to build soil organic matter in rotating forage crops in the crop rotation cycle, the opportunity to use surplus feeds and crop residues, the use of livestock as an alternative method of marketing crops produced on the farm, and the opportunity to use surplus labor, land, and other resources at certain times of the year.

Successful intensive pasture systems have these characteristics in common: (a) high yields of forage dry matter per unit of land, (b) seasonal periods of very high quality forage production that can be exploited by the sheep production system's peak nutrient needs, and (c) reasonably good distribution of pasture growth throughout the year. On-farm access or relatively economical external sources of supplemental feeds are usually available to these systems. The stocking rate of the ewe flock is set by determining how many ewes can be supported during the lowest period of pasture growth during the growing season. Lush growth periods coincide with the lactation and lamb growth phase of the production cycle, with pasture in surplus of sheep needs either grazed by cattle or harvested as hay or silage for use during winter or drought periods.

Nutritional Stress—Drought, Cold, Survival

The normal objective of any production system is to maintain optimum production; however, there are times when the objective changes to survival. These conditions may be short-term, such as during severe winter storms, or they may be long-term, as during prolonged drought periods.

Ewes can survive relatively severe weight losses over prolonged periods. Australian scientists have shown that ewes in reasonably good condition can survive up to 30 percent weight loss for as long as 6 months with no significant effects on future performance. The level of feed intake over extended periods for survival is apparently in the range of 60 percent of the NRC recommended levels for dry, mature ewes. Moderate levels of lamb and wool production can generally be maintained at 75–80 percent of NRC recommended levels (1).

As remaining forages become dry, protein may be the first nutrient supplement required. As the dry forage becomes limited in supply, the primary supplement ingredient should be energy, with supplemental protein provided once energy needs are met. The first mineral required to supplement dry range forages is usually P.

Extremely cold temperatures and periods where the range may be covered with snow will also cause severe nutritional stress. With winter and spring lambing systems, these stress periods generally coincide with the ewe's peak nutrient demands. The nutrient most urgently needed during these periods is usually energy. Extreme cold may increase energy needs by as much as 40 percent over normal. If the feed supply is covered by snow, then a complete ration should be provided in adequate amounts to meet normal and stress period needs. Disturbances or sudden changes in feeding during late gestation, which is often the situation in winter, may result in pregnancy toxemia, abortion, or both.

Water

An adequate supply of fresh, clean water is essential to successful sheep production. Sheep will not drink adequate amounts of stagnant, poor-quality water to sustain maximum production. The most efficient sheep operations are planned around adequate, high-quality water supplies. In situations where water is not available at the feed source, then water must be transported to the sheep.

Water intake is affected by the sheep's stage of production, ambient temperature, feed composition and level of consumption, body metabolism, body size, and wool covering. The lactating ewe nursing twins may consume up to three times more water than the nonpregnant ewe or a ewe in early gestation. Ambient temperature may affect water consumption, with ambient temperatures above 80° F increasing water intake by close to 100 percent above the amount required at 60° F. Lactating ewes have been observed to consume up to 10 times more water in hot summer weather than dry ewes in 40° F winter temperatures.

Voluntary water consumption is generally two or three times the volume of dry-matter consumption and increases with the consumption of high-salt or high-protein diets. Sheep grazing on lush, high-water-content, growing forages or on high-silage diets will have reduced water consumption. Water containing salt or minerals in excess of 1.3 percent may not be palatable, thus affecting water intake and performance.

Dry ewes with winter conditions of 0–40° F may consume adequate water through clean, fresh snow. However, ewes in late gestation or lactation would be unable to consume adequate water from snow without negatively affecting rumen metabolism. Water temperature is important. Hot or warm, stagnant water will not be consumed as readily as cool, fresh water. Extremely cold water will reduce rumen temperatures and thus metabolism. Ewes that rely on snow for their water source can be observed consuming small amounts several times daily, thus minimizing its effect on body or rumen temperature.

Sheep prefer fresh water from streams. If water troughs are required, they should be cleaned frequently. Winter temperatures may force the use of heated waterers. Heated waterers should be cleaned daily. Contamination from feed, dirt, bedding, and nasal and oral discharges in heated water bowls provide optimum growing conditions for infectious bacteria and viruses.

Toxic Plants

Certain plants produce poisonous substances that are toxic to sheep. Toxicity may vary with growing conditions, stage of growth, and level of intake relative to other nontoxic feed consumption. In other situations, plants may become toxic due to environmental conditions such as freezing temperatures or toxic nutrients from the soil or fertilizers. Treatments have not been developed for most plant toxicities, so management to avoid or minimize intake is recommended. The following are recommended practices:

A. Know the toxic plants in your area, and avoid grazing during periods of high toxicity.

B. Make certain that animals are not hungry or thirsty when turned on new pasture that may contain toxic plants.

C. Provide adequate salt, minerals (especially P), and water at all times.

D. Avoid using "inexperienced" animals. There is growing evidence that offspring learn what to eat from their mother. Sheep raised in areas with toxic plants tend to avoid them if other desirable plants are available and they are not too hungry, and this tendency can be passed from ewe to lamb.

The Poisonous Plants Laboratory of the USDA Agricultural Research Service at Logan, Utah, has developed an excellent publication that lists the most common plants toxic to sheep in the United States. Location, conditions under which these plants may be toxic, signs of poisoning, appearance of gross lesions caused by toxic plants, and methods of prevention and control of toxicity are discussed for each plant species. Producers in areas where toxic plants are a problem are strongly encouraged to obtain a copy of this publication.

Forage Crops

Probably the most popular supplemental forage crops worldwide are the root crops such as turnips, swedes, and mangels. Turnips have been used for hundreds of years in Great Britain and Europe and for many years in New Zealand and other countries as a winter forage crop. They are becoming increasingly popular in the United States. Turnips are a highly productive fall growth crop that can be double-cropped behind small grain crops or even interseeded into pastures. They "stockpile" well, in that there is minimal nutrient deterioration as fall growth reaches maturity, and they resist moderate frost damage. As a result, they make an excellent late fall-early winter grazing crop when pasture growth is generally dormant. Best grazing results are achieved with strip or controlled grazing to force total and uniform consumption of both the higher-protein forage top and the higher-energy turnip root.

Forage crops such as kale, rape, fodder radishes, and hybrid sorghum-Sudan grass are reasonably high in protein, minerals, and vitamins and are often used as supplemental forage crops when ewes are suckling lambs, for flushing prior to breeding, and for grazing during dry periods when pasture growth is limited. These crops work best when they are intensively grazed for short periods, then rested for regrowth and subsequent regrazing. Due to potential goitrogenic and/or anemia-inducing problems, crops such as kale should not be grazed continuously. Hybrid sorghum-Sudan grass should not be grazed after frost or in severely dry periods due to increases in prussic acid content that may cause toxicity problems.

Cereal grain grazing has been previously discussed, but is worthy of mention again. Wheat, barley, oat, and rye pastures in temperate climates are capable of rapid growth following fall planting. Cereal forage is generally of very high quality, with the only potential problems being inadequate dry-matter content that limits nutrient intake and hypomagnesemia if excessive levels of K fertilizer are used. The fall growth may be moderately grazed throughout the fall and winter period, and spring growth may be grazed up to approximately 1 week prior to jointing without affecting crop yields. Small grain pasture, due to its high nutrient quality, is excellent for lactating ewes and for lamb growth. Intake should be limited during maintenance periods of the ewe production cycle.

Supplement Feeds

The producer must recognize those periods of the forage and sheep production cycles when nutrient needs are not being met. There may also be periods, such as when the ewe is dry or in early gestation, when slight nutrient deficiencies that result in minor weight losses may be acceptable. These deviations, however, cannot be severe or extended in duration if life cycle production objectives are to be met. To meet production objectives, a clear understanding of nutrient requirements at various stages of the ewe production cycle and the nutrient content of available feedstuffs is required. These are provided in detail in NRC publications (1).

These points can be illustrated by evaluating the nutrient requirements of the ewe during early gestation and late gestation relative to the nutrient content of various feedstuffs, as shown in Table 17–1. An example of crested wheatgrass in the late vegetative stage versus mature stem-cured wheatgrass as available forages is shown in the table. A ewe in early gestation could meet her protein and energy needs with the consumption of approximately 1.3 kg of wheatgrass in the late vegetative stage, but limited supplementation of Ca and P would be required. If this is during the winter period, the crested wheatgrass is standing, cured forage. The ewe in early gestation would then require approximately 1.5 kg forage to meet energy needs, plus a supplement containing 90 g crude protein and supplemental P and Ca. The winter period often corresponds to mid- and late-gestation in range situations. If forage is limited, then supplemental hay or silage may be required. The type of hay or silage used will determine its adequacy in meeting nutrient deficiencies.

If protein is the limiting nutrient, as in the mature crested wheatgrass illustration, then the most economical supplement will be one of protein supplement feeds such as soybean meal, cottonseed meal, or possibly dehydrated alfalfa pellets. As shown in Table 17–1, a supplement of 0.2 kg of soybean meal or cottonseed meal or 0.5 kg of dehydrated alfalfa pellets should provide the 90 g of supplemental protein required. A mineral supplement of Ca and P would still be required with soybean or cottonseed meal, and a small amount of supplemental P would be required with alfalfa pellets.

If energy is the limiting nutrient, the appropriate supplement will include one of the feed grains. When energy is limiting, supplemental protein may be used as an energy source. Therefore, it is necessary to first meet energy needs before providing supplemental protein to meet protein deficiencies. Feed grains are always less expensive than protein supplements. The choice of grain or protein supplement depends on availability and cost to provide the deficient nutrients.

Most producers, particularly in areas where winter conditions limit forage availability, will plan on hay or silage feeding from late winter to early spring forage growth. As shown in Table 17–1, alfalfa or clover hay at 1.5–2.0 kg/d will meet the nutrient needs of the gestating ewe. Grass hay may require supplemental protein, Ca, and P. If corn silage is used, supplemental protein, Ca, and P will be required.

TABLE 17-1

Nutrient requirements and composition of selected common feedstuffs for sheep

	Dry Matter		Digestible Energy, Mcal	Crude Protein, g	Ca, g	P, g	Vit. A, IU
	%	kg					
Requirements							
154-lb ewe, first 15 wks gestation		1.4	3.4	164	5.7	3.2	3290
154-lb ewe, last 4 wks gestation		1.8	4.7	193	6.2	5.6	5590
Feedstuff Composition							
Crested wheatgrass, late vegetative	34	1.0	2.69	140	2.3	2.0	
Crested wheatgrass, mature stem-cured	81	1.0	2.34	33	2.0	0.9	low
Alfalfa hay, sun-cured, mid-bloom	90	1.0	2.47	170	14.1	2.4	
Crested wheatgrass hay, sun-cured, mid-bloom	96	1.0	2.47	132	3.0	1.5	
Red clover hay, sun-cured, mid-bloom	88	1.0	2.73	160	14.8	2.6	
Corn silage, well eared	33	1.0	3.09	81	2.3	2.2	low
Corn, no. 2 yellow	88	1.0	3.84	100	0.2	3.5	
Barley	88	1.0	3.79	135	0.5	3.8	low
Wheat, hard red winter	88	1.0	3.88	144	0.5	4.3	low
Soybean meal, solvent extracted	90	1.0	3.88	499	3.4	7.0	low
Cottonseed meal	91	1.0	3.13	452	1.8	12.1	low
Alfalfa pellets, dehydrated	92	1.0	2.65	189	15.2	2.5	

Source: NRC (1). Nutrient requirements are on a dry-matter basis. With the exception of % dry matter, feedstuff composition data are on a dry-matter basis.

Under certain conditions, supplemental vitamin A may be required. The ewe is able to store large amounts of vitamin A in the liver, so the need for supplementation will depend on the duration of the period on feeds low in vitamin A. Under most conditions, dry range forages that are low in vitamin A are not the primary feed source for a period long enough to result in deficiency problems.

Ca and P are usually provided in a salt-mineral mix. When salt is continuously available, intake will normally be 15–30 g/d. Intake will be higher when ewes are grazing lush, high-moisture forages and lower when dry, cured forages are consumed. There are several areas of the United States where Se deficiency is a problem. In these cases, a commercial salt containing supplemental Se should be provided.

SUMMARY

Sheep are raised in many different areas over the world, with the exception of arctic areas and wet, tropical areas. They are more adapted to arid areas than are most domestic grazers, and if predators can be controlled and water can be provided, sheep can exist in very dry climates. On the other hand, sheep can utilize high-quality forage to advantage for the production on grass of market-ready lambs. As a rule sheep utilize appreciably less concentrate feed than is the norm for cattle production.

The majority of sheep production occurs in areas where feed is not sufficient for some portion of the year, the result being that either supplementary feed must be supplied or that the animals will lose body condition. The amount of body reserves that can be lost without permanent effects varies somewhat, but sheep are capable of withstanding substantial nutritional stress. Adequate body reserves result in higher lamb crops, greater milk production, and fewer death losses. Ewes can make efficient use of many different crop residues as well as pasture or rangeland forages of different types. In many areas lambs raised on rangeland ewes must be fattened with supplemental feed or in feedlots (see Ch. 19) to meet market demands in the United States and other countries. Nutrients often critical for ewes on dryland ranges are energy and protein with, as time passes, P, vitamin A, and, sometimes, Ca and Se.

REFERENCES

1. NRC. 1985. *Nutrient requirements of sheep.* 6th ed. Washington, D.C.: Nat. Acad. Press.
2. ARC. 1980. *The nutrient requirements of farm livestock. No. 2: Ruminants.* 2d ed. Slough, England: Commonwealth Agr. Bureaux.

18

The Young Lamb

M. Thériez

INTRODUCTION

This chapter deals with the period from lamb birth to weaning. This period is of the utmost importance and corresponds to two critical phases of adaptation—adaptation to the outside world at birth and adaptation to autonomy at weaning.

Important changes are associated with each of these events, namely in nutrition of the young lamb. At birth, the animal makes the transition from a sterile and insulated environment to a contaminated one where climatic conditions are very variable. *In utero* nutrition, which is characterized by a continuous supply of nutrients in the form of glucose and amino acids for energy and N requirements, gives way to discontinuous feedings (suckings) that supply mainly lipids, carbohydrates, and proteins. In the same manner, the young lamb has to make physiological and behavioral adjustments to new changes at weaning. Volatile fatty acids (VFA) then make up its main source of energy, and owing to rumen flora, the lamb will be able to utilize nonprotein N.

This stage lasts from 4 to 16 weeks, de-pending on the husbandry system, animal performance, and on the type of production sought. It can take up the entire phase of rearing-fattening (as in dairy farming systems in Mediterranean areas where lambs are slaughtered around 5–6 weeks, or in pen rearing, for example, the 100-day-old lamb in France) or only part of this period. Thus it corresponds to animal production in which fattening takes place after weaning.

THE NEWBORN LAMB

Variations in and Effect of Birth Weight

Lamb birth weight can vary from 1.5 to 6 kg. These differences, which are linked to dam age, feeding, or litter size, express *in utero* growth differences. Differences can have very important effects on lamb rearing, as we shall see further on. A reduction in birth weight, whatever the origin, has the following main effects:

A. A great increase in mortality, which some authors have quantified as a 12

323

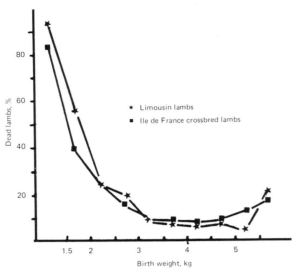

FIGURE 18-1. Birth weight and mortality from birth to weaning at 42 days. From Villette (13).

percent increase per kg of reduced initial weight and which is illustrated in Fig. 18-1.

B. A lessened growth rate. This reduction, which is always high from the first 4–6 weeks, can increase or remain constant after weaning, but never decreases. With artificial rearing, when the amount of milk available is not a limiting growth factor, a 1-kg difference at birth can be expressed by a discrepancy of 2.6 kg at 42 d.

C. An increase in carcass fatness at a constant slaughter weight (Table 18-1) or a reduction in weight at slaughter to avoid excessive fattening.

The First Hours of Life; Colostrum

During the first hours of life, the lamb must develop a certain number of physiological activities: respiration and digestion, for instance, but especially thermogenesis to maintain a constant body temperature.

TABLE 18-1

Lipid content of lambs slaughtered at 35 kg (Effects of birth weight)

| Birth Weight | Whole Body Lipid Content, kg | |
	Males	Females
High > 4.5 kg	4.9 ± 0.6	6.2 ± 0.6
Low < 2.5 kg	6.3 ± 1.6	7.2 ± 0.4

Source: Y. Villette (unpublished).

TABLE 18-2

Effects of birth weight and type of coat on cold resistance of lambs

Lamb Birth Weight, kg	Type of Coat	Air Temperature Producing Hypothermia (with Wind)
2	short	+ 23° C
2	long	+ 13° C
4	short	+ 4° C
4	long	− 14° C

Source: Slee (11).

Lambs with low birth weights suffer from several handicaps during the first few hours of life. The insulation afforded by fleece is limited because it is shorter and less thick than that of lambs of greater weight. The mass to surface ratio is unfavorable. This ratio, which amounts to 0.12 M^2/kg in a 1-kg animal, is only 0.07 M^2/kg in a 4-kg animal (2). Thus they must expend more energy per weight unit than heavier animals. The maximum metabolic level, that is, the highest amount of heat produced, is proportional to weight. Lambs of lower weight shiver at a higher temperature than the temperature at which heavier lambs shiver (Table 18-2).

All of these forms of adaptation are made first at the expense of lamb body reserves, then from energy intake in the first suckings. Alexander estimated these body reserves to be about 1,000 kcal, of which 60–70 percent were lipids and 15 percent carbohydrates (glycogen); the rest came from muscle catabolism (2).

Lambs with low birth weight have smaller energy reserves per weight unit than heavier lambs, which accentuates their disadvantage. The lower the weight and the more difficult the environmental conditions, the shorter the survival period of a fasted lamb.

If the lamb cannot suckle its dam rapidly to obtain a supplementary energy supply, it will die quickly from exhaustion. The shepherd's role during the first days of life is, thus, to avoid placing the lamb in environmental conditions that are too rigorous, and to facilitate the dam-offspring bonding by separating the pair from the rest of the flock into lambing pens.

During the first days after lambing the ewe secretes colostrum, which has a dual role both nutritive and preventive. Owing to its high concentration (Table 18–3), colostrum supplies a great amount of nutritive elements to the lamb which thereby acquires antibodies as well. These antibodies, which can cross the intestinal wall

TABLE 18-3

Milk and colostrum composition, wet basis

	Dry Matter, %	Proteins, %	Fat, %	Lactose, %	Energy, Mcal/kg
Colostrum	23.4	6.5	12.9	4.1	1.84
Milk	19.7	5.5	8.8	4.7	1.31

Source: Peart et al. (9).

TABLE 18-4

Lamb birth weight and mortality rate

No. of Lambs	Birth Weight, kg	Blood γ-Globulin Content of Viable Lambs, g/ℓ	Birth Weight of Lambs that Died, kg	Blood γ-Globulin of Dead Lambs, g/ℓ
Single	5.8	3.3	4.2	1.8
Twins	4.5	2.5	3.3	1.2
Triplets	3.5	2.2	2.8	0.7

Source: Doxey (4).

for the first 12–24 h of life, have a major role in survival. The antibody content depends on several factors, among which are dam age (Fig. 18–2) and the number of lambs in the same litter (Table 18–4).

Ewes with no colostrum at lambing can be detected and their lambs can be fed colostrum that has been frozen previously (milked from other ewes of the same flock that are adapted to the local microbial flora, or, when sheep colostrum is not available, goat or cow colostrum). Ewes with only small amounts of colostrum are more difficult to detect, which is why the systematic distribution of colostrum to lambs whose dams have slightly developed udders or

who are members of 3-lamb litters or more, is strongly recommended. Colostrum with a high γ-globulin content should be collected at the first milking of the female donor. The necessary amount is between 50 and 100 ml for a newborn lamb.

LAMB GROWTH

Evolution with Age

During the growth period, from birth to the beginning of fattening, the lamb has a growth rate that can vary, according to breed, sex, and feed, from 50–100 g/d up to 350–400 g/d. This regular development corresponds to the successive stages of growth, more or less rapid, of the different organs and tissues. With regard to nutrition, the birth to weaning period features a marked change in the anatomy and physiology of the digestive tract.

The abomasum, which functions as the sole stomach in lambs fed exclusively milk, is more developed than is the rumen at birth (Table 18–5), and feeding methods must allow this compartment of the digestive tract to start functioning as soon as possible. Anatomical modifications are concomitant with changes in body gain composition. The latter, which has a very high protein and water content during the first few weeks, is enriched in lipids and its energy value increases (Table 18–6) as the lamb gets older and heavier. The corresponding values are difficult to quote precisely because they depend on lamb age and on growth rate; thus the amount of fixed energy goes from 3.5 to 4.5 Mcal/kg of gain be-

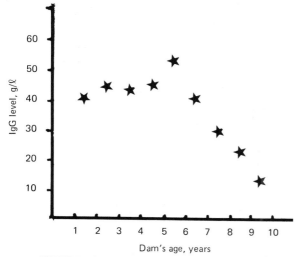

FIGURE 18–2. Dam's age and immunoglobulin (IgG) level in blood at 24–48-hour-old lambs. From Villette (14).

TABLE 18-5

Evolution of rumen and abomasum volumes

| Stomach Part[a] | Age, Weeks | | | | | |
	Birth	2	4	6	8	16
Reticulo-rumen	0.024	0.155	0.595	1.280	2.375	10.250
Omasum-abomasum	0.018	0.218	0.231	0.250	0.375	1.000

[a]Twin lambs reared by ewe on grass.
Source: Wardrop and Coombe (16).

TABLE 18-6

Empty body weight and gain composition (wool excluded)

| Item | Composition | | | |
| | Proteins, g/kg | | Lipids, g/kg | |
	♂	♀	♂	♀
EBW				
10	178	178	56	75
20	166	157	111	147
30	159	146	166	219
40	154	138	220	290
EBW gain				
10	159	145	111	148
20	148	128	221	291
30	142	119	330	432
40	138	113	438	572

Source: ARC (1).

tween the second and sixth weeks for a growth rate of 280 g/d. When live weight gain increases from 50 to 300 g/d, the energy fixed per kg gain increases by 38 percent during the first month.

The effect of feeding level decreases with age, and many authors have shown that body composition is fairly independent of early diet for heavy lambs. This means that gain composition can vary according to earlier treatments and tends to reduce the effect of initial feeding,

as shown in Table 18–7. In many circumstances differences in body gain are not so important, but differences induced by management (weaning, for example) may still be significant at slaughter. That's the reason early weaning of lambs can be used to reduce fatness at slaughter or to increase slaughter weight.

In these conditions the main factor which modifies animal composition is its weight or, more precisely, its maturity. The higher the maturity of a lamb, that is, the higher its actual weight compared to its potential mature weight, the more the weight gain will be high in lipids and energy. Ash content varies little during growth. Corresponding values are reported in Table 18–8.

Growing Lamb Requirements

Whatever the needs of growing lambs (energy, N, minerals, vitamins), they fall into two groups: maintenance requirements that correspond to supplies which the animal needs to stay alive without production (energy needed to maintain constant body temperature, to move about and eat, N required to ensure digestive secretions, tissue renewal), and production requirements (energy, N, mineral, and vitamins required for weight increase in growing animals).

TABLE 18-7

Effect of rearing method on body composition at different empty body weights and on body gain composition at the end of the finishing period

| Group | Body Composition at | | Gain Composition, g/kg |
	20 kg EBW	25 kg EBW	
Indoors			
Lipids	148	161	213
Proteins	165	164	160
Range			
Lipids	115	149	285
Proteins	182	169	115

TABLE 18-8

Mineral composition of growing lambs, g/kg EBW

Animal	Mineral				
	Ca	P	Mg	K	Na
Newborn	13	7	0.5	1.7	2.4
Fattening	11	6	0.4	1.8	1.2

Source: ARC (1).

Energy Requirements. Maintenance needs decrease with age in connection with reduced metabolism and activity, ranging from 315 kcal per day of NEm for lambs weighing 10 kg to 1053 kcal/d for lambs weighing 50 kg (see the appendix tables).

The tables of energy needs established by the NRC (7) and the ARC (1) were set up by the factorial method from published results which showed that the amount of fixed energy per unit of weight gain is independent of growth rate, and varies with lamb weight. The requirement tables set up by INRA (6) are based on the global method and, according to these tables, the amount of energy fixed in 100 g gain decreases, at the same weight, when growth rate increases.

Nitrogen Requirements. The maintenance requirements of growing lambs are based on the amounts of N needed to compensate for urinary losses (around 1 g/d in a growing lamb) and N fixed in wool (1 g/d as well, on the average). The production needs that correspond to the amount of proteins fixed by a growing animal depend on the composition of the gain and on the diet. Some trials (10) have shown clearly that the crude protein (CP) content of the diet has effects on growth rate and body gain composition. When the CP content of the diet fed to lambs weighing between 20 and 40 kg increases from 8–10 percent (on a DM basis) to 16–18 percent, their growth rate increases, and the proportion of lipids in the gain lessens. Given the variations in gain composition with weight, a decrease in the optimum concentration of the lamb's diet is noted (Table 18-9).

This mode of expressing protein needs amounts to the most common situation in which the animal is fed ad libitum: milk, grass and/or concentrates, and hay. When the lambs are limited to less than ad libitum consumption, their requirements can also be expressed on a basis of CP content per kg of DM in the feed or in grams of CP/d (see the Appendix).

The CP system is a rough system which takes into account neither N digestibility nor its utilization in the digestive tract (see Ch. 9, 12). That is why other systems have been proposed (1, 6) to take into account the alimentary proteins that reach the duodenum and the microbial proteins synthesized in the rumen directly.

Mineral and Vitamin Requirements. The mineral requirements of the lamb are presented in the Appendix. However, the different characteristics of the growing lamb and their interaction with minerals must be emphasized.

Phosphorus (P) and calcium (Ca). The mineral supplement given to lambs fed diets with a high cereal content must rectify the Ca shortage. When the Ca supply is too low or when the Ca to P ratio is less than two, serious metabolic disorders can occur (urolithiasis). The latter can reduce growth rate but can also induce death. Ammonium chloride incorporation into the diet (1 percent of DM) prevents these disorders.

Trace elements. These minerals, which are absolutely vital to sustaining a high growth rate, must be incorporated at a very low level (less than 1 mg per kg DM up to 50 mg/kg DM). Their incorporation rate must be kept within a margin corresponding to deficiency or to toxicity. Among these trace elements, Cu and Se are to be stressed as far as sheep nutrition is concerned. The safety margin of these two trace elements is very narrow: the Cu content must be kept between 7 and 15 mg/kg DM. A lower content induces the muscular disease known as swayback, while a higher Cu content induces liver disorders. The Se margin is somewhat larger, with 0.1 mg/kg DM as a deficiency level (white muscle disease) and 0.5 mg/kg DM as a

TABLE 18-9

Recommended crude protein of diets for growing lambs, DM basis

Body weight, kg	15	15 to 20	20 to 30	30 to 35	>35
CP of diet, %	20.0[a]	18.0	15.0	13.5	12.0

[a]Artificially reared lambs.
Source: INRA (6).

toxicity threshold. This is why a normal supply of these two elements must be ensured, which is not easy. Manufacturing a lamb concentrate in a feed plant just after a pig or poultry feed has been made in the same equipment can be sufficient to reach the Cu toxicity level in the lamb diet.

FEEDING THE YOUNG LAMB

Milk Consumption

During the first 2 or 3 weeks of life the young lamb consumes only milk (Fig. 18–3). The nutrient supply based on hay and concentrate, which is negligible during the first month, becomes greater as the lamb gets older and its dam's milk production decreases. However, even with a high-concentrate intake, the lamb's weaning weight strongly depends on the ewe's milk production.

If the milk production of a lactating ewe cannot be measured easily, its estimation is possible when lamb performances during the first month are known (when the milk represents the only source of nutrients). During this period lamb growth rate varies with milk intake, and the corresponding relation is very close. Feed efficiency can vary with sex, age, and rearing type, but 5 liters/kg of gain can be considered to be a good estimation.

Feeding Suckling Lambs

The first month's production accounts for 45–50 percent of the total milk yield of a 14–16 week lactation. Milk production decreases after the peak; the decline rate is 15–20 g less/d during

FIGURE 18–3. An Ile de France ewe with twin lambs. (Courtesy of G. Bechet, INRA.)

the second and third months and 10 g/d later. This means that daily production during the second, third, and fourth months of lactation amount to 75, 35, and 20 percent of the average daily values of the first month. Table 18–10 gives an example of milk production estimates in ewes.

Different experiments carried on with mother-fed or artificially reared lambs have shown that the lower the milk supply, the earlier and the higher is the complementary feed consumption (Table 18–11). That's why concentrate, high-quality roughage (legume or regrowth hay), as well as fresh water must be made available to the lamb by the second or third week of its life. This method allows young lambs to get accustomed to dry food and to compensate for a shortage of milk without any reduction of growth rate.

Creep Feed Composition

There are two main aspects of creep feeding: composition and palatability of the supplement. Palatability is the most important factor. As soon as possible, lambs must consume dry food as a supplement to mother's milk. This creep feed can be very simple, for instance bran or cereals. Of the cereals, corn and barley are more palatable than wheat or oats. These cereals, which can be offered as whole grain to 2-month-old lambs, should be rolled for younger animals. Propionic acid-treated moist cereals are also well accepted by lambs even as whole grains. When no legume hay is available, cereals alone can be protein-deficient for the young lamb and creep feed should be a pelleted mixture. When lambs are early-weaned, the starter diet can be used as creep feed if the pellets are not too hard and their diameter is limited (2 or 5 mm).

Mineral and vitamin supplements can be incorporated into creep feed pellets. When whole grain cereals are used, they can be mixed with a mineral mixture in the trough or, more simply, commercial vitamin and mineral pellets can be offered ad libitum in separate feeders. Among the different components available for creep feeding of the lamb, special mention must be made of urea. Urea is not toxic for the ad libitum fed lamb, and this is true for two reasons: first, food intake in lambs is never as rapid as in ewes, and second, when the urea concentration of a concentrate is too high (1.5–2 percent), the concentrate's palatability decreases sharply and intake falls. Urea can be incorporated into all the lamb feeds, even for unweaned lambs. Urea can

TABLE 18-10

Effects of number of lambs milked on crossbred ewes, milk production at grass, kg/ewe

Number of Lambs	Milk Production		
	From Birth to 4th Week	From 5th to 12th Week	Total
1	53	72	125
2	82	94	176
3	100	92	192

Source: Peart et al. (9).

TABLE 18-11

Effect of milk intake on dehydrated grass intake, g OM/lamb/day

Diet	Age, days			
	25	35	45	55
Low group				
Milk	160	140	120	110
Dehydrated grass	30	160	260	380
High group				
Milk	320	280	240	220
Dehydrated grass	8	50	150	290

Source: Hodge (5).

be incorporated during pellet processing, but it can also be sprayed over whole grains. The mixture (50 percent urea and 50 percent water, hot for easier dilution) can be used at the rate of 2 or 3 kg per 100 kg of grain.

Although the mechanical properties of the diets and cereal processing can be of importance to the very young lamb, as soon as it reaches 5 or 6 weeks of age, they are of less importance. The growing lamb can ingest whole grains as well as pelleted diets and the efficacy is similar for whole grains or treated cereals, because the grain can't pass through the reticulo-omasal orifice as long as its diameter is too large and the grain must be ground by chewing before reaching the abomasum. In general, lambs chew cereal grains rather well before swallowing.

Roughages for Lambs

As indicated above, lambs begin to consume roughages during their third week of age. Digestibility and water content of food are the main limiting factors of young lambs' intake. That's why even if silages (grass, corn, sorghum), beet pulp, or roots can be used early, it is better not to begin with them earlier than the third month of age. The length of chopped grass in silage can dramatically modify lambs' con-

sumption, because the longer the particles, the longer the time spent ruminating and the lower the daily intake. Roots and silage (corn) can be good sources of energy and legumes or young grasses are good protein sources for fattening lambs. Their utilization before weaning can be recommended mainly as a method of accustoming the lambs to food with which they will be fattened later. Listeriosis, a disease more frequently observed on silage-fed ewes, can occur in young lambs despite their low silage intake because they frequently eat refusals found in their dams' troughs.

A straw-concentrate diet can promote a high growth rate and high efficiency as a result of the high energy content (a 30-kg live-weight lamb consumes less than 200 g of straw daily and 1 kg or more of concentrate). However this diet can induce soft subcutaneous fat and rumenitis. Replacement of straw by a more palatable roughage (high-quality hay) can help to prevent the disorder.

The Grazing Lamb

Most lambs are reared at pasture by their dams, and their growth rate depends strongly on milk consumption. Indeed, if the lambs try to compensate for a shortage of milk with a higher grass

TABLE 18-12

Effects of milk intake on grazed herbage by lambs

Lamb Age, days	Milk Offered from Birth to 90 Days			
	50 kg	70 kg	90 kg	100 kg
34–38	177[a]	171	158	140
	(16.7)[b]	(13.1)	(10.2)	(8.5)
62–66	495	474	527	531
	(28.0)	(22.0)	(22.0)	(20.6)
83–87	593	618	718	820
	(26.7)	(24.3)	(24.0)	(24.9)

[a]177 = grass OM intake/lamb/day.

[b](16.7) = grass OM intake/kg live weight/day.

Source: Penning and Gibb (10).

intake (Table 18–12), the energetic concentration of the latter is too low to allow them to maintain a high growth rate until they are at least 3 months old. High-milk-producing ewes are essential to obtain good performances at pasture and, in some circumstances, it would probably be more efficient to wean slow-growing lambs early (6–8 weeks) and to fatten them indoors with concentrates than to maintain them on pasture with their dam. High milk production from ewes and high daily growth rate for lambs cannot be obtained without good pasture management, that is, with palatable species and a sufficient daily amount of grass available to the animals.

Legumes (alfalfa or white clover) are among the most desirable plants for lactating ewes; good performances can also be obtained from different grasses if they are grazed at the leafy stage. The amount of pasture to be offered to animals is close to 50–60 g DM/kg body weight/d.

An easy method to achieve this level is to control plant height by modifying stocking rate so that ewes are always grazing a 6–8 cm pasture. If grass amounts (or height) are not sufficient or if quality is low, creep feeding of lambs can be considered. This expensive method must be considered carefully and will never be justified on good-quality pasture, because, in such a case, concentrate takes the place of grass and increases the cost of feeding without any improvement in performance.

Early Weaning

In many sheep production systems the lamb may have to be weaned before it has reached slaughter weight in order to prevent growth rate decline when pastures or ranges dry in summer, to dry its dam before rebreeding in accelerated lambing programs, or to milk the ewe in cheese-making flocks. Good weaning doesn't impair the lamb's growth rate, but different precautions must be taken to prevent a growth check.

The lamb should not be weaned too early, never before 21 d of age, or before it attains a minimum weight. Weaning can be done when the lamb has doubled its initial birth weight and consumes a minimum of complementary food (200 g/d at least). When lambs are kept on grass after weaning or when the complementary foods are not highly palatable, it is better to delay weaning up to 5–6 weeks when actual weight is three times the birth weight.

Weaning can be abrupt or gradual. Abrupt weaning can induce a growth rate check and can promote mastitis in the ewes. This is why gradual weaning is preferable. The lambs suckle their dams for 10–20 minutes at increasing intervals (24, 48, and 72 h). A decrease in milk production before weaning makes it easier and induces creep feed consumption. This can be achieved by grazing sparse pastures or by reducing the concentrate given to the ewes a week prior to weaning. Weaning should always be carried out in conjunction with an antiparasite treatment against intestinal worms (round and flat worms) and coccidiosis, because weaning always involves stress to which host animals are more sensitive.

After weaning, the lamb should be given a diet to promote a high growth rate, such as grazing on good-quality pastures kept free of parasites, or concentrate diets offered together with high-quality hay. The early-weaned lamb's nutrient requirements are exactly the same as those of the milk-fed lamb, except that it cannot drink milk any longer. For this reason it is much more sensitive to nutrient deficiency and

TABLE 18-13

Example of diet for early-weaned lambs with high growth rate potential

Component[a]	%
Corn grain	79.5
Soybean meal	14.0
Ammonium chloride	1.0
Urea	1.0
Salt	1.0
Molasses	1.0
Minerals[b]	2.5

[a]Vitamins per 100 kg of concentrate: vit. A, 800,000 IU; vit D₃, 15,000 IU; vit. E, 2500 IU.

[b]For 100 g of minerals: calcium carbonate, 80 g; magnesium oxide, 17.2 g; zinc sulfate, 0.8 g; manganese sulfate, 0.8 g; sulfur, 1.0 g; copper sulfate, 0.09 g; cobalt sulfate, 0.006 g; calcium iodate, 0.0024 g; and sodium selenite, 0.0008 g.

TABLE 18-14

Voluntary dry matter intake by early-weaned lambs, kg/lamb/day

Lamb Weight, kg	Roughage in Diet, %	
	<25%	>25%
15	0.6	0.5
20	0.9	0.85
25	1.0	1.1
30	1.2	1.4
35	1.4	1.55
40	1.6	1.75

Source: INRA (6).

to feed quality. The main factor to control is protein quality. The early-weaned lamb's requirements are very high, and it must be fed diets containing low-degradability proteins to ensure a proper essential amino acid supply. Nevertheless, the postweaning diet can also be very simple. The diet proposed in Table 18-13, when given ad libitum to early-weaned lambs along with high-quality hay, allows 350–400 g/d as daily gain from 42 d up to slaughter at 120 d.

Daily DM intake varies according to weight and the proportion of forage in the diet. The values listed in Table 18–14 can be used as an estimation basis. With a diet composed of excellent-quality hay ad libitum, along with a concentrate similar to the one in Table 18–13, the diet then includes a 20 percent hay and 80 percent concentrate.

ARTIFICIAL REARING

Artificial rearing, which involves separating the lamb from its dam at birth, may be used for different purposes. In systems of biannual lamb-ing, it allows better ewe fertility by eliminating lactation anestrus. Second, in a system that uses ewe milk for human food, ewe milking can begin immediately after lambing instead of after 30–45 d of lactation. Furthermore, when ewes are prolific, it allows all lamb offspring of triplet or quadruplet litters to have fast growth, higher than when they are dam-fed.

This method, which is commonly used in North America and Europe by farmers (around 500,000 lambs per year, or 5 percent of all lambs reared in France), remains a costly one, both in time and money. It is especially time-consuming because about 30 minutes of care per lamb is needed, and this care must be available during the second and third days when all the flock still require considerable watching-over (lambing period). For this reason, it should be limited to a minimum of lambs. Many articles have elaborated on the method (12, 13) which is why only the main points will be dwelt upon here.

Milk Replacers

Milk replacers are essentially composed of skimmed cow's milk powder with added fat from less expensive sources (tallow or vegetable oils) to which vitamins A, D, and E and possibly lactobacilli (bacterial preparations to control intestinal flora) and antibiotics are added. Part of the milk powder can be replaced by whey or other sources of protein. Different trials have made clear the optimum protein and lipid contents of these milk replacers as well as their essential amino acid and fatty acid composition.

When energy intake is high, the growth rate increases with protein level when the latter goes from 15 to 25–30 percent of the DM. This optimum crude protein content of 25 percent is the level used for most of the available milk substitutes on the market. It is higher than actual requirements, which are close to only 20 percent around 3 weeks of age, provided that very good quality proteins are available (nonpasteurized or low-temperature dehydrated cow's milk), and it includes a margin of security for the manufacturers.

These proteins make up the only N source of lambs in the first 3 or 4 weeks of life. Thus they should cover essential amino acid requirements. The most restrictive amino acids are methionine and lysine. Three-week-old lambs' needs are almost 2 g/d for the former and 5 g/d for the latter.

Different sources of substitute proteins can be used: soybean, whey, buttermilk, fish hydrolysate, and others. The results obtained are comparable to or slightly less than those of skimmed milk when the essential amino acid supply is adequate. The use of alternate proteins is justified mainly for economic reasons.

The effects of an increasing lipid content on lamb performances are identical to those observed with proteins. An increase of up to 20 percent allows performances to improve (growth and feed efficiency). Contents that exceed 30 percent, in contrast, bring on a reduction in performance. The most frequently used levels are close to a 25 percent value, which is a compromise between too high a level, which could bring on various disorders (diarrhea, hepatic disorders) and too low a level, which, although ensuring better performances after weaning, leads to fatty carcasses with oily appearances because of excess water in external fat depots.

The balance between fatty acids of the milk substitute depends on the nature of fat used. Tallow, which is rich in long-chain fatty acids (C_{16} and C_{18}), is not as well digested as copra oil, which is rich in short-chain fatty acids (C_{12} and C_{14}). The digestibility of long-chain fatty acids depends on the maturity of the newborn lamb and particularly on its birth weight. It varies by 5 percent for a 1 kg deviation from birth weight, while that of short-chain fatty acids is independent of the weight. A mixture of two-thirds tallow to one-third copra oil provide a fat source in which fatty acids are similar to those observed in ewe milk. This mixture, which will avoid abomasal bloat and minimize composition defects of external fatty depots at slaughter, is the most commonly used in France.

Substitutes should be mixed with water before feeding the lamb. The optimum level is close to 16 percent (200 g powder/kg water). Lower contents reduce DM intake and lamb performances; higher concentrations do not allow the intake level to be increased and make weaning more difficult.

Lamb Rearing

A number of rules must be followed to succeed in artificial lamb rearing. Lambs should be separated from their dams 12–24 h after birth, long enough to allow them to consume some colostrum, and early enough to avoid problems in learning to suck from a teat. Deciding which lambs should be selected for artificial rearing should be done very early. It is advisable to separate the heaviest lamb or lightest lamb in

FIGURE 18–4. One example of a very simple and inexpensive feeder which will feed 12 lambs at one time. (Courtesy of G. Bechet, INRA.)

a litter of three in order to leave the dam with two offspring of similar weight.

Lambs should be reared in an environment close to 14° C. Too low a temperature would raise the intake index and could bring on loss by suffocation because the lambs may pile up to keep warm.

Milk can be prepared with an automatic machine according to needs, or given to the lambs in large containers (Figs. 18–4, 18–5, 18–6, 18–7). In the latter case, the preparation can be made daily or at longer intervals with an additive (1 ml formalin per gallon). The milk temperature has only little effect on lamb per-

FIGURE 18–5. A simple, low-cost, gravity-fed teat bar for feeding small groups of lambs. The bucket is attached by tubing to the rear bar. (Courtesy of J. W. G. Nicholson.)

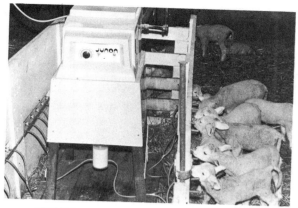

FIGURE 18-6. Lambs suckling from one type of automated feeder for milk replacers. (Courtesy of G. Bechet, INRA.)

formance. According to available methods, milk can be given cold (+4° C), at room temperature (10° to 14° C), or warm (+37° C). The learning process is easier with warm milk.

Weaning. Lambs reared artificially are weaned early; the minimum age is 4 weeks, but it is preferable to wait until 6 weeks of age to reduce risks of slowing down the growth rate. In contrast, it is useless to carry out milk feeding beyond the age of 6 weeks. The requirements of artificially reared lambs and good weaning conditions are the same as those in natural dam-offspring suckling. To facilitate weaning, it is recommended to reduce the daily milk supply from 21 d of age on. The amount to be given varies according to size: 1.5 kg (or 240 g DM) for

FIGURE 18-7. Lambs weaned at one day of age and reared on cold milk replacer continuously circulated to teat bar at the far end of the pen. Note the pen floor is an expanded metal screen which helps to keep cleaning chores to a minimum. (Courtesy of the Director, ARI, Ottawa.)

average-sized breeds (60 kg live weight for ewes) to 1.8 kg (300 g DM) for large-sized breeds (75 kg for adults).

The amount of milk substitute needed for one lamb in artificial rearing is close to 12 kg on the average and can reach 15 kg. Higher intake is costly and does not improve performances; lower amounts (10 kg and even 5 kg) should not be considered unless the starter feed is of good quality and well consumed.

CARCASS QUALITY

Carcass quality is estimated from several criteria. Some are genetic in origin, such as conformation, while others depend on the feeding or rearing applied. The amount and quality of fat are the most critical factors in most grading systems. These factors are linked to the feed or type of rearing and can involve a modification in the fattening state, depending on birth weight, dietary N content, daily amount of energy consumed, and weaning age. These factors will be dwelt upon in Ch. 19, so they will be simply summarized here as follows:

Birth Weight. The lamb's weight at birth expresses the level of nutrition attained by the fetus during its prenatal development. Effects have been shown in the preceding tables and figures. The birth weight is a major factor in the success of rearing the young lamb, and it is practically impossible to modify its postpartum effects.

Dietary N Content. A diet with a CP content or N quality that is insufficient to cover lamb requirements reduces growth rate and increases in the proportion of lipids in the body and carcass. It is vital to satisfy protein requirements during rearing and fattening stages. Early weaning, which occurs when the lamb weighs 12–15 kg, makes very high quality diets compulsory.

Energy Supply. When protein requirements are met, the energy supply (kcal/lamb/d) and the energy concentration have no clear effect on the fattening condition. Lamb weight, or more precisely, stage of maturity (slaughter weight/potential adult weight) is the most important factor in the fattening state. The effects of restricted feeding in late fattening or the use of low-concentrate diets that bring on an increased intake are limited and of no practical use.

Weaning. Whatever the weaning age, it always corresponds to a temporary reduction in the energy supply level. This reduction can have limited effects on growth, as the digesta greatly increase during this period, which disguises the lamb's weight loss. At the same age and with the same weight, early-weaned are always less fat than nonweaned lambs.

Carcass Fat Quality

The intensification of sheep production requires artificial rearing and high-energy diets with a high proportion of cereals during the fattening period. The latter two methods can both induce external soft carcass fat at slaughter.

Artificial Rearing. A low fat content (20 percent) and a high proportion of unsaturated

fatty acids in the milk replacer can modify carcass fatty acid composition. With low-fat milk replacers, the water percentage of external depots is higher than the corresponding values observed for dam-fed lambs or artificially fed lambs with 30 percent fat artificial milk (Table 18–15). In the latter situation the fatty acid composition of external carcass depots is different from the corresponding values observed with mother-fed lambs; unsaturated fatty acids with a lower melting point account for a higher percentage of fat depots (Table 18–16).

To avoid this defect, the utilization of lamb-adapted milk substitutes is required, using a high fat content (higher than 20 percent) and a high percentage of short-chain fatty acids (such as in coconut oil; see Table 18–16) and an increased ruminant phase (weaning to slaughter) to reduce the artificial-rearing-induced defects (Table 18–17).

Fattening. High-energy diets with a low roughage content (0–10 percent) or ground and pelleted diets are efficient to promote high growth rates. These diets induce a high propionic acid percentage in the rumen. This fatty acid is used efficiently for growth. However, the total amount of synthesized propionic acid can be too high and may overload liver enzymes. When this occurs, the fatty acids synthesized by

TABLE 18-15

Effects of milk substitute fat content on external fatty depot water content

Type of Rearing	Milk Fat Content, %	Water Content of Depot, %
Dam	—	21.3
Artificial rearing	30	19.5
Artificial rearing	20	24.3

Source: Theriez (12).

TABLE 18-16

Effects of milk fatty acid composition on external carcass depots composition

Type of Rearing	Type of Milk Replacer Fat	At Weaning (42 d)				At Slaughter (120 d)			
		C_{14}	C_{16}	C_{18}	Total Saturated	C_{14}	C_{16}	C_{18}	Total Saturated
Dam		9.9	29.9	48.8	49.9	4.8	26.7	50.1	43.0
Artificial rearing	Tallow	2.0	21.5	61.0	38.8	2.1	21.0	69.2	34.6
" "	Coconut	17.3	28.9	33.7	58.8	8.8	18.9	53.9	34.9
" "	Palm oil	1.8	30.7	57.9	42.5	1.5	19.3	58.2	31.5

(Header note: External Fat Depots Composition, % of Total Fatty Acids)

Source: Aurousseau et al. (3).

TABLE 18-17

Effects of ruminant phase length on external fatty depots of artificially reared lambs

Weaning Age, d	Slaughter Age, d	Fattening Period Length, d	Saturated Fatty Acids in External Depots, %
28	129	101	41.9
42	116	74	38.8
56	117	61	33.8

Source: Theriez (14).

adipocytes have a high percentage of odd-length fatty acids (15 and 17 carbon atoms) with a lower melting point than is typical of the corresponding C_{16} and C_{18} fatty acids.

To reduce the frequency of this defect, the following practices must be applied: the roughage proportion of diets (15–20 percent at least, hay rather than straw) must be increased, cereals as whole grain are to be preferred to ground and pelleted diets, and the amount of concentrate given during the last weeks of the fattening period must be reduced.

CONCLUSIONS

The rearing period from birth to weaning is the tricky period of lamb meat production. Its success has a determinant effect on the fattening period and on carcass quality. But this period depends on the initial growth potential of the lamb, which is affected by the lamb's nutrition *in utero*. A low birth weight induced by erroneous ewe nutrition has all the previously cited consequences: early mortality rate increase, growth rate reduction, and increased carcass fatness. These effects cannot be reduced in the rearing or fattening period. It must be borne in mind that in a very intensive system, a lamb can reach slaughter weight (38–48 kg according to breed) as early as 80–90 days of age, which corresponds to only 55–65 percent of the *in utero* growth period. Good performances and low loss percentages can never be obtained with lambs born of undernourished ewes, which is why the nutrient allowances for pregnant ewes must be carefully heeded. This is the key to success in good lamb rearing.

REFERENCES

1. ARC. 1980. *The nutrient requirements of ruminant livestock.* London: Commonwealth Agr. Bureaux.
2. Alexander, G. 1974. *Ciba Foundation Symp. 27.* London.
3. Aurousseau, B., M. Theriez, and M. Daniel. 1973. *Ann. Biol. Anim. Biochim. Biophysics.* 13:93.
4. Doxey, D. L. 1975. In: *Perinatal losses in lambs.* A collection of papers from a symposium at Stirling University (Feb. 1975): 35–37.
5. Hodge, R. W. 1966. *Aust. J. Exp. Agr. Animal Husb.* 21:139.
6. INRA. 1988. *Alimentation des bovines ovines et caprines.* R. Jarrige, ed. Paris: INRA.
7. NRC. 1985. *Nutrient requirements of sheep,* 6th ed. Washington, D.C.: Nat. Acad. Press.
8. Ørskov, E. R., et al. 1971. *J. Agr. Sci.* 77:351.
9. Peart, J. N., R. A. Edwards, and E. Donaldson. 1975. *J. Agr. Sci.* 85:315.
10. Penning, P. D., and M. J. Gibb. 1979. *Animal Prod.* 29:53.
11. Slee, J. 1977. In: *Perinatal losses in lambs.* A collection of papers from a symposium at Stirling University (Feb. 1975): 30–34.
12. Thériez, M. 1975. In: *L'allaitement artificiel des agneaux et des chevreaux,* 78000 Versailles: INRA Publications (route de St. Cyr): 21–44.
13. Villette, Y., and A. Brelurut. 1980. *Bull. Techn. CRZV Theix. INRA* 40:5.
14. Villette, Y., and D. Levieux. 1981. *Ann. Rech. Vet.* 12:227.
15. Villette, Y., and M. Thériez. 1982. *Ann. Zoot.* 30:151.
16. Wadrop, I. D., and J. B. Coombe. 1960. *J. Agr. Sci.* 54:140.

19

Finishing Lambs for Market

D. G. Ely

INTRODUCTION

Lambs marketed for slaughter are derived from many management and feeding systems. From a broad standpoint, the sources of slaughter lambs include (a) those marketed directly off the ewe at weaning, (b) those weaned before 120 d of age and finished to slaughter weights at some later date, and (c) those weaned at 120 d or older and finished on pasture or in drylot (feeder lambs). Most slaughter lambs are produced through sources (b) and (c).

The process of feeding lambs from weaning until they reach desired slaughter weights, and with adequate fat to grade choice, is termed "finishing." Lambs derived from sources (b) and (c) have to be finished before the producer is to receive a reasonable price and before the carcasses can be sold at the retail level.

Finishing lambs to market weights of 95–130 lb can be accomplished with rations ranging from all roughage (Fig. 19–1) to all concentrate (Fig. 19–2). These same lambs can have small, medium, and large frames. The frame size dictates the type of ration to feed, the length of

FIGURE 19–1. Finishing lambs with roughage rations. (Courtesy of M. E. Benson, Michigan State University, East Lansing, MI.)

the feeding period, and the weight when the finished lambs should be marketed.

The goal of the lamb feeder is to produce a lamb of satisfactory quality that will make the greatest profit. The purpose of this chapter is to describe the basic principles of finishing lambs that will lead to the attainment of both of these goals.

FIGURE 19–2. Finishing lambs with high-concentrate rations. (Courtesy of Harper Livestock Co., Eaton, CO.)

NUTRIENT REQUIREMENTS

Producers in the business of finishing lambs for the slaughter market must have in mind the ideal type of finished product. According to Tatum et al. (1), the ideal "lean" slaughter lamb produces a carcass that has 2.54–6.35 mm of back fat, less than 3.5 percent kidney and pelvic fat, and a yield grade of 2.67 to 3.67. After determining the type of lamb to produce, the producer must decide how to most efficiently feed to get this end product. This question becomes even more complex because of the wide variation in the types of lambs finished for slaughter (age, weight, sex, breed, and so on). Perhaps the first step towards answering this question is to analyze the nutrient requirements.

The lamb is born with a nonfunctional rumen that requires dietary nutrients be provided from milk or milk replacer. If lambs are provided access to dry feed immediately after birth, some degree of functionality becomes apparent by 2 weeks of age (2, 3). Continual access to ad libitum dry feed to 6–8 weeks of age produces an anaerobic microbial system in the rumen capable of digesting and synthesizing protein to an extent that milk is no longer essential for efficient production. Table 19–1 shows how the rumen-reticulum and omasum-abomasum tissue weights change with age.

Protein

Microorganisms in the functioning rumen digest dietary protein and nonprotein nitrogen (NPN) and convert it into their own cellular protein. The microbial protein, along with any dietary

TABLE 19-1

Changes in the tissue weight ratios of the rumen-reticulum (RR) to the omasum-abomasum (OA) at different ages (RR:OA)

Age	RR:OA
Birth	1:2
30 d	1.4:1
62 d	2.6:1
Adult	2.7:1

Source: Church et al. (4).

protein that is not digested by the microbes, passes from the rumen-reticulum through the omasum to the abomasum and small intestine, where both are subjected to digestive processes similar to those of the nonruminant. The microbial protein reaching the small intestine accounts for 40–80 percent of the total protein reaching this area of the digestive tract (5).

Rumen bacteria degrade dietary protein to ammonia, amino acids, and peptides and incorporate these into cellular protein. Ammonia is also derived from dietary NPN sources such as urea. This ammonia is preferentially used by the bacteria to synthesize cellular protein (6, 7). Any lack of ammonia may limit microbial growth when the intake of protein is low or ruminal degradation of the dietary protein is low. Concentrations of 5–10 mg ammonia/dl of rumen fluid appear to optimize bacterial protein production (8).

When developing dietary requirements, accountability must be made for the extent of utilization of the protein by rumen microorganisms, the amount that escapes digestion in the rumen, the extent of digestion in the small intestine, energy content of the diet, as well as age and weight of the lamb. Some dietary protein sources may be essentially 100 percent degraded in the rumen but inefficiently used for growth (see Ch. 8, 14, 15). Others may resist both rumen and small intestinal digestion, making the protein unavailable to the animal. Efficient use of protein in either of these situations is dependent on the availability of dietary energy. Furthermore, age and weight of the lamb, as well as the level of performance desired, influence the protein requirement.

The protein requirements of finishing lambs are presented in Table 19–2. Although the requirements are separated for age, weight, and gain, no differentiation is made between protein sources and how they are utilized.

Energy

Although dietary energy is the most important nutrient required for maximum gain in lambs, it can also be the most deterrent. That is, too little dietary energy inhibits gain whereas excess can cause extensive fat deposition at the expense of muscle growth. When either of these situations occur, economic inefficiency results.

Measures of energy requirements, expressed as total digestible nutrients (TDN), digestible energy (DE), and metabolizable (ME), are presented in Table 19–2. Metabolizable energy can be further divided into net energy for maintenance (NEm) and for gain (NEg). These values have been computed for varying growth rates of small, medium, and large frame genotype lambs (9). These requirements should be strictly adhered to in order to prevent oversupplying energy to finishing lambs, one of the most wasteful practices in the industry.

Minerals

Fifteen minerals have been demonstrated to be essential for sheep. Seven major minerals are sodium (Na), chlorine (Cl), calcium (Ca), phosphorus (P), magnesium (Mg), potassium (K), and sulfur (S). Trace elements required are iodine (I), iron (Fe), molybdenum (Mo), copper (Cu), cobalt (Co), manganese (Mn), zinc (Zn), and selenium (Se). Other elements may prove to be essential in the future.

Na and Cl requirements are considered together and are expressed as salt requirements. Salt should be added at a rate of 0.5–1.0 percent of the total diet. Salt can be used to limit free-choice supplement intake if plenty of fresh, cool water is available. These mixtures are usually 10–15 percent salt, depending on the desired amount of ration to be consumed. Trace mineral salt should not be used for this purpose because of the possible excessive intake of Cu.

Ca requirements range from 0.35 to 0.82 percent, and P requirements range from 0.19 to 0.38 percent of the complete diet (Table 19–2). For maximum use of each mineral, adequate vitamin D must be present. Calculations of the requirements in Table 19–2 reveal the recommended dietary Ca:P ratio is approximately 2:1. If this ratio becomes narrower, the incidence of urinary calculi may be increased.

Mg and K requirements range from 0.12 to 0.18 and 0.50 to 0.80 percent of the dietary dry matter, respectively (9). Although these minerals fulfill many physiological functions, cereal grains and harvested forages provide adequate amounts to prevent any deficiencies with good feeding regimens.

The S requirements for finishing lambs range from 0.18 to 0.26 percent of the dietary dry matter (9). Generally, the dietary N:S ratio should be maintained at 10:1. Common feedstuffs contain about 0.1 percent S, thus there is usually no reason to supplement finishing lamb rations with S. Exceptions might be when mature grass hay makes up a large portion of the ration or when NPN supplements replace portions of common protein supplements (soybean, cottonseed, or linseed meal). In these cases, methionine is the supplemental S source recommended.

For specific trace mineral requirements, one should refer to the latest edition of the NRC

TABLE 19-2
Dietary nutrient requirements for finishing lambs (% of dry matter)

BW,[a] kg	WC,[a]/d, g	Energy			Diet Proportions		CP,[a] %	Ca,[a] %	P,[a] %	Vitamin A, IU/kg	Vitamin E IU/kg
		TDN, %	DE, Mcal/kg	ME, Mcal/kg	Concentrate, %	Roughage, %					
Finishing lambs—4–7 mo old											
30	295	72	3.2	2.5	60	40	14.7	0.51	0.24	1,085	15
40	275	76	3.3	2.7	75	25	11.6	0.42	0.21	1,175	15
50	205	77	3.4	2.8	80	20	10.0	0.35	0.19	1,469	15
Early-weaned lambs—moderate and rapid growth potential											
20	300	78	3.4	2.8	85	15	16.9	0.54	0.24	940	20
30	325	78	3.3	2.7	85	15	15.1	0.51	0.24	1,085	15
40–60	400	78	3.3	2.7	85	15	14.5	0.55	0.28	1,253	15

[a]BW = body weight, WC = weight change, CP = crude protein, Ca = calcium, P = phosphorus.
Source: NRC (9).

(9). Toxicities of Cu and F can be potential problems, as can deficiencies, particularly of I and Se. Se can be provided through selenized trace mineral salt either ad libitum or mixed with the complete diet. Iodine can be provided through iodized salt.

Vitamins

The rumen microorganisms normally synthesize all of the B-vitamins and vitamin K in amounts required for maximum lamb performance. However, polioencephalomalacia, caused from a thiamin deficiency, can occur in feedlot lambs consuming high-concentrate diets.

Vitamins A and E must be supplied through the diet and vitamin D through the diet or from sunlight. The most recent requirements for A and E are published in NRC (9).

Vitamin A deficiencies are rarely encountered in finishing lambs, particularly if any green roughage is fed. Alfalfa hay is the best source of carotene, the precursor to vitamin A. Sun-cured hays are excellent sources of vitamin D. Common feedstuffs (corn, milo, soybean meal, and alfalfa hay) used in lamb finishing rations may be deficient in α-tocopherol (vitamin E) or the vitamin may be destroyed before it reaches the absorption site in the small intestine portion of the digestive tract.

Toxicities of vitamins A, D, and E are relatively hard to precipitate. Therefore, as a safety measure, a vitamin A, D, and E mixture containing 4 million, 800,000, and 500 IU/lb, respectively, should be mixed with the complete ration at 0.05 percent.

Water

Compared with other nutrients, water requirements are many times assumed to be incidental. However, provision of all the other nutrients in exact amounts will be a worthless endeavor if strict attention is not paid to water quantity and quality.

Water consumption by lambs is affected by ambient temperature, size, wool covering, and feed composition (9). These factors also affect feed consumption. Therefore, water intake is related to feed consumption by the following formula (9):

Total water intake
$$= (3.86 \times \text{dry-matter intake}) - 0.99$$

Water consumption is also dependent on water cleanliness and temperature. If the water supply is dirty, stagnate, hot, or cold, consumption will be low, as will feed intake and ultimate performance. Finishing lambs should always have access to clean water that is 40–50° F. Then, one can predict they will consume 2–3 lb of water per lb of dry matter consumed.

FEEDSTUFFS FOR FINISHING LAMBS

Concentrates

Carbonaceous concentrates are fed for energy. The primary feeds used to finish lambs include shelled corn, ground ear corn, wheat, sorghum, oats, and barley. These feeds are deficient in Ca and carotene and contain relatively small amounts of protein (see Ch. 7). The protein present is poorly digested and deficient in lysine and tryptophan. Therefore, if this protein is to provide any significant benefit to the lamb, it must be converted to microbial protein in the rumen.

Based on the energy content, the relative feeding values of these, plus liquid molasses, are presented in Table 19–3. Shelled corn is given a value of 100 with the other sources expressed as a percentage of this value. The quantities of each source required to produce equal performance of 1 lb of shelled corn are shown in the right-hand column. Wheat has a higher feeding value than shelled corn, but it should not make up more than 50 percent of the total ration grain because of possible digestive disturbances. Ear corn must be ground and mixed with 5 percent liquid molasses to have a value of 88.

These feeding values were used to compute the relative dollar values of the energy sources when shelled corn is valued at $2 to $4 per bushel (Table 19–4). The lamb feeder must use these relative values before maximum economic efficiency can be obtained because of different feeding values and different weights per bushel. Furthermore, some energy sources are marketed on a pound rather than a bushel basis.

Although dried molasses is relatively rich in energy, it is not as concentrated as shelled corn, milo, or barley. Liquid molasses, condensed soybean solubles, liquid whey, and hemicellulose extract provide only small amounts of dietary energy because of their high water content. Their cost per unit of energy is prohibitive if added to the ration strictly as an energy source. Instead, their use should be confined to increasing palatability of other ingredients or as binders in the manufacture of pellets.

TABLE 19-3

Relative feeding values of carbonaceous concentrates for finishing lambs

Feedstuff	Relative Feeding Value, %	Pounds Required to Provide Equal Energy to 1.0 lb of Shelled Corn
Shelled corn	100	—
Sorghum	95	1.05
Barley	90	1.10
Oats	80	1.25
Wheat[a]	105	0.95
Ground ear corn[b]	88	1.14
Liquid molasses[c]	70	1.43

[a]When fed at not more than 50% of the total ration grain.

[b]95% ground ear corn mixed with 5% liquid molasses.

[c]When fed at not more than 5% of the total ration.

Alternative carbonaceous energy sources include beet pulp, citrus pulp, cassava meal, cooked, raw, and ensiled potatoes, and wastes from food processing plants. Small amounts of animal fats (less than 5 percent) can be added to lamb finishing rations to reduce dust and increase palatability.

Although alternative sources can be used to finish lambs successfully, in most situations performance will not equal that obtained with cereal grains.

Proteinaceous concentrates most commonly fed to finishing lambs are soybean meal (SBM), cottonseed meal (CSM), linseed meal (LSM), sunflower meal, and dehydrated alfalfa meal, although corn gluten meal, brewers grains, distillers grains, feather meal, fish meal, and blood meal appear to be increasing in popularity.

Dietary protein is either digested in the rumen or escapes undigested to the lower part of the digestive tract (9). The undigested portion, bypass or escape protein, is either digested postruminally or excreted in the feces.

Protein sources have been classified on the basis of the percentage that bypasses or escapes ruminal digestion (10, 11, 12). Low-bypass sources (less than 40 percent) include casein, SBM, sunflower meal, and peanut meal; medium-bypass sources (40–60 percent) are cottonseed meal, dehydrated alfalfa meal, corn grain, and brewers dried grains; and high-bypass sources (greater than 60 percent) include meat meal, distillers dried grains, corn gluten meal, blood meal, feather meal, fish meal, and formaldehyde-treated proteins. Feed processing conditions, animal variability, other dietary constituents, and changes in the rumen microbial population affect dietary protein bypass, but

TABLE 19-4

Relative dollar values of carbonaceous concentrates for finishing lambs

	Shelled Corn, $/bu				
	2.00	2.50	3.00	3.50	4.00
Relative value ($/bu.)[a]					
Barley	$1.54	$1.93	$2.31	$2.70	$3.09
Oats	0.91	1.14	1.37	1.60	1.83
Wheat[b]	2.25	2.81	3.38	3.94	4.50
Ear corn[c]	1.92	2.46	3.02	3.57	4.12
Relative value ($/100 lb.)[a]					
Sorghum	$3.39	$4.24	$5.09	$5.94	$6.78
Ground ear corn[d]	3.14	3.92	4.71	5.49	6.28
Liquid molasses[e]	2.50	3.12	3.75	4.37	5.00

[a]Computations have been adjusted for difference in weight/bu and relative feeding values.

[b]When fed at not more than 50% of the total ration grain.

[c]Unground.

[d]Includes cost of grinding plus mixing with 5% liquid molasses.

[e]When fed at not more than 5% of the total ration.

these effects have not been well quantitated (9). When high-bypass proteins are fed, blending with NPN (urea) and/or a low-bypass supplement is required to maintain ruminal ammonia levels for adequate ruminal microbial protein synthesis.

Microbial protein synthesis is essential for two reasons. First, a rumen microbial population must be maintained to digest other dietary ingredients and, second, increased bypass of dietary protein does not always mean animal growth will be increased. Bypassed protein may be poorly digested postruminally, the balance of amino acids available for absorption from the small intestine may be poor, or other nutrients may limit production (13, 5).

Roughages

A wide variety of roughages can be fed to finishing lambs. When deciding how much roughage to feed, the main question to keep in mind is: Why am I feeding this roughage? Many roughages contribute little to the nutritive value of the ration and may be added simply to keep lambs on feed. Others make significant contributions of energy, protein, minerals, and vitamins.

Carbonaceous roughages contribute dietary energy. Corn silage is used more extensively than sorghum, grass, or grass-legume silages because it provides more readily available energy (contains more grain) and promotes faster and more efficient gain. Any time maximum gain is desired and silage is used as the roughage source, supplementation with grain and protein is essential. The level of per-

formance is always dictated by the level of energy provided by concentrates rather than by the roughages.

Other carbonaceous roughages that can be fed are grass hays, ground corn cobs, cottonseed hulls, chicken litter, cotton gin trash, stovers, and straws. All of these are considered low-quality roughages because they are so indigestible and, therefore, contribute very little to the nutritive value of the ration. If the ration contains more than 20 percent of these sources, they should be fed in pelleted form to increase consumption.

Even though most roughages are classed as energy sources, when compared with concentrates they are relatively poor suppliers of energy. Corn silage and some common hays fed for this purpose are compared with shelled corn in Table 19–5. Because of the lower energy content, digestibility, and feeding value, they become expensive energy sources (Table 19–6). For example, if shelled corn costs $3 per bushel, timothy hay would have to cost less than $30 per ton before it would be a more economical energy supplier.

Proteinaceous roughages (legumes) are excellent sources of protein. They should be fed for this purpose although they do also provide energy, minerals, and vitamins. Table 19–5 shows that the legume hays have higher feeding values, for energy, than do grass hays. However, they are usually too expensive to feed for any nutritive purpose other than provision of dietary protein (Table 19–6).

Alfalfa is the classic roughage for finishing lambs. Although the roughage portion of the ra-

TABLE 19-5

Relative feeding values of some common roughages for finishing lambs

Source	Relative Feeding Value, %[a]	Pounds Required to Provide Equal Energy to 1.0 lb of Shelled Corn
Shelled corn	100	—
Corn silage[b]	37	2.67
Alfalfa hay	58	1.75
Clover hay	56	1.79
Grass-legume hay	55	1.81
Orchardgrass hay	54	1.85
Fescue hay	38	2.63
Timothy hay	28	3.57
Bluegrass hay	26	3.85

[a]All sources are compared with shelled corn with a value of 100.
[b]40% dry matter.

TABLE 19-6

Relative dollar values of shelled corn ($/bu) and some roughages ($/ton) when fed for energy to finishing lambs

| | Shelled Corn, $/bu | | | | |
	2.00	2.50	3.00	3.50	4.00
Relative value ($/ton)					
Corn silage[a]	$26.40	$33.00	$39.66	$46.25	$52.84
Alfalfa hay	41.41	51.74	62.18	72.50	82.82
Clover hay	39.27	49.06	58.96	68.75	78.54
Grass-legume hay	39.98	49.95	60.03	70.00	79.97
Orchardgrass hay	38.56	48.17	57.89	67.50	77.11
Fescue hay	27.13	33.90	40.74	47.50	54.26
Timothy hay	19.99	24.98	30.02	35.00	39.98
Bluegrass hay	18.56	23.19	27.87	32.24	37.13

[a]40% dry matter.

tion can be provided as silage or pasture, hay is used more extensively. Alfalfa hay is highly palatable, very digestible, provides some energy (Table 19–5), is relatively rich in protein, is an excellent source of Ca, and is the ultimate supplier of carotene (vitamin A).

Other legume hays can be used as a source of protein almost as successfully as alfalfa. However, performance from grass-legume hays will be lower because the lower protein content of the grass dilutes the leguminous protein.

Mineral Supplements

Na and Cl (salt) receive highest priority for supplementation. Salt should be fed only in a loose form, because instead of licking block salt, sheep will try to bite it. The result will usually be broken teeth and insufficient intake.

Salt must be available at all times, either as 0.5–1.0 percent of the mixed ration or provided ad libitum. A shortage of salt intake will reduce water and feed intake. If lambs go without salt for a period of time and then are suddenly allowed ad libitum access, toxicity can result.

Common Ca supplements used in finishing lamb rations are ground limestone, dicalcium phosphate, and steamed bone meal. Ground limestone should be added to rations when only Ca is deficient. Grains are virtually devoid of Ca, thus rations that contain upwards of 90 percent concentrates are likely to be deficient, and especially so if the roughage is from any source other than legumes.

The ration Ca content can be increased with defluorinated dicalcium phosphate or steamed bone meal, but the P level will also be increased. Dicalcium phosphate and steamed bone meal contain Ca and P in approximately a 1 to 1 ratio. Therefore, supplementing for Ca alone with either of these sources may provide excess P and create a total ration Ca to P ratio less than 2 to 1. If this occurs, urinary calculi may be encountered, particularly in wether lambs.

Mineral deficiencies might be encountered in certain situations, even though rations may be balanced according to the NRC requirements (9). Some research on the "availability" of minerals in some supplements has been conducted with nonruminants (14). Whether this can be a problem in finishing lambs is not known, but if deficiencies occur when the ration supposedly provides adequate amounts, availability should be suspected.

The trace minerals I, Fe, Mo, Cu, Co, Mn, Zn, and Se can be provided through trace mineral salt. The trace mineral salt should contain Se unless the feeds are produced in an area with high Se soil levels. Any trace mineral salt other than that mixed specifically for sheep should not be fed because of the possibility of mineral toxicities, especially Cu.

Vitamin Supplements

A vitamin A, D, E premix (see vitamin requirement section) can be added to finishing rations. This premix should be added at 0.05 percent of the complete ration. Although most finishing rations provide adequate amounts of vitamins A, D, and E, supplementation is so inexpensive that it is wise to add these as a safety measure to guard against any possible deficiency.

FEED ADDITIVES

Antibiotics are added to finishing lamb rations to maintain health, primarily by reducing digestive disturbances and enterotoxemia incidence. Health maintenance, in turn, allows consistent improvements in gain and feed efficiency. Chlortetracycline, oxytetracycline, and neomycin are cleared for singular use in finishing rations (see Ch. 10).

Lasalocid and monensin are rumen fermentation modifiers that promote growth, increase feed efficiency, and prevent coccidiosis. Although lasalocid can be used as a growth promotant and coccidiostat, monensin can be used in lamb rations only as a coccidiostat.

Antibiotics should always be fed according to the manufacturer's specifications. Feeding less than the recommended amounts may eliminate any benefits expected, whereas feeding excessive amounts may be detrimental to the animal's health.

Buffer additions (2 percent $NaHCO_3$ or $KHCO_3$) can effectively prevent digestive disturbances, particularly when adjusting lambs to finishing rations or changing abruptly from high-roughage to high-concentrate rations. However, if a relatively long period (21 d) of adjustment to high-concentrate rations (80–90 percent) is employed, there appears to be little benefit to adding buffers. Furthermore, once the lambs are on feed, there is probably no benefit from buffer additions.

FEED PROCESSING

Ørskov (15, 16, 17) fed whole barley, oats, corn, and wheat to lambs and found acidosis and rumenitis were decreased, rumination time was increased, and carcasses contained firmer outside fat cover than those produced from the same grains fed as pellets. Feed efficiencies from whole corn, barley, and oats were higher than those obtained from the same ground grains. Other work has demonstrated improved gains and feed efficiencies from whole grains when compared with pellets (18, 19, 20). On the other hand, cracking, rolling, or flaking sorghum grains will increase efficiency of utilization.

The most critical factor to consider in determining whether to process grains for finishing lambs is the physical form of the complete ration. If protein, mineral, and vitamin supplementation is through pellets, they should be mixed with whole grains to prevent sifting in self-feeders and preferential consumption of self-fed or hand-fed rations. Conversely, if the supplements are provided in meal form, the grains should be ground or cracked before mixing to encourage desired consumption of all nutrients.

Hay that is mixed with ration concentrates should be chopped or coarsely ground to facilitate mixing, encourage uniform consumption of ration ingredients, and reduce wastage when compared with feeding as long hay. Fine grinding of hay increases ration dustiness, reduces intake, and leads to poorer lamb performance.

If large amounts of hay are fed, pelleting will increase consumption and performance, especially if the hay is of low quality. If hay is pelleted, then it can be mixed efficiently with the whole grain portion of the ration. Pelleting the entire ration for finishing lambs is usually not a viable option because the increased benefits are usually not large enough to offset the pelleting costs.

FEEDING EARLY-WEANED LAMBS

Early weaning is defined as separating ewes from lambs when the lambs reach any age less than 120 d. Under practical conditions, this operation usually occurs when lambs are 60–90 d of age. Since the rumen is adequately developed (Table 19–1), lambs can be early-weaned to pasture (Fig. 19–3) or drylot (Fig. 19–4) and finished for slaughter as milk-fed slaughter lambs. Economically, early weaning is a more efficient method of producing this type of lamb than allowing the lamb(s) to nurse

FIGURE 19–3. Finishing early-weaned lambs on pasture. (Courtesy of S. Umberger, VPI and SU, Blacksburg, VA.)

FIGURE 19–4. Early-weaned lambs in drylot. (Courtesy of North Dakota State University, Hettinger Experiment Station.)

the ewe (Fig. 19–5) until reaching milk-fed slaughter weights (21).

For early weaning to pasture to be successful, several management practices must be accomplished. Lambs should have access to a concentrate creep ration throughout the preweaning phase. They should also be allowed to consume pasture with the ewes prior to weaning. If lambs are raised in confinement prior to early weaning to pasture, some depressed performance can be expected. The following steps should be taken to prevent as much weaning stress as possible:

A. Vaccinate for enterotoxemia, shear, and keep lambs in preweaning surroundings for 14 d after ewes are moved out of hearing distance.

B. Continue to provide preweaning creep feed ad libitum for 7 d after weaning.

C. During the next 7 d provide ad libitum a 50:50 mixture of the preweaning

FIGURE 19–5. Lambs nursing ewes until reaching slaughter weights. (Courtesy of S. Umberger, VPI and SU, Blacksburg, VA.)

creep ration and the grain to be fed on pasture. Daily intake will average 0.5–0.7 lb/hd.

D. Supplement with grass-legume hay ad libitum during the last 7 d. Daily intake will average about 1.0 lb/hd.

E. Lambs can be turned to pasture 7 d after weaning but must have access to the preweaning facility to consume the concentrate mix and hay.

F. If lambs do not have access to pasture during the last 7 d, the total 14-d postweaning adjustment period should be in the preweaning facility.

Spring growth of cool season grasses (bluegrass, fescue, bromegrass, orchardgrass), legumes, grass-legume mixtures, and small grains are excellent pastures for early-weaned lambs. Supplemental energy, provided ad libitum, is essential for optimum performance (22). Shelled corn is ideal, but other grains and ground ear corn mixed with 5 percent liquid molasses can be used successfully. The choice of grains is dependent on grain availability and relative dollar values (Table 19–4). Grains do not need to be processed, because there is no reason to mix any other ingredients with the grain. On the average, lambs will consume about 2 lb of grain/hd daily from weaning until reaching slaughter weights of 95–120 lb. Have loose trace mineral salt with Se available at all times in covered salt boxes near the grain feeders.

Candidates for early weaning to pasture weigh a minimum of 50 lb. Expected gains are dependent on genetic growth potential, but early-weaned lambs finished on pasture plus a concentrate supplement reach slaughter weight as rapidly as drylot-fed lambs (100–150 d of age) (23). An illustration of this fact is shown in Table 19–7. Although lambs in this study were supplemented with a 13 percent crude protein-100 percent concentrate mix, whole grain will produce similar performances (22). Furthermore, early-weaned lambs finished on pasture plus supplement produced leaner carcasses.

Lambs early-weaned to drylot should be creep-fed an all-concentrate mixture (89 percent ground corn, 10 percent soybean meal, 1 percent antibiotic, for example) throughout preweaning. Vaccinate for enterotoxemia, shear, and leave lambs in their preweaning environment for 7 d postweaning. Continue to provide the preweaning creep ration ad libitum. On day 7, mix the preweaning creep with the drylot ration (half

TABLE 19-7

Performance of pasture-fed and drylot-fed lambs (initial weight = 31.8 kg; slaughter weight = 49.9 kg)

Treatment	Daily Gain, g	Feed Consumed, kg/d	Feed:Gain Ratio	Carcass Fat, %
Pasture	156	—	—	23.9
Pasture + supplement[a]	263	1.00	3.89	27.3
Drylot, 13% CP	267	2.07	7.98	33.2
Drylot, 16% CP	246	1.74	7.23	31.6

[a]13% crude protein supplement; same as drylot, 13% crude protein.

Source: Ely et al. (23).

TABLE 19-8

Example rations for finishing early-weaned lambs in drylot (%)

Ingredient	Ration 1	Ration 2
Ground shelled corn	67.5	—
Ground ear corn	—	74.5
Cottonseed hulls	10.0	—
Soybean meal (44% CP)	14.0	17.0
Liquid cane molasses	5.0	5.0
Ground limestone	1.0	1.0
Trace mineral salt + Se	1.0	1.0
Aureomycin crumbles[a,b]	1.0	1.0
Ammonium sulfate	0.5	0.5
Vitamin A, D, E premix	[b]	[b]

[a]Contains 2 g active ingredient/lb of premix.

[b]Mix according to manufacturer's directions.

and half) and feed ad libitum. Daily intake will average 1.1–1.2 lb/hd. On day 14, move lambs to the drylot and feed the finishing ration ad libitum. Two examples of rations for finishing early-weaned lambs in drylot are presented in Table 19–8. These rations will be the same as those used during the last 7 d of the 14-d adjustment period. Substitution of other grains for shelled or ear corn should follow the relative feeding and price values described in Tables 19–3 and 19–4, respectively. Coarsely ground or chopped dry roughages can replace equivalent cottonseed hulls, depending on cost of purchase and grinding. Other protein supplements may be substituted for soybean meal, but the choice should be dependent on purchase costs. If high-bypass supplements (corn gluten meal, distillers dried grains, or the like) are fed with these diets, restrict the amount to a maximum of 10 percent of the total ration.

FINISHING FEEDER LAMBS

Feeder lambs can be finished on pasture (plus supplemental concentrates) or in drylot. Weight

of lambs at purchase should govern the types of feed used for finishing. Lightweight lambs (50–70 lb) can use more roughage, whereas heavier lambs (70–80 lb) require more concentrates and a shorter feeding period. Lightweight lambs are more desirable for pasture finishing, while heavier lambs perform best in the drylot. Small-, medium-, and large-frame lambs can fit into either the lightweight or heavyweight categories.

The feeder should plan to market the lambs when they have adequate finish regardless of their weight (1). Small-frame lambs should be marketed between 95 and 105 lb, medium-frame lambs between 105 and 115 lb, and large-frame lambs between 115 and 130 lb. Feeding beyond these weights for each frame size is too expensive because of the decline in feed efficiency and increase in carcass fat (24).

Handling New Lambs

The success of a feeder lamb finishing system depends on the first 2 weeks after arrival. Lambs have usually been transported many miles and will probably be scared, tired, hungry, and thirsty. The following guides should be followed during this period.

Rest the lambs for 2–3 h after unloading in a dry, clean area. Provide shelter from rain or snow. After resting, offer grass hay or mixed grass-legume hay. A small pasture area can be used, but the grass should not be lush. Lambs can overeat on pasture! After feeding hay, offer fresh, cool water.

Hand-feed salt during the first 2 weeks, then provide trace mineral salt with Se and dicalcium phosphate in a compartmental trough. Lambs should be drenched for stomach and tape worms, treated for external parasites, and vaccinated for enterotoxemia Type C and D after 5–7 d. A vitamin A, D, E injection can be given at the same time if lambs originated from droughty conditions. Revaccinate for enterotoxemia 2 weeks later and drench again after 30 d.

Consider antibiotic feeding or injection, particularly during the first 2 weeks, to prevent respiratory infections. If the lambs are to be finished in drylot, sort by weight and feed separately. Isolate sick and weak lambs daily.

None of the lambs should be worked until they have recovered from the stress of shipping. They should be worked only during clear weather. Expected death losses should not exceed 2 percent for the total finishing period.

Shear all lambs sometime during the feeding period. Shearing prevents lambs from picking up mud and tags (25). Feed consumption and gains will also be increased, especially in warm weather. Lambs with number 1 pelts (½ to 1 inch of wool) sell at a premium to full-fleeced lambs. Usually 40–60 d are required to produce a number 1 pelt after shearing. Based on expected gains, the feeder can predict the minimum time needed to produce a number 1 pelt if lambs are sheared anytime after the first 2-week period.

Finishing Lambs on Pasture

Lightweight lambs make the best use of pasture. They can be used to clean weed fields, fence rows, soybean stubble, and corn fields. Lush, cool season grasses or alfalfa provide excellent fall pasture (and winter pasture in certain geographical areas). Rape (Fig. 19-6) and other brassicas (Fig. 19-7) can be used in the early fall. Depending on the targeted marketing date, supplemental concentrates can be fed ad libitum throughout the finishing period or during the last 30–40 d. Lambs grazing cool season grasses or alfalfa need only an energy source, such as whole cereal grains or rolled milo. Those clean-

FIGURE 19-6. Fall grazing of rape pasture. (Courtesy of S. Umberger, VPI and SU, Blacksburg, VA.)

FIGURE 19-7. Finishing lambs on cabbage. (Courtesy of Harper Livestock Co., Eaton, CO.)

ing weed fields, fence rows, soybean stubble, or corn fields will require a 90:10 ground grain: protein supplement. Brassica pastures also need to be supplemented with this grain-protein mixture.

The most profitable pasture is winter wheat or rye if they can be grown. Although lambs can be finished on small grain pasture alone, gains can be increased significantly by supplementing with whole grain. The grain can be limit-fed throughout the finishing phase or self-fed during the last 30–40 d to produce optimally finished "lean" lambs. The choice of grain is dependent on relative dollar values (Table 19–4). Supplemental protein is not required as long as lambs graze lush, green pasture.

If the final phase of the finishing period is conducted in drylot, gradually adjust lambs to a ration of 54–64 percent ground shelled corn, 30–40 percent ground grass hay, 5 percent liquid molasses, and 1 percent aureomycin premix for 30 d. Once in the drylot, replace ground hay with a protein supplement to raise the ration protein to 12–13 percent. Provide this ration ad libitum until marketing.

Trace mineral salt with Se in loose form, and protected from rain or snow, should be available continuously. Locate it in the same area as the water supply and the grain feeders.

Finishing Lambs in Drylot

Finishing heavy lambs in drylot allows for a rapid turnaround time, makes the most efficient use of facilities, and eliminates the need to adjust the ration composition as lambs increase in weight (Fig. 19-8).

Finishing lightweight lambs in drylot usually requires ration changes for at least three periods: period 1—first 3 weeks or until lambs reach 70 lb; period 2—70–80 lb; period 3—80 lb to market. There are many practical feeding programs, thus feeders should build theirs around

FIGURE 19-8. Finishing feeder lambs in drylot. (Courtesy of Harper Livestock Co., Eaton, CO.)

available feeds that will produce the most efficient gains at the least cost.

Three example feeding programs are shown in Table 19-9. The principles used to describe the data in Tables 19-3 and 19-4 should be employed if alternative feedstuffs are to be substituted in these programs. All of these example rations should contain an antibiotic and a vitamin A, D, E premix in the amounts prescribed by the manufacturer. Substitution of $NaHCO_3$ or $KHCO_3$ (2.0 percent of the ration)

for equivalent amounts of corn may reduce the incidence of acidosis during the 3-week period when starting lambs on feed.

All of these rations can be bunk-fed daily or self-fed. Both types of feeders require protection from rain or snow to maintain consistent intakes. If lambs are bunk-fed, allow 12 inches of trough space per lamb. If self-fed, each linear foot can serve 6–10 lambs.

Lambs can be fed in open fields. A windbreak or open shelter for winter feeding and a shade for summer feeding will aid in producing maximum growth and feed utilization. The ideal drylot will have some slope to the land to facilitate drainage. No more than 500 lambs should be fed per lot. Each lamb fed in this environment requires 15–20 square feet.

Lambs that are fed in a barn or shed require 5 square feet of housing plus 5 square feet of loafing area adjacent to the structure. If lambs are fed on slotted floors, each lamb requires only 4 square feet. Waterers and feeders must be located outside the feeding floor. Because of the cost of this type of feeding system, infestation

TABLE 19-9

Example feeding programs for finishing lambs in drylot

	Lamb Weight		
Rations	To 70 lb %	70–80 lb %	80 lb–market %
Ration 1			
Ground or cracked corn	51.0	61.0	71.0
Ground corn cobs	20.0	10.0	—
Soybean meal, 44% CP	11.5	11.5	11.5
Dehydrated alfalfa meal	10.0	10.0	10.0
Liquid molasses	5.0	5.0	5.0
Dicalcium phosphate	1.0	1.0	1.0
Trace mineral salt + Se	1.0	1.0	1.0
Ammonium sulfate	0.5	0.5	0.5
Ration 2			
Ground or cracked corn	48.0	58.0	68.0
Chopped grass hay	33.0	23.0	13.0
Soybean meal, 44% CP	11.5	11.5	11.5
Liquid molasses	5.0	5.0	5.0
Dicalcium phosphate	1.0	1.0	1.0
Trace mineral salt + Se	1.0	1.0	1.0
Ammonium sulfate	0.5	0.5	0.5
Ration 3			
Ground ear corn	60.0	30.0	—
Ground or cracked corn	—	30.0	60.0
Ground alfalfa hay	27.5	27.5	27.5
Soybean meal, 44% CP	6.0	6.0	6.0
Liquid molasses	5.0	5.0	5.0
Trace mineral salt + Se	1.0	1.0	1.0
Ammonium sulfate	0.5	0.5	0.5

of internal parasites and incidence of diseases must be eliminated before it will be economically viable.

Clean, fresh, cool water must be available at all times to encourage feed consumption and maximize ration digestibility and nutrient metabolism. Each foot of water space will serve 25–40 lambs.

POTENTIAL NUTRITIONAL PROBLEMS

The incidence of nutritional problems with finishing lambs is dependent on the severity of stress, the innate ability of the lambs to withstand this stress, and the level of management imposed by the feeder.

Enterotoxemia Type D is the most common nutritional problem encountered. Stress and sudden changes in rations precipitate this syndrome. Lambs to be early-weaned should be vaccinated twice prior to weaning. Older feeder lambs that are transported to the finishing area should be vaccinated twice during the first 2 weeks after arrival, whether they are destined to be finished on pasture or in drylot. Mixing a buffer in the ration when putting lambs on feed or when increasing the concentrate portion of the ration will shorten the adjustment period by reducing the incidence of acidosis. Offering broad-spectrum antibiotics any time concentrates are fed will aid in the maintenance of healthy lambs and thereby allow them to better withstand any stress imposed during the finishing period.

Urinary calculi can be a common occurrence in wethers in drylot (19). Maintenance of recommended Ca to P ratios will aid in prevention. The closer the ratio is to 1:1 the greater the probability of encountering urinary calculi. Provision of a continual supply of fresh, clean, cool water, with adequate waterer space, will aid in prevention. Mixing 1.0 percent trace mineral salt with Se will encourage maximum water consumption and thereby aid in the prevention of calculi.

Ammonium chloride (0.5 percent of the complete ration) has been used for many years to prevent urinary calculi. However, it has recently been taken off the market. Until it becomes available again, inclusion of 0.5 percent of ammonium sulfate is the recommended preventive. Include ammonium sulfate even if the Ca:P ratio is optimum, salt intake is adequate, and consistent and high-quality water is available at all times.

Feeding pelleted high-roughage rations may increase the incidence of rectal prolapse (26). Excessive ration dustiness may increase coughing, which can lead to rectal prolapse. Regardless of the ration fed, prolapse can still occur because the tendency to prolapse may be genetically controlled. Lambs with short-docked tails are more prone to rectal prolapse than those with long docks.

Early-weaned lambs may contract more coccidiosis than older lambs, particularly if they are fed in crowded conditions where feces can contaminate the drinking water. Usually, good sanitation practices will prevent coccidiosis.

Early-weaned lambs also appear to be more prone to Se and/or vitamin E deficiencies culminating in stiff lamb disease. Feeding high-quality rations with an adequate amount of green roughage will usually provide required amounts of vitamin E. Even so, adding a vitamin A, D, E premix to all rations is an inexpensive preventive measure.

A Se deficiency is more apt to occur than a deficiency of vitamin E, particularly if the grain was raised on Se-deficient soils. As long as the lambs have continual access to selenized trace mineral salt, either in the mixed ration or provided separately ad libitum, Se intake should be adequate to prevent any problems. As is the case with the vitamin A, D, E premix, providing a continual supply of selenized trace mineral salt is an economical investment.

Although Cu toxicity can occur in isolated situations, it should not be a significant problem for the lamb feeder if the selenized trace mineral salt that is fed is manufactured specifically for sheep.

SUMMARY

Many different feedstuffs can be used to provide all the nutrients required to economically finish lambs. The combination to use depends on the relative costs of the feedstuffs, the type and weight of lamb being finished, the management imposed, and the end product the feeder wants to market.

Early-weaned lambs are usually fed higher-quality feedstuffs (roughages and concentrates) than are older lambs so gains and feed efficiencies can be maximized. Although older lambs can be fed more roughage and lower-quality concentrate rations early in the feeding period, high-concentrate rations that promote maximum performance are required in the latter portion of the finishing phase. Feeding lambs beyond the point where they will produce "lean" carcasses is an economically unsound management practice.

The most critical period of the finishing phase, for both the feeder and the lambs, is the first 2–3 weeks. Handling lambs to minimize stress, promoting disease resistance, and getting the lambs on feed will determine how successful the total operation will be. If a high degree of management expertise is applied during this period and if all the nutrient requirements are met during the remainder of the finishing phase, nutritionally related problems will be minimal.

REFERENCES

1. Tatum, J. D., et al. 1988. *SID Res. J.* 5(1):23.
2. Poe, S. E., et al. 1971. *J. Animal Sci.* 32:989.
3. Poe, S. E., et al. 1972. *J. Animal Sci.* 34:826.
4. Church, D. C., ed. 1975. *Digestive physiology and nutrition of ruminants. Vol. 1: Digestive physiology.* 2d ed. Corvallis, OR: O & B Books.
5. Owens, F. N., and W. G. Bergen. 1983. *J. Animal Sci.* 57(Suppl. 2):498.
6. Bryant, M. P., and I. M. Robinson. 1963. *J. Dairy Sci.* 46:150.
7. Hungate, R. E. 1966. *The rumen and its microbes.* New York: Academic Press.
8. Satter, L. D., and L. L. Slyter. 1974. *Brit. J. Nutr.* 32:199.
9. NRC. 1985. *Nutrient requirements of sheep.* Washington, D.C.: Nat. Acad. Press.
10. Chapula, W. 1975. *J. Dairy Sci.* 58:1198.
11. Satter, L. D., and R. E. Roffler. 1975. *J. Dairy Sci.* 58:1219.
12. ARC. 1980. *The nutrient requirements of ruminant livestock.* London: Commonwealth Agr. Bureaux.
13. Young, A. W., et al. 1981. *J. Animal Sci.* 52:1421.
14. Burnell, T. W., et al. 1989. *J. Animal Sci.* 67 (Suppl. 1):38.
15. Barnes, B. J., and E. R. Ørskov. 1982. *World Anim. Rev.* 42:38.
16. Ørskov, E. R., et al. 1974. *Brit. J. Nutr.* 32:59.
17. Ørskov, E. R. 1979. *Livestock Prod. Sci.* 6:335.
18. Hanke, H. E., and R. M. Jordan. 1963. *J. Animal Sci.* 22:1097.
19. Pope, A. L., et al. 1984. *Univ. Wisconsin Sheep Day Proc.* (Spooner):15.
20. Pope, A. L., et al. 1985. *Univ. Wisconsin Sheep Day Proc.* (Spooner):26.
21. Ragland, K. K., et al. 1988. *Univ. Kentucky Sheeprofit Day Proc. Prog. Rpt.* 310:23.
22. Ely, D. G., et al. 1980. *Univ. Kentucky Sheeprofit Day Proc. Prog. Rpt.* 248:11.
23. Ely, D. G., et al. 1979. *J. Animal Sci.* 48:32.
24. Kemp, J. D., et al. 1976. *J. Animal Sci.* 42:575.
25. SID. 1987. *Sheep production handbook.* Denver, CO: Sheep Industry Development Program.
26. Church, D. C., ed. 1979. *Digestive physiology and nutrition of ruminants. Vol. 2: Nutrition.* 2d ed. Corvallis, OR: O & B Books.

20

Goats and Goat Nutrition

J. E. Huston

INTRODUCTION

Goats are small ruminants that are distributed widely throughout the geographic and climatic regions of the world. Although the dry conditions, rough terrain, and sparsely distributed vegetation of the steppe regions are most suitable, goats adapt quickly and with proper management can be productive under almost any circumstance.

Goats in the United States include dairy (intensive), Angora (mostly extensive), and Spanish or "meat" goats (mostly extensive). The Angora, and to a lesser extent the meat goat, is found primarily in the Edwards Plateau region of Texas. Goats are valuable to that region as a source of income from the sale of fiber (mohair) and animals for slaughter; they are also important in stabilizing the vegetation by retarding encroachment of brush species. The dairy goat industry is expanding rapidly, but it remains very minor in comparison with the dairy cattle industry. Most large goat dairies are located near metropolitan areas. Many smaller herds (5–20 goats) are kept as backyard operations, producing milk that is sold to neighbors and friends.

Although goats are important worldwide because of their socioeconomic contribution (mainly in lesser developed countries), the most unique thing about goats is their inquisitive feeding behavior. This alone is sufficient justification for dedicating this separate chapter to goats and goat nutrition.

FEEDING BEHAVIOR

Goats are unlike all other species of domestic livestock in choosing and consuming a diet. They discriminate between plant fractions or feed particles that appear identical, consuming one and leaving the other. They are insistent that their diet is fresh, clean, and previously untouched. They are versatile in diet selection.

Feeding in Confinement

Goats are very particular about what they eat even when fed a hay or mixed ration in a feed trough. Mobile lips and precise tongue movements (21) make it possible for the goat to sort through the offered feed, literally pushing the unchosen plant fragments and feed particles

FIGURE 20–1. A dairy goat at a feed bunk containing stem refusals from an earlier offering of hay.

aside and taking only the most preferred (Fig. 20–1).

This particular behavior has two important effects on diet. First, diet composition differs from the feed offered. The values in Table 20–1 show the difference in the composition of hay offered and refused. In this case the diet of the goats was 12.5 and 16.5 percent greater in net energy and protein, respectively, than the hay offered. Although the highly developed selectivity is usually advantageous to the goat, lower productivity or health problems could result from imbalances created by selective consumption. Pelleted rations offer less risk of such imbalances.

The second effect of goats' particular eating habits is that goats will eat more if they have more from which to select (Fig. 20–2). At a lower feeding level, only a small amount will be refused. As feeding rate increases, both refusals and net consumption also increase. It is important to not allow refusals to accumulate. Once the offering has been refused, little if any will be consumed at a later time without a serious effect on productivity.

TABLE 20-1

Feeding value of alfalfa hay offered, refused, and eaten by dairy goats

	Offered	Refused	Ingested
Leaves, %	46.2	23.9	59.9
Stems, %	53.8	76.1	41.4
Nutrient value			
Energy, Mcal/kg DM	0.88	0.7	0.99
Digestible crude protein, %	12.1	8.5	14.1

Source: Computed from values reported by Morand-Fehr and Sauvant (27).

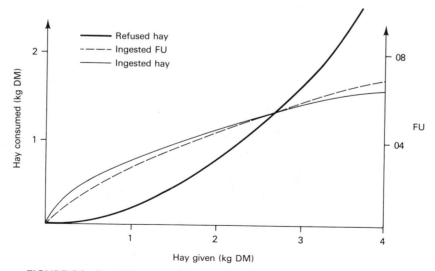

FIGURE 20–2. Influence of feeding level of alfalfa hay to adult Alpine goats on the relative amounts of hay refused and ingested and feed units (FU) ingested. Taken from Morand-Fehr (25).

Diet Selection and Composition on Range

The goat is active and inquisitive in its foraging behavior. Given an opportunity to be selective, the goat will graze (browse) from all plant types (trees, shrubs, herbaceous dicots, and grasses) and almost all species within a plant type. Occasionally, a single plant will be identified and totally defoliated while another of the same species will be completely avoided. However, both are exceptions to the general pattern of selecting a diversified diet from a relatively large area. Goats, known for their dexterity, often stand on high cliffs or climb onto low-hanging tree limbs. A common stance for browsing is on hind legs only with the front legs and head hidden in the lower branches of trees. The term "browse line" describes the appearance of a landscape where heavy use by goats has occurred (Fig. 20–3). Trees and shrubs take on a flattened-underline appearance 4–6 feet above the ground, the height that is within reach of the goat in a bipedal stance.

Although goats will select all types of foliage, they are particularly attracted to trees and shrubs. This behavioral characteristic, unique among livestock species, has been exploited for control of undesirable brush or weed species in several countries. Depending on the circumstances, goats can remove undesired woody species from rangeland (24), reduce its presence and prevent encroachment (4, 17, 31), or just improve its value for browsing by other livestock (32). The meat goat appears to be a slightly more effective browser than the Angora (44). In some instances income from "brushy" pastures is highest under goat browsing, in which case the shrubs should be maintained and used by goats, not overused to the point of their demise (38).

The nutritional value of a goat's selected diet is usually higher and more stable than that of the average available vegetation. Grasses and herbaceous legumes are generally considered higher in nutrients than shrubs and tree leaves and often comprise the major portion of the goat's diet. At other times the diet will contain the most tender and palatable leaves from trees, leaf tips from shrubs, fallen mast (for example, oak acorns), flowers and/or buds from xeric plants, grass seed heads, and so on. All of these minor plant parts contain high concentrations of one or more required nutrients. If the range vegetation is comprised of a complex assemblage of plants, the goat's diet also will be complex. Moreover, the diet composition will change drastically, often from day to day, as the array of plants simultaneously emerge, mature, fruit, senesce, drop leaves, and so on (45). The net result is that the selected diet is higher than the average of the available vegetation and, compared with diets of less adaptable livestock species, is rather stable in nutrient composition. However, on pastures or ranges where there is little or no plant diversity, diets selected by goats, sheep, and cattle would be similar.

PRODUCTIVITY OF GOATS

Goats are raised for milk, meat, and fiber (and hides). Although there exists some overlap in roles of individual goat types (meat and milk, fiber and meat), goats have developed into specific types to supply primary products.

Meat Goats

Meat goats fit into a category that is highly variable in appearance. In some countries of the world, meat goat breeds have occasionally established characteristic appearances. The Boer goat of Africa serves as an example of an established meat goat breed. In the United States, the meat goats have received little controlled genetic selection; therefore, they are a myriad of color patterns, horn and waddle types, milking ability, hair characteristics, and conformations.

Reproductive rate is relatively high in meat goats (18) and, except for a 2-month anestral period in March and April, these goats will breed year-round (37). Twinning is frequently observed, and litters of three or four offspring do occur. Although two sets of offspring

FIGURE 20–3. Meat goats foraging in the Edwards Plateau region of Texas. Note the browse line on the trees and associated shrubs. (Photo by Kenneth Bales.)

within a 12-month period are theoretically possible, a reasonable expectation for reproductive rate is approximately 180 live kids per 100 females per year.

Does produce approximately 2 lb of milk per day at peak lactation (21 d postpartum) and gradually reduce milk production to about 0.7 lb/d at 120 d lactation (6). Higher milk production would be expected from meat goats having a substantial infusion of milk goat breeding.

Newborn kids weigh 5–7 lb and gain approximately 0.25 lb/d to 120 d of age. Thus kids weaned at 6 months of age should weigh 35–40 lb depending on sex of the kid (males slightly heavier), number of kids in the litter, and environmental, primarily nutritional, conditions.

Slaughtered goats have a lower dressing percent (less than 50 percent yield) compared with sheep (41), partially because of a lower tendency to deposit fat (Fig. 20–4). Goat muscle is less tender (2) but is flavorful, especially when included in processed meat such as wieners, chili, and the like, irrespective of the age of the goat (22). Much of the meat goat product, especially that of young goats (cabrito), is used on a whole-carcass basis for outdoor, open-fire barbecues.

Hair on these goats is distinctly different from mohair of the Angora (Fig. 20–3). Most meat goats produce two types of hair, a very coarse type (guard hair) that has no marketable value and a very fine fraction (cashmere) that is currently in great demand. Cashmere production is quite variable in meat goats and usually very low (less than 50 g/yr). However, there is presently much interest in developing a cashmere industry from selected individuals from within the meat goat population.

Angora Goats

The Angora is the product of a long history of genetic selection for a single trait, mohair production. These goats are smaller than most other breeds, have higher nutrient requirements, especially for protein, and frequently suffer from less than optimal nourishment. They are more susceptible to parasitism and harsh environmental conditions.

The reproductive rate of Angora goats is low compared to that of the meat goat. Both the male and female have a restricted breeding season. Initiation of the estrous cycle in females and "rutting" in males usually corresponds with a cooling trend in late summer and continues until mid-winter or, for the female, until con-

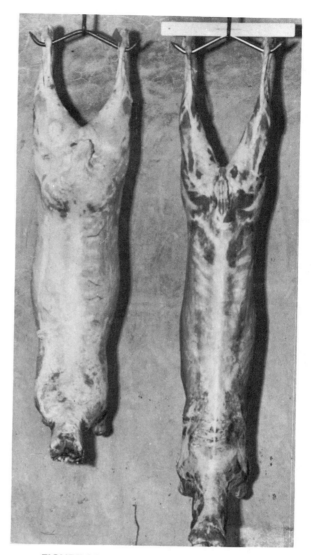

FIGURE 20–4. The carcass of a yearling sheep (left, 15.0 kg) compared to one of a Saanen goat (right, 15.4 kg) in New Zealand. Note that the goat carcass is leggier and carries very much less fat cover. (Courtesy of A. H. Kirton, Rukura Animal Res. Station, Hamilton, New Zealand.)

ception occurs. The most active breeding period occurs between mid-September and mid-November. Although ovulation rate often exceeds 125 percent, several adverse occurrences reduce weaning percentage to approximately one-half of ovulation (36). Major losses include failure to conceive, embryo death, abortion, perinatal losses, and predator losses. Many of these losses can be circumvented or reduced by good nutrition management.

Kids at birth are comparable in size to kids of meat goats (5–7 lb), but small, weak kids that die at birth are common in undernourished flocks. Kids will weigh 25–45 lb at weaning (6 months) and 50–60 lb at first breeding (18–20 months). The period between weaning and first breeding is critical, and underdeveloped yearlings have reduced lifetime productivity (39).

Meat characteristics of Angora goats are comparable to those of meat goats (42). However, young Angoras are seldom slaughtered. Because of the low reproductive rates and high attrition rates in Angora flocks, essentially all female kids must be held for replacements. Male offspring that are determined to be unsuitable for breeding are castrated (6–18 months of age) and held as wether or "mutton" goats for mohair production. Therefore, only cull or aged Angoras go into the meat trade in any appreciable numbers.

Angoras are raised for mohair. This fiber has a diameter greater than cashmere and the fine wools but less than the coarse, guard hairs of meat and milk goats and the wools of the long-wool breeds of sheep (Fig. 20–5). Average production of an Angora flock (including kids and yearlings) is about 7 lb (clean-fiber basis) per goat per year (43), but young adults (2–5 yr) exceed this level of production (Fig. 20–6). With advancing age, mohair production increases to a peak and then declines, fiber diameter increases but at a decreasing rate, and staple length remains relatively constant. Angora goats are shorn twice annually during late

winter and late summer. Mohair is sold on the basis of fineness (fiber diameter), with the highest price paid for the finer grades. Three broad grades are used in the U.S. mohair trade. Kid hair (less than 30 μm) is the finest and demands the highest price, followed by young adult (30 to 34 μm) and adult (greater than 34 μm), respectively. In some areas of the world trade, objective measurements (fiber diameter, staple length, strength, and so on) are used in place of a grading system to assess value.

Milk Goats

Milk goat numbers are increasing rapidly in the United States, but goat milk remains a specialty product and does not currently rival dairy cow milk. The average herd is small, but several large goat dairies are located near metropolitan areas, and modern equipment adapted for goats is readily available (Fig. 20–7). A 1981 survey in Texas recorded that 48 dairies were enrolled in Dairy Herd Improvement Association (DHIA) and represented 505 goats, estimated as one-third of the total number (46).

Similar to the Angora's being selected for mohair, milk goats are selected for milk yield with less emphasis placed on other characteristics. Reproductive rate in milk goats is higher

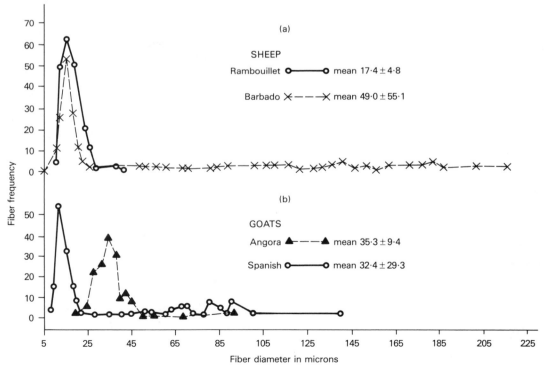

FIGURE 20–5. The fiber diameter distributions of Rambouillet and Barbado sheep are shown in (a) and Angora and meat goats in (b). Taken from Gallager and Shelton (5).

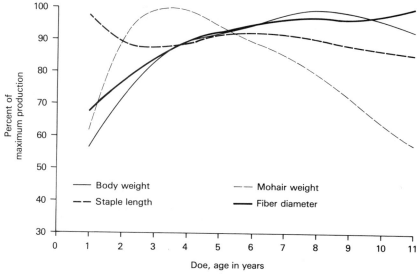

FIGURE 20–6. The relation of mohair weight, staple length, fiber diameter, and body weight to age in Angora females. Taken from Shelton (35).

FIGURE 20–7. An example of modern dairy equipment available for milking dairy goats.

than in Angoras but probably less than in meat goats (34). However, in milk goats reproduction is associated with freshening and thus with milk production. Seasonality of breeding is a significant constraint for dairies in the liquid milk market (1). Light modification to increase photoperiod in the spring months aids in breeding during this otherwise anestral period.

Birth weight and growth rate of kids vary among breeds, but both tend to be slightly higher than for meat goats. A kid weighing 8–9 lb at birth should gain 0.28 lb/d and reach 55–60 lb at 6 months of age (26). Meat characteristics are similar to those of meat goats except carcasses are larger and higher yielding.

Milk yield is highly variable. Reported yields of 1300–1600 lb (23, 46) are far below

those reported by individuals and what is considered potential production (9). Fat content of goat milk is reported at 4.2 percent (46). As in dairy cattle, milk yield and composition in goats are highly influenced by the level of nutrition in both prefreshening and lactation periods (23, 28).

NUTRITIVE REQUIREMENTS

Generally, goats must consume more dry matter (relative to body weight) or the dry matter consumed must contain higher concentrations of nutrients compared with the dietary requirements of other ruminant livestock. The reticulorumen of the goat is smaller according to body size, and retention time of feed particles tends to be shorter (Table 20–2). Whereas diet may be

TABLE 20-2

Rumen retention time (RT), turnover rate (TR), and digestibility of diets selected by cattle, sheep, and goats from a common range in the Edwards Plateau region of Texas (values averaged over four seasons)

Species	RT, hours	TR, %/h	Digestibility, %	
			in vitro[a]	in vivo[b]
Cattle	36	5.2	55	51
Sheep	34	5.2	57	50
Goats	28	7.1	56	45

[a]Calculated according to Van Soest et al. (47).
[b]Calculated according to Lippke et al. (19).
Source: Huston et al. (14).

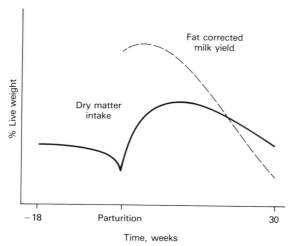

FIGURE 20-8. Variation of dry matter intake in dairy goats yielding 750 kg of milk/lactation. Taken from Morand-Fehr and Sauvant (27).

of similar digestibility (*in vitro* estimate), actual digestibility is lower in goats (*in vivo* estimate) because of the shorter residence time in the reticulo-rumen. This allows a faster turnover of feed particles and an elevated level of consumption. The net result is a higher level of intake and lower digestibility, but a higher level of consumption of digested nutrients compared with other ruminant livestock (11).

Energy Requirements

Energy is required for body maintenance, growth, reproduction, lactation, fiber growth, and activity. These concurrent body functions and associated requirements influence the voluntary dry-matter intake dramatically (Fig. 20-8). Perhaps no other livestock species varies as widely in energy requirements as the goat. This variation in requirements is a result of the extremes of type, productivity, and activity level. The NRC published its first edition on the nutrient requirements of the goat and attempted to account for this recognized variation (30). Requirements tables from NRC are given in Appendix Table 21. Energy requirements are expressed according to the relationship of 100 kcal of gross energy (GE) = 76 kcal digestible energy (DE) = 62 kcal metabolizable energy (ME) = 35 kcal net energy (NE). Also, 1 kg digestible organic matter (DOM) = 1.05 kg total digestible nutrients (TDN) = 4.62 Mcal DE. The approach allows the user to pick and choose between size of goat, level of activity, physiological stage (pregnant or nonpregnant), rate of growth, level and composition of milk yield, and fleece

production as they apply to a particular goat type.

Maintenance energy requirements vary with body size and are expressed according to the following relationship:

$$DE = 124 \text{ kcal/W}^{0.75}$$

This expression should be considered to have some latitude of precision because the efficiency of use of DE is not constant for different feedstuffs. Also, the fractional power (0.75) is the accepted value for interspecies comparisons but differs from the average value of 0.64 reported by Brody for goats (3). Additional energy costs for activity are expressed as either 0.25, 0.50, or 0.75 times maintenance for goats in confinement, on relatively small pastures, or under extensive grazing on rough terrain, respectively. Whereas at minimal activity (stall-fed condition) the maintenance energy requirements of goats are comparable to those of other livestock species, they are somewhat elevated under the more extensive conditions. This reflects the goat's active foraging behavior. The energy requirements for growth in goats is estimated at 8.84 kcal DE/g of liveweight gain (30). Again, this estimate should be interpreted as an average of a relatively large range of values depending on type of goat, environment, and diet.

Successful reproduction in goats requires adequate energy intake prior to and at breeding and elevated energy intake during the final 2 months of pregnancy. This 2-month period is especially critical in the Angora, which is subject to nutritional stress abortion (48). The NRC estimate of energy requirement for the last 2 months of pregnancy is 1.74 Mcal DE, irrespective of body size of the pregnant female (30). This level of energy intake is often difficult to achieve, especially in smaller goats. It is the author's opinion that this requirement for pregnancy is slightly overestimated for average reproducing goats. Small and intermediate-sized goats carrying a single fetus require approximately half the estimated value. However, the estimate is likely applicable for large goats and/or goats producing a high incidence of multiple births.

The energy requirements for lactation are expressed per kg milk at 2.5–6 percent fat content. The values are based on an estimated 1.52 Mcal DE/kg of 4 percent fat-corrected milk (FCM) with an adjustment of 19.9 kcal for each 0.5 percent change in milk fat content (30).

FIGURE 20-9. Mohair removal (shearing) from a typical adult Angora female at a Texas ranch.

The energy requirements for fiber production refer specifically to mohair produced by Angora goats (Fig. 20–9), although there appears to be an increasing interest in cashmere-producing goats. The low energy input into fiber relative to other body functions makes the direct measurement of energy costs difficult. The expressed values were derived from somewhat intuitive calculations (12). However, goats having high fiber production capability are recognizably benefited by elevated energy intake.

Protein Requirements

The protein requirements are expressed in Appendix Table 21 as total crude protein (TP) and digestible crude protein (DP) for different-sized goats and for different metabolic functions (30). The maintenance estimates reflect a calorie to protein ratio of 1 Mcal DE to 22 g DP. Although research data are not available on protein costs of activity in goats, estimates of requirements are increased correspondingly with increased energy costs. Requirements for growth equals 0.195 g DP/g live weight gain. The pregnancy requirements are estimated at 57 g DP/d for all pregnant goats during the last 2 months of gestation. As suggested for energy, this level of protein for pregnancy applies to the large goat and/or a goat producing multiple births. Small goats and those producing single offspring require approximately half the recommended protein for pregnancy. Digestible protein requirements for lactation were estimated at 51 g DP/kg 4 percent FCM and were adjusted for fat content according to recommendations for dairy cattle (29). This value compares favorably with that determined recently by Lu et al. (20). Requirements for fiber growth were based on work by Huston et al. (12).

Mineral Requirements

The mineral requirements reported in NRC for goats were adapted from experimental data obtained using other domestic animals (30). It is almost certain that minor differences exist in some aspects of mineral metabolism between goats and other species, but up to the present, none has been described that would justify changing the recommendations as presented in the NRC.

Macrominerals. Ca and P are the two major minerals that should be given the most attention in diet formulation. The recommended daily requirements for these two minerals are included in Appendix Table 21. Both are important in bone development and maintenance and in milk synthesis. A deficiency of either or both in young animals will result in poorly developed and malformed bones (rickets). In adult animals, especially those that are lactating, Ca and P are commonly mobilized from the bone to fulfill high-priority needs (such as milk synthesis). Normally, these bone deposits will be repleted once dietary intake exceeds current needs. In a dietary deficiency, continued removal from the bone can result in a thinning and loss of strength (osteomalacia) resulting in brittleness of bones.

The Ca:P ratio should be maintained between 1.2 and 2.5. A lower ratio (below 1:1) endangers the animal to the development of urolithiasis (urinary calculi or kidney stones), especially in males. A high intake of Ca has not been associated with an acute hazardous effect, but it can interfere with absorption and cause deficiencies of P and certain divalent cations (Mg, Mn, and others).

High-producing dairy goats can suffer parturient paresis (milk fever) as a result of metabolic hypocalcemia (low blood Ca). Although this condition can be related to dietary Ca, it is confounded by action of the parathyroid hormone, which is involved in freeing Ca from the bone. A failure or delay of activity of the parathyroid hormone with the onset of lactation results in a drop in the blood Ca and the placid outward appearance of milk fever. The condition is less frequently observed in dairy goats than in dairy cows but, when observed, is treated similarly by intravenously administering a solution containing Ca and glucose.

P is an extremely important mineral element for maintaining proper feed (forage) intake and intraruminal metabolism. In grazing cattle, low P is associated with a rough hair coat, un-thriftiness, loss of weight, depraved appetite, and low reproductive rate. Providing supplemental P as various inorganic phosphates is a very effective and rewarding practice in reducing or eliminating these symptoms. Goats tend to be less affected by low P, but a proper intake of the element is still considered essential for satisfactory productivity. The goat's intensive selectivity undoubtedly results in a diet higher in P than would be apparent from gross forage analysis and higher than would be obtained by less discriminating grazers. Attention to P level (and Ca:P ratio) is more important in formulation of complete diets using harvested or formulated feedstuffs.

Other macrominerals include Na, Cl, Mg, K, and S. Of these, only Na and Cl (salt) should be provided routinely free choice. A Mg deficiency can occur on lush pasture and cause grass tetany. K is most likely deficient in animals grazing dormant vegetation, in which case intake and performance will be reduced. S can be low, primarily for Angora goats, which have a high requirement for S-containing amino acids. Most common forage and feedstuffs will contain adequate Mg, K, and S.

Microminerals. The microminerals of main concern include Fe, I, Cu, Mo, Zn, Co, Mn, and Se. None of these elements should be considered as routinely deficient. Potential deficiencies are regional, and inclusion of these elements in feed formulations should be on a regional basis. Because some microminerals have a narrow span between amounts producing deficiency and toxicity, specific circumstances should be considered before providing liberal addition of microelements to goat diets.

Vitamin Requirements

In monogastric animals (nonruminants), vitamins must be supplied in the diet. In the goat (ruminant), only a few are likely to be periodically limiting, since most are synthesized by the ruminal microorganisms. The fat-soluble vitamins include vitamins A, D, E, and K. Of these, only vitamin A is likely to be deficient to the point of limiting productivity in goats. The B-vitamins are all synthesized in adequate amounts by ruminal bacteria, with the possible exception of vitamin B_{12} in regions with a cobalt deficiency.

Vitamin A is not contained in plant tissue but is synthesized within animals from vitamin A precursors that are present in plants. The levels of these precursors are generally in proportion to plant pigments (green, yellow, and so on). Whereas actively growing plants are high in provitamin A activity, weathered vegetation contains very little. Once synthesized, vitamin A can be stored in the liver of animals and metabolized as needed. The seasonal, cyclic nature of forage growth and the selective grazing behavior displayed by goats almost preclude a vitamin A deficiency in free-ranging goats. A vitamin A deficiency can occur in pen-fed goats and in goats feeding in extended dry and/or cold conditions during which vitamin A stores are depleted and little or no green plant material is consumed. Requirements for vitamins A and D were estimated by NRC (30) and are included in Appendix Table 21.

Vitamin B_{12} is a large compound that includes cobalt in its central structure. Thus vitamin B_{12} is deficient in animals that are consuming diets low in cobalt. Again, this is a very regional problem and is not likely to occur under most circumstances.

Water Requirements

The quantity, quality, and placement of water is a very important aspect of goat health and nutrition. Because water intake is related to feed intake and feed intake is correlated with productivity, the general recommendation is that goats be given free access to water to maximize water intake and thereby not limit feed (forage) intake. Goats are often more sensitive than other species to water quality and tend to refuse to drink water fouled by fecal and urine contamination. This is an interesting behavioral trait, because the goat may be the most incriminated among livestock species for actually fouling feed and water by direct defecation and urination. Designing the watering facilities to provide readily accessible water yet to protect it against contamination is crucial.

The quantity and frequency of water intake varies greatly among goat types, their locations, and associated diets. The small black Bedouin goat of the desert in Israel was reported by Shkolnik and Silanikove to drink enormous amounts of water (up to 47 percent of dehydrated body weight) on an infrequent basis as a strategy to extend the grazing range to 2-days' distance from water (40). The goat is generally reported to consume less water than sheep and cattle on a metabolic size basis (7), but this may be influenced by diet. Huston et al. (15) found that goats consumed less water than sheep when both were fed wheat straw, but water intake was higher in goats when the diet was oat hay (higher protein and digestibility). In this circumstance, water intake was closely related to feed intake, that is, the relative level of feed intake of the goat to the sheep was lower when fed the low-quality forage and higher when fed the high-quality forage.

Lactation affects water consumption. Giger et al. (8) found that in a temperate climate the maintenance requirement for water by a lactating goat was 145.6 g/kg$^{0.75}$ and that an additional 1.43 kg of water was required for each 1 kg of milk produced.

Other factors such as water content of the vegetation, salt intake, environmental temperature, water temperature, and electrolyte concentration in the water affect water intake. However, it is still recommended that goats be allowed free access to clean, cool water that is as free of contaminants as possible.

FEEDING AND MANAGEMENT

Animals will reach potential productivity only if provided adequate nutrients in proper balance in an acceptable setting. Such circumstances are rare in animal agriculture. More realistically, we search for the most economic return, which involves identifying the management strategy where the difference between value of products and costs of production is at a positive maximum. This section will discuss the relative value of feedstuffs for goat diets and nutritional and management factors that affect productivity.

Feedstuffs

Goats can utilize any feedstuff that is safe for ruminant consumption. Ingredients that appear in goat rations in the different countries of the world are those feedstuffs that are locally available and usually in low demand for human consumption. The most economic productivity results from maximizing the use of forages or roughage products combined with an adequate but minimal level of concentrates. Feedstuffs appearing in Table 20–3 are common ingredients used in ration formulation and serve as examples of feeds of varying nutrient content.

Forages. Forages vary greatly in chemical composition and thus in nutrient content. Range vegetation is highly seasonal, that is, it is nutritious and palatable during the rapidly growing period (usually during spring-summer) and unpalatable and low in nutrients during the dormant period. In the Edwards Plateau region of Texas, range vegetation is comprised of five functional components (Table 20–4). Goats pick

TABLE 20-3

Levels of nutrients in some common feeds

Feedstuff	Energy		Protein		Minerals		Carotene,[a] mg/lb
	TDN, %	DE, Mcal/lb	CP, %	DP, %	Ca, %	P, %	
Dry forage or roughage							
Bermuda grass hay	50	1.0	15	11	0.43	0.16	53
Annual ryegrass hay	53	1.1	9	5	0.53	0.29	113
Alfalfa hay	57	1.1	18	14	1.38	0.26	83
Wheat straw	39	0.8	4	0	0.16	0.04	1
Energy feeds							
Oats, grain	68	1.4	12	8	0.07	0.33	—
Sorghum, grain	78	1.6	10	7	0.03	0.28	—
Corn, grain	77	1.6	9	7	0.06	0.24	1
Molasses, cane	54	1.1	4	2	0.75	0.08	—
Protein feeds							
Fish meal	67	1.3	61	49	5.20	2.9	—
Soybean meal	79	1.6	45	42	0.30	0.6	—
Cottonseed meal	69	1.4	41	37	0.20	1.1	—
Sunflower meal	60	1.2	46	42	0.40	1.0	—

[a]Carotene contents are not reported for some feedstuffs. The expected levels in these feeds are usually negligible, but fish meal may be relatively high in vitamin A.

Source: NRC (30).

TABLE 20-4

Nutritional components of range vegetation in the Edwards Plateau region of Texas

Component	Plant Type	Nutritional Description
Production	Perennial, warm-season grasses	Low to moderate in protein (3–13 %) and digestibility (25–63%)
Quality	Perennial, warm-season forbs, legumes, and browse	Moderate to high in protein (10–30%) and digestibility (50–89%) when palatable
Level	Long-season or evergreen plants	Moderately low to moderately high in protein (6–12%) and digestibility (40–60%)
Bonus	All desirable annual plants	High in protein (15–30%) and digestibility (60–80%)
Toxic	All plant or plant parts that are poisonous or injurious to livestock	Low to high in all nutrients

Source: Huston et al. (13).

and choose from these plant groups, and if the range is sufficiently diverse, the nondairy goats can satisfy their nutrient requirements from the vegetation alone. Under a depleted circumstance as a result of drought, overgrazing, or the like, options for diet selection become limited and diet quality follows the pattern of the limited options. If only the production component is present, then diet quality fluctuates with the nutrient content of this component. Then, high productivity is achievable only with supplemental feeding of concentrates to bring the overall diet quality to a satisfactory level. Rangelands in other regions of the world have assemblages of plants that differ from the one described for the Edwards Plateau region of Texas, but the principle of fluctuating quality and importance of diversity holds for all rangelands.

Forages in the temperate climates are likely grown on tame pastures (monocultures) that are either grazed directly at a relatively high stocking rate or harvested and fed as hay. These forages are characteristically higher in quality compared with range forages and would typify forage fed to dairy goats. Alfalfa, various clovers, and ryegrass are examples of these forages.

Roughage Products. Roughage can be included in goat rations to reduce the risk of gastrointestinal disturbances and as a diluent to reduce the nutrient content of a mixture of ingredients to a desired level. There is no absolute requirement for roughage in goat rations, but as roughage is reduced below about 30–40 percent of the diet, greater attention to possible

digestive upsets is needed. Products such as cottonseed hulls, peanut hulls, cereal straw, and corn cobs are low in nutrients but provide good roughage factors.

High-Energy Feeds. Feedstuffs such as corn, barley, sorghum, other grains, and molasses that are high in soluble carbohydrates (starch and sugars) contain high concentrations of digestible energy. Grains require some kind of mechanical processing (grinding, cracking) for maximum utilization, but grain processing is less important for goats than for cattle. These high-energy feedstuffs are relatively low in protein content (usually less than 12 percent crude protein).

High-Protein Feeds. Protein concentrates are commonly by-products of an extraction process. Cottonseed meal, soybean meal, linseed meal, peanut meal, sunflower seed meal, and others are residues from the extraction of oil from the raw products. These by-products from plant sources are usually but not always more economical than animal by-product meals such as fish meal and meat meal. Either can be utilized effectively by goats, but because of the goat's particular nature, any ingredient possessing an objectionable odor may reduce consumption and should be kept at a low level in the diet. Protein concentrates are moderate in energy content.

Nonprotein Nitrogen (Urea). Any ammonia-releasing compound can be used to satisfy at least a part of the protein requirements in goats. Urea is the most commonly used nonprotein N product. It is recommended that no more than one-third of the protein in a goat diet be supplied by urea. Higher levels are possible but may not result in satisfactory performance and under some circumstances can become toxic.

Feeding Goats According to Requirements

It is important that the goat's nutrient requirements and nutrients provided in the consumed diet be matched to within a narrow zone of safety. Underfeeding, either from amount of dry matter or the nutrient concentration, will cause the animal to produce at a lower than expected level. Overfeeding will be wasteful and can reduce productivity also. Minor deviations should not be of concern because depletion and repletion of storage tissue are normal metabolic processes. A feeding plan should consider the nutrient requirements according to stage of production (dry, pregnant, lactating), level of feeding, and diet composition (or ration formulation).

Table 20–5 includes information derived from the larger and more detailed NRC requirements table (Appendix Table 21). The DE and CP requirements were calculated for dry and pregnant goats (non-Angora), for does in low (meat goats) and high (milk goats) lactation, for kids growing at three rates, and for lactating Angora does producing 8.8 lb of mohair per year. The necessary feed level and protein contents for diets of increasing energy density are listed in the six columns on the right-hand side of Table 20–5.

Nutrient requirements can be satisfied by either a large amount of a diet containing lower concentrations of nutrients or less of a diet containing higher concentrations of nutrients. A 60-lb dry doe (refer to Table 20–5) would receive equal protein and energy nutrition from either 1.7 lb of a 55 percent TDN (1.1 Mcal/lb), 7.7 percent CP feed, or 1.2 lb of a 75 percent TDN (1.5 Mcal/lb), 10.7 percent CP feed. Requirements increase as animals become larger and metabolic activity increases. A 100-lb doe requires more nutrients than does an 80-lb doe. A 20-lb kid requires more if gaining 150 g/d compared with only 50 g/d. However, a 60-lb doe that is lactating requires more nutrients than a 100-lb doe that is dry (3.24 versus 2.72 Mcal DE, respectively). Higher requirements can be satisfied by feeding more feed up to a level of maximum voluntary intake. Once maximum volun-

tary intake has been reached, additional intake of nutrients must be achieved by increasing the concentration of nutrients in the feed.

Voluntary intake (self-feeding) is the target management strategy of many if not most goat production systems. Goats in range and pasture settings have free access to the standing forage (grasses, forbs, shrubs, mast) and consume to their voluntary limit. Whether the nutrient requirements are met depends on the nutrient composition of the forages selected. If one or more nutrients are too low, these can be provided supplementally. Goats fed in confinement are dependent on the skill of the manager in determining the proper formulation so that voluntary intake (free-choice feeding) results in proper nutrient intake. Unfortunately, voluntary intake is affected by many factors (diet digestibility, genotypic factors, environmental factors, and so on) and is very difficult to predict. For discussion purposes, the following "rules of thumb" for maximum voluntary intake are suggested (16):

Goat Class	Maximum Voluntary Intake, % of body wt
Kids	4.5
Dry doe	2.8
Early pregnant doe	3.0
Late pregnant doe	2.7
Lactating doe, low	4.0
Lactating doe, high	5.0

The practical value of these numbers is in determining the appropriate minimum energy content of a ration for a goat of a particular size and in a particular productive state.

EXAMPLE 1.

Dry doe weighing 80 lb.

$$\text{Maximum intake} = 80 \text{ lb} \times 2.8\%$$
$$= 2.2 \text{ lb/d}$$

Required nutrients/d: DE = 2.3 Mcal
CP = 74 g

Required intake @: 1.1 Mcal/lb = 2.1
1.3 Mcal/lb = 1.8
1.5 Mcal/lb = 1.5

Conclusion: Because 2.1 lb is less than the 2.2-lb maximum intake limit, a ration containing 1.1 Mcal/lb DE and 7.7% CP would adequately supply the required energy and protein for the dry doe.

TABLE 20-5

Nutrient requirements and feeding levels for meat, milk, and Angora goats (example)

Class and State	Body Weight, lb	Daily Gain, g/d	DE, Mcal/d	CP, g/d	Required Intake @ Feed Energy Level, Mcal/lb			Required CP @ Feed[a] Energy Level, Mcal/lb		
					1.1[b]	1.3[b]	1.5[b]	1.1[b]	1.3[b]	1.5[b]
					----------- lb/d -----------			------------- % -------------		
Does, dry and	60		1.85	59	1.7	1.4	1.2	7.7	9.2	10.7
early pregnant	70		2.08	67	1.9	1.6	1.4	7.7	9.2	10.7
	80		2.30	74	2.1	1.8	1.5	7.7	9.2	10.7
	90		2.51	80	2.3	1.9	1.7	7.7	9.2	10.7
	100		2.72	87	2.5	2.1	1.8	7.7	9.2	10.7
Does, late	60		2.83	90	2.6	2.2	1.9	7.7	9.2	10.7
pregnant	70		3.06	98	2.8	2.4	2.0	7.7	9.2	10.7
	80		3.28	105	3.0	2.5	2.2	7.7	9.2	10.7
	90		3.49	111	3.2	2.7	2.3	7.7	9.2	10.7
	100		3.70	118	3.4	2.8	2.5	7.7	9.2	10.7
Does, low	60		3.24	104	2.9	2.5	2.2	7.7	9.2	10.7
lactation	70		3.47	111	3.2	2.7	2.3	7.7	9.2	10.7
	80		3.69	118	3.4	2.8	2.5	7.7	9.2	10.7
	90		3.90	125	3.5	3.0	2.6	7.7	9.2	10.7
	100		4.10	131	3.7	3.2	2.7	7.7	9.2	10.7
Does, high	80		6.46	207	5.9	5.0	4.3	7.7	9.2	10.7
lactation	100		6.88	220	6.3	5.3	4.6	7.7	9.2	10.7
	120		7.28	233	6.6	5.6	4.9	7.7	9.2	10.7
	140		7.66	245	7.0	5.9	5.1	7.7	9.2	10.7
	160		8.03	257	7.3	6.2	5.4	7.7	9.2	10.7
Kids, growing	20	50	1.25	40	1.1	1.0	0.8	7.7	9.2	10.7
		100	1.69	54	1.5	1.3	1.1	7.7	9.2	10.7
		150	2.13	68	1.9	1.6	1.4	7.7	9.2	10.7
	30	50	1.54	49	1.4	1.2	1.0	7.7	9.2	10.7
		100	1.98	63	1.8	1.5	1.3	7.7	9.2	10.7
		150	2.42	77	2.2	1.9	1.6	7.7	9.2	10.7
	40	50	1.81	58	1.6	1.4	1.2	7.7	9.2	10.7
		100	2.25	72	2.0	1.7	1.5	7.7	9.2	10.7
		150	2.69	86	2.4	2.1	1.8	7.7	9.2	10.7
Angora does,	60		3.39	121	3.1	2.6	2.3	8.5	10.0	11.5
low lactation,	70		3.62	128	3.3	2.8	2.4	8.5	10.0	11.5
8.8 lb/yr mohair	80		3.84	135	3.5	3.0	2.6	8.5	10.0	11.5
	90		4.05	142	3.7	3.1	2.7	8.5	10.0	11.5
	100		4.25	148	3.9	3.3	2.8	8.5	10.0	11.5

[a]Protein content must be increased with increasing energy in diets in order to provide adequate protein at lower feeding levels.
[b]Feed energy levels 1.1, 1.3, and 1.5 Mcal/lb are approximately equivalent to 55, 65, and 75% TDN, respectively.
Source: NRC (30).

EXAMPLE 2.

Kid weighing 30 lb and gaining 100 g/d.

Maximum intake = 30 lb × 4.5%
                        = 1.35 lb/d

Required nutrients/d: DE = 1.98 Mcal
                                  CP = 63 g

Required intake @: 1.1 Mcal/lb = 1.8
                            1.3 Mcal/lb = 1.5
                            1.5 Mcal/lb = 1.3

Conclusion: Because 1.3 is similar to the 1.35 lb/d maximum intake limit, a ration containing 1.5 Mcal/lb DE and 10.5% CP is adequate to achieve desired gain of 100 g/d.

EXAMPLE 3.

Lactating Angora doe weighing 70 lb and producing 8.8 lb/yr mohair.

$$\text{Maximum intake} = 70 \text{ lb} \times 4.0\%$$
$$= 2.8 \text{ lb/d}$$

Required nutrients/d: DE = 3.62 Mcal
CP = 128 g

Required intake @: 1.1 Mcal/lb = 3.3
1.3 Mcal/lb = 2.8
1.5 Mcal/lb = 2.4

Conclusion: Because 2.8 lb equates to the required intake, a ration containing 1.3 Mcal/lb DE and 10% CP would provide the approximate required energy and protein for a lactating Angora.

For example 1, ingredients from Table 20–3 could be used to provide the indicated energy and protein requirements as follows:

A. Annual ryegrass, free choice (2.2 lb/d)

$$\text{DE} = 2.2 \text{ lb/d} \times 1.1 \text{ Mcal/lb}$$
$$= 2.4 \text{ Mcal/d}$$
$$\text{CP} = 2.2 \text{ lb/d} \times 9\%$$
$$= 90 \text{ g/d}$$
(Note: 1 lb = 454 g)

Both DE and CP exceed requirements.

B. Alfalfa hay, free choice (2.2 lb/d)

$$\text{DE} = 2.4 \text{ Mcal/d}$$
$$\text{CP} = 180 \text{ g/d}$$

Both DE and CP exceed requirements.

C. Bermuda grass hay, corn mixture (2.2 lb/d)

	lb	DE, Mcal	CP, g
Bermuda grass hay	2.0	2.0	136
Corn	0.2	0.3	8
Total	2.2	2.3	144

DE equals and CP exceeds requirements.

D. Wheat straw, corn, soybean meal mixture (2.2 lb/d)

	lb	DE, Mcal	CP, g
Wheat straw	1.50	1.2	27
Corn	0.59	0.9	24
Soybean meal	0.11	0.2	22
Total	2.20	2.3	73

Both DE and CP approximate requirements.

Both annual ryegrass and alfalfa hays contain adequate energy and excess protein concentrations for an 80-lb dry doe fed free choice. Bermuda grass hay contains excess protein but is slightly low in energy. Combining nutrients provided by 0.2 lb of corn with that in 2 lb of Bermuda grass hay satisfies energy and protein requirements. Wheat straw is low in both energy and protein, and provision of both a high-energy and a high-protein ingredient is necessary to achieve the optimal balance. Rations that would satisfy the energy and protein requirements for examples 2 and 3 follow:

30-lb kid gaining 100 g/d

	lb	DE, Mcal	CP, g
Alfalfa hay	0.35	0.38	29
Corn	1.00	1.60	41
Total	1.35	1.98	70

70-lb Angora doe, lactating

	lb	DE, Mcal	CP, g
Alfalfa hay	0.28	0.31	23
Wheat straw	0.84	0.67	15
Corn	1.54	2.46	63
Soybean meal	0.14	0.22	29
Total	2.80	3.66	130

These examples consider only energy and protein required by the goat and supplied in the diet. Although these nutrients are the major considerations for selecting proper feedstuffs, minerals and vitamins must not be ignored. As suggested, Ca and P are the main mineral elements for consideration. The NRC table (Appendix Table 21) lists the actual requirements for the different classes of goats. In most cases, goats will not encounter a mineral imbalance if the diet contains at least one and one-half times as much Ca as P, and salt (NaCl) is offered free choice. In large, commercial operations it is suggested that a more precise formulation be exercised. Similarly, vitamin nutrition is probably adequate if green, leafy hays that are high in carotene (see Table 20–3) are included in the diet. If complete, mixed rations are fed, it is suggested that vitamin A be added at 2000 IU/lb.

Supplements for Goats on Rangeland

Proper supplementation is achieved only if the range diet and supplemental feed combine to properly supply the required nutrients (Fig. 20–10). Usually, protein is the first limiting nutrient for animals (nonpregnant, nonlactating) producing at a low level. Thus a small amount (100–300 g/d) of a high-protein feed (32–45 percent) is usually adequate. High-quality forages (alfalfa) can occasionally be a good alternative, but rarely should a low-quality roughage be fed on rangeland. Animals in a high stage of production may need both supplementary protein and energy. The proper balance is difficult to estimate. The author prefers to feed a supplemental feed with a protein safety factor to assure that protein does not become limiting. Kids and yearlings on average to dormant rangeland should be fed up to 350 g/d of a 30–35 percent protein concentrate. Under the same circumstances, developing billies, breeding does, and does in late pregnancy should receive up to 500 g/d of a 25 percent protein concentrate. Dry does and does between breeding and the fourth month of gestation could be fed less of a higher-protein concentrate as indicated to prevent loss of weight.

FIGURE 20–10. Adult Angora females in a 5-month fleece eating whole corn (*Zea mays*) off the ground. Note earthen pond in the background. (Photo by Kenneth Bales.)

Feeding Plan for Dairy Goats

Dairy goats require special consideration because of the large variation in nutrient requirements within the annual production cycle (28). Good nutrition management in dairy goats requires a keen understanding of forages and concentrates and their use in supplying (but not oversupplying) the needed nutrients.

The period of lowest requirements is during the dry, early-pregnant stage. Highest requirements occur between early and mid-lactation. Actually, energy requirements during peak lactation exceed the goat's capacity to take in energy. As a result, energy is mobilized from deposited body fat at a rapid rate. Because appetite is often depressed during late gestation and early lactation, fat reserves must be deposited during the low requirement periods (late lactation, early gestation).

A good feeding plan would begin with a close scrutiny of body fatness during the latter stage of lactation (early pregnancy). If the doe is very thin, increase the level of nutrients (especially energy) in the diet. This can be accomplished either by feeding a high-quality hay, grazing a good pasture, feeding concentrates liberally, or supplying an appropriate combination of these. Once the doe has increased in condition to the desired level (well-conditioned but not overly fat), decrease the nutrient intake level by reversing the above strategy (decrease hay quality, lower concentrate feeding, and so on) so that weight is maintained or only slightly increasing.

The next decision point is at about 6 weeks before kidding. Again, the level of nutrition should be increased to adjust for the increasing requirements of fetal development and the tendency for the doe to have a reduced appetite. Good-quality hay should be fed along with concentrates, beginning at about 1/3 lb/d and slowly increasing to 1 lb/d at kidding time. After kidding, concentrate feeding should continue and after about 3 weeks it should reach 2 lb/d for average producers and 3 lb/d for high producers. Feeding of good-quality hay (or pasture) should continue. Concentrate feeding just before and just after parturition is important for the prevention of pregnancy toxemia and ketosis, respectively. After the peak lactation period (3–4 months), concentrate feeding can be decreased slowly, allowing the elevated forage portion of the diet to encourage continued milk yield.

Feeding Breeding Males

Males should go into the breeding season in good, vigorous condition but not overly fat. Breeding males naturally reduce feeding time, thus they are expected to lose weight. Although some weight loss is acceptable, a highly depleted state can result in low breeding efficiency. It is recommended that concentrate feeding be practiced (1–1.5 lb/d) for 3–4 weeks before the beginning of the breeding period until breeding has ended and body condition is recovered. Feeding between breeding seasons can be at a maintenance level.

Unique Management Needs of the Angora

Early body development is important for good lifetime productivity of Angoras (35). The female kid should reach minimum weights of 35 lb (15.9 kg) at 6 months (weaning) and 60 lb (27.2 kg) at 18 months (first breeding). Optimal development (Fig. 20–11) will vary according to the normal mature size of the flock, but goats that are underdeveloped at first breeding will be low producers during their productive lifetimes.

Reproductive rate in Angora females can be increased by flushing (increasing the feeding level or nutritional status about 3 weeks prior to breeding and continuing 3 weeks into the breeding season). This can be accomplished in several ways, including increasing the feeding rate, increasing the concentrate level of the feed, increasing the amount of concentrates fed on pasture or range, moving animals to a fresh pasture of higher quality, treating animals for internal parasites, and so on. Flushing will not give a consistent response. The most likely positive response will occur when the females are in fair to good (not poor or excellent) condition and have been slightly underfed. Goats that are in good to excellent condition and are well fed likely will not respond to increased concentrate feeding (10).

The Angora is very sensitive to rapid changes in environmental conditions. Abortion at about the fourth month of pregnancy and death from hypothermia following shearing are at least related to a nutrition and environment interaction. Abortion occurs when the glucose level drops and triggers an endocrine mechanism (48). Since the goat is so sensitive to rapid change, a change in diet, location, or weather, shearing, or drenching can cause the doe to change her eating pattern or to refuse to eat, resulting in a drop in blood glucose. The routine of Angora females should not be changed after the 80th day and until the 120th day of pregnancy, especially the feeding routine. Changes made after the 120th day should not increase the nutritional stress on the goats.

Death from hypothermia following shearing is as risky in the late summer as during winter. The shock comes as a result of the

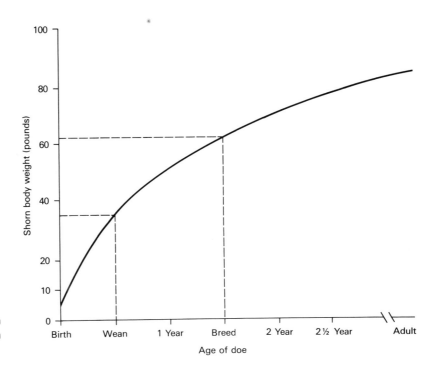

FIGURE 20–11. Optimal growth curve for Angora females. Taken from Huston et al. (12).

change (drop) in temperature (not just low temperature), wet conditions, and air velocity. A cold, blowing rain in August can kill freshly shorn goats at above 70° F. This is especially hazardous when goats that are freshly shorn and have been held off feed for several hours are returned to pasture without protection just before a cold, blowing rain. Freshly shorn goats should be either protected from the weather (shedded) and fed or turned into an area with natural protection (caves, cliffs, dense brush area) and with enough time to fill up with good-quality feed or forage.

SUMMARY

Goats are ruminant animals with an inquisitive and enterprising grazing-browsing behavior. They are uniquely attracted to trees and shrubs and are often used to reduce or prevent encroachment of undesired, brushy plants. Goats are physically agile and able to reach areas that are too remote or otherwise unavailable for use by other livestock species.

Three general goat types include dairy, Angora, and Spanish (or meat) goats. Nutrient requirements for goats are determined as the sum of the requirements for the different physiological processes carried on simultaneously (maintenance, pregnancy, and lactation). The lactating dairy goat is the most productive and requires the highest levels of nutrients. The Angora is the most sensitive to dietary and environmental changes. The Spanish goat is more rugged and fertile than the Angora and tends to be a more aggressive and effective browser. Nutrient requirements and example rations for different types and classes of goats were computed and discussed.

Certain periods of the annual cycle are critical, especially for the Angora, and require special managerial attention. Early life development (prior to first breeding) is important to establish an optimal adult body size and high lifetime productivity. The nutritional status at breeding should be good to assure proper ovulation and conception. Increased feeding at breeding (flushing) should be practiced when the goat has marginal body condition. The Angora goat is highly subject to nutritional stress abortion at about 90–100 d gestation. Changes in routine (feeding, watering, pasture location) should be avoided during this period. Perinatal losses of kids result if the does are underfed during late pregnancy. Dairy goats should be relatively fat at parturition to prepare for the mobilization of energy to support the high energy demands of early lactation.

REFERENCES

1. Ashbrook, P. F. 1982. *Proc. 3d Int. Conf. Goat Prod. Dis.*:153.
2. Bowling, R. A., et al. 1976. *Tex. Agr. Exp. Sta.* PR-3408:48.
3. Brody, S. 1938. *Mo. Agr. Exp. Sta. Res. Bull.* 291.
4. Davis, G. D., L. E. Bartell, and C. W. Cook. 1975. *J. Range Manage.* 28:216.
5. Gallagher, J. R., and Maurice Shelton. 1973. *Tex. Agr. Exp. Sta.* PR-3190:36.
6. Gathuka, Z. G., et al. 1982. *Tex. Agr. Exp. Sta.* CPR-4026:23.
7. Ghosh, T. K. 1987. *Proc. IV Int. Conf. on Goats* 2:1267. Brasilia, Brazil.
8. Giger, Sylvie, et al. 1981. In: P. Morand-Fehr, A. Bourbouze, and M. de Simiane, eds. Nutrition and systems of goat feeding. *Proc. Int. Symp.* (May 12–15):254. Tours, France.
9. Haenlein, G. F. W. 1980. Nutrient requirements of dairy goats—past and present. *Int. Goat and Sheep Res.* 1:79.
10. Hunt, L. J., et al. 1987. Influence of supplemental feeding on voluntary forage intake and on reproductive efficiency in Angora does. *SID Research Digest* (Summer):18.
11. Huston, J. E. 1978. *J. Dairy Sci.* 61:988.
12. Huston, J. E., Maurice Shelton, and W. C. Ellis. 1971. *Tex. Agr. Exp. Sta. Bull.* 1105.
13. Huston, J. E., et al. 1981. *Tex. Agr. Exp. Sta. Bull.* B-1357:16.
14. Huston, J. E., et al. 1986. *J. Animal Sci.* 62:208.
15. Huston, J. E., B. S. Engdahl, and K. W. Bales. 1988. *Small Ruminant Res.* 1:81.
16. Huston, J. E. 1989. Unpublished data.
17. Lambert, M. G., D. A. Clark, and K. Betteridge. 1987. *Proc. IV Int. Conf. on Goats* 2:1307. Brasilia, Brazil.
18. Lawson, J. L., D. W. Forrest, and Maurice Shelton. 1983. *Tex. Agr. Exp. Sta.* CR-4171:3.
19. Lippke, H., W. C. Ellis, and B. F. Jacobs. 1986. *J. Dairy Sci.* 69:403.
20. Lu, C. D., T. Sahlu, and J. Marcos Fernandez. 1987. *Proc. IV Int. Conf. on Goats* 2:1229. Brasilia, Brazil.

21. Mahler, C. 1945. *East Afr. Agr. J.* 11:115.

22. Marshall, W. H., et al. 1976. *Tex. Agr. Exp. Sta.* PR-3410:51.

23. Martinez Parra, R. A., et al. 1981. *Proc. Int. Symp. Nutr. Syst. Goat Feed:*369.

24. McGee, A. C. 1957. *Tex. Agr. Exp. Sta.* MP-208:8.

25. Morand-Fehr, P. 1981. In: C. Gall, ed., *Goat production:*193. New York: Academic Press.

26. Morand-Fehr, P., et al. 1982. *Proc. 3rd Int. Conf. Goat Prod. Dis.:*90.

27. Morand-Fehr, P., and D. Sauvant. 1985. In: D. C. Church, ed., *Livestock feeds and feeding.* 2nd ed.: 372. Englewood Cliffs, NJ: Prentice Hall.

28. Morand-Fehr, P., and D. Sauvant. 1987. *Proc. 4th Int. Conf. Goats:*1275.

29. NRC. 1978. *Nutrient requirements of dairy cattle.* 5th ed. Washington, D.C.: Nat. Acad. Press.

30. NRC. 1981. *Nutrient requirements of goats.* Washington, D.C.: Nat. Acad. Press.

31. Oates, A. V. 1956. *Rhodesia Agr. J.* 53:68.

32. Provenza, F. D., et al. 1983. *Utah Science* (Winter):91.

33. Rector, B. S. 1983. Diet selection and dietary forage intake by cattle, sheep and goats grazing in different combinations. Ph.D. dissertation: 173. Texas A&M Univ., College Station.

34. Riera, S. 1982. *Proc. 3rd Int. Conf. Goat Prod. Dis.:*162.

35. Shelton, M. 1961. *Tex. Agr. Exp. Sta.* MP-496.

36. Shelton, M., and J. R. Stewart. 1973. *Tex. Agr. Exp. Sta.* PR-3187:28.

37. Shelton, M., and D. Spiller. 1977. *Tex. Agr. Exp. Sta.* PR-3445:1.

38. Shelton, M., et al. 1982. *Tex. Agr. Exp. Sta.* CPR-4026:83.

39. Shelton, M., and J. Groff. 1984. *Tex. Agr. Exp. Sta.* B-1485.

40. Shkolnik, A., and N. Silanikove. 1981. In: P. Morand-Fehr, A. Bourbouze, and M. de Simiane, eds. Nutrition and systems of goat feeding:236. *Proc. Int. Symp.* (May 12–15). Tours, France.

41. Smith, G. C., B. W. Berry, and Z. L. Carpenter. 1972. *Tex. Agr. Exp. Sta.* PR-3027:31.

42. Smith, G. C., Z. L. Carpenter, and Maurice Shelton. 1978. *J. Animal. Sci.* 46:1229.

43. TDA. 1985. *Tex. livestock, dairy and poultry statistics.* Austin, TX: Tex. Dept. Agr.

44. Taylor, C. A., Jr. 1985. Multispecies grazing research overview. *Proc. Conf. on Multispecies Grazing:*65. Morrilton, AR: Winrock Int.

45. Taylor, C. A., Jr. 1983. Foraging strategies of goats as influenced by season, vegetation and management. Ph.D. dissertation:129. Texas A&M Univ., College Station.

46. Tomaszewski, M. A., and R. W. Blake. 1982. *Tex. Agr. Exp. Sta.* CPR-4026:42.

47. Van Soest, P. J., R. H. Wine, and L. A. Moore. 1966. *Proc. 10th Int. Grassl. Congr.* 10:438.

48. Wentzel, D. 1987. *Proc. of the IV Int. Conf. on Goats* 2:571. Brasilia, Brazil.

21

Feeding Swine

Gary L. Cromwell

INTRODUCTION

Nutrition and feeding management are very important aspects of swine production. In recent years, feed costs have accounted for 60–75 percent of the total costs of production. Therefore, it is extremely important that swine producers have a good understanding of the nutrient requirements of pigs during each phase of the life cycle, a knowledge of the feedstuffs that can be used in pig feeding, and an appreciation for the finer points of feeding management in order to raise pigs economically.

The feeding program has a major impact on animal performance and on overall profitability of the swine herd. High-quality feeds are needed in order to attain an optimal rate and efficiency of growth from birth to market and a high level of reproductive performance in the breeding herd.

This chapter will discuss the nutrient requirements of swine and identify feedstuffs that can be used to meet these requirements. It will describe feeding programs that optimize growth and reproductive performance of pigs.

NUTRIENTS REQUIRED BY SWINE

The pig has the ability to obtain nutrients from a wide variety of feedstuffs. Historically, the wild pig was omnivorous, consuming both vegetative and animal food sources. In the early days, domestic pigs were allowed to forage on grass, roots, acorns, refuse, and whatever else was available. Later, pigs were confined to dirt lots or pasture and fed ear corn and tankage or skim milk. Today, the majority of the pigs in the United States are raised in total confinement and fed highly fortified, grain-based diets in which the majority of the protein supplement consists of soybean meal.

The pig is a simple-stomached animal (see Ch. 3), so it must rely largely on feeds having readily digestible carbohydrates to meet its energy needs. The more complex carbohydrates (cellulose, hemicellulose) found in roughages and other fibrous feeds are broken down by microbial fermentation only. The pig does not have a rumen, thus the fibrous components of the diet are not utilized as efficiently as they are in ruminants. Also, simple-stomached animals like the pig are dependent upon certain essential amino acids present in dietary protein from which to build their own body proteins. Unlike the ruminant animal, the pig cannot synthesize the essential amino acids from poor-quality protein or from NPN sources. Thus the relative amounts of the essential amino acids in the protein are extremely important to pigs.

The nutrient requirements for growing pigs of various weights and the requirements of breeding swine are shown in Appendix Tables 6 through 9. These nutrient levels are established by the NRC and are estimates of the minimum amount of a nutrient required by animals under average conditions (1). While the NRC standards serve as an excellent guideline, they do not include safety margins to allow for variability among animals or among feedstuffs. Therefore, recommended nutrient allowances made by nutritionists at universities and feed companies often are slightly higher than the NRC standards.

Water

Water is so common that it is seldom thought of as a nutrient, yet it is one of the most important nutrient classes. Swine of all ages should have free access to fresh, clean water at all times. Limiting water intake will result in reduced rate and efficiency of gain in pigs and reduced milk production in lactating sows. A severe limitation of drinking water can cause death in pigs.

The requirement for water is influenced by many factors including environmental temperature and humidity, composition of the feed, and weight of the pig. A useful guideline is that about 2–3 lb (1–1.5 quarts) of water is required for every 1 lb of feed consumed. A lactating sow will require more water because of the high water content of the milk she produces.

Water is often supplied from automatic drinking fountains (Fig. 21–1). In cold environments, water fountains need to be equipped with heaters to keep the water from freezing. In heated buildings or in the mild climates of the southern United States, nipple-type waterers are common (Fig. 21–2); they are less expensive and the water stays cleaner. When cup waterers are used, at least one cup should be provided for every 20–25 pigs. When nipple waterers are used, one nipple should be provided for every 15 pigs.

FIGURE 21–1. A freeze-proof bowl-type automatic waterer for pigs.

Energy

Nursing pigs derive most of their energy from fat and sugar (lactose) in milk. Most of the energy for growing pigs is derived from the metabolism of starch in cereal grains. Baby pigs are unable to utilize starch because of insufficient amylase and maltase (starch-digesting enzymes) in the small intestine. Protein in excess of the requirement can be used as an energy source, but it is too costly to be fed solely for energy. In older animals (sows and finishing pigs), a limited amount of energy can be derived from volatile fatty acids, products produced by bacterial fermentation of fiber in the large intestine.

FIGURE 21–2. A nipple-type waterer for pigs.

Energy requirements of pigs are expressed as digestible energy (DE) and metabolizable energy (ME). For all weight classes of pigs, the ME requirement is approximately 96 percent of the DE requirement. Energy requirements of pigs are influenced by their weight (which influences the maintenance requirement), by their genetic capacity for lean tissue growth or milk synthesis, and by the environmental temperature in which they are housed. The energy requirement for maintenance is directly related to metabolic body weight and is approximately 110 kcal of DE per kg body weight$^{0.75}$. (Metabolic weight can be determined on a hand calculator by multiplying pounds by 0.454, cubing the result, then calculating the square root twice. For a 100-lb pig, the metabolic weight is 100 × 0.454 = 45.4 kg; 45.4 × 45.4 × 45.4 = 93,577; $\sqrt{93,577}$ = 307; $\sqrt{307}$ = 17.5 kg.) The total daily energy requirement for growing pigs is about 3.6–3.8 times the maintenance requirement in young pigs and 3.2–3.4 times the maintenance requirement in finishing pigs, when both are housed in a comfortable (thermoneutral) environment.

During the growth period, energy requirements increase as the pig increases in weight. For example, the ME requirement of a 200-lb pig (10,000 kcal/d) is greater than that of a 20-lb pig (2000 kcal/d) because of its greater maintenance requirement and a faster rate of accretion of body tissue (fat and muscle). The ME requirement of the lactating sow (14,500–20,500 kcal/d) is much greater than that of a pregnant sow (5800–6500 kcal/d). In fact, high-producing lactating sows are capable of producing 15–20 lb of milk/d, and they generally cannot consume enough energy to maintain energy balance; hence they lose weight during lactation.

Energy requirements are greater at low environmental temperatures than at high environmental temperatures because of the pig's need to produce heat for body warmth. For example, a 100-lb pig requires about 750 kcal more ME/d at 40° F than at 60° F to achieve the same weight gain. When full-fed, the pig simply consumes more feed in a cold environment to meet its increased energy needs. This is the reason why feed efficiency (feed:gain ratio) of pigs is better in summer than in winter.

Pigs that are full-fed will generally eat to meet their energy requirement, which means that they will consume more of a low-energy feed, such as a diet with oats or barley as the grain source, than they will consume of a diet based on corn. In contrast, if given a high-energy diet, such as a diet with added fat, their voluntary intake will decrease, because their energy requirement is met with less total feed. Therefore, feed conversion efficiency is influenced greatly by the energy density of the diet. Feeding high-energy diets results in a better feed:gain ratio—less feed is required per unit of gain. Conversely, feeding low-energy diets increases the amount of feed required to produce a unit of body weight gain. Growth rate is influenced slightly by energy intake, but to a much lesser degree than is feed:gain ratio.

Carcass quality also is influenced by energy intake of pigs. Reducing the energy intake by incorporating high levels of fibrous feedstuffs in the diet or by restricting feed intake will produce a leaner carcass. Adding fat to the diet tends to produce a slightly fatter carcass.

Protein and Amino Acids

The pig requires 10 essential amino acids in its diet for normal body functions. A good-quality protein is one that provides these amino acids in the amounts and proportions necessary for the particular need of the pig (growth, reproduction, lactation). Unfortunately, the protein in cereal grains is of very poor quality (see Ch. 9). Table 21–1 shows that 5 of the 10 amino acids required by a 50-lb growing pig are deficient in corn. Failure to supplement corn with sufficient amounts of a high-quality protein source such as a soybean meal results in poor growth, inefficient feed utilization, an increase in carcass fatness, and general unthriftiness (Table 21–2).

Traditionally, swine diets have been formulated on the basis of crude protein. Protein levels are established for the various weight classes of pigs so that the most limiting amino acid (lysine) will be present in adequate amounts. This system works well when corn and soybean meal are the major sources of energy and protein. Table 21–1 illustrates that supplementing corn with soybean meal (79 percent corn, 19 percent soybean meal) to provide a 15 percent protein level meets the lysine and other amino acid requirements of a 50-lb pig.

Amino acid requirements are influenced mostly by age and weight of the pig. On a daily basis, the requirements increase as the pig increases in weight; however, when the requirements are expressed on a percentage basis, the requirements decrease with increasing weight of the pig. For example, a 200-lb pig requires more grams of protein/d than a 20-lb pig (400

TABLE 21-1

Essential amino acids likely to be deficient in corn and corn plus soybean meal (44% protein) for the growing pig

Item	Corn	Corn + Soybean Meal (79% corn : 19% SBM)	Requirement,[a] 50-lb pig
Protein, %	8.5	15.1	15[b]
Amino acids, %			
Arginine	0.43	0.95	0.25
Histidine	0.27	0.43	0.22
Isoleucine	0.35[c]	0.66	0.46
Leucine	1.19	1.58	0.60
Lysine	0.25[c]	0.75	0.75
Methionine + cystine	0.40[c]	0.54	0.41
Phenylalanine + tyrosine	0.84	1.35	0.66
Threonine	0.36[c]	0.61	0.48
Tryptophan	0.09[c]	0.19	0.12
Valine	0.48	0.76	0.48

[a]From NRC (1).

[b]The pig does not have a protein requirement as such, but a corn-soybean meal diet with this level of dietary protein will meet the requirement for the most limiting amino acid, lysine.

[c]Deficient.

TABLE 21-2

Effects of feeding a protein-deficient diet on performance of growing pigs[a]

Item	Corn[b] 8% Protein	Corn-Soybean Meal[b] 16% Protein
Daily gain, lb	0.37	1.85
Daily feed, lb	2.50	4.83
Feed/gain	6.76	2.61

[a]Summary of 3 Univ. of Kentucky experiments, 12 pigs/treatment, 47–80 lb.

[b]Both diets supplemented with minerals and vitamins.

versus 100 g/d), but the heavier pig requires less protein when expressed on a percentage basis (13 versus 20 percent of the diet).

Minerals

Compared with energy and protein, minerals are required in very small amounts. Thirteen minerals are required in the diet by pigs (Table 21–3). The minerals most likely to be deficient in grain-soybean meal diets are calcium (Ca), phosphorus (P), sodium (Na), chlorine (Cl), and the trace minerals iron (Fe), zinc (Zn), iodine (I), and selenium (Se).

The two minerals required in the greatest amounts by pigs are Ca and P. Adequate levels of both Ca and P must be included in the diet for strong skeletal structure. If either Ca or P is deficient, poor bone mineralization will occur, which can lead to deformation of the legs (rickets), lameness, or bone fractures. Sound feet and legs are especially important in pigs reared on concrete or slatted floors in confinement facilities. A deficiency of P also will result in slow and inefficient growth. Ca deficiency seldom depresses growth, unless the deficiency is severe.

Ca and P need to be kept in proper balance in the diet. An excess of Ca can cause problems, especially if the P level is marginal. The most favorable ratio of Ca:P is between 1:1 and 1.5:1.

Feed grains are extremely deficient in both Ca and P (Table 21–3). In addition, most (60–80 percent) of the P in grains and oilseed meals is in the form of phytate, an organic complex which is not well utilized by pigs. The total P supplied by corn and soybean meal amounts to about 0.34 percent of the diet, but only about 0.08 percent is available to the pig. The requirement for total P takes into account that a large portion of the P in the natural feedstuffs is unavailable.

The amount of P in feedstuffs that is ac-

TABLE 21-3
Minerals likely to be deficient in corn and corn plus soybean meal (44% protein) for the growing pig

Item	Corn	Corn + Soybean Meal (79% corn + 19% SBM)	Requirement,[a] 50-lb pig
Major minerals, %			
Calcium	0.03[b]	0.08[b]	0.60
Phosphorus	0.28[b]	0.34[b]	0.50
Phosphorus, available	0.04[b]	0.08[b]	0.23
Sodium	0.01[b]	0.02[b]	0.10
Chlorine	0.05[b]	0.05[b]	0.08
Magnesium	0.11	0.14	0.04
Potassium	0.33	0.66	0.23
Sulfur	0.11	0.17	—[c]
Trace minerals, ppm			
Copper	3.5[b]	7.2	4.0
Iron	33.0[b]	53.0[b]	60.0
Manganese	5.7	10.3	2.0
Zinc	9.0[b]	25.0[b]	60.0
Iodine	0.03[b]	0.06[b]	0.14
Selenium[d]	0.07[b]	0.07[b]	0.15

[a]From NRC (1).
[b]Deficient.
[c]The requirement is unknown but is met by the sulfur in methionine and cystine.
[d]Level in corn is variable, depending on area where grown.

tually available to the pig is quite variable (Table 21–4). For many years, nutritionists used as a guideline that one-third of the P in feedstuffs of plant origin was available to the pig. Recent research findings now indicate that this rule of thumb is not valid (2). For example, in cereal grains the following differences exist: the availability of P in corn and grain sorghum is low (12–19 percent), it is intermediate in oats and barley (30 percent), and it is high in wheat, triticale, and high-moisture grain (43–50 percent). The P in sunflower meal, peanut meal, and cottonseed meal is poorly available (3–15 percent), in soybean meal it is intermediate in availability (25–35 percent), and in most animal protein sources the P is highly available (76–100 percent). The P in inorganic phosphate supplements is considerably more available than that in natural feedstuffs. Formulating swine diets on an available P basis is recommended when ingredients are used that have P availability values considerably different from those of corn and soybean meal.

Na and Cl also are required for normal growth and body functions. Most feeds are low in Na and marginal in Cl. The requirement for both minerals can be met by supplementing the diet with 0.25 percent salt. Failure to supply salt to pigs causes depressed feed intake and poor growth rate. Pigs are able to cope with high levels (5–7 percent) of salt in the diet as long as they have free access to fresh water.

Potassium (K), magnesium (Mg), and sulfur (S) are required by pigs, but they do not need to be supplemented because the natural feedstuffs contain ample amounts of these minerals (Table 21–3).

Zn is required for normal growth and healthy skin. A deficiency of Zn causes slow growth and a scabby appearance of the skin, a condition called parakeratosis. This condition is similar to the appearance of a pig heavily infested with mange. The skin lesions are reversible with Zn administration. High levels of dietary Ca tend to interfere with Zn absorption, so if high levels of Ca are fed, Zn levels also should be increased. Also, high levels of phytate tend to bind Zn and make it unavailable. Thus the Zn requirement is much higher in a grain-soybean meal diet (which is high in phytate) than in a diet in which a large portion of the protein is of animal origin. As a guide, a grain-soybean meal diet should contain 100 ppm of supplemental Zn for each 1 percent of Ca in the diet.

Fe is needed for hemoglobin synthesis in pigs. A deficiency of Fe results in depressed hemoglobin levels in the blood, a condition called anemia. Baby pigs develop anemia in the first week of life if not given supplemental Fe.

TABLE 21-4

Biological availability of the phosphorus in feedstuffs for pigs

Ingredient	Availability of P, %[a]	Ingredient	Availability of P, %[a]
Grains		High-protein meals—plant origin	
Corn	14	Soybean meal, dehulled	25
Corn, high moisture	49	Soybean meal	35
Corn, pelleted	12	Cottonseed meal	15
Grain sorghum	19	Peanut meal	12
Grain sorghum, high moisture	43	Canola meal	21
Barley	31	Sunflower meal	3
Oats	30	Palm kernel cake	11
Wheat	50	High-protein meals—animal origin	
Triticale	46	Fish meal	102
Grain by-products		Meat and bone meal	76
Hominy feed	14	Blood meal	92
Corn gluten meal	59	Dried whey	76
Distillers grain	71	Inorganic phosphate sources	
Wheat bran	35	Dicalcium phosphate	105
Wheat middlings	45	Defluorinated rock phosphate	87
Rice bran	25	Steamed bone meal	82
Miscellaneous			
Alfalfa meal	>100		
Soybean hulls	78		

[a]Relative to the availability of P in monosodium phosphate, which is given a value of 100. All values are based on slope ratio assays of bone ash and/or bone breaking strength in pigs.
Source: Cromwell (2).

In white pigs, anemia shows up as a pale color around the eyes, nose, and ears—tissues that otherwise are pink. In advanced stages of anemia "thumping," or spasmodic breathing, may occur. Growth rate is seldom depressed; in fact, the largest pig in the litter is often the first one to show symptoms of anemia because of its fast growth rate and the rapid dilution of its body Fe supply.

There are several reasons why the baby pig is very susceptible to anemia. The newborn pig grows exceptionally fast, quadrupling its weight in only 3 weeks. During this time, its only food is milk, which is extremely deficient in Fe. The pig has relatively low Fe reserves at birth and has little opportunity to obtain any Fe from its environment when it is raised in confinement. Pigs raised in dirt lots generally obtain sufficient Fe from the soil to meet their needs.

Anemia can be prevented by giving an intramuscular injection of 100–200 mg of Fe (as Fe-dextran, Fe-dextrin, or gleptoferrin) before 3 d of age (Fig. 21–3) or by oral administration. Fe deficiency is seldom encountered in older pigs because most feedstuffs contain some Fe, and the P supplements (such as dicalcium phosphate and defluorinated rock phosphate) contain relatively high levels of Fe.

Cu also is needed for hemoglobin synthesis, but the Cu requirement is much less than the Fe requirement. Cu deficiency is seldom seen in pigs. This mineral is unique in that when high dietary levels (100–250 ppm) are fed, Cu stimulates growth rate in pigs much like that obtained when antibiotics are fed. This will be discussed later under the section on feed additives.

Iodine is deficient in feedstuffs grown in certain areas of the country. In addition, many feedstuffs (soybeans, rapeseeds, linseed, and others) contain goitrogens, compounds that interfere with I absorption or the incorporation of I into thyroxine. Failure to supplement a grain-soybean meal diet with I will cause four- to five-fold enlargement of the thyroid, a condition called goiter. Iodine can be provided conveniently by using iodized salt in the diet.

Se deficiency is frequently a problem in swine. Crops grown in the Pacific Northwest, the Northeast, and the states around the Great Lakes are very low in Se. Failure to supplement the diet with Se can result in liver necrosis, heart lesions, pale muscles, and sudden death in pigs, a condition called "hepatosa dietetica." This trace mineral is regulated by the FDA, and the maximum level of supplementation is 0.3 ppm in swine feeds.

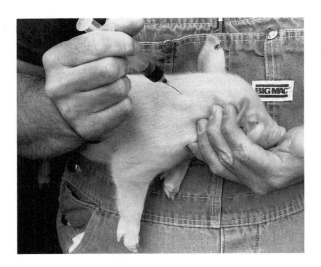

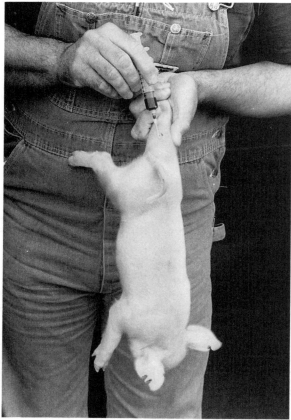

FIGURE 21–3. Anemia can be prevented by giving baby pigs an iron solution injection in the neck or ham.

One additional mineral, fluorine (F), is not considered as essential, but care should be taken to prevent excessive levels in the diet. Excessive F intake is generally associated with the feeding of unprocessed, high-F rock phosphate as a P source. Excessive F can cause mottling and erosion of teeth and abnormal bone formation. Pigs can tolerate up to 225 ppm F when rock phos-

phate is the source, and up to 150 ppm F when the F is in a more soluble form, such as Na fluoride.

Vitamins

Fourteen vitamins are required by pigs, all in very small amounts. Cereal grains and plant protein supplements are very poor sources of many of the vitamins (Table 21–5). Those most likely to be deficient in grain-soybean meal diets are vitamins A and D and the B-complex vitamins, riboflavin, pantothenic acid, niacin, and vitamin B_{12}.

Vitamin A occurs as its precursor, carotene, in yellow corn and green plants. However, it is risky to rely on the carotene in corn to meet the vitamin A requirements of pigs. Some of the carotenes in corn are not converted efficiently to vitamin A. Also, heat damage or the use of organic acids to preserve high-moisture corn destroys much of the carotene. From a practical standpoint, vitamin A should be added to pig feed (as vitamin A palmitate) at levels of at least 2–3 times the requirement; first, because it is relatively cheap, and second, because vitamin A is relatively unstable in mixed feeds.

Vitamin D is essentially absent from most feedstuffs that are commonly fed to pigs. Swine can synthesize vitamin D when exposed to sunlight; however, because many pigs are raised in confinement and away from direct sunlight, vitamin D should be supplemented. Although pigs can utilize either the form found in plants (D_2) or the form found in animal products (D_3), there is evidence that pigs, like chicks, utilize vitamin D_3 better than vitamin D_2 (1).

Vitamin E may be adequate in grain and plant protein sources, but it is likely to be marginal or deficient in some instances. Therefore, it is recommended that pig diets be fortified with vitamin E. This vitamin serves as a natural antioxidant in feeds and, when deficient, will cause symptoms that are similar to those of a Se deficiency (liver necrosis, pale muscles, and the like).

Vitamin K is present in some feeds and is synthesized by microorganisms in the hind gut of the pig. Generally, microbial synthesis is assumed to provide adequate levels of vitamin K for pigs, provided that the pigs have access to their feces. However, deficiencies have been encountered when pigs are fed moldy grain or other feeds with mold damage, or when fed diets with excessive levels of Ca. One symptom is prolonged blood clotting time, resulting in excessive

TABLE 21-5

Vitamins likely to be deficient in corn and corn plus soybean meal (44% protein) for the growing pig

Vitamin	Corn	Corn + Soybean Meal (79% corn : 19% SBM)	Requirement,[a] 50-lb Pig
Fat-soluble vitamins			
Vitamin A, IU/lb	200[b]	158[b]	590
Vitamin D, IU/lb	—[b]	—[b]	68
Vitamin E, IU/lb	10	7.7	5
Vitamin K mg/lb	—	—	0.2[c]
Water-soluble vitamins, mg/lb			
Vitamin C	—	—	?[d]
B-complex			
Riboflavin	0.5[b]	0.64[b]	1.1
Pantothenic acid	2.3[b]	3.2[b]	4.6
Niacin, available	—[b]	2.5[b]	4.5
Vitamin B_{12}	—[b]	—[b]	0.005
Choline	227	404	136
Pyridoxine	2.8	2.7	0.5
Thiamin	1.7	1.9	0.5
Folic acid	0.14	0.16	0.14
Biotin	0.03	0.05	0.02

[a]From NRC (1).
[b]Deficient.
[c]Requirement generally met by microbial synthesis.
[d]Requirement unknown. Sufficient amounts are present in natural ingredients and/or are synthesized in the body to meet the requirements.

bleeding and bruising. Death often will result from internal hemorrhage. The deficiency can be corrected by injection of vitamin K or by including it in the feed. For insurance purposes, vitamin supplements should contain a small amount of vitamin K.

Cereal grains and plant protein supplements are very poor sources of riboflavin, niacin, and pantothenic acid, and they contain no vitamin B_{12}. In addition, the niacin in cereal grains is chemically bound and totally unavailable to the pig. A deficiency of one or more of these vitamins can cause retarded growth, and if the deficiency is severe, chronic diarrhea can occur. Vitamin supplements should always contain these four B-vitamins.

A deficiency of biotin will cause cracking of the hooves in pigs. Although feedstuffs fed to growing pigs should contain ample biotin, there is recent evidence suggesting that biotin supplementation of sow diets results in improved reproductive performance (3). A deficiency of biotin is more likely to occur when barley or wheat is the grain source, because the availability of biotin is considerably lower in these grains than in corn.

The choline requirement of growing pigs is generally met by natural ingredients, but choline supplementation has been shown to improve litter size in pregnant sows (4). Under ex-

perimental conditions, choline deficiency in sows has been shown to cause a spraddle-legged condition in newborn pigs. Choline supplementation of a corn-soybean meal diet for sows has not been effective, however, in preventing the spraddle-legged pig condition occasionally seen in practice.

Thiamin, pyridoxine, and folic acid are adequately supplied to the growing pig by natural ingredients. But like biotin and choline, supplemental folic acid has recently been found to benefit reproductive performance in sows (5). Therefore, for insurance purposes, it may be advisable to supplement sow feeds with the three B-vitamins biotin, choline, and folic acid.

Vitamin C is synthesized in adequate amounts by pigs, and research has not shown any consistent benefit from the addition of this vitamin. An exception might be under high-stress conditions, such as immediately post-weaning, in which case vitamin C supplementation occasionally has been shown to improve performance of early-weaned pigs.

FEEDSTUFFS USED IN SWINE DIETS

This section will describe the more common feed ingredients used in swine diets in the United States. Additional details on these and other feedstuffs not covered in this section are provided in Ch. 6–9 and in other publications (6, 7, 8).

Energy Sources

Cereal Grains. Corn accounts for over 85 percent of the grain fed to swine in the United States. It is an excellent feed for swine of all ages because it is high in digestible starch and low in fiber, it is very palatable, and it can be fed in a variety of ways. For these reasons, corn is the standard to which other grains are compared (Table 21–6). In spite of its many virtues, corn is low in protein (8.5 percent), is extremely deficient in lysine (0.25 percent) and tryptophan (0.07 percent), and is deficient in many of the essential minerals and vitamins, as shown in Tables 21–1, 21–3, and 21–5. However, when these deficiencies are corrected with appropriate amounts of protein, mineral, and vitamin supplementation, corn makes an excellent feed for pigs.

Several genetic mutants of corn have been discovered in recent years that are 50–75 percent higher in lysine and tryptophan than normal hybrid corn (see Ch. 8). The lysine content of these mutant cultivars varies from 0.32 to 0.45 percent, compared with about 0.25 percent lysine in normal corn. Because of the higher lysine content, less protein supplement is required to meet the amino acid requirements of pigs. For example, the soybean meal can be reduced by 75–100 lb/ton when high-lysine corn is fed to pigs. Unfortunately, most high-lysine varieties of corn do not produce as high yields as normal hybrid corn, and they are more susceptible to harvesting damage because of the softer, more floury kernel. Table 21–7 shows the yield reduction that a producer can afford to take when high-lysine corn is raised and fed to swine.

Grain sorghum (milo) is grown in the southern and southwestern states and is the second

TABLE 21-6

Relative value and maximum replacement for corn of energy feedstuffs for swine

Feedstuff	Relative Value[a]	Maximum Replacement[b]
Corn	100	100
Fat, feed-grade	230	5–10
Rice polishings	100	100
Oat groats	100	100[c]
Bakery waste, dehydrated	100	50–80
Wheat	98	100
Hominy feed	97	100
Grain sorghum (milo)	97	100
Rice, polished, broken	96	100
Triticale	89	75
Millet, proso	89	100
Barley	89	100
Rye	88	25
Wheat middlings	87	30
Wheat shorts	84	30
Rice bran	84	10
Oats	80	25
Beet pulp	79	10
Wheat bran	63	10
Molasses, cane	59	5
Alfalfa meal	50	5
Potatoes, cooked	25	25

[a]Based on ME value.
[b]Maximum replacement for corn in diets for growing-finishing swine. Two to three times these levels of the fibrous, feedstuffs (oats, wheat bran, rice bran, alfalfa meal, beet pulp) can be used in sow diets.
[c]Cost prohibits the inclusion of more than 10–20% in starter diets.

most common cereal grain fed to pigs. The energy value of grain sorghum for swine is similar to that of corn, and it contains about the same levels of protein and lysine as corn. The overall feeding value of grain sorghum is nearly equivalent to corn for growing-finishing pigs (Table 21–8). Some grain sorghums have been devel-

TABLE 21-7

Affordable percent yield reduction of high-lysine corn compared with normal corn (% yield reduction)[a]

Normal Corn, $/bu	Soybean Meal (44% protein), $/ton				
	150	200	250	300	350
2.00	6.0	9.4	12.7	15.6	18.4
2.50	3.8	6.7	9.4	12.0	14.5
3.00	2.3	4.8	7.2	9.4	11.6
3.50	1.1	3.4	5.5	7.5	9.4

[a]Based on 0.25% lysine in normal corn and 0.40% lysine in high-lysine corn.

TABLE 21-8

Comparison of corn, wheat, grain sorghum (milo), and barley as energy sources for growing-finishing pigs

Comparisons	Corn	Other Grains
Corn vs. grain sorghum (milo)[a]		
Avg daily gain, lb	1.60	1.57
Feed/gain	3.33	3.44
Corn vs. barley[b]		
Avg daily gain, lb	1.76	1.69
Feed/gain	3.13	3.45
Corn vs. wheat[c]		
Avg daily gain, lb	1.67	1.68
Feed/gain	3.19	3.17

[a]Ten experiments, 508 pigs, 51–221 lb.
[b]Four experiments, 280 pigs, 42–225 lb.
[c]Fifteen experiments, 984 pigs, 47–215 lb.

oped that are resistant to bird damage, but the feeding value of most bird-resistant varieties is considerably lower than conventional grain sorghum because of their high tannin content. The bird-resistant varieties are seldom grown in the major grain sorghum producing areas of the United States.

Barley is commonly fed to pigs in the northern states and in Canada. Barley is higher in fiber and lower in energy than corn; therefore, it has a lower feeding value (Table 21–8). Also, barley is quite variable in its composition and its feeding value. Some of the variability is attributed to the amount of β-glucans present in the barley. β-glucans are complex carbohydrates (polymers of glucose) that cause gels to form in the tract which interfere with nutrient digestibility.

Barley and oats are generally considered to have 85–90 percent and 75–80 percent, respectively, of the feeding value of corn (Table 21–6). However, both are slightly higher in protein and lysine than corn is. Barley can replace a part or all the corn in the diet, but oats should not replace more than 25 percent of the corn for growing-finishing pigs. Higher levels can be used in sow diets.

Wheat is an excellent feed for pigs (Table 21–8), but generally it is too expensive to be used as a feed ingredient. However, at certain times, wheat compares quite favorably with corn on a cost basis. Wheat is similar to corn on an energy basis, and it is higher in protein, lysine, and available P than corn. On an energy basis, wheat has slightly less value than corn (98 percent), but when the additional lysine in wheat is taken into account, wheat has about 105 per-

cent of the value of corn. Furthermore, on a bushel basis, wheat has about 112 percent of the value of corn because of its greater weight/bushel (60 versus 56 lb/bu). Wheat that is damaged moderately by disease, insects, or frost, or wheat that is contaminated with wild garlic bulblets, cannot be used for milling, but it makes excellent feed for swine. Wheat can replace a part or all of the corn in the diet.

Rye is quite high in energy, but it is not as palatable as the other cereal grains. Also, rye contains high levels of pectin, a complex carbohydrate, which reduces its feeding value. In addition, rye is susceptible to ergot (a fungus) infection which can cause abortion in sows and markedly reduce performance in growing pigs.

Triticale has a feeding value that is better than rye but somewhat less than wheat. Triticale possesses a trypsin inhibitor, which limits its feeding value if fed as the sole source of grain to pigs. Some cultivars of triticale have been developed for the southern United States and have been shown to give excellent performance when fed to pigs. An example of one of these cultivars is Beagle—31.

It is very important to remember that when cereal grains other than corn are used, either the grain should be substituted for corn on a pound-for-pound basis, or the diet must be formulated on the basis of the lysine content of the grain, not on the basis of its protein content. Because most grains are higher in protein than corn is, formulating the diet on a protein basis will result in a deficiency of lysine. An example of the difference in pig performance when diets are formulated on a protein basis instead of a lysine basis is shown in Table 21–9.

TABLE 21-9

Effects of method of diet formulation on performance of finishing pigs fed corn and wheat-based diets

Method of Diet Formulation:	Corn	Wheat (weight basis)[a]	Wheat (lysine basis)[a]	Wheat (protein basis)[a]
Grain in diet, %	83.0	83.0	86.0	90.6
Soybean meal in diet, %	14.5	14.5	11.6	6.9
Protein in diet, %	14.0	16.8	15.7	14.0
Lysine in diet, %	0.66	0.74	0.66	0.53
Avg daily gain, lb	1.65	1.69	1.67	1.38
Feed/gain	3.17	3.18	3.26	3.63

[a]Method of diet formulation.

Source: Cromwell et al. (9). Two trials, 36 pigs/treatment, 90–217 lb.

Damaged Grain. Cereal grains can be damaged by a number of different causes, one of which is a lack of rainfall during the growing season. Drought-damaged grain is lighter than normal in test weight, but its feeding value is generally equal to normal grain when compared on a weight basis.

Grains can also be damaged by molds (see Ch. 4). Mold growth can occur in the field prior to harvest or after the grain is in storage. Grains are particularly susceptible to mold damage if they are not properly dried or if stored under warm (80–100° F), humid conditions. Broken kernels or insect damage also makes grain more vulnerable to mold infestation. Besides grains, peanuts and cottonseeds (and thus peanut meal and cottonseed meal) are also quite susceptible to certain molds. Molds themselves are not harmful, but they produce toxins (mycotoxins) that can be harmful to animals.

One of the major mycotoxins of concern is aflatoxin, produced by the mold *Aspergillus flavus.* Several aflatoxins have been identified, with four of the more common ones labeled B_1, B_2, G_1, and G_2. Corn may be infected with this fungus, yet not be visibly moldy. The presence of the fungus can be detected by placing corn under ultraviolet light (black light), in which case a bright, greenish-yellow fluorescence will occur if the mold is present. The detection of the mold by this screening procedure does not necessarily mean that the grain is contaminated with aflatoxin, and a further chemical test must be conducted to determine whether or not aflatoxin is present and at what levels.

Aflatoxin is a potent carcinogen, and the FDA has placed certain restrictions on the interstate movement of grain containing this mycotoxin. At low levels (20–50 ppb), aflatoxins do not cause any problems in growing pigs, but high levels cause reduced gain, lower resistance to disease, prolonged blood clotting time, and liver damage. Grain with up to 200 ppb aflatoxin can be fed to finishing pigs, but it should not be fed to young pigs or breeding animals.

Certain zeolites, such as hydrated Na Ca aluminosilicate (trade name NovaSil), have recently been shown to protect against aflatoxin toxicity when added to aflatoxin-contaminated diets (10). This compound ordinarily is used in feeds as an anticaking agent. Apparently the zeolite binds the alfatoxin and prevents its absorption. Recent studies have also shown that feeding elevated levels of dietary protein or supplementing the diet with lysine offers some protection against aflatoxin toxicity (11).

The trichothecenes, produced by *Fusarium* fungi, are potent mycotoxins. Deoxynivalenol (commonly called vomitoxin or feed refusal factor), T-2 toxin, and diacetoxyscirpenol are examples of toxins in this class. Grains containing these toxins cause reduced feed intake, reduced growth, impaired immune function, nervous disorders, and vomiting. As little as 10 ppm vomitoxin has been found to reduce feed intake by 50 percent, and levels of 20 ppm or higher may result in nearly total feed refusal. The tolerance level for vomitoxin is about 1 ppm, whereas the tolerances for T-2 toxin and diacetoxyscirpenol are not known.

Zearalenone, one of the most frequently encountered mycotoxins, is produced by *Fusarium roseum* and *Gibberella zeae.* This compound produces estrogenic effects such as reddening and swelling of the vulva and nipples, irregular estrual cycles, and pseudopregnancy in gilts and sows. High levels can cause vaginal and rectal prolapses. The tolerance for zearalenone in contaminated feed is 20 ppm for growing swine and considerably less for breeding animals. From day 7 to day 10 after breeding (that is, at about the time of implantation of the embryos into the uterine wall) is an especially critical time; if bred animals consume zearalenone at that time, they likely will lose their litter and not recycle for a considerable length of time.

Ochratoxin and citrinin are less common mycotoxins that may be present in mold-infected barley and other small grains. Ergot is an alkaloid-like mycotoxin produced by fungi that may affect rye or wheat. Ergot is quite toxic, and ergot-contaminated grain should not be fed to pigs.

If mycotoxins are suspected in grain or other feeds, they should be subjected to a laboratory test to determine which ones are present and at what levels. If levels of mycotoxins are within the tolerance levels, the grains may be fed to finishing pigs, but it is best not to feed mycotoxin-contaminated feeds to young pigs. It is advisable not to feed mycotoxin-suspect feed to replacement gilts, and it should never be fed to pregnant animals. Blending of contaminated grain with sound grain to bring the grain within the tolerance range is an option when the grain is fed to hogs on the farm.

Grain By-Products. Wheat shorts, bran, and middlings are higher in fiber and lower in energy than wheat, but often they are an economical ingredient to use in pig feeds. Feed manufacturers like to use small amounts (5–10 percent) of wheat middlings when feeds are pelleted, because they have good binding properties and give a hard, cohesive pellet. Wheat bran is often used in sow farrowing feed because of its laxative properties. Rice bran is another fibrous feed that can be used in sow feeds. Rolled oat groats are very palatable and make an excellent addition to starter feeds for pigs, but their high cost limits their usage in other pig feeds.

Fat. Feed-grade fat can be used as an energy source in swine diets. As a rule of thumb, in order for fat to be economical as a feed ingredient, it must be no more than 2.5–3.0 times the cost of corn. Table 21–10 shows that when fat is added at a level of 5 percent, growth rate is improved slightly, feed intake is reduced, and feed efficiency is improved. However, when fed fat, pigs tend to consume more calories, so backfat often will be increased slightly. With 5 percent added fat, a 0.1-inch increase in backfat should be expected. Because feed intake is reduced when fat is added, it is important to increase the level of protein so that the daily

TABLE 21-10

Supplemental fat for growing-finishing swine fed a corn-soybean meal diet[a]

Item	Added Fat, %	
	0	5
Daily gain, lb	1.68	1.77
Daily feed, lb	5.44	5.22
Feed/gain	3.24	2.95
Carcass backfat, in.	1.20	1.31
Ham-loin, % of carcass	43.4	42.3

[a]Five experiments, 88 pigs/treatment, 57–208 lb. Univ. of Kentucky and Univ. of Nebraska.

intake of protein is maintained. As a general rule, the protein level should be increased by 0.2 percentage units for every 1 percent addition of dietary fat.

Fat is utilized more efficiently in a hot environment than in a moderate or cold environment. This is so because the amount of heat produced when fat is metabolized is less than when carbohydrate or protein is metabolized. Therefore, fat is most beneficial when added to diets in the summertime or when used in the hotter regions of the country.

Several types of fat are available; however, feed-grade tallow, white or yellow grease, hydrolyzed animal-vegetable fat (a by-product of the soap industry), or mixtures of these fats are the types of fat most widely used in swine feeds. The maximum amount of fat that can be added to a diet is 6–7 percent; higher levels will cause the feed to bridge up in self-feeders. Small amounts of fat (1–2 percent) are commonly added to commercial hog feeds to improve the physical characteristics of the feed, to facilitate pelleting, to control dust in feed mills, and to reduce segregation of the fine particles in mixed feed. The inclusion of 3–5 percent fat in swine feeds has another major benefit in that it reduces feed dust in confinement hog buildings. Recent research has shown that this reduced dustiness and improved air quality in hog buildings results in fewer respiratory problems in confinement-reared pigs. The major disadvantage to using fat in farm-mixed feeds is that it requires heating prior to mixing.

There is some interest in feeding fat to sows during late gestation and early lactation, in that it results in improved survival of newborn pigs, especially if the pigs are small at birth (12).

Miscellaneous Energy Sources. Bakery wastes and certain roots and tubers (pota-

TABLE 21-11

Relative value of protein sources for swine

Ingredient	Protein, %	Lysine, %	Relative Value[a]	Maximum Inclusion Rate, %[b]
Plant sources				
Soybean meal, dehulled	48.5	3.10	100	20
Soybean meal	44.0	2.80	100	20
Peas, cull	23.8	1.52	100	80
Soybean, full fat, cooked	37.0	2.40	100	25
Beans, cull	26.7	1.68	99	50
Canola meal	38.0	2.27	94	10
Alfalfa meal	17.5	0.85	76	5
Safflower meal	29.0	1.30	71	8
Cottonseed meal, low gossypol	41.7	1.70	64	8
Sunflower meal	45.5	1.68	58	8
Linseed meal	33.0	1.20	57	5
Brewers dried grains	27.3	0.88	51	15
Copra meal	20.0	0.64	50	5
Peanut meal	49.0	1.45	47	10
Sesame meal	45.0	1.26	44	5
Corn gluten feed	23.3	0.64	43	10
Distillers dried grains + solubles	27.0	0.70	41	20
Corn gluten meal	61.2	1.03	26	5
Animal sources				
Blood meal, spray dried[c]	86.0	7.44	136	3
Fish meal, menhaden	61.2	4.74	122	5
Skim milk, dried	33.3	2.54	120	—[d]
Whey, dried	13.3	0.94	111	—[d]
Meat and bone meal[c]	50.9	2.89	89	5
Meat meal[c]	55.6	3.09	87	5
Feather meal	84.9	1.67	31	2
Synthetic sources				
Lysine HCl	—	78.0	—	0.20[e]

[a]Based on the lysine content, as a percent of the protein.
[b]Maximum inclusion in grower-finisher diets without depressing performance.
[c]Although high in lysine, these sources are quite low in tryptophan and isoleucine.
[d]Cost is the factor that limits the maximum amount.
[e]This level supplies 0.15% lysine.

toes, artichokes, cassava) are examples of other energy sources that can be used in swine feeds. Potatoes need to be cooked in order to destroy enzyme inhibitors and to maximize their feeding value.

Protein Sources

Feedstuffs that are high in protein (greater than 20 percent) are added to swine diets to correct the amino acid deficiencies of the cereal grains and other energy sources. The relative value of various protein supplements is related to the overall protein content as well as the proportions of the essential amino acids in the protein. One can roughly assess the relative value of protein supplements based on their lysine content (Table 21–11), because lysine generally is the first limiting amino acid in pig diets.

Plant Proteins. Soybean meal is the major protein source used in pig diets, accounting for over 85 percent of all protein supplements fed to pigs. Soybean meal is unsurpassed by any other plant protein in biological value, and therefore it is the standard to which other protein sources are compared (Table 21–11). It has an excellent balance of amino acids and is especially high in lysine, tryptophan, and threonine, the amino acids that are most deficient in cereal grains. Soybean meal is very palatable and is readily available throughout the major swine producing areas in the United States. It is available in two forms, as 44 percent protein meal and as dehulled meal, which ranges in protein from 48 to 50 percent. The dehulled meal is lower in fiber, 3.4 versus 7.3 percent, so it is more desirable for young pigs. Dehulled soybean meal contains about 3.10 percent lysine, and the 44 percent protein meal contains about 2.85 percent lysine. When soybean meal is blended with corn to met the recommended protein level for the various weight classes of swine, all of the amino acid requirements are met (Table 21–1).

Whole soybeans contain about 35–37 percent protein and 18–19 percent oil. Whole soybeans can be fed to pigs, but they must first be heated to a temperature above 250° F to destroy the trypsin inhibitor and other enzyme inhibitors (see Ch. 9). Young pigs do not digest or utilize raw soybeans very well because of these inhibitors; older animals appear to tolerate raw soybeans better than younger animals do. Recent research has shown that, during gestation, sows can be fed raw soybeans as the only source of supplemental protein with no detrimental effects (13).

Cooking or roasting of whole soybeans and toasting of soybean meal must be controlled carefully, because overheating will tie up some of the lysine and reduce the biological value of the meal. When properly roasted, ground, full-fat soybeans make an excellent protein supplement for pigs. In addition, feeding whole soybeans allows one to take advantage of the benefits of fat (discussed previously) supplied by the whole bean.

Cottonseed meal is considerably lower in lysine than is soybean meal (Table 21–11), and it is higher in fiber. Also, cottonseed meal contains gossypol, a compound that is toxic to pigs. Only low-gossypol cottonseed meal (less than 0.04 percent free gossypol) should be used in pig feeds. To protect against gossypol toxicity, Fe sulfate should also be added to provide the same level of Fe as the free-gossypol level. The Fe binds with gossypol and prevents its absorption.

Rapeseed meal is slightly lower in lysine and higher in fiber than soybean meal, but it serves as an excellent supplement when substituted for up to half of the soybean meal, provided the newer varieties, called Canola, are used. Canola includes those cultivars that have been specifically bred to be low in antinutritional factors (see Ch. 8).

Peanut meal is relatively high in protein, but it is much lower in lysine than is soybean meal. Its usage in the United States is mostly limited to the peanut-producing states in the Southeast. Peanut meal is quite susceptible to the fungus *Aspergillus flavus,* which is capable of producing aflatoxin.

Other plant proteins that have limited usage in pig feeds in the United States include sunflower meal, sesame meal, linseed meal, safflower meal, and copra (coconut) meal. Most of these have only average protein quality, in that the lysine is quite low compared with the lysine in soybean meal.

Cull peas and beans are often an economical feed ingredient in the Pacific Northwest, and they can serve as a source of both energy and protein. Certain types of beans (kidney, navy, pinto) and peas (cowpeas, pigeon peas) require heat treatment to destroy enzyme inhibitors, while others (field beans, horsebeans, field peas) do not require heating. When the majority of the protein is supplied by these products, methionine supplementation may be necessary.

Protein sources derived from grain, such as corn gluten meal, distillers dried grains, and brewers dried grains, can be used to supply a portion of the protein supplement, but the biological value of the protein is very poor. The amino acid pattern is similar to that of the grain from which they are produced.

Animal Proteins. Animal proteins are good sources of lysine and other amino acids. Also, the animal protein sources are much higher in Ca, P, and B-vitamins (particularly vitamin B_{12}) than the plant proteins. However, they are more variable in nutrient content and are subjected to high drying temperatures during processing for dehydration and sterilization. If drying time and temperature are not controlled carefully, the bioavailability of lysine, tryptophan, and other amino acids can be reduced markedly.

Packinghouse by-products such as meat meal and meat and bone meal are high in lysine but relatively low in tryptophan. In addition, the biological availability of tryptophan in these products is quite low. Also, these products tend to be somewhat unpalatable, so diets for growing pigs should not contain more than 4–5 percent meat by-products or performance may be reduced. Higher levels can be used in growing pig diets if supplemental tryptophan is provided. Sow feeds may contain higher levels, up to one-third of the protein supplement.

Dried blood meal is very high in protein (85–90 percent) and in lysine (7–8 percent). Much of the lysine was destroyed by the older drying methods, but the newer drying processes (ring-drying or flash-drying) result in a product with a high level of available lysine. Blood meal tends to be low in the amino acid isoleucine, and this protein source is not very palatable, so it should not be added at levels exceeding 3 percent of the diet.

Fish meal is an excellent protein supplement for pigs, however the high cost of fish meal in the United States limits its use. Fish meals are quite variable, depending on the type of fish used and the type of processing employed. Some marine meals are made from residues, such as shrimp meal, and these are less nutritious. Certain long-chained fatty acids in fish oil can cause a fishy flavor in pork, so the amount of fish meal in pig feed should not exceed 6–7 percent. Inclusion of fish meal or fish solubles in starter diets has recently been shown to improve performance of early-weaned pigs.

Dried milk products are excellent protein supplements. They are very palatable, highly digestible, and have an excellent balance of amino acids; however, they are very expensive ingredients (especially dried skim milk). Dried whey is commonly used in prestarter (15–30 percent) and starter diets (5–15 percent) for young pigs, but it is too expensive to be used in feeds for older pigs.

Liquid skim milk, buttermilk, or whey are sometimes available at low cost around processing plants. Though these products are excellent sources of protein and other nutrients, they are so high in water that pigs are not able to consume enough to meet their dry-matter requirements. However, if transportation costs are not too great and if proper feeding equipment is available, these products do make excellent protein supplements.

Other Protein Sources. Bacteria grown on petroleum and other wastes have been shown to be a good protein supplement for pigs. However, the cost of producing single-cell protein currently is too expensive to justify its use as a feedstuff.

Synthetic Amino Acids. Pigs can utilize synthetic amino acids to meet a portion of their dietary requirements. Currently, lysine and methionine are the only amino acids that are economically feasible to use in feeds. However, because methionine is the fourth or fifth limiting amino acid in most pig diets, there is no need for supplemental methionine in practical swine diets. New biotechnology procedures have been developed for the production of tryp-

tophan and threonine, so their use may be economically feasible in the not-too-distant future.

Lysine is commercially available as lysine hydrochloride. When lysine HCl (which contains 78 percent lysine) is used as a supplement, the protein level of a grain-soybean diet can be reduced by up to 2 percentage units and 0.15 percent lysine can be added. Put another way, 96 lb of corn and 4 lb of lysine HCl can replace 100 lb of dehulled soybean meal in a ton of swine feed. With this amount of protein reduction and lysine supplementation, there is no reduction in pig performance. Greater reductions in protein, however, will reduce pig performance, even if additional amounts of lysine are added. This is due to the fact that other amino acids become limiting. NPN sources, such as urea, are of no practical nutritional value to pigs.

Mineral Sources

Most swine diets need to be supplemented with minerals, especially if the diet consists mainly of plant proteins. Mono- and dicalcium phosphate, defluorinated rock phosphate, and steamed bone meal are good sources of highly available Ca and P. High-F rock phosphate, soft rock phosphate, and fertilizer-grade phosphates should be avoided, because the P is less available and the high F level can be toxic. Ground limestone (Ca carbonate) is commonly used as an additional source of Ca. Oyster shell flour, aragonite, marble dust, and gypsum are also good sources of Ca, but dolomitic limestone, which is high in Mg, should be avoided because the Ca is poorly available.

Common salt is the most practical way of meeting the dietary requirements for Na and Cl. If iodized salt is used, the I needs of pigs will also be met.

Generally, a trace mineral mix is added as a premix to swine diets to supply the necessary trace minerals. An example of a trace mineral mix is shown in Table 21–12. This mix can be added at variable levels (2 lb/ton in starter and sow feeds, 1.5 lb/ton in grower feeds, 1 lb/ton in finisher feeds) to meet the trace mineral requirements. Another means of providing trace minerals is in the form of trace-mineralized salt.

Pigs that are self-fed shelled corn and a protein supplement can also be self-fed a mineral mixture consisting of 50 percent dicalcium phosphate or defluorinated phosphate, 30 percent ground limestone, and 20 percent trace-mineralized salt. However, if appropriate levels

TABLE 21-12

Trace mineral premix[a]

Mineral Element[b]	Concentration in Premix, %	1 Lb of Premix Supplies to Diet, ppm
Copper	1.0	5.0
Iodine[b]	0.10	0.50
Iron	15.0	75.0
Manganese	2.0	10.0
Selenium[c]	0.03	0.15
Zinc	15.0	75.0

[a]Use 2 lb/ton in prestarter, starter, gestation, and lactation diets, 1.5 lb/ton in grower diets, and 1 lb/ton in finisher diets. These amounts should be mixed in 10–20 lb of corn prior to blending in a ton of feed.

[b]Iodine not needed if iodized salt is fed.

[c]Selenium not needed in high-selenium areas.

of minerals are provided in the diet, the free-choice feeding of additional minerals is not necessary.

Vitamin Sources

Alfalfa meal, fermentation by-products, and animal protein sources are good sources of many of the vitamins. However, synthetic vitamins are relatively inexpensive and are generally added to swine diets in the form of a premix. An example of a vitamin premix is shown in Table 21–13. This supplement can be added at various levels (1–2 lb/ton) to meet the requirements during the different stages of growth and reproduction.

Choline is commonly added to sow feed as a 50 percent choline chloride supplement (43 percent choline). Choline should not be combined with the other vitamins in a concentrated premix, as it tends to promote the destruction of other vitamins, especially vitamin A. If biotin and/or folic acid are added to sow feeds, they may be added as a separate premix. Table 21–14 shows the composition of choline, biotin, and folic acid premixes that are recommended for sow diets.

Feed Additives

Feed additives used in swine diets include antibiotics, chemotherapeutics, and anthelmintics

TABLE 21-13

Composition of vitamin premix[a]

Vitamin	Amount in 1 Lb of Premix	1 Lb of Premix/Ton Supplies These Levels/Lb of Diet
Vitamin A	3,000,000 IU	1500 IU
Vitamin D₂ or D₃	200,000 IU	100 IU
Vitamin E	10,000 IU	5 IU
Vitamin K	2 g	1 mg
Riboflavin	4 g	2 mg
Pantothenic acid	12 g	6 mg
Niacin	16 g	8 mg
Vitamin B₁₂	12 mg	6 mcg
Carrier (to 1 pound total)	+	

[a]Use 2 lb/ton in prestarter, starter, gestation, and lactation diets, 1.5 lb/ton in grower diets, and 1 lb/ton in finisher diets. These amounts should be mixed in 10–20 lb of corn prior to blending them in a ton of feed.

TABLE 21-14

Composition of choline premix and biotin-folic acid premix for sows[a]

Premix	Amount in 1 Lb of Premix	1 lb of Premix/Ton Supplies These Levels/Lb of Diet
Choline chloride mix	195 g choline	98 mg choline
Biotin-folic acid mix	200 mg biotin 1 g folic acid	100 mcg biotin 500 mcg folic acid

[a]Add 2 lb of choline mix and 1 lb of biotin-folic acid mix per ton of sow gestation and lactation feed. These amounts should be mixed in 10–20 lb of corn prior to blending them in a ton of feed.

(dewormers). Antibacterial agents are added to pig feeds to stimulate growth and efficiency of feed utilization and reduce mortality and morbidity. Anthelmintics are used at certain times to remove ascarids (roundworms) or other internal parasites. These compounds are considered as drugs, and their use is regulated by the FDA (see Ch. 5, 10).

Only certain types, levels, and combinations of antibacterials are approved for swine (14). Some require withdrawal from the feed prior to slaughter in order to prevent carcass residues (see Ch. 10). It is important that swine producers who mix their own feed be familiar with proper usage of antimicrobial agents and that they mix feeds properly to prevent carry-over of drugs from one feed to the next. This is especially important when feeds containing sulfamethazine are mixed. The sulfa drugs are electrostatic and tend to accumulate in feed dust. Failure to clean mixers and feed conveying equipment can result in cross-contamination of feed with drugs, and very small amounts of certain drugs (such as sulfamethazine) will cause violative residues in pork carcasses (15).

The greatest benefit from antibiotics is in the very young pig. Young pigs are more susceptible to stress and disease organisms than are older pigs. The passive immunity that the baby pig acquires from the sow's colostrum nearly disappears by the time it reaches 3 weeks of age (Fig. 21–4). Since the baby pig does not synthesize antibodies very well, its immunity remains low until 6–8 weeks of age. As pigs become older, they produce specific immunoglobulins which give them protection against disease-causing organisms in their environment. Table 21–15 shows the relative response to an-

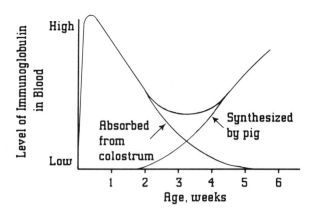

FIGURE 21–4. Development of disease resistance in young pigs.

tibiotics in pigs during the starter phase, the grower phase, and for the entire growing-finishing stage.

The overall health of the pigs and the cleanliness of the environment also influence the pig's response to antibiotics. In general, the higher the disease level, the less sanitary the environment, and the poorer the management, the greater is the response from antibiotic usage. However, antibiotics should never be considered as a substitute for good management.

Antibiotics have been shown to be beneficial for sows and gilts at breeding time in that they tend to improve conception rate and litter size (Table 21–16). A high level (0.5–1 g/d) of an absorbable antibiotic (such as one of the tetracyclines) is recommended for this purpose.

Antibiotics are of little value during gestation, but they are generally considered to be beneficial just before and after farrowing, because this is a high-stress period. Antibiotics have been shown to reduce the incidence of

TABLE 21-15

Effects of age and weight of pigs on response to antibiotic feeding[a]

Growth Stage	Control	Antibiotic	Improvement, %
Starter phase (16–55 lb)			
Daily gain, lb	0.86	0.99	16.4
Feed/gain	2.28	2.13	6.9
Grower phase (37–108 lb)			
Daily gain, lb	1.30	1.45	10.6
Feed/gain	2.91	2.78	4.5
Grower-finisher phase (53–197 lb)			
Daily gain, lb	1.52	1.59	4.2
Feed/gain	3.30	3.27	2.2

[a]Data from 1194 experiments, involving 32,555 pigs.
Source: Hays (18) and Zimmerman (19).

TABLE 21-16

Effects of antibiotics in the feed at breeding on reproductive performance[a]

Item	Control	Antibiotics[b]
Farrowing rate, %[c]	75.4	82.1
Live pigs/litter	10.0	10.4

[a]Data from 9 experiments involving 1931 sows.
[b]In most cases 0.5–1.0 g of antibiotics/sow/d.
[c]No. of sows farrowed/no. bred.

agalactia (lack of milk) and uterine infections that occur occasionally in sows shortly after farrowing. The data in Table 21–17 suggest that pig survival and pig weaning weights are im-

proved slightly when antibiotics are included in the lactation diet.

Cu sulfate acts as a growth stimulant when fed at high levels in the diet (16). A level of 125–250 ppm of Cu (or 1–2 lb of Cu sulfate/ton) results in improved growth rate and feed efficiency in pigs, similar to that resulting from the feeding of antibiotics (Table 21–18). Recent studies show that a combination of Cu and antibiotics in starter feeds stimulates growth of young pigs to a greater degree than when either Cu or antibiotics are added singly (Table 21–19). Cu can be toxic at high levels (greater than 250 ppm), so if Cu sulfate is used as a supplement, it must never exceed 2 lb/ton.

TABLE 21-17

Antimicrobial agents in the prefarrowing and lactation diet for sows[a]

Item	Control	Antimicrobial[b]
Live pigs born/litter	10.3	10.6
Pigs weaned/litter	8.2	8.6
Survival, %	84.9	87.1
Avg. pig weaning weight, lb	10.23	10.34

[a]Summary of 11 experiments with 2105 litters.
[b]Tetracyclines, ASP-250, tylosin, bacitracin, or Cu sulfate fed from 3–5 d prepartum through 7–21 d of lactation.

TABLE 21-18

Effect of copper sulfate on performance of weanling and growing-finishing pigs

Growth stage	Copper, ppm[a]		Improvement, %
	0	250	
Starting period (15–31 lb)			
Daily gain, lb	0.51	0.62	24.0
Feed/gain	2.04	1.86	9.7
Growing period (40–123 lb)			
Daily gain, lb	1.47	1.57	6.9
Feed/gain	2.80	2.70	3.6
Growing-finishing period (40–205 lb)			
Daily gain, lb	1.57	1.62	3.1
Feed/gain	3.18	3.10	2.5

[a]Does not include the copper supplied by the trace mineral mix.
Source: Cromwell et al. (16). Summary of 12 starter experiments involving 462 pigs and 18 growing-finishing experiments involving 672 pigs.

TABLE 21-19

Effect of copper and antibiotics on performance of weanling pigs from 15 to 40 lb[a]

Antibiotics:	−	+	−	+
Copper sulfate (250 ppm Cu):	−	−	+	+
Daily gain, lb	0.57	0.66	0.68	0.75
Daily feed, lb	1.19	1.28	1.30	1.40
Feed/gain	2.10	1.95	1.91	1.84

[a]Summary of 14 experiments involving 1700 pigs conducted at 6 experiment stations.

TABLE 21-20

Efficiency of acidifying agents in pig starter diets

Item	Basal	+ Acid	Improvement, %
Studies with citric acid[a]			
Avg daily gain, lb	0.65	0.69	5.2
Feed/gain	1.88	1.75	7.2
Studies with fumaric acid[b]			
Avg daily gain, lb	0.68	0.71	4.1
Feed/gain	1.86	1.73	6.9

[a]Summary of 5 trials, 311 pigs, 19-35 lb, 24 d on test.
[b]Summary of 5 trials, 386 pigs, 20-38 lb, 27 d on test.

Three excellent reviews on antibiotics in animal feeds have been prepared by CAST (17), Hays (18), and Zimmerman (19).

Probiotics (*Lactobacillus acidophilus, Streptococcus faecium*) and yeast cultures (*Saccharomyces cerevisiae*) are products that may be added to feeds in an effort to promote the colonization in the gut of desirable microorganisms and reduce the numbers of potentially undesirable ones (such as pathogenic *E. coli*). There is some evidence from field studies that these types of additives may benefit young pigs under stress conditions; however, the majority of experiments conducted under controlled research conditions have failed to show any consistent benefit in pig performance from the feeding of probiotics or yeast culture.

Mixtures of enzymes are available as additives, but most research shows that they are not generally effective. In certain instances, β-glucanase has been shown to improve the utilization of barley when the barley is high in β-glucans and low in naturally occurring β-glucanase.

Two organic acids, citric acid and fumaric acid, have recently been shown to benefit early-weaned pigs when included in starter diets at levels of 1–3 percent (Table 21–20). The mode of action of these acids is not known, but it is thought that they may lower the pH of the stomach of the weanling pig, thereby serving to increase the activity of the digestive enzyme, pepsin. The lower pH also may help to reduce the proliferation of undesirable bacteria in the stomach and small intestine. Generally, the response to acidifying agents is greater when they are added to simplified diets than when added to complex, high-milk diets.

PROCESSING FEEDS

Grinding

Feed grains must be ground before complete-mixed diets can be prepared. Corn, sorghum, and wheat should be ground medium to fine through a hammer mill, using a ³⁄₁₆, ¼, or ⅜ in. screen. For other grains (barley, oats) a coarser screen (½ in.) can be used. Research has shown that finely ground corn is utilized more efficiently than is coarsely ground corn (see Ch. 11). However, exceptionally fine grinding requires more grinding time, causes feed to be overly dusty, and may cause feed to bridge in feeders. If grain is ground too coarse, pigs tend to sort out the larger particles and wastage becomes a problem. If grains are processed in a roller mill, the rollers need to be set relatively close.

Pelleting

Pigs that are fed pelleted diets tend to gain slightly faster and utilize their feeder more efficiently than pigs fed diets in meal form (Table 21–21). Pelleting especially improves feed utilization in diets containing barley, oats, or other fibrous feeds. Pelleting also reduces dustiness and helps to prevent segregation and wastage of feed. It is very important that pellets be hard and not crumbly. A soft pellet breaks up when handled mechanically, and variable particle size makes it difficult, if not impossible, to adjust feeders properly to prevent feed wastage.

Cooking and Roasting

Grains are not improved sufficiently by cooking or roasting to offset the cost. Micronizing is a

TABLE 21-21

Effect of steam pelleting of corn diets on performance of growing-finishing pigs[a]

Item	Meal	Pellet	Improvement, %
Avg daily gain, lb	1.65	1.71	3.6
Feed/gain	3.29	3.16	4.0

[a]Summary of 25 experiments involving 796 pigs (9 stations).

processing method that may improve the utilization of grain sorghum, but it also is a rather expensive process. Soybeans and certain types of peas and beans are improved greatly by roasting or other forms of heating. Potatoes must be cooked before feeding them to pigs. Where garbage feeding is permitted, laws require that it be cooked to control transmission of trichinosis and other diseases.

Liquid Feeding

Several mechanical feeders are being marketed that allow feed and water to be mixed in a gruel. Liquid feeding may help to prevent feed wastage, but there is no research evidence to indicate that performance of pigs is consistently improved by liquid feeding. Therefore liquid feeding should be evaluated solely on its merits as a means of dispensing feed to pigs. Wet feeding is sometimes used to increase feed intake in lactating sows when the environmental temperature is high.

High-Moisture Grains

High-moisture shelled corn and other grains are essentially equal to dry grain on a dry-matter basis. High-moisture grain can be fed free choice with a complete supplement, or the grain can be rolled and mixed with the supplement. However, it must be prepared daily, or it will heat, spoil, and cake up in feeders. Propionic acid-treated, high-moisture grain can be kept for longer periods of time without spoilage. Less supplemental P is needed when high-moisture grain is fed, because the P is 3–4 times more available in high-moisture grain than in dry grain.

FEEDING MANAGEMENT

Prebreeding

Gilts kept for breeding purposes should be selected at market weight, then removed from the self-feeder and hand-fed 6–7 lb of feed/d. They should be kept in a good gaining condition but not allowed to become overfat.

Gilts are normally bred at 7–8 months of age. Earlier breeding is possible, but it will result in smaller litter size. If gilts are thin at time of breeding, they may be "flushed" by full-feeding them for 1–2 weeks prior to breeding. Flushing will increase the number of eggs ovulated and may result in larger litters. If gilts are flushed, they should be returned to a moderate

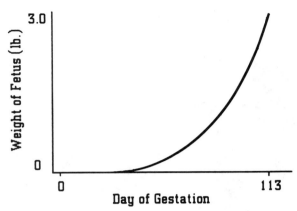

FIGURE 21–5. Fetal development during the gestation period.

feeding level (4–6 lb/d) immediately after breeding. An absorbable antibiotic should be included in the breeding diet at a high level (200–300 g of chlortetracycline/ton) to maximize conception rate and reduce embryonic mortality (Table 21–16).

Gestation

The nutrient requirements of the pregnant sow are really quite low, particularly during the first two-thirds of gestation. The majority of the fetal development occurs during the last month of gestation (Fig. 21–5). Sows should be fed at a level to accommodate the growth of the fetuses and the placenta, approximately 40 lb (Table 21–22), along with an increase of 30–40 lb of their own body weight. Gilts should be fed to gain more of their own body weight (50–60 lb) because they have not yet reached their mature size. Thus the targeted pregnancy weight gain should be 75 lb for sows and 100 lb for gilts.

TABLE 21-22

Components of gestation weight gain

Component	Lb
Pigs and placenta	
Pigs, 11 at 2.9 lb	32
Placental membranes	5
Placental fluids	3
	40
Sow	
Uterus	7
Udder and blood	8
Body muscle and fat	25–45
	40–60
Total gestation weight gain	80–100

Source: Adapted from NRC (1) and Whittemore and Elsley (20).

FIGURE 21-6. Sows in confinement gestation stalls.

FIGURE 21-7. Individual sow feeding stalls.

Both overfeeding and underfeeding should be avoided. Overfeeding is costly and wasteful, and overfat sows may have smaller litters and more farrowing difficulty. They are more likely to crush their pigs by overlay. If sows are underfed, pigs will be smaller and weaker at birth, and the sow may not have sufficient body stores to produce sufficient milk for a large litter. In addition, she may be too thin at weaning and be less likely to recycle.

Approximately 5800–6500 kcal of ME/d, or about 4–4.5 lb/d, of a corn-soybean meal diet (containing 1450 kcal ME/lb) in a moderate climate will generally result in the right amount of gain in gilts and sows. If lower-energy feeds such as oats or barley are fed, more feed is necessary. The feeding level should be increased to 5–6 lb/d for sows that are housed outside in a cold environment. Conversely, less feed (3–3.5 lb/d) may be necessary to produce adequate weight gains during gestation for animals in warmer climates, or for sows housed in individual crates in confinement gestation houses (Fig. 21–6).

If sows are not penned individually, the use of feeding stalls is recommended in order to prevent boss sows from taking more than their share of feed (Fig. 21–7). Sows should be penned separately from gilts when animals are group-penned. Once-daily feeding is recommended.

A protein level of 14 percent and Ca and P levels of 0.80 and 0.65 percent, respectively, are recommended, when a 4 lb/d feeding level is used. If sows are fed 3 lb/d, the nutrient percentages should be adjusted upwards so that sows will receive a minimum of 250 g of protein, 14.5 g of Ca, and 11.5 g of P/d (Table 21–23). Sows may either be fed a complete-mixed diet or they can be fed 3–4 lb of grain and 1 lb of a complete protein supplement daily.

Examples of diets are shown in Table 21–24. A grain-soybean meal diet fortified with minerals and vitamins is adequate for sows, however some animal protein, alfalfa meal, or by-product feedstuffs may also be included in the diet.

Sows are able to utilize roughages better than are younger pigs. Corn silage, haylage, alfalfa hay, and good-quality grass-legume pasture can be used to provide a portion of the nutrients of the sow (Fig. 21–8). Generally, 8–12 sows/acre is the recommended stocking rate. The feeding of 12–15 lb of corn silage plus 1 lb of complete supplement/day or self-feeding high-quality alfalfa hay to sows during gestation has resulted in good reproductive performance.

Attempts to devise a system for self-feeding of sows have met with limited success. Allowing sows access to a self-feeder for 2–4 h every third day will result in weight gains and reproductive performance similar to hand-fed sows, but a system like this needs to be managed very carefully. Self-feeding a bulky diet does not seem to work, unless extremely high levels of a low-energy ingredient (ground hay, saw-dust, or the like) are included in the feed.

TABLE 21-23

Percentages of protein, calcium, and phosphorus at three feeding levels for sows during gestation

Daily Feeding Level, lb	Dietary Levels Needed, %[a]		
	Protein	Ca	P
3	17	1.10	0.85
4	14	0.80	0.65
5	12	0.65	0.55

[a]These levels will provide a minimum daily amount of 250 g (0.55 lb) of protein, 14.5 g of Ca, and 11.5 g of P.

TABLE 21-24

Gestation diets for pregnant sows and gilts[a]

Ingredient	1	2	3	4	5
Corn or milo, ground	1616	—	1146	1583	1497
Wheat or barley, ground	—	1692	—	—	—
Oats, ground	—	—	500	—	—
Soybean meal (44%)[b]	314	242	285	176	194
Meat and bone meal	—	—	—	110	—
Alfalfa meal	—	—	—	100	—
Wheat middlings	—	—	—	—	200
Fish meal	—	—	—	—	50
Dicalcium phosphate	37	29	36	14	26
Limestone, ground	16	20	16	—	16
Salt	10	10	10	10	10
Vitamin mix[c]	2	2	2	2	2
Choline mix[c]	2	2	2	2	2
Biotin-folic acid mix[c]	1	1	1	1	1
Trace mineral mix[c]	2	2	2	2	2
Total	2000	2000	2000	2000	2000

[a]Provide 14–15% protein, 0.65% lysine, 0.80% Ca, and 0.65% P. Feed at a level of 4 lb/d.
[b]If dehulled soybean meal is used, reduce level by 10% and replace difference with grain.
[c]See Tables 21–12, 21–13, and 21–14.

There has been recent interest in the use of high levels of supplemental fat in the sows' feed during late gestation. Research has shown that birth weights of pigs are improved slightly and pig survival is increased when sows are fed fat. Some of the benefit is attributed to a higher fat level in the colostrum and milk and a slight increase in milk production as a result of feeding fat to sows (12). A new compound, 1–3 butane-diol, has recently been cleared by the FDA for use in sow feed during late gestation. This compound, like fat, improves survival in young pigs (21).

Farrowing

The farrowing diet should be laxative in nature to prevent constipation, a problem often en-

countered when sows are moved into the farrowing crate. Wheat bran or dried beet pulp can be added to the diet at levels of 10–15 percent to provide a laxative effect. As an alternative, Mg sulfate (Epsom salts) or KCl, added at levels of 0.75–1.0 percent (15–20 lb/ton) will also serve to soften the feces. An advantage to these chemical laxatives is that they do not reduce the energy content of the diet. Examples of farrowing diets are given in Table 21–25.

A high level of an absorbable antibiotic is recommended in the prefarrowing and post-farrowing diet. Antibiotics tend to reduce the incidence of MMA (mastitis, metritis, agalactia) that sometimes occurs shortly after a sow farrows. In addition, small amounts of the antibiotic may be passed on to the pigs through the milk.

Lactation

The nutrient requirements of the sow during lactation are three to four times higher than the requirements during gestation because of the high demands for milk production. A sow with 10 pigs produces 15–20 lb of milk/d by the third week of lactation (Fig. 21–9), and the milk is much higher in fat, protein, and total dry matter than is cow milk (Table 21–26).

Although the daily requirements for all nutrients are higher during lactation than during gestation, they are about the same as during gestation when the requirement is expressed

FIGURE 21-8. Pasture provides additional nutrients for sows.

TABLE 21-25

Farrowing and lactation diets for sows and gilts[a]

Ingredient	1	2	3	4	5
Corn or milo, ground	1530	—	1493	1385	1598
Wheat or barley, ground	—	1298	—	—	—
Oats, ground	—	400	—	—	—
Soybean meal (44%)[b]	302	236	174	287	316
Meat and bone meal	—	—	100	—	—
Wheat bran	100	—	100	—	—
Alfalfa meal	—	—	100	—	—
Wheat middlings	—	—	—	200	—
Fat	—	—	—	60	—
Potassium chloride or magnesium sulfate	—	—	—	—	15
Dicalcium phosphate	33	30	12	32	38
Limestone, ground	18	19	4	19	16
Salt	10	10	10	10	10
Vitamin mix[c]	2	2	2	2	2
Choline mix[c]	2	2	2	2	2
Biotin-folic acid mix[c]	1	1	1	1	1
Trace mineral mix[c]	2	2	2	2	2
Antibiotics[d]	+	+	+	+	+
Total	2000	2000	2000	2000	2000

[a]Provides 14–15% protein, 0.65% lysine, 0.80% Ca, and 0.65% P. Feed 4–5 lb/d prior to farrowing and full-feed after farrowing.

[b]If dehulled soybean meal is used, reduce level by 10% and replace difference with grain.

[c]See Tables 21–12, 21–13, and 21–14.

[d]Broad spectrum, absorbable antibiotics are recommended. Add to supply 50–150 g/ton.

as a percentage of the diet. The requirements of the lactating sow can generally be met by full-feeding the gestation diet during lactation. Sows will consume 12–15 lb of feed daily during lactation and still lose weight if they are good milkers and are nursing a large litter of pigs.

Failure to give high-producing sows all they will consume can result in excess losses of body weight and condition, especially if they are thin at farrowing. Conversion of body fat to milk

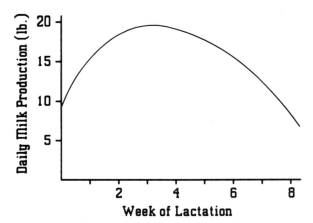

FIGURE 21-9. Milk production of a sow during lactation.

TABLE 21-26

Composition of sow's milk and cow's milk

Item	Sow Milk %	Cow Milk %
Fat	6–8	4
Protein	6	3
Lactose	5	5
Ash	1	0.7
Total solids	18–20	12.7

energy is very efficient in sows, but drawing from body protein reserves to meet milk protein needs is not an efficient process. Also, if feed is restricted during lactation, bone mineral reserves can be depleted, especially if the diet is marginal in Ca and P. Bone fractures or paralysis can occur in mineral-depleted sows toward the end of lactation or during the rebreeding period, particularly if animals are penned together and fighting occurs. Sows should not be allowed to get excessively thin during the lactation period; otherwise, they may have extended delay to estrus following weaning.

Some producers gradually increase the sow's feed after farrowing until they are on full

FIGURE 21-10. Baby pigs receive all of their nutrients from sow milk.

cent, respectively. Examples of lactation diets are given in Table 21–25.

Baby Pigs

The baby pig receives most of its nutrients from the sow's milk during its first 2–3 weeks of life (Fig. 21–10). The first milk secreted by the sow (colostrum) is exceptionally rich in immunoglobulins (antibodies). The newborn pig is capable of absorbing these antibodies intact for the first 12–24 h of life (Fig. 21–4), which gives it passive immunity. Newborn pigs depend entirely on colostrum for their immunity, and those that do not receive colostrum stand little chance of survival. During the first 24–48 h postpartum, the colostrum gradually changes to a composition that is typical of milk (Table 21–26).

The requirements for protein, minerals, and other nutrients are quite high at birth, but these requirements are adequately met by milk alone, because milk is quite high in protein, energy, Ca, P, and other nutrients, on a dry-matter basis (Table 21–27).

Fe is the only nutrient required by baby pigs that is deficient in milk. The pig is born with about 50 mg of Fe in its body. A pig requires 6–8 mg of Fe/d for hemoglobin synthesis, and milk supplies only about 1 mg/d, so if not given supplemental Fe, the pig will become anemic within 3–4 d. The simplest method of supplying supplemental Fe is to give an intramuscular injection of 100–200 mg of Fe (as Fe-dextran, Fe-dextrin, or gleptoferrin) before the pig is 3 d of age. The injection can be given in the ham or in the neck muscles (Fig. 21–3). This will generally meet the pig's need until it begins eating dry feed. Sprinkling an Fe-rich medium on the floor of the pen, or swabbing the sows udder with an Fe-rich solution is effective, but it must be done on a daily basis. Feeding a high level of Fe to the sow also is effective—not

feed within 5–7 d. Others begin full-feeding immediately after farrowing. Either practice is acceptable. Feed intake of lactating sows often will be reduced if the farrowing house is hot. Supplemental fat, either incorporated in the diet at 5–8 percent or top-dressed on the feed, will help to offset the reduced energy intake. Drip cooling (a system that drips water on the sow's neck and shoulders) also is beneficial in this regard.

A protein level of 14 percent is recommended for the lactating sow. Ca and P are critical and should be kept at 0.80 and 0.65 per-

TABLE 21-27

Comparison of sow colostrum and sow milk on a wet and dry basis

Item	Colostrum		Milk	
	Wet Basis	Dry Basis	Wet Basis	Dry Basis
Total solids, %	25	100	20	100
Protein, %	15	60	5.5	28
Fat, %	5	20	7.5	38
Lactose, %	4	16	5	25
Calcium, %	0.05	0.20	0.22	1.1
Phosphorus, %	0.10	0.40	0.16	0.8

because it increases the Fe content of her milk, but because the pen becomes contaminated with Fe-rich feces from the sow. Some of the Fe-rich feces is tracked onto the sow's udder and ingested by the pigs while nursing.

If a sow does not milk properly, the pigs should be transferred to another sow. The transfer should be made within 24 h after the foster dam has farrowed. Transferring a few pigs from an excessively large litter to a sow with a small litter is a recommended procedure in that it will result in more uniform weaning weights of the pigs. Pigs can be bottle-fed or pan-fed cow's milk, but these procedures are very laborious and are successful only if excellent sanitation is used and only if pigs first receive colostrum. Sow's milk contains an appreciably higher nutrient concentration than does cow's milk, so if cow's milk is used, condensed milk or dry milk replacer should be added to increase the dry-matter content to 20 percent (Table 21–26). Commercial equipment recently has become available for mechanically feeding artificial milk diets to baby pigs.

Pigs will begin to eat dry feed at about 3 weeks of age. A palatable starter diet containing 18–20 percent protein (1.2 percent lysine) should be placed in a creep feeder at about 3–4 weeks of age. Table 21–28 gives examples of starter diets for pigs. The diet should contain some dried milk products (such as dried whey) because the young pig utilizes the carbohydrates (lactose) and proteins in milk products very efficiently. Also, milk products are very palatable. Most commercial starter diets contain a small amount (3–5 percent) of sucrose as an attractant. Baby pigs have a "sweet tooth," and when given a choice, they will select a diet with sugar over one without sugar. However, when not given a choice, pigs will generally perform just as well on diets without sugar or other flavoring agents.

The starter should contain a high level of antibiotics. Copper sulfate (250 ppm Cu) also is recommended in the starter diet. It is very important that the starter feed be kept fresh. Young pigs will not eat stale feed very well.

Most pigs are weaned between 3 and 6 weeks of age. Earlier weaning is possible, but a more complex prestarter diet with high dried milk products (Table 21–28) and an exceptionally warm and clean environment are required.

Starting Pigs

The starter phase is the period between weaning (10–20 lb) and about 40–50 lb. Pigs need a

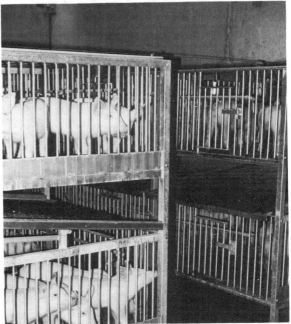

FIGURE 21–11. Early-weaned pigs in raised, decked pens *(top)* and in tiered decks *(bottom)*.

warm and exceptionally dry and draft-free environment during this stage. Rearing pigs on raised decks with totally slotted floors (Fig. 21–11) is recommended for this stage of production because their dunging habits are not yet established. A highly medicated diet containing 18–19 percent protein (1.0 percent lysine) should be full-fed in a nursery-type feeder (Fig. 21–12). Again, dried whey at 10–20 percent of the diet is beneficial, particularly during the first 2–3 weeks following early weaning. Examples of starter diets are shown in Table 21–28.

TABLE 21-28

Prestarter and starter diets for young pigs

Ingredient	Prestarter[a]					Starter[b]					
	1	2	3	4	5	1	2	3	4	5	6
Corn or milo, ground	1265	830	670	761	1023	1413	723	1195	1143	1055	1316
Wheat or barley, ground	—	—	—	—	—	—	720	—	—	—	—
Oat groats, rolled	—	—	—	200	—	—	—	—	—	200	—
Soybean meal (49%)	672	525	435	404	470	531	503	458	410	312	378
Fish meal	—	—	—	100	—	—	—	—	—	100	—
Dried whey	—	600	400	400	400	—	—	300	200	200	200
Dried skim milk	—	—	200	—	—	—	—	—	100	—	—
Sucrose	—	—	200	50	—	—	—	—	50	50	—
Fat	—	—	50	50	50	—	—	—	50	50	50
Lysine HCl (78% lysine)	—	—	—	—	4	—	—	—	—	—	4
Dicalcium phosphate	35	21	24	15	29	27	23	20	21	11	26
Limestone, ground	15	11	8	7	11	16	18	14	13	9	13
Salt	7	7	7	7	7	7	7	7	7	7	7
Vitamin mix[c]	2	2	2	2	2	2	2	2	2	2	2
Trace mineral mix[c]	2	2	2	2	2	2	2	2	2	2	2
Copper sulfate	2	2	2	2	2	2	2	2	2	2	2
Antibiotics[d]	+	+	+	+	+	+	+	+	+	+	+
Total	2000	2000	2000	2000	2000	2000	2000	2000	2000	2000	2000

[a] For pigs from 3 to 6 weeks of age (10–20 lb). Diets contain 19–20% protein, 1.2% lysine, 0.8% Ca, and 0.7% P.

[b] For pigs from 6 to 10 weeks of age (20–50 lb). Diets contain 18–19% protein (16% for starter diet 6), 1.00% lysine, 0.7% Ca, and 0.6% P.

[c] See Tables 21–12, 21–13, and 21–14.

[d] Antibiotics added to provide 100–250 g/ton.

FIGURE 21-12. A nursery-type self feeder.

Growing-Finishing Pigs

From 50 lb to market weight, pigs are generally full-fed complete mixed diets in self-feeders (Fig. 21–13). There should be a feeder space for every 4 to 5 pigs. Grain-soybean meal diets, adequately fortified with minerals and vitamins, are commonly fed to growing-finishing pigs. The recommended protein level for corn- or sorghum-soybean meal diets is 16 percent during the growing phase (to 100–125 lb) and 13–14 percent for the finishing phase (thereafter to 230 lb). Recommended lysine levels for these two stages are 0.80 and 0.65 percent, respectively. Other

grains or protein supplements can be used when economically feasible. Examples of grower and finisher diets are shown in Tables 21–29 and 21–30, respectively.

Feed for growing-finishing pigs can be purchased as mixed feed from a feed manufacturer, or diets can be prepared on the farm. Stationary screw mixers, volumetric proportional mixers, and tractor-driven, portable grinder-mixers are popular means of on-farm mixing.

A common practice among larger swine producers who mix their own feed is to purchase soybean meal in bulk and mix it on the farm with ground corn and a "base mix." A base mix is a mineral-vitamin pack that is added to the grain-soybean meal mixture to make the diet complete. Examples of base mixes are shown in Table 21–31.

Another system commonly used by smaller producers is to purchase a commercial supplement which is then mixed with grain on the farm. These types of supplements contain various protein, mineral, and vitamin sources and are formulated to supply all of the pig's nutritive requirements when blended with grain in the proper proportion. Examples of a complete supplement are shown in Table 21–32. One part of a complete supplement containing 40 percent

TABLE 21-29

Diets for growing pigs (50–125 lb)[a]

Ingredient	1	2	3	4	5	6	7	8	9
Corn or milo, ground	1561	1525	—	—	1243	1489	1631	1388	1638
Corn, high lysine, ground	—	—	1603	—	—	—	—	—	—
Wheat or barley, ground	—	—	—	1597	—	—	—	—	—
Oats, ground	—	—	—	—	300	—	—	—	—
Soybean meal (49%)	390	—	—	—	—	—	—	—	—
Soybean meal (44%)	—	427	348	360	410	330	247	415	308
Meat and bone meal	—	—	—	—	—	80	—	—	—
Wheat middlings	—	—	—	—	—	80	—	—	—
Fish meal	—	—	—	—	—	—	40	—	—
Blood meal	—	—	—	—	—	—	40	—	—
Distillers grains/solubles	—	—	—	—	—	—	—	100	—
Fat	—	—	—	—	—	—	—	50	—
Lysine HCl (78% lysine)	—	—	—	—	—	—	—	—	4
Dicalcium phosphate	25	24	26	16	23	4	22	23	27
Limestone, ground	16	16	15	19	16	9	12	16	15
Salt	5	5	5	5	5	5	5	5	5
Vitamin mix[b]	1.5	1.5	1.5	1.5	1.5	1.5	1.5	1.5	1.5
Trace mineral mix[b]	1.5	1.5	1.5	1.5	1.5	1.5	1.5	1.5	1.5
Antibiotics[c]	+	+	+	+	+	+	+	+	+
Total	2000	2000	2000	2000	2000	2000	2000	2000	2000

[a]Provides 16–17% protein (14%, diet 9), 0.8% lysine, 0.65% Ca, and 0.55% P.
[b]See Tables 21–12, 21–13, and 21–14.
[c]Add to provide 50–100 g/ton. Copper sulfate may also be included to provide 100–250 ppm copper.

protein would be mixed with 3.2 parts of corn to provide a 16 percent protein level and mixed with 4.7 parts of corn to provide a 14 percent protein level.

Still another feeding system is to give pigs free-choice access to shelled corn and a commercial supplement. This system works better for corn than for other grains, but it requires close management to ensure that pigs consume from ¾ to 1 lb of protein supplement daily. This system works better for finishing pigs (125–235 lb) than for younger pigs.

Mechanical feeding systems are commercially available which dispense feed on the floor or in troughs at prescribed time intervals (Fig. 21–14). These systems generally necessitate a restricted feeding regimen in order to prevent wastage of feed. Pigs that are restricted to 85–90 percent of full feed gain slower and require more days to reach market weight, but have less backfat and a higher percentage of lean cuts in their carcass. The effects of feed restriction on efficiency of feed conversion are sometimes (but not always) improved.

Regardless of the feeding system used, it is very important that self-feeders be adjusted properly to prevent feed wastage. This is especially important when pigs are kept on slotted floors, because considerable amounts of wasted feed can be lost through the slats and go undetected.

FIGURE 21–13. Two types of self feeders for growing-finishing pigs.

TABLE 21-30

Diets for finishing pigs (125–235 lb)[a]

Ingredient	1	2	3	4	5	6	7	8
Corn or milo, ground	1670	1644	—	1363	1609	1578	1514	1758
Wheat or barley, ground	—	—	1722	—	—	—	—	—
Oats, ground	—	—	—	300	—	—	—	—
Soybean meal (49%)	285	—	—	—	—	—	—	—
Soybean meal (44%)	—	312	239	294	215	318	—	192
Soybeans, full fat, roasted	—	—	—	—	—	—	436	—
Meat and bone meal	—	—	—	—	80	—	—	—
Wheat middlings	—	—	—	—	80	—	—	—
Fat	—	—	—	—	—	60	—	—
Lysine HCl (78% lysine)	—	—	—	—	—	—	—	4
Dicalcium phosphate	22	21	12	20	—	22	28	24
Limestone, ground	16	16	20	16	9	15	15	15
Salt	5	5	5	5	5	5	5	5
Vitamin mix[b]	1	1	1	1	1	1	1	1
Trace mineral mix[b]	1	1	1	1	1	1	1	1
Antibiotics[c]	+	+	+	+	+	+	+	+
Total	2000	2000	2000	2000	2000	2000	2000	2000

[a]Provides 14–15% protein (12%, diet 8), 0.65% lysine, 0.6% Ca, and 0.5% P.
[b]See Tables 21–12, 21–13, and 21–14.
[c]Add to provide 20–50 g/ton.

TABLE 21-31

Composition of mineral-vitamin base mixes

Ingredients	1	2
Defluorinated rock phosphate	32	—
Dicalcium phosphate	—	26
Ground limestone	10	16
Salt	5	5
Vitamin mix	1.5	1.5
Trace mineral mix	1.5	1.5
Total	50 lb	50 lb

Diet will contain 0.65–0.75% Ca, 0.55–0.66% P, and 0.25% salt when 50 lb of this mix is added to 1950 lb of grain and soybean meal.

Feeding Boars

The requirements of breeding boars are not well known but are assumed to be similar to those of sows. Boars should be hand fed 4–6 lb daily of the sow's gestation feed. Boars should be kept in fairly trim condition, not too thin and not too fat. During heavy use, breeding boars may require a bit of extra feed to remain in good condition.

Purebred breeders who raise boars should feed diets that are 2–3 percent higher in protein (0.15–0.25 percent higher in lysine) and 0.1–0.2 percent higher in Ca and P during the develop-

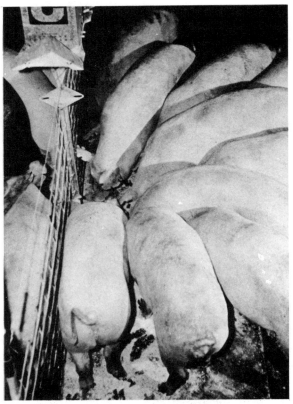

FIGURE 21–14. A floor feeding system for limit-fed pigs.

TABLE 21-32

Complete supplements for growing-finishing pigs and sows

Ingredient	Growing-Finishing[a]		Sows[b]	
	1	2	1	2
Soybean meal (44%)	1284	—	752	1197
Soybean meal (49%)	—	1341	—	—
Meat and bone meal	400	200	600	300
Alfalfa meal	—	160	500	—
Wheat middlings	200	120	—	250
Dicalcium phosphate	36	85	63	115
Limestone, ground	42	56	—	53
Salt	30	30	50	50
Vitamin mix[c]	4	4	10	10
Choline mix[c]	—	—	10	10
Biotin-folic acid mix[c]	—	—	5	5
Trace mineral mix[c]	4	4	10	10
Antibiotics[d]	+	+	—	—
Total	2000	2000	2000	2000

[a]Contains 40% protein, 3.3% Ca, and 1.75% P. Mix 1 part supplement with 3.2 parts grain for growing pigs (50–125 lb) and 1 part supplement with 4.7 parts grain for finishing pigs (125–235 lb).

[b]Contains 36% protein, 4.0% Ca, 2.25% P. Mix 1 part supplement with 4 parts grain.

[c]See Tables 21–12, 21–13, and 21–14.

[d]Add to provide 100–300 g/ton.

ment period than the levels used in conventional growing-finishing diets. Boars grow faster, consume less feed per unit of gain, and are leaner than barrows and gilts, so their nutritional requirements are higher.

Feed Requirements

Records indicate that it takes approximately 375–400 lb of feed for each 100 lb of pork marketed in a well-managed, farrow-to-finish swine operation. This value may be as low as 330 or even less in highly productive, well-managed herds. This includes the feed consumed by the breeding herd as well as that consumed by the pigs from birth to market.

The approximate distribution of feed required to produce a 235-lb market hog is shown in Table 21–33. About 15–20 percent of the feed is consumed by the breeding herd that produces the pig, and about 80–85 percent is consumed by the pig itself. Analysis of farm records shows that those farms having the best herd feed conversion are the ones that are the most profitable.

A number of factors can influence feed conversion in a swine herd. Genetically lean pigs are more efficient in converting feed to weight gain than are fat hogs, because lean tissue is more energetically efficient to produce than fat tissue. Marketing hogs at heavy weights has a negative effect on feed conversion; conversely, marketing hogs at lighter weights will improve overall herd feed conversion. As hogs increase in weight, a greater proportion of the gain is fat and a lesser proportion is lean. Other factors that reduce efficiency of feed conversion are cold

TABLE 21–33

Total feed required to produce a 235-lb market hog[a]

Stage	Lb
Boar feed	10
Sow gestation feed	100
Sow lactation feed	50
Starter feed (to 40 lb)	50
Grower feed (40–125 lb)	250
Finisher feed (125–235 lb)	420
Total	880[b]

[a]Based on 2.0 litters/sow/year and 8.0 pigs marketed/litter.
[b]Feed conversion 880 ÷ 235 = 3.74.
Growing-finishing feed conversion = 670 ÷ 195 = 3.43.

or excessively hot environmental temperatures, poor housing, failure to control feed wastage, feeding low-quality diets, and failure to maintain parasite and disease control in the herd.

SUMMARY

A sound nutrition program during all phases of the life cycle is essential for raising swine profitably. The current trends in the swine industry such as early weaning, confinement rearing, and intensive production systems place added importance on the quality of the feeding program. Raising pigs will continue to be a profitable undertaking for those producers who use top-level management in their operation. Efficient swine production will ensure a readily available supply of pork as a palatable and nutritious food for humans.

REFERENCES

1. NRC. 1988. *Nutrient requirements of swine.* 8th ed. Washington, D.C.: Nat. Acad. Press.
2. Cromwell, G. L. 1989. *Proc. Pitman-Moore Nutrition Conf.* Terre Haute, IN.
3. Tribble, L. R., J. D. Hancock, and D. E. Orr, Jr. 1984. *J. Animal Sci.* 59(Suppl. 1):245 (abstr.).
4. North Central Region-42 Committee on Swine Nutrition. 1976. *J. Animal Sci.* 42:1211.
5. Lindemann, M. D., and E. T. Kornegay. 1989. *J. Animal Sci.* 67:459.
6. National Pork Producers Council. 1990. *Pork industry handbook.* Cooperative Exten. Serv., Purdue Univ., W. Lafayette, IN.
7. Pond, W. G., and J. H. Maner. 1974. *Swine production in temperate and tropical environments.* San Francisco, CA: W. H. Freeman.
8. Krider, J. L., J. H. Conrad, and W. E. Carroll. 1982. *Swine production.* New York: McGraw-Hill.
9. Cromwell, G. L., T. S. Stahly, and H. J. Monegue. 1984. *J. Animal Sci.* 59(Suppl. 1):103 (abstr.).
10. Lindemann, M. D., et al. 1989. *J. Animal Sci.* 67(Suppl. 2):36 (abstr.).
11. Coffey, M. T., W. M. Hagler, Jr., and J. M. Cullen. 1989. *J. Animal Sci.* 67:465.
12. Pettigrew, J. E. 1981. *J. Animal Sci.* 53:107.
13. Danielson, M. 1985. *Pig News Info.* 6(1):35.
14. Feed Additive Compendium. 1990. Minnetonka, MN: Miller Publ. Co.
15. Cromwell, G. L., et al. 1981. *J. Animal Sci.* 53(Suppl. 1):95 (abstr.).
16. Cromwell, G. L., W. D. Williams, and T. S.

Stahly. 1981. *Proc. Distillers Feed Res. Conf.* Cincinnati, OH.

17. CAST. 1981. Antibiotics in animal feeds. *Council Agri. Sci. Tech. Rpt.* No. 88. Iowa State Univ., Ames, IA.

18. Hays, V. W. 1977. *The Hays Report.* Long Beach, CA: Rachelle Laboratories, Inc.

19. Zimmerman, D. R. 1986. *J. Animal Sci.* 62(Suppl. 3):6.

20. Whittemore, C. T., and F. W. H. Elsley. 1977. *Practical pig production.* Ipswich, Suffolk, England: Farming Press Ltd.

21. Stahly, T. S., G. L. Cromwell, and H. J. Monegue. 1985. *J. Animal Sci.* 61:1485.

22

Feeding Poultry

H. S. Nakaue and G. H. Arscott

Some idea of the relative importance of nutrition and feeding of poultry is indicated by the fact that about 43 percent of all commercially prepared feed in the United States is now fed to poultry. This value does not, of course, include the tremendous tonnage of farm-grown feed that is fed to animals and not processed through commercial mills. Another point of interest is that about 75 percent of the cost of production in raising or maintaining poultry may be attributed to feed costs, with three-fourths of this cost being allotted to maintenance needs and the remainder for productive purposes.

The scope of information presented in this chapter does not permit presentation of information other than that strictly related to nutrition and feeding of poultry. For further details on poultry management and nutrition the reader is referred to textbooks by Card and Nesheim (1), North (2), or Scott et al. (3).

NUTRIENT REQUIREMENTS

The nutrient requirements of poultry, particularly broiler chicks and layer hens, are de-

fined more precisely than those for other domestic animals. This is so because of the nature of the birds, the rather specific conditions under which they are produced, and because the short periods of time involved, particularly for broilers, allow the development of much more information for a given cost than with other species.

One of the best sources of information concerning the nutrient requirements of avian species, including chickens, turkeys, pheasants, quail, ducks, and geese, is contained in the NRC publication (4), the requirement tables of which are included in the appendix tables.

With regard to tabulated values on nutrient requirements, it should be noted that the recommendations do not provide any margin of safety. Where margins of safety are indicated, the resulting figures are considered allowances. Allowances are generally applied to those nutrients subject to potential destruction in feedstuffs during processing and storage, particularly the vitamins. In the absence of information concerning stability characteristics of various vitamin supplements, suggested allowance factors for some of these are: vitamin A, 66 percent; vitamins D and E, 50 percent; vitamin K, 25 percent; and all B-complex vitamins, 15-20 percent.

With regard to the nutrient requirements of birds, it should be recognized that birds generally eat to satisfy their energy needs. Furthermore, energy needs are affected by the environmental conditions to which birds are subjected, with temperature being a major factor. Thus as temperature increases, the need for energy-producing feeds will decrease and the amount of feed consumed will be reduced, and vice versa. While this may appear desirable, the specific nutrients required for growth or egg production must still be provided and, if feed consumption decreases, the quantities of essential nutrients must be increased accordingly by increasing their concentration in the diet. Therefore, it should be evident that protein and amino acid requirements can be defined accurately only in relation to the energy concentration of the diet, which may vary within certain ranges. To this end, Scott (5) has recently reported protein requirements in terms of dietary energy content for broilers and replacement pullets (Table 22–1), commercial layers and broiler breeder hens (Table 22–2), and turkeys of various ages (Table 22–3).

Other considerations include the fact that interactions exist between specific nutrients. For example, both the amino acids cystine and tyrosine should be considered in ration formulation to lower the total amounts of dietary methionine and phenylalanine, respectively, required in a diet, because methionine can be converted to cystine and phenylalanine to tyrosine. However, it should be emphasized that neither cystine nor tyrosine can be converted to methionine or phenylalanine. Further, cystine may actually be required under certain conditions and could be considered an essential amino acid in its own right because the bird is not always capable of synthesizing it in adequate amounts. Likewise, tryptophan can spare (reduce) the need for niacin. Thus it is prudent to include adequate levels of niacin in the diet to reduce the conversion of tryptophan to this vitamin and permit the use of tryptophan for tissue synthesis. Similarly, methionine spares the requirement for choline, thus more choline in the diet is desirable when methionine levels are marginal, depending on the economics of the supplements involved. There are many other important interrelationships which are covered in greater detail elsewhere in discussions of specific nutrients.

TABLE 22-1

Protein requirements of broilers and flock replacement chickens in relation to energy content of diet

| ME of Diet kcal/kg | Broilers | | |
	Starter Diet 0-2 wk, %	Grower Diet 2-6 wk, %	Finisher Diet 6 wk-mkt, %
2860	23.3	19.7	—
2970	24.2	20.5	18.7
3180	25.1	21.1	19.3
3190	26.0	22.0	20.0
3300	26.9	22.7	20.5
3410	—	—	21.2

| ME of Diet kcal/kg | Replacement Chickens | | | | | |
| | Starter Diet 0-2 wk, % | | Grower Diet 2-8 wk, % | | Developer Diet 8-18 wk, % | |
	LBW[a]	HBW[b]	LBW[a]	HBW[b]	LBW[a]	HBW[b,c]
2460	—	—	18.0	17.1	13.5	14.1
2695	—	—	18.6	17.7	13.6	14.6
2805	20.0	20.0	19.5	19.0	14.5	15.2
2905	20.8	20.8	20.0	19.5	15.1	15.7
3000	21.5	21.5	20.7	20.2	—	16.2
3100	22.2	22.2	21.4	20.9	—	—

[a]LBW = 3.75 lb mature body weight.
[b]HBW = 4.2 lb mature body weight.
[c]Restricted to about 90% of ad libitum consumption.
Source: Scott (5).

TABLE 22-2

Protein requirements of White Leghorn and broiler breeder hens as related to energy content of diet and environmental temperature

	White Leghorns					
	Environmental Temperatures[a]					
	55-65° F (13-18° C)		65-75° F (18-24° C)		78-88° F[b] (26-31° C)	
ME of Diet kcal/kg	LBW, %	HBW, %	LBW, %	HBW, %	LBW, %	HBW %
2695	—	—	16.4	15.6	18.0	17.1
2750	—	—	16.7	15.9	18.4	17.5
2805	16.0	15.2	16.9	16.0	18.6	17.7
2860	16.4	15.6	17.3	16.4	19.0	18.0
2915	16.7	15.9	17.6	16.7	19.4	18.4
2970	17.0	16.2	18.0	17.1	19.8	18.8

| | Broiler Breeders | |
| | Moderate Climate[c] | Hot Climate |
	%	%
2530	14.5	16.0
2640	15.1	16.7
2750	15.8	17.4
2860	16.3	18.1
2970	17.0	18.8

[a]Protein levels are about 1% above minimum requirements as a margin of safety.
[b]These diets should contain at least 4% fat, which supplies energy but a low level of heat increment.
[c]These values are based on a protein requirement of 24 g/hen/d and an expected ME intake of 420 kcal/hen/d in moderate climate and 380 kcal/hen/d in hot weather.
Source: Scott (5).

At present there are no fixed quantitative requirements for water. There are too many factors which influence the birds' needs for water to permit the establishment of firm requirements. These include dietary factors, physical form of the diet, inhibitors in feed ingredients, carbohydrate sources, age, breed, rate of production, environmental temperature, and contaminants in feed or water systems. In addition, source of water is a factor and includes drinking water, water in feed, and metabolic water. A convenient rule of thumb is that the bird consumes 1.5-2 times as much water as it does feed.

Nutrient requirements vary depending upon the type of poultry enterprise involved, particularly for young birds. Accordingly, the needs of broiler chicks are considered more critically and extensively in formulating rations

TABLE 22-3

Relation of protein requirements to dietary energy levels and to age of turkeys

| | Protein Requirements, % | | | | |
ME of Diet, kcal/kg	Starter, 0-4 wk	Grower #1, 4-12 wk	Grower #2, 12-18 wk	Finisher[a]	Breeder
2640	28	22	16.5	13.0	16.5
2750	29	23	17.0	13.5	17.0
2860	30	24	18.0	14.0	17.5
2970	31	25	18.5	14.5	18.0
3080	32	26	19.0	15.0	18.5
3300	—	—	—	15.5	—

[a]Turkey hens reach structural maturity at about 16 wk and therefore could be fed the finishing diets after that age.
Source: Scott (5).

TABLE 22-4

Suggested protein requirements for different ages and species

Species, Age	Ration			
	Starter	Grower	Finisher	Layer-Breeder
Chickens				
Broilers				
0-3 weeks	23-25[a]	—	—	—
3-5 weeks	—	21[a]	—	—
5-7 weeks	—	—	18[a]	—
Pullets				
0-6 weeks	20	—	—	—
6-10 weeks	—	16	—	—
10-20 weeks	—	12	—	—
Layers	—	—	—	15
Ducks	16[af]	16[a]	16[a]	15
Partridges	28	22	16	17
Geese	22	16[ab]	16[a]	15
Guinea	28	22	16	17
Pheasants	28	22	16	17
Pigeons	—	—	—	14[cg]
Quail				
Bobwhite	28	22	—	16
Coturnix or Japanese	28	22[d]	—	16
Turkeys[e]				
0-8 weeks	28	—	—	—
8-13 weeks	—	20	—	—
13-17 weeks	—	17	—	—
17 weeks to market age	—	—	15	—
Breeders	—	—	—	14

[a]Pellets preferred.
[b]After 3 weeks.
[c]Pellets or whole grains.
[d]After 2 weeks.
[e]Sexes not separated.
[f]When increased growth is desired use 22% for first 2 weeks.
[g]Recommendation by W. D. Holderread, Corvallis, OR, is acknowledged and appreciated.

than the needs of layers, and close scrutiny is given to virtually all nutrients for which requirement data are available (see Appendix Tables 29, 30, and 33–36). With the advent of computers and software for least-cost linear programming, this has become more or less routine. The same relationship exists with turkeys, although requirements probably are less quantitative (Appendix Tables 37 and 38).

For flock replacement chickens, nutrients of major concern include protein plus the essential amino acids, usually likely to be limiting—arginine, cystine, lysine, methionine, and tryptophan; vitamins A, D, riboflavin, pantothenic acid, and niacin; and Ca, P, Na (as salt), and Mn.

With adult layers for either commercial or hatching egg production, particular attention is usually given to the protein requirement and the five amino acids mentioned earlier, plus those vitamins and minerals necessary for egg pro-

duction. Further, when chicken breeder rations are involved, added fortification involving vitamin E, riboflavin, pantothenic acid, pyridoxine, biotin, folacin, Mn, Ca, Fe, and Zn is necessary, as noted in Appendix Tables 29, 33, and 36.

The nutrient requirements of other domestic or game birds (Appendix Tables 40–44), when not known, are often estimated by comparison to the most appropriate domestic species. The protein requirement, if known, may be used as a bench mark. When feeding free-ranging birds, it may be desirable to provide highly fortified rations to insure against possible deficiencies in natural feedstuffs.

From the foregoing, it can be seen that much attention is given to individual nutrient requirements. This is especially so now that computers are used in formulating rations. Since many feeding systems, to be discussed later in this chapter, are still closely tied to protein levels, a summary of suggested protein requirements for various types of avian species has been developed and is shown in Table 22-4.

FEEDSTUFFS FOR POULTRY

There is extensive information available regarding feedstuffs and their chemical composition. The NRC (4, 6) provides much pertinent data on this subject, some of which are excerpted and presented in Appendix Tables 3-6. In addition, many commercial companies also provide current publications, often in leaflet form, with similar information that is available on request.

However, at the present time the major ingredients utilized in poultry rations center on extensive use of corn for energy and soybean meal for protein, although many other feedstuffs may be used in smaller amounts. In general, the variety of ingredients used in a given ration tends to be greater than for most other animal species.

General Considerations

In selecting feedstuffs for use in poultry rations, a number of factors should be considered. Ration palatability is important and while it may be inherent in the feedstuff, such as presence of tannins in some milos, it may also be affected by such factors as moisture content, variety of ingredients, and contaminants such as molds. Habits of the bird may likewise alter consumption. For example, birds that are in the habit of consuming whole or cracked corn may fail to eat when suddenly exposed to whole barley as a source of grain. Birds may be attracted to feeds by light reflections from granite grit or differences in color, factors which are sometimes considered in feeding newly hatched poults (young turkeys). Physical condition of the feed, such as fineness of particle size or its hydroscopic properties, can also influence feed consumption.

In addition to factors that have been mentioned, physiological effects on both the bird or the product it produces must be considered. For example, care must be taken to avoid excessive use of feedstuffs which contain growth inhibitors or other undesirable substances that are often found in common plant protein sources (see Ch. 9). Similarly, both yellow corn and alfalfa contain xanthophyll pigments which may be undesirable when present in excess as far as yolk color is concerned, but which are desirable for broiler skin pigmentation.

Nutrient availability is also a factor. Availability may be affected by differences among feed ingredients, fiber content, presence of fat, amino acid balance, and other factors.

Presence of sufficient volume of a feedstuff in the marketplace is an additional item. If only a small tonnage of a given feedstuff is present, it may not be economical to change rations just to utilize such an ingredient. Finally, the cost of the ingredients involved is a critical factor.

Feed Grains

High-energy grains suitable for poultry are corn, milo, wheat, rice, triticale, and oat groats. Medium-energy grains are barley and heavy oats, while low-energy grains are oats and spelt. Corn, milo, wheat, and barley are the most important grains used currently in poultry rations. Grain milling by-products (except for hominy) are low-energy sources for poultry.

The relative values of various grains, using corn as a standard for poultry, are shown in Table 22-5. It is evident that none of the commonly available western-grown grains appear comparable to corn. However, in recent studies with newer varieties of white wheat, the difference is decreasing with broilers and has largely disappeared for turkey poults. Egg production appears unaffected by grain source, although relative efficiency figures proved inferior for wheat, barley, and oats due probably to increased feed consumption.

Protein Supplements

Vegetable protein concentrates used routinely include oil meals from soybean, cottonseed, sunflower seed, safflower, peanuts, and limited amounts of other plant protein supplements such as corn gluten meal, rapeseed (Canola) meal, and pea meal. By far the most important of these for poultry are soybean and degossypolized cottonseed meals.

Soybean meal is an excellent source of protein; it may vary in protein content from 44-50 percent with the higher values resulting from the removal of hulls. Hull-less meals are often used in broiler rations because of their lower fiber and higher energy contents. Methionine may be slightly marginal in diets where soybean meal constitutes the major protein source.

As pointed out in Ch. 9, raw soybeans contain a trypsin inhibitor and other substances

TABLE 22-5
Comparative values of grains for poultry

Grain	Broilers	Layers	Poults
Eastern corn			
Growth (egg production)	100	(100)	100
Feed consumption	100	100	100
Relative efficiency	100	100	100
Western corn			
Growth (E.P.)	97	(98)	100
Feed consumption	98	101	97
Relative efficiency	99	97	103
Milo			
Growth (E.P.)	95	(99)	—
Feed consumption	97	98	—
Relative efficiency	100	100	—
Wheat (grains)[a]			
Growth (E.P.)	95	(100)	93[c]
Feed consumption	102	106	99
Relative efficiency	93	95	93
Wheat[b]			
Growth (E.P.)	97	—	110
Feed consumption	103	—	112
Relative efficiency	96	—	98
Barley			
Growth (E.P.)	92	(99)	93
Feed consumption	107	106	103
Relative efficiency	83	95	90
Oats			
Growth (E.P.)	78	(97)	—
Feed consumption	84	107	—
Relative efficiency	93	89	—
Spelt			
Growth (E.P.)	99	—	98
Feed consumption	112	—	112
Relative efficiency	86	—	85
Triticale[d]			
Growth (E.P.)	—	—	102
Feed consumption	—	—	95
Relative efficiency	—	—	94

[a]Note: An earlier study with broilers and turkeys involving hard red wheat provided values of 99, 98, and 98 (8) and 105, 106, and 101 (9), respectively.
[b]Includes Nu Gaines, Yamhill, and Beaver varieties (10).
[c]From Harper (10).
[d]From Nakaue et al. (11).

which are growth inhibitors. Proper heat processing inactivates these compounds. In some circumstances unextracted soybeans may be desirable to use in broiler rations, but the beans must be processed by either extruding or roasting. This will result in a product which can be utilized by poultry with up to 19 percent fat and 38 percent protein. Care must be exercised not to overheat soybeans because this renders lysine and other amino acids unavailable.

Cottonseed meals may be used to replace up to half of the usual amount of soybean meal in grower poultry rations, but further use must be restricted because of the content of gossypol and sterculic acid (see Ch. 9). Gossypol levels of more than 0.04 percent will cause an olive-green yolk color, particularly with eggs subjected to storage. Thus even with lower gossypol levels, the use of cottonseed meal for layers is restricted to a maximum of 10 percent of the diet. The addition of 0.05–0.1 percent of iron sulfate will alleviate the gossypol problem partially; there are also biologically tested meals that have been developed for use with poultry (12). Further, sterculic acid, a cyclopropenoid fatty acid present in cottonseed oil, causes pink albumens.

Linseed meal proves toxic when fed to poultry in excess of 2-3 percent of the diet. The inhibitor (linatine) results in reduced growth (13). Water treatment by soaking and drying largely inactivates the inhibitor, as do high levels of pyridoxine, but the meal processed in this manner is not used because of the cost involved.

Canola meal is used in poultry rations as a source of protein. The meal is only slightly goitrogenic, because its glucosinolate content is low. Furthermore, sufficient heat during the early extraction process destroys the enzyme myrosinase, which is responsible for the conversion of progoitrin to goitrin, the principal goitrogenic factor in canola meal. Incomplete destruction of myrosinase, or myrosinase getting into mixed feed as a grain contaminant, does not affect poultry seriously (14). The levels of canola meal should not exceed 10 percent, 15 percent, 15 percent, 20 percent, and 20 percent in the rations of laying-breeding chickens, broilers, turkey breeders, market turkeys, and waterfowl, respectively (14). Inclusion of canola meal in rations for brown egg layers is not recommended. Brown egg layers are apparently unable to oxidize trimethylamine (TMA) (which has a fishy odor) to odorless TMA-oxide rapidly enough to prevent TMA from being deposited in the eggs.

Alfalfa meals are used in poultry rations as a source of vitamins, protein, and skin or yolk pigmentation (xanthophylls). They also contain toxic substances which influence growth and mortality of chicks when levels exceed 10 percent of the diet. The toxic substances are related to saponins (15). Since alfalfa meal contains a relatively high level of fiber, it usually is not used in excess of 2-3 percent of the diet in poultry rations.

Animal protein sources commonly used are fish meals, meat meal, meat and bone meal, poultry by-products meal, and hydrolyzed feather meal. Except for feather meal, these feedstuffs are considered good to excellent sources of amino acids, with use limitations dependent on cost, P, or salt content.

Fish meals are frequently used at the 2-5 percent level as a source of unidentified growth or hatchability factors in addition to their favorable amino acid profile. Cost, at times, may be high. The meat products often are priced economically so that they may replace an equivalent amount of soybean meal protein up to about 10 percent of the diet, with greater levels possibly providing too much P and/or salt.

Miscellaneous Ingredients

Feed ingredients that are particularly rich in vitamins, amino acids, and minerals tend to fall in the category of supplements. Vitamin supplements include sun-cured and dehydrated alfalfa meals, corn gluten meal, distillery and brewery by-products, fish solubles, and brewers yeast, as well as crystalline or highly concentrated forms of individual vitamins. Synthetic sources of amino acids currently include methionine, methionine hydroxy analogue, lysine, threonine, and tryptophan. A wide variety of mineral supplements may be used involving ingredients containing Ca, P, Na, Mn, and Zn.

Vegetable or animal fats are used frequently as energy sources and can serve as a replacement for energy furnished by grains. When incorporating fat into the diet, it must be recognized that fat supplies only energy and essential fatty acids; thus other nutrients are diluted, and appropriate adjustments in nutrient concentrations must be made to such rations.

Other feeds that are sometimes utilized include molasses. Although molasses is a good source of energy, it does exert a laxative effect on the bird, which limits its use to not more than 2 percent of the diet. Grits of varying size serve poultry as a mechanism for grinding feed in the gizzard and may be needed, particularly when birds are fed whole grains. However, their use in present day commerical rations is optional.

In addition to the known nutrients, it appears that other unidentified factors may be present in some feedstuffs. This is based on the fact that ingredients such as fish solubles, fish and meat meals, distillers dried solubles, whey, and green forages often provide a response to growth, hatchability, or, in some instances, egg production. For these reasons many nutritionists include small amounts of these ingredients in poultry rations. However, it may be that these feedstuffs provide optimal combinations of nutrients or that the nutrients contained are more highly available to the bird.

Several stimulatory nonnutritive additives are also used to promote efficient performance, presumably by bringing about favorable changes in the intestinal tract, resulting in improved growth and feed efficiency. For broiler chicks and market turkeys these include such substances as antibiotics, organic arsenicals, and nitrofurans. Responses in egg production have been more variable, and their use in such rations is limited. Further, use of these and other compounds is closely regulated by the FDA (16). Amylolytic but not proteolytic enzyme supplements also have beneficial effects on growth when added to diets containing western barley. These barleys are known to be lacking in β-glucanase, which is present in most other grains or in barley when it is grown outside the Pacific Northwest.

As pointed out in Ch. 11, processing of poultry feeds is primarily that of grinding the cereal grains and pelleting all or parts of the diet. Pelleting or cubing followed in many instances by crumbling results in a physical increase in density and tends to prohibit sorting of ingredients by the bird. Pelleting is a particularly useful practice when an increase in feed consumption is desired to enhance growth of chicks or broilers. The advantages of pelleting include the following: feed wastage is minimized, each pellet is a complete diet, pellets are readily adaptable to automatic equipment, less food storage and feeder space are required, greater simplification results, improved palatability is obtained for a number of feedstuffs, and salmonella organisms may be destroyed by heat. Some of the disadvantages are the following: feed costs are increased, nutrients may be destroyed by heat, incidence of cannibalism may be increased, camouflaging of feed ingredients may occur, and water and feed consumption are increased without an increase in egg production.

In feeding birds of different ages, it is a common practice to use pellet sizes ranging from about 1/8 in. (0.32 cm) to 3/8 in. (0.95 cm). The length of the pellets must also be considered, so that pellets are not too long for the bird consuming it. Crumbling allows the feed manufacturer to employ a larger die size, thus increasing pellet mill volume and thereby reducing cost even though an added process is involved.

METHODS OF FEEDING

In discussing this subject, it will be broken down into two sections; namely, feeding systems and feeding practices. The former describes the actual methods involved while the latter refers to the terminology in general relating to the various modifications to the systems. In any discussion of this subject, it should be understood clearly that no one system is superior to any other. The success of any program is dependent, to a large degree, on a knowledge by the poultry producer of the nutrients, their requirements, and the feedstuffs involved for the particular class of poultry.

Feeding Systems

Feeding systems generally used in the past or present include the whole grain method, the mash-scratch (grain) method, and the all-mash method. The whole grain method is of historical interest only and was the original system involved in feeding poultry. It required that a diet of grain be supplemented by natural sources of nutrients such as insects, worms, kitchen slops, green vegetation, and so forth. Over the years it was modified to include supplements of skim milk, meat meal, or other products.

The mash-scratch method of feeding once was the most popular system, particularly for adult poultry. In certain situations it is still used to advantage by poultry producers, especially those who have access to locally grown grains. This method is sometimes used for market turkeys, replacement pullets, or adult chickens and turkeys. For layers, it involves keeping mash available to the birds on a free-choice basis and restricting the scratch grain portion to about half of the hen's total daily intake. The conventional system usually involves a mash containing 20 percent protein. Thus, because most grains contain 10 percent protein, the total protein intake will equal 15 percent (which meets the layers' protein requirement; Table 22–4 and Appendix Table 29). The advantages of this system are: the poultry producer can vary dietary protein and energy content as influenced by stage or rate of production and environmental temperatures; it permits some use of locally grown or locally available grains; and, in floor

pen operations, it can be used as an aid in maintaining good litter condition. One of the disadvantages is that it is often difficult for some poultry producers to adjust the grain to the mash intake so that the birds' requirements are met, as there is a tendency to overfeed on grain. Another disadvantage is that the appearance of the end product (birds or eggs) may be less uniform because the grain composition and consumption may vary. It should also be recognized that no one grain mixture is best. It is usually recommended that at least two or more grains be utilized, to permit birds to obtain some degree of familiarity for different grains should the composition of a mixture be changed. Further, while often overlooked by the producer, the use of scratch grains, as noted above, does permit one to regulate energy intake. During cold weather, mixtures of high-energy grains readily meet energy needs; during the summer and periods of high temperatures, when feed intake generally tends to decrease, the use of low-energy grains may stimulate feed intake.

The all-mash system of feeding is presently the most common method used in North America. It is employed in all types of poultry operations starting with day-old chicks to layers and breeders. It is the system of choice with broilers and is also used extensively with laying hens and turkeys. In some instances, as mentioned previously and in Ch. 11, the diet may be fed in pelleted or crumbled form rather than as a mash. Advantages are as follows: it is simple, because one complete feed is all that is fed; less skill is required; there is more uniformity of product; and it is adaptable to mechanical feeders. Some of the disadvantages are that all grains need to be ground, resulting in increased cost; the system is inflexible; and, if litter condition is a factor, there is no help with this system.

Feeding Practices

As noted previously, feeding practices are generally modifications of the systems just discussed. These are described briefly.

Protein Concentrates. This term refers to mashes with protein levels in excess of 20 percent and up to 40 percent. Such concentrates are generally utilized by poultry producers who have access to locally available grains. Concentrate mashes are designed to meet the protein, vitamin, and mineral needs of the birds, with energy needs being made up by grains. Protein concentrates may be used with layers, developing pullets, and growing turkeys. In utilizing protein concentrates, it is important that the correct proportion of mash to grain be fed. The grain can be either whole or in ground form and is, therefore, applicable to either the mash-scratch, or, if properly mixed, the all-mash systems of feeding. The Pearson square technique can be utilized to calculate the proper amount of mash and grain to use with a particular protein concentrate and a protein intake level (Ch. 12).

Free Choice or Cafeteria Feeding.
This is a modification of the controlled feeding systems mentioned previously. In this case layers, for example, are fed both mash and scratch on a free-choice basis. Much controversy exists over this system, and it now appears that, if applicable, it can be utilized only by White Leghorns and not by the heavy American-type breeds used as replacement stock for broilers. Even with the light breeds, its use is recommended only with protein concentrates containing 30 percent or more protein.

Supplemental Feeding.
Supplemental feeding is utilized in an attempt to maintain high feed consumption of layers by stimulating feed intake and, in the process, possibly minimizing sudden drops during the egg production cycle (see Fig. 22–1). The most common practice is to utilize a high level of an antibiotic (50-100 g/ton) for a 2-4 d period when decreases in production are observed. This can be done either on a regular basis or when conditions indicate a change. The level used is dependent on the antibiotic available and regulations regarding its use (16). Two other less commonly used methods involve the use of pellets (2 lb/100 birds/d) or a wet mash at a similar rate. Another supplementary practice, not commonly used now, involves the use of green feeds. Once started, the use of

pellets, wet mash, or green feed supplement must be continued, because layers seem to become accustomed to these practices.

Restricted Feeding.
Restricted feeding of growing birds, particularly the heavy breeds, is now being practiced extensively (17,18). This practice involves limiting feed intake in some manner during the growing period. Its success is dependent upon the use of highly fortified diets to meet nutritional requirements in order to overcome the imposed feed restriction.

Restricted feeding in the growing of replacement pellets is desirable for the following reasons: it slows the rate of sexual maturity, it permits the development of larger final body size, it results in larger egg weights at an earlier age (which is desirable for production of hatching eggs), it appears to reduce mortality, and it increases egg production. In addition, while not fully substantiated, there may be a reduction in total feed consumption during the developing period.

There are several types of restricted feeding programs which, in some instances, involve the use of high-fiber diets. One of the earlier ones was known as the Quaker Oats program (19). At 2 mo of age, birds are given as much mash and oats as they will consume during 1-2 h in the morning 5 d a week. In the late afternoon, 7 d a week, the birds are fed all the oats they will consume in a 10-min period. The morning feeding is usually skipped on Sundays and Wednesdays.

Another program developed later by Texas workers involves feeding a diet containing 15-20 percent fiber utilizing oat hulls. One of the disadvantages of this program is the fact that the birds tend to overconsume to satisfy energy needs and may eat up to 50 percent more feed. A modification of this, also developed at the Texas Agricultural Experiment Station, involved feeding a conventional, adequately fortified feed at 70 percent of what birds fed a normal diet free choice would be consuming. This program does require adequate records, additional labor, and careful supervision.

The skip-a-day program, also commonly known as the Arbor Acres program, was developed subsequently (20). This program is carried on during the growing period to 24 weeks of age. It involves doubling up on feed available minus 2 lb/100 pullets the day before restriction is to commence, no mash on the odd days except for 2 lb of oats/100 birds spread on the litter, full feed minus 2 lb/100 birds on even days and the

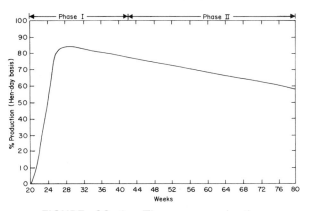

FIGURE 22–1. The egg production curve in relation to phase feeding.

use of a ration containing 15 percent protein and 6 percent fiber. The feed weights and age schedule/100 birds/d follows: 10-14 weeks, 26 lb; 14-16 weeks, 28 lb; 16-22 weeks, 30 lb; 22-24 weeks, 32 lb.

Much interest has also occurred over the use of lysine-deficient rations as a means for delaying sexual maturity. This work was first initiated in Connecticut in the middle 1960s and involved the feeding of lysine-deficient diets to chicks from 0-12 weeks, after which time the birds were fed a conventional developer mash. Considerable variability in uniformity of body weight occurred, and some evidence has since been reported regarding an adverse effect on subsequent layer performance. The Texas workers modified this practice by reversing the program in using an adequate diet for the first 6-7 weeks and feeding a lysine-deficient diet thereafter to 19-22 weeks depending on age at first egg. This change, while accomplishing restriction, has so far shown no adverse effects on subsequent layer performance. Results have also been reported from the Maryland Experiment Station involving the use of imbalanced protein diets fed in a similar manner to that described above. In general, these programs have consistently delayed sexual maturity and resulted in an increase in the number of hatchable eggs obtained.

Restricted Feeding of Heavy Breeds.
Attempts have been made in recent years to control energy intake and prevent overeating in heavy breed layers and males kept for broiler chick replacement purposes. By observing the body weight status of a given flock one can, by restricting the birds' feed intake, prevent them from becoming overly fat. It is important when using this program that one considers the environmental conditions to which the birds are exposed as well as the strain of bird involved. When used properly, feed savings of up to 15 percent may be obtained. The major breeding organizations provide detailed management guides for their particular line of birds.

Phase Feeding.
Phase feeding may be characterized as a system that utilizes feeds of varying nutrient densities for increased economic returns throughout the production cycle of the layer. It generally relates to protein intake, with energy playing a regulatory role (3). This practice requires maintaining detailed records by the producer involving stage and rate of production, body weight, and feed consumption. Other data involving energy and protein content of the diet,

environmental temperatures, and type of management are also necessary. As originally proposed, the system involved up to three phases in the production cycle. Phases I and II are noted (see Fig. 22–1 and Table 22–2). Phase I may be defined as about 20-42 weeks, at which time the hen is still growing and peaks in production. Phase II is from about 42 weeks to about 65 percent production or 80 weeks of age. Protein requirements during these phases are now estimated as 17 g/bird/d, and diets are formulated to reflect these changes. Energy requirements are affected by environmental temperatures and the energy level in the diet. The system requires that rations must be tailored to fit very specific needs. Research on phase feeding has shown both positive and negative results.

Multiple Versus Single Stage Rations for Broilers and Market Turkeys.
Multiple stage rations for use with broilers are analogous in many ways to phase feeding used with laying hens. This system involves feeding diets with varying energy and protein contents and is related to age. As now constituted, the protein level of the diet may consist of two, three, and, in some instances, four stages, with the first stage often referred to as a prestarter stage. Protein levels in the diet may range up to 24 percent for the prestarter and decrease to 18–20 percent for the finisher. The prestarter may be fed for the first 0.5–1.0 lb of feed consumed, depending upon recommendations of the feed manufacturer. Generally, birds are switched to a different stage on the basis of age at 3-4 weeks and 5-6 weeks. As the protein content decreases, the energy content either remains constant or increases slightly.

When single stage rations are used throughout the broiler period, they usually contain less total protein content than do the prestarter or starter feeds, but slightly more protein than do the final finisher feeds. Use of either type is dependent on economics.

An examination of the protein and energy needs of turkeys (Appendix Table 36) shows that they should also receive multiple stage rations over the growing period. A fairly recent development, and one that may be observed to a greater extent in the future, is the use of specific rations on the basis of segregating the sexes.

Other Miscellaneous Practices.
There are a number of practices that may or may not be directly related to the feeding of poultry but which should be mentioned. These include the use of artificial lights, beak trimming, dubbing

of combs, and management of broody hens. For further information on these topics, the reader should consult various sources on poultry management (1, 2, 21).

RATIONS FOR POULTRY

Examples of various types of rations fed to poultry are given in Tables 22–6 to 22–8. These formulas have, for the most part, been formulated using the NRC publication (4) as a major guide. Layer rations are given for both moderate and warm climates. These formulas may differ somewhat from those in actual use in various areas, due primarily to feed ingredient availability and cost. The vitamin and trace mineral supplements used should at least meet the minimums noted in the tables. The levels of antibiotics and other drugs used are dependent on the product available and regulations regarding their use. These rations will be referred to in more detail subsequently.

While ration formulation is treated in more detail in Ch. 12, a few comments providing basic information for avian species might be helpful to the overall understanding of this subject. Performance standards for various types of poultry, especially for broilers, growing chickens, layers, and turkeys, are available from several sources (4, 21, 22) but, it should be emphasized, are subject to continual change as improvements occur.

Ration formulation and feed manufacturing are handled commercially by feed companies; however, the amount of feed mixing occurring in poultry operations is on the increase. Producers have to make an independent decision as to whether to mix their own feed or not. There are many factors that need to be considered. In addition to flock size these are: cost as it relates to capital investment, equipment, and building; quality control; the need for adequate mixing; servicing aspects usually provided by feed manufacturers; keeping up-to-date on recent developments in the nutrition field; the proper use of medicaments, and the diversion of time from husbandry-related activities.

Water, feed, feed conversion, and growth standards for broilers are shown in Appendix Tables 32 and 39. Currently, broilers are being marketed at 7 weeks of age or less, at which time mixed sexes will have an average weight of about 4.5 lb on about 8.6 lb of feed.

For flock replacement pullets, information on water consumption is provided in Appendix

Table 39. For white-shelled egg pullets about 16-17 lb of feed are required to 22 weeks of age, while for brown-shelled egg types 20-21 lb of feed are needed. Pullet breeder flocks for broiler production require about 25 lb of feed to 25 weeks of age, while cockerels require up to 35 lb of feed.

Detailed standards are provided in the appendix tables for layers. Because three-fourths of feed consumed by layers is used for maintenance purposes, it can be seen that body size markedly influences feed consumption and feed efficiency. For production rates of 60–90 percent, feed consumption and feed/dozen eggs range from about 21 to 29 lb and 4.9 to 3.3 lb, respectively.

Extensive performance standards for turkeys are currently reported and updated annually by Sell (22). For more detailed information regarding individual sexes and body size, the reader should refer to the current reference noted above.

FEEDING-MANAGEMENT OF POULTRY

Broilers

Broiler chicks are provided feed on a free-choice basis to 7 weeks or whenever they are marketed. The feed may be in the form of mash, pellets, or crumbles. Protein requirements vary with age, thus multiple stage rations are usually employed. An example of a two-stage ration is shown in Table 22–6. Required protein levels for starter feeds are approximately 23-24 percent and for the finisher, 18 percent. Energy levels may range from 2750 to 3300 kcal/kg (Table 22–1) with slightly higher values present in the finisher feeds. Starter feeds are generally used for no longer than 3 weeks, followed by grower and finisher feeds. Feed is provided daily either manually by trough, tube-, or tank-type feeders, or by means of mechanized, electrically controlled, automated feeding equipment in troughs or tube-type feeders (Fig. 22–3). Water is provided by means of troughs, fountains, or watering cups. Broiler diets should contain an antibiotic as a growth stimulant and a coccidiostat or coccidiocide for the control of coccidiosis. Care must be exercised in following FDA regulations relating to drug withdrawal prior to marketing birds (16).

Flock Replacement Pullets

Flock replacement pullets are usually fed an all-mash starter diet containing 20 percent protein

TABLE 22-6

Suggested two-stage broiler rations

Ingredients	Starter[a] 23% Protein (3134 kcal/kg) lb	Finisher[b] 20% Protein, (3192 kcal/kg) lb
Corn, yellow gr.	1134.6	1237.4
Fat, animal[c]	80	80
Soybean meal, solv. (47.5% prot.)[d]	645	550
Meat and bone meal (50% prot.)	100	100
Alfalfa meal, dehy. (17% prot.)	20	20
Limestone flour	7	2.6
Dicalcium phosphate	8.4	5
Salt, iodized	5	5
Total	2000	2000
Supplements to supply at least:[e]		
Vitamin A, IU × 10⁶	3.3	3.0
Vitamin D₃, IU × 10⁶	1.0	1.0
Vitamin E, IU × 10³	1.0	1.0
Vitamin K (menadione), g	0.5	0.5
Riboflavin, g	3.0	3.0
d-Pantothenic acid, g	5.0	5.0
Niacin, g	20.0	20.0
Choline, g	175.0	175.0
Vitamin B₁₂, mg	4.0	4.0
Manganese, g	60.0	60.0
Methionine, g[f]	1362.0	908.0
Antibiotics, g[g]	4–50	4–50
Coccidiostat[g]	+	+

[a]To be fed first 3 weeks in mash or pellet form.

[b]To be fed from fourth week on.

[c]Prime tallow or equivalent energy source—adequately stabilized with suitable antioxidant.

[d]May be replaced by not more than 200 lb of meat and bone meal (50% protein) with appropriate adjustment for protein, Ca, P, and salt.

[e]Added at the expense of ground corn when 5 lb or more are involved. Vitamin-trace mixtures with greater fortification than noted are permissible.

[f]Or other equivalent sources.

[g]Level used is dependent upon product available, treatment desired, and manufacturer's recommendation.

FIGURE 22-2. Broiler houses typical of large operations in the United States.

FIGURE 22-3. Broilers under intensive confinement conditions.

for the first 6 weeks of life, followed by a 15-16 percent protein developer feed up through 12 weeks of age, with a further decrease to 12-13 percent protein up to 18-20 weeks of age. Pelleted or crumbled feeds may be used but are not necessary. Suggested protein levels for the various ages are given in Table 22-4. Energy levels utilized during the starting and developer periods may range from 2640 to 3080 kcal/kg (Table 22-1), but may vary considerably depending upon the feed ingredients involved and the environmental conditions encountered. Examples of starter and developer feeds are given in Table 22-7. Beginning with the first developer ration, the operator may utilize a mash-scratch system of feeding throughout the growing period (see footnote b, Table 22-7).

However, in view of the extensive use of all-mash laying feeds, it is probably now more advisable to provide developing pullets with all-mash feeds. With commercial egg-type pullets, feed and water are available daily on a free-choice basis. For broiler flock replacement stock, developing pullets are fed any of the restricted feeding programs described previously, subject to the specific recommendations of the particular franchise breeder whose strain is being used. While a low-level antibiotic may be desirable in the starter ration, its need in developer rations is questionable. A coccidiostat should be employed that imparts some degree of immunity from coccidiosis to ensure protection during the bird's productive life. The use of a coccidiocide is not recommended under these circumstances.

TABLE 22-7
Suggested chick starter, grower, and developer rations

Ingredients	Starter[a] 20% Protein, (2947 kcal/kg) lb	Grower[b] 15% Protein, (3079 kcal/kg) lb	Developer[c] 13% Protein, (3095 kcal/kg) lb
Corn, yellow gr.[d]	900	1160	1150
Barley, gr.	100	200	300
Milo, gr.	353	267	273
Soybean meal, solv. (47.5% prot.)	460	210	120
Meat and bone meal (50% prot.)	100	100	100
Alfalfa meal, dehy. (17% prot.)	50	50	50
Dicalcium phosphate	32	8	2
Salt, iodized	5	5	5
Total	2000	2000	2000
Supplements to supply at least:[e]			
Vitamin A, IU × 10^6	3.0	2.0	2.0
Vitamin D_3, IU × 10^6	0.7	0.35	0.35
Vitamin E, IU × 10^3	1.0	—	—
Vitamin K (menadione), g	0.5	—	—
Riboflavin, g	2.0	0.5	0.5
d-Pantothenic acid, g	4.0	2.0	2.0
Niacin, g	10.0	—	—
Vitamin B_{12}, mg	3.0	—	—
Manganese, g	40.0	10.0	10.0
Methionine, kg[g]	1.0	1.0	0.5
Antibiotic, g[h]	4-50	4-50[f]	4-50[f]
Coccidiostat[h]	+	+	+[e]

[a]Fed as all-mash (0-6 wk). Limited scratch may be used commencing at 5-6 wk of age but not exceeding 25% of total intake at 6 wk. If a mash-scratch program is used from 7-18 wk, reformulate the 15% protein grower by removing 1000 lb of corn or grain and use a scratch mixture that does not exceed 50% intake (7-12 wk) and 70% intake (13-18 wk).

[b]Fed as all-mash (7-12 wk).

[c]Fed as all-mash (13-18 wk).

[d]Wheat may be substituted for part or all the corn and milo, dependent on price.

[e]Added at expense of gr. grain component when 5 lb or more are involved. Vitamin-trace mineral premixes with greater fortification than noted above are permissible.

[f]Optional.

[g]Or other equivalent source.

[h]Level used is dependent on product, treatment desired, and manufacturer's recommendations.

TABLE 22-8

Suggested layer-breeder* rations

| | Moderate Climate | | Warm Climate |
| | All-Mash 15% Protein, (2870 kcal/kg) | Mash-Scratch[a] 21% Protein, (2417 kcal/kg) | All-Mash 17% Protein, (2752 kcal/kg) |
Ingredients	lb	lb	lb
Corn, yellow gr.[b]	963	926	752
Barley, gr.	100	—	200
Milo, gr.	100	—	400
Soybean meal, solv. (47.5% prot.)	240	480	338
Meat and bone meal (50% protein)	100	200	100
Alfalfa meal, dehy. (17% prot.)	50	100	50
Limestone flour[c]	134	268	145
Dicalcium phosphate	8	16	9
Salt, iodized	5	10	6
Total	2000	2000	2000
Supplements to supply at least:[d]			
Vitamin A, IU × 10⁶	3.0	6.0	3.0
Vitamin D₃, IU × 10⁶	0.7	1.4	0.7
Vitamin E, IU × 10³	0-1*	0-2*	0-1*
Vitamin K (menadione), g	0-0.5*	0-1*	0-0.5*
Riboflavin, g	2-3*	4-6*	2-3*
d-Pantothenic acid, g	1-2*	2-4*	1-2*
Niacin, g	10.0	20.0	10.0
Vitamin B₁₂, mg	0-2	0-4	0-2
Methionine, g[e]	136	272	181
Manganese, g	0-20*	0-40*	0-20*

*Points out need for increased breeder ration fortification.

[a]Adapted from 15% protein ration and to be fed with about equal parts of scratch grain(s).

[b]Wheat may be substituted for part or all the corn and milo, dependent on price.

[c]May be reduced by 50% with substitution of med. oyster shell on lb for lb basis.

[d]Added at expense of gr. grain component when 5 lb or more are involved. Vitamin-trace mineral mixtures with greater fortification than noted are permissible.

[e]Or other equivalent source.

Chicken Layers and Breeders

At the onset of sexual maturity, which may be defined as the age at first egg (approximately 18-20 weeks in many strains), a layer or breeder ration containing an adequate level of Ca as well as other nutrients needs to be made available to the birds. This should preferably be in mash form, although pellets may be used if deemed advisable. Suggested layer and breeder rations are shown in Table 22–8. While rations are formulated in moderate climates to provide a protein intake of 15 percent, it may be necessary, depending upon the strain and rate of production, to provide diets with up to 18 percent protein in warm climates. This is also the case in areas of the country where phase feeding is successfully practiced (see Table 22–2, Fig. 22–1). Where a single stage ration is used throughout, levels of 15-16 percent protein can be utilized unless environmental temperatures are high or for some reason very high energy diets are being used. Energy levels may range from 2530 to 3190 kcal/kg as related to breed and purpose (Table 22–8) and should vary around these figures dependent on feed ingredients involved. For commercial egg producing strains, feed is provided daily on a free-choice basis, regardless of whether birds are housed in cages or on the floor. For heavy breed layers, on the other hand, some degree of restriction is necessary, with the amount of restriction closely correlated to the bird's production rate, body weight, and current environmental temperatures.

For birds that are kept for breeding purposes, males should be introduced at least 4 weeks before fertile eggs are required. Feeds should also be formulated to contain increased levels of the fat-soluble vitamins, E and K; the water-soluble vitamins, riboflavin, pantothenic acid, pyridoxine, biotin, and folacin; and the trace minerals, copper (Cu), iron (Fe), manganese (Mn), selenium (Se), and zinc (Zn). Other nutrients are sometimes needed in increased amounts; these have been discussed earlier but are not critical in the diet described here.

While most diets are now formulated to be complete from the standpoint of all nutrients, on occasion, one might encounter a diet requiring supplemental Ca. If this is the case, it may be provided on a free-choice basis by means of oystershell granules or some other form of grits containing Ca. With the trend towards smaller body size, plus the increased egg production pressure placed on the bird, the need for Ca in very high rates of production may be higher than the 3.25 percent indicated by the NRC. A method has been reported by the Maryland group (23) for estimating Ca needs for layers using the criteria of feed/dozen eggs. A summary of Ca needs for various efficiencies is shown in Table 22–9.

Often little attention is paid to the management and feeding of male chickens, which in flock matings are usually treated similarly to layers. Research has shown that, when holding adult males separately, they may be fed a simplified ration containing not more than 9 percent protein and 1 percent Ca without any adverse affect on subsequent reproductive performance (24). However, it is necessary that body weights in such birds have plateaued before using such rations. This usually occurs by 24 weeks. Further, before mating, males should be exposed to 12-14 h of light 4-6 weeks before fertile eggs are required. Males should be checked periodically for body weight, because weight losses of 10-15 percent have been shown to decrease fertilizing capacity. Figs. 22–4, and 22–5 provide examples of commercial egg production facilities.

TABLE 22-9

Estimated levels of calcium in rations for varying amounts of feed required per dozen eggs

Feed/Doz. Eggs, lb	Calcium in Ration, %[a]
3.0	4.0
3.5	3.4
4.0	3.0
4.5	2.7
5.0	2.4
5.5	2.2
6.0	2.0

[a]Calculated from (0.12 ÷ feed/doz. eggs) × 100, assuming 1.2 lb of dietary Ca is required to produce a doz. 2-oz eggs.
Source: Ott (23).

FIGURE 22-4. Hens in a cage layer operation typical of current production methods.

FIGURE 22-5. Mechanized egg collection equipment.

Starter, Grower, and Breeder Turkeys

As Appendix Table 31 indicates, protein requirements decrease by age and are also influenced by sex. This decreases from 28 percent with poults to 12 and 14 percent for holding turkeys and mature breeders, respectively. Energy requirement levels, on the other hand, tend to increase during the growing stage, ranging from 2640 to 3300 kcal/kg (Table 22–3) and dropping back to 2900 kcal/kg for breeders. Suggested turkey starter-developer and breeder rations are shown in Table 22–10. Turkeys may be fed all-mash-type rations throughout their growing and laying periods. Mash-scratch feeding programs are sometimes utilized during the developing period. Mash feeds may be used; however, pelleted feeds are more desirable for market turkeys. An antibiotic and coccidiostat

TABLE 22-10

Suggested turkey rations

Ingredients	Starter[a] 28% Protein, (2760 kcal/kg) lb	Grower[b] 20% Protein, (2844 kcal/kg) lb	Breeder[c] 15% Protein, (2989 kcal/kg) lb
Corn, yellow gr.[d]	855	1210	1508
Soybean meal, solv. (47.5% prot.)	900	400	107
Meat and bone meal (50% prot.)	100	170	200
Whey, dried	50	50	50
Alfalfa meal, dehy. (17% prot.)	50	100	50
Limestone flour	20	30	40
Dicalcium phosphate	15	30	40
Salt, iodized	10	10	5
Total	2000	2000	2000
Supplements to supply per ton:[e]			
Vitamin A, IU $\times 10^6$	5.0	5.0	5.0
Vitamin D_3, IU $\times 10^6$	1.5	1.0	1.0
Vitamin E supplement, IU $\times 10^3$	5.0	5.0	5.0
Vitamin K (menadione), g	0.5	0.5	0.5
Riboflavin, g	5.0	5.0	4.0
Pantothenic acid, g	7.0	7.0	8.0
Niacin, g	40.0	30.0	30.0
Choline chloride, g	400.0	400.0	400.0
Folacin, g	0.5	0.5	0.5
Vitamin B_{12} (cobalamin), mg	8.0	8.0	8.0
Manganese, g	55.0	55.0	25.0
Methionine, g	908.0	908.0	454.0
Antibiotic, g[g]	4-50	4-50[f]	—
Antioxidant, g[g]	113.5	113.5	113.5
Coccidiostat[h]	+	+[f]	—

[a]Feed day-old to 8 wk of age.

[b]Feed 9-13 wk of age. Mix 600 lb ground corn with 1400 lb grower = 17% protein for 13-17 wk of age. Mix 1000 lb ground corn with 1000 lb grower = 15% protein for 17–24 wk or market age.

[c]Feed at time of lighting through breeder period.

[d]White western wheat and milo may be substituted for part or all the corn dependent on price. Barley may replace up to ¾ of the corn.

[e]Added at expense of gr. grain component when 5 lb or more are involved.

[f]Optional.

[g]Level used is dependent on product, treatment desired, and manufacturer's recommendations.

[h]Coccidiostat fed first 8 wk; level used is dependent on product, treatment desired, and manufacturer's recommendations.

are desirable in starter rations but their use in developer rations is optional. The grower feeds shown are designed to provide a protein intake of 20 percent for 8–13 weeks, and then are reduced to 17 percent through 17 weeks (as noted in footnote c of Table 22–10) with a further reduction to 15 percent protein through market age. Breeder rations should start with the commencement of the lighting program, which usually occurs about 30 weeks of age. Figs. 22–6 and 22–7 show current turkey facilities.

Other Poultry

Rations for ducks, geese, pheasants, and other birds may for the most part be patterned after appropriate poultry formulas, using the indicated protein requirements as a guide and making necessary adjustments for either the vitamin and/or mineral levels as indicated by the NRC (4) or any other sources of information, including reference to Table 22–4 for suggested protein levels (Appendix Tables 40–44).

In feeding ducks, regardless of age, it is usually recommended that pelleted-type rations be utilized because they are easier to consume and tend to minimize feed wastage. Pellet size should be 1/8 in. for starter diets and then may be increased to 3/16 in. thereafter. Ducklings should be fed a starter diet for the first 2 weeks of age, following which they may be placed on a finisher-type diet to market age. Potential

FIGURE 22-6. Young market turkeys under intensive confinement.

FIGURE 22-7. A modern semiconfinement operation with a turkey capacity of 25,000 birds.

breeders should be placed on a breeder-developer diet about one month prior to the date of expected egg production. Because ducks have a higher requirement for niacin than do chickens, supplemental niacin should be provided if chicken rations are substituted.

As noted with ducks, geese should receive pelleted-type diets. Goslings should be fed a starter-type feed for the first 3 weeks of life, followed by a suitable grower feed containing 15-16 percent protein. Pellet size may be similar to that used with ducks. Geese are known as excellent foragers, thus they can be expected to obtain a good portion of their feed by this means by the time they are 5-6 weeks of age. With adequate succulent forage, feed may be restricted to about 1-2 lb/feed/bird/week until they are 12 weeks of age. From 12 weeks to market age, the birds should have access to pellets on a free-choice basis. Either an all-mash or a mash-scratch system of feeding may be utilized, providing the system meets the bird's protein requirements of at least 15 percent after the initial 3-week period. Geese are marketed when they are about 5-6 months of age. Those used for breeding purposes should be provided with a suitable breeder-type ration containing approximately 18 percent protein. This level is somewhat higher than required for other kinds of breeders but, since geese tend to forage extensively, a portion of their diet may consist of material containing less protein. In the absence of a specially designed goose breeder ration, a good chicken breeder ration containing 15-17 percent protein may be utilized. As noted with ducks, supplemental niacin may be needed.

Guinea fowl are fed in a manner very similar to turkeys. They may be fed either mash or pellets. Developer feeds are supplied to keets after about 6 weeks of age. Guineas are marketed generally around 14 weeks of age. As in the case with guineas, the nutritional requirements of pheasants are quite similar to the turkey, and feeding methods described for that species may be utilized in raising these birds.

Experience in the writer's laboratory has shown that Japanese quail may be raised successfully by utilizing a turkey starter diet containing 28 percent protein for the first 2 weeks followed by a well-fortified chicken broiler ration to sexual maturity at 5-6 weeks. For adult quail, a chicken layer or breeder ration containing 15-16 percent protein has given satisfactory results.

SUMMARY

Poultry production has reached a high stage of development in the mid 1990s. This has been made possible by improved knowledge of poultry nutrition and management, disease control, and the development and use of a wide variety of feed additives. In addition, information is constantly being added on the nutritional value of various feedstuffs and environmental problems. Poultry geneticists have been able to produce crossbred birds that can be sexed by feather color and that grow to satisfactory market size in 6 to 7 weeks. Advancements have also resulted in greater layer production at improved efficiency. At this point in time, turkeys are the most efficient warm-blooded farm animals. They can be grown on less feed per pound than chickens and marketing and processing costs are less per pound. Large pieces of flesh are available for production of turkey "hams" and other products that compete directly with cured pork. Ducks, geese, and some quail are also grown in relatively large numbers, but they cannot at this time be managed as easily as chickens or turkeys.

REFERENCES

1. Nesheim, M. C., R. E. Austic, and L. E. Card. 1979. *Poultry production.* Philadelphia: Lea and Febiger.

2. North, M. O. 1984. *Commercial chicken production manual.* 3d ed. Westport, CT: AVI Pub. Co.

3. Scott, M. L., M. C. Nesheim, and R. J. Young. 1982. *Nutrition of the chicken.* 3d ed. Ithaca, NY: M. L. Scott and Assoc.

4. NRC. 1984. *Nutrient requirements of poultry.* 8th ed. Washington, D.C.: Nat. Acad. Press.

5. Scott, M. L. 1987. *Feedstuffs Reference Issue* 59(31):72, 74.

6. NRC. 1982. *United States-Canadian tables of feed composition.* 3d ed. Washington, D.C.: Nat. Acad. Press.

7. Arscott, G. H. 1957. *Oregon Agr. Exp. Sta. Misc. Paper* 35.

8. Arscott, G. H. 1960. In: *Proc. 18th Oregon Animal Industry Conf., Feb. 4–5.* Oregon State Univ., Corvallis, OR.

9. Harper, J. A. and G. A. Arscott. 1974. In: *Proc. 9th Pac. N.W. Animal Nutrition Conf.* Victoria, BC.

10. Harper, J. A. 1973. *Oregon Agr. Exp. Sta. Spec. Rpt.* 397.

11. Nakaue, H. S., J. A. Harper, and R. J. Metzger. 1981. In: *Proc. 16th Annual Pac. N.W. Animal Nutr. Conf., Nov. 4–5.* Boise, ID.

12. Holloran, H. R., and G. C. Cavanagh. 1960. *Poultry Sci.* 39:18.

13. Klosterman, H. J., G. L. Lamoureaux, and J. L. Parsons. 1967. *Biochem.* 6:170.

14. Clandinin, D. R. 1981. *Canola meal for livestock and poultry.* Canola Council of Canada Pub. 59.

15. Cheeke, P. R. 1971. *Can. J. Animal Sci.* 51:621.

16. Anon. 1989. *Feed additive compendium.* Minnetonka, MN: Miller Pub. Co.

17. Couch, J. R. 1968. *Proc. Distillers Feed Res. Coun.* 23:35.

18. Couch, J. R., et al. 1970. *Proc. Distillers Feed Res. Coun.* 25:35.

19. Kent, O. B. 1953. *Feedstuffs* 25(39):32.

20. Knight, C. M., M. C. Wilkening, and W. H. Gosset. 1965. *Feedstuffs* 37(43):30.

21. Anon. 1974, 1989. *Poultry management and business analysis manual for the 80's.* Coop. Ext. Ser., Univ. of Maine, N. Hampshire, Mass., Conn., Rhode Island, and Vermont Bul. 566 (revised).

22. Sell, J. L. 1989. *Turkey World* 56(1):8.

23. Combs, G. F., and N. V. Helbacka. 1960. *Feedstuffs* 32(40):32.

24. Arscott, G. H., and J. E. Parker. 1966. *Poultry Sci.* 45:1266.

23

Feeding Horses

E. A. Ott

INTRODUCTION

Providing suitable feeding programs for horses has been a challenge ever since the species was domesticated 5000-6000 years ago. Variations in availability of feedstuffs and the nutrient content of these feedstuffs have plagued horse-raisers for many years. Through trial and error, individual feedstuffs and combinations of feedstuffs were found to result in desirable responses by the animal. Horse feeding thus became an art, and those techniques which proved advantageous were passed from one generation to the next.

Only in this century and particularly during the past 20 years has sufficient information been assembled to allow the scientific formulation of horse rations to meet the nutrient requirements of the animal. There are still many gaps in this information, and continued research is needed on the nutrient requirements of different classes of horses. It is interesting to note that many of the feeding techniques used years ago have been shown to have provided satisfactory levels of essential nutrients needed by horses.

Planning feeding programs for horses requires that consideration be given to the digestive tract of the animal. The horse is a monogastric herbivore—a simple-stomached animal that has developed the ability to utilize forages. The unusual nature of this digestive system necessitates that feeding programs be compatible with physical limitations of the animal. This aspect of feeding horses will be discussed in greater detail later in this chapter.

CRITICAL NUTRIENTS

Energy requirements of the horse are expressed by the NRC as megacalories (Mcal) of digestible energy (DE)/d or per unit of feed (19). The daily DE requirements for maintenance is represented by the following equation:

$$DE \ (Mcal/d) = 1.4 + 0.03 \ BW$$

where BW is body weight in kg. The requirement table and the nutrient composition table (Appendix Tables 45 and 46) are based on digestibility studies where available. When suit-

417

able values were not present in the literature, appropriate calculations were made from available data to provide a best estimate of the information.

Protein requirements (NRC, 20) are expressed as crude protein (N × 6.25). Digestible protein (DP) is not used because there is little information on the DP requirements of horses or the DP content of feeds. In reality, the horse requires amino acids just as do other nonruminant animals. Lysine is the only amino acid that has been studied extensively, and recommendations are included in the appendix tables.

Ca and P are particularly important to the horse, as they influence the structure and durability of the skeletal system. Inadequate Ca and P intakes will result in osteoperosis or inadequate bone mineralization, which is accompanied by lameness, tenderness of joints, and sometimes spontaneous fractures. Ca and P needs are shown in Appendix Table 45.

Na and Cl (salt) are needed in greater amounts by horses than by other domestic species. This is due to salt loss in perspiration. Inadequate salt intake will result in dehydration, acid base imbalance, and loss of appetite. Adequate Na intake will normally ensure adequate Cl intake. Mg is required as an activator of enzymes involved in energy, lipid, and amino acid metabolism. Horses appear to have lower requirements for Mg than cattle because they can graze pastures that cause grass tetany in cattle without problems. K is generally provided in adequate quantities when horses graze high-quality forages or consume high-quality hay. Horses on high-concentrate diets may need K supplementation. S is an integral part of the amino acids cystine and methionine. Adequate intake of high-quality protein will usually ensure adequate S intake.

Fe, Zn, Mn, Cu, Co, I, and Se supplementation of diets should be considered if horses are raised on areas known to be low in any of these minerals. Horses fed feed ingredients from undocumented sources should also be supplemented as a matter of insurance against possible deficiencies. These trace minerals are required in very small quantities and can be added to the concentrate or free-choice salt.

Vitamin A, D, and E requirements are shown in Appendix Table 46. Vitamin A requirements are usually met by the conversion of carotene in forages to vitamin A. Horses on good-quality pastures will not need vitamin A supplementation. Horses on hay should be supplemented with vitamin A, since carotene content of the hay and utilization of the carotene decreases with storage time (9). Vitamin D is not required if animals are given sufficient exposure to direct sunlight (8). Stalled horses should receive supplemental vitamin D. Vitamin E recommendations have been increased based on data that indicates that it is required for maximum immune response in the animal (4). Dietary supplementation of vitamins C and K should not be required by the horse because considerable synthesis occurs in the gut. The B-complex vitamins are also synthesized in adequate quantities in the gut of most horses, so supplementation is not needed for most horses. Performance horses and show horses that are under stress may respond to B-vitamin supplementation. Estimated daily requirements and suggested supplementation needs are shown in Table 23-1.

FACTORS INFLUENCING THE NUTRIENT REQUIREMENTS

The nutrient requirements for different classes of horses vary with the animal's size and use. The maintenance requirements must first be

TABLE 23-1

Estimated daily B-complex vitamin requirements and suggested supplementation levels for horses

Vitamin	Daily Need	Suggested Supplementation Level
Thiamin, mg	36	18-36
Riboflavin, mg	60	0-45
Niacin, mg	300	0-150
Pantothenic acid, mg	150	0-75
Folic acid, mg	10	5-10
Biotin, mg	2	1-2
Choline, mg	10,000	0-5000
B_{12}, μg	200	0-200

satisfied, followed by those needs imposed by the additional activities of reproduction, growth, and exercise. Maintenance needs include those necessary to maintain the animal without weight loss and normal activities associated with feeding. Thus many mature horses not being used for breeding purposes or daily riding have only maintenance requirements.

Maintenance

Maintenance requirements are influenced primarily by the animal's size, the environment in which it exists, and the variation between individuals, including metabolic activity and digestive efficiency. It must be understood, therefore, that the requirement tables cannot take into account all of the possible variations. Modifications in nutrient intake are required for extremes in environment and those individuals who may be classified as "hard keepers" and "easy keepers." The eye of the master is, therefore, still important in maintaining the desired body condition of each horse.

The needs for maintenance can usually be met by simple rations. Reproduction, growth, and exercise increase these needs, requiring a conscious effort to balance the ration to satisfy the total needs of the animal. The requirements for the various activities may be expressed as an increment above maintenance, or the total needs of the animal may be combined into a single value.

Reproduction

The increased demands for reproduction are mediated primarily through the mare. The open mare and the mare in early gestation are considered to have only a maintenance requirement. The open mare should be placed on an in-

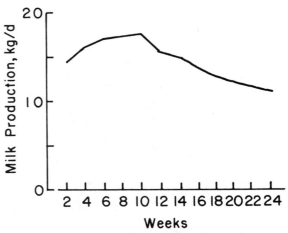

FIGURE 23–1. Mean daily milk production of mares. From Bouman and Van Der Schee (3).

creased plane of nutrition a few weeks prior to and during the breeding season to help stimulate ovarian activity. During the last 90 d of the gestation period, about 60 percent of the weight of the fetus develops (5). Increased intake of energy, protein, minerals, and vitamins is needed to support this rapid development, but this increased demand is still small in comparison to that which occurs after the foal is born. During the first 3 months of lactation the typical mare of light horse breeding will produce 32-38 lb (14.5-17.5 kg) of milk daily (3, 18). Milk production peaks 9-10 weeks after parturition and gradually declines (Fig. 23–1). Mare's colostrum is high in solids and protein but declines quickly. Solids, protein, lipids, energy, Ca, and P will decline gradually during lactation, while lactose increases (Table 23–2).

Average mare's milk contains 525 kcal GE/kg, 2.2% CP, 875 mg Ca/kg, and 526 mg P/kg. The mare must, therefore, meet her maintenance needs plus that for the milk she is pro-

TABLE 23-2

Composition of mare's milk

	Total Solids, %	Crude Protein, %	Lipids, %	Lactose, %	Calcium, mg/kg	Phos., mg/kg	Gross Energy, kcal/kg
Partum	25.2	19.1	0.7	4.6	1000	850	1350
12 h	11.5	3.8	2.4	4.8	1050	800	640
24 h	11.4	3.3	2.5	5.2	1050	800	620
48 h	12.0	3.3	2.5	5.8	1199	700	620
5 d	11.6	3.1	2.1	5.9	1199	700	590
Weeks 1–4	10.8	2.7	1.8	6.4	1148	698	575
Weeks 5–8	10.4	2.1	1.5	6.6	951	596	525
Weeks 9–17	10.2	2.0	1.2	6.5	724	557	500

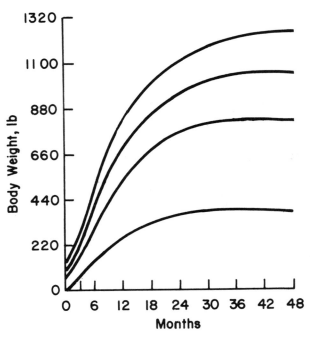

FIGURE 23–2. Growth rates of horses of four different mature weights (19).

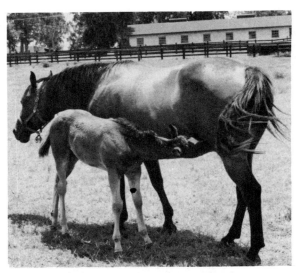

FIGURE 23–3. Milk is the foal's primary source of nutrients during the first few months of life.

ducing. Failure to meet both demands results in reduced milk production, weight loss, or both.

The stallion's requirements increase during the breeding season, primarily as a result of the increased physical activity. His needs are most closely related to those of a performance horse.

Growth

The nutrient requirements of the growing foal are directly related to the growth rate of the animal (Fig. 23–2). The nursing foal may gain in excess of 3 lb (1.4 kg)/d, while the yearling will gain 0.5–1.5 lb (0.23–0.68 kg) daily. Fig. 23–3 illustrates the rate of development of several types of horses. Conversely, rate of gain is influenced by energy and protein intake. Restricting energy intake will slow growth and decrease muscle and fat deposition. The protein

needs are directly related to the availability and quality of the protein supplied. The amino acid lysine has been shown to be the first limiting amino acid in typical diets for growing foals. The weanling requires about 36 g and the yearling 40 g of lysine daily, or about 0.7 and 0.5 percent lysine in the total diet, respectively, assuming feed intakes of 2.5 lb/100 lb BW (16, 24).

Most of the bone development of a foal occurs during the first year of life, thus Ca and P intakes are particularly critical during this period. In addition to meeting the minimum requirements for these two minerals, it is also important to maintain a proper ratio. Table 23–3 provides recommendations on the proper Ca:P ratio for growing foals and mature horses. It should be noted that the younger the foal, the more critical the ratio.

Exercise (Work)

Exercise primarily influences the energy requirement of the animal. Energy requirements for work are added to the maintenance require-

TABLE 23-3

Calcium to phosphorus ratio for complete rations

	Minimum Ca:P	Maximum Ca:P	Optimum Ca:P
Nursing foal	1:1	1.5:1	1.2:1
Weanling	1:1	2.0:1	1.5:1
Yearling	1:1	3.0:1	2.0:1
Long yearling	1:1	3.0:1	2.0:1
Mature	1:1	5.0:1	2.0:1

TABLE 23-4

Digestible energy (DE) expenditures of horses at work[a]

Activity	Speed		DE, kcal/kg/h
	Miles/h	m/min	
Walk	4	107	2.86
Brisk walk or slow trot	6	161	4.68
Slow canter	8	215	7.26
Med. trot or canter	10	268	10.85
Hand gallop	15	402	27.96
Breeze	30	805	402.45

[a]Calculated from the data of Pagan and Hintz (26).

TABLE 23-5

Effect of exercise on daily sweat and mineral losses by horses (500-kg horse)

	Work[a]		
	Light	Moderate	Heavy
Sweat loss, liters[b]	2.5	10	25
Calcium, g	0.48	1.9	4.75
Phosphorus, g	0.55	2.2	5.50
Sodium, g	8.25	33.0	82.5
Potassium, g	4.5	18.0	45.0
Chloride, g	15.25	61.0	152.5
Magnesium, g	0.30	1.2	3.0
Iron, mg	50	200	500
Manganese, mg	0.5	2.0	5.0
Zinc, mg	25	100	250
Copper, mg	10	40	100

[a]Work is a function of intensity and duration of exercise.
[b]Sweat loss will also be influenced by ambient temperature and humidity.
Source: Adapted from Meyer (17).

ments and are a function of type of activity, time, and weight moved (13). DE requirements for various activities are shown in Table 23–4. The DE expenditure must be multiplied by the weight of the horse and rider in kg and the number of hours the horse is worked and added to the maintenance requirement to get total DE requirements. Other nutrients necessary for energy metabolism are increased in proportion to the increased energy requirement.

Exercise also has a direct effect on other nutrient requirements due to nutrient loss in perspiration. Although perspiration loss will vary with work intensity and duration, training status, and ambient environment, estimated perspiration losses times perspiration composition provides a useable projection of the effect of exercise on nutrient loss by the animal (Table 23–5).

FEEDSTUFFS FOR HORSES

The horse is relatively flexible with regard to feedstuffs that it will eat. In maintenance situations, forages can make up most of the daily diet. Only minerals may need to be supplemented. However, when energy demands are high, such as for the performance horse, a diet providing as much as 75 percent concentrate can be fed if managed properly.

Forage

Pasture. Most grasses can be used as pasturage for horses. These include: bluegrass, Bermuda grass, bluestem, bahiagrass, timothy, orchard grass, bromegrass, fescue, and cereal grains as well as many native grasses, forbs, and browse. Sorghum and sorghum-Sudan hybrids are generally not recommended for horses, as they have been linked to cystitis problems in mares. Grass-legume mixtures using one or more legumes including lespedeza, ladino and red clovers, birdsfoot trefoil, and alfalfa with the above grasses also make excellent pastures. Horses are selective and tend to graze the youngest and most tender forage. Palatability of grasses will vary with season, maturity, and species. Excellent management including proper fertilization, rotational grazing with cattle, and/or mowing are essential for maximum utilization and productivity of pastures. During peak growing seasons, well-managed pastures may support up to two animals/acre. At other times, 3–4 acres may be required/animal to prevent overgrazing.

Hay. If pasture is unavailable, of poor quality, or not practical in the feeding program, a high-quality hay free from weeds, dust, and mold will be an essential part of the daily diet. Hay should be green and leafy, an indication that it was cured properly and will likely have a high nutritive value. The type of hay used will depend upon availability, economics, and the horseraiser's preference.

Timothy, orchard grass, bromegrass, Bermuda grass, bluestem, grama, ryegrass, and several native grasses make excellent hays for horses. These hays are palatable and are usually less dusty and less likely to be moldy than legume hays. The nutrient content of grass hays tends to be low, and their exclusive use will necessitate higher levels of supplementation than are necessary when mixed hays or straight legume hays are used (see Ch. 6). The legumes are high in nutrient content and palatable to the horse, and they may be fed by themselves or in combination with grass hays. Legume hays are more dense and difficult to cure properly and are thus more prone to mold and dustiness. Alfalfa hay is more laxative than grass hays and will result in less well-formed feces. This does not seem to be detrimental to the horse. A few horses (perhaps 2–3 percent) appear to be allergic to alfalfa. They produce excessive amounts of dark urine if given even small quantities of the hay. Changing to another type of hay will alleviate the problem with no apparent permanent effects. Its use for other horses should not be precluded on this basis.

Composition, digestibility, and nutritive value index of three cuttings of alfalfa, timothy, and bromegrass hays are shown in Table 23–6. The nutritive value index (the product of the relative intake times the energy digestibility of

the hay) demonstrates the difficulty in assessing the value of hay from its composition. There was a general decrease in the value of the hay with each subsequent cutting. The relative value of the three species varies with each cutting.

Dehydrated Alfalfa Meal. Dehydrated alfalfa meal is an excellent ingredient for horse rations. It is a rich source of protein (17–20 percent), minerals, vitamins, and unidentified factors. Whenever alfalfa meal is used, it should be of the highest quality, with a bright green color, and it should contain a minimum of 17 percent crude protein and 100,000 IU of vitamin A activity/lb. High-quality alfalfa meal is the closest substitute for green pasture and may be particularly valuable during periods of the year when green pastures are not available. Dehydrated alfalfa meal may be included in grain rations at levels of 5–15 percent and up to 30 percent in complete rations. Higher levels may cause some palatability problems. It is best to use pelleted dehydrated alfalfa in coarse type grain rations. Dehydrated alfalfa is laxative in nature and due to its small particle size should be fed with some coarser roughages.

Silage, Haylage. Haylage and silage can both be fed to horses and are excellent sources of nutrients. Their use in North America is low due to the risk of mycotoxicosis from improperly ensiled material or the spoilage of the feed after it is fed. With proper management, the use of haylage and silage could provide an excellent alternative to hay in areas where hay curing is difficult.

Energy Feeds

Grains. In North America, oats is the most popular grain for horses. It is the standard by which all other grains are compared. Oats is a less concentrated source of energy than the other grains because of the bulky hulls. This results in a tendency to form a loose mass in the stomach, whereas some of the other grains tend to form a dense mass. It is best to roll or crush oats for horses with poor teeth or for young foals. Oats vary in weight from less than 32 to greater than 42 lb/bu. Heavy, bright, clean oats, which contain a small percentage of hull, are preferred for horses. Musty oats should never be fed because they may cause digestive disturbances and result in colic.

Corn is the second most popular grain for horses. It is higher in energy than oats and can

TABLE 23-6

Composition and digestibility of three cuttings of alfalfa, timothy, and orchard grass hay by horses

| | Cutting* | | |
	First	Second	Third
Composition			
Crude protein, %			
Alfalfa	15.05	14.40	9.05
Timothy	9.99	8.32	6.47
Orchard grass	14.00	10.87	6.53
Crude fiber, %			
Alfalfa	28.32	32.66	38.74
Timothy	32.47	35.12	36.38
Orchard grass	30.86	32.26	37.98
Digestibility			
Crude protein, %			
Alfalfa	74.5[1a]	72.1[1c]	55.2[2f]
Timothy	65.2[3b]	62.1[2d]	55.3[4f]
Orchard grass	68.3[5b]	66.9[5c]	52.4[6f]
Digestible energy, %			
Alfalfa	64.8[1a]	55.9[2d]	51.6[3f]
Timothy	63.0[4b]	56.5[5d]	55.1[5g]
Orchard grass	58.0[6c]	54.8[7e]	49.1[8h]
Nutritive value index†			
Alfalfa	77.1[1a]	61.0[2d]	42.0[3f]
Timothy	63.8[4b]	61.3[4d]	56.6[5g]
Orchard grass	58.6[6c]	54.6[7e]	50.6[8h]

*Within each category, means on the same line having different superscript numbers differ ($P < .05$). Within each category, means in the same column having different superscript letters differ ($P < .05$).

†Product of the relative intake times percent DE.

Source: Darlington and Hershberger (7).

be used to increase the energy content of the diet. Corn can be fed as the only grain, but it is best utilized in a mixture with oats or other less dense ingredients. Corn should be cracked, coarsely ground, or rolled. Finely ground corn should not be fed except in pelleted form, and then only if mixed with bulky ingredients to prevent impaction and colic.

Barley is very popular and used quite extensively for horses in the western part of the United States and Canada and in many other countries. Most horseraisers who use barley in North America prefer to mix it with oats in about equal parts. Barley is hard, thus it should be coarsely ground or, preferably, steam-rolled.

Wheat is not generally fed in large quantities to horses. Because of its hardness, it should be processed prior to feeding. When ground, it is rather doughy and tends to ball up with moisture. Grain sorghums have similar characteristics. Both wheat and sorghum grains are best rolled and mixed at low levels with bulky

feeds such as oats or wheat bran or ground and incorporated into pellets.

All grains should be of good quality and not moldy, dusty, or spoiled. Processing grains will improve digestive efficiency for young horses, performance horses, and those animals that do not chew feed adequately (Table 23–7). Any processing method used should facilitate enzymatic action on the grain without producing a dusty, floury product that will be low in palatability or cause doughy compaction in the digestive tract (22).

By-Products. Wheat bran can be used as both an energy and a protein source. It is a common ingredient in commercial horse feeds and farm-mixed rations. Most horse owners extol this ingredient for its high P content and its bulky, laxative characteristics. In contrast to its popularity, it also has a notorious history. In the late 19th and early 20th centuries, it was identified as one of the primary causes of Bighead or Miller's disease. Horses fed high levels of mill-

TABLE 23-7

Effect of processing grains on their use by horses

Process	Type of Animal Fed	Advantage for Processing
Ground grain vs. whole	Yearlings	9%
Shelled corn vs. corn meal	Mature horses	0
Ground ear corn and oats vs. whole grain	Yearlings	25%
Crushed oats vs. whole oats	Working horses	5-6%
Crushed oats vs. whole oats	Weanlings & yearlings	21-24%

Source: Ott (22).

ing by-products developed nutritional-secondary hyperparathyroidism as a result of consuming high levels of P in the absence of adequate Ca. Proper balancing of rations eliminated this problem, however, the use of high levels of wheat bran as dietary supplements added at the farm will sometimes unbalance otherwise satisfactory feeding programs. It is recommended that concentrates contain 7-15 percent wheat bran when fed with grass hay to improve the laxative characteristics of the diet. P in wheat bran is about half as available to the animal as P from NaH_2PO_4 and other inorganic sources (14).

Wheat middlings and closely related milling by-products can be used as grain substitutes in pelleted diets. They are floury and dusty and are not suitable in other diet forms unless incorporated into a pelleted supplement. The energy and protein in these products are readily available to the horse.

Molasses is a good energy source and can be included at levels of 5-15 percent in the grain mixture. Liquid molasses enhances the palatability of the feed, reduces dustiness, and helps to texturize the feed. Its ability to stick the ingredients together to prevent separation is one of its biggest assets.

Hominy feed may be used as a partial substitute for grain in pelleted diets. It is not suitable for use in coarse type diets unless it is incorporated into a pelleted supplement.

Citrus pulp can be used as an energy source in pelleted diets, however, it is not very palatable to horses and is, therefore, not acceptable in coarse diets. Digestion studies have indicated that the substitution of citrus pulp for oats at 15 or 30 percent of the diet results in a small increase in energy digestibility (23). Protein digestibility is somewhat lower, indicating that this product should not be used for growing foals.

Dried beet pulp is not well liked by horses but, when combined with molasses and other ingredients, it can be fed as a substitute for grain and as a source of bulk. It has been fed successfully in both loose and pelleted form. Some companies have used beet pulp as a roughage substitute in antiallergenic diets.

Rice bran can be fed as a source of energy and bulk. Its high fat content requires that the product be stabilized for maximum shelf life. Additional antioxidant should be added to the diet when this ingredient is used.

Oat mill feed and oat hulls can be used to dilute the energy content of corn and other high-energy grains. Their nutrient values are quite low and they should therefore be used only to control the energy content of products.

Animal fats and vegetable oils can be used as highly concentrated energy sources for horses. Animal fats are generally lower in palatability than vegetable oils. Blended fats are usually acceptable. These products can also be used as a source of essential fatty acids when other dietary ingredients are too low in fat to meet the animal's needs. Vegetable oils are valued for their ability to put a bloom on the animal.

Protein Supplements

Oil seed meals are the most popular sources of supplemental protein for horses. Today, soybean meal is the most popular. In North America it is available in 44 and 49 percent protein levels (as-fed basis). Soybean meal is higher in lysine and methionine than the other oil meals and combines with grains to produce a ration with a high-quality protein. Some horses find soybean meal unpalatable and will sort it out of a coarse type ration. The addition of molasses or pelleting the grain ration will minimize this problem.

Linseed meal (flax seed meal) was at one time a very popular ration ingredient for horses. The expeller processed meal is high in fat and results in a bloom and hair coat luster which is difficult to achieve by other means. Linseed meal is now processed by solvent extraction and is, thus, low in fat. Its amino acid composition is inferior to that of soybean meal, thus it is no longer used in large quantities. Linseed meal is usually the most expensive of the oilseed meals.

Cottonseed meal has a lower-quality protein than soybean meal. The high gossypol content of poorly processed cottonseed meal may cause problems for young foals. Good-quality cottonseed meal properly supplemented with lysine will support excellent growth in yearlings (16). It can be fed at low levels to mature horses without lysine supplementation.

Milk protein products, such as dried skimmed milk, are high in nutritive value but are usually more expensive than vegetable protein. They are usually economically impractical except when it becomes necessary to feed a young foal to supplement or replace mare's milk (Fig. 23–3).

Fish meal is also a very high-quality protein (29). It is seldom fed to horses in North America because of palatability problems and its high cost. Fish meal is used successfully in horse rations in Europe.

Brewers dried grains (BDG) can be used as both an energy and protein source for horses. Data from the Florida Experiment station (23) indicate that this ingredient has a DE content of 3.0 Mcal/kg (as fed) when fed at 20 percent of the diet and 2.7 Mcal/kg (as fed) when fed at 40 percent of the diet. The substitution of 20 or 40 percent BDG for oats and soybean meal did not result in a lower crude protein digestibility by horses. Protein quality of BDG is fairly low. Lysine content is about 1.0 percent, which is considerably less than the 1.43 percent lysine provided by a mixture of oats and soybean meal that will provide the same amount of protein. Research results with growing foals indicate that BDG will not provide adequate lysine for growing foals when used as the sole source of supplemental protein (23, 24). It is recommended that concentrates containing BDG as the primary protein supplement be fortified with 0.1 percent lysine for yearlings and 0.2 percent lysine for weanlings.

Distillers dried grains with or without solubles can be substituted for part of the grain and provide part of the protein supplement for horses. The protein in this ingredient is also low in lysine, and appropriate supplementation is recommended for growing foals. Distillers dried grains with solubles has been shown to stimulate cecal fermentation, but the factor appears to be digested and absorbed prior to reaching the cecum in intact horses.

Corn gluten meal can be used as both an energy and protein source in pelleted products. Its protein quality is relatively low due to its low lysine level. Horses have been shown to digest a smaller portion of corn gluten meal protein than fish meal protein, thus requiring a higher protein intake for a positive N balance (27).

Other oil meals and by-product protein sources such as rapeseed meal, safflower meal, sunflower meal, or legume seed screenings have found little use by horse feeders. The amino acid content of many of these feeds make them more suitable for ruminants than for horses.

Water

A supply of clean fresh water should always be available to horses except immediately after heavy exercise (Fig. 23–4). Following heavy exercise or a period of water deprivation, small quantities (a few swallows) of water should be allowed at 5–10 minute intervals until thirst is quenched. This will prevent digestive disturbances and possible founder from excess water intake.

Horses should never be allowed to drink from stagnant ponds or polluted streams. Automatic water systems which incorporate a float valve or other mechanisms for controlling the flow of water into durable, safe receptacles are desirable. Stalled horses should be provided water via individual automatic waters or buckets. Either system should allow for easy cleaning of the receptacle. Watering in buckets has the advantage of allowing easy appraisal of consumption levels but requires more labor to ensure that the buckets are kept filled.

Water consumption will vary with the individual horse, ration fed, exercise type and

FIGURE 23–4. A used concrete culvert equipped with a float valve makes an excellent watering trough for horses.

TABLE 23-8

Feeding programs for horses

	Pasture	Hay	Grain[a]	Free-Choice Minerals[b]	Water	Examples
1	+	−	−	+	+	Maintenance, pleasure horses, mares in early gestation
2	+	−	+	+	+	Lactating mares, working horses
3	+	+	+	+	+	Early or late pasture season
4	−	+	+	+	+	Horses in training, show and race horses
5	Complete ration			+	+	Pleasure and show horses with limited space

[a]Grain may be a single grain or a mixed grain ration including supplements.
[b]Salt and a mineral mixture providing Ca, P, and trace minerals.

amount, and weather conditions. Adequate water intake is as important as feed intake.

METHODS OF FEEDING

Feeding programs for horses vary from one area to another and among farms within an area. The primary factors influencing the selection of a feeding program include: pasture availability and cost; climate and season of the year; animal type, including reproductive status, age, breed, and sex; exercise level; facilities available; and expected feed intake. Typical feeding programs are shown in Table 23–8.

Feed consumption by horses will vary with the type of animal being fed, the form of the ration, and the previous feeding program. Typical feed intakes are shown in Table 23–9. Some variations from this may occur and should be recognized as normal in those animals because animals differ in their ability to consume food. Consequently, it may be necessary to shift the forage and grain ratios to achieve the desired energy consumption. Such limitations must be considered when formulating rations.

Feeding Pleasure Horses

Many pleasure horses are only ridden once or twice each week. For these animals maintenance levels of nutrient intake will usually be adequate. Ample high-quality pasture will provide adequate energy, protein, and vitamin needs of most of these animals. Free-choice minerals and water will complete their needs. When pasture availability and quality are limited, hay may be used to provide most of the nutrients. A concentrate or grain ration is usually used to supplement the hay to ensure adequate levels of required nutrients and to reduce "hay belly." Pleasure horses receiving daily exercise will need some grain with hay or pasture to maintain satisfactory body condition.

Feeding the Broodmare

Open mares should be kept at moderate body condition and placed on an increased plane of nutrition 30–45 d before the breeding season and kept at this level until in foal. Feeding 0.5–1.0 lb/100 lb BW of grain ration is usually sufficient if adequate forage is available. Pregnant mares

TABLE 23-9

Expected daily feed consumption by different classes of horses expressed as a percentage of body weight

	Forage Intake	Grain Intake	Total Intake
Weaning foals	0.5–1.5	1.5–2.5	2.5–3.5
Yearling foals	1.0–1.5	1.0–1.5	2.0–3.0
Two-year-olds	1.0–1.5	1.0–1.5	2.0–2.5
Mature horses			
Maintenance	1.5–2.0	0.0–0.5	1.5–2.0
Late gestation	1.0–2.0	1.5–2.0	2.0–2.5
Lactation	1.0–1.5	1.0–2.0	2.5–3.5
Performance	1.0–1.5	1.0–1.5	2.0–3.0

will usually maintain satisfactory body condition on high-quality pasture or hay until 90 d before foaling. Nutrient intake should be increased by feeding 0.5–0.75 lb/100 lb BW of a grain ration; the amount should be increased to 1.0 lb/100 lb BW during the last 30 d. After foaling, the grain ration should be increased to 1.5 lb/100 lb BW to maintain satisfactory milk production. Grain ration feeding levels may need to be varied to suit individual animals. Hard keepers may require 20–40 percent above the recommendations and easy keepers 20–40 percent below the above recommendations. Adequate quantities of high-quality pasture or hay should be available to the mares in addition to the grain rations.

Feeding Foals

Most of the nutrients the foal needs for the first 2–3 months will come from the dam's milk. Most foals will start eating the mare's grain ration, grass, and hay at an early age, but it has been shown that foals from good milk producers do not eat as much feed as foals from poor milk producers. Milk production peaks when the foal is 2–3 months of age and after that time provides a smaller and smaller portion of the foal's needs. If the mare is receiving a grain ration, most foals eat with the mare, but the nutrient concentrations of the mare's ration are usually less than that needed by the foal for maximum growth (Fig. 23–5). A grain ration designed specifically for the foal should be fed in a separate feeder in the stall or creep feeder in the pasture. Typical foals will eat a pound of grain ration/month of age/d but will increase this intake after weaning. Foals may be weaned anytime after 3 months of age if they are eating well.

FIGURE 23–5. One type of creep feeder which allows the foal continuous access to feed while excluding the mare.

Weanlings should be fed a grain ration to appetite two or three times daily. They will eat 1.5–1.7 lb/100 lb BW daily. They should also receive high-quality hay, about 1 lb/100 lb BW/d, or have access to high-quality pasture. Due to variations in rate of eating or social dominance, foals should be fed individually whenever possible. This will increase uniformity of development. Paired feeding programs also work well if the paired foals are similar in temperament and attitude. Group feeding systems, although handled well on some farms, generally result in more variations in development and increased risk of digestive upsets.

Yearlings should be grouped by sex in pastures and paddocks that will accommodate 6–10 animals. Grain rations should be fed individually twice daily. Yearlings will eat 1.6–1.8 lb/100 lb BW/d of grain and should be limited to no more than 2.0 lb/100 lb BW/d to prevent digestive upsets and obesity. Hay should be fed at 1.0 lb/100 lb BW/d unless adequate high-quality pasture is available. Feed adjustments will be necessary as the animals approach their 2-year-old year. Yearlings not being trained will need less grain and more forage. Animals in training may need greater concentrate levels to maintain suitable body conditions.

Feeding the Performance Horse

Horses in training for various performance events are generally ridden daily and have relatively high energy expenditures. These horses are usually stalled and thus most of their forage intake will be hay. Equal quantities of hay and concentrate work well for most animals, but hard-working horses may need more concentrate than forage to satisfy energy requirements (Fig. 23–6). In no case should they receive less than 1 lb forage/100 lb BW daily.

At high levels of feed intake, multiple feedings may be necessary to minimize digestive disturbances. Concentrate intake for a 1000–1100 lb animal should be limited to 6–7 lb/feeding. An animal receiving 7 lb or less can be fed once daily, but those receiving 8–14 lb should be fed twice daily and those receiving over 14 lb should be fed three times daily. Traditional concentrates for performance horses are predominantly oats, however, pelleted concentrates combining other energy sources such as corn with high-fiber feeds to give a digestible energy level similar to oats will give comparable results.

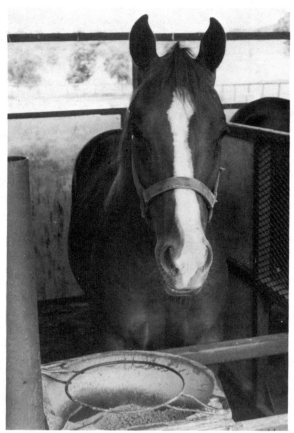

FIGURE 23–6. Mineral supplements may be fed in feeders such as the type illustrated here.

FORMULATING RATIONS

The purpose of formulating rations is to combine the available ingredients into a mixture which, when fed to the horse, will meet its daily nutrient requirements. A review of the nutrient requirement tables in the Appendix indicates that it would be possible, but not practical, to formulate a different ration for each horse on the farm due to the variation present in size and activity. Therefore, those animals with similar requirements should be grouped and a single ration formulated which, when fed in different amounts, will meet each animal's needs. A farm should seldom need more than three or four different rations, and most farms will do well with only one or two.

Variations in ingredient availability and cost will influence ration formulations and result in considerable variation between different areas of the country. Rations may be extremely simple or complex, depending on the nutrient requirements of the animal being fed. A ration containing 4 or 5 major ingredients can be just

as nutritious as one providing the same nutrients with 15 or 20 ingredients.

Example Formulas for Horses

A great variety of ingredient combinations can be used to provide the nutrients required by the horse. Horse owners should resist the temptation to classify any single ingredient as essential in the feeding program. Likewise, a long list of ingredients should not be considered preferable to a well-planned but more simple program. For example, alfalfa hay, shelled corn, free-choice minerals, and water will provide a satisfactory feeding program for some horses. Adding other ingredients may improve the diet's physical form, appearance, and texture, but would not necessarily improve its ability to meet the animal's nutritional requirements. However, such simple formulas may require greater management skills than other programs because of their high nutrient density.

More typical formulations are shown in Table 23–10. All of the formulas shown may be fed in either coarse or pelleted form except formula A, which contains too much molasses to pellet readily. Other ingredients may be substituted for those shown, where availability or economics dictate. The trace mineral and vitamin premixes should be selected to provide suitable nutrient levels discussed earlier. The amount of premix may need to be varied depending on the concentration of the products available.

Formula A is a sweet feed or high-molasses concentrate. It is formulated to be used as a grain ration to supplement good-quality forage for mature horses. This type of product is also frequently blended with oats and other ingredients to make a farm-formulated ration. When used in this way, it should be recognized that the sweet feed is usually lower in protein than oats and the oats are lower in Ca than the sweet feed.

Formula B is a coarse-grain concentrate designed to supplement good-quality grass forage for 2-year-old and older horses. This formula will meet the needs of horses in training and of stallions and mares in late gestation.

Formula C is a pelleted grain concentrate designed to supplement good-quality grass forage for yearlings and lactating mares.

Formula D is a pelleted grain concentrate designed to use as a creep feed for nursing foals and for weanlings receiving good-quality grass forage.

TABLE 23-10

Example formulas for horses (figures are percents)

Ingredients	Concentrates (Grain Rations)				Protein Supplement	Complete Ration
	A	B	C	D		
Alfalfa hay, s.c.	—	—	—	—	—	65.00
Oats, rolled	44.50	38.00	30.25	30.00	—	—
Corn, cracked	25.00	30.00	39.00	30.00	—	25.50
Soybean meal, 44% protein	—	3.00	11.00	19.75	58.00	—
Wheat bran	7.00	10.00	7.00	7.00	21.00	—
Alfalfa, dehy., 17% protein	10.00	10.00	10.00	10.00	8.00	—
Molasses	12.00	7.00	—	—	7.00	8.00
Limestone	0.50	0.50	0.75	1.00	1.00	—
Dicalcium phosphate	—	0.25	0.75	1.00	3.00	0.50
Salt	0.75	0.75	0.75	0.75	1.00	0.50
Trace mineral premix	0.12	0.25	0.25	0.25	0.50	0.125
Vitamin premix	0.12	0.25	0.25	0.25	0.50	0.125
Calculated analyses (as fed)						
Digestible energy, Mcal/kg	2.84	2.88	2.88	2.95	2.92	2.31
Crude protein, %	10.90	12.25	14.90	18.23	30.00	11.80
Calcium, %	0.48	0.51	0.66	0.85	1.50	0.90
Phosphorus, %	0.31	0.40	0.51	0.59	1.00	0.30
Form	coarse	coarse	pelleted[a]	pelleted[a]	pelleted[a]	pelleted[a]

[a] Grains must be ground for pelleted products.

When alfalfa, clover, or legume-grass mixed hays having at least 50 percent legume are fed, the protein content of the concentrate can be reduced two or three percentage units and the Ca levels reduced to equal the P content of the concentrate. When poor-quality forages are fed, the nutrient content of the concentrate or the amount of concentrate may need to be increased.

Feed Additives

A number of nonnutritive feed additives are added to horse feeds. Antioxidants such as ethoxyquin, BHT, and BHA are added to feeds to stabilize fats and reduce the oxidation of vitamins. Antibiotics may be added to stimulate gain and feed efficiency in young animals or reduce environmental stress on animals. At present, only Aureomycin (chlortetacycline) is approved for use in horse feeds (see Ch. 10).

Chelates are used to alter the availability of minerals to the animal. Some chelates increase mineral availability and some decrease the availability. Some chelated trace minerals appear to be much more available than the salts of these minerals.

Nutritive feed additives have value only as sources of required nutrients. No sources of unidentified nutrients have been documented for the horse. Multiple sources of the same nutrients have no documented value over single sources.

Other Considerations

In addition to providing the nutrient needs of the horse, the ration must also be of suitable density, be palatable, impart an acceptable physical environment in the digestive tract, and, if the product is to be sold commercially, have a good sensory appeal to the buyer. Feed processing and ingredient selection must be considered important aspects of ration formulation.

FEED PREPARATION

Preparation of feeds for horses varies from the feeding of whole grains to the cooking of ingredients (for example, flax seeds and barley). Research information available to date indicates that there is little advantage to processing grains for horses if the animals chew their feed adequately (22). Unfortunately, many do not, thus making it preferable to process some ingredients. Feed ingredients which must be processed to destroy undesirable factors for other monogastric animals should also be processed for horses (for example, soybean meal).

Grain rations are generally fed in one of two forms: coarse, in which the grains are whole,

TABLE 23-11

Influence of form on intake, digestibility, and nutritive value of alfalfa hay by horses

Form of Hay	Relative Intake,[a] %	Total Digestible Nutrients, %	Nutritive Value Index,[b] %
Pellets	122	47	57
Cubes[c]	119	50	59
Loose	90[d]	48	44[d]

[a]Relative intake = $\dfrac{100 \times \text{observed intake in grams}}{80\,(BW^{0.75})}$

[b]Nutritive value index = relative intake × total digestible nutrients.

[c]Lundell-type machine.

[d]Significantly different (P < .01) from other means in the same columns.

Source: Haenlein et al. (11).

cracked, or steamed-rolled to varying degrees, or pelleted, in which the grains are ground and then formed into small-size pellets. Grinding of grains is usually avoided due to the dustiness and subsequent reduced palatability, unless the grain is to be combined with other ingredients and incorporated into pellets.

Hay may be fed loose, cubed, pelleted, or chopped. Cubes and pelleted hay may not provide as much bulk as desired under some circumstances, but they may provide compensatory advantages. Although pelleting and cubing of hay appear to increase the rate of passage and subsequently reduce digestibility of the crude fiber portion of the ration, increased relative intake results in pelleted and cubed hay having a greater nutritive value index than loose hay (Table 23-11) (11,12). Ground hay may also be fed but will usually require the addition of molasses to reduce the dust. Water may also be used for this purpose, but care should be taken to prevent molding of the hay.

DIGESTIVE DISTURBANCES

Colic and founder (laminitis) may be caused by digestive disturbances. Care should be taken to minimize the likelihood of these problems through proper formulation, ingredient selection, and feeding programs. Colic is the horse's reaction to a pain in the abdominal cavity. Signs of colic include looking at the flank, kicking the belly, restlessness, violent rolling, listlessness, and perspiration. Colic may be caused by compaction due to poor mastication, high-fiber feeds, or inadequate water intake; gas production due

to rapid fermentation of grains; or excessive sand retention due to improper feeding practices. Ensuring that the total ration is somewhat laxative will minimize these problems.

Nutritionally induced founder is usually caused by intentional or unintentional consumption of high levels of readily fermentable feedstuffs such as grain or early spring pastures. Care should be taken to keep consumption levels moderate at any one feeding or restrict grazing times until the animal has adjusted to the pasture.

Heaves, an allergy problem in horses which affects their breathing, appears to be aggravated by dusty feeds. Horses with heaves must be fed without hay. Special bulky rations or complete pellets are most desirable. It may also be necessary to restrict exposure to dusty grains and pollens.

A number of equine vices are probably related to diet and feeding programs. Wood chewing may be caused by nutrient deficiencies, inadequate bulk or fiber intake, and restricted feed intake, but it also may be due to boredom or a desire for the taste of wood. Soil ingestion often occurs when horses are restricted to paddocks and pastures with inadequate forage, resulting in the horses digging up the roots of the grass. Deliberate soil ingestion by foals has no known cause. Coprophagy (manure consumption) by foals is common and is probably the method by which the foal establishes desirable microflora in the gut. Coprophagy in older horses is rare.

FEEDING HINTS

A. Match the feeding program to the dietary requirements of the animal.

B. Feed only high-quality feedstuffs to horses. Low-quality ingredients and moldy and dusty feeds should be avoided.

C. Horses should receive at least 1 lb/100 lb BW of high-quality hay or pasture equivalent daily. Higher levels will be desirable for some animals.

D. Feed small quantities of feed often. Limit concentrate intake to no more than 0.5 lb/100 lb BW/feeding for mature horses. Weanlings and yearlings can usually consume up to 1.0 lb/100 lb BW/feeding without problems.

E. Make all diet changes slowly to allow

FIGURE 23-7. Feeding horses individually is important when nutritional needs are critical. Horses may be fed in box stalls, tied to fences, or in individual stalls as shown here.

the animal's digestive system and microbial population to adjust to the new feedstuffs.

F. Adjust feeding levels to maintain desired body condition of the animal.

G. Provide free-choice, clean, fresh water to all animals. Water should be restricted after hard exercise until the animal is cooled out.

H. Control internal parasites by using a regular deworming program. Parasites reduce digestive efficiency, take nutrients from the animal, and are a major cause of colic in horses.

I. Free-choice salt should be available to all horses (Fig. 23–7). A free-choice Ca and P supplement should also be available to all horses not receiving a balanced diet. Trace minerals should be included in at least one portion of the animal's diet.

SUMMARY

Horses are adaptable creatures, well suited to the open range but capable of adjusting to stall confinement for 20–23 h per day. Under range conditions the nutritional needs of the mature horse are generally satisfied by natural ingredients with little input by humans except to ensure the availability of adequate minerals and quality water. However, when the animal is confined, meeting its nutritional needs is more of a challenge. Increased activity including maximum growth, high reproductive efficiency, and performance demands increase nutrient requirements, and confining the animal necessitates that the feeds offered provide suitable concentrations of nutrients. Research during the past 20 years has provided a wealth of knowledge on which to base feeding programs for all types of horses. The next 20 years will provide even greater information, so we will be able to feed for optimum development and maximum performance from our animals.

REFERENCES

1. Anwer, M. S., et al. 1975. *J. Animal Sci.* 41:179.
2. Baucus, K. L., et al. 1987. *Proc. 10th Equine Nutr. Physiol. Soc. Sym.,* p. 179. Ft. Collins, CO.
3. Bouman, H., and W. Van der Schee. 1978. *Z. Tierphysiol, Tierer nahrg. U. Futtermittelkde.* 40:39.
4. Bendick, A., E. Gabriel, and L. J. Machlin. 1986. *J. Nutr.* 116:675.
5. Bergin, W. C., et al. 1967. *Proc. Amer. Assoc. Equine Pract.,* December, p. 179.
6. Breedveld, L., S. G. Jackson, and J. P. Baker. 1987. *Proc. 10th Equine Nutr. Physiol. Soc. Sym.,* p. 159. Ft. Collins, CO.
7. Darlington, J. M., and T. V. Hershberger. 1968. *J. Animal Sci.* 27:1572.
8. El Shorafa, W. M., et al. 1979. *J. Animal Sci.* 48:882.
9. Fonnesbeck, P. V., and L. D. Symons. 1967. *J. Animal Sci.* 26:1030.
10. Gibbs, P. D., et al. 1982. *J. Animal Sci.* 54:496.
11. Haelein, G. F. W., R. D. Holdren, and Y. M. Yoon. 1966. *J. Animal Sci.* 25:740.
12. Hintz, H. F., and R. G. Loy. 1966. *J. Animal Sci.* 25:1059.
13. Hintz, H. F., et al. 1971. *J. Animal Sci.* 32:100.
14. Hintz, H. F., et al. 1973. *J. Animal Sci.* 36:522.
15. Lukas, V. K., et al. 1972. *J. Animal Sci.* 34:350 (Abstr.)
16. McCall, M. A., G. D. Potter, and J. L. Kreider. 1981. *Proc. 7th Equine Nutri. & Physiol. Symp.,* p. 82.
17. Meyer. 1987. In: *Equine exercise physiology 2.* San Diego, CA: ICEEP Publications.

18. Neuhaus, Von U. 1959. *Zeit. Fur Tierzuchtung and Zuchtung skrologie.* 73:370.

19. NRC. 1978. *Nutrient requirements of horses.* 4th rev. ed. Washington, D.C.: Nat. Acad. Press.

20. NRC. 1989. *Nutrient requirements of horses.* 5th rev. ed. Washington, D.C.: Nat. Acad. Press.

21. Oftedal, O. T., H. F. Hintz, and H. F. Schryver. 1983. *J. Nutr.* 113:2169.

22. Ott, E. A. 1973. *Symposium on Effect of Processing on the Nutritional Value of Feeds.* Washington, D.C.: Nat. Acad. Sci., p. 373.

23. Ott, E. A. 1977. *Proc. U. S. Brewers Assoc. Feed. Conf.* St. Louis, MO, p. 84.

24. Ott, E. A., et al. 1979. *J. Animal Sci.* 49:983.

25. Ott, E. A., R. L. Asquith, and J. P. Feaster. 1981. *J. Animal Sci.* 53:1496.

26. Pagan, J. D., and H. F. Hintz. 1986. *J. Animal Sci.* 63:822.

27. Robinson, D. W., and L. M. Slade. 1974. *J. Animal Sci.* 39:1045.

28. Schryver, H. F., et al. 1986. *J. Nutr.* 116:2142.

29. Slade, L. M., et al. 1970. *J. Animal Sci.* 30:753.

30. Ullrey, D. E., et al. 1966. *J. Animal Sci.* 25:217.

31. Ullrey, D. E., E. T. Ely, and R. L. Covert. 1974. *J. Animal Sci.* 38:1276.

24

Feeding and Nutrition of the Dog and Cat

Diane A. Hirakawa

INTRODUCTION

Dogs and cats have lived as companions to humans for thousands of years. Both domestic dogs and cats are members of the order *Carnivora*, which are flesh-eating mammals. Living families of the present day order *Carnivore* are *Canidae* and *Felidae*, commonly referred to as the dog and cat families.

Carnivora possess anatomical features which support their carnivorous feeding behavior through evolution (Fig. 24–1). The canine teeth allow these animals to successfully catch and consume prey. The carnassids, flat molars, facilitate the reduction in food particle size to ease the swallowing of prey.

Archaeological records indicate the special relationship between human and dog is at least 12 thousand years old. In what is now known as northern Israel, the remains of a wolf or dog pup were discovered with the burial remains of a human child some 12 thousand years old.

FIGURE 24–1. Evolution of the domestic dog. (Courtesy of The Iams Co., Dayton, OH.)

Archaeological evidence suggests that the first domesticated canid appeared before the agricultural phase, making the dog a likely candidate as the first animal domesticated by humans. It is believed that the wild canid ran in packs for hunting and for protection. First brought into close contact with humans by hunting the same prey humans hunted, the wild canid probably learned to scavenge scraps left by human hunting parties. More than likely, it was the young offspring of these scavengers who were adopted and hand-raised by humans, which led to further domestication.

The domesticated dog continued to serve humans on the hunt and in protective capacities even when agricultural development progressed. It is likely that selective breeding of dogs was routinely practiced at this time.

The tremendous breed variation seen today is a result of 12 thousand years of planned matings. Today's dog may weigh as much as 100 kg or as little as 1 kg. Hair length ranges from that of the Afghan's very long fibers to that of the Mexican hairless' coat, and nose shapes range from the collie's to the pug's. Some breeds, such as the retriever, have retained their innate desire for the hunt. Other breeds, such as the toys, are better suited for pampering.

A younger relationship exists between humans and cats. Findings in Egypt dated to approximately 3000 years ago suggest that cats were kept in captivity. However, unlike the dog, few anatomical changes have occurred in the cat during its domestication; therefore, the precise date of a clear association with humans is unclear. By 1600 BC cats were surely domesticated and considered as sacred beings by the Egyptians. Whether the first domesticated cat was revered as a sacred animal, kept as a beloved companion, or kept for its keen hunting capabilities, as a method of rodent control, remains to be elucidated.

Although both dog and cat are classified in the order *Carnivore*, the divergence of the order occurred early in the evolutionary pathway; therefore, considerable distinction between the domestic dog and cat is present today. It is the evolution of the domestication process for the dog and cat which enhances our current understanding of their nutritional requirements. The domestic cat (*Felis domesticus*) is a strict carnivore whose nutritional requirements have remained quite specialized through domestication. On the other hand, the domestic dog (*Canis familia*) is often considered an omnivore. Considering the phenotypic diversity among dog breeds, it is evident that the dog has acquired anatomical and physiological differences which directly affect nutritional requirements.

ECONOMIC AND SOCIAL SIGNIFICANCE OF DOGS AND CATS

In 1987 approximately 5 billion dollars were spent on veterinary care for companion animals, with 91 percent of that attributed to the health care of dogs and cats. A recent profile of the pet food industry in the United States revealed that 220 million dollars were invested in advertisements by the manufacturers of pet foods in multimedia campaigns.

As a result, pet owners purchased 9.3 billion pounds of pet food products in 1987. That is equivalent to spending 5.3 billion dollars. It has been estimated that 2.46 billion pounds of vegetable protein and 1.5 billion pounds of animal protein were used in the manufacture of pet food. Because domestic animal research is focused on efficient use of foodstuffs, it seems reasonable that nutritional research with companion animals should be viewed with as much interest as that existing in nutritional research with food-producing animals.

Approximately 39 percent of all households in the United States own at least one dog, and an average of two cats occupy approximately 30 percent of all homes. In fact, there are approximately 51 million dogs and 56 million cats in the United States alone. Recently, for the first time in the United States, the cat population has surpassed that of dogs. The increase in the cat population is, most probably, due to the changing life style of today's fast-paced family. Owning a cat yields animal companionship; however, the independent behavior of the domestic cat allows it to adjust to changing life styles.

Recent research efforts have focused on the importance of the human-animal bond. In addition to filling traditional roles as hunting companions, guard dogs, guides for the sight- and hearing-impaired, service dogs for the physically disabled or scent dogs for narcotics, explosives, and missing people, the companionship of dogs and cats has been shown to lower blood pressure, have a positive effect on surgical recovery, and enhance psychological health of humans. Companion animals are currently being used, for example, in therapy programs for elderly individuals in long-term care facilities, emotionally disturbed children, and criminally insane prisoners.

Establishment of the economic and social importance of companion animals in our environment strongly justifies future experimentation concerning nutritional requirements and factors affecting these requirements, although this is not an easy task. There are no economic benefits to increased growth rates or improved reproductive efficiency, per se, in companion animals. Thus it is difficult to define response criteria to assess nutrient requirements in this class of animals. The nutritional efficacy of a companion animal diet is based on maintenance of health, well-being, and longevity, an unusual response parameter for a nutritionist, except when dealing with other pets or animals used for exhibition, but an area that warrants investigation.

NUTRIENT REQUIREMENTS OF DOGS AND CATS

The nutrient requirements for today's dog and cat can be supplied in a variety of ways through the use of commercial diets available in most grocery and pet supply stores. There are hundreds of brands of commercial pet food one can choose from. They vary from 10–78 percent moisture, 12–35 percent protein, 5–30 percent fat, and 1–10 percent fiber. How does a pet owner provide complete and balanced nutrition and understand the options without becoming a specialist in companion animal nutrition?

The dietary requirements for dogs and cats were originally established by the NRC. These recommendations were revised and updated in 1985 and 1986 for the dog and cat, respectively (13, 29). The recommendations for each individual nutrient are based on minimum dietary requirements that were founded primarily on research employing the growing puppy or kitten. The experimental diets were often purified in composition, containing crystalline amino acids, vitamins, and minerals, thereby providing nutrients with high availability. Therefore, caution must be advised in applying these nutrient requirements to the practical setting. Upon formulating a diet with feedstuffs common to the pet food industry, the nutrient digestibility, availability, nutrient interactions, and effects of processing must be considered.

Nutrient requirements cannot be defined simply as being at a single level; requirements should be given as a range that provides sound nutrition, thereby avoiding states of nutrient deficiencies or toxicities. As stated, the NRC publications provide minimum requirements, which may be defined as "adequate" nutrition. Optimal nutrition for dogs and cats often requires nutrients above minimum requirements. These are dependent on other nutrients in the diet, the individual animal being fed, and the desired response criteria as measured and seen by the pet owner.

The suggested wide range of nutrient requirements is not surprising when one considers breed diversity of the canine species. The mature adult weight of the canine can vary 100-fold, from the Chihuahua weighing as little as 1 kg to the Great Dane weighing more than 100 kg. In addition, bone length and density, hair type and length, desired skin condition, muscle tone, and other physiological differences can contribute to difficulty in the assessment of nutrient requirements. Environmental factors and physiological phases such as growth, gestation, lactation, and physical stress must be considered as well. A paucity of information exists on definitive nutrient requirements related to breed, age, and sex. Lack of uniformity in the canine species makes it difficult, but by no means impossible, to establish such requirements.

Nutrient requirement estimates for dogs and cats have been established for energy, protein, fat, vitamins, minerals, and, of course, water. Rather than address the six nutrient classes and respective minimum requirements within each class, tables of reference are provided for dogs (Table 24–1) and for cats (Table 24–2). The nutritional information emphasized here is intended to enhance the reader's general knowledge of canine and feline nutrition as well as impart information about specific nutritional idiosyncrasies of feline diets.

Water

Water, although often overlooked, is of utmost importance for life. It is known that an animal can survive approximately ten times longer without food than without water. The amount of body water is inversely related to body fat or positively correlated to lean body mass. Thus it is not surprising that both growing puppies and kittens and racing sled dogs have a high lean body composition and also have a high body water content. Therefore, hydration or dehydration is a primary concern in these animals.

The water requirement of an animal is provided by the moisture content of food, water of metabolism (primarily oxidation), and the consumption of drinking water or other fluids.

Water content of commercial diets can range from 10 to 78 percent, thus consumption of water will vary accordingly. Needed water intake is affected by the amount of water lost in the process of thermoregulation (primarily excretion via the lungs) and excretion of metabolic waste

TABLE 24-1

Minimum requirements for growing dogs

Nutrient	Unit	Units per 1000 kcal ME
Fat	g	13.60
Linoleic acid	g	2.70
Protein		
Arginine	g	1.37
Histidine	g	0.49
Isoleucine	g	0.98
Leucine	g	1.59
Lysine	g	1.40
Methionine-cystine	g	1.06
Phenylalanine-tyrosine	g	1.95
Threonine	g	1.27
Tryptophan	g	0.41
Valine	g	1.05
Dispensable amino acids	g	17.07
Minerals		
Calcium	g	1.60
Phosphorus	g	1.20
Potassium	g	1.20
Sodium	g	0.15
Chloride	g	0.23
Magnesium	g	0.11
Iron	mg	8.70
Copper	mg	0.80
Manganese	mg	1.40
Zinc	mg	9.70
Iodine	mg	0.16
Selenium	mg	0.03
Vitamins		
Vitamin A	IU	1011.00
Vitamin D	IU	110.00
Vitamin E	IU	6.10
Vitamin K[a]	—	—
Thiamin	mg	0.27
Riboflavin	mg	0.68
Pantothenic acid	mg	2.70
Niacin	mg	3.00
Vitamin B$_6$	mg	0.30
Folic acid	mg	0.05
Biotin[a]	—	—
Vitamin B$_{12}$	mg	7.00
Choline	mg	340.00

[a]Dogs have a metabolic requirement, but it is not a dietary requirement when practical diets are fed.

Source: Edited from NRC (13).

TABLE 24-2

Minimum requirements for growing kittens

Nutrient	Unit	Units per 1000 kcal ME
Fat		
Linoleic acid	g	1.00
Arachidonic acid	mg	40.00
Protein	g	48.00
Arginine	g	2.00
Histidine	g	0.60
Isoleucine	g	1.00
Leucine	g	2.40
Lysine	g	1.60
Methionine-cystine	g	1.50
Methionine	g	0.80
Phenylalanine-tyrosine	g	1.70
Phenylalanine	g	0.80
Taurine	mg	80.00
Threonine	g	1.40
Tryptophan	g	0.30
Valine	g	1.20
Minerals		
Calcium	g	1.60
Phosphorus	g	1.20
Magnesium	g	0.08
Potassium	g	0.80
Sodium	g	0.10
Chloride	g	0.38
Iron	mg	16.00
Copper	mg	1.00
Iodine	mg	0.07
Zinc	mg	10.00
Manganese	mg	1.00
Selenium	mg	0.02
Vitamins		
Vitamin A	IU	666.60
Vitamin D	IU	100.00
Vitamin E	IU	6.00
Vitamin K[a]	μg	20.00
Thiamin	mg	1.00
Riboflavin	mg	0.80
Vitamin B$_6$	mg	0.80
Niacin	mg	8.00
Pantothenic acid	mg	1.00
Folic acid	mg	0.16
Biotin[a]	μg	14.00
Vitamin B$_{12}$	μg	4.00
Choline	mg	480.00

[a]Cats have a metabolic requirement, but it is not a dietary requirement unless antimicrobial agents or antivitamin compounds are present in the diet.

Source: Edited from NRC (29).

436   *Part III / Feeding Livestock*

products through the urine. The quality of drinking water may be as important as the nutrient content of the diet. For example, hard and soft water may contain high levels of specific minerals that may adversely affect the mineral balance of the diet.

Energy

Following water, dietary energy is the nutrient required in largest amounts. Energy requirements are influenced by the animal's metabolic efficiency, environmental factors (temperature, humidity), physical exercise and activity level, the animal's age (Fig. 24–2), and the stage of production (Fig. 24–3). In addition, the energy requirement of a dog and cat (as with any other warm-blooded animal) per unit of body weight decreases as the size of the animal increases.

Traditionally, commercial pet food analysis has been presented so that the percentage composition of the food was listed. While this accurately shows the chemical breakdown of the diet, it does not fully explain the balance of the various nutrients to a common factor other than "as fed" or dry matter.

Ten years ago the concept of nutrient digestibility was introduced to the pet food

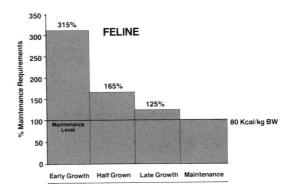

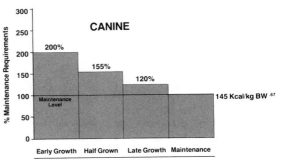

FIGURE 24–2. Feline and canine metabolizable energy requirements for growth.

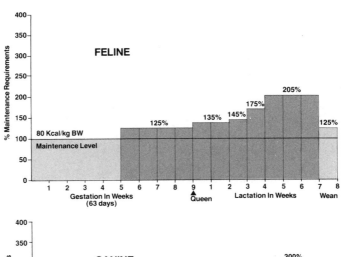

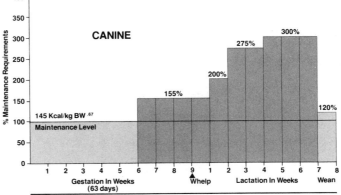

FIGURE 24–3. Feline and canine metabolizable energy requirements for production.

market; this complicated the relatively simple process of feeding a pet. Digestibility was introduced as a means of judging pet food quality. The higher the digestibility, the better the nutritional quality of the diet (see Ch. 2 and 3). The principle holds true for all nutrients. Some pet food manufacturers have begun to provide nutritional information based on metabolizable energy (ME). The concept has been in existence for decades among nutritionists, but the need for educating consumers about ME is recent (see Ch. 3).

Animals offered a balanced diet tend to eat primarily to satisfy their energy need, thus the logical comparison involves evaluating a diet on the basis of units of a nutrient per unit of energy. Separate diets can then be compared more accurately, and actual nutrient intake can be determined knowing the caloric content.

A study employing growing puppies fed four diets containing different levels of gross energy (GE) illustrated the phenomenon that puppies consume feed to meet their ME needs. Interestingly, on one commercial diet puppies consumed 23 percent more GE to rectify the inefficient digestibility of the fibrous feedstuffs (7).

Carbohydrates

Grain starches provide an important and economical source of dietary energy in most pet foods. Whether the carbohydrate source is supplied by corn, rice, wheat, or oats is less important than the method of processing. Utilization of starch in cereal grains is enhanced significantly when grains are finely ground and properly heat-treated (see Ch. 11). Mild heat treatments will allow the starch molecule to swell and enhance its digestion. Failure of proper heat treatment will leave raw starches that may ferment in the intestinal tract, thereby creating flatulence and by-products of potential detriment to the efficiency of the digestive process.

The cat has an abnormally low activity of a liver enzyme required for the metabolism of glucose. Therefore, the cat is unable to efficiently metabolize a diet containing high levels of glucose (15). This finding is supportive of the cat's carnivorous feeding regimen of high protein and fat and low carbohydrates.

The pet food industry uses the term crude fiber to represent the fiber fraction of pet foods. However, this value is often an underestimate of the actual level of dietary fiber. For example, beet pulp provides a quality source of dietary fiber in pet foods. The analysis of beet pulp reveals 19 percent crude fiber but 77 percent total dietary fiber, the difference being due to soluble "fiber" sources such as pectins. Fiber sources common to commercial pet foods are fruit pomaces, cereal brans, and vegetable pulps.

Fiber has been shown to decrease nutrient utilization in the adult dog, but to a degree that varies with the type and physical composition of the fiber. A recent study examined the nutrient availability of diets containing 0–12.5 percent beet pulp. As the level of beet pulp increased, protein and energy availability of the diet decreased. In addition, the inclusion of graded levels of fiber resulted in a linear decrease in diet retention time, thereby increasing the rate of passage through the digestive tract. Dietary fiber has been shown to increase losses of amino acids and reduce dietary amino acid availability, both of which can influence the amino acid requirement. Sloughing of intestinal mucosal cells and elevated mucous production are primarily responsible for the increase in loss of amino acids. It is thought that fiber decreases amino acid availability by forming gels around the amino acids or by absorbing digestive enzymes, thereby diminishing their activities. With the emergence of low-calorie, high-fiber commercial pet foods, the availability of dietary nutrients may be a concern.

Fats

In commercial pet foods fat serves as a concentrated source of energy, a carrier for fat-soluble vitamins, a source of essential fatty acids, and an enhancer of diet palatability. Fat is a very concentrated source of energy with an energy efficiency ratio of approximately 2.25:1 for either fat to protein or fat to carbohydrates. Fats are routinely added to commercial pet foods to increase the caloric density. Some quality fat sources have a digestibility value of 95 percent or more. Fats are also more digestible than carbohydrates, thus the available caloric contribution of fat is very high.

A low-fat diet or the use of poor-quality, unstable fat may limit the absorption of fat-soluble vitamins. Therefore, inferior quality or quantity may result in clinical cases of fat-soluble vitamin deficiencies in both dogs and cats.

The optimal quantity of dietary fat is not exclusively in the total percentage of fat in the diet, but rather in the relationship of metabolizable fat to metabolizable nutrients. For example, when a diet contains a limited quantity or inferior quality protein, the percentage of dietary fat (energy) desired may be as low as 5–10 percent. However, as protein quality and/or quantity are increased, a concomitant increase in fat will be warranted to maintain proper nutrient balance.

As with most animal species, the dog and cat have an essential fatty acid requirement for linoleic acid. In addition, the fatty acid, arachidonic acid, is essential for the cat. The cat appears to lack adequate amounts of the liver enzyme △ 6-desaturase, which converts linoleic to linolenic and arachidonic acid (25). Sources of fat commonly employed in commercial pet foods are tallow, lard, poultry fat, and numerous vegetable oils; however, not all of these contain the required essential fatty acid. Fish oil is the richest source of arachidonic acid. Poultry and lard contain appreciable quantities. However, tallow contains a relatively lower level and vegetable oils lack arachidonic acid entirely. This unique requirement for arachidonic acid found in the cat has also been found in other strict carnivore species. A deficiency in arachidonic acid results in poor growth, inferior fur quality, skin lesions by the mouth and hocks, slow wound healing, increased susceptibility to infection, and poor reproductive performance.

Protein

Pet food sales have increased steadily throughout the years, and efforts have been intensified to find economical protein sources of high quality with high amino acid availability. Ideally, the optimum use of an intact protein feedstuff is to supply required levels of the ten essential amino acids, thus allowing efficient formulation of pet foods. However, with regard to practical diets, relatively little is known about the quantitative amino acid requirements for the canine and feline and subsequent factors affecting those requirements.

Early investigations suggested that the qualitative amino acid needs of most animal species were probably very similar. However, only in recent years has a quantitative assessment of canine and feline amino acid requirements been undertaken. The establishment of a purified crystalline amino acid diet has provided a very useful research tool. The resulting amino acid requirements were incorporated into the revised NRC guidelines. However, as previously stated, caution must be advised in the application of these requirements to practical diets.

Vegetable proteins such as soybean meal and corn gluten meal and animal proteins such as poultry, meat, and respective by-products are common ingredients in commercial pet foods. Although cereals provide a major source of energy in cereal-based products, they also supply a significant portion of the protein, which may often be deficient in an essential amino acid. Fresh meats, meat and poultry meals, and various meat by-products are often added to complement the amino acid profile of cereal-based products. Animal sources of protein vary considerably in protein quality. Some sources provide amino acids of poor availability and others are highly available; overall quality is dependent on the source and processing methods of the renderer (see Ch. 8).

The development of an optimal feeding program for dogs or cats is highly dependent on the selection of the proper source of dietary protein. To determine the nutritional efficacy of a specific protein source, consideration must be given to digestibility and assimilation of the essential amino acids present in the protein. A study that established the lysine requirement for the growing puppy using a purified crystalline amino acid diet and an intact protein diet supplemented with crystalline lysine illustrates the importance of availability. The results suggest a lysine requirement for maximal growth and feed efficiency of approximately 0.7 percent for a purified L-amino acid diet and 0.8 percent for a diet based upon intact protein-containing ingredients. The best explanation for this difference is that the crystalline lysine is virtually 100 percent available, whereas lysine present in intact protein is not. Therefore, it is readily apparent that the lower lysine bioavailability of dietary components contained in the intact protein diet had the expected effect on the lysine requirement (6). This by no means challenges the validity of the requirement estimates that have been obtained with crystalline amino acid diets, but the high availability must be considered when formulating a diet to meet the essential amino acid requirements of the dog and cat.

It is generally accepted that the requirement for most essential amino acids, expressed as a percent of the diet, will be affected by the age, sex, and breed of the animal. A study clearly showed that the tryptophan requirement of growing dogs, expressed as a percent of the diet, decreases substantially as age and weight of the dog increases (3). In contrast, the protein requirement of the cat remains relatively high.

The impact of sex has variable results. In some studies the amino acid requirement of young puppies was not affected by sex. In contrast, a study with immature beagle dogs suggested that the lysine requirement for maximal growth and N balance was greater for the immature male dog than for the immature female (9).

With respect to breeds, it has been observed that Labradors have a higher requirement for S amino acids than do beagles (2). In addition, a study revealed that the S amino acid requirement of pointer puppies is also different from those of either beagles or Labradors (5). The diversity among requirements is not surprising when one considers the genetic diversity of the canine species.

The cat, a strict carnivore, is unique in its protein and amino acid nutritional requirements. The cat and other carnivores have substantially higher protein requirements than do omnivores such as the dog. The metabolic reason for the high protein requirement of the cat is the high activity of the amino acid catabolic enzymes in the liver. These enzymes are nonadaptive, therefore the obligatory N loss is high even when cats are fed low-protein diets or fasted (21). This is a major concern with respect to pet owners who feed dog food to their cats. Although some dog food products provide high levels of dietary protein, most would be considered deficient for the cat.

Although not of practical importance, it has been shown that cats are very sensitive to a deficiency of the amino acid arginine. The feeding of a single meal that is devoid in arginine will result in hyperammonemia in less than an hour. It has been suggested that the cat's sensitivity to an arginine deficiency is related to the metabolism of urea cycle intermediates. Other carnivores reveal similar but less severe responses to an arginine-free diet (22).

Of more practical concern is the cat's high requirement for S amino acids relative to other mammals. It has been suggested that the cat's high protein requirement may be a result of its high S amino acid requirement. It is postulated that the presence of high dietary S amino acid levels may be required to support the cat's thick hair coat, which is high in the S amino acid cysteine (21).

The cat's unique requirement for taurine, a β-amino sulfonic acid, has recently received considerable scientific and public attention.

Taurine is a by-product of S amino acid metabolism produced in the liver and other tissues, such as the brain. It functions as a bile acid conjugate and is present in a few peptides, but it is not a component of body proteins. The cat appears to be very inefficient at synthesizing taurine as well as having a higher physiological requirement for it than other mammals have. The concentration of taurine in the cat's eye is considerable, and it is required to prevent central retinal degeneration (CRD) (19). In addition, a study on reproductive performance has shown that low plasma taurine concentration is related to poor reproductive performance in cats (27). Recently, research revealed that a low concentration of plasma taurine was associated with congestive cardiomyopathy in cats. Oral supplementation of taurine resulted in normalization of plasma taurine concentrations and heart function (23).

Of practical concern is the established requirement estimate for dietary taurine. Taurine is present in only animal sources of protein, with shellfish and mollusks containing the highest levels. Therefore, caution is advised in the feeding of commercial dog foods to cats which employ protein sources of vegetable rather than animal origin. Although most commercial cat foods contain adequate levels of taurine, it has been shown that taurine bioavailability may be compromised during specific processing methods. Current research endeavors are examining factors that may affect taurine availability. This unique requirement for taurine supports the strict carnivorous feeding requirements of the feline.

Vitamins in Pet Foods

In the case of fat-soluble vitamins, it is essential that a quality stable fat source be employed in the diet to assure vitamin absorption and utilization. Therefore, many pet food manufacturers add an antioxidant to assure the stabilization of dietary fat. Water-soluble vitamins are carefully selected and added in commercial pet foods in excess of minimum requirements to compensate for losses associated with heat processing and extended shelf life.

Vitamin A

The cat, like all mammals, has a dietary requirement for vitamin A. This fat-soluble vitamin occurs in several different chemical forms in nature. β-carotene, a carotenoid pigment, is a vitamin A precursor found in plant products. Most mammals have the ability to convert β-carotene to active vitamin A through the action of two enzymes located in the intestinal mucosa, however, unlike the dog, the cat is unable to convert dietary β-carotene to active vitamin A due to a deficiency in the intestinal enzyme β-carotene-15-15'-dioxygenase. As a result, the cat has a dietary requirement for preformed vitamin A, found only in animal tissues (17). Products containing high levels of vitamin A include beef, chicken, and pork liver as well as whole milk. The richest sources of vitamin A are the fish oils. Cod liver oil is especially high in vitamin A.

In contrast to other mammals, the cat is more susceptible to the overconsumption of vitamin A. Because the cat consumes preformed vitamin A that is not regulated by the intestinal mucosa, as is β-carotene, a toxic level may be readily absorbed into the body. The susceptibility of vitamin A toxicity may be exacerbated by the common practice of feeding food items to domestic cats that contain excessively high levels of vitamin A, such as liver, kidney, and various fish oils.

Niacin

With respect to water-soluble vitamins, the cat appears to have a unique dietary requirement for niacin. In most mammals the niacin requirement can be met with dietary tryptophan. In contrast, the cat cannot meet its physiological niacin requirement by consuming tryptophan (21) but must have preformed niacin in its diet.

Minerals in Pet Foods

There is a paucity of data on quantitative and qualitative mineral requirements in dog and cat nutrition. To assure dietary adequacy, commercial pet foods provide essential minerals, thereby eliminating the need for additives and supplements. Practical applications have repeatedly shown that supplementation of commercial pet foods may create nutritional imbalances which can influence the expression of health or disease in the animal.

Calcium and Phosphorus

Ca constitutes 1.5–2 percent of the total body weight and is the most abundant cation in the body. More than 99 percent of the bone is Ca with a Ca:P ratio of 2:1. The Ca:P ratio of a diet also affects the absorption of Ca. If a diet contains an excess of either mineral, the absorption of the other mineral will be compromised.

Many dog owners believe that growing puppies need additional Ca in their diet to prevent the development of chronic skeletal problems. Numerous controlled studies have demonstrated that supplementation of a previously adequate diet with Ca will not alleviate or prevent skeletal problems. In fact, these studies have demonstrated that the addition of excess Ca to a growing dog's diet can actually be harmful. Excessive dietary Ca causes skeletal changes and may ultimately result in the development of skeletal disorders such as osteochondritis dissecans (OCD), Wobbler's syndrome, hypertropic osteodystrophy (HOD), and hip dysplasia.

Due to the carnivorous feeding behavior of the cat and palatability response of the dog, many consumers believe the addition of meat is of nutritional benefit. However, sources of fresh meat, poultry, and fish can supply a Ca:P of 1:15–20. The addition of such ingredients can imbalance the desired Ca:P ratio of 1:1 for cats and 1.2–1.4:1 for dogs.

Feline Urologic Syndrome

Feline Urologic Syndrome (FUS) is a generally accepted term that describes lower urinary tract disease in the domestic cat occurring as a result of urethritis or cystitis. Approximately 90–97 percent of all urinary calculi in cats with FUS are composed exclusively or primarily of struvite (magnesium-ammonium-phosphate). One of the factors necessary for the formation of struvite in urine is the presence of sufficient concentrations of Mg, P, and ammonium. Feline urine always contains high amounts of ammonium due to the cat's high protein requirement and intake. Urinary phosphate in the normal healthy cat is also high enough for struvite formation, regardless of dietary P intake. The concentration of urinary Mg, on the other hand, is normally quite low and can be directly affected by the level of dietary intake (26).

Magnesium

Several studies demonstrate the relationship between increased dietary Mg and increased rate of calculi formation and obstruction in cats; however, the practical significance of the role of dietary Mg remains uncertain. The levels of dietary Mg fed to cats in these studies were all substantially higher than those typically found in commercial cat foods. Although commercial cat foods do contain more Mg than is required by the cat, they do not approach the levels used in experimental studies to induce urolithiasis (0.4–1.0 percent). It must be recognized that Mg intake is not singularly responsible for the development of this disease, and its level of importance in relation to other contributing factors may be insignificant.

Acidifying Properties of a Diet

Struvite is more soluble in acid than in alkaline medium. As a result, the pH of a cat's urine can have the most profound effect on the development of FUS. It has been demonstrated that a linear relationship exists between urinary pH and the formation of struvite crystals. Struvite calculi will form in feline urine with a pH of 7.0 or greater, and its solubility greatly increases at a pH of 6.6 or less (24).

Compared to an omnivorous or herbivorous diet, a true carnivorous diet has the effect of increasing net acid excretion and decreasing urinary pH. This urinary acidifying effect is due primarily to the high level of S-containing amino acids contained in meats. The oxidation of these amino acids results in the excretion of sulfate in the urine and a concomitant decrease in urinary pH (20). In addition, a high-meat diet is lower in K salts than is a diet containing high amounts of cereal grains, the metabolism of which has been shown to produce alkaline urine (18). The inclusion of high amounts of cereal grains and low amounts of meat products in some brands of commercial cat food may, therefore, be a contributing factor to the development of FUS in cats.

Diets that are high in caloric density and highly digestible will be consumed in smaller quantities, thus lowering both dry-matter and Mg intake. Therefore, the percentage of Mg in the diet is not as important as is the total amount of Mg that the cat will be consuming. While some researchers feel that Mg concentration in the diet should be 0.1 percent or less on a dry-matter basis, others maintain that FUS risk is only increased when Mg levels reach 0.25 percent or greater (16). Factors of Mg level, caloric density, digestibility, and, perhaps most important, the acidifying properties of the diet should be considered when selecting a commercial cat food for the prevention of FUS.

COMMERCIAL DIETS FOR DOGS AND CATS

In response to consumer preference, the pet food industry produces primarily three types of foods. They are categorized according to moisture content as dry (6–12 percent moisture), semimoist (23–40 percent moisture), and canned (60–78 percent moisture).

Dry Pet Foods

Dry dog food, favored by dog owners, represents over 55 percent of dog food sales and 65 percent by weight. Dry cat food ranks second to canned products and represents approximately 35 percent of cat food sales. Most dry pet foods are produced by processing through an extruder (see Ch. 11). Ingredients common to dry foods are protein meals of plant and animal origin, such as corn gluten meal, soybean meal, poultry and meat meal, respective by-products, as well as fresh animal protein sources. Raw cereals and cereal by-products of corn, wheat, and rice are used as carbohydrate sources. Fats can be of animal or vegetable origin, and vitamins and minerals are added in the milling process to provide a homogeneous, complete, and balanced mixture for processing.

Extrusion is a high-temperature, short-time process. It is used for cooking, forming, and expanding cereals as well as texturizing proteins. The combination of high temperature, pressure, and shear optimizes expansion and dextrinization of starches. In addition, the exposure to high heat acts as a sterilization technique against pathogenic organisms. The extruded diet is then dried, cooled, and packaged. A process option is the application of fats and dry or liquid digests postextrusion. Such options may be employed to enhance palatability.

Another method of producing a dry diet is pelleting. Binding agents, such as molasses, are often added to the ingredient mixture to regulate the hardness of the pellets. The carbohydrate and protein ingredients are often precooked to gelatinize the starch and kill pathogenic organisms.

A less common process is baking, as in the production of kibbled dog foods or treat products. Prior to the use of extrusion in the pet food industry, commercial products were provided in meal form. To alleviate problems associated with raw starch, corn flakes were commonly employed in dog foods. Vegetable and animal protein sources were vat cooked, cooled, and mixed with corn flakes, vitamins, and minerals.

Dry pet foods are diverse in nutrient composition, ingredient selection, process method, and physical appearance. Although they all contain approximately 10 percent moisture, the protein level can range from 12 to over 30 percent and fat can range from 6 to over 25 percent. When evaluating differences in dry foods, one must consider the caloric density, bulk density, and ingredient composition. Considering the aforementioned, it is easy to understand that a cup of dry food can provide 200–600 kcal of ME. The major advantages associated with the feeding of dry pet food are that it is most economical to feed, it is convenient to feed, and its abrasive texture aids in dental hygiene.

Semimoist Pet Foods

Semimoist foods have fallen in popularity. The dollar sales of semimoist dog and cat foods account for a mere 6 and 11 percent of the market, respectively. These foods represent a very diverse group of commercial products. The moisture content can vary dramatically, but primarily these products contain 35–40 percent moisture. Most semimoist foods are extruded like dry foods. Depending on the selection of ingredients, the food may be cooked prior to extrusion. The unusual factor associated with the production of semimoist products is that the added water requires the addition of other ingredients to prevent product spoilage. Sugar, corn syrup, and salts are added to bind the water fraction and render it unavailable for the growth of bacteria. The sweet taste associated with many semimoist foods is attributed to the external application of propylene glycol. Propylene glycol functions to bind moisture in the food, thereby supporting its pliable form through the prevention of moisture loss. The major advantages in feeding a semimoist food are its convenience of feeding, intermediate cost, and good palatability.

Canned Pet Foods

Canned foods are extremely popular, especially in the cat food market. Canned cat foods account for over 50 percent of cat food sales, but less than 30 percent of dog food sales. Due to the popularity of domestic cats, the canned cat food market is likely to continue its growth.

The canning process is a high-temperature, long-time process. Ingredients are mixed, cooked, and filled into template cans which are lidded, seared, and retorted at temperatures of 230–275° F for 15–325 minutes, depending on type of retort and container size. Associated high temperatures are necessary to sterilize the diet. Canned diets contain up to 78 percent moisture. The presence of high moisture provides a highly palatable product that is attractive to consumers who have finicky pets; however, canned foods are relatively more expensive due to the cost associated with processing.

There are presently two types of canned foods: canned ration and canned meat. Canned rations may contain a variety of both dry and wet ingredients. The carbohydrate fraction is supplied by cereal grains, and the protein is derived from fresh meats, poultry and meat meals, and soybean meal. Fats are primarily of animal origin and, to provide a complete and balanced diet, vitamins and minerals are added.

Canned meat-type foods are composed primarily of fresh meat and poultry and respective by-products. Carbohydrates are present in very small quantities, approximately 5–10 percent. Due to the high protein content of these foods, protein is often used as an energy source. Soy flour is frequently added in the form of expanded chunks that resemble meat. This processing technique usually enhances the texture of the product. Vitamins and minerals are added.

Processing Effects on Nutritional Quality

The manufacturing of dry, semimoist, and canned pet foods all involve heat processing. There are several benefits associated with the heat treatment process which result in improved food quality. These have been discussed in some detail in Ch. 11.

Heat processing may also be detrimental to the nutritional quality of foods. Amino acid availability may be compromised in the preparation of pet foods. The loss of vitamins may be 10–100 percent, depending on the vitamins of concern, type of diet, and heat process employed. Fat-soluble vitamins are very sensitive to oxidation during processing, and specific water-soluble vitamins are extremely thermolabile. As a result, vitamins are added at higher levels in pet foods to compensate for such losses. Therefore, the quality of a diet is dependent on the processing method and subsequent controls enforced by the pet food manufacturer.

Puppy and Kitten Foods

Puppy and kitten foods are provided in the form of dry, semimoist, and canned foods. Pet food marketing has done an excellent job of convincing the consumer that the puppy and kitten have special nutritional requirements that can be met only with a diet designed especially for growth; however, this is not actually the case. Rapidly growing puppies and kittens require more energy and only specific nutrients on a unit-per-body-weight basis. Puppies and kittens should be fed a quality diet that is highly digestible and, thereby, meets the nutritional demands for growth without a substantial increase in food volume. Many adult foods meet these nutrient needs and provide for optimal growth of puppies or kittens.

Hard Work and Stress Nutrition

The use of dogs as a means of transportation, although a traditional role for the Alaskan sled dog, has recently received considerable attention due to the popularity of sled dog racing. The physiological stress encountered during endurance training for the 1000 mile Iditarod race across the rugged terrain and inclement weather of Alaska represents undoubtedly the highest nutritional demand for the canine in any type of organized contest (Fig. 24–4). Other animals, such as the field trial dog and racing greyhound,

FIGURE 24–4. Racing sled dogs during the grueling Iditarod race in Alaska. (Courtesy of Trot-A-Long Kennels, Two Rivers, AK.)

may have increased nutrient requirements as well.

These animals have a high caloric need which must be balanced with nutrients required for body maintenance. Due to the high caloric and digestibility value of fat, such diets simply require a higher level of dietary fat. However, protein must be supplied to maintain muscle mass and not be inefficiently used for energy demands. The caloric distribution for such a diet may contain the following caloric contribution: ME from protein, fat, and carbohydrates at levels of 30, 50, and 20 percent, respectively. The ingredients employed in the diet should provide highly available nutrients, thereby supporting optimal performance. If nutrient availability is inferior, ratio adjustments will be warranted.

Geriatric Nutrition

Geriatric diets are also available in dry, semi-moist, and canned products. The difficulty in providing a geriatric diet is that one cannot employ a general definition for the geriatric animal. One has to assess the overall health and well-being of the geriatric animal before a nutritional recommendation can be made. A geriatric pet food should be designed to maximize health and longevity with subsequent prevention of disease.

Some geriatric pet foods provide reduced levels of dietary protein. This dietary regimen is based on the increase of renal insufficiency seen in some geriatric dogs. However, there is a paucity of research information to support that a normal or high-protein diet increases the incidence of renal disease. In fact, several studies have examined the effect of protein level on induced renal dysfunction and reported no adverse effects due to high levels of dietary protein (4).

Physiological changes associated with aging reveal that the protein requirement of the geriatric animal is equal to, if not greater than, that of younger animals. In fact, factors such as a reduction in muscle mass, efficiency of N metabolism, increased requirement for specific amino acids, and inefficient digestive functions, as well as an increased susceptibility to disease due to a reduction in immune function, may support an increase in protein quantity and quality.

A study concerning the feeding of four diverse diets to geriatric dogs revealed that the nutritional requirements were not different from their respective young adult controls. While the study did show that a diet containing reduced protein levels resulted in a significantly lower serum N level, the clinical response would be desired only in a state of renal disease (10).

Geriatric animals are often associated with a decrease in physical activity and metabolism, hence they are often overweight. As a result, some low-calorie, high-fiber diets are fed. The nutrients contained in such diets may interact with a subsequent reduction in availability. For example, high levels of dietary fiber can decrease energy and protein absorption, as well as that of specific minerals. Considering the inefficient digestive functions of some geriatric dogs, this nutritional regimen may be contraindicated.

In general, it appears that the nutritional requirements of the geriatric animal must be considered on an individual animal basis. A diet of high nutrient availability that has been validated as complete and balanced by animal feeding studies may provide the best option.

Weight-Reducing Pet Foods

Obesity may be defined as the condition in which a pet's body weight is 10–15 percent above ideal body weight. The incidence of obesity is approximately 30 percent in dogs and 9 percent in cats. Grossly obese animals are considered to be 25 percent or more over ideal body weight. The concern with such pets is the predisposition to physiological diseases, such as skeletal changes due to the stress associated with excess weight. If an animal is in a state of physical compromise, a commercial diet severely restricted in caloric content may be required to precipitate rapid weight loss. However, prolonged underfeeding could be detrimental to the maintenance of lean body mass and metabolic functions.

A more general category represents animals that simply are above ideal body weight due to the intake of dietary energy exceeding that of energy expenditure. Animals included in this category are those that are slightly above ideal body weight to the grossly obese. The incidence of such an animal may be as high as 60 percent of the dog and 50 percent of the cat population. Factors such as insufficient exercise and the hormonal, metabolic, and behavioral changes associated with neutering define many of these animals.

In contrast to performance animals, pets require fewer calories due to a reduction in energy expenditure. Such a diet should provide reduced ME while providing nutrients required for body maintenance. The process of weight reduction is relatively simple. A 25 percent reduction relative to an animal's maintenance requirements should provide a gradual loss of body weight. However, many pet owners find it difficult to reduce the volume of food offered to their dog or cat. In addition, a subsequent reduction in food volume consumed by an animal may result in displays of undesirable behavior patterns. Therefore, the development of a reduced-calorie diet would be based on an increase in carbohydrates with a subsequent reduction in fat, while still providing adequate levels of essential fatty acids. Likewise, the level of protein must supply essential amino acids for the maintenance of protein-containing tissues and metabolic functions. The caloric distribution of such a food may provide metabolizable calories from protein, fat, and carbohydrates of 20, 30, and 50 percent, respectively.

Some weight-reducing commercial pet foods dilute the caloric density by substituting fiber for fat. However, dietary fiber above that required for regulation of digesta flow, maintenance of the intestinal villi, and formation of normal stools may be unnecessary for proper weight control. Excess fiber in the intestinal tract has been shown to reduce the availability of other dietary nutrients which may be required for body maintenance. In addition, excess fiber will result in increased defecation frequency, stool volume, and changes in fecal consistency, hence, loose or soft stools to hard, excessively dry stools.

Generic Pet Foods

Generic pet foods were introduced to the consumer market due to their economic appeal. Although some provide adequate nutrition, others were of inferior quality. A study demonstrated that dogs fed a generic food developed skin problems associated with a zinc deficiency (11). An additional study examined the nutrient digestibility of generic products. This study revealed significant differences in digestibility and growth rate of puppies despite identical label guaranteed analyses. These results supported the misrepresentation of some pet food label guarantees and actual differences in the nutritional quality of pet foods (8).

Premium Pet Foods

The exposure of some inferior-quality generic pet foods influenced the rapid proliferation of high-quality, energy-dense diets. These premium products represent a direct contrast to other disciplines of domestic animal feeding. Rather than be derived purely by economics and, subsequently, least-cost formulation, these products employ quality ingredients of high nutritional availability. Although these products are more expensive, their rapid growth in the pet food industry suggests that some consumers are willing to pay the price for high-quality nutrition.

PET FOOD LABELS

Commercial pet foods are fed as an animal's only source of nutrition and are expected to maintain optimal health and well-being. It is difficult to assess the quality of a pet food when commercial diets are presented with the influence of marketing cleverness. A pet food label contains a tremendous amount of useful information and, when correctly interpreted, can distinguish a quality commercial product from those of inferior quality but reduced cost.

The information required on pet food labels (Fig. 24–5) is prepared and approved by the joint federal and state Association of American Feed Control Officials (AAFCO). Regulation PF2: Label Format requires the following information (14): the product name; the net weight; an ingredient list; a guaranteed analysis; the name and address of the manufacturer, packer, or distributor; the designation of "Dog Food" or "Cat Food"; and a nutritional statement suggesting the adequacy of dietary purpose.

NUTRITIONAL STATEMENTS

Although pet food labels provide ingredient lists and guaranteed analyses, they lack information on nutrient content and availability. It is feasible for two labels to present identical ingredient lists and guaranteed analyses but provide products of different nutritional value (8). Differences in processing methods and selection of quality raw materials can create one product of superior nutritional quality and another that is completely unsatisfactory. Although select manufacturers provide product literature as consumer education tools which enhance one's understanding of nutrition, this is rare. The reputation of the pet food manufacturer and information concerning animal nutritional testing of a product will assist in food selection.

Nutritional statements as to the nutritional adequacy of the diet are presented on the label by some manufacturers. A simple statement, such as "complete and balanced," or a specific statement with a support claim, such as "meets the nutritional requirements as established by the National Research Council" or "as determined by protocol feeding studies established by AAFCO," signify the nutritional value of a product.

Nutritional Adequacy of Pet Foods

Nutritional adequacy claims for a complete and balanced diet or one specified for a particular life stage, such as growth, maintenance, or gesta-

FIGURE 24–5. Pet food label requirements shown on a simulated label.

tion/lactation, could be validated in one of three ways. The first method involves calculating the nutrient composition of a diet and comparing the summed values to those listed in the NRC requirement publication for dogs (1974) and cats (1978) (12, 28). The second method requires analytical evaluation of the food. The third, and most qualitative, method involves animal feeding trials during different stages of the life cycle.

Due to recent research information concerning nutritional requirements for both dogs and cats, the NRC published a revised requirement of the dog in 1985 and the cat in 1986 (13, 29). The primary difference between the former NRC publication and the revised version is the presentation of minimum nutrient requirements. Without determination of nutrient availability in practical diets, the use of minimum requirements in diet formulation is a concern.

The AAFCO Pet Food Committee developed Policy Statement 21 as a testing method to validate nutritional adequacy claims for all pet foods with the exception of treats and those foods administered under veterinarian supervision (14). According to Policy Statement 21, nutritional adequacy can be claimed by two methods. The first method is an analytical evaluation of dietary nutrients that meet the AAFCO approved nutrient profile. In addition, a short-term digestibility trial to quantify digestible dry matter and protein must be conducted in accordance with AAFCO procedures. The second method includes feeding trials plus determination of digestible dry matter and protein. Although the policy is in its early stages, it provides greater assurance as to nutritional adequacy claims.

Physical Evaluation of Pet Foods

Physical evaluation of a pet food can provide considerable information concerning product quality. First, evaluate the package or container. Dry and semimoist foods should be provided in tightly sealed multilayer packages. The presence of an inner liner aids in the prevention of moisture migration, fat wicking, and infestation. The liner also keeps product aroma in to maintain palatability. Canned products that are dented or swollen signify bacteria fermentation and should not be fed.

Product appearance should meet your quality standards. Consistency of product color, size, and shape as well as a pleasant aroma should all be considered. The presence of foreign

FIGURE 24-6. Palatability evaluation being conducted by an animal care technician. (Courtesy of the Iams Co., Dayton, OH.)

material, ingredient-related foreign material (large ingredient fragments, hair, feathers), and excessive fines are indicators of a manufacturer's inferior quality assurance program.

Palatability Evaluation

Pet foods are routinely tested for acceptability. After all, if your animal refuses to eat it, even the most nutritious pet food is of no benefit. Palatability evaluations offer an animal two products, one of which is a control of known acceptability (Fig. 24-6). Many pet foods market the palatability of their product; however, highly palatable foods are not always the most nutritious. In fact, the addition of ingredients such as garlic and cheese powder or phosphoric acid that is palatable to the cat provide no nutritional value to the diet. In addition, a highly palatable food may entice an animal to eat over its caloric needs, resulting in obesity. Product odor, taste, texture, shape, and moisture content affect the palatability of a diet.

If selecting a pet food is still confusing, request information from the pet food manufacturer concerning their testing methods in determining nutritional adequacy. A reputable manufacturer conducts numerous analytical and animal feeding tests to assure the nutritional quality of a diet, and information about these tests should be available to customers.

COMMON ERRORS IN FEEDING

Most commercial pet food manufacturers guarantee that all required nutrients are present in the proper quantities. The availability of well-balanced commercial foods makes the supplementation of dog and cat diets unnecessary.

Indiscriminate supplementation may, in fact, upset the nutritional balance of commercial pet foods, depriving the animal of optimal nutrition.

Egg Supplementation

Eggs provide a good source of protein, Fe, vitamin A, vitamin D, and numerous B-vitamins. Many pet owners believe that the addition of eggs will improve coat quality, increase the level of protein, and increase the acceptability of commercial rations. While eggs may improve the performance of an inferior commercial product, there are several potential problems associated with such supplementation.

Egg white contains avidin and a trypsin-inhibitor. Avidin functions to bind biotin, a B-vitamin, and render it unavailable for absorption. This problem may be negated by the large amount of biotin present in the yolk of eggs. However, the feeding of raw egg white alone can cause a biotin deficiency to develop. The presence of a trypsin-inhibitor will decrease normal digestion of protein. The supplementation of raw egg will result in a decrease in the protein digestibility of the diet. Cooking eggs will destroy the activity of avidin as well as the trypsin-inhibitor, thereby eliminating this potential problem.

Milk and Dairy Products

Although milk is an excellent source of protein, Ca, P, and several vitamins, excessive intake often causes diarrhea in dogs and cats. This is due to the fact that milk contains the sugar lactose, which requires the enzyme lactase for absorption. Many dogs and cats do not produce sufficient lactase to handle the quantity of lactose present in milk. This results in an inability to completely digest milk that is added to the diet and will subsequently cause digestive upsets and diarrhea. Dairy products, such as cheese, buttermilk, and yogurt, contain slightly lower levels of lactose. While these products may be more easily tolerated by some animals, they still have the potential for causing diarrhea and dietary imbalances.

Fish

Fish is highly palatable to most cats. As a result, many cat owners supplement their cat's diet with various seafoods. Although fish is a good source of protein, most deboned fish are deficient in Ca, Na, Fe, Cu, and several vitamins. Tuna fish is commonly fed to cats. Canned tuna that is packed in oil contains high levels of polyunsaturated fatty acids. The excessive intake of these oils, coupled with the fact that oils are low in vitamin E, can result in a vitamin E deficiency. This may result in steatitis or "yellow fat disease" in the cat. A second problem associated with feeding large amounts of tuna involves the high levels of Mg. The intake of high-Mg foods has been shown to be a causative factor in the development of FUS. In addition, raw fish should never be fed to cats. Certain types of fish, such as carp or herring, contain thiaminase. Thiaminase destroys the thiamin present in a diet and may result in a thiamin deficiency.

Liver

Liver provides an excellent source of protein, Fe, Cu, vitamin D, and several B-vitamins; however, it is severely deficient in Ca and excessively high in vitamin A. Both of these nutritional imbalances can cause the development of bone disorders in the cat. Vitamin A toxicity can develop slowly over a period of years in cats that are regularly fed fresh liver as their primary source of protein. The bone deformities of vitamin A toxicity form gradually and may be asymptomatic for several years.

Oils and Fats

Animal fats and fish oils are often added to commercial pet foods to improve palatability. Although fish oils provide an excellent source of vitamin A and vitamin D, when consumed in excess they are toxic. Both vitamins are stored in the liver—the effects of excess intake are cumulative and may develop over long periods of time. In addition, oversupplementation with fat may result in obesity or in an eventual decrease in dietary intake due to the fact that energy needs will be met with less food. Deficiencies of other nutrients may then occur.

Chocolate

Most dogs love chocolate. However, chocolate contains theobromine, a compound toxic to dogs and cats. The content of theobromine is highest in unsweetened baking chocolate and lowest in milk chocolate. The consumption of only 3 oz of chocolate has the potential to cause death in a 25-lb dog. Signs of theobromine toxicity include depression, vomiting, diarrhea, increased urination, and muscular tremors.

Onions

Contrary to common belief, the addition of onions to a dog's diet will not prevent fleas or parasites. Although many dogs enjoy the taste, onions contain a compound that may cause severe anemia. A dog consuming 0.5 percent or more of its body weight in dehydrated onion will exhibit symptoms of hemolytic anemia within 1–3 days.

Vitamin C

Vitamin C is not required in the diet, but it is often supplemented with hopes of preventing certain skeletal diseases, such as hypertrophic osteodystrophy (HOD) or hip dysplasia. However, this claim has not been scientifically confirmed through controlled research. Likewise, although vitamin C requirements increase with stress, vitamin C supplementation does not enhance a dog's stamina or performance. In fact, excessive vitamin C supplementation increases the risk for the formation of kidney or bladder stones.

B-Complex Vitamins and Brewer's Yeast

B-complex vitamins, or B-complex in the form of brewer's yeast, are often supplemented in the hope of repelling fleas or improving athletic performance. Scientific studies have shown that such supplementation has no effect on flea infestation or increasing performance, provided a well-balanced diet is being fed.

METHODS OF FEEDING

The selection of an appropriate diet is only the first step in assuring the health and well-being of a dog or cat. Selecting the appropriate method of feeding can influence animal health as well. The method of feeding will be influenced by the type of diet, age and physical condition of the animal, environmental factors and social interactions, as well as the attitude and life style of the owner.

There are two basic methods of feeding both dogs and cats. The first method is ad libitum or free choice and the second is portion-controlled or meal feeding. A free-choice regimen provides more food than the animal will consume at one time. In contrast, a portion-controlled regimen provides food in restricted quantities as one, two, or three meals per day.

Feeding Management of Cats

Due to the feeding patterns of the cat, the most common method of feeding is ad libitum. It has been shown that the cat is a nibbler, meaning it will eat 10–20 times in a 24-h period. Whether it is night or day seems to have an insignificant effect on the frequency of feeding. The frequent small meal sizes displayed by most cats suggest that they consume food to meet their caloric needs. Although mature cats meet their nutritional needs when meal fed, unless they are overweight and warrant a portion-controlled regimen, free-choice feeding is the method of choice.

Growing kittens and queens in a stage of gestation and lactation have the highest caloric needs. To maximize caloric intake, nutrient-dense, highly digestible foods should be offered. Sudden changes in the surrounding environment, such as excessive noise, a change in lighting, or the relocation of a feed bowl, may upset a cat and result in anorexia. Social interactions (multiple cat households) may adversely affect feeding behavior. In multiple cat households each cat should have an individual feeding bowl in a separate location. This will allow the assessment of individual food intake, as well as prevent competitive feeding that may predispose an animal to obesity.

Feeding Management of Dogs

If an adult dog consumes food to meet its energy needs, a free-choice regimen is the most convenient method. Dry pet foods are the most suitable for a free-choice program. Canned foods may be inappropriate because they are susceptible to bacterial growth due to their high moisture content and because they often dry out, resulting in reduced acceptability. In contrast, diets should be portion-controlled when fed to obese dogs who are unable to self-regulate caloric needs. The maintenance of ideal body weight is the best assessment of the appropriateness of a feeding regimen.

Similar to the cat, caloric needs of the dog are increased in the growing puppy and during periods of gestation and lactation. The puppy is in a linear stage of growth and, depending on breed, will reach its adult weight in 10 months. Other breeds, such as the giant breeds, do not reach mature weight even at 24 months of age (Fig. 24–7). Puppies should be fed a diet of high caloric content. If a diet of inferior energy availability is fed, the puppy may not be able to con-

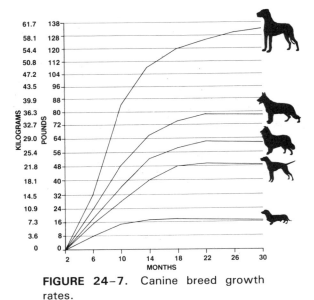

FIGURE 24-7. Canine breed growth rates.

sume sufficient quantities to meet its nutritional needs due to a limitation in stomach capacity.

A portion-controlled feeding regimen should be used for growing puppies. Although a free-choice method supports maximal weight gain, this is not a benefit to the rapidly growing dog. Such a condition can predispose a puppy to a state of obesity, as well as compromise normal skeletal development. A study with growing Labradors compared these two feeding regimens and recorded a 17 percent increase in food consumption when puppies were fed free choice. In addition, puppies on a portion-controlled regimen had a lower incidence of osteodystrophic changes that were correlated to a reduction in caloric intake and subsequent lower weight gain than their respective free-choice controls (1).

The caloric requirement for gestation is not substantially increased until the last trimester. However, the caloric needs to support peak lactation periods may exceed the maintenance requirement in excess of threefold. The consumption of excess calories resulting in too much weight gain is rarely a concern during lactation. Rather, it is the maintenance of ideal body weight that a feeding program should be based upon. A free-choice feeding regimen is most suitable for maximal performance.

Environmental factors can significantly affect energy requirements. Exposure to cold temperatures will increase energy expenditure, thereby increasing energy requirements. It has been estimated that energy requirement of a dog exposed to cold temperatures may increase 25 percent over that required for maintenance.

It has been demonstrated that dogs housed together will consume more food than if housed individually. In part, this response may be due to an increase in energy expenditure of dogs housed together. However, it has been shown that satiated dogs introduced into a neutral territory will resume eating when pair fed. The respective individually fed controls did not initiate further food consumption once satiated. Therefore, competition at the feeder results in caloric consumption over that required. To prevent such an occurrence in homes with more than one dog, individual food bowls should be provided in separate locations. A portion-controlled feeding program may be necessary.

SUMMARY

Nutritional research with companion animals has not been generally recognized as part of the animal science tradition. Although companion animals are frequently employed as animal models in other areas of biological science, assessment of specific nutrient requirements for dogs and cats has only received attention recently.

Nutrition for the dog and cat can be supplied by a vast array of ingredient compositions, processed by diverse techniques, and provided in various forms. The selection of the proper diet warrants a basic understanding of the nutritional requirements for dogs and, especially, cats and the factors that affect nutritional quality and efficacy, as well as the appropriate method of feeding. The proper diet for a dog or cat should not simply provide an adequate level of nutrition, but should express an optimum state of health and well-being.

REFERENCES

Dogs

1. Alexander, J. E., and L. L. H. Wood. 1987. *Canine Practice* 14(2):41.
2. Blaza, S. E., et al. 1982. *J. Nutr.* 112:2033.
3. Czarnecki, G. L., and D. H. Baker. 1982. *J. Anim. Sci.* 55:1405.
4. Finco, D. R. 1980. *Clinical biochemistry of domestic animals.* 3d ed. New York: Academic Press.

5. Hirakawa, D. A., and D. H. Baker. 1985. *Nutr. Research* 5:631.

6. Hirakawa, D. A., and D. H. Baker, 1986. *Nutr. Research* 6:527.

7. Hirakawa, D. A., and D. H. Baker. 1988. *Comp. Animal Pract.* 2:25.

8. Huber, T. L., R. C. Wilson, and S. A. McGarity. 1988. *J. Amer. Anim. Hosp. Assoc.* 22:571.

9. Milner, J. A. 1981. *J. Nutr.* 111:40.

10. Sheffy, B. E., et al. 1985. *Cornell Vet.* 75:324.

11. Sousa, C. A., et al. 1988. *JAVMA* 192:676.

12. NRC. 1974. *Nutrient requirements of dogs.* Washington, D.C.: Nat. Acad. Press.

13. NRC. 1985. *Nutrient requirements of dogs.* Washington, D.C.: Nat. Acad. Press.

14. Anon. 1989. *AAFCO official publication.* Atlanta, GA: Assoc. Amer. Feed Control Officials, Inc.

Cats

15. Ballard, F. J. 1965. *Comp. Biochem. Physiol.* 14:437.

16. Burger, I. H. 1987. *J. Small Anim. Pract.* 28:447.

17. Gershoff, S. N., et al. 1957. *Lab. Invest.* 6:227.

18. Harrington, J. T., and J. Lemann. 1970. *Med. Clinics N. Amer.* 54:1543.

19. Hayes, K. C., R. E. Carey, and S. Y. Schmidt. 1975. *Science* 188:949.

20. Kane, E., and G. M. Douglas. 1986. *Feline Pract.* 16:9.

21. MacDonald, M. L., Q. R. Rogers, and J. G. Morris. 1984. *Ann. Rev. Nutr.* 4:521.

22. Morris, J. G., and Q. R. Rogers. 1978. *Science* 199:431.

23. Pion, P. D., et al. 1987. *Science* 237:764.

24. Rich, L. J., and R. W. Kirk. 1969. *JAVMA* 154:153.

25. Reveis, J. P. W. 1982. *J. Small Anim. Pract.* 23:563.

26. Sauer, L. S., D. Hamar, and L. D. Lewis. 1985. *Feline Pract.* 15:10.

27. Sturman, J. A., et al. 1986. *J. Nutr.* 116:655.

28. NRC. 1978. *Nutrient requirements of cats.* Washington, D.C.: Nat. Acad. Press.

29. NRC. 1986. *Nutrient requirements of cats.* Washington, D.C.: Nat. Acad. Press.

25

Feeding Rabbits

Hugo Varela-Alvarez

INTRODUCTION

Rabbits are used for meat, for fur and hair production, for vocational projects, as laboratory animals, as teaching tools, as animal research models, and for pets (Fig. 25–1). Because of their use in a wide range of enterprises it is necessary to have a good knowledge of the different aspects of their management and nutrition.

Rabbit feeding and nutrition information increased significantly during the 1980s. Most of the research in these areas has been done by European researchers, most notably those of France. It is in Europe where meat rabbit production has become a true industry, and rabbit meat consumption is relatively high.

Feeding and nutrition are important aspects of any animal production enterprise. Cost of feed accounts for a large percentage of the total production cost, and therefore, a good understanding of proper nutrition and feeding is essential for successful economic rabbit production.

FIGURE 25–1. California rabbits, one breed often used for meat production. (Courtesy of Mrs. G. Absolon, Doebank, Palmerston North, New Zealand.)

DIGESTIVE SYSTEM

The function of the digestive system is to transform the ingested feed, through chemical, physical, and biological processes, in such a way that the organism can use the nutrients of the feed for maintenance, growth, and production.

Relative Size

The digestive system of the rabbit (illustrated in Ch. 2, Fig. 2–5) is well adapted for the utilization of forages and feeds of plant origin. The digestive system occupies a large portion of the body cavity. In the New Zealand White adult rabbit (4–4.5 kg) the digestive tube can be as long as 5 m. The development of the digestive system is almost completed at 9 weeks of age. The cecum and the colon start to develop around 3–5 weeks of age, when feed ingestion, other than milk, starts to be significant, and the microflora population becomes important in those organs.

The size of the different parts of the digestive system varies with age, breed, physiological status, and type of feed given to the rabbit. Close to 80 percent of the digesta is contained in the stomach and the cecum (Table 25–1). These two compartments are the ones with the largest capacity. The relative organ size is also presented in Table 25–1.

Retention in the Stomach

The amount of time that the feed stays in the digestive system affects the amount of time enzymes and microorganisms can act over the ingested material, therefore affecting both nutrient absorption and utilization. The average retention time of ingested material in the digestive tract is 17–18 h, being less for large particles (14–16 h) and longer for finer particles (20–21 h). The longest retention time occurs in the stomach and in the cecum. Retention time in the small intestine is relatively low. The rabbit's stomach is almost always full. Gastric secretion is continuous and very acid (pH 1–2), the result of HCl secretion. Gastric digestion is characterized by a significant production of lactic acid (1) that is absorbed directly by the gastric mucosa or in the small intestine (2).

Type of Feces Produced

The rabbit produces two kinds of feces: hard feces and soft feces or cecotrophs (3). The rabbit has a specialized mechanism which retains digesta in the proximal colon and cecum for microbial utilization of nutrients and also to allow the formation of the two types of feces. The reingestion of the soft feces by the rabbit is called cecotrophy. The production of two types of feces and the ingestion of only one type of these distinguishes cecotrophy from coprophagy. This process is one of the important characteristics of the digestive physiology of the rabbit which allows the animal maximal utilization and absorption of total ingested nutrients (4). The soft feces are higher in water, electrolytes, and nitrogen (N) content, and lower in fiber (5). A significant proportion of the total N content of cecotrophs (60–80 percent) is from cecal microbial cells (6). Total N from cecotrophs represents an important source of protein for the animal and could amount to up to 20 percent of the total N intake of the rabbit. Cecotrophs contribute approximately 20 percent of the protein and 10 percent of the energy for maintenance, vitamins, and minerals. Producers should take advantage of this characteristic in order to feed rabbits with nontraditional ingredients (7).

TABLE 25-1

Values for different parts of the rabbit digestive system[a]

Digestive System Part	Weight, g	Length, cm	Capacity, g	DM, %	pH
Stomach	20		90–100	17	1.5–2.0
Small intestine	60	330	20–40	7	7.2
Cecal appendix	10	13	1		
Cecum	25	40	100–120	20	6.0
Colon	30		10–30		
Proximal colon		50		20–25	6.5
Distal colon		90		20–40	

[a]Values from 12-week-old New Zealand rabbits fed a pelleted complete diet.
Source: Lebas et al. (9).

The cecotrophs are removed directly from the anus and are swallowed whole. When they reach the stomach they do not mix immediately with the rest of the stomach contents but lie in a mass in the fundic region for 6–8 h (8). From there on the cecotrophs follow a digestion pattern as does any other ingested feed.

FEEDING BEHAVIOR

Feed and Water Intake

Quantifying feed and water intake is important in order to ascertain the economics of the rabbit enterprise. It would also help in the early detection of health problems whose first sign could be a lack of appetite or an excess of drinking.

Knowledge of feed intake helps the manager to decide whether or not there is an excess of feed waste. Feed and water intake values are helpful in diet formulation and disease control, so that concentration of nutrient or medicine can be formulated according to requirements, age, or body weight.

During the first 3 weeks of life, the rabbit consumes only maternal milk. When milk production is not enough, then the rabbit starts to consume solid food and water. The animal then changes from one or two feedings a day to several feedings in 24 h.

During a 24-h period, adult and growing rabbits (4 weeks or older), will consume feed in several meals of small amounts (feed and water), utilizing usually 2–4 h/d for feeding. Feed and water consumption in g/meal is lower during the day (time with light) than during the night (dark hours). In lactating does, feed consumption occurs mostly during the night. This behavior must be taken into consideration for feeding practices.

The average feed and water consumption varies according to age and physiological status of the animal. In general, rabbits will consume water in quantities close to twice their dry feed intake. Adult animals (4 kg body weight) will consume on the average 200–300 ml of water/d, while lactating females can drink 3–4 liters/d (10). Lactating females increase their feed intake proportionally to milk production and number of suckling rabbits (11, 12).

Water and feed consumption vary according to environmental temperature and humidity. There is a direct relationship between dry feed intake and water intake (13). As temperature rises, water consumption increases, but at high temperatures (30° C and over) feed and water consumption decline, affecting the performance of growing and lactating animals (14).

NUTRIENT REQUIREMENTS

Water

Water should be supplied ad libitum. Rabbits have a high requirement for water in relation to their body weight. Water is necessary for maintenance, production, and lactation. Because dry matter intake is related to water intake, any restriction in water causes a decline in dry matter consumption. However, if feed is restricted, water intake may increase. Water should be clean, fresh, and free from biological and chemical contaminants. One example of a watering device for rabbits is shown in Fig. 25–2.

Protein

The adult rabbit (probably) obtains 10–20 percent of its total protein intake from cecotrophy as good-quality bacterial protein. Gidenne reported that in 6-week-old young New Zealand rabbits, independent of the type of diet, cecotrophy accounted for 29 percent of the total protein intake (16). Part of the amino acids produced in the cecum by microorganisms are absorbed directly by the cecum wall, and after cecotrophy, the rest are absorbed by the small intestine. The contribution of microbial protein to young rabbits (4–8 weeks old) is very small, and steps should be taken to supply good-quality protein to growing animals. Rabbits require a good-quality protein intake in terms of quantity and quality. The essential amino acids are the same as in other species (see Ch. 3). Glycine can be synthesized in adequate amounts in the adult

FIGURE 25–2. An automatic nipple drinking system that works well for rabbits. (Courtesy of Mrs. G. Absolon, Doebank, Palmerston North, New Zealand.)

TABLE 25-2

Essential amino acid minimum requirements for rabbits

Amino Acid	Growth	Gestation	Lactation
Arginine, %	1.00	0.80	1.11
Glycine, %	0.40	0.40	0.40
Histidine, %	0.45	0.42	0.45
Isoleucine, %	0.70	0.70	0.71
Leucine, %	1.05	1.05	1.25
Lysine, %	0.70	0.70	0.85
Methionine + cystine, %	0.60	0.60	0.95
Phenylalanine + tyrosine, %	1.20	1.20	1.20
Threonine, %	0.55	0.60	0.64
Tryptophan, %	0.15	0.15	0.15
Valine, %	0.70	0.75	0.82

Source: Varela-Alvarez (15).

rabbit. However, in the fast-growing rabbit the rate of synthesis of glycine is not adequate, therefore, glycine should be supplemented in diets for these animals (15). The amino acid requirements are presented in Table 25–2. Protein quality is related to feed intake and thus to performance.

Total crude protein requirements for maintenance in adult rabbits is 13 percent of the ration. Digestible protein requirements for growing rabbits can be computed using the following formulas:

$$\text{Minimum DP} = \frac{\text{DE}}{250}$$

$$\text{Maximum DP} = \frac{\text{DE}}{230}$$

Digestible protein requirements for lactating does can be obtained by the following formulas:

$$\text{Minimum DP} = \frac{\text{DE}}{200}$$

$$\text{Maximum DP} = \frac{\text{DE}}{180}$$

where DP = percent digestible protein in the diet and where DE = digestible energy, kcal/kg in the diet.

The protein requirements for lactating does are higher than those for growing rabbits due to the protein demands during lactation. There is a high secretion of protein and energy in the milk during lactation. This secretion is directly proportional to milk production. The producer should take into account that protein levels below 18 percent without the proper levels of energy have a negative effect on milk produc-

tion and, therefore, on the rate of gain of the suckling rabbits.

Protein nutrition is of special concern in fur- and hair-producing rabbits. Because the final product (pelt and hair) is high in N-containing compounds and S-containing amino acids, the level in dietary protein should be high, with a minimum of 17 percent crude protein and a minimum of 0.6 percent of S-containing amino acids (methionine, cystine). It should be noted that, in the usual rabbit feeds, the first limiting amino acids are the S-containing ones, followed by lysine.

Energy and Fiber

Most of the required energy in the rabbit is supplied by carbohydrates, to a lesser extent by lipids, and in some cases by excess protein. Rabbits, like most other animals, adjust their feed intake to maintain a relatively constant energy intake. Therefore, when formulating a diet, nutrients should be supplied in relation to energy.

Energy requirements vary according to factors such as animal age and size (younger and smaller animals require more energy), physiological status (growing animals require more energy than inactive adults; lactating does require more energy than nonlactating animals), environmental temperature and humidity (animals in cold and humid environments require more energy in order to maintain body temperature and level of production), diet fiber concentration, and type of enterprise.

For the growing period the average daily digestible energy (DE) requirement for maintenance and production can be estimated by the following formula:

$$DE = 4MW (20 - WW) + 55WW + 3.6DG - 50$$

For lactating animals, the average daily DE requirement can be estimated by the following formula:

$$DE = 290 + 65DW + 35G$$

where: DE = daily digestible energy, kcal/d
MW = estimated market weight, kg
WW = weaning weight, kg
DG = expected average daily gain, g
DW = doe weight, kg
G = number of suckling rabbits

EXAMPLE

For a rabbit that is going to be marketed at 2 kg, with a weaning weight of 0.6 kg, and an expected daily gain of 30 g, the estimated DE requirement per day for the growing period would be

$$4 \times 2(20 - 0.6) + 55(0.6) \\ + 3.6(30) - 50 = 246.2 \text{ kcal/d}$$

If the feed utilized contains 2500 kcal DE/kg, then feed consumption/animal/d (waste not included) will be

$$\frac{246.2 \times 1000}{2500} = 98.48 \text{ g of feed}$$

For primiparous lactating females, the energy requirement should include an increase in energy to fulfill the requirements for growth of the female. That can be quantified as an extra 6.5 kcal/d/kg body weight.

As lactation progresses, the lactating female increases her feed intake to a maximum in order to satisfy her energy needs. If the ration does not contain a high level of energy/kg, then the female will use part of her body reserves in order to maintain milk production. This will cause the female to lose condition, affecting future breeding performance and efficiency (15). Furthermore, if the feed is of a low caloric density, the young rabbits will not be able to maintain a high growth rate when they start to consume dry feed. This has been shown to also affect growth rate and feed efficiency in the postweaning period.

With the estimated energy requirement and the estimated level of intake per day, it is possible to calculate the energy concentration in the diet. Diets with a minimum concentration of 2500 kcal DE/kg will satisfy the requirements of growing rabbits, and 2500–3000 kcal DE/kg

will be sufficient for lactating does with more than seven pups. Rations with 2200 kcal/kg are adequate for inactive adults.

With an increase in fiber content in the diet there is a reduction in the utilization of energy and organic matter. This relationship seems to be linear. However, some minimum level of fiber must be present in the diet (12–14 percent crude fiber for growing rabbits) in order to maintain proper digestion and gut motility, and to prevent some metabolic disorders such as diarrhea. For each 1 percent increase in cellulose content in the diet there is a decrease of 0.7 units in organic matter digestibility (8). French researchers have estimated that by replacing the diet's starch with cellulose there is a reduction of the DE in a proportion of 60 kcal DE/kg diet for every percent point increase of cellulose (17).

Digestibility is the combined effect of rate of passage and the digestibility coefficient of the feed itself. An increase in crude fiber will increase feed intake and decrease feed efficiency. In general, an increase in retention time increases the digestibility of the diet, but in the rabbit it also increases the incidence of digestive disorders. It has been suggested that a low retention time is a normal characteristic in the rabbit (8). Gidenne (18) reported that increasing lignin concentration in rabbit diets decreases protein digestibility and to a lesser extent energy and cellulose.

Part or all of the fiber should be given in the form of large particles (2–4 mm) in order to decrease the incidence of digestive disorders, reduce weight loss, and promote gut function and hard feces formation. Part of the fiber could be ground below the 2 mm size to permit longer cecal retention and increase digestibility. Research is needed in this area to determine the minimum proportion of long fiber needed by growing and by lactating animals.

Minerals

Rabbits require Ca, P, Mg, K, Na, Cl, Mn, Zn, Cu, Fe, I, Co, and Se. Other minerals such as chromium and fluoride, which are essential for other mammals, have not been reported as having an important role in rabbit nutrition. Mineral requirements are higher during lactation because they are either secreted in milk or are required for milk secretion. Available information on rabbit mineral nutrition and requirements is scarce and contradictory. Data presented here refer to mineral levels based on a 2500-kcal/kg feed mix. The minimum requirements for each of the important minerals are presented in Table 25-3.

Ca and P requirements are highest for the lactating females because of the higher amounts of these minerals that are secreted in the milk. The recommended ratio of Ca to P is 2:1, however, rabbits can tolerate up to a 12:1 ratio. Although rabbits can tolerate high amounts of Ca in the diet, this can bring on a Zn or a Mg deficiency in growing animals and a P deficiency in lactating does. Some of the feed Ca comes from buffers added to the diets. Buffers can be added to rabbit diets in order to lower the pH of the cecal contents, which in turn increases feed intake (19). Ca deficiencies are rare in commercial rabbit production because most of the ingredients utilized in rabbit diets are high in this mineral. Ca can be supplemented in the diet as inorganic Ca with calcium carbonate ($CaCO_3$) or dicalcium phosphate (HP_4Ca_2).

The best sources of P are ingredients of animal origin, but these ingredients are not popular in rabbit diets. Most of the P ingested is of plant origin and is present in phytate form which is poorly utilized by the animals. There seems to be a microbial process in the cecum that frees the P, making it available through cecotrophy. However, it does not cover the animal's requirements, making it necessary to supplement with P. The best supplements are in the form of Ca salts; of these the best is monocalcium phosphate.

Mg is required for proper growth, gestation, and lactation. Mg requirements increase during gestation and lactation due to fetus uptake and milk synthesis. Deficiencies of this element cause retarded growth, fur chewing, poor fur condition, and whitening of the ears. Excess of Mg can cause diarrhea.

Zn is required in rabbits to maintain a normal pregnancy, for proper fetus growth, and for proper pre- and postweaning growth. Zn also plays a role in the quality of hair and fur. A level of 50-70 ppm in the diet seems to be appropriate. However, these levels should be increased if the diet contains more than 2 percent Ca. Pregnant does fed diets low in Zn pull little or no hair for nest building.

Under normal conditions K will not be a limiting mineral in rabbit diets. High-energy diets will be lower in K due to the high grain concentration. Some of the K is excreted via the milk. K levels in the diet should be increased to their maximum under high-temperature conditions, especially for lactating does. If K is increased, total Na should also be increased. An imbalance of K and Na may cause renal problems. High levels of K (greater than 2 percent) can cause low fertility rates and low embryonic survival (20).

Addition of chelated salts of Cu, Co, Fe, Zn, Mn, and I to rabbit diets have been reported to increase rate of growth, dressing percentage, and feed efficiency (21).

When diets are supplemented with crystalline synthetic amino acids, the levels of Cl and Na in the diet should be adjusted both in quantity and in ratio. This is due to the fact that most of the synthetic amino acids are of the hydrochloride form, thus adding extra Cl to the diet.

Vitamins

In the adult rabbit, B-complex vitamins are synthesized in the cecum. However, not all B-

TABLE 25-3
Mineral minimum requirements for rabbits[a]

Mineral	Growth	Breeding	Lactation
Calcium, %	0.9-1.0	0.9-1.0	1.0-1.2
Phosphorus, %	0.6-0.7	0.6-0.7	0.8-1.0
Potassium, %	1.3	0.75	1.3
Sodium, %	0.4	0.25	0.4
Chloride, %	0.4	0.2-0.25	0.4
Manganese, ppm	8.5	8.5	8.5
Magnesium, ppm	400-500	400-500	400-500
Cobalt, ppm	1	1	1
Copper, ppm	5	5	5
Zinc, ppm	50-70	50-70	50-70
Iodine, ppm	0.2	0.2	0.2

[a]Assumes a 2500 kcal DE/kg diet.
Source: Varela-Alvarez (15).

TABLE 25-4

Recommended vitamin supplementation for growing and adult rabbits

Compound	Premix Units/kg
Vitamin A, IU	3,530,000
Vitami D$_3$, IU	353,000
Vitamin E, IU	15,985
Vitamin B$_{12}$, mg	5
Riboflavin, mg	1325
Niacin, mg	19,845
d-Pantothenic acid, mg	4765
Choline chloride, mg	242,510
Menadione SBC, mg	620
Thiamine mononitrate, mg	480
Pyridoxine HCl, mg	1060
Biotin, mg	40
Folic acid, mg	80
β-Carotene	4410

Source: Frye (22).

complex vitamins are synthesized in the needed amount for fast-growing rabbits, therefore they should be supplied in growing rabbit diets to obtain a high performance in the commercial meat operation. The absence of a vitamin or its inadequate amount in the diet will result in poor performance and, if severe, in specific deficiency symptoms. Vitamins should be present for normal absorption and utilization of the other required nutrients. Frye (22) recommended the vitamin premix presented in Table 25-4 to be used as a supplementation for growing rabbits. This premix should be used at a minimum rate of 2.5 kg/1000 kg of complete feed. Vitamin C (ascorbic acid) supplementation is recommended for diets of rabbits under stress (23).

Some of the factors that can affect the amount of a given vitamin in a diet are: improper formulation, low-quality supplemental vitamin product, amount of time the feed is stored, and environmental conditions such as temperature and humidity. Vitamins will be degraded under conditions of high temperature and humidity. It is recommended that feed should be utilized within a maximum of 3–4 months after blending in order to have the proper nutritive value. If feed is contaminated by mold, insects, or rodents, the shelf life may be much less than 3–4 months.

Factors that can influence the vitamin requirement level in rabbits are: general health of the animals (parasites and diseases damage the lining of the digestive tract and increase the requirements), environmental stress, medication (especially with antibiotics, which decrease the rate of B-complex synthesis), rate of growth (animals that grow faster require more quantities of vitamins per day), quality of the product being used as a source for the vitamin (bioavailability), and system of production: intensive versus extensive (animals under intensive systems of production have a higher requirement).

Dietary levels below the requirement for vitamins A, D, E, and K will produce deficiency symptoms similar to those in other species. Excess vitamin A and D are known to cause health problems in rabbits. Supplementation of fat-soluble vitamins in the diet may be necessary but should be done with care.

Additives

In some cases, it may be desirable to use additives in rabbit diets. The most common additives are antibiotics, coccidiostats, and antioxidants. These additives, when included in any diet, should be in accordance with FDA regulations (see Ch. 10).

Molasses may be added to rabbit diets to increase the energy content of the diet, to increase palatability, or to reduce dustiness of the mix. Caution should be taken when using molasses because high levels (greater than 6 percent) may produce diarrhea. Buffers and pellet binders are also added to the diets. Of the pellet binders, Ca and Na lignosulphonates have been reported to produce high incidences of colon ulcerations and high mortality, while Mg lignosulphonates appear to have no such effects (24, 25).

FEEDSTUFFS FOR RABBITS

The major ingredients used in rabbit diets are feed grains, milling by-products, protein supplements, forages, fats, synthetic amino acids, and mineral and vitamin supplements. Selection of ingredients should be done on the basis of availability, freshness, nutrient content, price, and palatability.

Feed Grains

Feed grains are used as a source of energy. Barley, wheat, oats, corn, sorghum, and triticale can be included in rabbit diets. Grain milling by-products can be utilized in rabbit diets as a source of fiber and a limited source of protein. The contribution of feed grains to diet protein is limited.

Protein Supplements

Most of the protein supplements used in rabbit diets are of plant origin. However, when offered, animal protein supplements (fish meal, meat meal) will be consumed by rabbits, but to a lesser extent than those from plant sources. Plant protein sources are usually cheaper than those of animal origin. The most common protein supplements are soybean meal, cottonseed meal, peanut meal, rapeseed meal (canola meal), sesame seed meal, sunflower meal, and safflower meal. Caution should be taken when feeding cottonseed meal and rapeseed meal (see Ch. 9). Cottonseed meal can contain high levels of gossypol, making the ration unpalatable and toxic. Problems may also be encountered with rapeseed meal if the levels of erucic acid are high. Rapeseed meal has been reported to cause problems in fertility and reproduction in does. Peanut meal should be used with caution because this feedstuff may sometimes contain aflatoxins.

In some parts of the world, beans have been used as a protein source. Some raw beans (including raw soybeans) as well as soybean meal have been reported to affect animal performance due to high contents of antitrypsin factors and other growth depressant compounds (see Ch. 9). Proper heat treatment of beans and soybean meal inactivates these compounds.

Forages

Forages are used in rabbit diets as a source of fiber and bulk. Forages can be directly incorporated into a completely pelleted feed or be used as a complement to pellets. It is more convenient from the point of view of handling and knowledge of animal intake to include forages in the pellets. However, in some situations, direct use could be more convenient, as is the case in backyard and other small operations. When given apart from the pellets, it is better to offer forages in the form of hay. Care should be taken to avoid moldy forages, because these can cause digestive disorders in rabbits.

Of all forages, alfalfa is the most widely used and preferred by the animals. This legume provides not only a good source of fiber, but good levels of protein and Ca. However, caution should be taken when using very young alfalfa. Alfalfa from very early cuts is high in protein (greater than 20 percent) and xanthophylls, but when used in growing rabbit diets it may cause diarrhea.

The following plants have been listed by Bender (26) as undesirable rabbit feeds: arrowgrass, bracken fern, brownweed, buckeye, burdock, castor beans, chinaberry, fireweed, foxglove, goldenrod, hemlock, horehound, jimson weed, Johnsongrass, larkspur, laurel, lupine, mesquite, milkweed, miner's lettuce, oak, oleander, poppy, sweet clover, and tarweed.

Fats

Fats can be added to rabbit diets as a concentrated source of energy and a source of essential fatty acids. Rabbit diets will contain, on the average, 3 percent fats that come from the different feedstuffs used for typical diets. Added fats increase the diet energy density, but sometimes they also increase the price of feed. An economic analysis comparing price to performance will be required to ascertain whether increasing feed price per unit will increase profitability. It has been reported that adding fats increases the feed to gain ratio in growing rabbits (27), and that this increase was noted with fat additions up to 6 percent. However, high levels of fat present a problem for pelleting. Pelleting will be done properly if the added fat does not exceed 3 percent. Fat could be sprayed on the pellets.

Other Nonconventional Feedstuffs

Other materials have been used as feedstuffs for rabbits as a partial substitute for the conventional grains and forages or as a primary source, as is the case of some tropical plants. Pomaces, the residue of industrial processing of some fruits (apples, grapes, tomatoes, pears), have been utilized without detrimental effects in diets of growing and adult rabbits. These pomaces have variable levels of fiber and soluble carbohydrates and are low in protein.

In tropical areas cassava root meal, coconut meal, tropical kudzu, palm oil, whole corn plant meal, amaranthus, carrot leaves, bananas, sweet potatoes, sugar cane, and NaOH-treated straw have been used as feedstuff for rabbits. The following legumes, some of them of tropical origin, have been utilized in rabbit diets: *Indigofera arrecta*, *Lespedeza spp*, *Leucaena leucocephala*, *Pueraria spp*, *Stylosanthes spp*, and *Trifolium alexandrium* (9). All of these legumes have a good level of protein.

There is need for comprehensive research into the utilization of tropical legumes and forages for rabbit production.

FEEDING MANAGEMENT

Rabbit production success depends on the profit made, that is, the difference between production cost and gross returns from animal sales. Producers can increase this difference by reducing production cost. Because feed represents a large proportion of production cost, proper feed formulation and feeding practices can help to increase profits.

Diet Formulation

One important factor to consider in rabbit diet formulation is the quality of the ingredients, because these will have a direct impact on rabbit health and performance. Quality includes shelf life and nutrient profile.

In compliance with state and federal laws, feed manufacturers provide a feed label tag (See Ch. 6) where information regarding composition and feed analysis is displayed. Rabbit producers should read these labels carefully, but the label guarantee does not imply consistent nutrition or performance in some cases because required information is not sufficient to make an evaluation. Performance of a mix is obtained by comparing those feeds on actual feeding tests. The best policy is to buy feed produced by a reputable feed company.

Producers formulating their own feeds should follow the nutritional recommendations and select the feed ingredients as described earlier in this chapter. Formulating a diet for rabbits may be approached as follows: (A) identify the target animal (gestating, lactating, growing, breeding) for which the diet is intended; (B) select the appropriate nutrient re-

quirements (see Tables 25–2, 25–3, and 25–4); (C) select appropriate feed ingredients in order to formulate a diet that is nutritionally balanced, palatable, and safe; (D) formulate the ration based on nutrition, efficiency, and cost (see Ch. 12).

Feed manufacturers have three types of pellets available in the market: all-grain pellets, all-hay pellets, and complete pellets (grain and forage together). The type of pellet required will depend on the type of feeding management adopted in the rabbitry. An all-grain pellet requires a supplementation of hay; use of a hay pellet requires a supplementation of grain; a complete pellet does not require supplementation of any kind.

Mixing of rabbit diets should have the end result of satisfying all of the minimum daily requirements for energy, protein, minerals, and vitamins within the limits of the animal's normal feed intake. Supplementation, therefore, should not be necessary. If the mix is adequate, extra supplementation will cause a nutritional imbalance which leads to suboptimal performance. Examples of some sample diets for rabbits are presented in Table 25–5.

A feed mix of uniform quality is the ideal target for rabbit feeding. Formulas may vary according to local feed price changes. If a change is economically necessary, keep in mind that significant variations during a short period of time in ingredient or nutritional composition will alter the cecal environment. This change will alter the cecal bacterial composition and its byproducts and will change the rabbit's ability to utilize nutrients. To obtain a uniform mix, the ingredients of the ration should be ground and

TABLE 25-5

Sample diets for rabbits

Int'l. Feed Number	Ingredient	Mainte-nance	Growth		Lactation	
1-00-068	Alfalfa hay, %	52.4	40.0	45.0	36.4	34.9
4-00-549	Barley, %	18.1	15.9	34.0	—	—
4-02-935	Corn, %	—	—	2.7	32.5	41.1
4-03-309	Oats, %	9.6	15.8	—	—	—
5-04-604	Soybean meal, %	—	10.4	—	16.3	—
5-04-739	Sunflower meal, %	3.5	—	11.1	—	17.8
4-05-190	Wheat bran, %	13.0	12.5	2.1	10.2	1.7
4-04-696	Cane molasses, %	1.5	3.0	3.0	1.6	1.5
6-01-080	Dicalcium Phosphate, %	1.1	1.6	1.3	2.2	2.2
	Salt (NaCl), %	0.5	0.5	0.5	0.5	0.5
	Supplement,[a] %	0.3	0.3	0.3	0.3	0.3

[a]The supplement must contain the sources to balance microminerals, vitamins, and amino acids.

then pelleted. Pellets should be 3–4 mm in diameter and no longer than 8 mm. Pelleting prevents selection by the animal, should reduce waste, and increases total dry matter intake.

Feed Storage

Feed should be stored in containers (bins or silos) that can be emptied and cleaned on a regular basis to maintain the quality of the diet. Nutrient stability in complete mixed rabbit diets is inversely related to environmental temperature and humidity. Knapka (28) reported that although the quality of rabbit diets may decrease during the shelf life period, there is no research documentation of problems as a direct result of this loss in quality. The same author recommended to feed rabbit diets as soon as possible after manufacture and not to use diets when there is doubt regarding their quality. In general, it is recommended that feed should be used as soon as possible after mixing, and to have the objective of not keeping feed more than 4–6 weeks in storage.

Feeding Schedule

In any type of rabbit operation, time of feeding should be constant, since rabbits can be influenced by changes in routine. Any changes in routine should be done in a stepwise fashion. Time of feeding will depend on the type of exploitation. If the operation is an extensive one, in which feed is available to animals at all times, the filling of feeders should be done at the same time every day, making sure the animals will not run out of feed between refillings. Operators

FIGURE 25–3. Growing New Zealand White rabbits. (Courtesy of Mrs. G. Absolon, Doebank, Palmerston North, New Zealand.)

should verify feed consumption, as reflected by the time between refills, because any changes in consumption will indicate problems, like diseases, or waste, and these should be corrected quickly. If the animals are fed several times daily, the routine should be maintained.

Caution should be taken to feed late in the day, because rabbits are more active during the night and feed consumption is highest during that period. The producer must make sure that feeders are at the appropriate level before leaving in the evening. Feeders should be checked in the morning to verify consumption. This practice will alert the producer to possible problems which usually begin with reduced feed intake. A number of different types of feeder are available (Fig. 25–3).

Breeding Animals

Feeding young breeding animals properly is very important because it affects the lifetime reproductive capacity of the animals. Proper feeding and nutrition during their growing period will result in a higher production for a long time. Growing breeding rabbits must have adequate nutrition in order to fulfill all of their growing needs, but not above these levels, or they may become overweight. Overweight breeding animals must be avoided because it causes poor reproductive performance, may cause metabolic problems (young doe syndrome), and also wastes feed.

Overweight may also cause breeding failures during the periods of high temperature (summer months). Temperatures in the rabbitry should be maintained at 21–24° C. During periods of high temperature, rabbits' physical activity decreases, thus reducing energy use. The excess energy could result in extra body weight.

Growing breeding animals should be fed a diet in an amount that keeps the animals in good physical condition and promotes normal growth, but that prevents them from becoming fat. These animals should be observed closely and their feed should be adjusted accordingly. Restriction of feed can be done by physically reducing the amount of diet offered or by offering forage (hay).

When feeding growing breeding stock, care should be taken to ensure enough floor and feeder space (Fig. 25–4). When animals are kept in a group (up to 12–13 weeks of age), floor space should be a minimum of 0.07 m/animal. The feeder space should be such that all animals can

FIGURE 25-4. A commercial flat-deck system operation used for efficient rabbit production. (Courtesy of Mrs. G. Absolon, Doebank, Palmerston North, New Zealand.)

FIGURE 25-5. A New Zealand White doe with a nest box. (Courtesy of Mrs. G. Absolon, Doebank, Palmerston North, New Zealand.)

eat at the same time. This practice will ensure proper intake and growth by all animals and will reduce the risk of diseases.

Adult males and nonpregnant and nonlactating adult females should be restricted in their feed intake when not reproductively active, to avoid body overconditioning. During the breeding activity period the amount of feed offered to bucks and does should be increased moderately. When rabbits are restricted in their feed, the producers should monitor on a regular basis the condition of the animals to adjust accordingly the amount being offered. The ideal situation is to maintain the body weight of the animals without overweight or weight loss.

Pregnant Does

Pregnant does should also be restricted in their feed intake during the gestation period to control their body weight. Feeding pregnant does ad libitum will result in reduction of litter size, problems at kindling, and waste of feed.

In pregnant females, feed and water consumption increase to a maximum around the tenth day of gestation. From the tenth day on, consumption is kept constant and then decreases at the end of the gestation period. A day or two before kindling, some does consume almost no feed and water. An adult New Zealand White doe will consume on the average 105–115 g/day of feed (2500 kcal/kg) in the first 10 days, and then level at 150–160 g/day until kindling. A nest box used for rabbits is shown in Fig. 25–5.

Lactating Does and Litters

Lactating females have a high nutrient demand due to their milk production level. Milk produc-

tion is associated with litter size and nutrient intake. Proper feed intake will ensure proper nutrient intake, which will be reflected in the milk output, and hence, in the initial rate of growth of the rabbits. Overall feed digestibility diminishes with the advance of lactation in lactating does (29, 30), thus the importance of providing feed with the proper nutrient density to these animals. Preweaning rate of growth is directly associated with postweaning rate of growth and feed efficiency. Improper feeding of lactating does not only affects milk production and litter performance but also will have a negative effect on future reproduction performance and productive longevity of the doe.

Lactating does must be fed a good-quality feed. This will ensure the availability of nutrients required for milk production. After the second week of lactation some of the young rabbits will start to come out of the nest and will also start to consume some of the doe's feed, so it is important to have feed available at all times for the doe and her litter. A good manager will check several times a day the level of feed in feeders for lactating does and her litters. The most economical gains of growing rabbits are made during the time they are with the doe.

After kindling, feed and water consumption increase as milk production increases (Fig. 25–6). Feeding the lactating does ad libitum right after kindling may cause a carbohydrate overload or increase the possibility of mastitis. The amount offered to does the day of kindling should be around half the normal amount. From the second day on, feed offered to lactating does should be increased gradually to ad libitum, usually in a week's time. Feed consumption may reach 500 g/d (2500 kcal/kg) in New Zealand does. The amount of feed and water consump-

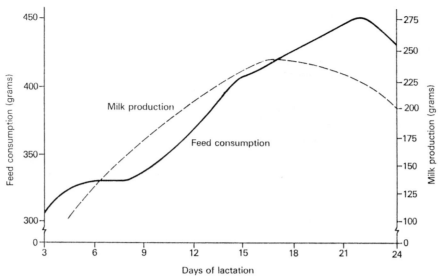

FIGURE 25-6. Doe milk production and feed consumption during lactation. From Varela-Alvarez (15).

tion depends on the milk production level of the doe. Feed intake will increase in order to fulfill the nutrient demand of lactation, however the doe may not be able to eat enough feed to meet those requirements because of the physical gut fill limitation of the animal. Some producers recommend a special lactating diet which has a higher caloric density. Animals eating a high-caloric-density diet consume less volume of feed to obtain the required amount of nutrients.

The feed offered to lactating does could be the same as that offered to fast-growing animals. Having only one diet has the advantages of reducing feeding and storage for different diets, and because the young animals consume their mother's feed they will continue to use the same feed after weaning without going through a period of adaptation.

Feeders utilized for lactating does with a litter should have a capacity for at least 2–3 days' feed supply. Feeders should be checked regularly for contamination, ease of flow, and level of feed. The physical location of the feeder should be low enough for the small animals to have easy access to the feed, but high enough to prevent the litter climbing and laying on the feed.

Creep feeding is practiced in some rabbit enterprises. This system consists of offering a special type of feed, usually higher in energy and protein than the doe diet. This diet will allow the young animals to grow faster, allowing an earlier weaning. The creep feed is offered in special feeders from which the young can eat but

the doe cannot. The adoption of this practice depends on the economics of it.

Does that are producing a high amount of milk at weaning time should be restricted to a minimum in the amount of concentrate offered. These animals should be offered a good-quality hay. When the does dries off, then feeding of concentrate could be resumed, in a progressive manner. This practice is intended to reduce mastitis problems in heavy milkers.

Growing Rabbits (Weaning to Slaughter)

In meat rabbit production, the growing animals and the lactating females are the ones with the highest nutrient demand. These animals should have feed of good quality and fresh water available at all times.

For intensive meat rabbit operations, feeding is done almost exclusively with pelleted complete mixes, and there is no need for additional supplementation of either grains or forages. In less intensive operations it may be necessary to feed animals forage in order to limit energy intake. In these cases, forages should not be ground. It is recommended that they be fed as hay and cut to at least 7–10 cm for best results.

Growing rabbits of 5–10 weeks of age will have an average daily dry feed consumption of 80–95 g/kg body weight (2500 kcal/kg). For practical feeding, allowances should be made for feed waste in order to buy and store appropriate amounts of feeds for the rabbit operation. Daily water consumption will be 135–150 ml/kg body weight.

Feeding management for meat rabbits should be done based on specific targets. These targets include the expected feed conversion and average daily gain. Feed conversion should be calculated in terms of total feed utilized and total gain obtained. Feed conversion varies widely among rabbit breeds and managements. An average feed conversion for meat-producing rabbits should be 3:1, that is, 3 kg of feed for each kg of live weight gain. Feed conversion decreases with increase in age, especially after 10 weeks of age. For a good economic return it is important to produce rabbits that reach slaughter weight in the shortest time. Total feed utilized includes both feed consumed and feed wasted, the latter being one of the targets for reduction in the operation because waste has a negative impact on feed efficiency. A good feed efficiency and average daily gain can be obtained through good animal genetic selection, proper nutrition and health, good feeding practices, and constant management improvement.

Hair- and Fur-Producing Rabbits

For hair and pelt rabbit production, it should be noted that production is done with adult animals, and thus feeding should be of good quality but restricted. In this type of operation postweaning rate of gain is not as important as for the meat rabbit enterprise. Protein levels, and in particular, S-containing amino acids, are critical for proper performance because the final product (pelt and hair) consist mainly of protein material, primarily keratin. The minimum recommended level of total protein is 17 percent, with a minimum of 0.65–0.70 percent of total S-containing amino acids in the diet.

In order to restrict pellet consumption and at the same time maintain a high protein level in the diet, good-quality alfalfa hay and oats can be used together with the pelleted ration.

It is recommended to fast the animals at least once a week. This practice will ensure the emptying of the stomach, reducing in a significant way accumulation of ingested hair. Ingested hair has the tendency to aggregate in "balls" that obstruct the pylorus of the rabbit, causing the animal's death.

Health Problems

Health of the animals is related to proper feeding and nutrition practices. Proper feeding and nutrition will give the animals the basis for building resistance and maintaining their immunological system in good working condition.

Health problems associated with feeding could be the result of nutrient imbalances, improper feed or fiber particle size, or inappropriate feeding schedules. A significant imbalance between protein and fiber can increase the risk of enteritis. It is recommended that the protein level be kept between 16 and 18 percent and the fiber at a level of 12–15 percent. Other nutrient balances to keep in mind are Ca:P and K and Na. Fiber particle size could be a problem if it is too finely ground. This will increase feed retention time in the digestive tract and in turn could modify the cecum microflora. Modification of the microflora will bring as a result a change in the volatile fatty acid rate of production and induce a series of reactions that produce amines and ammonia, changing the cecal pH and favoring increases in coliform bacteria. Feeding in irregular patterns (lack of a systematic schedule), could favor enteritis. Irregular patterns of work will cause stress to the animals. Stress may cause diarrhea, especially in growing rabbits, producing a Na and K imbalance. To avoid these problems, all routine work in the rabbitry (feeding, breeding, cleaning) should be done at the same time every day if possible.

For certain health-related problems, such as cecum stasis or lung edema, the cause could be associated with pellet size, feed grinding, or particle size. A routine inspection of particle size will help prevent some of the associated digestive problems in rabbits.

When feeding forages to rabbits it is recommended to use a good-quality hay rather than green feed. Green forage may cause noninfectious diarrhea, thus affecting animal performance and economic returns.

SUMMARY

Feeding and nutrition of the rabbit depend primarily on the type of exploitation, animal size, and physiological and environmental conditions. It is important to match the feeding program with the nutritional requirements of the animal. In order to calculate the energy requirements for animals of different sizes, formulas have been included in this chapter to calculate the energy requirements, taking into consideration size and performance. From these energy requirements an estimation of the expected feed intake can be obtained. Quality feeds, health problem prevention, regular labor practices, and an understanding of the unique digestive process of the rabbit will help ensure success in the rabbit feeding program. Rabbit producers should have a goal level of production (average daily gain and feed efficiency, amount of hair/year) in order to evaluate their nutrition and feeding programs, as well as their management practices.

REFERENCES

1. Alexender, F., and A. K. Chowdury. 1958. *Brit. J. Nutr.* 12:65.
2. Parker, D. S., and A. J. Mould. 1977. *Proc. Nutr. Soc.* 36:5A.
3. Lebas, F., and J. P. Laplace. 1974. *Ann. Zootech.* 23:577.
4. Colin, M. 1975. *Le Lapin: regles d'élevage et d'hygiene.* Ministere de l'agriculture, France: Informations Techniques des Directions des Services Veterinaires.
5. Proto, V. 1980. *Coniglicoltura.* 17:17.
6. Marty, J., P. Raynaud, and J. Carles. 1973. *Ann. Biol. Anim. Bioch. Biophys.* 13:429.
7. Salse, A. 1984. *Cuni Sciences.* 1:28.
8. Lang, J. 1981. *Nutr. Abstr. Rev. Ser. B* 51:197.
9. Lebas, F., et al. 1984. *Le Lapin. Élevage et pathologie.* Collection FAO: Production et santé animales. No. 21. Rome: Food and Agriculture Organization of the United Nations.
10. Mercier, P. 1978. *Le Courrier Avicole.* France No. 708, p. 12.
11. Varela-Alvarez, H. E. Grobet, and A. Gómez-de-Varela. 1975. *J. Animal Sci.* 41:239.
12. Lebas, F. 1987. *Reprod. Nutr. Develop.* 27:207.
13. Laffolay, B. 1985. *Bull. Soc. Vet. Prat. de France.* 69:117.
14. Prud'hon, M. 1976. *I Intern. Rabbit Congress,* Communication No. 14. Dijon, France.
15. Varela-Alvarez, H. 1985. *Summaries.* 1985 Rabbit Conference. June 14–15, 1985. pp. 13–23, College of Agriculture, Pennsylvania State University.
16. Gidenne, T. 1987. *Ann. Zootech.* 36:85.
17. Lebas, F. 1975. *Ann. Zootech.* 24:281.
18. Gidenne, T. 1987. *Ann. Zootech.* 36:95.
19. Bhattacharya, A. N., and R. G. Warner. 1968. *J. Animal Sci.* 27:1418.
20. Colin, M. 1974. *Alimentation et techniques d'élevage du lapin de chair, mise au point sur les acides amines du lapin en croissance.* France: ITAVI.
21. Bonomi, A., et al. 1982. *Annali della Facolta di Medicina Veterinaria di Parma.* 2:179.
22. Frye, T. M. 1987, pp. 16–18. *Summaries.* 1987 Rabbit Conference. Mar 20–21, 1987. College of Agriculture, Pennsylvania State University.
23. Verde, M. T., and J. G. Piquer. 1986. *J. Appl. Rabbit Res.* 9:181.
24. Lang, J. 1981. *Nutr. Abstr. Rev. Ser. B* 51:287.
25. Marcus, S. N., and J. Watt. 1977. *Vet. Rec.* 100:452.
26. Bender, M. E. 1987. Rabbit production. Unpublished Notes. Modesto Junior College. Modesto, CA.
27. Stillions, M. C., and A. Cooper. 1987. *Summaries. 1987 Rabbit Conference,* Mar 20–21, 1987, pp. 19–20. College of Agriculture, Pennsylvania State University.
28. Knapka, J. J. 1987. *Summaries. 1987 Rabbit Conference.* Mar 20–21, 1987, pp. 24–25. College of Agriculture, Pennsylvania State University.
29. Gaudreault, M., and A. Sylvstre. 1980. *Symposium en Production cunicole "Situation Actuelle en Cuniculture."* 6 Dec. 1980. Institut de Tech. Agr. de St-Hyacinte. Canada: Conseil des productions animals du Quebec. M.A.P.A.Q.
30. Lebas, F. 1975. *Le lapin de chair, ses besoins nutritionnels et son alimentation pratique.* France: ITAVI.

Appendix

Appendix tables have been included primarily to provide readily accessible information on some of the compositional values of feedstuffs consumed by domestic animals and on nutrient requirements of domestic animals as defined by the various committees of the National Research Council (NRC).

Appendix Table 1 presents information on nutrient composition of forage and other feedstuffs consumed by ruminants and horses. The international feed numbers (IFN) have been added for this edition because they provide some help in identifying similar products. It is a common practice with the NRC booklets to present data on a number of different types of energy terms. However, many of the feeds listed in Appendix Table 1 have not been evaluated for energy utilization (particularly net energy) using animals, and values have been arrived at by using different regression equations based on chemical analyses.

It is obvious after examination of some of the data that there are many differences in values listed for beef and dairy cattle. In the writer's opinion we have made some backward strides, because now it is necessary to use values quoted for beef cattle to formulate rations or calculate requirements for beef cattle—data quoted for dairy cattle or sheep will not fit. This is so because the committees have gone their own ways and have recalculated energy values and requirements and, rather than the results coming closer together, the differences are exaggerated.

With regard to nutrient content of feedstuffs, the reader is cautioned that average values are just that. All feed ingredients vary in composition, and averages may or may not be applicable to a given feed or for a particular species of animal or in conditions where the environment may alter nutrient utilization, particularly for the various energy values listed.

Other tables that the reader may find useful have been included. For example, Appendix Table 2 gives values on ruminal undegradability of various proteins in natural feedstuffs. Appendix Table 3 contains information on composition of feedstuffs commonly consumed by poultry and swine (on an as-fed basis, because that is the way they are presented in the NRC booklets). Appendix Table 4 contains information on amino acid composition of selected feeds; limited data on vitamins are presented in Table 5; and data on mineral supplements are found in Table 6. Most of the remaining tables give data on either feed consumption or on estimated nutrient requirements. More detail may be found in the NRC booklets or in other sources.

Composition of feedstuffs commonly fed to cattle, sheep, and horses (data from NRC publications)

Feed Name and Description	Intl. Feed Number	Typical DM, %	Composition, Dry Basis, %						Energy Utilization, Dry Basis, Mcal/kg Beef Cattle				TDN,[a] %
			CP	CF	NDF	ADF	Ca	P	DE	ME	NEm	NEg	
1. Alfalfa, fresh, late veg.	2-00-181	21	20.0	23	38	29	2.19	0.33	2.78	2.28	1.41	0.83	63
2. Alfalfa, fresh	2-00-196	24	20.0	26	—	—	1.96	0.30	2.69	2.27	1.31	0.61	61
3. Alfalfa, hay, S-C, early bloom	1-00-059	90	18.0	23	42	31	1.41	0.22	2.43	1.99	1.14	0.58	60
4. Alfalfa, hay, S-C, mature	1-00-071	91	13.0	38	58	44	1.13	0.18	2.21	1.81	0.97	0.42	50
5. Alfalfa, meal, dehy 17%	1-0C-023	92	18.9	26	45	35	1.52	0.25	2.69	2.21	1.34	0.77	61
6. Alfalfa, silage, wilted midbloom	3-00-217	38	15.5	30	47	35	—	—	2.56	2.10	1.24	0.68	58
7. Alfalfa, silage, 30-50% dry matter	3-08-150	43	9.8	19	—	—	1.39	0.27	—	—	—	—	—
8. Bakery waste, dried	4-00-466	92	10.7	1	18	13	0.14	0.26	3.92	3.22	2.21	1.52	89
9. Barley grain	4-00-549	88	13.5	6	19	7	0.05	0.38	3.70	3.04	2.06	1.40	84
10. Barley grain, Pacific Coast	4-07-939	89	10.8	7	21	9	0.06	0.39	3.79	3.11	2.12	1.45	86
11. Barley straw	1-00-498	91	4.3	42	80	49	0.30	0.07	1.76	1.45	0.60	0.08	40
12. Bean, Navy, seeds	5-00-623	89	25.3	5			0.18	0.59	3.70	3.04	2.06	1.40	84
13. Beet, Sugar, pulp, dehy.	4-00-669	91	9.7	20	54	33	0.69	0.10	3.26	2.68	1.76	1.14	74
14. Bermuda grass, fresh	2-00-712	34	12.0	26	—	—	0.53	0.21	2.65	2.17	1.31	0.74	60
15. Bermuda grass hay, SC	1-00-703	90	6.0	31	78	38	0.43	0.20	2.16	1.77	0.93	0.39	49
16. Bluegrass, Kentucky fresh, early veg.	2-00-777	31	17.4	25	55	29	0.50	0.44	3.17	2.60	1.70	1.08	72
17. Bluestem, fresh, early veg.	2-00-821	27	12.8	25	—	—	0.63	0.20	3.00	2.46	1.57	0.97	68
18. Brewer's grains, dehy.	5-02-141	92	29.4	14	46	24	0.33	0.55	2.91	2.39	1.51	0.91	66
19. Brome, fresh, early veg.	2-00-892	34	18.0	24	56	31	0.50	0.30	3.26	2.68	1.76	1.14	74
20. Brome hay, late bloom, S-C	1-00-888	89	10.0	37	68	43	0.30	0.35	2.43	1.99	1.14	0.58	55
21. Citrus pulp, dehy.	4-01-237	91	6.7	13	23	22	1.84	0.12	3.62	2.97	2.00	1.35	77
22. Clover, Crimson, hay, S-C	1-01-328	87	18.4	30	—	—	1.40	0.22	2.51	2.06	1.21	0.64	57
23. Clover, Ladino, fresh, early veg.	2-01-380	19	27.2	14	—	—	1.93	0.35	3.00	2.46	1.57	0.97	68
24. Clover, Ladino, hay, S-C	1-01-378	90	22.0	21	36	32	1.35	0.31	2.65	2.17	1.31	0.74	65
25. Clover, Red, fresh, early bloom	2-01-428	20	19.4	23	40	31	2.26	0.38	3.04	2.50	1.60	1.00	69
26. Clover, Red, hay, S-C	1-01-415	89	16.0	29	56	36	1.53	0.25	2.43	1.99	1.14	0.58	55
27. Corn, Dent, fodder	1-28-231	81	8.9	25	55	33	0.50	0.25	2.87	2.35	1.47	0.88	65
28. Corn, Cobs, ground	1-28-234	90	3.2	36	89	35	0.57	0.10	2.21	1.81	0.97	0.42	50
29. Corn distillers grains, dehy.	5-28-235	94	23.0	12	43	17	0.11	0.43	3.79	3.11	2.12	1.45	86
30. Corn ears, ground	4-28-238	87	9.0	9	28	11	0.07	0.27	3.66	3.00	2.03	1.37	83
31. Corn gluten, meal	5-28-241	91	46.8	5	37	9	0.16	0.50	3.79	3.11	2.12	1.45	86
32. Corn gluten feed	5-28-243	90	25.6	10	45	12	0.36	0.82	3.66	3.00	2.03	1.37	83
33. Corn grain, #2	4-02-931	88	10.1	2	9	3	0.02	0.35	3.97	3.25	2.24	1.55	90
34. Corn grain, flaked	4-28-244	86	11.2	1	9	3	0.03	0.29	4.19	3.44	2.38	1.67	95
35. Corn grain, high moisture	4-20-770	72	10.7	3	9	3	0.02	0.32	4.10	3.36	2.33	1.62	93
36. Corn silage, well-eared	3-28-250	33	8.1	24	51	28	0.23	0.22	3.09	2.53	1.63	1.03	70
37. Cotton, seed hulls	1-01-599	91	4.1	48	90	64	0.15	0.09	1.85	1.52	0.68	0.15	42
38. Cottonseeds	5-01-614	92	23.9	21	39	29	0.16	0.75	4.23	3.47	2.41	1.69	96

[a]TDN values apply to both beef and dairy cattle.

| | Energy Utilization, Dry Basis, Mcal/kg | | | | | | | | | | | |
| | Dairy Cattle | | | | | Sheep | | | | | Horses | |
	DE	ME	NEm	NEg	NEℓ	DE	ME	NEm	NEg	TDN, %	DE	TDN, %
1.	—	—	—	—	—	—	—	—	—	—	2.94	—
2.	—	—	—	—	—	2.56	2.10	1.24	0.68	58	2.51	57
3.	2.65	2.22	1.31	0.74	1.35	2.47	2.03	1.18	0.61	56	2.48	55
4.	—	—	—	—	—	2.38	1.95	1.11	0.55	54	—	—
5.	2.69	2.27	1.34	0.77	1.38	2.65	2.17	1.34	0.77	60	2.36	—
6.	—	—	—	—	—	—	—	—	—	—	—	—
7.	—	—	—	—	—	2.56	2.10	1.24	0.68	58	—	—
8.	3.92	3.51	2.20	1.52	2.06	—	—	—	—	—	—	—
9.	3.70	3.29	2.06	1.40	1.94	3.79	3.11	2.12	1.45	86	3.60	82
10.	3.79	3.38	2.12	1.45	1.99	3.88	3.18	2.18	1.50	88	3.68	79
11.	2.16	1.73	0.93	0.53	1.08	2.12	1.74	0.90	0.35	48	1.62	37
12.	3.70	3.29	2.06	1.40	1.94	3.84	3.15	2.15	1.48	87	—	—
13.	3.44	3.02	1.88	1.24	1.79	2.96	2.43	1.60	1.04	67	2.56	65
14.	—	—	—	—	—	—	—	—	—	—	2.07	50
15.	—	—	—	—	—	1.97	1.62	0.85	0.35	45	—	—
16.	3.17	2.76	1.69	1.08	1.64	2.87	2.35	1.47	0.88	65	2.09	56
17.	—	—	—	—	—	—	—	—	—	—	—	—
18.	2.91	2.49	1.51	0.91	1.50	3.09	2.53	1.63	1.03	70	2.75	68
19.	3.26	2.85	1.75	1.13	1.69	3.53	2.89	1.94	1.30	80	3.00	68
20.	2.60	2.18	1.27	0.70	1.33	—	—	—	—	—	2.38	54
21.	3.40	2.98	1.86	1.22	1.77	3.70	3.04	2.06	1.40	84	2.99	68
22.	2.51	2.09	1.21	0.64	1.28	2.43	1.99	1.14	0.58	55	2.16	49
23.	3.00	2.58	1.57	0.97	1.55	—	—	—	—	—	2.50	—
24.	2.87	2.45	1.47	0.88	1.47	2.91	2.39	1.51	0.91	66	2.56	51
25.	3.04	2.62	1.60	1.00	1.57	3.00	2.46	1.57	0.47	68	2.01	57
26.	2.43	2.00	1.14	0.58	1.23	2.65	2.17	1.31	0.74	60	2.22	49
27.	—	—	—	—	—	2.78	2.28	1.41	0.83	63	2.06	—
28.	2.21	1.78	0.97	0.42	1.11	2.25	1.84	1.07	0.45	51	1.36	31
29.	3.79	3.38	2.12	1.45	1.99	3.84	3.15	2.12	1.48	87	3.08	70
30.	3.66	3.25	2.03	1.37	1.91	3.66	3.00	2.03	1.37	83	3.49	74
31.	3.79	3.38	2.12	1.45	1.99	3.88	3.18	2.18	1.50	88	3.29	—
32.	3.66	3.25	2.03	1.37	1.91	3.66	3.00	2.03	1.37	83	—	—
33.	3.53	3.12	1.94	1.30	1.84	3.84	3.15	2.15	1.48	87	3.84	88
34.	3.88	3.47	2.18	1.50	2.04	—	—	—	—	—	—	—
35.	3.88	3.47	2.18	1.50	2.06	—	—	—	—	—	—	—
36.	3.09	2.67	1.63	1.03	1.60	3.09	2.53	1.63	1.03	70	2.68	—
37.	1.98	1.55	0.78	0.25	0.98	2.16	1.77	0.93	0.39	49	1.89	33
38.	4.23	3.83	2.41	1.69	2.23	—	—	—	—	—	—	—

| | | | Composition, Dry Basis, % | | | | | | Energy Utilization, Dry Basis, Mcal/kg | | | | |
| | | | | | | | | | Beef Cattle | | | | |
Feed Name and Description	Intl. Feed Number	Typical DM, %	CP	CF	NDF	ADF	Ca	P	DE	ME	NEm	NEg	TDN,[a] %
39. Cottonseed, meal, mech. extd., 41% protein	5-01-617	93	44.3	13	28	20	0.21	1.16	3.44	2.82	1.88	1.24	78
40. Cottonseed, meal, solv. extd., 41% protein	5-01-621	91	45.2	13	26	19	0.18	1.21	3.35	2.75	1.82	1.19	76
41. Fat, animal-poultry	4-00-409	99	—	—	—	—	—	—	7.80	6.40	4.75	3.51	177
42. Fescue, Kentucky 31, fresh, early veg.	2-01-900	28	22.1	21	—	—	0.53	0.39	—	—	—	—	67
43. Fescue hay, S-C, early bloom	1-09-186	91	20.2	25	59	32	0.35	0.24	—	—	—	—	64
44. Fescue hay, S-C, late bloom	1-01-871	92	9.5	37	72	39	0.30	0.26	2.12	1.74	0.90	0.35	48
45. Flax, seed, solvent extd. (linseed meal)	5-02-048	90	38.3	10	25	19	0.43	0.89	3.44	2.82	1.88	1.24	78
46. Grass-legume silage	3-02-303	29	11.3	32	—	—	0.25	0.08	—	—	—	—	—
47. Lespedeza, common fresh, late veg.	2-26-028	32	16.4	32	—	—	—	—	2.60	2.13	1.28	0.71	—
48. Milk, cattle, fresh	5-01-168	12	26.7	—	—	—	0.95	0.76	5.60	5.43	3.80	3.80	129
49. Milk, sheep, fresh	5-08-510	19	24.7	—	—	—	1.05	0.79	—	—	—	—	—
50. Millet, Foxtail, fresh	2-03-101	28	9.5	32	—	—	0.32	0.19	2.78	2.28	1.41	0.83	63
51. Molasses, beet	4-00-668	78	8.5	—	—	—	0.17	0.03	3.48	2.86	1.91	1.27	75
52. Molasses, citrus	4-01-241	68	8.2	—	—	—	1.72	0.13	3.31	2.71	1.79	1.16	75
53. Molasses, sugarcane	4-04-696	75	5.8	6	—	—	1.00	0.11	3.17	2.60	1.70	1.08	72
54. Oats, grain	4-03-309	89	13.3	12	32	16	0.07	0.38	3.40	2.78	1.85	1.22	77
55. Oats, grain, Pacific Coast	4-07-999	91	10.0	12	—	—	0.11	0.34	3.44	2.82	1.88	1.24	78
56. Oat hay, S-C	1-03-280	91	9.3	30	66	42	0.24	0.22	2.43	1.99	1.14	0.58	55
57. Oat silage, dough stage	3-03-296	35	10.0	33	—	—	0.47	0.33	2.51	2.06	1.21	0.64	—
58. Oat straw	1-03-283	92	4.4	40	70	54	0.24	0.06	1.98	1.63	0.79	0.25	45
59. Orchard grass, fresh, early, veg.	2-03-439	23	18.4	25	55	31	0.58	0.54	3.17	2.60	1.70	1.08	72
60. Orchard grass, hay, late bloom	1-03-428	91	8.4	37	72	45	0.26	0.30	2.38	1.95	1.11	0.55	54
61. Pea seeds	5-03-600	89	25.3	7	—	—	0.15	0.44	3.84	3.15	2.15	1.48	87
62. Potato, tubers, fresh	4-03-787	23	9.5	2	—	—	0.04	0.24	3.57	2.93	1.97	1.32	81
63. Potato, tubers, silage	4-03-768	25	7.6	4	—	—	0.04	0.23	3.62	2.97	2.00	1.35	82
64. Poultry feathers, hydrolyzed	5-03-795	93	91.3	1	—	—	0.28	0.72	3.09	2.53	1.63	1.03	—
65. Poultry manure, dehy.	5-14-015	90	28.2	13	38	15	9.31	2.52	2.29	1.88	1.04	0.49	—
66. Prairie plants, midwest, hay, S-C	1-03-191	92	5.8	34	—	—	0.43	0.15	2.25	1.84	1.00	0.45	51
67. Rape, fresh, early bloom	2-03-866	11	23.5	16	—	—	—	—	3.31	2.71	1.79	1.16	75
68. Rape, seed, meal, solvent extd.	5-03-871	91	40.6	13	—	—	0.67	1.04	3.04	2.50	1.60	1.00	69
69. Redtop, fresh	2-03-897	29	11.6	27	64	—	0.46	0.29	2.78	2.28	1.41	0.83	63
70. Redtop, hay, S-C, midbloom	1-03-886	94	11.7	31	—	—	0.63	0.35	2.51	2.06	1.21	0.64	57
71. Rice, bran	4-03-928	91	14.1	13	33	18	0.08	1.70	3.09	2.53	1.63	1.03	70
72. Rice, ground	4-03-938	89	8.9	10	—	—	0.07	0.32	3.48	2.86	1.91	1.27	79
73. Rice, straw	1-03-925	91	4.3	35	71	55	0.21	0.08	1.81	1.48	0.64	0.11	41
74. Rye, fresh	2-04-018	24	15.9	28	—	—	0.39	0.33	3.04	2.50	1.60	1.00	69
75. Rye, grain	4-04-047	88	13.8	3	—	—	0.07	0.37	3.70	3.04	2.06	1.40	84
76. Rye, straw	1-04-007	90	3.0	43	—	—	0.24	0.09	1.37	1.12	0.26	—	31

[a]TDN values apply to both beef and dairy cattle.

	Dairy Cattle					Sheep					Horses	
	DE	ME	NEm	NEg	NEl	DE	ME	NEm	NEg	TDN, %	DE	TDN, %
39.	3.44	3.02	1.88	1.24	1.79	3.31	2.71	1.79	1.16	75	—	—
40.	3.35	2.93	1.82	1.19	1.74	3.13	2.57	1.67	1.06	71	3.01	—
41.	7.30	7.30	5.84	5.84	5.84	—	—	—	—	—	8.00	—
42.	2.91	2.49	1.51	0.92	1.50	3.22	2.64	1.73	1.11	73	2.22	—
43.	2.82	2.40	1.44	0.85	1.45	2.73	2.24	1.38	0.80	62	—	—
44.	2.12	1.69	0.90	0.36	1.06	—	—	—	—	—	—	—
45.	3.44	3.02	1.88	1.24	1.79	3.48	2.86	1.91	1.27	79	3.04	69
46.	—	—	—	—	—	2.73	2.24	1.38	0.80	62	—	—
47.	—	—	—	—	—	—	—	—	—	—	1.89	—
48.	5.69	5.29	3.34	2.16	3.04	—	—	—	—	—	—	—
49.	—	—	—	—	—	6.00	5.82	4.07	161	—	—	—
50.	2.78	2.36	1.41	0.83	1.42	—	—	—	—	—	—	—
51.	3.31	2.89	1.79	1.16	1.72	3.40	2.78	1.85	1.22	77	3.40	72
52.	3.31	2.89	1.79	1.16	1.72	—	—	—	—	—	3.40	—
53.	3.17	2.76	1.69	1.08	1.64	3.48	2.86	1.91	1.27	79	3.50	74
54.	3.40	2.98	1.86	1.22	1.77	3.40	2.78	1.85	1.22	77	3.36	76
55.	3.44	3.02	1.88	1.24	1.79	3.44	2.82	1.88	1.24	78	3.20	77
56.	2.43	2.00	1.14	0.58	1.23	2.34	1.92	1.14	0.58	53	1.92	47
57.	—	—	—	—	—	—	—	—	—	—	—	—
58.	—	—	—	—	—	2.07	1.70	0.79	0.25	47	1.76	40
59.	3.17	2.76	1.69	1.08	1.64	2.95	2.42	1.54	0.94	67	2.42	55
60.	2.38	1.96	1.11	0.55	1.20	—	—	—	—	—	1.90	—
61.	3.84	3.42	2.16	1.48	2.01	—	—	—	—	—	3.45	—
62.	3.57	3.16	1.97	1.32	1.87	—	—	—	—	—	—	—
63.	3.62	3.20	2.01	1.35	1.89	—	—	—	—	—	—	—
64.	—	—	—	—	—	—	—	—	—	—	—	—
65.	—	—	—	—	—	—	—	—	—	—	—	—
66.	—	—	—	—	—	—	—	—	—	1.62	46
67.	—	—	—	—	—	3.31	2.71	1.79	1.16	75	—	—
68.	3.04	2.62	1.60	1.00	1.57	3.26	2.68	1.76	1.14	74	—	—
69.	2.78	2.36	1.41	0.83	1.42	—	—	—	—	—	—	—
70.	2.51	2.09	1.21	0.64	1.28	2.47	2.03	1.18	0.61	56	1.97	—
71.	3.09	2.67	1.63	1.03	1.60	3.26	2.68	1.76	1.14	74	—	—
72.	3.48	3.07	1.91	1.27	1.82	—	—	—	—	—	2.51	—
73.	—	—	—	—	—	—	—	—	—	—	—	—
74.	—	—	—	—	—	—	—	—	—	—	—	—
75.	3.70	3.29	2.06	1.40	1.94	3.75	3.07	2.09	1.43	85	3.84	80
76.	—	—	—	—	—	1.98	1.63	0.79	0.25	45	—	—

Feed Name and Description	Intl. Feed Number	Typical DM, %	Composition, Dry Basis, %						Energy Utilization, Dry Basis, Mcal/kg Beef Cattle				
			CP	CF	NDF	ADF	Ca	P	DE	ME	NEm	NEg	TDN,[a] %
77. Ryegrass, Italian, fresh	2-04-073	25	14.5	24	—	—	0.65	0.41	2.65	2.17	1.31	0.74	60
78. Ryegrass, Italian, hay, S-C, early bloom	1-04-066	88	11.4	36	69	45	0.62	0.34	2.38	1.95	1.11	0.55	54
79. Ryegrass, perennial, fresh	2-04-086	27	10.4	23	—	—	0.55	0.27	3.00	2.46	1.57	0.97	68
80. Ryegrass, perennial, hay, S-C	1-04-077	86	8.6	30	41	30	0.65	0.32	2.65	2.17	1.31	0.74	60
81. Safflower seeds, meal, solvent extd.	5-04-110	92	25.4	32	58	41	0.37	0.81	2.51	2.06	1.21	0.64	57
82. Safflower seeds w/o hulls, meal, solvent extd.	5-07-959	92	46.9	15	—	—	0.38	1.40	3.22	2.64	1.73	1.11	73
83. Sage, Black, browse, fresh	2-05-564	65	8.5	—	—	—	0.81	0.17	2.16	1.77	0.93	0.39	49
84. Saltgrass, hay, S-C	1-04-168	89	8.9	32	—	—	—	—	2.25	1.84	1.00	0.45	51
85. Sedge, hay, S-C	1-04-193	89	9.4	32	—	—	—	—	2.29	1.88	1.04	0.49	52
86. Sorghum, fodder	1-07-960	89	7.5	27	—	—	0.52	0.13	2.56	2.10	1.24	0.68	58
87. Sorghum, grain 8–10% protein	4-20-893	87	10.1	3	18	9	0.04	0.34	3.70	3.04	2.06	1.40	84
88. Sorghum, grain, flaked	4-16-295	85	10.1	3	—	—	0.04	0.34	4.06	3.33	2.30	1.60	92
89. Sorghum, grain, reconstituted	4-16-296	70	10.1	3	—	—	0.04	0.34	4.10	3.36	2.33	1.62	93
90. Sorghum, milo, heads	4-04-446	90	10.0	9	—	—	0.13	0.25	—	—	—	—	—
91. Sorghum, silage	3-04-323	30	7.5	28	—	38	0.35	0.21	2.65	2.17	1.31	0.74	60
92. Sorghum, Sudan grass, fresh, early veg.	2-04-484	18	16.8	23	55	29	0.43	0.41	3.09	2.53	1.63	1.03	70
93. Sorghum, Sudan grass, hay, S-C	1-04-480	91	8.0	36	68	42	0.55	0.30	2.47	2.03	1.18	0.61	56
94. Sorghum, Sudan grass, silage	3-04-499	28	10.8	33	—	—	0.46	0.21	2.43	1.99	1.14	0.58	55
95. Soybean, hay, S-C	1-04-538	94	17.8	30	—	40	1.26	0.27	—	—	—	—	53
96. Soybean, hulls	1-04-560	91	12.1	40	67	50	0.49	0.21	2.34	1.92	1.07	0.52	57
97. Soybean, seeds	5-04-610	92	42.8	6	—	10	0.27	0.65	4.01	3.29	2.27	1.57	91
98. Soybean, meal, solvent extd., 44% protein	5-20-637	89	49.9	7	—	10	0.33	0.71	3.70	3.04	2.06	1.40	84
99. Soybean, straw	1-04-567	88	5.2	44	70	54	1.59	0.06	1.85	1.52	0.68	0.15	42
100. Sunflower, seeds, meal, solvent extd.	5-09-340	90	25.9	35	40	33	0.23	1.03	1.94	1.59	0.75	0.22	44
101. Sunflower, seeds w/o hulls, solvent extd.	5-04-739	93	49.8	12	—	—	0.44	0.98	2.87	2.35	1.47	0.88	65
102. Timothy, fresh, late veg.	2-04-903	26	18.0	32	—	—	0.39	0.32	3.17	2.60	1.70	1.08	72
103. Timothy, hay, S-C, late veg.	1-04-881	89	17.0	27	55	29	0.66	0.34	2.73	2.24	1.38	0.80	62
104. Timothy, hay, S-C, midbloom	1-04-883	89	9.1	31	67	36	0.48	0.22	2.51	2.06	1.21	0.64	57
105. Trefoil, Birdsfoot, fresh	2-20-786	24	21.0	25	—	—	1.91	0.22	2.91	2.39	1.51	0.91	66
106. Triticale, grain	4-20-362	90	17.6	4	—	8	0.06	0.33	3.70	3.04	2.06	1.40	84
107. Turnip, roots, fresh	4-05-067	9	11.8	12	44	34	0.59	0.26	3.75	3.07	2.09	1.43	85

[a]TDN values apply to both beef and dairy cattle.

| | Energy Utilization, Dry Basis, Mcal/kg | | | | | | | | | | | |
| | Dairy Cattle | | | | | Sheep | | | | | Horses | |
	DE	ME	NEm	NEg	NEl	DE	ME	NEm	NEg	TDN, %	DE	TDN, %
77.	—	—	—	—	—	—	—	—	—	—	1.73	—
78.	2.38	1.96	1.11	0.55	1.20	2.51	2.06	1.21	0.64	57	1.94	—
79.	—	—	—	—	—	—	—	—	—	—	—	—
80.	2.82	2.40	1.44	0.85	1.45	—	—	—	—	—	—	—
81.	2.51	2.09	1.21	0.64	1.28	2.47	2.03	1.18	0.61	56	—	—
82.	3.22	2.80	1.73	1.11	1.67	—	—	—	—	—	—	—
83.	—	—	—	—	—	2.16	1.77	0.93	0.39	49	—	—
84.	—	—	—	—	—	2.25	1.84	1.00	0.45	51	—	—
85.	—	—	—	—	—	—	—	—	—	—	—	—
86.	2.56	2.13	1.25	0.68	1.30	2.56	2.10	1.24	0.68	58	—	—
87.	3.53	3.12	1.94	1.30	1.84	—	—	—	—	—	3.56	80
88.	—	—	—	—	—	—	—	—	—	—	—	—
89.	—	—	—	—	—	—	—	—	—	—	—	—
90.	—	—	—	—	—	3.70	3.04	2.06	1.40	84	—	—
91.	2.65	2.22	1.31	0.74	1.35	2.51	2.06	1.21	0.64	57	—	—
92.	3.09	2.67	1.63	1.03	1.60	2.78	2.28	1.41	0.83	63	—	—
93.	2.47	2.04	1.18	0.62	1.25	2.43	1.99	1.14	0.58	55	—	—
94.	2.43	2.00	1.14	0.58	1.23	2.34	1.92	1.07	0.52	53	—	—
95.	2.34	1.91	1.08	0.52	1.18	—	—	—	—	—	—	—
96.	—	—	—	—	—	2.51	2.06	1.21	0.64	57	1.88	48
97.	4.01	3.60	2.27	1.57	2.11	4.14	3.40	2.35	1.65	94	4.05	92
98.	3.70	3.29	2.06	1.40	1.94	3.88	3.18	2.18	1.50	88	3.52	82
99.	—	—	—	—	—	1.90	1.56	0.72	0.18	43	—	—
100.	1.94	1.51	0.75	0.22	0.96	1.98	1.63	0.75	0.25	45	—	—
101.	2.87	2.45	1.47	0.88	1.47	3.35	2.75	1.82	1.19	76	3.12	71
102.	—	—	—	—	—	2.69	2.21	1.34	0.77	61	1.70	—
103.	2.91	2.49	1.51	0.92	1.50	2.87	2.35	1.47	0.88	65	—	—
104.	2.56	2.13	1.25	0.68	1.30	2.65	2.17	1.31	0.74	60	1.99	45
105.	2.91	2.49	1.31	0.92	1.50	2.78	2.28	1.41	0.83	63	2.18	—
106.	3.70	3.29	2.06	1.40	1.94	—	—	—	—	—	—	—
107.	3.75	3.34	2.10	1.43	1.96	3.79	3.11	2.12	1.45	86	—	—

Feed Name and Description	Intl. Feed Number	Typical DM, %	Composition, Dry Basis, %						Energy Utilization, Dry Basis, Mcal/kg				
									Beef Cattle				
			CP	CF	NDF	ADF	Ca	P	DE	ME	NEm	NEg	TDN,[a] %
108. Urea, 281% protein equivalent	5-05-070	99	280.0	—	—	—	—	—	—	—	—	—	—
109. Vetch, fresh, late veg.	2-05-108	22	20.8	28	—	—	—	—	—	—	—	—	—
110. Vetch, hay, S-C	1-05-106	89	20.8	31	48	33	1.18	0.32	2.51	2.06	1.21	0.64	57
111. Wheat, bran	4-05-190	89	17.1	11	51	15	0.13	1.38	3.09	2.53	1.63	1.03	70
112. Wheat, flour by-product (middlings)	4-05-205	89	18.4	8	37	10	0.13	0.99	3.04	2.50	1.60	1.00	69
113. Wheat, fresh, early veg.	2-05-176	22	28.6	17	52	30	0.42	0.40	3.22	2.64	1.73	1.11	73
114. Wheat, grain, hard red spring	4-05-258	88	17.2	3	—	—	0.04	0.43	3.92	3.22	2.21	1.52	89
115. Wheat, grain, hard red winter	4-05-268	88	14.4	3	—	4	0.05	0.43	3.88	3.18	2.18	1.50	88
116. Wheat, grain, soft red winter	4-05-294	88	13.0	2	—	—	0.05	0.43	3.92	3.22	2.21	1.52	89
117. Wheat, grain, soft white winter	4-05-337	89	11.3	3	14	4	0.07	0.36	3.92	3.22	2.21	1.52	89
118. Wheat, grain, soft white winter, Pacific Coast	4-08-555	89	11.2	3	—	—	0.10	0.34	3.88	3.18	2.18	1.50	88
119. Wheat, mill run	4-05-206	90	17.2	9	—	—	0.11	0.13	3.48	2.86	1.91	1.27	79
120. Wheat, silage, full bloom	3-05-185	25	8.1	31	—	—	—	—	2.60	2.13	1.28	0.71	59
121. Wheat, straw	1-05-175	89	3.6	42	70	54	0.18	0.05	1.81	1.48	0.64	0.11	41
122. Wheatgrass, Crested fresh, early veg.	2-05-420	28	21.5	22	—	—	0.46	0.34	3.31	2.71	1.79	1.16	75
fresh, post ripe	2-05-428	80	3.1	40	—	—	0.27	0.07	2.16	1.77	0.93	0.39	49
hay, S-C	1-05-418	93	12.4	33	—	36	0.33	0.21	2.34	1.92	1.07	0.52	53
123. Whey, cattle, dehy.	4-01-182	93	14.2	—	—	—	0.92	0.82	3.57	2.93	1.97	1.32	81
124. Whey, cattle, fresh	4-08-134	7	13.0	—	—	—	0.73	0.65	4.14	3.40	2.35	1.65	94
125. Yeast, Brewers, dehy.	7-05-527	93	46.9	3	—	—	0.13	1.49	3.48	2.86	1.91	1.27	79

[a]TDN values apply to both beef and dairy cattle.

| | Energy Utilization, Dry Basis, Mcal/kg | | | | | | | | | | | |
| | Dairy Cattle | | | | | Sheep | | | | | Horses | |
	DE	ME	NEm	NEg	NEl	DE	ME	NEm	NEg	TDN, %	DE	TDN, %
108.	—	—	—	—	—	—	—	—	—	—	—	—
109.	—	—	—	—	—	2.60	2.13	1.28	0.71	59	—	—
110.	2.51	2.09	1.21	0.64	1.28	2.43	1.99	1.14	0.58	55	—	—
111.	3.09	2.67	1.63	1.03	1.60	3.13	2.57	1.67	1.06	71	2.94	67
112.	3.04	2.62	1.60	1.00	1.57	3.62	2.97	2.00	1.35	82	3.42	—
113.	3.22	2.80	1.73	1.11	1.67	3.31	2.71	1.79	1.16	75	2.88	—
114.	—	—	—	—	—	3.97	3.25	2.24	1.55	90	—	—
115.	3.88	3.47	2.18	1.50	2.04	3.88	3.18	2.18	1.50	88	3.86	87
116.	3.92	3.51	2.20	1.52	2.06	3.88	3.18	2.18	1.50	88	3.86	87
117.	3.92	3.51	2.20	1.52	2.06	—	—	—	—	—	3.92	87
118.	—	—	—	—	—	3.92	3.22	2.21	1.52	89	—	—
119.	3.48	3.07	1.91	1.27	1.82	—	—	—	—	—	—	—
120.	—	—	—	—	—	—	—	—	—	—	—	—
121.	1.94	1.51	0.75	0.22	0.96	1.81	1.48	0.64	0.11	41	1.62	34
122.	—	—	—	—	—	3.31	2.71	1.79	1.16	75	2.54	—
	—	—	—	—	—	2.38	1.95	1.11	0.55	54	—	—
	—	—	—	—	—	2.34	1.92	1.07	0.52	53	—	—
123.	3.57	3.16	1.97	1.32	1.87	—	—	—	—	—	4.06	—
124.	3.57	3.16	1.97	1.32	1.87	—	—	—	—	—	—	—
125.	3.48	3.07	1.91	1.27	1.82	—	—	—	—	—	3.30	75

APPENDIX TABLE 2

Ruminal undegradability of protein in selected feeds (from 1989 NRC on dairy cattle)

| Feed | Number of Determinations | Undegradability | | |
		Mean	S.D.[a]	C.V.[b]
Alfalfa, dehydrated	8	0.59	0.17	29
Alfalfa hay	12	0.28	0.07	25
Alfalfa silage	6	0.23	0.08	36
Alfalfa-bromegrass	1	0.21		
Barley	16	0.27	0.10	37
Barley, flaked	1	0.67		
Barley, micronized	1	0.47		
Barley silage	1	0.27		
Bean meal, field	1	0.46		
Beans	2	0.16	0.02	14
Beet pulp	4	0.45	0.14	30
Beet pulp molasses	2	0.35	0.03	8
Beets	3	0.20	0.03	16
Blood meal	2	0.82	0.01	1
Brewers dried grains	9	0.49	0.13	27

Feed	Number of Determinations	Undegradability		
		Mean	S.D.[a]	C.V.[b]
Bromegrass	1	0.44		
Casein	3	0.19	0.06	32
Casein, HCHO[c]	2	0.72	0.08	11
Clover, red	3	0.31	0.04	12
Clover, red, silage	1	0.38		
Clover, white	1	0.33		
Clover-grass	2	0.54	0.11	21
Clover-grass silage	7	0.28	0.06	22
Coconut	1	0.57		
Coconut meal	5	0.63	0.07	11
Corn	11	0.52	0.18	34
Corn, 0% cottonseed hulls	1	0.46		
Corn, 7% cottonseed hulls	1	0.43		
Corn, 14% cottonseed hulls	1	0.59		
Corn, 21% cottonseed hulls	1	0.48		
Corn, 10.5% protein, 0% $NaHCO_3$	1	0.36		
Corn, 10.5% protein, 3.5% $NaHCO_3$	1	0.30		
Corn, 12% protein, 0% $NaHCO_3$	1	0.29		
Corn, 12% protein, 3.5% $NaHCO_3$	1	0.24		
Corn, dry-rolled	6	0.60	0.07	12
Corn, dry-rolled, 0% roughage	1	0.54		
Corn, dry-rolled, 21% roughage	1	0.49		
Corn, flaked	1	0.58		
Corn, flakes	1	0.65		
Corn, high-moisture acid	1	0.56		
Corn, high-moisture ground	1	0.80		
Corn, micronized	1	0.29		
Corn, steam-flaked	1	0.68		
Corn, steam-flaked, 0% roughage	1	0.51		
Corn, steam-flaked, 21% roughage	1	0.47		
Corn gluten feed	1	0.25		
Corn gluten feed dry	2	0.22	0.11	51
Corn gluten feed wet	1	0.26		
Corn gluten meal	3	0.55	0.08	14
Corn silage	3	0.31	0.06	20
Cottonseed meal	21	0.43	0.11	25
Cottonseed meal, HCHO[c]	2	0.64	0.15	23
Cottonseed meal, prepressed	2	0.36	0.02	6
Cottonseed meal, screwpressed	2	0.50	0.10	20
Cottonseed meal, solvent	6	0.41	0.13	32
Distillers dried grain with solubles	4	0.47	0.18	39
Distillers dried grains	1	0.54		
Distillers wet grains	1	0.47		
Feather meal, hydrolyzed	1	0.71		
Fish meal	26	0.60	0.16	26
Fish meal, stale	1	0.48		
Fish meal, well-preserved	1	0.78		
Grapeseed meal	1	0.45		
Grass	4	0.40	0.10	26
Grass pellets	2	0.46	0.05	11
Grass silage	20	0.29	0.06	20
Guar meal	1	0.34		
Linseed	1	0.18		
Linseed meal	5	0.35	0.10	27
Lupin meal	1	0.35		
Manoic meal	1	0.36		

Feed	Number of Determinations	Undegradability		
		Mean	S.D.[a]	C.V.[b]
Meat and bone meal	5	0.49	0.18	37
Meat meal	1	0.76		
Oats	4	0.17	0.03	15
Palm cakes	6	0.66	0.06	9
Peanut meal	8	0.25	0.11	45
Peas	4	0.22	0.03	15
Rapeseed meal	10	0.28	0.09	31
Rapeseed meal, protected	1	0.70		
Rye	1	0.19		
Ryegrass, dehydrated	4	0.22	0.14	66
Ryegrass, dried artifically	1	0.71		
Ryegrass, dried artificially, chopped	1	0.30		
Ryegrass, dried artificially, ground	1	0.73		
Ryegrass, dried artificially, pelleted	1	0.54		
Ryegrass, fresh	1	0.48		
Ryegrass, fresh or frozen	3	0.41	0.18	44
Ryegrass, frozen	1	0.52		
Ryegrass silage, HCHO[c]	1	0.93		
Ryegrass silage, HCHO[c] dried	1	0.83		
Ryegrass silage, unwilted	1	0.22		
Sanfoin	1	0.81		
Sorghum grain	2	0.54	0.02	4
Sorghum grain, dry-ground	1	0.49		
Sorghum grain, dry-rolled	2	0.64	0.08	12
Sorghum grain, micronized	1	0.64		
Sorghum grain, reconstituted	2	0.42	0.32	75
Sorghum grain, steam-flaked	2	0.47	0.07	15
Soybean meal	39	0.35	0.12	33
Soybean meal, dried 120 C	1	0.59		
Soybean meal, dried 130 C	1	0.71		
Soybean meal, dried 140 C	1	0.82		
Soybean meal, 35% concentrate	1	0.18		
Soybean meal, 65% concentrate	1	0.46		
Soybean meal, HCHO[c]	3	0.80	0.11	14
Soybean meal, unheated	1	0.14		
Soybean-rapeseed meal, HCHO[c]	2	0.78	0.02	3
Soybeans	2	0.26	0.11	40
Subterranean clover	2	0.40	0.18	45
Sunflower meal	9	0.26	0.05	20
Timothy, dried artificially, chopped	1	0.32		
Timothy, dried artificially, pelleted	1	0.53		
Wheat	4	0.22	0.06	27
Wheat bran	4	0.29	0.10	34
Wheat gluten	1	0.17		
Wheat middlings	3	0.21	0.02	11
Yeast	1	0.42		
Zein	1	0.60		

[a]S.D. = standard deviation.

[b]C.V. = coefficient of variation.

[c]HCHO = formaldehyde treatment.

APPENDIX TABLE 3

Composition of feedstuffs commonly fed to poultry and swine (from NRC publications on swine and poultry)

Feed Class and Ingredient Name	Int'l. Feed Number	Composition, As Fed — Dry Matter, %	Crude Protein, %	Crude Fiber, %	Ca, %	P, %	Poultry ME, kcal/kg	As Fed Basis — Swine: Digest. Protein, %	DE, kcal/kg	ME, kcal/kg	TDN, %
Roughage											
Alfalfa, dehy, mn 15% CP	1-00-022	93.1	15.2	26.4	1.23	0.22	1587	7.0	1436	1331	32
Alfalfa, dehy, mn 17% CP	1-00-023	93.0	17.9	24.3	1.33	0.24	1653	8.3	1435	1322	32
Alfalfa, dehy, mn 20% CP	1-00-024	93.1	20.6	20.2	1.52	0.27	1720	12.6	2217	2029	50
Alfalfa, dehy, mn 22% CP	1-00-851	92.9	22.5	18.5	1.48	0.28	1764	13.7	2253	2052	51
Alfalfa hay, s-c, grnd	1-00-111	92.2	16.7	25.8	—	—	—	7.7	1382	1276	31
Alfalfa leaf meal	1-00-246	88.8	21.3	14.6	2.11	0.26	1580	13.0	2192	2000	50
Pasture grass, closely grazed		20.0	5.2	3.4	—	—	—	3.5	517	—	12
Energy sources (<20% CP)											
Animal fat	4-00-409	99.5	—	—	—	—	7090	—	8130	7900	199
Barley grain	4-00-530	89.0	11.6	5.0	0.08	0.42	2646	8.2	3080	2876	70
Buckwheat grain	4-00-994	88.0	11.1	9.0	0.11	0.33	2712	8.0	3026	2829	69
Corn germ meal	5-02-898	93.0	18.0	12.0	0.10	0.40	1700	—	—	—	—
Corn grain	4-02-935	86.0	8.8	2.0	0.03	0.27	3417	7.0	3488	3275	79
Corn hominy feed	4-02-887	90.6	10.7	5.0	0.05	0.53	2866	8.5	3595	3365	82
Millet grain	4-03-098	90.0	12.0	8.0	0.05	0.28	—	8.8	2897	2703	66
Molasses, beet	4-00-668	77.0	6.7	—	0.16	0.03	1962	—	—	—	—
Molasses, cane	4-04-696	75.0	3.2	—	0.89	0.08	1962	—	2464	2343	56
Oats, grain	4-03-309	89.0	11.8	11.0	0.10	0.35	2535	9.9	2860	2668	65
Oats, groats	4-03-331	91.0	16.7	3.0	0.07	0.43	3549	14.0	3250	2999	74
Potatoes, cooked	4-03-784	22.5	2.2	0.7	0.01	0.05	—	1.6	863	811	20
Potato meal	4-07-850	90.3	5.9	1.4	0.07	0.20	3527	5.0	3345	3168	76
Rice bran	4-03-928	91.0	13.5	11.0	0.06	1.82	1630	10.2	3256	3028	74
Rice grain w/hulls, grnd	4-03-938	89.0	7.3	9.0	0.04	0.26	2668	5.5	2511	2367	57
Rye grain	4-04-047	89.0	11.9	2.0	0.06	0.34	2888	9.6	3300	3079	75
Sorghum grain, milo	4-04-444	89.0	11.0	2.0	0.04	0.29	3250	7.8	3453	3229	78
Wheat bran	4-05-190	89.0	16.0	10.0	0.14	1.17	1146	12.2	2512	2321	57
Wheat grain	4-05-211	89.0	12.7	3.0	0.05	0.36	3071	11.7	3520	3277	80
Wheat middlings	4-05-203	89.0	18.0	2.0	0.08	0.52	2756	16.0	3212	2952	73
Wheat mill run	4-05-206	90.0	15.3	8.0	0.09	1.02	1764	12.2	3168	2934	72
Wheat shorts	4-05-201	90.0	18.4	5.0	0.11	0.76	2646	15.4	3168	2912	72
Whey, dried	4-01-182	94.0	13.8	—	0.87	0.79	1852	12.6	3432	3191	78

Feed Class and Ingredient Name	Int'l. Feed Number	Composition, As Fed					Poultry ME, kcal/kg	As Fed Basis — Swine			
		Dry Matter, %	Crude Protein, %	Crude Fiber, %	Ca, %	P, %		Digest. Protein, %	DE, kcal/kg	ME, kcal/kg	TDN, %
Plant protein sources (>20% CP)											
Barley malt sprouts	5-00-545	93.0	26.2	14.0	0.22	0.73	1411	20.7	1558	1406	35
Brewer's dried grains	5-02-141	92.0	25.9	15.0	0.27	0.50	2513	20.4	1892	1708	43
Coconut meal, solv. extd	5-01-573	92.0	21.3	15.0	0.17	0.61	1540	15.5	3123	2852	71
Corn distillers grains w/solubles, dehy.	5-02-843	92.0	27.4	9.0	0.09	0.37	2425	—	—	—	—
Corn dist. sol., dehy	5-02-844	92.0	26.9	4.0	0.35	1.37	2932	16.1	3300	2976	75
Corn gluten meal	5-02-900	91.0	42.9	4.0	0.16	0.40	3307	—	—	—	—
Cottonseed meal, prepress solv. extd.	5-07-874	92.5	50.0	8.5	0.16	1.01	2150	45.0	3018	2569	68
Pea seed, grnd	5-03-598	91.0	22.5	9.0	0.17	0.50	2601	19.3	3531	3213	80
Peanut meal, solv. extd.	5-04-650	92.0	47.4	13.0	0.20	0.65	2205	44.5	3408	2920	77
Rapeseed meal, solv. extd	5-03-871	90.3	39.4	13.8	0.40	0.90	—	32.3	2747	2396	62
Soybean meal, solv. extd.	5-04-604	89.0	45.8	6.0	0.32	0.67	2249	41.7	3300	2825	75
Soybean meal, dehulled, solv. extd.	5-04-612	89.8	50.9	2.8	0.26	0.62	2425	46.3	3405	2881	77
Sunflower meal, solv. extd.	5-04-739	93.0	46.8	11.0	0.40	1.00	1760	42.1	3034	2604	69
Wheat germ meal	5-05-218	90.0	26.2	3.0	0.07	1.04	3086	23.6	3770	3397	86
Yeast, brewer's dried	7-05-527	93.0	44.6	3.0	0.13	1.43	2425	39.2	3076	2654	70
Animal and fish protein sources											
Blood meal	5-00-380	91.0	79.9	1.0	0.28	0.22	2844	62.3	2684	2101	61
Blood flour	5-00-381	91.0	82.2	1.0	0.45	0.37	—	64.1	2608	2029	59
Buttermilk, dried	5-01-160	93.0	32.0	—	1.34	0.94	2756	29.8	3388	3015	77
Casein, dried	5-01-162	90.0	81.8	—	0.61	0.99	4120	76.0	3532	2740	80
Fish meal, anchovy	5-02-985	93.0	66.0	1.0	4.50	2.85	2900	60.7	2994	2446	68
Fish meal, herring	5-02-000	92.0	70.6	1.0	2.94	2.20	2976	66.3	3650	2938	83
Fish meal, menhaden	5-02-009	92.0	61.3	1.0	5.49	2.81	2866	56.4	3123	2580	71
Fish solubles, dried	5-01-971	92.0	62.8	1.0	—	—	2866	60.3	3408	2801	77
Liver meal	5-00-389	92.6	66.5	1.3	0.50	1.25	—	64.4	3920	3195	89
Meat meal	5-00-385	93.5	53.4	2.4	7.94	4.03	1984	47.5	3010	2543	68
Meat meal tankage	5-00-386	92.0	59.8	2.0	5.94	3.17	2646	37.1	2475	2052	56
Meat and bone meal	5-00-388	94.0	50.6	2.2	10.57	5.07	1984	45.0	2859	2434	65
Milk, dried skim	5-01-175	94.0	33.5	—	1.26	1.03	2513	32.8	3784	3360	86

Amino acid composition of selected feedstuffs

	Crude Protein	Amino Acids, As Fed Basis, %												
		Arginine	Cystine	Glycine	Histidine	Isoleucine	Leucine	Lysine	Methionine	Phenylalanine	Threonine	Tryptophan	Tyrosine	Valine
Forage-roughage														
Alfalfa, dehy, 15% CP	15.2	0.60	0.17	0.70	0.30	0.68	1.10	0.60	0.20	0.80	0.60	0.40	0.40	0.70
Alfalfa, dehy, 20% CP	20.6	0.90	—	1.00	0.40	0.80	1.50	0.90	0.30	1.10	0.90	0.50	0.70	1.19
Alfalfa leaf meal, s-c	21.3	0.90	0.34	0.90	0.33	0.90	1.25	0.95	0.30	0.80	0.70	0.25	0.60	0.90
Grass, dehy	14.8	0.99	0.19	0.72	0.46	1.38	1.98	1.06	0.31	1.30	0.89	0.31	0.46	1.57
Energy feeds														
Barley grain	11.6	0.53	0.18	0.36	0.27	0.53	0.80	0.53	0.18	0.62	0.36	0.18	0.36	0.62
Corn hominy feed	10.7	0.50	0.18	0.50	0.20	0.40	0.80	0.40	0.18	0.30	0.40	0.10	0.50	0.50
Corn germ meal	18.0	1.20	0.32	—	—	—	1.70	0.90	0.35	0.80	0.90	0.30	1.50	1.30
Corn grain	8.8	0.50	0.09	0.43	0.20	0.40	1.10	0.20	0.17	0.50	0.40	0.10	—	0.40
Millet grain	12.0	0.35	0.08	—	0.23	1.23	0.49	0.25	0.30	0.59	0.44	0.17	—	0.62
Oats grain	11.8	0.71	0.18	—	0.18	0.53	0.89	0.36	0.18	0.62	0.36	0.18	0.53	0.62
Potato meal	8.2	0.43	—	—	0.11	0.48	0.30	0.47	0.07	0.29	0.21	0.15	—	0.39
Rice grain w/hulls	7.3	0.53	0.10	0.80	0.09	0.27	0.53	0.27	0.17	0.27	0.18	0.10	0.60	0.51
Rye grain	11.9	0.53	0.18	—	0.27	0.53	0.71	0.45	0.18	0.62	0.36	0.09	0.27	0.62
Sorghum grain, milo	11.0	0.36	0.18	0.40	0.27	0.53	1.42	0.27	0.09	0.45	0.27	0.09	0.36	0.53
Wheat grain	12.7	0.71	0.18	0.89	0.27	0.53	0.89	0.45	0.18	0.62	0.36	0.18	0.45	0.53
Wheat shorts	18.4	0.95	0.20	0.40	0.32	0.70	1.20	0.70	0.18	0.70	0.50	0.20	0.40	0.77
Whey dried	13.8	0.40	0.30	0.30	0.20	0.90	1.40	1.10	0.20	0.40	0.80	0.20	0.30	0.70
Plant protein sources														
Brewers dried grains	25.9	1.30	—	—	0.50	1.50	2.30	0.90	0.40	1.30	0.90	0.40	1.20	1.60
Corn dist. solv., dehy	26.9	1.00	0.60	1.10	0.70	1.50	2.10	0.90	0.60	1.50	1.00	0.20	0.70	1.50
Corn gluten meal	42.9	1.40	0.60	1.50	1.00	2.30	7.60	0.80	1.00	2.90	1.40	0.20	1.00	2.20
Cottonseed meal, solv.	50.0	4.75	1.00	2.35	1.25	1.85	2.80	2.10	0.80	2.75	1.70	0.70	0.80	2.05
Peanut meal, solv.	47.4	4.69	—	—	1.00	2.00	3.10	1.30	0.60	2.30	1.40	0.50	—	2.20
Rapeseed meal, solv.	39.4	2.16	0.67	1.88	1.05	1.43	2.63	2.09	0.76	1.49	1.65	0.48	0.83	1.90
Soybean meal, solv.	45.8	3.20	0.70	2.10	1.10	2.50	3.40	2.90	0.60	2.20	1.70	0.60	1.40	2.40
Sunflower meal, solv.	46.8	3.50	0.70	2.70	1.10	2.10	2.60	1.70	1.50	2.20	1.50	0.50	—	2.30
Yeast, brewer's dried	44.6	2.20	0.50	1.70	1.10	2.10	3.20	3.00	0.70	1.80	2.10	0.50	1.50	2.30
Animal and fish protein sources														
Blood meal	79.9	3.50	1.40	3.40	4.20	1.00	10.30	6.90	0.90	6.10	3.70	1.10	1.80	6.50
Buttermilk, dried	32.0	1.10	0.40	0.60	0.90	2.70	3.40	2.40	0.70	1.50	1.60	0.50	1.00	2.80
Casein, dried	81.8	3.40	0.30	1.50	2.50	5.70	8.60	7.00	2.70	4.60	3.80	1.00	4.70	6.80
Fish meal, anchovy	66.0	4.46	1.00	5.10	1.84	3.40	7.01	5.40	2.19	2.48	3.04	0.80	1.77	3.54

Fish meal, herring	3.20	2.10	0.90	2.60	2.60	2.00	5.10	7.30	3.20	1.30	5.00	1.60	4.00	70.6
Fish meal, menhaden	3.60	1.60	0.60	2.90	2.70	1.80	5.00	5.30	4.10	1.60	4.40	0.94	4.00	61.3
Liver meal	4.20	1.70	0.60	2.60	2.90	1.30	5.40	4.80	3.40	1.50	5.60	0.90	4.10	66.5
Meat meal	2.60	0.90	0.30	1.80	1.90	0.80	3.50	3.80	1.90	1.10	2.20	0.60	3.70	53.4
Meat and bone meal	2.40	0.80	0.20	1.80	1.80	0.70	3.10	3.50	1.70	0.90	6.60	0.60	4.00	50.6
Meat meal tankage	4.20	—	0.70	2.40	2.70	0.80	5.10	4.00	1.90	1.90	—	—	3.60	59.8
Milk, dried skim	2.20	1.30	0.40	1.40	1.50	0.80	3.30	2.80	2.30	0.90	0.20	0.50	1.20	33.5

APPENDIX TABLE 5

Vitamin content of selected feedstuffs, fresh basis (ppm)

	Carotene	Vitamin E	Choline	Niacin	Pantothenic acid	Riboflavin	Thiamin	Vitamin B6	Vitamin B12
Plant sources									
Alfalfa, dehy., 15% CP	102	98	1550	42	21	11	3.0	6.5	—
Alfalfa leaf meal, s-c	62	—	1600	55	33	15	—	11	—
Barley grain	—	11	1030	57	6.5	2.0	5.1	2.9	—
Brewers dried grains	—	—	1587	43	8.6	1.5	0.7	0.7	—
Corn dist. sol., dehy.	1	55	4818	115	21	17	6.8	10	—
Corn grain	4	22	537	23	5	1.1	4.0	7.2	—
Cottonseed meal, solv., 41% CP	—	15	2860	40	14	5.0	6.5	6.4	—
Oats grain	—	36	1073	16	13	1.6	6.2	1.2	—
Peanut meal, solv.	—	3	2000	170	53	11	7.3	10	—
Rice grain w/hulls	—	14	800	30	3.3	1.1	2.8	—	—
Rye grain	—	15	—	1.2	6.9	1.6	3.9	—	—
Sorghum grain, milo	—	12	678	43	11	1.2	3.9	4.1	—
Soybean meal, solv., 45% CP	—	3	2743	27	14	3.3	6.6	8.0	—
Wheat grain	—	34	830	57	12	1.2	4.9	—	—
Wheat middlings	—	58	1100	53	14	1.5	19	11	—
Yeast, brewers dried	—	—	3885	447	110	35	92	43	—
Animal sources									
Buttermilk, dried	—	6	1808	9	30	31	3.5	2.4	0.02
Fish meal, herring	—	27	4004	89	11	9.0	—	3.7	219
Fish meal, menhaden	—	9	3080	56	9	4.8	0.7	—	0.1
Meat meal	—	1	1955	57	4.8	5.3	0.2	3.0	51
Meat and bone meal	—	1	2189	48	3.7	4.4	1.1	2.5	45
Liver meal	—	—	—	204	45	46	0.2	—	501
Milk, cow's, dried skim	—	9	1426	11	34	20	3.5	3.9	42
Whey, dried	—	—	20	11	48	30	3.7	2.5	0.03

APPENDIX TABLE 6

Composition of mineral supplements for animal feeds, dry-matter basis (from 1989 NRC dairy publication)[a]

Feed Name Description	International Feed Number	Dry Matter, %	Protein Equivalent — N × 6.25, %	Macrominerals, %							Microminerals, mg/kg							
				Calcium	Chlorine	Magnesium	Phosphorus	Potassium	Sodium	Sulfur	Cobalt	Copper	Fluorine	Iodine	Iron	Manganese	Selenium	Zinc
Ammonium																		
Phosphate, monobasic, $(NH_4)H_2PO_4$	6-09-338	97	70.9	0.28	—	0.46	24.74	0.01	0.06	1.46	10	10	2500	—	17,400	400	—	100
Phosphate, dibasic, $(NH_4)_2HPO_4$	6-00-370	97	115.9	0.52	—	0.46	20.60	0.01	0.05	2.16	—	10	2100	—	12,400	400	—	100
Sulfate	6-09-339	100	134.1	—	—	—	—	—	—	24.10	—	1	—	—	10	1	—	—
Bone																		
Charcoal (bone black, bone char)	6-00-402	90	9.4	30.11	—	0.59	14.14	0.16	—	—	—	—	—	—	—	—	—	—
Meal, steamed	6-00-400	97	13.2	30.71	—	0.33	12.86	0.19	5.69	2.51	—	—	—	—	26,700	—	—	100
Calcium																		
Carbonate, $CaCO_3$	6-01-069	100	—	39.39	—	0.05	0.04	0.06	0.06	—	—	—	—	—	300	300	—	—
Phosphate, monobasic, from defluorinated phosphoric acid	6-01-082	97	—	16.40	—	0.61	21.60	0.08	0.06	1.22	10	10	2100	—	15,800	360	—	90
Phosphate, dibasic, from defluorinated phosphoric acid (dicalcium phosphate)	6-01-080	97	—	22.00	—	0.59	19.30	0.07	0.05	1.14	10	10	1800	—	14,400	300	—	100
Sulfate, dihydrate, $CaSO_4 \cdot 2H_2O$, cp[b]	6-01-089	97	—	23.28	—	—	—	—	—	18.62	—	—	—	—			—	—
Colloidal clay																		
Clay (soft rock phosphate); see also phosphate	6-03-947	100[c]	—	17.00	—	0.38	9.00	—	0.10	—	—	—	15,000	—	19,000	1000	—	—
Cobalt																		
Carbonate, $CoCO_3$	6-01-566	99[c]	—	—	—	—	—	—	—	0.20	460,000	—	—	—	—	—	—	—
Copper (cupric)																		
Sulfate, pentahydrate, $CuSO_4 \cdot 5H_2O$, cp[b]	6-01-720	100	—	—	—	—	—	—	—	12.84	—	254,500	—	—	—	—	—	—
Curacao																		
Phosphate	6-05-586	99[c]	—	34.34	—	0.81	14.14	—	0.20	—	—	—	5500	—	3500	—	—	—
Ethylenediamine																		
Dihydroiodide	6-01-842	98[c]	—	—	—	—	—	—	—	—	—	—	—	803,400	—	—	—	—
Iron (ferrous)																		
Sulfate, heptahydrate	6-20-734	98[c]	—	—	—	—	—	—	—	12.35	—	—	—	—	218,400	—	—	—
Limestone																		
Limestone, ground	6-02-632	100	—	34.00	0.03	2.06	0.02	0.12	0.06	0.04	—	—	—	—	3500	—	—	—
Magnesium (dolomitic)	6-02-633	99[c]	—	22.30	0.12	9.99	0.04	0.36	—	—	—	—	—	—	770	—	—	—
Magnesium																		
Carbonate, $MgCO_3 \cdot Mg(OH)_2$	6-02-754	98[c]	—	0.02	—	30.81	—	—	—	—	—	—	—	—	220	—	—	—
Oxide, MgO	6-02-756	98	—	3.07	—	56.20	—	—	—	—	—	—	200	—	—	100	—	—

Feed Name Description	International Feed Number	Dry Matter %	Protein Equivalent— N × 6.25, %	Macrominerals, %							Microminerals, mg/kg							
				Calcium	Chlorine	Magnesium	Phosphorus	Potassium	Sodium	Sulfur	Cobalt	Copper	Fluorine	Iodine	Iron	Manganese	Selenium	Zinc
Manganese (manganous)																		
Oxide, MnO, cp[b]	6-03-056	99[c]	—	—	—	—	—	—	—	—	—	—	—	—	—	774,500	—	—
Carbonate, MnCO$_3$	6-03-036	97	—	—	—	—	—	—	—	—	—	—	—	—	—	478,000	—	—
Oystershell																		
Ground (flour)	6-03-481	99	—	38.00	0.01	0.30	0.07	0.10	0.21	—	—	—	—	—	2870	100	—	—
Phosphate																		
Defluorinated	6-01-780	100	—	32.00	—	0.42	18.00	0.08	4.90	—	10	20	1800	—	6700	200	—	60
Rock	6-03-945	100	—	35.00	—	0.41	13.00	0.06	0.03	—	10	10	35,000	—	16800	200	—	100
Rock, low-fluorine	6-03-946	100	—	36.00	—	—	14.00	—	—	—	—	—	—	—	—	—	—	—
Rock, soft (see also Calcium)	6-03-947	100	—	17.00	—	0.38	9.00	—	0.10	—	—	—	15,000	—	19,000	1000	—	—
Phosphate, monobasic, monohydrate, NaH$_2$PO$_4$·H$_2$O (see also Sodium)	6-04-288	97	—	—	—	—	22.50	—	16.68	—	—	—	—	—	—	—	—	—
Phosphoric acid																		
H$_3$PO$_4$	6-03-707	75	—	0.05	—	0.51	31.60	0.02	0.04	1.55	10	10	3100	—	17,500	500	—	130
Potassium																		
Bicarbonate, KHCO$_3$, cp[b]	6-29-493	99[c]	—	—	—	—	—	39.05	—	—	—	—	—	—	—	—	—	—
Chloride, KCl	6-03-755	100	—	0.05	47.30	0.34	—	50.00	1.00	0.45	—	—	—	—	600	—	—	—
Iodide, KI	6-03-759	100[c]	—	—	—	—	—	21.00	—	—	—	—	—	681,700	—	—	—	—
Sulfate, K$_2$SO$_4$	6-06-098	98[c]	—	0.15	1.55	0.61	—	41.84	0.09	17.35	—	—	—	—	710	10	—	—
Sodium																		
Bicarbonate, NaHCO$_3$	6-04-272	100	—	—	—	—	—	—	27.00	—	—	—	—	—	—	—	—	—
Chloride, NaCl	6-04-152	100	—	—	60.66	—	—	—	39.34	—	—	—	—	—	—	—	—	—
Phosphate, monobasic, monohydrate, NaH$_2$PO$_4$·H$_2$O (see also Phosphate)	6-04-288	97	—	—	—	—	22.50	—	16.68	—	—	—	—	—	—	—	—	—
Selenite, Na$_2$SeO$_3$	6-26-013	98[c]	—	—	—	—	—	—	26.60	—	—	—	—	—	—	—	456,000	—
Sulfate, decahydrate, Na$_2$SO$_4$·10H$_2$O, cp[b]	6-04-292	97[c]	—	—	—	—	—	—	14.27	9.95	—	—	—	—	—	—	—	—
Tripolyphosphate, Na$_5$P$_3$O$_{10}$	6-08-076	96	—	—	—	—	25.00	—	31.00	—	—	—	—	—	40	—	—	—
Zinc																		
Oxide, ZnO	6-05-533	100	—	0.02	—	—	—	—	—	—	—	—	—	—	—	—	—	780,000
Sulfate, monohydrate, ZnSO$_4$·H$_2$O	6-05-555	99[c]	—	—	0.015	—	—	—	—	17.68	—	—	—	—	10	10	—	363,600

[a]Note: The compositions of hydrated mineral ingredients (e.g., CaSO$_4$·2H$_2$O) are shown including the waters of hydration. Mineral compositions of feed-grade mineral supplements vary by source, mining site, and manufacturer. The manufacturer's analysis should be used when it is available.

[b]cp = Chemically pure.

[c]Dry matter values have been estimated for these minerals.

Some common trace nutrients and feed additives and concentrations of active ingredients as received from manufacturers or suppliers of premixes

Active Ingredient	Concentration from the Manufacturer	Concentration Typical of Premix Use
Fat-soluble vitamins		
Vitamin A acetate,[a] gelatin-coated feed grade	325,000, 500,000, or 600,000 IU/g	same, 30,000 IU/g
Vitamin A palmitate,[a] gelatin-coated	325,000 IU/g	same
Vitamin D_3 acetate dry feed grade	500,000 ICU/g[b]	same, 26,455 ICU/g
Vitamin E acetate, dry feed grade	250 IU/g	same, 44 IU/g
Vitamin K, menadione Na bisulfate complex	pure	same, 16 g/lb
Vitamin A acetate & vitamin D_3 acetate mix	500,000 IU/g of A 167,000 IU/g of D_3	50,000 IU/g 16-20,000 IU/g
Vitamin A, D_3, E premix		40-50,000 IU/g A 10,000 IU/g D_3 50 IU/g E
B-complex vitamins		
Riboflavin	0.50 g/g	same, 60 g/lb
Thiamin	pure	same
Pridoxine	pure	same
Niacin	0.98 g/g	same
Pantothenate, Ca DL	0.414 g/g of D pantho. acid	same
Choline chloride	0.435 g/g of choline	same
Cyanocobalamin (B_{12})	1.32 mg/g	same
Folic acid	0.45 g/g	same
Biotin	pure	various
Amino acids		
Methionine, DL	0.995 g/g	same
Methionine hydroxy analog, Ca salt	0.93 g/g	same
Lysine, L	0.769 g/g	same
Antibiotics		
Terramycin	10, 50 g/lb	same
Aureomycin	10, 50 g/lb	same
Neoterramycin	20 g/lb	same
Zinc bacitracin	40 g/lb	same
Erythromycin	50 g/lb	same
Penicillin	136 g/lb	same
Rumensin (Na monensin)	60 g/lb	same
Tylosin phosphate	10 g/lb	same
Miscellaneous		
Arsanilic acid	20, 40, 227 g/lb	same
Sodium arsanilate	pure	same
Roxarsone	45.4 g/lb	same
Ethylenediamine dihydriodide	0.99 g/g	42 g/lb
Melengestrol acetate	100, 500 mg/lb	0.4, 0.5 mg/lb

[a]Other concentrations available from manufacturers; vitamin A is also available in water-dispersible and gelatin-coated preparations, water miscible, in oil, or in injectable preparations.

[b]ICU = international chick units.

APPENDIX TABLE 8

Net energy requirements of growing and finishing beef cattle (Mcal/d) (from 1984 NRC on beef)

Body Weight, kg:	150	200	250	300	350	400	450	500	550	600
NEm Required:	3.30	4.10	4.84	5.55	6.24	6.89	7.52	8.14	8.75	9.33
Daily gain, kg	NEg Required									
Medium-frame steer calves										
0.2	0.41	0.50	0.60	0.69	0.77	0.85	0.93	1.01	1.08	
0.4	0.87	1.08	1.28	1.47	1.65	1.82	1.99	2.16	2.32	
0.6	1.36	1.69	2.00	2.29	2.57	2.84	3.11	3.36	3.61	
0.8	1.87	2.32	2.74	3.14	3.53	3.90	4.26	4.61	4.95	
1.0	2.39	2.96	3.50	4.02	4.51	4.98	5.44	5.89	6.23	
1.2	2.91	3.62	4.28	4.90	5.50	6.69	6.65	7.19	7.73	
Large-frame steers, compensating medium-frame yearling steers, and medium-frame bulls										
0.2	0.36	0.45	0.53	0.61	0.68	0.75	0.82	0.89	0.96	1.02
0.4	0.77	0.96	1.13	1.30	1.46	1.61	1.76	1.91	2.05	2.19
0.6	1.21	1.50	1.77	2.03	2.28	2.52	2.75	2.98	3.20	3.41
0.8	1.65	2.06	2.43	2.78	3.12	3.45	3.77	4.08	4.38	4.68
1.0	2.11	2.62	3.10	3.55	3.99	4.41	4.81	5.21	5.60	5.98
1.2	2.58	3.20	3.78	4.34	4.87	5.38	5.88	6.37	6.84	7.30
1.4	3.06	3.79	4.48	5.14	5.77	6.38	6.97	7.54	8.10	8.64
1.6	3.53	4.39	5.19	5.95	6.68	7.38	8.07	8.73	9.38	10.01
Large-frame bull calves and compensating large-frame yearling steers										
0.2	0.32	0.40	0.47	0.54	0.60	0.67	0.73	0.79	0.85	0.91
0.4	0.69	0.85	1.01	1.15	1.29	1.43	1.56	1.69	1.82	1.94
0.6	1.07	1.33	1.57	1.80	2.02	2.23	2.44	2.64	2.83	3.02
0.8	1.47	1.82	2.15	2.47	2.77	3.06	3.34	3.62	3.88	4.15
1.0	1.87	2.32	2.75	3.15	3.54	3.91	4.27	4.62	4.96	5.30
1.2	2.29	2.84	3.36	3.85	4.32	4.77	5.21	5.64	6.06	6.47
1.4	2.71	3.36	3.97	4.56	5.11	5.65	6.18	6.68	7.18	7.66
1.6	3.14	3.89	4.60	5.28	5.92	6.55	7.15	7.74	8.31	8.87
1.8	3.56	4.43	5.23	6.00	6.74	7.45	8.13	8.80	9.46	10.10
Medium-frame heifer calves										
0.2	0.49	0.60	0.71	0.82	0.92	1.01	1.11	1.20	1.29	
0.4	1.05	1.31	1.55	1.77	1.99	2.20	2.40	2.60	2.79	
0.6	1.66	2.06	2.44	2.79	3.13	3.46	3.78	4.10	4.40	
0.8	2.29	2.84	3.36	3.85	4.32	4.78	5.22	5.65	6.07	
1.0	2.94	3.65	4.31	4.94	5.55	6.14	6.70	7.25	7.79	
Large-frame heifer calves and compensating medium-frame yearling heifers										
0.2	0.43	0.53	0.63	0.72	0.81	0.90	0.98	1.06	1.14	1.21
0.4	0.93	1.16	1.37	1.57	1.76	1.95	2.13	2.31	2.47	2.64
0.6	1.47	1.83	2.16	2.47	2.78	3.07	3.35	3.63	3.90	4.16
0.8	2.03	2.62	2.98	3.41	3.83	4.24	4.63	5.01	5.38	5.74
1.0	2.61	3.23	3.82	4.38	4.92	5.44	5.94	6.43	6.91	7.37
1.2	3.19	3.97	4.69	5.37	5.03	6.67	7.28	7.88	8.47	9.03

APPENDIX TABLE 9

Protein requirements of growing and finishing cattle (g/d) (from 1984 NRC on beef)

Body Weight, kg:	150	200	250	300	350	400	450	500	550	600
Medium-frame steer calves										
Daily gain, kg										
0.2	343	399	450	499	545	590	633	675	715	
0.4	428	482	532	580	625	668	710	751	790	
0.6	503	554	601	646	688	728	767	805	842	
0.8	575	621	664	704	743	780	815	849	883	
1.0	642	682	720	755	789	821	852	882	911	
1.2	702	735	766	794	822	848	873	897	921	
Large-frame steer calves and compensating medium-frame yearling steers										
0.2	361	421	476	529	579	627	673	719	762	805
0.4	441	499	552	603	651	697	742	785	827	867
0.6	522	576	628	676	722	766	809	850	890	930
0.8	598	650	698	743	786	828	867	906	944	980
1.0	671	718	762	804	843	881	918	953	988	1021
1.2	740	782	822	859	895	929	961	993	1023	1053
1.4	806	842	877	908	938	967	995	1022	1048	1073
1.6	863	892	919	943	967	989	1011	1031	1052	1071
Medium-frame bulls										
0.2	345	401	454	503	550	595	638	680	721	761
0.4	430	485	536	584	629	673	716	757	797	835
0.6	509	561	609	655	698	740	780	819	856	893
0.8	583	632	677	719	759	798	835	871	906	940
1.0	655	698	739	777	813	849	881	914	945	976
1.2	722	760	795	828	860	890	919	947	974	1001
1.4	782	813	841	868	893	917	941	963	985	1006
Large-frame bull calves and compensating large-frame yearling steers										
0.2	355	414	468	519	568	615	661	705	747	789
0.4	438	494	547	597	644	689	733	776	817	857
0.6	519	574	624	672	718	761	803	844	884	923
0.8	597	649	697	741	795	826	866	905	942	979
1.0	673	721	765	807	847	885	922	958	994	1027
1.2	745	789	830	868	904	939	973	1005	1037	1067
1.4	815	854	890	924	956	986	1016	1045	1072	1099
1.6	880	912	943	971	998	1024	1048	1072	1095	1117
1.8	922	942	962	980	997	1013	1028	1043	1057	1071
Medium-frame heifer calves										
0.2	323	374	421	465	508	549	588	626	662	
0.4	409	459	505	549	591	630	669	706	742	
0.6	477	522	563	602	638	674	708	741	773	
0.8	537	574	608	640	670	700	728	755	781	
1.0	562	583	603	621	638	654	670	685	700	
Large-frame heifer calves and compensating medium-frame yearling heifers										
0.2	342	397	449	497	543	588	631	672	712	751
0.4	426	480	530	577	622	665	707	747	787	825
0.6	500	549	596	639	681	721	759	796	832	867
0.8	568	613	654	693	730	765	799	833	865	896
1.0	630	668	703	735	767	797	826	854	881	907
1.2	680	708	734	758	781	803	824	844	864	883

APPENDIX TABLE 10

Calcium and phosphorus requirements of growing and finishing cattle (g/d) (from 1984 NRC on beef)

Body Weight, kg	Mineral	150	200	250	300	350	400	450	500	550	600
Medium-frame steer calves											
Daily gain, kg											
0.2	Ca	11	12	13	14	15	16	17	19	20	
	P	7	9	10	12	13	15	16	18	19	
0.4	Ca	16	17	17	18	19	19	20	21	22	
	P	9	10	12	13	14	16	17	18	20	
0.6	Ca	21	21	21	22	22	22	22	23	23	
	P	11	12	13	14	15	17	18	19	20	
0.8	Ca	27	26	25	25	25	25	24	24	24	
	P	12	13	14	15	16	17	19	20	21	
1.0	Ca	32	31	29	29	28	27	26	26	25	
	P	14	15	16	16	17	18	19	20	21	
1.2	Ca	37	35	33	32	31	29	28	27	26	
	P	16	16	17	17	18	19	20	21	21	
1.4	Ca	42	39	37	35	33	32	30	29	27	
	P	17	18	18	19	19	20	20	21	22	
Large-frame steer calves, compensating medium-frame yearling steers, and medium-frame bulls											
0.2	Ca	11	12	13	14	16	17	18	19	20	22
	P	7	9	10	12	13	15	16	18	20	21
0.4	Ca	17	17	18	19	19	20	21	22	23	24
	P	9	10	12	13	15	16	17	19	20	22
0.6	Ca	22	22	23	23	23	24	24	24	25	25
	P	11	12	13	15	16	17	18	20	21	22
0.8	Ca	28	27	27	27	27	27	27	27	27	27
	P	13	14	15	16	17	18	19	20	22	23
1.0	Ca	33	32	31	31	30	30	29	29	29	28
	P	14	15	16	17	18	19	20	21	22	23
1.2	Ca	38	37	36	35	34	33	32	31	30	30
	P	16	17	18	18	19	20	21	22	23	24
1.4	Ca	44	42	40	38	37	36	34	33	32	31
	P	18	18	19	20	20	21	22	22	23	24
1.6	Ca	49	47	44	42	40	38	37	35	34	32
	P	20	20	20	21	21	22	22	23	24	24
Large-frame bull calves and compensating large-frame yearling steers											
0.2	Ca	11	12	13	15	16	17	18	20	21	22
	P	7	9	10	12	13	15	17	18	20	21
0.4	Ca	17	18	19	19	20	21	22	23	24	25
	P	9	11	12	13	15	16	18	19	21	22
0.6	Ca	23	23	23	24	24	25	25	26	27	27
	P	11	12	14	15	16	18	19	20	22	23
0.8	Ca	28	28	28	28	28	29	29	29	29	30
	P	13	14	15	16	18	19	20	21	22	24
1.0	Ca	34	34	33	33	32	32	32	32	32	32
	P	15	16	17	18	19	20	21	22	23	24
1.2	Ca	40	39	38	37	36	36	35	35	34	34
	P	17	17	18	19	20	21	22	23	24	25
1.4	Ca	45	44	42	41	40	39	38	37	36	36
	P	18	19	20	20	21	22	23	24	25	26
1.6	Ca	51	49	47	45	44	42	41	40	39	38
	P	20	21	21	22	23	23	24	25	25	26
1.8	Ca	56	54	51	49	47	45	44	42	41	39
	P	22	22	22	23	23	24	25	25	26	26

APPENDIX TABLE 10 (Cont.)

Body Weight, kg	Mineral	150	200	250	300	350	400	450	500	550	600
Medium-frame heifer calves											
0.2	Ca	10	11	12	13	14	16	17	18	19	
	P	7	9	10	11	13	14	16	17	19	
0.4	Ca	15	16	16	16	17	17	18	19	19	
	P	9	10	11	12	14	15	16	18	19	
0.6	Ca	20	20	19	19	19	19	19	19	19	
	P	10	11	12	13	14	16	17	18	19	
0.8	Ca	25	23	23	22	21	20	20	19	19	
	P	12	12	13	14	15	16	17	18	19	
1.0	Ca	29	27	26	24	23	22	20	19	19	
	P	13	14	14	15	16	16	17	18	19	
Large-frame heifer calves and compensating medium-frame yearling heifers											
0.2	Ca	11	12	13	14	15	16	17	18	20	21
	P	7	9	10	12	13	15	16	18	19	21
0.4	Ca	16	16	17	17	18	19	19	20	21	22
	P	9	10	11	13	14	15	17	18	20	21
0.6	Ca	21	21	21	21	21	21	21	21	22	22
	P	10	12	13	14	15	16	17	19	20	21
0.8	Ca	26	25	24	24	23	23	23	22	22	22
	P	12	13	14	15	16	17	18	19	20	21
1.0	Ca	31	29	28	27	26	25	24	23	23	22
	P	14	14	15	16	17	18	18	19	20	21
1.2	Ca	35	33	31	30	28	27	25	24	23	22
	P	15	16	16	17	17	18	19	20	20	21

APPENDIX TABLE 11

Approximate total daily water intake of beef cattle (from 1984 NRC on beef)

| Weight | | Temperature in °F (°C)[a] | | | | | | | | | | |
| | | 40 (4.4) | | 50 (10.0) | | 60 (14.4) | | 70 (21.1) | | 80 (26.6) | | 90 (32.2) | |
kg	lb	liter	gal	liter	gal	liter	gal	liter	gal	liter	gal	liter	gal
Growing heifers, steers, and bulls													
182	400	15.1	4.0	16.3	4.3	18.9	5.0	22.0	5.8	25.4	6.7	36.0	9.5
273	600	20.1	5.3	22.0	5.8	25.0	6.6	29.5	7.8	33.7	8.9	48.1	12.7
364	800	23.8	6.3	25.7	6.8	29.9	7.9	34.8	9.2	40.1	10.6	56.8	15.0
Finishing cattle													
273	600	22.7	6.0	24.6	6.5	28.0	7.4	32.9	8.7	37.9	10.0	54.1	14.3
364	800	27.6	7.3	29.9	7.9	34.4	9.1	40.5	10.7	46.6	12.3	65.9	17.4
454	1000	32.9	8.7	35.6	9.4	40.9	10.8	47.7	12.6	54.9	14.5	78.0	20.6
Wintering pregnant cows[b]													
409	900	25.4	6.7	27.3	7.2	31.4	8.3	36.7	9.7	—	—	—	—
500	1100	22.7	6.0	24.6	6.5	28.0	7.4	32.9	8.7	—	—	—	—
Lactating cows													
409+	900+	43.1	11.4	47.7	12.6	54.9	14.5	64.0	16.9	67.8	17.9	61.3	16.2
Mature bulls													
636	1400	30.3	8.0	32.6	8.6	37.5	9.9	44.3	11.7	50.7	13.4	71.9	19.0
727+	1600+	32.9	8.7	35.6	9.4	40.9	10.8	47.7	12.6	54.9	14.5	78.0	20.6

[a]Water intake of a given class of cattle in a specific management regime is a function of dry matter intake and ambient temperature. Water intake is quite constant up to 40° F (4.4° C).

[b]Dry matter intake has a major influence on water intake. Heavier cows are assumed to be higher in body condition and to require less dry matter and, thus, less water intake.

APPENDIX TABLE 12

Nutrient requirements of breeding cattle (metric) (from 1984 NRC on beef)

Weight[a], kg	Daily Gain[b], kg	Daily DM[c], kg	Energy — Daily — ME, Mcal	TDN, kg	NEm, Mcal	NEg, Mcal	Energy — In Diet DM — ME, Mcal/kg	TDN, %	NEm, Mcal/kg	NEg, Mcal/kg	Total Protein — Daily, g	DM, %	Calcium (In Diet) — Daily, g	DM, %	Phosphorus — Daily, g	DM, %	Vitamin A[d] — Daily, 1000 IU
Pregnant yearling heifers—Last third of pregnancy																	
325	0.4	7.1	14.2	3.9	8.04	NA[e]	2.00	55.2	1.15	NA[e]	591	8.4	19	0.27	14	0.20	20
325	0.6	7.3	15.7	4.3	8.04	0.77	2.15	59.3	1.29	0.72	649	8.9	23	0.32	15	0.21	20
325	0.8	7.3	17.2	4.8	8.04	1.67	2.35	64.9	1.47	0.88	697	9.5	27	0.37	16	0.22	20
350	0.4	7.5	14.8	4.1	8.38	NA	1.99	55.0	1.14	NA	616	8.3	20	0.27	15	0.21	21
350	0.6	7.7	16.5	4.6	8.38	0.81	2.14	59.1	1.28	0.71	674	8.8	24	0.32	16	0.21	22
350	0.8	7.8	18.1	5.0	8.38	1.76	2.34	64.6	1.46	0.88	720	9.3	27	0.35	17	0.22	22
375	0.4	7.8	15.5	4.3	8.71	NA	1.98	54.7	1.13	NA	641	8.2	21	0.27	15	0.19	22
375	0.6	8.1	17.2	4.8	8.71	0.86	2.13	58.8	1.27	0.70	697	8.6	25	0.31	17	0.21	23
375	0.8	8.2	19.0	5.2	8.71	1.86	2.32	64.1	1.45	0.86	743	9.1	27	0.33	18	0.22	23
400	0.4	8.2	16.1	4.5	9.04	NA	1.97	54.4	1.12	NA	664	8.1	22	0.27	16	0.20	23
400	0.6	8.5	18.0	5.0	9.04	0.90	2.12	58.6	1.26	0.69	721	8.5	25	0.30	18	0.21	24
400	0.8	8.6	19.8	5.5	9.04	1.95	2.31	63.8	1.44	0.85	764	8.9	28	0.33	18	0.20	24
425	0.4	8.6	16.8	4.6	9.36	NA	1.96	54.1	1.11	NA	687	8.0	23	0.27	17	0.20	24
425	0.6	8.9	18.7	5.2	9.36	0.94	2.11	58.3	1.25	0.69	743	8.4	26	0.30	18	0.20	25
425	0.8	9.0	20.7	5.7	9.36	2.04	2.30	63.5	1.43	0.84	786	8.8	28	0.31	19	0.21	25
450	0.4	8.9	17.3	4.8	9.67	NA	1.95	53.9	1.10	NA	710	8.0	23	0.26	18	0.20	25
450	0.6	9.2	19.4	5.4	9.67	0.98	2.10	58.0	1.25	0.68	765	8.3	26	0.29	19	0.21	26
450	0.8	9.4	21.5	5.9	9.67	2.13	2.29	63.3	1.42	0.84	807	8.6	28	0.30	20	0.21	26
Dry pregnant mature cows—Middle third of pregnancy																	
350	0.0	6.8	11.9	3.3	6.23	NA	1.76	48.6	0.92	NA	478	7.1	12	0.16	12	0.18	19
400	0.0	7.5	13.1	3.6	6.89	NA	1.76	48.6	0.92	NA	525	7.0	13	0.17	13	0.17	21
450	0.0	8.2	14.3	4.0	7.52	NA	1.76	48.6	0.92	NA	570	7.0	15	0.17	15	0.18	23
500	0.0	8.8	15.5	4.3	8.14	NA	1.76	48.6	0.92	NA	614	7.0	17	0.19	17	0.19	25
550	0.0	9.5	16.7	4.6	8.75	NA	1.76	48.6	0.92	NA	657	6.9	18	0.19	18	0.19	27
600	0.0	10.1	17.8	4.9	9.33	NA	1.76	48.6	0.92	NA	698	6.9	20	0.20	20	0.20	28
650	0.0	10.7	18.9	5.2	9.91	NA	1.76	48.6	0.92	NA	739	6.9	22	0.21	22	0.21	30
Dry pregnant mature cows—Last third of pregnancy																	
350	0.4	7.4	14.7	4.1	8.38	NA	1.98	54.7	1.13	NA	609	8.2	20	0.27	15	0.20	21
400	0.4	8.2	16.0	4.4	9.04	NA	1.96	54.1	1.11	NA	657	8.0	22	0.27	16	0.20	23
450	0.4	8.9	17.2	4.8	9.67	NA	1.94	53.6	1.10	NA	703	7.9	23	0.26	18	0.21	24
500	0.4	9.5	18.3	5.1	10.29	NA	1.92	53.1	1.08	NA	746	7.8	25	0.26	20	0.21	27
550	0.4	10.2	19.5	5.4	10.90	NA	1.91	52.8	1.07	NA	790	7.8	26	0.25	21	0.21	29
600	0.4	10.8	20.6	5.7	11.48	NA	1.90	52.5	1.06	NA	832	7.7	28	0.26	23	0.21	30
650	0.4	11.5	21.7	6.0	12.06	NA	1.89	52.2	1.05	NA	872	7.6	30	0.26	25	0.22	32
Two-year-old heifers nursing calves—First 3–4 months postpartum—5.0 kg milk/d																	
300	0.2	6.9	16.6	4.6	9.30[f]	0.72	2.41	66.6	1.53	0.93	814[g]	11.8	26	0.38	17	0.25	27
325	0.2	7.3	17.4	4.8	9.64[f]	0.77	2.37	65.5	1.49	0.90	841[g]	11.5	27	0.37	18	0.25	28
350	0.2	7.8	18.1	5.0	9.98[f]	0.81	2.34	64.6	1.46	0.88	866[g]	11.2	27	0.35	19	0.24	30
375	0.2	8.2	18.9	5.2	10.31[f]	0.86	2.31	63.8	1.44	0.85	892[g]	10.9	28	0.34	19	0.23	32

APPENDIX TABLE 12 (Cont.)

Weight[a], kg	Daily Gain[b], kg	Daily DM[c], kg	Energy Daily ME, Mcal	Energy Daily TDN, kg	Energy Daily NEm, Mcal	Energy Daily NEg, Mcal	In Diet DM ME, Mcal/kg	In Diet DM TDN, %	In Diet DM NEm, Mcal/kg	In Diet DM NEg, Mcal/kg	Total Protein Daily, g	Total Protein DM, %	Calcium Daily, g	Calcium DM, %	Phosphorus Daily, g	Phosphorus DM, %	Vitamin A[d] Daily, 1000 IU
400	0.2	8.6	19.7	5.4	10.64[f]	0.90	2.29	63.3	1.42	0.84	916[g]	10.7	28	0.33	20	0.23	34
425	0.2	9.0	20.4	5.6	10.96[f]	0.94	2.27	62.7	1.40	0.82	939[g]	10.5	29	0.32	21	0.23	35
450	0.2	9.4	21.1	5.8	11.27[f]	0.98	2.25	62.2	1.38	0.80	963[g]	10.3	29	0.31	22	0.23	37
Cows nursing calves—Average milking ability—First 3–4 months postpartum—5.0 kg milk/d																	
350	0.0	7.7	16.6	4.6	9.98	NA	2.15	59.4	1.29	NA	814[g]	10.6	23	0.30	18	0.23	30
400	0.0	8.5	17.9	4.9	10.64[f]	NA	2.11	58.3	1.25	NA	864[g]	10.2	25	0.29	19	0.22	33
450	0.0	9.2	19.1	5.3	11.27[f]	NA	2.08	57.5	1.23	NA	911[g]	9.9	26	0.28	21	0.23	36
500	0.0	9.9	20.3	5.6	11.89[f]	NA	2.05	56.6	1.20	NA	957[g]	9.7	28	0.28	22	0.22	39
550	0.0	10.6	21.5	5.9	12.50[f]	NA	2.03	56.1	1.18	NA	1001[g]	9.5	29	0.27	24	0.23	41
600	0.0	11.2	22.6	6.2	13.08[f]	NA	2.01	55.5	1.16	NA	1044[g]	9.3	31	0.28	26	0.23	44
650	0.0	11.9	23.9	6.6	13.66[f]	NA	2.00	55.3	1.15	NA	1086[g]	9.1	33	0.28	27	0.23	46
Cows nursing calves—Superior milking ability—First 3–4 months postpartum—10.0 kg milk/d																	
350	0.0	6.2	18.5	5.1	13.73[f]	NA	3.00	82.9	2.03	NA	1009[g]	16.4	36	0.58	24	0.39	24
400	0.0	7.6	21.4	5.9	14.39[f]	NA	2.80	77.4	1.86	NA	1099[g]	14.4	37	0.49	25	0.33	30
450	0.0	9.1	23.2	6.4	15.02[f]	NA	2.56	70.7	1.66	NA	1186[g]	13.1	39	0.43	26	0.29	35
500	0.0	10.0	24.6	6.8	15.64[f]	NA	2.45	67.7	1.56	NA	1246[g]	12.4	40	0.40	28	0.28	39
550	0.0	10.9	25.8	7.1	16.25[f]	NA	2.38	65.8	1.50	NA	1299[g]	12.0	42	0.39	30	0.27	42
600	0.0	11.6	27.0	7.5	16.83[f]	NA	2.32	64.1	1.45	NA	1348[g]	11.6	43	0.37	31	0.27	45
650	0.0	12.4	28.2	7.8	17.41[f]	NA	2.28	63.0	1.41	NA	1394[g]	11.3	45	0.36	33	0.26	48
Bulls, maintenance and regaining body condition																	
<650 For growth and development use requirements for bulls in Appendix Tables 8, 9, and 10																	
650	0.4	12.3	24.3	6.7	9.91	2.06	1.98	54.8	1.13	0.57	904	7.4	25	0.20	23	0.19	48
650	0.6	12.6	26.7	7.4	9.91	3.21	2.11	58.4	1.25	0.69	957	7.6	27	0.21	24	0.19	49
650	0.8	12.8	28.7	7.9	9.91	4.40	2.24	62.0	1.37	0.79	998	7.8	29	0.23	25	0.20	50
700	0.4	13.0	25.7	7.1	10.48	2.18	1.98	54.8	1.13	0.57	942	7.3	26	0.20	25	0.20	51
700	0.6	13.4	28.2	7.8	10.48	3.40	2.11	58.4	1.25	0.69	994	7.4	29	0.22	26	0.20	52
700	0.8	13.5	30.3	8.4	10.48	4.66	2.24	62.0	1.37	0.79	1032	7.6	30	0.22	26	0.19	53
800	0.0	12.9	22.6	6.3	11.58	NA	1.75	48.4	0.91	NA	882	6.8	27	0.21	27	0.21	50
800	0.2	13.7	25.5	7.1	11.58	1.12	1.86	51.5	1.02	0.47	956	7.0	27	0.20	27	0.20	53
900	0.0	14.1	24.7	6.8	12.65	NA	1.75	48.4	0.91	NA	958	6.8	30	0.21	30	0.21	55
900	0.2	15.0	27.9	7.7	12.65	1.23	1.86	51.5	1.02	0.47	1031	6.9	31	0.21	31	0.21	58
1000	0.0	15.3	26.8	7.4	13.69	NA	1.75	48.4	0.91	NA	1032	6.8	33	0.22	33	0.22	60

[a] Average weight for a feeding period.

[b] Approximately 0.4 ± 0.1 kg of weight gain/d over the last third of pregnancy is accounted for by the products of conception. Daily 2.15 Mcal of NEm and 55 g of protein are provided for this requirement for a calf with a birth weight of 36 kg.

[c] Dry matter consumption should vary depending on the energy concentration of the diet and environmental conditions. These intakes are based on the energy concentration shown in the table and assuming a thermoneutral environment without snow or mud conditions. If the energy concentrations of the diet to be fed exceed the tabular value, limit feeding may be required.

[d] Vitamin A requirements per kilogram of diet are 2800 IU for pregnant heifers and cows and 3900 IU for lactating cows and breeding bulls.

[e] Not applicable.

[f] Includes 0.75 Mcal NEm/kg of milk produced.

[g] Includes 33.5 g protein/kg of milk produced.

APPENDIX TABLE 13

Daily nutrient requirements of growing dairy cattle and mature bulls (from 1989 NRC on dairy)

Live Weight, kg	Gain, g	Dry Matter Intake[a], kg	NEm, Mcal	NEg, Mcal	ME, Mcal	DE, Mcal	TDN, kg	UIP, g	DIP, g	CP, g	Ca, g	P, g	A, 1000 IU	D, 1000 IU
					Energy				Protein		Minerals		Vitamins	
Growing large-breed calves fed only milk or milk replacer														
40	200	0.48	1.37	0.41	2.54	2.73	0.62	—	—	105	7	4	1.70	0.26
45	300	0.54	1.49	0.56	2.86	3.07	0.70	—	—	120	8	5	1.94	0.30
Growing large-breed calves fed milk plus starter mix														
50	500	1.30	1.62	0.72	5.90	6.42	1.46	—	—	290	9	6	2.10	0.33
75	800	1.98	2.19	1.30	8.98	9.78	2.22	—	—	435	16	8	3.20	0.50
Growing small-breed calves fed only milk or milk replacer														
25	200	0.38	0.96	0.37	2.01	2.16	0.49	—	—	84	6	4	1.10	0.16
30	300	0.51	1.10	0.52	2.70	2.90	0.66	—	—	112	7	4	1.30	0.20
Growing small-breed calves fed milk plus starter mix														
50	500	1.43	1.62	0.72	6.49	7.06	1.60	—	—	315	10	6	2.10	0.33
75	600	1.76	2.19	0.96	7.98	8.69	1.97	—	—	387	14	8	3.20	0.50
Growing veal calves fed only milk or milk replacer														
40	200	0.45	1.37	0.55	1.89	2.07	0.47	—	—	100	7	4	1.70	0.26
50	400	0.57	1.62	0.57	2.39	2.63	0.59	—	—	125	9	5	2.10	0.33
60	540	0.80	1.85	0.81	2.84	3.17	0.71	—	—	176	13	8	2.60	0.40
75	900	1.36	2.19	1.47	4.82	5.39	1.21	—	—	300	16	9	3.20	0.50
100	1,250	2.00	2.72	2.26	6.22	7.06	1.58	—	—	440	20	11	4.20	0.66
125	1,250	2.38	3.21	2.44	7.40	8.40	1.88	—	—	524	22	13	5.30	0.82
150	1,100	2.72	3.69	2.29	8.46	9.60	2.15	—	—	598	24	15	6.40	0.99
Large-breed growing females														
100	600	2.63	2.72	1.22	7.03	8.13	1.84	317	57	421	17	9	4.24	0.66
100	700	2.82	2.72	1.44	7.54	8.72	1.98	346	75	452	18	9	4.24	0.66
100	800	3.02	2.72	1.66	8.06	9.32	2.11	374	92	483	18	10	4.24	0.66
150	600	3.51	3.69	1.45	9.14	10.61	2.41	283	150	562	19	11	6.36	0.99
150	700	3.75	3.69	1.71	9.76	11.33	2.57	307	173	600	19	12	6.36	0.99
150	800	3.99	3.69	1.97	10.39	12.07	2.74	331	196	639	20	12	6.36	0.99
200	600	4.39	4.57	1.65	11.14	12.99	2.95	254	239	631	20	14	8.48	1.32
200	700	4.68	4.57	1.95	11.87	13.84	3.14	274	267	686	21	14	8.48	1.32
200	800	4.97	4.57	2.25	12.62	14.71	3.34	294	295	741	22	15	8.48	1.32
250	600	5.31	5.41	1.84	13.10	15.33	3.48	229	326	637	22	16	10.60	1.65
250	700	5.65	5.41	2.18	13.94	16.32	3.70	246	359	678	23	17	10.60	1.65
250	800	5.99	5.41	2.51	14.79	17.32	3.93	263	393	726	24	17	10.60	1.65
300	600	6.26	6.20	2.02	15.05	17.69	4.01	209	413	752	23	17	12.72	1.98
300	700	6.66	6.20	2.39	16.00	18.81	4.27	223	452	799	24	18	12.72	1.98
300	800	7.06	6.20	2.77	16.97	19.95	4.52	236	490	848	25	19	12.72	1.98
350	600	7.29	6.96	2.20	17.01	20.09	4.56	193	501	874	24	18	14.84	2.31
350	700	7.75	6.96	2.60	18.09	21.36	4.84	204	545	930	25	19	14.84	2.31
350	800	8.21	6.96	3.01	19.18	22.64	5.14	214	590	985	26	20	14.84	2.31
400	600	8.39	7.69	2.37	19.03	22.58	5.12	182	592	1007	25	19	16.96	2.64
400	700	8.92	7.69	2.80	20.23	24.00	5.44	190	641	1070	26	20	16.96	2.64
400	800	9.46	7.69	3.24	21.44	25.44	5.77	198	692	1135	26	21	16.96	2.64
450	600	9.59	8.40	2.53	21.12	25.18	5.71	176	686	1151	28	19	19.08	2.97
450	700	10.20	8.40	2.99	22.46	26.78	6.07	182	742	1224	28	20	19.08	2.97
450	800	10.82	8.40	3.46	23.81	28.40	6.44	187	799	1298	29	21	19.08	2.97
500	600	10.93	9.09	2.69	23.32	27.96	6.34	175	785	1311	28	20	21.20	3.30
500	700	11.63	9.09	3.18	24.81	29.74	6.75	179	848	1395	28	20	21.20	3.30
500	800	12.33	9.09	3.68	26.32	31.55	7.16	182	913	1480	29	21	21.20	3.30
550	600	12.42	9.77	2.84	25.67	30.95	7.02	180	891	1490	28	20	23.32	3.63
550	700	13.22	9.77	3.37	27.33	32.95	7.47	183	963	1587	28	20	23.32	3.63
550	800	14.04	9.77	3.90	29.02	34.99	7.94	185	1035	1685	29	21	23.32	3.63
600	600	14.11	10.43	3.00	28.23	34.24	7.77	193	1007	1694	28	20	25.44	3.96
600	700	15.05	10.43	3.55	30.09	36.50	8.28	194	1088	1805	28	21	25.44	3.96
600	800	15.99	10.43	4.11	31.98	38.79	8.80	195	1170	1919	29	21	25.44	3.96
Small-breed growing females														
100	400	2.41	2.72	0.91	6.34	7.35	1.67	249	38	386	15	8	4.24	0.66
100	500	2.64	2.72	1.16	6.92	8.03	1.82	275	59	422	16	8	4.24	0.66
100	600	2.86	2.72	1.40	7.51	8.71	1.98	300	80	458	17	9	4.24	0.66
150	400	3.31	3.69	1.09	8.39	9.78	2.22	222	129	512	17	10	6.36	0.99
150	500	3.60	3.69	1.39	9.12	10.63	2.41	243	156	567	18	11	6.36	0.99
150	600	3.89	3.69	1.69	9.86	11.50	2.61	263	185	622	19	11	6.36	0.99
200	400	4.24	4.57	1.26	10.38	12.16	2.76	201	217	513	19	13	8.48	1.32

Live Weight, kg	Gain, g	Dry Matter Intake[a], kg	NEm, Mcal	NEg, Mcal	ME, Mcal	DE, Mcal	TDN, kg	UIP, g	DIP, g	CP, g	Ca, g	P, g	A, 1000 IU	D, 1000 IU
			Energy					Protein			Minerals		Vitamins	
200	500	4.60	4.57	1.60	11.25	13.19	2.99	217	251	562	20	13	8.48	1.32
200	600	4.96	4.57	1.95	12.14	14.23	3.23	232	286	611	20	14	8.48	1.32
250	400	5.24	5.41	1.41	12.36	14.57	3.30	185	305	629	21	15	10.60	1.65
250	500	5.68	5.41	1.80	13.38	15.78	3.58	197	346	681	21	16	10.60	1.65
250	600	6.12	5.41	2.20	14.43	17.01	3.86	209	389	735	22	16	10.60	1.65
300	400	6.34	6.20	1.56	14.38	17.06	3.87	176	395	761	22	16	12.72	1.98
300	500	6.87	6.20	1.99	15.57	18.48	4.19	184	445	824	23	17	12.72	1.98
300	600	7.40	6.20	2.43	16.79	19.92	4.52	192	495	888	23	17	12.72	1.98
350	400	7.57	6.96	1.71	16.50	19.71	4.47	173	490	909	23	17	14.84	2.31
350	500	8.20	6.96	2.18	17.87	21.35	4.84	178	548	985	23	18	14.84	2.31
350	600	8.85	6.96	2.66	19.28	23.03	5.22	183	608	1062	24	18	14.84	2.31
400	400	8.98	7.69	1.84	18.77	22.58	5.12	177	592	1078	24	18	16.96	2.64
400	500	9.74	7.69	2.35	20.36	24.50	5.56	181	661	1169	24	19	16.96	2.64
400	600	10.52	7.69	2.87	21.98	26.45	6.00	183	730	1263	25	19	16.96	2.64
450	400	10.64	8.40	1.98	21.27	25.80	5.85	191	706	1276	27	18	19.08	2.97
450	500	11.56	8.40	2.52	23.12	28.04	6.36	193	786	1387	28	19	19.08	2.97
450	600	12.50	8.40	3.08	25.01	30.33	6.88	194	867	1500	28	19	19.08	2.97
Large-breed growing males														
100	800	2.80	2.72	1.42	7.48	8.66	1.96	401	65	448	18	10	4.24	0.66
100	900	2.97	2.72	1.60	7.92	9.16	2.08	433	79	475	19	10	4.24	0.66
100	1000	3.13	2.72	1.79	8.36	9.67	2.19	465	93	501	20	11	4.24	0.66
150	800	3.60	3.69	1.64	9.52	11.03	2.50	364	155	576	20	12	6.36	0.99
150	900	3.80	3.69	1.85	10.03	11.63	2.64	393	172	607	21	13	6.36	0.99
150	1000	3.99	3.69	2.07	10.55	12.22	2.77	422	190	639	22	13	6.36	0.99
200	800	4.43	4.57	1.84	11.48	13.34	3.03	333	241	709	22	15	8.48	1.32
200	900	4.66	4.57	2.08	12.06	14.02	3.18	359	262	745	23	15	8.48	1.32
200	1000	4.89	4.57	2.33	12.66	14.71	3.34	385	284	782	24	16	8.48	1.32
250	800	5.27	5.41	2.03	13.37	15.58	3.53	305	325	778	24	17	10.60	1.65
250	900	5.53	5.41	2.30	14.03	16.35	3.71	329	350	837	25	18	10.60	1.65
250	1000	5.80	5.41	2.57	14.70	17.13	3.89	352	375	897	26	18	10.60	1.65
300	800	6.13	6.20	2.21	15.22	17.80	4.04	281	408	771	25	19	12.72	1.98
300	900	6.43	6.20	2.51	15.96	18.66	4.23	302	436	827	25	19	12.72	1.98
300	1000	6.73	6.20	2.80	16.70	19.53	4.43	323	464	884	26	20	12.72	1.98
350	800	7.02	6.96	2.38	17.06	20.02	4.54	261	490	843	26	20	14.84	2.31
350	900	7.36	6.96	2.70	17.88	20.98	4.76	280	522	883	26	20	14.84	2.31
350	1000	7.70	6.96	3.02	18.70	21.94	4.98	298	554	924	27	21	14.84	2.31
400	800	7.96	7.69	2.55	18.91	22.27	5.05	244	572	955	26	21	16.96	2.64
400	900	8.34	7.69	2.89	19.80	23.32	5.29	260	608	1001	27	21	16.96	2.64
400	1000	8.72	7.69	3.24	20.71	24.39	5.53	277	644	1046	28	22	16.96	2.64
450	800	8.95	8.40	2.71	20.78	24.56	5.57	230	656	1074	29	21	19.08	2.97
450	900	9.37	8.40	3.08	21.76	25.72	5.83	245	696	1125	29	22	19.08	2.97
450	1000	9.80	8.40	3.44	22.75	26.89	6.10	259	736	1176	29	23	19.08	2.97
500	800	10.00	9.09	2.87	22.69	26.92	6.11	220	742	1201	29	21	21.20	3.30
500	900	10.48	9.09	3.25	23.76	28.19	6.39	233	786	1257	29	22	21.20	3.30
500	1000	10.95	9.09	3.64	24.84	29.47	6.68	246	830	1314	29	23	21.20	3.30
550	800	11.14	9.77	3.02	24.66	29.38	6.66	213	831	1336	29	21	23.32	3.63
550	900	11.66	9.77	3.43	25.82	30.76	6.98	225	879	1399	29	22	23.32	3.63
550	1000	12.19	9.77	3.84	27.00	32.16	7.29	236	927	1463	30	23	23.32	3.63
600	800	12.36	10.43	3.17	26.71	31.95	7.25	211	923	1483	29	21	25.44	3.96
600	900	12.95	10.43	3.60	27.97	33.47	7.59	221	976	1554	29	22	25.44	3.96
600	1000	13.54	10.43	4.03	29.25	34.99	7.94	231	1029	1624	30	23	25.44	3.96
650	800	13.69	11.07	3.32	28.86	34.67	7.86	212	1020	1643	29	21	27.56	4.29
650	900	14.35	11.07	3.77	30.24	36.33	8.24	222	1078	1722	29	22	27.56	4.29
650	1000	15.01	11.07	4.22	31.63	38.00	8.62	230	1137	1801	30	23	27.56	4.29
700	800	15.16	11.70	3.46	31.14	37.59	8.52	219	1124	1820	29	22	29.68	4.62
700	900	15.90	11.70	3.93	32.64	39.40	8.94	227	1187	1907	29	22	29.68	4.62
700	1000	16.63	11.70	4.40	34.16	41.23	9.35	235	1252	1996	30	23	29.68	4.62
750	800	16.79	12.33	3.60	33.59	40.73	9.24	232	1235	2015	29	22	31.80	4.95
750	900	17.62	12.33	4.09	35.23	42.73	9.69	239	1305	2114	29	23	31.80	4.95
750	1000	18.45	12.33	4.58	36.89	44.74	10.15	246	1376	2213	30	23	31.80	4.95
800	800	17.56	12.94	3.74	35.12	42.59	9.66	216	1303	2107	29	22	33.92	5.28
800	900	18.41	12.94	4.25	36.83	44.67	10.13	221	1377	2210	29	23	33.92	5.28
800	1000	19.28	12.94	4.76	38.55	46.76	10.61	227	1451	2313	30	23	33.92	5.28

Live Weight, kg	Gain, g	Dry Matter Intake[a], kg	Energy					Protein			Minerals		Vitamins	
			NEm, Mcal	NEg, Mcal	ME, Mcal	DE, Mcal	TDN, kg	UIP, g	DIP, g	CP, g	Ca, g	P, g	A, 1000 IU	D, 1000 IU
Small-breed growing males														
100	500	2.45	2.72	1.02	6.54	7.56	1.72	287	41	392	16	8	4.24	0.66
100	600	2.64	2.72	1.23	7.04	8.15	1.85	316	58	422	17	9	4.24	0.66
100	700	2.83	2.72	1.45	7.55	8.74	1.98	345	75	453	18	9	4.24	0.66
150	500	3.28	3.69	1.20	8.55	9.92	2.25	257	129	525	18	11	6.36	0.99
150	600	3.52	3.69	1.46	9.16	10.64	2.41	282	151	563	19	11	6.36	0.99
150	700	3.76	3.69	1.71	9.78	11.36	2.58	306	174	601	19	12	6.36	0.99
200	500	4.12	4.57	1.37	10.45	12.18	2.76	232	213	573	20	13	8.48	1.32
200	600	4.40	4.57	1.66	11.17	13.02	2.95	252	241	629	20	14	8.48	1.32
200	700	4.69	4.57	1.96	11.90	13.87	3.15	273	268	684	21	14	8.48	1.32
250	500	4.99	5.41	1.53	12.31	14.41	3.27	210	296	598	21	16	10.60	1.65
250	600	5.32	5.41	1.86	13.14	15.38	3.49	228	328	638	22	16	10.60	1.65
250	700	5.66	5.41	2.19	13.97	16.35	3.71	245	361	679	23	17	10.60	1.65
300	500	5.89	6.20	1.68	14.15	16.64	3.77	193	378	707	23	17	12.72	1.98
300	600	6.28	6.20	2.04	15.09	17.74	4.02	207	415	754	23	17	12.72	1.98
300	700	6.68	6.20	2.41	16.04	18.85	4.28	221	453	801	24	18	12.72	1.98
350	500	6.86	6.96	1.82	16.01	18.91	4.29	180	461	823	23	18	14.84	2.31
350	600	7.31	6.96	2.22	17.06	20.15	4.57	191	503	877	24	18	14.84	2.31
350	700	7.76	6.96	2.62	18.13	21.41	4.86	203	547	932	25	19	14.84	2.31
400	500	7.90	7.69	1.96	17.91	21.25	4.82	171	545	947	24	19	16.96	2.64
400	600	8.41	7.69	2.39	19.08	22.64	5.14	180	594	1010	25	19	16.96	2.64
400	700	8.94	7.69	2.82	20.27	24.06	5.46	189	644	1073	26	20	16.96	2.64
450	500	9.03	8.40	2.10	19.87	23.70	5.37	166	634	1083	28	19	19.08	2.97
450	600	9.62	8.40	2.55	21.18	25.26	5.73	174	689	1155	28	19	19.08	2.97
450	700	10.23	8.40	3.01	22.51	26.84	6.09	180	744	1227	28	20	19.08	2.97
500	500	10.28	9.09	2.23	21.93	26.29	5.96	167	726	1233	28	19	21.20	3.30
500	600	10.96	9.09	2.71	23.39	28.04	6.36	173	788	1315	28	20	21.20	3.30
500	700	11.65	9.09	3.20	24.87	29.81	6.76	177	851	1398	28	20	21.20	3.30
550	500	11.67	9.77	2.36	24.12	29.08	6.60	174	825	1400	28	19	23.32	3.63
550	600	12.46	9.77	2.87	25.75	31.05	7.04	178	895	1495	28	20	23.32	3.63
550	700	13.26	9.77	3.39	27.40	33.03	7.49	181	966	1591	28	20	23.32	3.63
600	500	13.25	10.43	2.48	26.50	32.14	7.29	187	933	1590	28	19	25.44	3.96
600	600	14.16	10.43	3.02	28.32	34.35	7.79	190	1012	1699	28	20	25.44	3.96
600	700	15.08	10.43	3.57	30.17	36.59	8.30	192	1091	1810	28	21	25.44	3.96
Maintenance of mature breeding bulls														
500	—	7.89	9.09	—	15.79	19.15	4.34	161	472	789	20	12	21.20	3.30
600	—	9.05	10.43	—	18.10	21.95	4.98	155	573	905	24	15	25.44	3.96
700	—	10.16	11.70	—	20.32	24.64	5.59	148	670	1016	28	18	29.68	4.62
800	—	11.23	12.94	—	22.46	27.24	6.18	142	764	1123	32	20	33.92	5.28
900	—	12.27	14.13	—	24.53	29.76	6.75	135	854	1227	36	22	38.16	5.94
1000	—	13.28	15.29	—	26.55	32.20	7.30	129	943	1328	41	25	42.40	6.60
1100	—	14.26	16.43	—	28.52	34.59	7.85	122	1029	1426	45	28	46.64	7.26
1200	—	15.22	17.53	—	30.44	36.92	8.37	115	1113	1522	49	30	50.88	7.92
1300	—	16.16	18.62	—	32.32	39.21	8.89	108	1196	1616	53	32	55.12	8.58
1400	—	17.09	19.68	—	34.17	41.45	9.40	102	1277	1709	57	35	59.36	9.24

Note: The following abbreviations were used: NEm, net energy for maintenance; NEg, net energy for gain; ME, metabolizable energy; DE, digestible energy; TDN, total digestible nutrients; UIP, undegraded intake protein; DIP, degraded intake protein; CP, crude protein.

[a]The data for DMI are not requirements per se, unlike the requirements for net energy maintenance, net energy gain, and absorbed protein. They are not intended to be estimates of voluntary intake but are consistent with the specified dietary energy concentrations. The use of diets with decreased energy concentrations will increase dry-matter intake needs; metabolizable energy, digestible energy, and total digestible nutrient needs; and crude protein needs. The use of diets with increased energy concentrations will have opposite effects on these needs.

APPENDIX TABLE 14

Daily nutrient requirements of lactating and pregnant cows

Live Weight, kg	Energy				Total Crude Protein, g	Minerals		Vitamins	
	NEℓ, Mcal	ME, Mcal	DE, Mcal	TDN, kg		Ca, g	P, g	A, 1000 IU	D, 1000 IU
Maintenance of mature lactating cows[a]									
400	7.16	12.01	13.80	3.13	318	16	11	30	12
450	7.82	13.12	15.08	3.42	341	18	13	34	14
500	8.46	14.20	16.32	3.70	364	20	14	38	15
550	9.09	15.25	17.53	3.97	386	22	16	42	17
600	9.70	16.28	18.71	4.24	406	24	17	46	18
650	10.30	17.29	19.86	4.51	428	26	19	49	20
700	10.89	18.28	21.00	4.76	449	28	20	53	21
750	11.47	19.25	22.12	5.02	468	30	21	57	23
800	12.03	20.20	23.21	5.26	486	32	23	61	24
Maintenance plus last 2 months of gestation of mature dry cows[b]									
400	9.30	15.26	18.23	4.15	890	26	16	30	12
450	10.16	16.66	19.91	4.53	973	30	18	34	14
500	11.00	18.04	21.55	4.90	1,053	33	20	38	15
550	11.81	19.37	23.14	5.27	1,131	36	22	42	17
600	12.61	20.68	24.71	5.62	1,207	39	24	46	18
650	13.39	21.96	26.23	5.97	1,281	43	26	49	20
700	14.15	23.21	27.73	6.31	1,355	46	28	53	21
750	14.90	24.44	29.21	6.65	1,427	49	30	57	23
800	15.64	25.66	30.65	6.98	1,497	53	32	61	24
Milk production—nutrients/kg of milk of different fat percentages (Fat %)									
3.0	0.64	1.07	1.23	0.280	78	2.73	1.68	—	—
3.5	0.69	1.15	1.33	0.301	84	2.97	1.83	—	—
4.0	0.74	1.24	1.42	0.322	90	3.21	1.98	—	—
4.5	0.78	1.32	1.51	0.343	96	3.45	2.13	—	—
5.0	0.83	1.40	1.61	0.364	101	3.69	2.28	—	—
5.5	0.88	1.48	1.70	0.385	107	3.93	2.43	—	—
Liveweight change during lactation—nutrients/kg of weight change[c]									
Weight loss	−4.92	−8.25	−9.55	−2.17	−320	—	—	—	—
Weight gain	5.12	8.55	9.96	2.26	320	—	—	—	—

Note: The following abbreviations were used: NEℓ, net energy for lactation; ME, metabolizable energy; DE, digestible energy; TDN, total digestible nutrients.

[a]To allow for growth of young lactating cows, increase the maintenance allowances for all nutrients except vitamins A and D by 20% during the first lactation and 10% during the second lactation.

[b]Values for calcium assume that the cow is in calcium balance at the beginning of the last 2 months of gestation. If the cow is not in balance, then the calcium requirement can be increased from 25 to 33%.

[c]No allowance is made for mobilized calcium and phosphorus associated with liveweight loss or with liveweight gain. The maximum daily nitrogen available from weight loss is assumed to be 30 g or 234 g of crude protein.

Daily nutrient requirements of lactating cows using absorbable protein (from 1989 NRC on dairy)

Live Weight, kg	Fat, %	Milk, kg	Live Weight Change, kg	Dry Matter Intake, kg	Energy			Protein		Minerals	
					NEℓ, Mcal/kg DM	NEℓ, Mcal	TDN, kg	UIP, g	DIP, g	Ca, g	P, g
Intake at 100% of the requirement for maintenance, lactation, and weight gain											
400	4.5	8.0	0.220	10.14	1.43	14.55	6.44	511	753	44	28
400	4.5	14.0	0.220	12.66	1.52	19.26	8.48	710	1052	65	41
400	4.5	20.0	0.220	14.91	1.61	23.96	10.51	880	1355	85	54
400	4.5	26.0	0.220	16.94	1.69	28.67	12.54	1026	1662	106	67
400	4.5	32.0	0.220	19.41	1.72	33.37	14.58	1220	1962	127	80
400	5.0	8.0	0.220	10.36	1.44	14.94	6.60	525	778	46	30
400	5.0	14.0	0.220	13.00	1.53	19.93	8.77	730	1096	68	43
400	5.0	20.0	0.220	15.35	1.62	24.93	10.93	902	1419	90	57
400	5.0	26.0	0.220	17.44	1.72	29.92	13.07	1048	1745	112	71
400	5.0	32.0	0.220	20.30	1.72	34.91	15.25	1277	2061	134	84
400	5.5	8.0	0.220	10.57	1.45	15.32	6.77	538	803	48	31
400	5.5	14.0	0.220	13.33	1.55	20.61	9.07	748	1140	71	45
400	5.5	20.0	0.220	15.77	1.64	25.89	11.34	923	1483	95	60
400	5.5	26.0	0.220	18.13	1.72	31.17	13.62	1091	1826	118	75
400	5.5	32.0	0.220	21.20	1.72	36.45	15.92	1334	2160	142	89
500	4.0	9.0	0.275	11.59	1.42	16.49	7.30	540	883	49	32
500	4.0	17.0	0.275	14.78	1.51	22.38	9.86	797	1257	75	48
500	4.0	25.0	0.275	17.62	1.61	28.27	12.40	1015	1635	101	64
500	4.0	33.0	0.275	20.14	1.70	34.15	14.93	1201	2018	126	80
500	4.0	41.0	0.275	23.29	1.72	40.04	17.49	1453	2392	152	95
500	4.5	9.0	0.275	11.84	1.43	16.92	7.49	556	911	51	33
500	4.5	17.0	0.275	15.20	1.53	23.20	10.21	821	1310	79	50
500	4.5	25.0	0.275	18.16	1.62	29.47	12.92	1043	1715	107	68
500	4.5	33.0	0.275	20.79	1.72	35.74	15.61	1230	2124	134	85
500	4.5	41.0	0.275	24.44	1.72	42.02	18.35	1526	2519	162	102
500	5.0	9.0	0.275	12.08	1.44	17.36	7.68	571	939	53	35
500	5.0	17.0	0.275	15.60	1.54	24.01	10.57	844	1364	83	53
500	5.0	25.0	0.275	18.68	1.64	30.67	13.44	1069	1795	113	71
500	5.0	33.0	0.275	21.71	1.72	37.33	16.31	1289	2226	142	89
500	5.0	41.0	0.275	25.58	1.72	43.99	19.21	1599	2646	172	108
600	3.0	10.0	0.330	12.52	1.42	17.79	7.87	533	974	52	34
600	3.0	20.0	0.330	16.20	1.49	24.18	10.67	845	1375	79	51
600	3.0	30.0	0.330	19.37	1.58	30.58	13.43	1102	1784	106	68
600	3.0	40.0	0.330	22.21	1.67	36.98	16.19	1323	2198	133	84
600	3.0	50.0	0.330	25.23	1.72	43.38	18.95	1565	2608	161	101
600	3.5	10.0	0.330	12.86	1.42	18.27	8.08	557	1004	54	35
600	3.5	20.0	0.330	16.70	1.51	25.15	11.08	874	1438	84	54
600	3.5	30.0	0.330	20.04	1.60	32.03	14.06	1137	1879	113	72
600	3.5	40.0	0.330	23.00	1.69	38.90	17.01	1360	2326	143	90
600	3.5	50.0	0.330	26.63	1.72	45.78	20.00	1654	2763	173	109
600	4.0	10.0	0.330	13.20	1.42	18.75	8.30	581	1034	56	37
600	4.0	20.0	0.330	17.19	1.52	26.11	11.50	902	1501	89	57
600	4.0	30.0	0.330	20.69	1.62	33.47	14.68	1170	1975	121	77
600	4.0	40.0	0.330	23.78	1.72	40.83	17.84	1395	2454	153	96
600	4.0	50.0	0.330	28.03	1.72	48.19	21.05	1744	2918	185	116
700	3.0	12.0	0.385	14.46	1.42	20.54	9.09	607	1154	61	40
700	3.0	24.0	0.385	18.75	1.50	28.21	12.44	968	1638	94	60
700	3.0	36.0	0.385	22.48	1.60	35.89	15.76	1269	2129	127	81
700	3.0	48.0	0.385	25.80	1.69	43.57	19.05	1525	2627	159	101
700	3.0	60.0	0.385	29.81	1.72	51.25	22.39	1857	3114	192	121
700	3.5	12.0	0.385	14.86	1.42	21.11	9.34	636	1190	64	42
700	3.5	24.0	0.385	19.34	1.52	29.37	12.94	1002	1713	100	64
700	3.5	36.0	0.385	23.26	1.62	37.62	16.50	1309	2244	135	86
700	3.5	48.0	0.385	26.72	1.72	45.88	20.04	1567	2781	171	108
700	3.5	60.0	0.385	31.48	1.72	54.13	23.65	1964	3300	207	130
700	4.0	12.0	0.385	15.20	1.43	21.69	9.60	658	1227	67	44
700	4.0	24.0	0.385	19.92	1.53	30.52	13.44	1035	1789	105	68

Live Weight, kg	Fat, %	Milk, kg	Live Weight Change, kg	Dry Matter Intake, kg	Energy NEℓ, Mcal/kg DM	Energy NEℓ, Mcal	Energy TDN, kg	Protein UIP, g	Protein DIP, g	Minerals Ca, g	Minerals P, g
700	4.0	36.0	0.385	24.02	1.64	39.35	17.25	1347	2359	144	91
700	4.0	48.0	0.385	28.03	1.72	48.19	21.05	1648	2930	182	115
700	4.0	60.0	0.385	33.16	1.72	57.02	24.91	2071	3485	221	139
800	3.0	14.0	0.440	16.36	1.42	23.24	10.29	682	1331	71	46
800	3.0	27.0	0.440	20.93	1.51	31.56	13.91	1064	1857	106	68
800	3.0	40.0	0.440	24.95	1.60	39.88	17.50	1388	2390	142	90
800	3.0	53.0	0.440	28.54	1.69	48.20	21.08	1665	2928	177	112
800	3.0	66.0	0.440	32.87	1.72	56.51	24.69	2022	3457	213	134
800	3.5	14.0	0.440	16.78	1.42	23.92	10.58	710	1374	74	49
800	3.5	27.0	0.440	21.59	1.52	32.86	14.47	1102	1942	113	72
800	3.5	40.0	0.440	25.82	1.62	41.80	18.33	1432	2517	151	96
800	3.5	53.0	0.440	29.57	1.72	50.75	22.17	1711	3099	190	120
800	3.5	66.0	0.440	34.72	1.72	59.69	26.07	2140	3661	228	144
800	4.0	14.0	0.440	17.17	1.43	24.59	10.88	734	1418	77	51
800	4.0	27.0	0.440	22.24	1.54	34.16	15.03	1139	2027	119	76
800	4.0	40.0	0.440	26.66	1.64	43.73	19.16	1474	2644	161	102
800	4.0	53.0	0.440	31.00	1.72	53.29	23.28	1800	3263	203	128
800	4.0	66.0	0.440	36.56	1.72	62.86	27.46	2259	3865	244	154

Intake at 85% of the requirement for maintenance and lactation

Live Weight, kg	Fat, %	Milk, kg	Live Weight Change, kg	Dry Matter Intake, kg	Energy NEℓ, Mcal/kg DM	Energy NEℓ, Mcal	Energy TDN, kg	Protein UIP, g	Protein DIP, g	Minerals Ca, g	Minerals P, g
400	4.5	20.0	−0.696	11.62	1.67	19.41	8.49	687	1066	85	54
400	4.5	26.0	−0.840	14.02	1.67	23.41	10.24	931	1310	106	67
400	4.5	32.0	−0.983	16.41	1.67	27.41	11.99	1187	1554	127	80
400	5.0	20.0	−0.726	12.11	1.67	20.23	8.85	720	1118	90	57
400	5.0	26.0	−0.878	14.65	1.67	24.47	10.71	987	1377	112	71
400	5.0	32.0	−1.030	17.20	1.67	28.72	12.56	1255	1635	134	84
400	5.5	20.0	−0.755	12.60	1.67	21.05	9.21	761	1169	95	60
400	5.5	26.0	−0.916	15.29	1.67	25.54	11.17	1042	1443	118	75
400	5.5	32.0	−1.077	17.98	1.67	30.03	13.14	1323	1717	142	89
500	4.0	25.0	−0.819	13.67	1.67	22.83	9.99	810	1286	101	64
500	4.0	33.0	−0.998	16.67	1.67	27.83	12.18	1134	1590	126	80
500	4.0	41.0	−1.178	19.66	1.67	32.84	14.37	1458	1894	152	95
500	4.5	25.0	−0.856	14.28	1.67	23.85	10.44	864	1350	107	68
500	4.5	33.0	−1.047	17.48	1.67	29.18	12.77	1205	1674	134	85
500	4.5	41.0	−1.238	20.67	1.67	34.52	15.10	1546	1998	162	102
500	5.0	25.0	−0.892	14.89	1.67	24.87	10.88	917	1414	113	71
500	5.0	33.0	−1.095	18.28	1.67	30.53	13.36	1275	1758	142	89
500	5.0	41.0	−1.298	21.67	1.67	36.19	15.83	1633	2103	172	108
600	3.0	30.0	−0.881	14.71	1.67	24.56	10.74	860	1399	106	68
600	3.0	40.0	−1.076	17.96	1.67	30.00	13.12	1223	1728	133	84
600	3.0	50.0	−1.271	21.22	1.67	35.44	15.50	1585	2057	161	101
600	3.5	30.0	−0.925	15.44	1.67	25.79	11.28	924	1476	113	72
600	3.5	40.0	−1.135	18.94	1.67	31.63	13.84	1308	1830	143	90
600	3.5	50.0	−1.344	22.44	1.67	37.48	16.40	1692	2184	173	109
600	4.0	30.0	−0.969	16.17	1.67	27.01	11.82	988	1552	121	77
600	4.0	40.0	−1.193	19.92	1.67	33.27	14.55	1393	1932	153	96
600	4.0	50.0	−1.418	23.67	1.67	39.52	17.29	1798	2311	185	116
700	3.0	36.0	−1.034	17.26	1.67	28.83	12.61	1054	1669	127	81
700	3.0	48.0	−1.268	21.17	1.67	35.36	15.47	1489	2064	159	101
700	3.0	60.0	−1.502	25.08	1.67	41.88	18.32	1924	2458	192	121
700	3.5	36.0	−1.087	18.15	1.67	30.30	13.26	1131	1761	135	86
700	3.5	48.0	−1.339	22.35	1.67	37.32	16.33	1591	2186	171	108
700	3.5	60.0	−1.590	26.55	1.67	44.34	19.40	2052	2611	207	130
700	4.0	36.0	−1.140	19.03	1.67	31.78	13.90	1208	1853	144	91
700	4.0	48.0	−1.409	23.52	1.67	39.28	17.19	1694	2308	182	115
700	4.0	60.0	−1.678	28.02	1.67	46.79	20.47	2180	2764	221	139
800	3.0	40.0	−1.147	19.15	1.67	31.98	13.99	1176	1871	142	90
800	3.0	50.0	−1.342	22.41	1.67	37.42	16.37	1538	2200	169	107
800	3.0	60.0	−1.537	25.66	1.67	42.86	18.75	1900	2529	196	124
800	3.5	40.0	−1.206	20.13	1.67	33.62	14.71	1261	1973	151	96

Live Weight, kg	Fat, %	Milk, kg	Live Weight Change, kg	Dry Matter Intake, kg	Energy			Protein		Minerals	
					NEℓ, Mcal/kg DM	NEℓ, Mcal	TDN, kg	UIP, g	DIP, g	Ca, g	P, g
800	3.5	50.0	−1.416	23.63	1.67	39.46	17.27	1645	2327	181	114
800	3.5	60.0	−1.625	27.13	1.67	45.31	19.82	2028	2682	211	133
800	4.0	40.0	−1.264	21.11	1.67	35.25	15.42	1346	2075	161	102
800	4.0	50.0	−1.489	24.86	1.67	41.51	18.16	1751	2455	193	122
800	4.0	60.0	−1.713	28.60	1.67	47.76	20.90	2156	2835	225	142

Note: The following abbreviations were used: NEℓ, Mcal/kg DM net energy for lactation/kg of dry matter; NEℓ, net energy for lactation; TDN, total digestible nutrients; UIP, undegraded intake protein; DIP, degraded intake protein.

APPENDIX TABLE 16

Dry-matter intake requirements to fulfill nutrient allowances for maintenance, milk production, and normal liveweight gain during mid- and late lactation (from 1989 NRC on dairy)

4% FCM,[a] kg	Live Weight,[b,c] kg				
	400	500	600	700	800
10	2.7	2.4	2.2	2.0	1.9
15	3.2	2.8	2.6	2.3	2.2
20	3.6	3.2	2.9	2.6	2.4
25	4.0	3.5	3.2	2.9	2.7
30	4.4	3.9	3.5	3.2	2.9
35	5.0	4.2	3.7	3.4	3.1
40	5.5	4.6	4.0	3.6	3.3
45	—	5.0	4.3	3.8	3.5
50	—	5.4	4.7	4.1	3.7
55	—	—	5.0	4.4	4.0
60	—	—	5.4	4.8	4.3

Note: The following assumptions were made in calculating DMI requirements shown in this table:

1. The reference cow used for the calculations weighed 600 kg and produced milk with 4% milk fat. Other live weights in the table and corresponding fat percentages were 400 kg and 5%; 500 kg and 4.5%; and 700 and 800 kg and 3.5% fat.

2. The concentrations of energy in the diet for the cow was 1.42 Mcal of NEℓ/kg of DM for milk yields equal to or less than 10 kg/d. It increased linearly to 1.72 Mcal of NEℓ/kg for milk yields equal to or greater than 40 kg/d.

3. The energy concentrations of the diets for all other cows were assumed to change linearly as their energy requirements for milk production, relative to maintenance, changed in a manner identical to that of the 600-kg cow as she increased in milk yield from 10 to 40 kg/d.

4. Enough DM to provide sufficient energy for cows to gain 0.055% of their body weight daily was also included in the total. If cows do not consume as much DM as they require, as calculated in this table, their energy intake will be less than their requirements. The result will be a loss of body weight, reduced milk yields, or both. If cows consume more DM than what is projected as required from the table, the energy concentration of their diet should be reduced or they may become overly fat.

[a]4% fat-corrected milk (kg) = (0.4) (kg of milk) + (15) (kg of milk fat).

[b]The probable DMI may be up to 18% less in early lactation.

[c]DMI as a percentage of live weight may be 0.02% less per 1% increase in diet moisture content above 50% if fermented feeds constitute a major portion of the diet.

APPENDIX 17

Recommended nutrient content of diets for dairy cattle (from 1989 NRC on dairy)

Cow weights, fat, gain, and corresponding milk yields for lactating cow diets

Cow wt, kg	Fat, %	Wt gain, kg/d	Lactating Cow Diets, Milk Yield, kg/d (1)	(2)	(3)	(4)	(5)
400	5.0	0.220	7	13	20	26	33
500	4.5	0.275	8	17	25	33	41
600	4.0	0.330	10	20	30	40	50
700	3.5	0.385	12	24	36	48	60
800	3.5	0.440	13	27	40	53	67

Recommended nutrient content

Nutrient	Lactating Cow Diets (1)	(2)	(3)	(4)	(5)	Early lactation, wks 0–3	Dry, pregnant cows	Calf milk replacer	Calf starter mix	Growing Heifers and Bulls[a] 3–6 mos	6–12 mos	12 mos	Mature bulls	Maximum tolerable levels[b,c]
Energy														
NEℓ, Mcal/kg	1.42	1.52	1.62	1.72	1.72	1.67	1.25	—	—	—	—	—	—	—
NEm, Mcal/kg	—	—	—	—	—	—	—	2.40	1.90	1.70	1.58	1.40	1.15	—
NEg, Mcal/kg	—	—	—	—	—	—	—	1.55	1.20	1.08	0.98	0.82	—	—
ME, Mcal/kg	2.35	2.53	2.71	2.89	2.89	2.80	2.04	3.78	3.11	2.60	2.47	2.27	2.00	—
DE, Mcal/kg	2.77	2.95	3.13	3.31	3.31	3.22	2.47	4.19	3.53	3.02	2.89	2.69	2.43	—
TDN, % of DM	63	67	71	75	75	73	56	95	80	69	66	61	55	—
Protein equivalent														
Crude protein, %	12	15	16	17	18	19	12	22	18	16	12	12	10	—
UIP, %	4.4	5.2	5.7	5.9	6.2	7.0	—	—	—	8.2	4.4	2.1	—	—
DIP, %	7.8	8.7	9.6	10.3	10.4	9.7	—	—	—	4.6	6.4	7.2	—	—
Fiber content (min.)[d]														
Crude fiber, %	17	17	17	15	15	17	22	—	—	13	15	15	15	—
Acid detergent fiber, %	21	21	21	19	19	21	27	—	—	16	19	19	19	—
Neutral detergent fiber, %	28	28	28	25	25	28	35	—	—	23	25	25	25	—
Ether extract (min.), %	3	3	3	3	3	3	3	10	3	3	3	3	3	—
Minerals														
Calcium, %	0.43	0.51	0.58	0.64	0.66	0.77	0.39[c]	0.70	0.60	0.52	0.41	0.29	0.30	2.00
Phosphorus, %	0.28	0.33	0.37	0.41	0.41	0.48	0.24	0.60	0.40	0.31	0.30	0.23	0.19	1.00
Magnesium, %[f]	0.20	0.20	0.20	0.25	0.25	0.25	0.16	0.07	0.10	0.16	0.16	0.16	0.16	0.50
Potassium, %[g]	0.90	0.90	0.90	1.00	1.00	1.00	0.65	0.65	0.65	0.65	0.65	0.65	0.65	3.00
Sodium, %	0.18	0.18	0.18	0.18	0.18	0.18	0.10	0.10	0.10	0.10	0.10	0.10	0.10	—
Chlorine, %	0.25	0.25	0.25	0.25	0.25	0.25	0.20	0.20	0.20	0.20	0.20	0.20	0.20	—
Sulfur, %	0.20	0.20	0.20	0.20	0.20	0.25	0.16	0.29	0.20	0.16	0.16	0.16	0.16	0.40
Iron, ppm	50	50	50	50	50	50	50	100	50	50	50	50	50	1000
Cobalt, ppm	0.10	0.10	0.10	0.10	0.10	0.10	0.10	0.10	0.10	0.10	0.10	0.10	0.10	10.00
Copper, ppm[h]	10	10	10	10	10	10	10	10	10	10	10	10	10	100
Manganese, ppm	40	40	40	40	40	40	40	40	40	40	40	40	40	1000
Zinc, ppm	40	40	40	40	40	40	40	40	40	40	40	40	40	500
Iodine, ppm[i]	0.60	0.60	0.60	0.60	0.60	0.60	0.25	0.25	0.25	0.25	0.25	0.25	0.25	50.00[j]
Selenium, ppm	0.30	0.30	0.30	0.30	0.30	0.30	0.30	0.30	0.30	0.30	0.30	0.30	0.30	2.00

Vitamins[k]												
A, IU/kg	3200	3200	3200	4000	4000	3800	2200	2200	2200	2200	3200	66,000
D, IU/kg	1000	1000	1000	1000	1200	600	300	300	300	300	300	10,000
E, IU/kg	15	15	15	15	15	40	25	25	25	25	15	2000

Note: The values presented in this table are intended as guidelines for the use of professionals in diet formulation. Because of the many factors affecting such values, they are not intended and should not be used as a legal or regulatory base.

a The approximate weight for growing heifer and bulls at 3–6 mos is 150 kg; at 6–12 mos, it is 250 kg; and at more than 12 mos, it is 400 kg. The approximate average daily gain is 700 g/d.

b The maximum safe levels for many of the mineral elements are not well defined and may be substantially affected by specific feeding conditions. Additional information is available in *Mineral Tolerance of Domestic Animals* (NRC, 1980).

c Vitamin tolerances are discussed in detail in *Vitamin Tolerance of Animals* (NRC, 1987).

d It is recommended that 75% of the NDF in lactating cow diets be provided as forage. If this recommendation is not followed, a depression in milk fat may occur.

e The value for calcium assumes that the cow is in calcium balance at the beginning of the dry period. If the cow is not in balance, then the dietary calcium requirement should be increased by 25–33%.

f Under conditions conducive to grass tetany (see text), magnesium should be increased to 0.25 or 0.30 %.

g Under conditions of heat stress, potassium should be increased to 1.2 %.

h The cow's copper requirement is influenced by molybdenum and sulfur in the diet.

i If the diet contains as much as 25 % strongly goitrogenic feed on a dry basis, the iodine provided should be increased two times or more.

j Although cattle can tolerate this level of iodine, lower levels may be desirable to reduce the iodine content of milk.

k The following minimum quantities of B-complex vitamins are suggested per unit of milk replacer: niacin, 2.6 ppm; pantothenic acid, 13 ppm; riboflavin, 6.5 ppm; pyridoxine, 6.5 ppm; folic acid, 0.5 ppm; biotin, 0.1 ppm; vitamin B_{12}, 0.07 ppm; thiamin, 6.5 ppm; and choline, 0.26 %. It appears that adequate amounts of these vitamins are furnished when calves have functional rumens (usually at 6 weeks of age) by a combination of rumen synthesis and natural feedstuffs.

APPENDIX TABLE 18

Daily nutrient requirements of sheep (100% dry matter basis) (from 1985 NRC on sheep)

Body Weight		Gain or Loss		Dry Matter[a]			Energy			Total Protein, g	DP,[c] g	Grams DP per Mcal DE	Nutrients per Animal		Caro-tene, mg	Vita-min A, IU	Vita-min D, IU
				Per Animal		% Live Wt	TDN, kg	DE,[b] Mcal	ME, Mcal				Ca, g	P, g			
kg	lb	g	lb	kg	lb												
Ewes[d]																	
Maintenance																	
50	110	10	0.02	1.0	2.2	2.0	0.55	2.42	1.98	89	48	20	3.0	2.8	1.9	1275	278
60	132	10	0.02	1.1	2.4	1.8	0.61	2.68	2.20	98	53	20	3.1	2.9	2.2	1530	333
70	154	10	0.02	1.2	2.6	1.7	0.66	2.90	2.38	107	58	20	3.2	3.0	2.6	1785	388
80	176	10	0.02	1.3	2.9	1.6	0.72	3.17	2.60	116	63	20	3.3	3.1	3.0	2040	444
Nonlactating and first 15 weeks of gestation																	
50	110	30	0.07	1.1	2.4	2.2	0.60	2.64	2.16	99	54	20	3.0	2.8	1.9	1275	278
60	132	30	0.07	1.3	2.9	2.1	0.72	3.17	2.60	117	64	20	3.1	2.9	2.2	1530	333
70	154	30	0.07	1.4	3.1	2.0	0.77	3.39	2.78	126	69	20	3.2	3.0	2.6	1785	388
80	176	30	0.07	1.5	3.3	1.9	0.82	3.61	2.96	135	74	20	3.3	3.1	3.0	2040	444
Last 6 weeks of gestation or last 8 weeks of lactation suckling singles[e]																	
50	110	175(+45)	0.39	1.7	3.7	3.3	0.99	4.36	3.58	158	88	20	4.1	3.9	6.2	4250	278
60	132	180(+45)	0.40	1.9	4.2	3.2	1.10	4.84	3.97	177	99	20	4.4	4.1	7.5	5100	333
70	154	185(+45)	0.41	2.1	4.6	3.0	1.22	5.37	4.40	195	109	20	4.5	4.3	8.8	5950	388
80	176	190(+45)	0.42	2.2	4.8	2.8	1.28	5.63	4.62	205	114	20	4.8	4.5	10.0	6800	444
First 8 weeks of lactation suckling singles or last 8 weeks of lactation suckling twins[f]																	
50	110	−25(+80)	−0.06	2.1	4.6	4.2	1.36	5.98	4.90	218	130	22	10.9	7.8	6.2	4250	278
60	132	−25(+80)	−0.06	2.3	5.1	3.9	1.50	6.60	5.41	239	143	22	11.5	8.2	7.5	5100	333
70	154	−25(+80)	−0.06	2.5	5.5	3.6	1.63	7.17	5.88	260	155	22	12.0	8.6	8.8	5950	388
80	176	−25(+80)	−0.06	2.6	5.7	3.2	1.69	7.44	6.10	270	161	22	12.6	9.0	10.0	6800	444
First 8 weeks of lactation suckling twins																	
50	110	−60	−0.13	2.4	5.3	4.8	1.56	6.86	5.63	276	173	25	12.5	8.9	6.2	4250	278
60	132	−60	−0.13	2.6	5.7	4.3	1.69	7.44	6.10	299	187	25	13.0	9.4	7.5	5100	333
70	154	−60	−0.13	2.8	6.2	4.0	1.82	8.01	6.57	322	202	25	13.4	9.5	8.8	5950	388
80	176	−60	−0.13	3.0	6.6	3.7	1.95	8.58	7.04	345	216	25	14.4	10.2	10.0	6800	444
Replacement lambs and yearlings[g]																	
30	66	180	0.40	1.3	2.9	4.3	0.81	3.56	2.92	130	75	21	5.9	3.3	1.9	1275	166
40	88	120	0.26	1.4	3.1	3.5	0.82	3.61	2.96	133	74	20	6.1	3.4	2.5	1700	222
50	110	80	0.18	1.5	3.3	3.0	0.83	3.65	2.99	133	73	20	6.3	3.5	3.1	2125	278
60	132	40	0.09	1.5	3.3	2.5	0.82	3.61	2.96	133	72	20	6.5	3.6	3.8	2550	333

Rams

Replacement lambs and yearlings[g]																	
40	88	250	0.55	1.8	4.0	4.5	1.17	5.15	4.22	184	108	21	6.3	3.5	2.5	1700	222
60	132	200	0.44	2.3	5.1	3.8	1.38	6.07	4.98	219	122	20	7.2	4.0	3.8	2550	333
80	176	150	0.33	2.8	6.2	3.5	1.54	6.78	5.56	249	134	20	7.9	4.4	5.0	3400	444
100	220	100	0.22	2.8	6.2	2.8	1.54	6.78	5.56	249	134	20	8.3	4.6	6.2	4250	555
120	265	50	0.11	2.6	5.7	2.2	1.43	6.29	5.16	231	125	20	8.5	4.7	7.5	5100	666
Lambs																	
Finishing[h]																	
30	66	200	0.44	1.3	2.9	4.3	0.83	3.65	2.99	143	87	24	4.8	3.0	1.1	765	166
35	77	220	0.48	1.4	3.1	4.0	0.94	4.14	3.39	154	94	23	4.8	3.0	1.3	892	194
40	88	250	0.55	1.6	3.5	4.0	1.12	4.93	4.04	176	107	22	5.0	3.1	1.5	1020	222
45	99	250	0.55	1.7	3.7	3.8	1.19	5.24	4.30	187	114	22	5.0	3.1	1.7	1148	250
50	110	220	0.48	1.8	4.0	3.6	1.26	5.54	4.54	198	121	22	5.0	3.1	1.9	1275	278
55	121	200	0.44	1.9	4.2	3.5	1.33	5.85	4.80	209	127	22	5.0	3.1	2.1	1402	305
Early-weaned[i]																	
10	22	250	0.55	0.6	1.3	6.0	0.44	1.94	1.59	96	69	36	2.4	1.6	1.2	850	67
20	44	275	0.60	1.0	2.2	5.0	0.73	3.21	2.63	160	115	36	3.6	2.4	2.5	1700	133
30	66	300	0.66	1.4	3.1	4.7	1.02	4.49	3.68	196	133	30	5.0	3.3	3.8	2550	200

[a] To convert dry matter to an as-fed basis, divide dry matter by percentage of dry matter.

[b] 1 kg TDN = 4.4 Mcal DE (digestible energy). DE may be converted to ME (metabolizable energy) by multiplying by 82%.

[c] DP = digestible protein.

[d] Values are for ewes in moderate condition, not excessively fat or thin. Fat ewes should be fed at the next lower weight, thin ewes at the next higher weight. Once maintenance weight is established, such weight would follow through all production phases.

[e] Values in parentheses are for ewes suckling singles last 8 weeks of lactation.

[f] Values in parentheses are for ewes suckling twins last 8 weeks of lactation.

[g] Requirements for replacement lambs (ewe and ram) start when the lambs are weaned.

[h] Maximum gains expected. If lambs are held for later market, they should be fed as replacement ewe lambs are fed. Lambs capable of gaining faster than indicated should be fed at a higher level. Lambs finish at the maximum rate if they are self-fed.

[i] A 40-kg early-weaned lamb should be fed the same as a finishing lamb of the same weight.

APPENDIX TABLE 19

Nutrient content of diets for sheep (nutrient concentration in diet dry matter) (from 1985 NRC on sheep)

Body Weight		Daily Gain or Loss		Daily Dry Matter[a]			Energy			Total Protein, %	DP,[c] %	Ca, %	P, %	Carotene, mg/kg	Vitamin A, IU/kg	Vitamin D, IU/kg
				Per Animal		% Live Wt	TDN, kg	DE,[b] Mcal/kg	ME, Mcal/kg							
kg	lb	g	lb	kg	lb											
Ewes[d]																
Maintenance																
50	110	10	0.02	1.0	2.2	2.0	55	2.4	2.0	8.9	4.8	0.30	0.28	1.9	1275	278
60	132	10	0.02	1.1	2.4	1.8	55	2.4	2.0	8.9	4.8	0.28	0.26	2.0	1391	303
70	154	10	0.02	1.2	2.6	1.7	55	2.4	2.0	8.9	4.8	0.27	0.25	2.2	1488	323
80	176	10	0.02	1.3	2.9	1.6	55	2.4	2.0	8.9	4.8	0.25	0.24	2.3	1569	342
Nonlactating and first 15 weeks of gestation																
50	110	30	0.07	1.1	2.4	2.2	55	2.4	2.0	9.0	4.9	0.27	0.25	1.7	1159	253
60	132	30	0.07	1.3	2.9	2.1	55	2.4	2.0	9.0	4.9	0.24	0.22	1.7	1177	256
70	154	30	0.07	1.4	3.1	2.0	55	2.4	2.0	9.0	4.9	0.23	0.21	1.9	1275	277
80	176	30	0.07	1.5	3.3	1.9	55	2.4	2.0	9.0	4.9	0.22	0.21	2.0	1369	296
Last 6 weeks of gestation or last 8 weeks of lactation suckling singles[e]																
50	110	175(+45)	0.39	1.7	3.7	3.3	58	2.6	2.1	9.3	5.2	0.24	0.23	3.6	2500	164
60	132	180(+45)	0.40	1.9	4.2	3.2	58	2.6	2.1	9.3	5.2	0.23	0.22	3.9	2684	175
70	154	185(+45)	0.41	2.1	4.6	3.0	58	2.6	2.1	9.3	5.2	0.21	0.20	4.2	2833	185
80	176	190(+45)	0.42	2.2	4.8	2.8	56	2.6	2.1	9.3	5.2	0.21	0.20	4.5	3091	202
First 8 weeks of lactation suckling singles or last 8 weeks of lactation suckling twins[f]																
50	110	−25(+80)	−0.06	2.1	4.6	4.2	65	2.9	2.4	10.4	6.2	0.52	0.37	3.0	2024	132
60	132	−25(+80)	−0.06	2.3	5.1	3.9	65	2.9	2.4	10.4	6.2	0.50	0.36	3.3	2217	145
70	154	−25(+80)	−0.06	2.5	5.5	3.6	65	2.9	2.4	10.4	6.2	0.48	0.34	3.5	2380	155
80	176	−25(+80)	−0.06	2.6	5.7	3.2	65	2.9	2.4	10.4	6.2	0.48	0.34	3.8	2615	171
First 8 weeks of lactation suckling twins																
50	110	−60	−0.13	2.4	5.3	4.8	65	2.9	2.4	11.5	7.2	0.52	0.37	2.6	1771	116
60	132	−60	−0.13	2.6	5.7	4.3	65	2.9	2.4	11.5	7.2	0.50	0.36	2.9	1962	128
70	154	−60	−0.13	2.8	6.2	4.0	65	2.9	2.4	11.5	7.2	0.48	0.34	3.1	2125	139
80	176	−60	−0.13	3.0	6.6	3.7	65	2.9	2.4	11.5	7.2	0.48	0.34	3.3	2267	148
Replacement lambs and yearlings[g]																
30	66	180	0.40	1.3	2.9	4.3	62	2.7	2.2	10.0	5.8	0.45	0.25	1.5	981	128
40	88	120	0.26	1.4	3.1	3.5	60	2.6	2.1	9.5	5.3	0.44	0.24	1.8	1214	159
50	110	80	0.18	1.5	3.3	3.0	55	2.4	2.0	8.9	4.8	0.42	0.23	2.1	1417	185
60	132	40	0.09	1.5	3.3	2.5	55	2.4	2.0	8.9	4.8	0.43	0.24	2.5	1700	222

Rams

Replacement lambs and yearlings[g]

40	88	250	0.55	1.8	4.0	4.5	65	2.9	2.4	10.2	6.0	0.35	0.19	1.4	944	123
60	132	200	0.44	2.3	5.1	3.8	60	2.6	2.1	9.5	5.3	0.31	0.17	1.7	1109	145
80	176	150	0.33	2.8	6.2	3.5	55	2.4	2.0	8.9	4.8	0.28	0.16	1.8	1214	159
100	220	100	0.22	2.8	6.2	2.8	55	2.4	2.0	8.9	4.8	0.30	0.17	2.2	1518	198
120	265	50	0.11	2.6	5.7	2.2	55	2.4	2.0	8.9	4.8	0.33	0.18	2.9	1962	256

Lambs

Finishing[h]

30	66	200	0.44	1.3	2.9	4.3	64	2.8	2.3	11.0	6.7	0.37	0.23	0.8	588	128
35	77	220	0.48	1.4	3.1	4.0	67	3.0	2.4	11.0	6.7	0.34	0.21	0.9	637	139
40	88	250	0.55	1.6	3.5	4.0	70	3.1	2.5	11.0	6.7	0.31	0.19	0.9	638	139
45	99	250	0.55	1.7	3.7	3.8	70	3.1	2.5	11.0	6.7	0.29	0.18	1.0	675	147
50	110	220	0.48	1.8	4.0	3.6	70	3.1	2.5	11.0	6.7	0.28	0.17	1.1	708	154
55	121	200	0.44	1.9	4.2	3.5	70	3.1	2.5	11.0	6.7	0.26	0.16	1.1	738	161

Early-weaned[i]

10	22	250	0.55	0.6	1.3	6.0	73	3.2	2.6	16.0	11.5	0.40	0.27	2.0	1417	112
20	44	275	0.60	1.0	2.2	5.0	73	3.2	2.6	16.0	11.5	0.36	0.24	2.5	1700	133
30	66	300	0.66	1.4	3.1	4.7	73	3.2	2.6	14.0	9.5	0.36	0.24	2.7	1821	143

[a] To convert dry matter to an as-fed basis, divide dry matter by percentage of dry matter.

[b] 1 kg TDN = 4.4 Mcal DE (digestible energy). DE may be converted to ME (metabolizable energy) by multiplying by 82%. Because of rounding errors, calculations between Appendix Table 18 and 19 may not give the same values.

[c] DP = digestible protein.

[d] Values are for ewes in moderate condition, not excessively fat or thin. Fat ewes should be fed at the next lower weight, thin ewes at the next higher weight. Once maintenance weight is established, such weight would follow through all production phases.

[e] Values in parentheses are for ewes suckling singles last 8 weeks of lactation.

[f] Values in parentheses are for ewes suckling twins last 8 weeks of lactation.

[g] Requirements for replacement lambs (ewe and ram) start when the lambs are weaned.

[h] Maximum gains expected. If lambs are held for later market, they should be fed as replacement ewe lambs are fed. Lambs capable of gaining faster than indicated should be fed at a higher level. Lambs finish at the maximum rate if they are self-fed.

[i] A 40-kg early-weaned lamb should be fed the same as a finishing lamb of the same weight.

APPENDIX TABLE 20

Yearly dry matter, energy, and protein requirements of 60-kg ewe[a] (from 1975 NRC on sheep)

	Maintenance, 15 wk	Early Gestation, 15 wk	Late Gestation, 6 wk	Early Lactation, 8 wk[b]		Late Lactation, 8 wk[b]		Yearly Total
Dry matter, kg/day	1.1	1.3	1.9	2.3 2.6	(S) (T)	1.9 2.3	(S) (T)	
kg/period	115.5	136.5	79.8	128.8 145.6	(S) (T)	106.4 128.8	(S) (T)	567.0 606.2
Metabolizable energy, Mcal/day	2.20	2.60	3.97	5.41 6.10	(S) (T)	3.97 5.41	(S) (T)	
Mcal/period	231.0	273.0	166.7	303.0 341.6	(S) (T)	222.3 303.0	(S) (T)	1196.0 1312.3
Digestible protein, g/day	53	64	99	143 187	(S) (T)	99 143	(S) (T)	
kg/period	5.6	6.7	4.2	8.0 10.5	(S) (T)	5.5 8.0	(S) (T)	30.0 35.0

[a]Refer to Fig. 1 in the NRC publication for daily and cumulative weight changes.

[b]S = ewes suckling singles; T = ewes suckling twins.

APPENDIX TABLE 21

Daily nutrient requirements of goats (from 1981 NRC on goats)

Body weight, kg	Feed Energy				Crude protein		Ca, g	P, g	Vita-min A, 1000 IU	Vita-min D, IU	Dry Matter per Animal			
											1 kg = 2.0 Mcal ME		1 kg = 2.4 Mcal ME	
	TDN, g	DE, Mcal	ME, Mcal	NE, Mcal	TP, g	DP, g					Total, kg	% of BW	Total, kg	% of BW
Maintenance only (includes stable feeding conditions, minimal activity, and early pregnancy)														
10	159	0.70	0.57	0.32	22	15	1	0.7	0.4	84	0.28	2.8	0.24	2.4
20	267	1.18	0.96	0.54	38	26	1	0.7	0.7	144	0.48	2.4	0.40	2.0
30	362	1.59	1.30	0.73	51	35	2	1.4	0.9	195	0.65	2.2	0.54	1.8
40	448	1.98	1.61	0.91	63	43	2	1.4	1.2	243	0.81	2.0	0.67	1.7
50	530	2.34	1.91	1.08	75	51	3	2.1	1.4	285	0.95	1.9	0.79	1.6
60	608	2.68	2.19	1.23	86	59	3	2.1	1.6	327	1.09	1.8	0.91	1.5
70	682	3.01	2.45	1.38	96	66	4	2.8	1.8	369	1.23	1.8	1.02	1.5
80	754	3.32	2.71	1.53	106	73	4	2.8	2.0	408	1.36	1.7	1.13	1.4
90	824	3.63	2.96	1.67	116	80	4	2.8	2.2	444	1.48	1.6	1.23	1.4
100	891	3.93	3.21	1.81	126	86	5	3.5	2.4	480	1.60	1.6	1.34	1.3
Maintenance plus low activity (= 25% increment, intensive management, tropical range, and early pregnancy)														
10	199	0.87	0.71	0.40	27	19	1	0.7	0.5	108	0.36	3.6	0.30	3.0
20	334	1.47	1.20	0.68	46	32	2	1.4	0.9	180	0.60	3.0	0.50	2.5
30	452	1.99	1.62	0.92	62	43	2	1.4	1.2	243	0.81	2.7	0.67	2.2
40	560	2.47	2.02	1.14	77	54	3	2.1	1.5	303	1.01	2.5	0.84	2.1
50	662	2.92	2.38	1.34	91	63	4	2.8	1.8	357	1.19	2.4	0.99	2.0
60	760	3.35	2.73	1.54	105	73	4	2.8	2.0	408	1.36	2.3	1.14	1.9
70	852	3.76	3.07	1.73	118	82	5	3.5	2.3	462	1.54	2.2	1.28	1.8
80	942	4.16	3.39	1.91	130	90	5	3.5	2.6	510	1.70	2.1	1.41	1.8
90	1030	4.54	3.70	2.09	142	99	6	4.2	2.8	555	1.85	2.1	1.54	1.7
100	1114	4.91	4.01	2.26	153	107	6	4.2	3.0	600	2.00	2.0	1.67	1.7
Maintenance plus medium activity (= 50% increment, semiarid rangeland, slightly hilly pastures, and early pregnancy)														
10	239	1.05	0.86	0.48	33	23	1	0.7	0.6	129	0.43	4.3	0.36	3.6
20	400	1.77	1.44	0.81	55	38	2	1.4	1.1	216	0.72	3.6	0.60	3.0
30	543	2.38	1.95	1.10	74	52	3	2.1	1.5	294	0.98	3.3	0.81	2.7
40	672	2.97	2.42	1.36	93	64	4	2.8	1.8	363	1.21	3.0	1.01	2.5
50	795	3.51	2.86	1.62	110	76	4	2.8	2.1	429	1.43	2.9	1.19	2.4
60	912	4.02	3.28	1.84	126	87	5	3.5	2.5	492	1.64	2.7	1.37	2.3

APPENDIX TABLE 21 (Cont.)

Body weight, kg	Feed Energy				Crude protein		Ca, g	P, g	Vita-min A, 1000 IU	Vita-min D, IU	Dry Matter per Animal			
											1 kg = 2.0 Mcal ME		1 kg = 2.4 Mcal ME	
	TDN, g	DE, Mcal	ME, Mcal	NE, Mcal	TP, g	DP, g					Total, kg	% of BW	Total, kg	% of BW
70	1023	4.52	3.68	2.07	141	98	6	4.2	2.8	552	1.84	2.6	1.53	2.2
80	1131	4.98	4.06	2.30	156	108	6	4.2	3.0	609	2.03	2.5	1.69	2.1
90	1236	5.44	4.44	2.50	170	118	7	4.9	3.3	666	2.22	2.5	1.85	2.0
100	1336	5.90	4.82	2.72	184	128	7	4.9	3.6	723	2.41	2.4	2.01	2.0
Maintenance plus high activity (= 75% increment, arid rangeland, sparse vegetation, mountainous pastures, and early pregnancy)														
10	278	1.22	1.00	0.56	38	26	2	1.4	0.8	150	0.50	5.0	0.42	4.2
20	467	2.06	1.68	0.94	64	45	2	1.4	1.3	252	0.84	4.2	0.70	3.5
30	634	2.78	2.28	1.28	87	60	3	2.1	1.7	342	1.14	3.8	0.95	3.2
40	784	3.46	2.82	1.59	108	75	4	2.8	2.1	423	1.41	3.5	1.18	3.0
50	928	4.10	3.34	1.89	128	89	5	3.5	2.5	501	1.67	3.3	1.39	2.7
60	1064	4.69	3.83	2.15	146	102	6	4.2	2.9	576	1.92	3.2	1.60	2.7
70	1194	5.27	4.29	2.42	165	114	6	4.2	3.2	642	2.14	3.0	1.79	2.6
80	1320	5.81	4.74	2.68	182	126	7	4.9	3.6	711	2.37	3.0	1.98	2.5
90	1442	6.35	5.18	2.92	198	138	8	5.6	3.9	777	2.59	2.9	2.16	2.4
100	1559	6.88	5.62	3.17	215	150	8	5.6	4.2	843	2.81	2.8	2.34	2.3
Additional requirements for late pregnancy (for all goat sizes)														
	100	0.44	0.36	0.20	82	57	2	1.4	1.1	213	0.71		0.59	
Additional requirements for growth—weight gain at 50 g per day (for all goat sizes)														
	100	0.44	0.36	0.20	14	10	1	0.7	0.3	54	0.18		0.15	
Additional requirements for growth—weight gain at 100 g per day (for all goat sizes)														
	200	0.88	0.72	0.40	28	20	1	0.7	0.5	108	0.36		0.30	
Additional requirements for growth—weight gain at 150 g per day (for all goat sizes)														
	300	1.32	1.08	0.60	42	30	2	1.4	0.8	162	0.54		0.45	
Additional requirements for milk production per kg at different fat percentages (including requirements for nursing single, twin, or triplet kids at the respective milk production level) (% Fat)														
2.5	333	1.47	1.20	0.68	59	42	2	1.4	3.8	760				

3.0	337	1.49	1.21	0.68	64	45	2	1.4	3.8	760
3.5	342	1.51	1.23	0.69	68	48	2	1.4	3.8	760
4.0	346	1.53	1.25	0.70	72	51	3	2.1	3.8	760
4.5	351	1.55	1.26	0.71	77	54	3	2.1	3.8	760
5.0	356	1.57	1.28	0.72	82	57	3	2.1	3.8	760
5.5	360	1.59	1.29	0.73	86	60	3	2.1	3.8	760
6.0	365	1.61	1.31	0.74	90	63	3	2.1	3.8	760

Additional requirements for mohair production by Angora at different production levels

Annual Fleece Yield (kg)						
2	16	0.07	0.06	0.03	9	6
4	34	0.15	0.12	0.07	17	12
6	50	0.22	0.18	0.10	26	18
8	66	0.29	0.24	0.14	34	24

APPENDIX TABLE 22

Nutrient requirements of swine allowed feed ad libitum (% or amount/kg of diet, 90% dry-matter basis)[a,b] (from 1988 NRC on swine)

	1–5	5–10	10–20	20–50	50–110
Live weight, kg	1–5	5–10	10–20	20–50	50–110
Expected weight gain, g/d	200	250	450	700	820
Expected feed intake, g/d	250	460	950	1900	3110
Expected efficiency, gain/feed	0.800	0.543	0.474	0.368	0.264
Expected efficiency, feed/gain	1.25	1.84	2.11	2.71	3.79
DE intake, kcal/d	850	1560	3230	6460	10570
ME intake, kcal/d	805	1490	3090	6200	10185
Energy concentration, kcal ME/kg diet	3220	3240	3250	3260	3275
Protein, %	24	20	18	15	13
Indispensable amino acids					
Arginine, %	0.60	0.50	0.40	0.25	0.10
Histidine, %	0.36	0.31	0.25	0.22	0.18
Isoleucine, %	0.76	0.65	0.53	0.46	0.38
Leucine, %	1.00	0.85	0.70	0.60	0.50
Lysine, %	1.40	1.15	0.95	0.75	0.60
Methionine + cystine, %	0.68	0.58	0.48	0.41	0.34
Phenylalanine + tyrosine, %	1.10	0.94	0.77	0.66	0.55
Threonine, %	0.80	0.68	0.56	0.48	0.40
Tryptophan, %	0.20	0.17	0.14	0.12	0.10
Valine, %	0.80	0.68	0.56	0.48	0.40
Linoleic acid, %	0.1	0.1	0.1	0.1	0.1
Mineral elements					
Calcium, %	0.90	0.80	0.70	0.60	0.50
Phosphorus, total, %	0.70	0.65	0.60	0.50	0.40
Phosphorus, available, %	0.55	0.40	0.32	0.23	0.15
Chlorine, %	0.08	0.08	0.08	0.08	0.08
Magnesium, %	0.04	0.04	0.04	0.04	0.04
Potassium, %	0.30	0.28	0.26	0.23	0.17
Sodium, %	0.10	0.10	0.10	0.10	0.10
Copper, mg	6.0	6.0	5.0	4.0	3.0
Iodine, mg	0.14	0.14	0.14	0.14	0.14
Iron, mg	100	100	80	60	40
Manganese, mg	4.0	4.0	3.0	2.0	2.0
Selenium, mg	0.30	0.30	0.25	0.15	0.10
Zinc, mg	100	100	80	60	50
Vitamins					
Vitamin A, IU	2200	2200	1750	1300	1300
Vitamin D, IU	220	220	200	150	150
Vitamin E, IU	16	16	11	11	11
Vitamin K (menadione), mg	0.5	0.5	0.5	0.5	0.5
Biotin, mg	0.08	0.05	0.05	0.05	0.05
Choline, g	0.6	0.5	0.4	0.3	0.3
Folacin, mg	0.3	0.3	0.3	0.3	0.3
Niacin, available, mg	20.0	15.0	12.5	10.0	7.0
Pantothenic acid, mg	12.0	10.0	9.0	8.0	7.0
Riboflavin, mg	4.0	3.5	3.0	2.5	2.0
Thiamin, mg	1.5	1.0	1.0	1.0	1.0
Vitamin B_6, mg	2.0	1.5	1.5	1.0	1.0
Vitamin B_{12}, µg	20.0	17.5	15.0	10.0	5.0

[a]These requirements are based upon the following types of diets: 1–5-kg pigs, a diet containing a substantial amount (25–75%) of milk products; 5–10-kg pigs, a corn-soybean meal diet that includes 5–25% milk products; 10–110 kg pigs, a corn-soybean meal diet. Based upon corn containing 8.5% and soybean meal containing 44% protein.

[b]The requirements listed are based upon the principles and assumptions described in the text of this publication. Knowledge of nutritional constraints and limitations is important for the proper use of this table.

APPENDIX TABLE 23

Daily nutrient intakes and requirements of swine allowed feed ad libitum (from 1988 NRC on swine)

Live weight, kg	1–5	5–10	10–20	20–50	50–110
Expected weight gain, g/d	200	250	450	700	820
Expected feed intake, g/d	250	460	950	1900	3110
Expected efficiency, gain/feed	0.800	0.543	0.474	0.368	0.264
Expected efficiency, feed/gain	1.25	1.84	2.11	2.71	3.79
DE intake, kcal/d	850	1560	3230	6460	10570
ME intake, kcal/d	805	1490	3090	6200	10185
Energy concentration, kcal ME/kg diet	3220	3240	3250	3260	3275
Protein, %	6.0	92.0	171.0	285.0	404.0
Indispensable amino acids					
Arginine, g	1.5	2.3	3.8	4.8	3.1
Histidine, g	0.9	1.4	2.4	4.2	5.6
Isoleucine, g	1.9	3.0	5.0	8.7	11.8
Leucine, g	2.5	3.9	6.6	11.4	15.6
Lysine, g	3.5	5.3	9.0	14.3	18.7
Methionine + cystine, g	1.7	2.7	4.6	7.8	10.6
Phenylalanine + tyrosine, g	2.8	4.3	7.3	12.5	17.1
Threonine, g	2.0	3.1	5.3	9.1	12.4
Tryptophan, g	0.5	0.8	1.3	2.3	3.1
Valine, g	2.0	3.1	5.3	9.1	12.4
Linoleic acid, g	0.3	0.5	1.0	1.9	3.1
Mineral elements					
Calcium, g	2.2	3.7	6.6	11.4	15.6
Phosphorus, total, g	1.8	3.0	5.7	9.5	12.4
Phosphorus, available, g	1.4	1.8	3.0	4.4	4.7
Chlorine, g	0.2	0.4	0.8	1.5	2.5
Magnesium, g	0.1	0.2	0.4	0.8	1.2
Potassium, g	0.8	1.3	2.5	4.4	5.3
Sodium, g	0.2	0.5	1.0	1.9	3.1
Copper, mg	1.50	2.76	4.75	7.60	9.33
Iodine, mg	0.04	0.06	0.13	0.27	0.44
Iron, mg	25.0	46.0	76.0	114.0	124.4
Manganese, mg	1.00	1.84	2.85	3.80	6.22
Selenium, mg	0.08	0.14	0.24	0.28	0.31
Zinc, mg	25.0	46.0	76.0	114.0	155.5
Vitamins					
Vitamin A, IU	550	1012	1662	2470	4043
Vitamin D, IU	55	101	190	285	466
Vitamin E, IU	4	7	10	21	34
Vitamin K (menadione), mg	0.02	0.02	0.05	0.10	0.16
Biotin, mg	0.02	0.02	0.05	0.10	0.16
Choline, g	0.15	0.23	0.38	0.57	0.93
Folacin, mg	0.08	0.14	0.28	0.57	0.93
Niacin, available, mg	5.00	6.90	11.88	19.00	21.77
Pantothenic acid, mg	3.00	4.60	8.55	15.20	21.77
Riboflavin, mg	1.00	1.61	2.85	4.75	6.22
Thiamin, mg	0.38	0.46	0.95	1.90	3.11
Vitamin B_6, mg	0.50	0.69	1.42	1.90	3.11
Vitamin B_{12}, μg	5.00	8.05	14.25	19.00	15.55

APPENDIX TABLE 24

Nutrient requirements of breeding swine (% or amount/kg of diet)[a,b] (from 1988 NRC on swine)

		Bred Gilts, Sows, and Adult Boars	Lactating Gilts and Sows
Digestible energy	kcal/kg diet	3340	3340
Metabolizable energy	kcal/kg diet	3210	3210
Crude protein	%	12	13
Indispensable amino acids			
Arginine, %		0.00	0.40
Histidine, %		0.15	0.25
Isoleucine, %		0.30	0.39
Leucine, %		0.30	0.48
Lysine, %		0.43	0.60
Methionine + cystine, %		0.23	0.36
Phenylalanine + tyrosine, %		0.45	0.70
Threonine, %		0.30	0.43
Tryptophan, %		0.09	0.12
Valine, %		0.32	0.60
Linoleic acid, %		0.1	0.1
Mineral elements			
Calcium, %		0.75	0.75
Phosphorus, total, %		0.60	0.60
Phosphorus, available, %		0.35	0.35
Chlorine, %		0.12	0.16
Magnesium, %		0.04	0.04
Potassium, %		0.20	0.20
Sodium, %		0.15	0.20
Copper, mg		5.00	5.00
Iodine, mg		0.14	0.14
Iron, mg		80.00	80.00
Manganese, mg		10.00	10.00
Selenium, mg		0.15	0.15
Zinc, mg		50.00	50.00
Vitamins			
Vitamin A, IU		4000	2000
Vitamin D, IU		200	200
Vitamin E, IU		22	22
Vitamin K (menadione), mg		0.50	0.50
Biotin, mg		0.20	0.20
Choline, g		1.25	1.00
Folacin, mg		0.30	0.30
Niacin, available, mg		10.00	10.00
Pantothenic acid, mg		12.00	12.00
Riboflavin, mg		3.75	3.75
Thiamin, mg		1.00	1.00
Vitamin B_6, mg		1.00	1.00
Vitamin B_{12}, μg		15.00	15.00

[a]These requirements are based upon corn-soybean meal diets, with corn containing 8.5% and soybean meal containing 44% protein, and based on feed intake levels listed in Appendix Table 25.

[b]The requirements listed are based upon the principles and assumptions described in the text of this publication. Knowledge of nutritional constraints and limitations is important for the proper use of this table.

APPENDIX TABLE 25

Daily nutrient intakes and requirements of intermediate weight breeding animals (from 1988 NRC on swine)

	Bred Gilts, Sows, and Adult Boars	Lactating Gilts and Sows
Mean gestation or farrowing wt, kg	162.5	165.0
Daily feed intake, kg	1.9	5.3
Digestible energy, Mcal/d	6.3	17.7
Metabolizable energy, Mcal/d	6.1	17.0
Crude protein, g/d	228	689
Indispensable amino acids		
Arginine, g	0.0	21.2
Histidine, g	2.8	13.2
Isoleucine, g	5.7	20.7
Leucine, g	5.7	25.4
Lysine, g	8.2	31.8
Methionine + cystine, g	4.4	19.1
Phenylalanine + tyrosine, g	8.6	37.1
Threonine, g	5.7	22.8
Tryptophan, g	1.7	6.4
Valine, g	6.1	31.8
Linoleic acid, g	1.9	5.3
Mineral elements		
Calcium, g	14.2	39.8
Phosphorus, total, g	11.4	31.8
Phosphorus, available, g	6.6	18.6
Chlorine, g	2.3	8.5
Magnesium, g	0.8	2.1
Potassium, g	3.8	10.6
Sodium, %	2.8	10.6
Copper, mg	9.5	26.5
Iodine, mg	0.3	0.7
Iron, mg	152.0	424.0
Manganese, mg	19.0	53.0
Selenium, mg	0.3	0.8
Zinc, mg	95.0	265.0
Vitamins		
Vitamin A, IU	7600	10600
Vitamin D, IU	380	1060
Vitamin E, IU	42	117
Vitamin K (menadione), mg	1.0	2.6
Biotin, mg	0.4	1.1
Choline, g	2.4	5.3
Folacin, mg	0.6	1.6
Niacin, available, mg	19.0	53.0
Pantothenic acid, mg	22.8	63.6
Riboflavin, mg	7.1	19.9
Thiamin, mg	1.9	5.3
Vitamin B_6, mg	1.9	5.3
Vitamin B_{12}, μg	28.5	79.5

APPENDIX TABLE 26

Requirements for several nutrients for breeding herd replacement animals allowed feed ad libitum, % of diet (from 1988 NRC on swine)

	Developing Gilts[a]		Developing Boars[a]	
Weight, kg	20–50	50–110	20–50	50–110
Energy concentration, kcal ME/kg diet	3255	3260	3240	3255
Crude protein, %	16	15	18	16
Lysine, %	0.80	0.70	0.90	0.75
Calcium, %	0.65	0.55	0.70	0.60
Phosphorus, total, %	0.55	0.45	0.60	0.50
Phosphorus, available, %	0.28	0.20	0.33	0.25

[a]Sufficient data are not available to indicate that requirements for other nutrients are different from those in Appendix Table 23 for this size animal.

APPENDIX TABLE 27

Daily energy and feed requirements of pregnant gilts and sows (from 1988 NRC on swine)

	Bred Gilts and Sows[a]		
Weight at mating, kg	120	140	160
Mean gestation weight, kg[b]	142.5	162.5	182.5
Energy required, Mcal DE/d			
Maintenance[c]	4.53	5.00	5.47
Gestation weight gain[d]	1.29	1.29	1.29
Total required	5.82	6.29	6.76
Feed required/d, kg[e]	1.8	1.9	2.0

[a]Assuming 25 kg maternal weight gain plus 20-kg increase in weight due to products of conception, total 45 kg.

[b]Weight at mating plus total weight gain × 0.5.

[c]Animal daily maintenance requirements; 110 kcal DE/kg$^{0.75}$.

[d]1.10 Mcal DE/d for maternal weight gain plus 0.19 Mcal DE/d for conceptus gain.

[e]Corn-soybean meal diet containing 3.34 Mcal DE/kg.

APPENDIX TABLE 28

Daily energy and feed requirements of lactating gilts and sows (from 1988 NRC on swine)

	Lactating Gilts and Sows[a]		
Weight postfarrowing, kg	145	165	185
Milk yield, kg	5.0	6.25	7.5
Energy required, Mcal DE/d			
Maintenance[a]	4.5	5.0	5.5
Milk yield[b]	10.0	12.5	15.0
Total required	14.5	17.5	20.5
Feed required/d, kg[c]	4.4	5.3	6.1

[a]Animal daily maintenance requirement; 110 kcal DE/kg$^{0.75}$.

[b]2.0 Mcal DE/kg milk.

[c]Corn-soybean meal diet containing 3.34 Mcal DE/kg.

APPENDIX TABLE 29

Nutrient requirements of leghorn-type chickens (as % or as milligrams or units/kg of diet) (from 1984 NRC on poultry)

Energy Base kcal ME/kg Diet[a]	Growing			Laying		Breeding
	0–6 Weeks 2900	6–14 Weeks 2900	14–20 Weeks 2900	2900	Daily Intake per Hen, mg[b]	2900
Protein, %	18	15	12	14.5	16,000	14.5
Arginine, %	1.00	0.83	0.67	0.68	750	0.68
Glycine and Serine, %	0.70	0.58	0.47	0.50	550	0.50
Histidine, %	0.26	0.22	0.17	0.16	180	0.16
Isoleucine, %	0.60	0.50	0.40	0.50	550	0.50
Leucine, %	1.00	0.83	0.67	0.73	800	0.73
Lysine, %	0.85	0.60	0.45	0.64	700	0.64
Methionine + cystine, %	0.60	0.50	0.40	0.55	600	0.55
Methionine, %	0.30	0.25	0.20	0.32	350	0.32
Phenylalanine + tyrosine, %	1.00	0.83	0.67	0.80	880	0.80
Phenylalanine, %	0.54	0.45	0.36	0.40	440	0.40
Threonine, %	0.68	0.57	0.37	0.45	500	0.45
Tryptophan, %	0.17	0.14	0.11	0.14	150	0.14
Valine, %	0.62	0.52	0.41	0.55	600	0.55
Linoleic acid, %	1.00	1.00	1.00	1.00	1100	1.00
Calcium, %	0.80	0.70	0.60	3.40	3750	3.40
Phosphorus, available, %	0.40	0.35	0.30	0.32	350	0.32
Potassium, %	0.40	0.30	0.25	0.15	165	0.15
Sodium, %	0.15	0.15	0.15	0.15	165	0.15
Chlorine, %	0.15	0.12	0.12	0.15	165	0.15
Magnesium, mg	600	500	400	500	55	500
Manganese, mg	60	30	30	30	3.30	60
Zinc, mg	40	35	35	50	5.50	65
Iron, mg	80	60	60	50	5.50	60
Copper, mg	8	6	6	6	0.88	8
Iodine, mg	0.35	0.35	0.35	0.30	0.03	0.30
Selenium, mg	0.15	0.10	0.10	0.10	0.01	0.10
Vitamin A, IU	1500	1500	1500	4000	440	4000
Vitamin D, ICU	200	200	200	500	55	500
Vitamin E, IU	10	5	5	5	0.55	10
Vitamin K, mg	0.50	0.50	0.50	0.50	0.055	0.50
Riboflavin, mg	3.60	1.80	1.80	2.20	0.242	3.80

APPENDIX TABLE 29 (Cont.)

Energy Base kcal ME/kg Diet[a] →	Growing			Laying		Breeding
	0-6 Weeks 2900	6-14 Weeks 2900	14-20 Weeks 2900	2900	Daily Intake per Hen, mg[b]	2900
Pantothenic acid, mg	10.0	10.0	10.0	2.20	0.242	10.0
Niacin, mg	27.0	11.0	11.0	10.0	1.10	10.0
Vitamin B_{12}, mg	0.009	0.003	0.003	0.004	0.00044	0.004
Choline, mg	1300	900	500	?	?	?
Biotin, mg	0.15	0.10	0.10	0.10	0.011	0.15
Folacin, mg	0.55	0.25	0.25	0.25	0.0275	0.35
Thiamin, mg	1.8	1.3	1.3	0.80	0.088	0.80
Pyridoxine, mg	3.0	3.0	3.0	3.0	0.33	4.50

[a]These are typical dietary energy concentrations.
[b]Assumes an average daily intake of 110 g of feed/hen daily.

APPENDIX TABLE 30

Body weights and feed requirements of leghorn-type pullets and hens
(From 1984 NRC on poultry)

Age, Weeks	Body Weight[a], g	Feed Consumption[b], g/week	Typical Egg Production, hen-day %
0	35	45	—
2	135	90	—
4	270	180	—
6	450	260	—
8	620	325	—
10	790	385	—
12	950	430	—
14	1,060	460	—
16	1,160	460	—
18	1,260	460	—
20	1,360	460	—
22	1,425	525	10
24	1,500	595	38
26	1,575	665	64
30	1,725	770	88
40	1,815	770	80
50	1,870	765	74
60	1,900	755	68
70	1,900	740	62

[a]Pullets and hens of leghorn-type strains are generally fed ad libitum but are occasionally control-fed to limit body weights. Values shown are typical but will vary with strain differences, season, and lighting. Specific breeder guidelines should be consulted for desired schedules of weights and feed consumption.
[b]Based on diets containing 2,900 kcal ME/kg. Consumption will vary depending upon the caloric density of the diet, environmental temperature, and rate of production (see Appendix Table 34).

APPENDIX TABLE 31

Nutrient requirements of broilers (as % or as milligrams or units/kg of diet)
(From 1984 NRC on poultry)

Energy Base kcal ME/kg Diet[a] ⟶	Weeks 0-3 3200	Weeks 3-6 3200	Weeks 6-8 3200
Protein, %	23.0	20.0	18.0
Arginine, %	1.44	1.20	1.00
Glycine + Serine, %	1.50	1.00	0.70
Histidine, %	0.35	0.30	0.26
Isoleucine, %	0.80	0.70	0.60
Leucine, %	1.35	1.18	1.00
Lysine, %	1.20	1.00	0.85
Methionine + Cystine, %	0.93	0.72	0.60
Methionine, %	0.50	0.38	0.32
Phenylalanine + Tyrosine, %	1.34	1.17	1.00
Phenylalanine, %	0.72	0.63	0.54
Threonine, %	0.80	0.74	0.68
Tryptophan, %	0.23	0.18	0.17
Valine, %	0.82	0.72	0.62
Linoleic acid, %	1.00	1.00	1.00
Calcium, %	1.00	0.90	0.80
Phosphorus, available, %	0.45	0.40	0.35
Potassium, %	0.40	0.35	0.30

APPENDIX TABLE 31 (Cont.)

Energy Base kcal ME/kg Diet [a] ⟶	Weeks 0-3 3200	Weeks 3-6 3200	Weeks 6-8 3200
Sodium, %	0.15	0.15	0.15
Chlorine, %	0.15	0.15	0.15
Magnesium, mg	600	600	600
Manganese, mg	60.0	60.0	60.0
Zinc, mg	40.0	40.0	40.0
Iron, mg	80.0	80.0	80.0
Copper, mg	8.0	8.0	8.0
Iodine, mg	0.35	0.35	0.35
Selenium, mg	0.15	0.15	0.15
Vitamin A, IU	1500	1500	1500
Vitamin D, ICU	200	200	200
Vitamin E, IU	10	10	10
Vitamin K, mg	0.50	0.50	0.50
Riboflavin, mg	3.60	3.60	3.60
Pantothenic acid, mg	10.0	10.0	10.0
Niacin, mg	27.0	27.0	11.0
Vitamin B_{12}, mg	0.009	0.009	0.003
Choline, mg	1300	850	500
Biotin, mg	0.15	0.15	0.10
Folacin, mg	0.55	0.55	0.25
Thiamin, mg	1.80	1.80	1.80
Pyridoxine, mg	3.0	3.0	2.5

[a]These are typical dietary energy concentrations.

APPENDIX TABLE 32

Body weights and feed requirements of broilers[a] (from 1984 NRC on poultry)

Age, weeks	Body Weights, g		Weekly Feed Consumption, g		Cumulative Feed Consumption, g		Weekly Energy Consumption, kcal ME/bird		Cumulative Energy Consumption, kcal ME/bird	
	M	F	M	F	M	F	M	F	M	F
1	130	120	120	110	120	110	385	350	385	350
2	320	300	260	240	380	350	830	770	1215	1120
3	560	515	390	355	770	705	1250	1135	2465	2255
4	860	790	535	500	1305	1205	1710	1600	4175	3855
5	1250	1110	740	645	2045	1850	2370	2065	6545	5920
6	1690	1430	980	800	3025	2650	3135	2560	9680	8480
7	2100	1745	1095	910	4120	3560	3505	2910	13,185	11,390
8	2520	2060	1210	970	5330	4530	3870	3105	17,055	14,495
9	2925	2350	1320	1010	6650	5540	4225	3230	21,280	17,725

[a]Typical for broilers fed well-balanced diets containing 3200 kcal ME/kg.

APPENDIX TABLE 33

Nutrient requirements of meat-type hens for breeding purposes[a]

Energy Base kcal ME/kg Diet $\longrightarrow$	2850[b]	Daily Intake Per Hen, mg
Protein, %	14.5	22,000
Arginine, %	0.74	1110
Glycine + serine, %	0.62	932
Histidine, %	0.14	205
Isoleucine, %	0.57	850
Leucine, %	0.83	1250
Lysine, %	0.51	765
Methionine + cystine, %	0.55	820
Methionine, %	0.35	520
Phenylalanine + tyrosine, %	0.75	1112
Phenylalanine, %	0.41	610
Threonine, %	0.48	720
Tryptophan, %	0.13	190
Valine, %	0.63	950
Calcium, %	2.75	4125
Phosphorus, available, %	0.25	375
Sodium, %	0.10	150

[a]Diets are generally fed on a limited intake basis to control body weight gains. Adjust quantity of feed offered based on desired body weights and egg production levels for specific breed or strain.

[b]Diets for laying hens generally are fed to provide daily energy intakes of 375–450 kcal ME/d based on body weight, environmental temperature, and rate of egg production. Percentage of nutrients shown is typical of hens given 425 kcal ME/d.

Typical body weights and feed allowances for male and female meat-type chickens (replacement stock)[a] (from 1984 NRC on poultry)

Age, weeks	Male Body Weight[b], g	Male Feed Consumption[c], g/week	Female Body Weight[b], g	Female Feed Consumption[c], g/week	Typical Egg Production, hen-day %
0	40	100	40	75	—
2	250	250	225	225	—
4	545	350–385	455	315–330	—
6	795	390–425	660	330–350	—
8	1020	405–475	840	350–400	—
10	1250	475–550	1000	385–445	—
12	1480	540–625	1180	425–480	—
14	1700	575–700	1360	460–550	—
16	1930	625–765	1550	495–600	—
18	2150	665–825	1730	525–670	—
20	2400	—[d]	1930	570–730	—
22	2640	—	2110	635–795	10
24	3200	—	2450	800–925	15
26	3540	—	2730	950–1050	30
28	3750	—	2880	1078–1141	56
30	3900	—	3000	1078–1141	75
32	4090	—	3090	1078–1141	80
34	4220	—	3130	1078–1141	78
36	4340	—	3160	1078–1141	76
38	4450	—	3180	1071–1134	73
40	4540	—	3180	1064–1127	72

[a]Broiler-breeder strains must be grown on a controlled feeding program to limit weight. Values shown are typical but will vary according to strain. Specific breeder guidelines should be consulted for desired schedule of weights and feed allotments.

[b]Values are typical for fall-hatched chicks. Spring-hatched chicks will have decreasing natural daylight during the time of sexual maturity and usually need to be heavier to attain sexual maturity at the desired age.

[c]Adjust as required to maintain desired body weight.

[d]Males and females intermingled.

Metabolizable energy required daily by chickens in relation to body weight and egg production[a] (from 1984 NRC on poultry)

Body Weight, kg	Rate of Egg Production, %					
	0	50	60	70	80	90
	Metabolizable Energy/Hen Daily, kcal[b]					
1.0	130	192	205	217	229	242
1.5	177	239	251	264	276	289
2.0	218	280	292	305	317	330
2.5	259	321	333	346	358	371
3.0	296	358	370	383	395	408
3.5	333	395	408	420	432	445

[a]A number of formulas have been suggested for prediction of the daily energy requirements of chickens. The formula used here was derived from that in *Effect of Environment on Nutrient Requirements of Domestic Animals* (NRC, 1981).

ME/hen daily = $W^{0.75}(173 - 1.95T) + 5.5\Delta W + 2.07EE$

where: W = body weight (kg),
       T = ambient temperature (°C),
    ΔW = change in body weight in g/d, and
    EE = daily egg mass (g).

[b]Temperature of 22°, egg weight of 60 g, and no change in body weight were used in calculations.

APPENDIX TABLE 36

Nutrient requirements of turkeys as percentages or as milligrams or units per kilogram of feed (from 1984 NRC on poultry)

				Age (weeks)				
Energy Base kcal ME/kg Diet[a] ⟶	M: 0–4 F: 0–4 2800	4–8 4–8 2900	8–12 8–11 3000	12–16 11–14 3100	16–20 14–17 3200	20–24 17–20 3300	Holding 2900	Breeding Hens 2900
Protein, %	28	26	22	19	16.5	14	12	14
Arginine, %	1.6	1.5	1.25	1.1	0.95	0.8	0.6	0.6
Glycine + serine, %	1.0	0.9	0.8	0.7	0.6	0.5	0.4	0.5
Histidine, %	0.58	0.54	0.46	0.39	0.35	0.29	0.25	0.3
Isoleucine, %	1.1	1.0	0.85	0.75	0.65	0.55	0.45	0.5
Leucine, %	1.9	1.75	1.5	1.3	1.1	0.95	0.5	0.5
Lysine, %	1.6	1.5	1.3	1.0	0.8	0.65	0.5	0.6
Methionine + cystine, %	1.05	0.9	0.75	0.65	0.55	0.45	0.4	0.4
Methionine, %	0.53	0.45	0.38	0.33	0.28	0.23	0.2	0.2
Phenylalanine + tyrosine, %	1.8	1.65	1.4	1.2	1.05	0.9	0.8	1.0
Phenylalanine, %	1.0	0.9	0.8	0.7	0.6	0.5	0.4	0.55
Threonine, %	1.0	0.93	0.79	0.68	0.59	0.5	0.4	0.45
Tryptophan, %	0.26	0.24	0.2	0.18	0.15	0.13	0.1	0.13
Valine, %	1.2	1.1	0.94	0.8	0.7	0.6	0.5	0.58
Linoleic acid, %	1.0	1.0	0.8	0.8	0.8	0.8	0.8	1.0
Calcium, %	1.2	1.0	0.85	0.75	0.65	0.55	0.5	2.25
Phosphorus, available, %	0.6	0.5	0.42	0.38	0.32	0.28	0.25	0.35
Potassium, %	0.7	0.6	0.5	0.5	0.4	0.4	0.4	0.6
Sodium, %	0.17	0.15	0.12	0.12	0.12	0.12	0.12	0.15
Chlorine, %	0.15	0.14	0.14	0.12	0.12	0.12	0.12	0.12
Magnesium, mg	600	600	600	600	600	600	600	600
Manganese, mg	60	60	60	60	60	60	60	60
Zinc, mg	75	65	50	40	40	40	40	65
Iron, mg	80	60	60	60	50	50	50	60
Copper, mg	8	8	6	6	6	6	6	8
Iodine, mg	0.4	0.4	0.4	0.4	0.4	0.4	0.4	0.4
Selenium, mg	0.2	0.2	0.2	0.2	0.2	0.2	0.2	0.2
Vitamin A, IU	4000	4000	4000	4000	4000	4000	4000	4000
Vitamin D[b], ICU	900	900	900	900	900	900	900	900
Vitamin E, IU	12	12	10	10	10	10	10	25
Vitamin K, mg	1.0	1.0	0.8	0.8	0.8	0.8	0.8	1.0
Riboflavin, mg	3.6	3.6	3.0	3.0	2.5	2.5	2.5	4.0
Pantothenic acid, mg	11.0	11.0	9.0	9.0	9.0	9.0	9.0	16.0
Niacin, mg	70.0	70.0	50.0	50.0	40.0	40.0	40.0	30.0
Vitamin B_{12}, mg	0.003	0.003	0.003	0.003	0.003	0.003	0.003	0.003
Choline, mg	1900	1600	1300	1100	950	800	800	1000
Biotin, mg	0.2	0.2	0.15	0.125	0.100	0.100	0.100	0.15
Folacin, mg	1.0	1.0	0.8	0.8	0.7	0.7	0.7	1.0
Thiamin, mg	2.0	2.0	2.0	2.00	2.0	2.0	2.0	2.0
Pyridoxine, mg	4.5	4.5	3.5	3.5	3.0	3.0	3.0	4.0

[a]These are typical ME concentrations for corn-soy diets. Different ME values may be appropriate if other ingredients predominate.

[b]These concentrations of vitamin D are satisfactory when the dietary concentrations of calcium and available phosphorus conform with those in this table.

Growth rate, feed and energy consumption of large-type turkeys (from 1984 NRC on poultry)

Age, weeks	Body Weight, kg		Feed Consumption per Week, kg		Cumulative Feed Consumption, kg		ME Consumption per Week, Mcal	
	M	F	M	F	M	F	M	F
1	0.11	0.11	0.10	0.10	0.10	0.10	0.30	0.30
2	0.27	0.24	0.20	0.17	0.30	0.27	0.60	0.50
3	0.58	0.47	0.45	0.39	0.75	0.66	1.1	0.80
4	1.0	0.70	0.61	0.46	1.36	1.12	1.7	1.2
5	1.5	1.1	0.70	0.60	2.06	1.72	2.3	1.6
6	2.0	1.6	0.86	0.76	2.92	2.48	2.9	2.1
7	2.6	2.1	1.08	0.89	4.00	3.37	3.5	2.6
8	3.3	2.6	1.30	1.04	5.30	4.41	4.1	3.1
9	4.0	3.1	1.51	1.18	6.81	5.59	4.8	3.6
10	4.7	3.7	1.78	1.34	8.59	6.93	5.2	4.1
11	5.5	4.3	1.99	1.47	10.58	8.40	5.7	4.6
12	6.3	4.8	2.25	1.59	12.83	9.99	6.3	5.1
13	7.1	5.3	2.51	1.70	15.34	11.69	7.1	5.5
14	8.0	5.8	2.66	1.75	18.00	13.44	7.8	5.8
15	8.8	6.3	2.89	1.82	20.89	15.26	8.4	6.1
16	9.7	6.7	3.05	1.92	23.94	17.18	8.8	6.4
17	10.5	7.1	3.13	2.03	27.03	19.21	9.6	6.7
18	11.3	7.5	3.27	2.07	30.34	21.28	10.2	6.9
19	12.1	7.8	3.43	2.15	33.77	23.43	10.9	7.1
20	12.8	8.1	3.60	2.23	37.37	25.66	11.6	7.3
21	13.5	—	3.71	—	41.08	—	12.5	—
22	14.2	—	3.82	—	44.90	—	12.9	—
23	14.8	—	3.94	—	48.84	—	13.2	—
24	15.4	—	4.05	—	52.89	—	13.5	—

APPENDIX TABLE 38

Body weights and feed consumption of large-type turkeys during holding and breeding periods[a] (from 1984 NRC on poultry)

Age, weeks	Hens			Toms	
	Weight, kg	Egg Production, %	Feed /Day, g	Weight, kg	Feed /Day, g
20	7.0	—	200	12.0	400
25	8.0	—	215	13.5	420
30	9.0	Start light stimulation	230	16.0	440
35	9.5	66	260	17.0	450
40	9.3	63	255	18.0	460
45	9.1	60	250	18.2	480
50	9.0	50	240	18.5	500
55	9.0	40	230	18.8	510
60	9.0	35	220	19.0	520

[a]These values are based on experimental data involving "in season" egg production (i.e., November through July) of commercial stock. It is estimated that summer breeders would produce 70–90% as many eggs and consume 60–80% as much feed, respectively, as "in season" breeders.

APPENDIX TABLE 39

Daily water consumption by chickens and turkeys of different ages[a] (from 1984 NRC on poultry)

| Age, week | Amounts per 1000 Birds | | | | | |
| | Chicken Broilers[b] | | Leghorn-Type Pullets | | Turkeys[b] | |
	Liters	Gallons[c]	Liters	Gallons[c]	Liters	Gallons[c]
1	20	5	19	5	38	10
2	50	13	38	10	76	20
3	90	24	45	12	114	30
4	140	37	64	17	151	40
5	200	53	83	22	189	50
6	260	69	95	25	227	60
7	320	85	106	28	284	75
8	380	100	114	30	360	95
9			132	35	435	115
10			144	38	473	125
12			151	40	568	150
15			158	42	606	160
20			170	45	757	200
			Laying or Breeding			
35			189	50	M 908	240
					F 492	130

[a]Will vary considerably depending on temperature and diet composition.
[b]Mixed sexes.
[c]U.S. measure.

APPENDIX TABLE 40

Nutrient requirements of geese as percentages or as milligrams or units per kilogram of diet[a] (from 1984 NRC on poultry)

Energy Base, kcal ME/kg Diet[b] ⟶	Starting (0–6 Weeks) 2900	Growing (after 6 Weeks) 2900	Breeding 2900
Protein, %	22.0	15.0	15.0
Lysine, %	0.9	0.6	0.6
Methionine + cystine, %	0.75	—	—
Calcium, %	0.8	0.6	2.25
Phosphorus, available, %	0.4	0.3	0.3
Vitamin A, IU	1500	1500	4000
Vitamin D, ICU	200	200	200
Riboflavin, mg	4.0	2.5	4.0
Pantothenic acid, mg	15.0	—	—
Niacin, mg	55.0	35.0	20.0

[a]For nutrients not listed, see requirements for chickens as a guide.
[b]These are typical dietary energy concentrations.

APPENDIX TABLE 41

Nutrient requirements of Pekin ducks as percentages or as milligrams or units per kilogram of diet[a] (from 1984 NRC on poultry)

Energy base, kcal ME/kg Diet[b] ⟶	Starting (0-2 weeks) 2900	Growing (2-7 weeks) 2900	Breeding 2900
Protein, %	22.0	16.0	15.0
Arginine, %	1.1	1.0	—
Lysine, %	1.1	0.9	0.7
Methionine + cystine, %	0.8	0.6	0.55
Calcium, %	0.65	0.6	2.75
Phosphorus, available, %	0.40	0.35	0.35
Sodium, %	0.15	0.15	0.15
Chlorine, %	0.12	0.12	0.12
Magnesium, mg	500	500	500
Manganese, mg	40.0	40.0	25.0
Zinc, mg	60.0	60.0	60.0
Selenium, mg	0.14	0.14	0.14
Vitamin A, IU	4000	4000	4000
Vitamin D, ICU	220	220	500
Vitamin K, mg	0.4	0.4	0.4
Riboflavin, mg	4.0	4.0	4.0
Pantothenic acid, mg	11.0	11.0	10.0
Niacin, mg	55.0	55.0	40.0
Pyridoxine, mg	2.6	2.6	3.0

[a]For nutrients not listed, see requirements for chickens as a guide.
[b]These are typical dietary energy concentrations.

APPENDIX TABLE 42

Typical body weights and feed consumption of Pekin ducks to 8 weeks of age (from 1984 NRC on poultry)

Age, weeks	Body Weight, kg		Feed Consumption by 1-week periods, kg		Cumulative Feed Consumption, kg	
	M	F	M	F	M	F
0	0.05	0.05	—	—	—	—
1	0.27	0.27	0.22	0.22	0.22	0.22
2	0.78	0.74	0.77	0.73	0.99	0.95
3	1.38	1.28	1.12	1.11	2.11	2.05
4	1.96	1.82	1.28	1.28	3.40	3.33
5	2.49	2.30	1.48	1.43	4.87	4.76
6	2.96	2.73	1.63	1.59	6.50	6.35
7	3.34	3.06	1.68	1.63	8.18	7.98
8	3.61	3.29	1.68	1.63	9.86	9.61

APPENDIX TABLE 43

Nutrient requirements of pheasants[a] and bobwhite quail[b] as percentages or as milligrams or units per kilogram of diet (from 1984 NRC on poultry)

Energy Base, kcal ME/kg Diet[c] →	Pheasant			Bobwhite Quail		
	Starting 2800	Growing 2700	Breeding 2800	Starting 2800	Growing 2800	Breeding 2800
Protein, %	30.0	16.0	18.0	28.0	20.0	24.0
Glycine + serine, %	1.8	1.0	—	—	—	—
Lysine, %	1.5	0.8	—	—	—	—
Methionine + cystine, %	1.1	0.6	0.6	—	—	—
Linoleic acid, %	1.0	1.0	1.0	1.0	1.0	1.0
Calcium, %	1.0	0.7	2.5	0.65	0.65	2.3
Phosphorus available, %	0.55	0.45	0.40	0.55	0.45	0.50
Sodium, %	0.15	0.15	0.15	0.15	0.15	0.15
Chlorine, %	0.11	0.11	0.11	0.11	0.11	0.11
Iodine, mg	0.30	0.30	0.30	0.30	0.30	0.30
Riboflavin, mg	3.5	3.0	—	3.8	—	4.0
Pantothenic acid, mg	10.0	10.0	—	13.0	—	15.0
Niacin, mg	60.0	40.0	—	30.0	—	20.0
Choline, mg	1500.0	1000.0	—	1500.0	—	1000.0

[a]For values not listed see requirements for turkeys as a guide.

[b]For values not listed see requirements for leghorn-type chickens as a guide.

[c]These are typical dietary energy concentrations.

APPENDIX TABLE 44

Nutrient requirements of Japanese quail (Coturnix) as percentage or as milligrams or units per kilogram of diet (from 1984 NRC on poultry)

Energy Base, kcal ME/kg Diet[a] ⟶	Starting and Growing 3000	Breeding 3000
Protein, %	24.0	20.00
Arginine, %	1.25	1.26
Glycine + serine, %	1.20	1.17
Histidine, %	0.36	0.42
Isoleucine, %	0.98	0.90
Leucine, %	1.69	1.42
Lysine, %	1.30	1.15
Methionine + cystine, %	0.75	0.76
Methionine, %	0.50	0.45
Phenylalanine + tyrosine, %	1.80	1.40
Phenylalanine, %	0.96	0.78
Threonine, %	1.02	0.74
Tryptophan, %	0.22	0.19
Valine, %	0.95	0.92
Linoleic acid, %	1.0	1.0
Calcium, %	0.8	2.5
Phosphorus, available, %	0.45	0.55
Potassium, %	0.4	0.4
Magnesium, mg	300	500
Sodium, %	0.15	0.15
Chlorine, %	0.20	0.15
Manganese, mg	90	70
Zinc, mg	25	50
Iron, mg	100	60
Copper, mg	6	6
Iodine, mg	0.3	0.3
Selenium, mg	0.2	0.2
Vitamin A, IU	5000	5000
Vitamin D, ICU	1200	1200
Vitamin E, IU	12	25
Vitamin K, mg	1	1
Riboflavin, mg	4	4
Pantothenic acid, mg	10	15
Niacin, mg	40	20
Vitamin B_{12}, mg	0.003	0.003
Choline, mg	2000	1500
Biotin, mg	0.3	0.15
Folacin, mg	1	1
Thiamin, mg	2	2
Pyridoxine, mg	3	3

[a]These are typical dietary energy concentrations.

APPENDIX TABLE 45

Daily nutrient requirements of horses (from 1989 NRC on horses)

Item	Weight, kg	lb	DE, Mcal	C. Protein, g	Lysine, g	Calcium, g	Phos., g	Mg, g	K, g	Na, g
Maintenance										
	400	880	13.4	536	18.8	16.0	11.2	6.0	20	6.7
	500	1100	16.4	656	23.0	20.0	14.0	7.5	25	8.2
	600	1320	19.4	776	27.2	24.0	16.8	9.0	30	9.7
Preg. mare										
9th mo.	400	880	14.9	654	22.9	28.3	21.4	7.1	24	6.6
	500	1100	18.2	801	28.0	34.6	26.2	8.7	29	8.1
	600	1320	21.5	947	33.2	40.9	31.0	10.3	34	9.6
10th mo.	400	880	15.1	666	23.3	28.8	21.8	7.3	24	6.7
	500	1100	18.5	815	28.5	35.2	26.7	8.9	30	8.2
	600	1320	21.9	965	33.8	41.7	31.6	10.5	35	9.7
11th mo.	400	880	16.1	708	24.8	30.6	23.2	7.7	26	6.7
	500	1100	19.7	866	30.3	37.4	28.3	9.4	31	8.2
	600	1320	23.3	1024	35.9	44.2	33.5	11.2	37	9.7
Lact. mare										
Early lact.	400	880	22.9	1141	39.9	44.8	28.9	8.7	37	8.8
	500	1100	28.3	1427	49.9	56.0	36.1	10.9	46	10.9
	600	1320	33.7	1712	59.9	67.2	43.3	13.0	55	12.9
Late lact.	400	880	19.7	839	29.4	28.8	17.8	6.9	26	8.1
	500	1100	24.3	1049	36.7	36.0	22.2	8.6	33	9.9
	600	1320	28.9	1259	44.1	43.2	26.7	10.3	40	11.8
Working horse										
Light work	400	880	16.7	670	23.4	20.4	14.6	7.7	25	20.5
	500	1100	20.5	820	28.7	25.0	17.8	9.4	31	25.1
	600	1320	24.2	970	33.9	29.6	21.1	11.2	37	29.7
Moderate work	400	880	20.1	804	28.1	24.5	17.5	9.2	31	22.8
	500	1100	24.6	984	34.4	30.0	21.4	11.3	37	27.8
	600	1320	29.1	1164	40.7	35.5	25.3	13.4	44	32.9
Intense work	400	880	26.8	1072	37.5	32.7	23.3	12.3	41	28.2
	500	1100	32.8	1312	45.9	40.0	28.5	15.1	50	34.5
	600	1320	38.8	1552	54.3	47.3	33.8	17.8	59	40.8

APPENDIX TABLE 46

Daily nutrient requirements of horses (from 1989 NRC on horses)

Item	Weight kg	Weight lb	Fe, mg	Mn, mg	Zn, mg	Cu, mg	Co, mg	I, mg	Se, mg	Vit A, IU	Vit D, IU	Vit E, IU
Maintenance	400	880	268	268	268	67	0.7	0.7	0.7	12,000	2010	335
	500	1100	328	328	328	82	0.8	0.8	0.8	15,000	2460	410
	600	1320	388	388	388	97	1.0	1.0	1.0	18,000	2910	485
Preg. mare												
9th mo.	400	880	331	264	264	66	0.7	0.7	0.7	24,000	3966	529
	500	1100	405	324	324	81	0.8	0.8	0.8	30,000	4854	647
	600	1320	479	383	383	96	1.0	1.0	1.0	36,000	5742	766
10th mo.	400	880	336	269	269	67	0.7	0.7	0.7	24,000	4038	538
	500	1100	412	329	329	82	0.8	0.8	0.8	30,000	4942	659
	600	1320	487	390	390	97	1.0	1.0	1.0	36,000	5846	779
11th mo.	400	880	335	268	268	67	0.7	0.7	0.7	24,000	4020	536
	500	1100	410	328	328	82	0.8	0.8	0.8	30,000	4920	656
	600	1320	485	388	388	97	1.0	1.0	1.0	36,000	5820	776
Lact. mare												
Early lact.	400	880	440	352	352	88	0.9	0.9	0.9	24,000	5286	705
	500	1100	544	435	435	109	1.1	1.1	1.1	30,000	6526	870
	600	1320	647	518	518	129	1.3	1.3	1.3	36,000	7767	1036
Late lact.	400	880	403	322	322	81	0.8	0.8	0.8	24,000	4833	644
	500	1100	496	397	397	99	1.0	1.0	1.0	30,000	5956	794
	600	1320	590	472	472	118	1.2	1.2	1.2	36,000	7079	944
Working horse												
Light work	400	880	273	273	273	68	0.7	0.7	0.7	12,000	2051	547
	500	1100	335	335	335	84	0.8	0.8	0.8	15,000	2510	669
	600	1320	396	396	396	99	1.0	1.0	1.0	18,000	2969	792
Moderate work	400	880	303	303	303	76	0.8	0.8	0.8	12,000	2275	607
	500	1100	371	371	371	93	0.9	0.9	0.9	15,000	2785	743
	600	1320	439	439	439	110	1.1	1.1	1.1	18,000	3294	878
Intense work	400	880	376	376	376	94	0.9	0.9	0.9	12,000	2821	752
	500	1100	460	460	460	136	1.4	1.4	1.4	18,000	4084	1089
	600	1320	545	545	545	136	1.4	1.4	1.4	18,000	4084	1089

APPENDIX TABLE 47

Daily nutrient requirements of growing horses (from 1989 NRC on horses)

Age, Mo.	Weight, kg	D. Gain, kg	DE, Mcal	C. Pro, g	Lysine, g	Calcium, g	Phos., g	Mg, g	K, g	Na, g
4	145[a]	0.75	12.6	630	26.4	29.8	16.5	3.1	9	4.3
6	180[a]	0.55	12.9	643	27.0	24.8	13.7	3.4	11	4.4
		0.70	14.5	725	30.5	29.6	16.4	3.6	11	5.0
12	265[a]	0.40	15.6	700	29.6	23.4	12.9	4.5	14	5.6
		0.50	17.1	770	32.5	26.6	14.7	4.6	15	6.1
18	330[a]	0.25	15.9	716	30.2	21.2	11.7	5.3	17	6.4
4	175[b]	0.85	14.4	720	30.2	34.2	19.0	3.7	11	5.0
6	215[b]	0.65	15.0	750	31.5	29.4	16.3	4.0	13	5.2
		0.85	17.2	860	36.1	35.8	19.9	4.3	13	5.9
12	325[b]	0.50	18.9	851	35.9	29.0	16.0	5.5	18	6.8
		0.65	21.2	956	40.4	33.8	18.7	5.7	18	7.6
18	400[b]	0.35	19.8	893	37.7	27.2	15.0	6.4	21	7.9
4	200[c]	1.00	16.5	826	34.7	40.0	22.2	4.2	13	5.7
6	245[c]	0.75	17.0	850	35.7	33.8	18.7	4.6	14	5.9
		0.95	19.2	960	40.3	40.2	22.3	4.9	15	6.6
12	375[c]	0.65	22.7	1024	43.2	35.8	19.8	6.4	21	8.1
		0.80	25.1	1129	47.7	40.6	22.5	6.6	21	9.0
18	475[c]	0.45	23.9	1077	45.5	33.4	18.5	7.7	25	9.6

[a]Expected mature weight 400 kg.
[b]Expected mature weight 500 kg.
[c]Expected mature weight 600 kg.

APPENDIX TABLE 48

Daily nutrient requirements of growing horses (from 1989 NRC on horses)

Age, mo.	Weight, kg	D. Gain, kg	Fe, mg	Mn, mg	Zn, mg	Cu, mg	Co, mg	I, mg	Se, mg	Vit a, IU	Vit D, IU	Vit E, IU
4	145[a]	0.75	217	174	174	43	0.4	0.4	0.4	4350	3474	347
6	180[a]	0.55	222	177	177	44	0.4	0.4	0.4	5400	3545	355
		0.70	250	200	200	50	0.5	0.5	0.5	5400	4000	400
12	265[a]	0.40	278	222	222	56	0.6	0.6	0.6	7950	4447	445
		0.50	306	245	245	61	0.6	0.6	0.6	7950	4891	489
18	330[a]	0.25	318	254	254	64	0.6	0.6	0.6	9900	5089	509
4	175[b]	0.85	248	199	199	50	0.5	0.5	0.5	5250	3973	397
6	215[b]	0.65	259	207	207	52	0.5	0.5	0.5	6450	4138	414
		0.85	297	237	237	59	0.6	0.6	0.6	6450	4745	475
12	325[b]	0.50	338	270	270	68	0.7	0.7	0.7	9750	5405	541
		0.65	379	304	304	76	0.8	0.8	0.8	9750	6071	607
18	400[b]	0.35	397	318	318	79	0.8	0.8	0.8	12,000	6351	635
4	200[c]	1.00	285	228	228	57	0.6	0.6	0.6	6000	4558	456
6	245[c]	0.75	293	235	235	59	0.6	0.6	0.6	7350	4690	469
		0.95	331	265	265	66	0.7	0.7	0.7	7350	5297	530
12	375[c]	0.65	406	325	325	81	0.8	0.8	0.8	11,250	6500	650
		0.80	448	358	358	90	0.9	0.9	0.9	11,250	7166	717
18	475[c]	0.45	479	383	383	96	1.0	1.0	1.0	14,250	7660	766

[a]Expected mature weight 400 kg.
[b]Expected mature weight 500 kg.
[c]Expected mature weight 600 kg.

APPENDIX TABLE 49

Table of equivalents

Volume
1 cubic inch	= 16.387 cubic centimeters
1 cubic foot	= 1728.0 cubic inches = 0.0283 cubic meters
1 cubic yard	= 27.0 cubic feet = 0.7646 cubic meters
1 cubic centimeter	= 1.0 milliliter = 0.061 cubic inch
1 cubic meter	= 35.315 cubic feet = 1.308 cubic yards
1 liquid pint (US)	= 28.875 cubic inches = 0.5 liquid quart = 0.47316 liter
1 liquid quart (US)	= 57.75 cubic inches = 0.9463 liter
1 liquid gallon (US)	= 231 cubic inches = 4.0 quarts = 3.7853 liters
1 liter	= 1.057 liquid quarts (US) = 0.2642 liquid gallons (US)
1 bushel	= 2150.42 cubic inches = 1.244 cubic feet
	= 9.309 liquid gallons (US) = 4 pecks

Weight
1 ounce (avdp.)	= 28.50 grams = 16 drams
1 pound (avdp.)	= 16.0 ounces = 453.6 grams = 7000 grains
1 kilogram	= 1000 grams = 2.205 pounds
1 ton	= 2000 pounds = 907.0 kilograms
1 metric ton	= 1000 kilograms = 2205 pounds = 1.102 tons

Length
1 inch	= 2.54 centimeters = 25.4 millimeters
1 foot	= 12.0 inches = 30.48 centimeters = 0.3048 meters
1 yard	= 3.0 feet = 0.9144 meters
1 millimeter	= 0.03937 inches
1 centimeter	= 0.3937 inches = 10 millimeters
1 meter	= 39.37 inches = 3.2808 feet = 1.09361 yards = 100 centimeters
1 kilometer	= 1000 meters = 0.6412 miles
1 mile	= 1.6093 kilometers

Area
1 square inch	= 6.452 square centimeters
1 square centimeter	= 0.155 square inches
1 square foot	= 0.929 square meter
1 square meter	= 1550.0 square inches = 10.764 square feet
1 square yard	= 9.0 square feet = 0.8361 square meters
1 acre	= 43,560 square feet = 4840.0 square yards = 0.4047 hectares
1 square mile	= 640.0 acres = 259.0 hectares
1 hectare	= 10,000 square meters = 2.471 acres
1 square kilometer	= 247.1 acres = 0.386 square miles

Temperature
Degrees Centigrade	= 5/9 (Degrees Fahrenheit − 32)
Degrees Fahrenheit	= (9/5 × Degrees Centigrade) + 32

Glossary

In addition to the terms listed and defined herein, a number of terms used in feed manufacturing are listed and defined in Ch. 5. Those terms will not be repeated here. It might also be noted that mineral elements, amino acids, and the vitamins are not listed separately, but will be found listed as a group under the topics minerals, amino acids, or vitamins.

Abomasum: The fourth compartment of a ruminant's stomach, which has functions similar to the glandular stomach of nonruminants.

Absorption: The movement of nutrients (or other compounds) from the digestive tract (or through other tissues such as the skin) into the blood and/or lymph system.

Acetic acid: One of the volatile fatty acids commonly found in silage, rumen contents, and vinegar as a result of microbial fermentation.

ADF: Acid detergent fiber; the fraction of a feedstuff not soluble by acid detergent; roughly comparable to a crude fiber plus lignin.

Additive: An ingredient or combination of ingredients added in small quantities to a basic feed mix for the purpose of fortifying the basic mix with trace nutrients, medicines, or drugs.

Ad libitum: Unrestricted consumption of feed or water.

Aerobic: Living or functioning in the presence of oxygen.

Albumin: A group of globular proteins; a major component of blood serum protein.

Alimentary: Having to do with feed or food.

Alimentary tract: A term synonymous with the digestive or gastrointestinal tract.

Amino acids: The simplest organic structure of which proteins are formed; all have the common property of containing a carboxyl group and an amino group on the adjacent carbon atom.

Amino acids, essential: Those which must be present in the diet; they include arginine, histidine, isoleucine, leucine, lysine, methionine, phenylalanine, threonine, tryptophan, and valine.

Amino acids, nonessential: Amino acids found in common proteins but which may be partly or completely synthesized by the animal's tissues; they include alanine, aspartic acid, citrulline, cystine, glutamic acid, glycine, hydroxyproline, proline, serine, and tyrosine.

Amylase: Any of several enzymes which can hydrolyze starch to maltose or glucose.

Anaerobic: Living or functioning in the absence of oxygen.

Anemia: A deficiency in the blood of red cells, hemoglobin, or both.

Antagonist: A substance that exerts a nullifying or opposing action to another substance.

Antibiotic: A substance produced by one microorganism which has an inhibitory effect on another microorganism.

Antioxidant: A substance that inhibits the oxidation of other compounds.

Antivitamin: A substance that interferes with the synthesis or metabolism of a vitamin.

Anus: The distal opening of the gastrointestinal tract.

Appetite: A desire for food or water; generally a long-term phenomenon, in contrast to short-term satiety.

Ascorbic acid: *See* Vitamins.

As fed: As consumed by the animal.

Ash: The residue remaining after complete incineration at 500–600° C of a feed or animal tissue. Only metallic oxides or contaminants such as soil should remain.

Balanced ration (or diet): A combination of feeds that will provide the essential nutrients in the required proportions.

Basal metabolic rate: The basal metabolism expressed in kilocalories per unit of body size; the heat production of an animal during physical, digestive, and emotional rest.

Beriberi: A deficiency (acute) of thiamin, one of the B-complex vitamins.

Bile: A secretion from the liver containing metabolites such as cholesterol and bile acids, which aid in digestion of fats.

Biological value: The efficiency with which a protein furnishes the required amounts of essential amino acids; usually expressed as a percentage.

Biopsy: The removal and examination of tissue or other material from the living body.

Bolus: A solid mass of ingesta (synonymous with cud) which, in ruminants, is regurgitated for remastication during rumination.

Bomb calorimeter: An instrument used for measuring the gross energy (GE) content of any material that will burn.

Buffer: Any substance that can reduce changes in pH when an acid or alkali is added to it.

Butyric acid: One of the volatile fatty acids commonly found in rumen contents and in poor-quality silages.

Calorie: The amount of energy required to raise the temperature of water from 14.5 to 15.5° C.

Calorimeter: The equipment used to measure the heat generated in a system.

Carbohydrate: Organic substances containing C, H, and O, with the H and O present in the same proportions as in water. Many different kinds are found in plant tissues; some are vital to animal metabolism.

Carcinogen: Any cancer-producing substance.

Cartilage: A connective tissue characterized by non-vascularity (absence of blood vessels) and firm texture.

Carotene: A yellow organic compound that is the precursor of vitamin A.

Carrier: An edible material used to facilitate the addition of micronutrients to a ration.

Casein: The protein precipitated from milk by acid and/or rennin.

Cassava: A tropical plant of the spurge family with edible starchy roots.

Catalyst: A substance that changes the rate of a chemical reaction but is not itself used up in the reaction. The use of platinum in hydrogenating unsaturated fats is an example

Cecum (or caecum): A blind pouch located at the junction of the small intestine with the colon (the appendix in humans); it is part of the large intestine.

Cellulose: A polymer of glucose characterized by a linkage between the glucose molecules that is resistant to hydrolysis by most digestive enzymes (except some produced by microorganisms).

Cholesterol: The most common member of the sterol group found in blood and many other animal tissues; not present in any plant tissues.

Cholic acid: A family of steroids comprising the bile acids; they are derived from metabolism of cholesterol by the liver.

Chyme: A semiliquid material produced by the action of gastric juice on ingested food.

Chymotrypsin: A proteolytic digestive enzyme secreted by the pancreas.

Coagulated: Curdled, clotted, or congealed.

Coenzyme: An organic molecule required by some enzumes to produce enzymic activity; vitamin coenzymes include niacin, pyridoxine, thiamin, riboflavin, panthothenic acid, and folic acid.

Collagen: A principal supportive protein in connective tissue.

Colon: Part of the large intestine; divided into the transverse, descending, and acending segments.

Convulsion: An involuntary spasm or contraction of muscles, often in very rapid sequence.

Colostrum milk: The milk secreted during the first day or two of lactation.

Complete feed: A single feed mixture used as the only source of food for an animal.

Concentrate: Any feed containing relatively low fiber (20 percent or less) and with 60 percent or more TDN. Opposite of roughage; or, a concentrated source of one or more nutrients used to supplement a feed mix.

Crude fat: That portion of a feed (or other material) which is soluble in ether; also referred to as ether extract.

Crude fiber: The fibrous, less digestible portion of a feed.

Crude protein: Total ammoniacal nitrogen × 6.25, based on the fact that feed protein, on the average, contains 16 percent nitrogen; many nonprotein nitrogen compounds may be included.

Cud: The solid mass of ingesta regurgitated and remasticated in the process of rumination (synonymous with bolus).

Curd: The semisolid mass that is formed when milk comes in contact with an acid or rennin.

Deamination: Removal of the amino group from an amino acid.

Defluorinated: Having the fluorine content reduced to a level that is nontoxic under normal feed use.

Degradation: Conversion of a chemical compound to one that is less complex.

Dermatitis: An inflammation of the skin.

Dextrin: An intermediate polysaccharide product obtained during starch hydrolysis.

Diet: A regulated selection or mixture of feedstuffs provided on a continuous or prescribed schedule.

Digestibility, apparent: That percentage of a feed or nutrient that is apparently absorbed from the GI tract as indicated by intake minus fecal output; it differs from true digestibility in that feces contain substances derived from the body, many microbial products, and various secretions as well as undigested food.

Digestibility, true: The percentage of a feed nutrient actually absorbed from the GI tract.

Digestion: The processes involved in preparing food for absorption.

Disaccharide: Any of several dimers (contains two simple sugar molecules); for example, sucrose (common table sugar) yields glucose and fructose.

Dispensable amino acid: Synonymous with nonessential amino acid.

Dry matter: That portion of a feed or tissue remaining after water is removed by drying in an oven.

Duodenum: The first segment of the small intestine.

Edema: An abnormal accumulation of fluid in a part of or in the entire body.

Element: Any one of the chemical atoms of which all matter is composed.

Emaciated: Excessive leanness; a wasted condition of the body.

Emulsify: To disperse small drops of liquid into another liquid.

Endemic: A disease of low morbidity that persists over a long period of time in a certain region.

Endocrine: Pertains to internal secretions that affect metabolic processes or specific target organs.

Endogenous: Originating from within the organism.

Enzyme: A protein formed in plant or animal cells that acts as an organic catalyst.

Ensilage: The same as silage.

Ensiled: Having been subjected to an anaerobic fermentation to form silage.

Enteritis: Inflammation of the intestines.

Epithelial: Refers to those cells that form the outer layer of the skin or which line body cavities.

Ergosterol: A sterol found chiefly in plant tissues; on exposure to ultraviolet irridiation it becomes vitamin D.

Eructation: Belching of gas by ruminants as a normal means of expelling gases of fermentation.

Esophagus: The passageway (tube) from the mouth to the stomach.

Estrogens: Estrus-producing hormones secreted by the ovaries.

Excreta: The products of excretion—primarily feces and urine.

Exogenous: Originating from outside of the body.

Fat-soluble: Soluble in fats and fat solvents but generally not soluble in water.

Fattening: The deposition of excess energy in the form of adipose tissue (fat).

Feces: The excreta discharged from the digestive tract through the anus; composed of undigested food residues, microorganisms, and various materials originating in the liver and intestinal tract.

Feed: Any material used as food by an animal; same as feedstuff.

Feed grade: Suitable for animal food but not permitted by regulating agencies to be used in human foods.

Fermentation: Chemical changes brought about by enzymes produced by various microorganisms.

Fibrous: High in content of cellulose and/or lignin (or in cell walls or NDF, neutral detergent fiber).

Finish: To fatten an animal in preparation for slaughtering for food; also, the degree of fatness of such an animal.

Fistula: An abnormal passage from some part of the body to another part or the exterior—sometimes surgically inserted.

Fodder: The entire above-ground part of nearly mature corn or sorghum in the fresh or cured form.

Forage: Crops used as pasture, hay, haylage, silage, or green chop for feeding animals.

Fortify: To add one or more nutrients to a feed to increase its content to a needed level.

Free choice: The method of feeding in which the animal may choose to eat its feed at will.

Fresh: Usually denotes the green or wet form of a feed or forage.

Fructose: A 6-carbon monosaccharide; one of the components of sucrose.

Galactose: A 6-carbon monosaccharide; one of the components of lactose.

Gall bladder: A membranous sac attached to the liver of farm livestock (except for the horse) in which bile is stored.

Gastric juice: A clear liquid secreted by the wall of the stomach; it contains HCl and the enzymes rennin, pepsin, and gastric lipase.

Gastritis: Inflammation of the stomach.

Gastrointestinal: Pertaining to the stomach and intestine.

Germ: When used as a feed term, the embryo of a seed.

Glucose: A 6-carbon monosaccharide found in the blood and as a component of sucrose and maltose and other sugars.

Glycerol: An alcohol containing three carbons and three hydroxy groups; a component of a fat.

Glycogen: A polysaccharide found in the liver and muscles as a reserve form of quickly available energy.

Goiter: An enlargement of the thyroid gland sometimes caused by an iodine deficiency.

Gossypol: A substance present in cottonseed (and meal) which is toxic to swine and some other non-ruminant species.

Green chop: Forage harvested and fed in the green, chopped form.

Groat: Grain from which the hull has been removed.

Gross energy: The total heat of combustion of material burned in a bomb calorimeter.

Growth: An increase in muscle, bone, vital organs, and connective tissue as contrasted to an increase in adipose tissue (fat deposition).

Hay: The aerial part of forage crops stored in the dry form for feeding to animals.

Heat increment: The heat that is unavoidably produced by an animal incidental with nutrient digestion and utilization.

Heat labile: Unstable to heat .

Hematocrit: The volume of whole blood made up by the red blood cells after centrifugation.

Hemoglobin: The oxygen-carrying red protein of the red corpuscles.

Hemorrhage: Copious loss of blood through bleeding.

Hepatitis: Inflammation of the liver.

Hormone: A chemical secreted in the body fluids by an endocrine gland that has a specific effect on other tissues.

Hunger: The desire for food; the antithesis of satiety.

Hydrogenation: The chemical addition of hydrogen to any unsaturated compound (double bond), often to fatty acids.

Hydrolysis: The chemical process whereby a compound is split into simpler units with the uptake of water.

Hypervitaminosis: An abnormal condition resulting from the intake of (or treatment with) an excess of one or more vitamins.

Ileum: The third section of the small intestine.

Inert: Relatively inactive.

Ingest: To eat or take in through the mouth.

Insulin: A hormone secreted by the pancreas into the blood; it is involved in regulation and utilization of blood glucose.

Intestinal tract: The small and large intestines.

Intrinsic factor: A chemical substance in the normal stomach necessary for absorption of vitamin B_{12}.

Inulin: A polysaccharide found in some root crops. Composed of fructose.

Iodine number: The amount of iodine (in grams) that can be taken up by 100 g of a fat or fatty acid; it is a measure of unsaturation.

Jejunum: The middle portion of the small intestine.

Kcal: An abbreviation for kilocalorie; 1000 calories.

Keratin: An S-containing protein found in tissues such as hair, wool, feathers, horn, and hooves.

Ketone: A group of chemicals that includes acetone, acetoacetic acid, and betahydroxy butyric acid; they are produced in excess when carbohydrate metabolism is low and fat is being metabolized for energy.

Labile: Unstable; easily destroyed.

Lactase: An enzyme present in the intestinal juice which acts on lactose to produce glucose and galactose.

Lactic acid: An organic acid commonly found in sour milk and silage, and one which is important in the body during anaerobic glycolysis.

Lesion: An unhealthy change in the structure of a part of the body.

Lignin: A biologically unavailable polymer that is a major structural component of the cell walls of plants.

Linoleic acid: An 18-carbon unsaturated fatty acid; one of the essential fatty acids; it occurs widely in plant glycerides.

Lipase: A fat-splitting enzyme; different lipases are produced by the stomach and the pancreas.

Lipids: Substances that are diverse in chemical nature but are soluble in fat solvents.

Lymph: The slightly yellow, transparent fluid occupying the lymphatic channels of the body.

Malignant: Virulent or destructive as applied to cancer.

Malnutrition: An overall term for poor nourishment.

Maltase: An enzyme which splits maltose to produce two molecules of glucose.

Manure: The refuse from animal quarters consisting of excreta with or without litter or bedding.

Megacalorie (Mcal): 1000 kcal or 1 million calories; synonymous with therm.

Metabolic size: The body weight raised to the 3/4 power ($W^{0.75}$); a means of relating body weight to heat production of an animal.

Metabolism: The sum of all the physical and chemical processes taking place in a living organism.

Metabolite: Any compound produced during metabolism.

Metabolizable energy (ME): Digestible energy minus the energy of the urine and combustible gases from the gastrointestinal tract (primarily methane).

Methane: A major product of anaerobic fermentation of carbohydrates; found in the rumen.

Microingredient: Any ration component normally measured in milligrams of micrograms/kg or in parts per million (ppm).

Minerals: As applied to animal nutrition, elements that are essential to the plant or animal and that are found in its tissues.

Minerals, macro: The major minerals (in terms of the amounts required in the diet or found in body tissues): calcium (Ca), chlorine (Cl), magnesium (Mg), phosphorous (P), potassium (K), sodium (Na), and sulfur (S).

Minerals, micro: The trace elements required by animal tissues and which must be in the diet: cobalt (Co), copper (Cu), chromium (Cr), fluorine (F), iodine (I), iron (Fe), manganese (Mn), molybdenum (Mo), nickel (Ni), selenium (Se), silicon (Si), vanadium (V), and zinc (Zn).

Miscible: Capable of being mixed easily with another substance.

Monosaccharide: Any one of several simple sugars.

Morbidity: A state of sickness.

Moribund: A dying state—near death.

Mucosa: The membranes that line the passages and cavities of the body.

Mucus: A slimy liquid secreted by the mucous glands and membranes.

Monogastric: The simple stomach; often used for nonruminant animals, but technically a misnomer because ruminants have only one stomach with four compartments.

Mycotoxin: A fungal toxin; quite often present in feeds, sometimes at lethal levels.

NDF: Neutral detergent fiber, the fraction containing mostly cell wall constituents of low biological availability.

Necrosis: Death of a part of the cells making up a living tissue.

Nephritis: Inflammation of the kidneys.

Net energy (NE): Metabolizable energy minus the heat increment.

Neuritis: Inflammation of the peripheral nerves.

NFE (nitrogen-free extract): Consists primarily of readily available carbohydrates such as sugars and starches; part of the proximate analysis.

Nonprotein nitrogen (NPN): Any one of a group of N-containing compounds which are not true proteins that can be precipitated from a solution; ammonia and urea are examples.

Nutrient: Any chemical substance that provides nourishment to the body.

Obesity: The accumulation of body fat beyond the amount needed for good health.

Oil: Usually a mixture of pure fats which is liquid at room temperature.

Oleic acid: An 18-carbon fatty acid that contains one double bond; it is found in animal and vegetable fat.

Omasum: The third compartment of the ruminant stomach.

Ossification: The process of deposition of bone salts in the cartilage of the bones.

Osteitis: Inflammation of a bone.

Osteomalacia: A weakening of the bones caused by inadequate Ca, P, and/or vitamin D or by some diseases.

Osteoporosis: A reduction in the normal amount of bone salts (often occurring with age) such that the bone becomes porous and brittle.

Oxidation: The union of a substance with oxygen; the increase of positive charges on an atom or loss of negative charges.

Palmitic acid: A saturated fatty acid with 16 carbon atoms.

Pancreas: An organ located near the stomach; it produces pancreatic juice which is secreted into the small intestine via the pancreatic duct. It is also an endocrine gland which secretes insulin and glucagon, hormones which control metabolism of glucose.

Pathogen: Any disease-producing microoganism or material.

Pentosan: An polysaccharide made up primarily of 5-carbon sugars; araban and xylan are examples.

Pentose: A 5-carbon sugar such as arabinose, xylose, or ribose.

Pepsin: A proteolytic enzyme produced by the stomach.

Permeable: Capable of being penetrated.

Physiological: Pertaining to the science that deals with the functions of living organisms or their parts.

Plasma: The fluid portion of the blood; serum is plasma from which the fibrinogen has been removed by the clotting process.

Polyneuritis: An inflammation encompassing many peripheral nerves.

Polyuria: An ecessive excretion of urine.

Precursor: A compound that can be used by the

body to form another compound, such as carotene used to produce vitamin A.

Premix: A uniform mixture of one or more microingredients and a carrier, used in the introduction of microingredients into a larger batch.

Proximate analysis: A combination of analytical procedures used to describe feeds, excreta, and other agricultural products.

Propionic acid: One of the volatile fatty acids commonly found in rumen contents.

Protein: Any of many complex organic compounds formed from various combinations of amino acids and, sometimes, other nonprotein components.

Putrefaction: The decomposition of proteins by microorganisms under anaerobic conditions.

Pyrexia: A feverish condition.

Radioactive: An element that emits particles during the disintegration of the nuclei; the emissions include alpha and beta particles and gamma rays.

Radioisotope: A radioactive form of an element; often used in experimental work with plants and animals to trace metabolic activity in the animal.

Rancid: A term used to describe fats that have undergone partial decomposition; rancid fats may have objectional tastes or odors and may be toxic.

Ration: A fixed portion of feed, usually expressed as the amount of a diet allowed daily.

Rennin: A milk-curdling enzyme present in the gastric juice of young mammals.

Reticulum: The first compartment of the ruminant stomach.

Reticular groove: A muscular structure at the lower end of the esophagus which, when closed, forms a tube allowing milk to go directly into the abomasum; sometimes called the esophageal groove.

Rumen: The second compartment of the ruminant stomach.

Ruminant: Any of a group of hooved mammals which have a four-compartmented stomach and that chew a cud while ruminating.

Rumination: The process of regurgitating previously eaten feed, reswallowing the liquids, and rechewing the solids (cud).

Satiety: The condition of being fully satisfied with food; the antithesis of hunger.

Salmonella: A pathogenic, diarrhea-producing organism sometimes present in contaminated feeds.

Saponifiable: Having the capacity to react with alkali to form soap.

Sarcoma: A tumor of fleshy consistency—often highly malignant.

Saturated fat: A fat that contains no fatty acids with double bonds.

Self-fed: Provided with part or all of the ration on a continuous basis so that the animal may eat at will.

Septicemia: A diseased condition resulting from the presence of pathogenic bacteria and their associated poisons in the blood.

Serum: *See* Plasma.

Silage: Feed resulting from the storage and fermentation of wet crops under anaerobic conditions.

Stabilized: Made more resistant to chemical change by the addition of a particular substance.

Starch: A polysaccharide that yields glucose on hydrolysis; found in high concentrations in most seed grains.

Stearic acid: An 18-carbon saturated fatty acid.

Sterol: An alcohol of high molecular weight, such as cholesterol; a basic compound used to synthesize many vital chemicals for both plants and animals.

Stomach: That part of the digestive tract in which chemical digestion is initiated in most animal species. It normally lies between the esophagus and the small intestine.

Stress: Any circumstance that tends to disrupt the normal, steady functioning of the body and its parts.

Sucrose: A disaccharide (common table sugar) composed of one molecule each of glucose and fructose.

Syndrome: A medical term meaning a set of symptoms that occur together.

Taste: The ability to distinguish flavors between or among solid or liquid components of the diet.

TDN (total digestible nutrients): A value that indicates the relative energy value of a feed for an animal.

Thyroxine: An iodine-containing hormone that is produced by the thyroid gland.

Trace minerals: *See* Minerals, micro.

Triglyceride (fat): An ester composed of glycerol and three fatty acids.

True protein: A precipitable protein rather than any of several nonprotein compounds.

Trypsin: A proteolytic digestive enzyme produced by the pancreas.

Unsaturated fat: A fat that contains from one to three fatty acids which contain one or more double bonds.

Urea: The chief end product of protein metabolism in mammals; one of the main nitrogenous constituents in urine; a synthetic product sometimes used as a nitrogen source in rations for ruminants.

Uric acid: A nitrogenous end product of purine metabolism; it is the principal N-containing component in urine of birds.

Urease: An enzyme that acts on urea to produce carbon dioxide and ammonia; it is present in numerous microorganisms in the rumen.

Uremia: A toxic accumulation of urinary constituents in the blood because of faulty kidney excretion.

VFA: Volatile fatty acids.

Villi: Small threadlike projections attached to the interior of the wall of the small intestine to increase absorptive surface area.

Viscera: The organs of the great cavities of the body which are removed at slaughter.

Viscosity: The freedom of flow of liquids.

Vitamin: One of a group of organic substances that are essential in small amounts for the lives of animals.

Vitamin, fat-soluble: Vitamins soluble in fats. This group includes vitamins A, D_2, D_3, E (tocopherol), and K.

Vitamins, water-soluble: Vitamins soluble in water. This group includes ascorbic acid (vitamin C) and the B-complex—biotin, choline, cobalamin or cyanocobalamin, folacin, niacin, pantothenic acid, pyridoxine, riboflavin, and thiamin.

Index

Toxins
  in cottonseed, 139, 140
  in hay, 74
  in rapeseed, 144
  in soybeans, 137
  in water, 16
Trace minerals, 169–72, 342, 346, 348
  needed in diet, 169, 170
Trials, comparative, 118
Triticale, 108, 116
  for finishing swine, 116
Turkeys, 413, 414
  rations, 414

U

Urea, 151–58
  supplements, 275
  toxicity, 20, 153
  usage, limitations on, 152–53
  utilization, methods of improving, 153–54
Urinary calculi, 348

V

Veal calves, 303, 304
Villi, 8
Vitamins, 26, 27, 248
  A, 440
    and D, 289
  C, 449
  deficiencies in, 27
  E, 289, 290
  fat-soluble, 26, 173–76
  for feedlot lambs, 339
  functions, 26
  in grains, 105, 108
  metabolism, 27
  for milk production, 289, 290
  in milk replacers, 299
  needed in diet, 173
  in pet foods, 440
  for rabbits, 457, 458
  requirements of goats, 358
  sources, 172–77
    for swine, 383
  stability of, 172–76
  supplements, 38
    for lambs, 342
  for swine, 374, 375
  tissue distribution, 26

  water-soluble, 26, 173, 174, 176, 290
Voluntary intake, 65

W

Water
  consumption of, 425
  for dogs and cats, 435–37
  for finishing lambs, 339
  functions and metabolism, 15, 16
  for horses, 425, 426
  losses, 16
  metabolic, 16
  for milk production, 291
  quality, 16
  for rabbits, 454
  requirements of goats, 358
  for sheep, 318, 319
  as source of mineral nutrients, 16
  for swine, 369
Weaning, 333
  calves, 300
  early, 344
    of lambs, 330, 331
Weather damage
  to hay, 72, 73
  of stored hay, 74
Weight-reducing pet foods, 445
Wet milling methods, 119, 120
Wheat, 108, 114–16
  by-products, 119, 120
  comparison with triticale, 116
  feed grain varieties, 115
  meal feeds, 119, 120
  protein, 115
  sprouted, 116
  types, 115
Wheat-grain sorghum, corn blends, 270, 271
Whey
  liquid, 125
  products, 124, 125
  protein concentrate, 149
Wintering systems, 262, 263

X

Xanthophylls, 110

Y

Yeast, irradiated, 151